NATIONAL GEOGRAPHIC

CONCISE HISTORY OF
SCIENCE&INVENTION

AN ILLUSTRATED TIME LINE

NATIONAL GEOGRAPHIC

CONCISE HISTORY OF
SCIENCE&INVENTION

AN ILLUSTRATED TIME LINE

EDITED BY JOLYON GODDARD

NATIONAL GEOGRAPHIC
WASHINGTON, D.C.

CONTENTS

ORIGINS OF SCIENCE
PREHISTORY–850 B.C.E.

CLASSICAL AND EARLY MEDIEVAL SCIENCE
849 B.C.E.-999 C.E.

LATE MEDIEVAL AND RENAISSANCE SCIENCE
1000-1624

THE SCIENTIFIC REVOLUTION
1625-1774

THE INDUSTRIAL REVOLUTION
1775-1839

CONTENTS

THE AGE OF STEAM
1840-1884

THE AGE OF ELECTRICITY
1885-1919

THE ATOMIC AGE
1920-1949

THE SPACE AGE
1950-1979

THE MODERN WORLD
1980-PRESENT

FOREWORD

I T IS EASY TO THINK OF SCIENCE AS A CHARACTERISTIC OF THE MODERN AGE. WE associate it perhaps with computers or with space exploration. In fact, science is very old: Its history is as long as the history of humankind's attempts to understand the world. In the words of the 19th-century biologist Thomas Henry Huxley, "Science is nothing but trained and organized common sense." As the time line in the *National Geographic Concise History of Science and Invention* shows, the story of scientific and technological advance has for most of the time taken the form of a series of small steps, each based on previous knowledge, rather than a sudden revelation of a new truth. The process began early in human history, when our ancestors first experimented with cultivating crops, domesticating animals, building shelters, and making tools—and it has continued ever since.

"One thing I have learned in a long life: That all our science, measured against reality, is primitive and childlike, and yet it is the most precious thing we have."

ALBERT EINSTEIN

Like all of the publications of the National Geographic Society—since it was established in 1888—this book sets out to promote knowledge of the world and its regions, in our case by providing global perspectives on the growth of human knowledge. This illustrated time line helps readers make sense of the apparently chaotic course of technological development and understand the historical background of cutting-edge scientific innovations. Even the newest scientific and technological advances are often the culmination of processes of discovery that stretch back decades or even centuries.

By tracing this development, the time line and accompanying illustrated essays make complex ideas easier to grasp. They show the reader what happened when and where and highlight the essential facts to understand. In that way, they help the reader avoid the bewilderment that led Nobel laureate Wolfgang Pauli to complain in the 1930s: "Physics is very muddled again at the moment; it is much too hard for me anyway, and I wish I were a movie comedian or something like that and had never heard anything about physics!"

TIME PERIODS AND DATES

The history of science is a multicultural discipline, and scholars and editors working today use terminology that does not impose the standards of one culture on others. This book uses the terms **B.C.E.** (before the Common Era) and **C.E.** (the Common Era). B.C.E. refers to the same period as B.C. (before Christ), and C.E. refers to the same time period as A.D. (*anno Domini*, a Latin phrase meaning "in the year of the Lord"). When a person is mentioned for the first time, his or her birth and death dates are provided where they are available. Dates preceded by r. (reigned) give the reign dates of monarchs. Cases where an exact date is not known are indicated by the use of ca (*circa*, Latin for "about") or fl. (*floruit*, Latin for "flourished").

INTRODUCTION

Each chapter opens with an introductory essay that surveys the major trends in science and invention of the era. The example here, which covers the period from prehistory to 850 B.C.E., describes the earliest technologies and inventions, from making tools and capturing fire to cultivating crops, domesticating animals, and forming early settlements. It also covers the single most important invention for the transmission of human knowledge—writing—and the roots of what many people consider to be the first true science, the study of astronomy.

ABOUT THIS BOOK

N*ATIONAL GEOGRAPHIC CONCISE HISTORY OF SCIENCE AND INVENTION: An Illustrated Time Line* chronicles the remarkable story of human knowledge through a versatile design that allows readers to learn in detail about particular periods or regions or to follow themes from prehistory to the modern world. The book traces inventions and discoveries in all fields of science and technology, including math, astronomy, biology, medicine, physics, chemistry, engineering, and invention. The book is divided into ten chapters covering major historical eras. Each chapter begins with an Introduction, outlining the key developments of that era, followed by The World at a Glance, which provides an overview of the chapter. The bulk of each chapter is a time line that traces the most important scientific discoveries and inventions by region and by scientific field. The time lines are supplemented by picture essays, sidebars, and boxes that provide additional detail about particularly important subjects.

Wherever possible, the book provides exact dates for events. However, in some cases it is difficult to say exactly when an invention occurred. This is true of the ancient past, when we rely on archaeological evidence or on written records to trace the development of technology, but it is also true of the modern world. Scientific advance is a continual process rather than a specific event; a breakthrough might be the cumulative result of a series of tiny advances. In such cases, the time lines provide approximate dates or use the dates commonly accepted by experts in the field. Again, it is sometimes not entirely clear who to credit with a specific development or even where it first took place. Scientists in different countries often work on similar subjects at the same time, either in collaboration or in competition. While this book acknowledges differing claims or the work of collaborators, it occasionally uses a degree of necessary simplification in order to place an entry in a particularly place in the time line.

THE WORLD AT A GLANCE

The World at a Glance displays the era's most important scientific developments chronologically from left to right and regionally from top to bottom. The four regions defined here—**Europe**, **The Americas** (North and South America), **Asia & Oceania**, and **Africa & the Middle East**—appear in the same order in the time line. This overview allows for quick comparison of developments occurring in different regions at the same time. The last vertical column here, for example, reveals that while Italian scientist Galileo Galilei was observing moons of Jupiter, ships were beginning to be built in North America and tobacco had reached the Ottoman Empire in western Asia.

TIME LINE

Each time line spread offers a view of scientific developments during the period defined in red at top left. (Time spans may vary in length, depending on the length of the era covered in each chapter.) Four vertical columns cover major areas of science and technology: **Astronomy & Math**, **Biology & Medicine**, **Physical Sciences**, and **Engineering & Invention**. The fifth, **World Events**, provides a broader historical context. Developments within those areas are listed chronologically within each region. At the right of each spread, sidebars highlight significant scientists, technologies, or inventions, and boxed features entitled **Turning Points**, **Inside Story**, and **How Things Work** give extra information on specific entries.

PICTURE ESSAY

Each chapter contains between two and seven picture essays that explore a particularly significant topic. These in-depth articles might focus on the background to a specific invention or discovery, or might describe the influence a particular form of technology had on an entire civilization, such as pyramid construction had on Mesoamerica. This example tells the story of the discovery of the structure of deoxyribonucleic acid (DNA). As here, all picture essays have key dates boxes. Many chapters also have quotes that define the era in the words of scientists, philosophers, and others who embodied their times.

CHAPTER 1

ORIGINS OF SCIENCE

T ODAY PEOPLE FREQUENTLY THINK OF SCIENCE AS A RELATIVELY modern field of knowledge. In its broadest terms, however, science is as old as humankind itself. In this sense, it describes the process of learning about the world through observation, and using reason and deduction to influence one's environment. As soon as modern humans evolved from their hominid ancestors more than three million years ago, they began to accumulate knowledge of what they saw around them and pass the information on to one another and to later generations. They used stones as tools, and then learned how to shape stones to make more efficient tools. As the tools improved, so people were able to use them to fashion weapons and other artifacts from bone, antler, and wood. They also learned how to capture fire from natural sources such as wild fires, and later to make fire for themselves by using the heat generated by friction or sparks from stones, or by concentrating the sun's heat.

Another major advance came when people began to domesticate plants. The earliest humans lived as hunter-gatherers, moving around through the year to follow the best sources of food. By carefully selecting the fattest grains of wild grasses to use as seeds, the first farmers produced better-yielding strains of wheat and other crops. As

Like all early civilizations, ancient Egypt was primarily an agricultural society that depended on its farmers to produce enough food to support its population. Egyptian technology was dedicated to maximizing food production, from building irrigation canals to carry water to the fields to creating a calendar that predicted the annual flooding of the Nile, when fertile sediment was washed over the land. The success of Egyptian farmers allowed a complex civilization to emerge and to achieve such remarkable feats of engineering as the building of the pyramids.

a result, some people were able to lead a more settled existence, tilling the ground and growing crops instead of gathering wild plants. They also domesticated animals, first for use as food and as a source of wool and hides, and later as draft animals to help with farming. Over the centuries the development of newer, more productive strains of plants and better tools for planting and harvesting enabled small agrarian communities to support larger populations, growing into villages and towns, even early cities. These population centers became the location for the exchange of practical knowledge and rapid technological development.

Recorded history began with the development of writing. Instead of passing on stories or knowledge by word of mouth, people could write them down. They could record quantities of farm animals and stocks of grain by developing numbers and ways of counting; this is turn made it easier to keep records of trade. To keep track of the seasons, early peoples devised calendars and linked the passage of time with phases of the moon and other changes they observed in the heavens. The need for accurate timekeeping, both to enable farmers to know when to sow or harvest their crops and to allow priests to know when to celebrate rituals, lay behind the observation of the stars and planets. Astronomy was therefore the first science to be formally studied, and the complex calculations it involved meant that advances in math soon followed.

Meanwhile, technological innovation constantly improved the tools people used to influence their world. There were few identifiable ancient "inventions." Instead tools such as the plow were slowly improved by tiny changes introduced by countless individuals over a period of time.

To that extent, early technological development is as representative of advances in human cooperation and communication than skill or ingenuity. An individual stone ax, for example, could be created by accident or random experimentation and used by its owner until it was lost or broken. To teach others how to make and use axes required a conscious desire to communicate knowledge.

With the invention of writing, the possibilities for human advancement increased dramatically. The written word is arguably the most important invention in the history of knowledge. It enables the transmission of information and ideas across generations, regions, and communities. It is an idea that we take for granted today, but with the development of writing, an individual who could read could possess not just the knowledge he or she had acquired through individual ingenuity and observation, but also the knowledge of every other person to whose writings he or she had access.

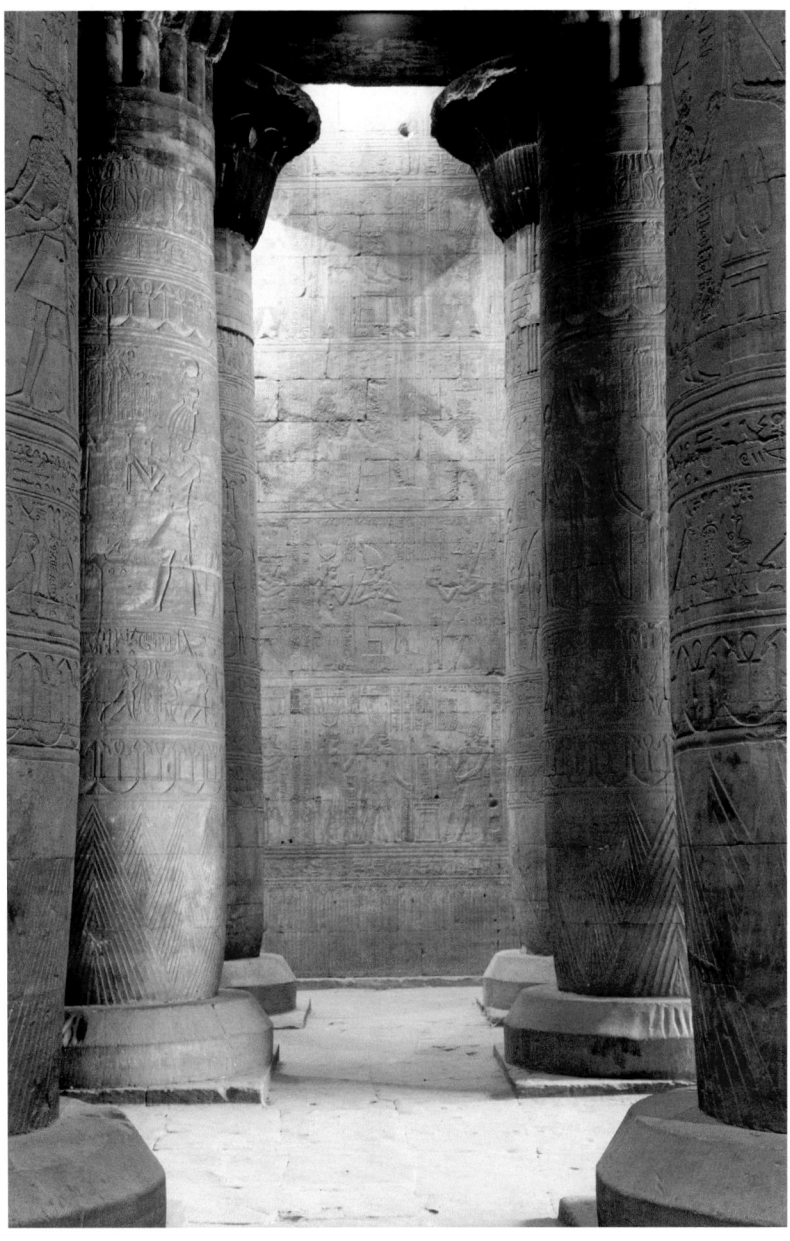

Ancient Egyptian builders constructed the temple at Dendara in about the fourth century B.C.E., using columns to support the weight of a stone roof while still retaining a light and airy interior for worshippers. The structure was so well designed that it still stands nearly 2,500 years after its completion.

CONCISE HISTORY OF SCIENCE AND INVENTION

	PREHISTORY	6000 B.C.E.	4000 B.C.E.	3000 B.C.E.	2500 B.C.E.	
EUROPE	ca **750,000** Fire is used by *Homo erectus*. ca **120,000** Neandertals appear in Europe. ca **40,000** Modern humans live alongside Neandertals. ca **28,000** Neandertals die out. ca **25,000** People begin to make ceramic models. ca **6300** Earliest known boat is made.	ca **6000** Scandinavians make sleds to travel on snow. ca **5000** People in Italy make mirrors from obsidian. ca **4300** People in France make canoes.	ca **4000** Horses are domesticated in Ukraine. ca **3100** The first stage of Stonehenge—an earth bank—is built in England.	ca **3000** Copper deposits are found and utilized in Cyprus. ca **3000** Marble sculptures are made in the Greek islands. ca **3000** Grapes and olives are cultivated by town-dwelling people in the Aegean around Greece.	ca **2300** Work begins on aligning the stones at Stonehenge.	
THE AMERICAS	ca **15,000** First settlements appear in America. ca **8,500** North Americans make stone arrowheads.	ca **6000** Pottery is made in South America. ca **5000** Arable farming begins in Mexico and Central America.	ca **4000** Potatoes are cultivated in the Andes.	ca **3000** North Americans begin making baskets and blankets. ca **3000** The llama is domesticated in Peru.	ca **2500** People in the Arctic make flint tools.	
ASIA & OCEANIA	ca **75,000** Modern humans reach Southeast Asia. ca **45,000** Modern humans reach Australia. ca **11,000** Clay pots are made in Japan. ca **6500** Rice is cultivated in China.	ca **5500** The jungle fowl is domesticated. ca **5200** People in Iran make wine.	ca **4000** The Chinese domesticate the water buffalo. ca **4000** Bronze is first made in Thailand. ca **4000** Farmers begin to settle the Indus Valley in India. ca **3500** The plow is invented in both China and Mesopotamia.	**3000** Boats in China are equipped with anchors. **2950** A lunar calendar is developed in China. ca **2900** Cotton is cultivated in India. ca **2700** The Chinese raise silkworms on mulberry leaves. **2637** Year 1 of the Chinese calendar.	ca **2500** The camel is domesticated in Asia. ca **2500** Clay pipes are used as drains in Pakistan. ca **2500** Chinese doctors begin using acupuncture. **2296** Chinese astronomers record the sighting of a comet.	
AFRICA & THE MIDDLE EAST	ca **1,000,000** *Homo erectus* uses stone tools. ca **160,000** *Homo sapiens* (modern man) evolves in Africa. ca **100,000** *Homo sapiens* moves out of Africa. ca **10,000** People in Palestine build houses from sun-dried bricks. ca **10,000** Dogs are domesticated. ca **8000** Goats and sheep are domesticated. ca **7500** Clay tokens are used for record keeping. ca **6500** Cattle are domesticated.	ca **6000** The world's first known city is built in Anatolia. ca **6000** People settle in the Nile Valley in Egypt. ca **5000** Northern African farmers grow millet. ca **5000** Cats are used to catch rodents. ca **5000** Copper is smelted in Egypt. ca **4400** Egyptians weave cloth on looms. **4236** Ancient Egyptians devise a 365-day calendar. ca **4000** The arch is used in construction in Egypt and Mesopotamia.	ca **4000** The Egyptians domesticate the donkey. ca **3500** The Egyptians develop a simple clock. ca **3500** Barges with sails are used in Egypt and Mesopotamia. ca **3500** The wheel is invented in Mesopotamia. ca **3400** Egyptians adopt numerals for quantities more than ten. ca **3200** Bronze is made in Mesopotamia. ca **3100** Egyptians begin using hieroglyphs.	ca **3000** The Sumerians introduce a 360-day calendar. ca **3000** Yams are cultivated in West Africa. ca **3000** Egyptians dam the Garawi River. ca **2800** Sumerians make soap. **2630** Egyptians begin building pyramids. **2600** Mesopotamians make glass. **2550** The Great Pyramid is completed.	ca **2500** Tin ore is mined and smelted in Turkey. ca **2400** Mesopotamians waterproof boats and buildings with tar. ca **2300** Babylonian astronomers study comets. ca **2300** People in the Middle East keep geese. ca **2300** Egyptians make wine from grapes. ca **2300** The earliest known maps are produced in Mesopotamia.	

2100 B.C.E.	1800 B.C.E.	1500 B.C.E.	1200 B.C.E.	1000–850 B.C.E.
ca 2000 The Minoans build palaces on Crete.	**ca 1700** Central Europeans trade metals and amber. **ca 1600** Bellows are used in glassmaking and metalworking.	**ca 1500** Copper from the Alps is exported to England. **ca 1500** Bathrooms in the Minoan palaces of Crete have running water. **ca 1500** People in the Aegean invent a press to squeeze grapes and olives. **ca 1400** Stonehenge is completed in England.	**ca 1150** Craftsmen in Greece and Cyprus use colored glass to decorate objects. **ca 1050** Ironworking is introduced to Greece.	**ca 1000** Etruscan craftsmen make false teeth from gold. **950** Oats are cultivated in northern and central Europe. **ca 900** Etruscans flourish in Italy.
ca 2000 Copper is mined in North America.	**ca 1750** Peruvians build a long canal to irrigate their crops.	**1400** Cassava (manioc) is grown in South America.	**1200** Fishermen in Peru make rafts and boats from reeds. **1200** Olmec sculptors carve figurines and giant human heads.	**ca 1000** Aleuts and Inuits have now successfully adapted to their Arctic homelands.
ca 2000 Austronesians settle on various islands in the South Pacific.	**ca 1550** Southeast Asian farmers make plowshares from bronze.	**1500** People in Asia make beer. **1450** The Chinese cultivate soybeans. **1361** Chinese astronomers record a solar eclipse.	**1150** Chinese metalworkers cast bronze bells. **1100** The Chinese invent spinning to make yarn. **1000** The Chinese begin writing on bamboo or paper made from bark. **1000** The Hindu calendar of 360 days is introduced in India.	**900** Chinese metalworkers cast coins. **850** The Chinese use natural gas for lighting.
ca 2100 Sumerians build a mud-brick ziggurat. **ca 2000** Babylonian mathematicians introduce a positional number system. **ca 2000** Egyptian armies develop a portable battering ram. **ca 2000** Medicine becomes an important science in Syria and Babylon. **ca 2000** Spoked wheels are made in Egypt and Mesopotamia. **ca 1950** Palestinian farmers make plows.	**ca 1800** Mesopotamian mathematicians discover the "Pythagorean theorem." **1750** Babylonian astronomers compile lists of planets and stars. **ca 1650** Egyptian mathematicians learn to solve simple equations. **ca 1600** Babylonian astronomers recognize the zodiac and the paths of the planets. **ca 1550** Egyptians are using about 700 drugs and medications.	**1500** Professional millers grind wheat in Egypt. **1450** Farmers in Mesopotamia use a seed drill. **1450** The Egyptians devise a water clock. **1350** The symptoms of leprosy are described in an Egyptian text. **1350** Egyptians learn to weld iron.	**1200** The Egyptians dig a canal to join the Nile River to the Red Sea. **1200** Babylonian astronomers make an instrument to determine when a star is due south of their observatory.	**1000** The Phoenicians develop an alphabet. **1000** Farmers use dung to fertilize crops. **975** The Hebrews devise a lunar calendar with 12 months. **950** The Phoenicians make a purple dye. **900** Farmers in Mesopotamia use an irrigation system to water crops. **850** The first-known arch bridge is built in Smyrna.

ASTRONOMY & MATH	BIOLOGY & MEDICINE	PHYSICAL SCIENCES

EUROPE

And God said, "Let the earth put forth vegetation, plants yielding seed, and fruit trees bearing fruit in which is their seed, each according to its kind, upon the earth."

GENESIS 1:11

TURNING POINTS

The World's First City

The settlement at Çatal Hüyük in Anatolia (modern Turkey) dates from about 6000 B.C.E. at the latest. The houses butted closely together and had flat roofs, reached by means of ladders. The people grew crops and irrigated the fields. They supplemented their diet by hunting animals. They wove cloth, made baskets and clay pots, and tanned hides to make leather. Nearby volcanoes produced a hard, glasslike obsidian, which the people of Çatal Hüyük made into knives and other tools. The obsidian was also traded with neighboring peoples. Each house had a religious shrine decorated with figurines and the heads and horns of animals. The dead were left outside exposed to the elements before their remains were buried under the houses.

THE AMERICAS

ca 8000 In Central America pumpkins and squash are domesticated, probably the first fruits cultivated for food.

ASIA & OCEANIA

ca 8000 The woolly mammoth becomes extinct.

ca 6500 Rice is domesticated in the delta of the Yangtze River in China.

Cultivated wheat yields about six times more grain than wild species.

AFRICA & THE MIDDLE EAST

ca 11,000 Hunter-gatherers in northern Syria cultivate rye.

ca 10,000 Dogs are domesticated in Mesopotamia, probably as food.

ca 9000 Einkorn wheat is grown in Palestine.

ca 8000 People in East Africa and Mesopotamia domesticate goats and sheep.

ca 8000 Barley is first grown in the Fertile Crescent in West Asia.

ca 7000 Pigs are domesticated in Turkey.

ca 6500 Cattle are domesticated in Africa and Asia.

The woolly mammoth became extinct about 10,000 years ago. Near-perfect specimens have been discovered in Siberia, preserved in the frozen earth.

ENGINEERING & INVENTION	WORLD EVENTS
ca 750,000 Fire is used by human ancestors, *Homo erectus*, in France.	**ca 120,000** Neandertals live in Europe.
ca 45,000 Stone-headed spears are used in Europe.	**ca 40,000** Modern humans move into Europe and live alongside Neandertals.
ca 25,000 People in central Europe make ceramic images by firing clay models.	**ca 28,000** Neandertals become extinct.
ca 20,000 The wooden bow and arrow are used in Spain and Saharan Africa. People in southern Europe use sewing needles made from bone.	
ca 6300 The earliest surviving dugout boat (hollowed from a tree trunk), found in the Netherlands, dates from this time.	
ca 8500 Indigenous people in North America make stone arrowheads.	**ca 15,000** Likely date for first settlement of America, although some scholars believe people arrived as early as 40,000 B.C.E.
ca 8000 The Folsom people living on the eastern side of the southern Rocky Mountains develop sophisticated tools.	
ca 11,000 The earliest-known clay pots are made in Japan.	**ca 75,000** Modern humans live in Southeast Asia.
	ca 45,000 Modern humans reach Australia.
ca 1,000,000 Human ancestors (*Homo erectus*) begin chipping flakes off stones to sharpen them for tools.	**ca 160,000** First appearance of *Homo sapiens*, the modern human race.
ca 1,000,000 *Homo erectus* use antlers to create tools for cutting and drilling.	**ca 100,000** *Homo sapiens* moves out of Africa.
ca 15,000 In Africa bone harpoons (barbed spears) are used for fishing.	**ca 6,000** Hunter-gatherers settle in farming communities in the Nile Valley in present-day Egypt. They will form the basis of the ancient Egyptian culture.
ca 10,000 People in Palestine make houses of sun-dried bricks and also weave baskets.	
ca 7500 Clay tokens are used for record keeping in Mesopotamia.	
ca 6000 People at Çatal Hüyük in Anatolia (modern Turkey) build the world's first known city.	

THE FIRST CROPS

Modern domestic plants are the result of rapid evolution in response to artificial selection by humans. Characteristics humans prefer, such as large size, flavor, and productivity, are not the same as those favored by natural selection.

The first deliberate cultivation appears to have taken place in West Asia about 10–11,000 years ago (9000–8000 B.C.E.) in the Fertile Crescent, an area running from the Nile Delta up the eastern coast of the Mediterranean and across present-day Iraq to the Persian Gulf. Cereal crops were the first to be cultivated systematically. Barley and wheat were probably first, then rice and oats. People began to sow some of the grain they collected from wild barley and wheat close to home, to make it easier to collect the grain the following year. Cultivation of rice began in China in around 6500 B.C.E. or a little later. The switch from gathering to cultivation made it possible for people to abandon the hunter-gatherer lifestyle in favor of a more settled, more predictable, and so more secure way of life.

A natural mutation produced a variety of wheat known as einkorn, in which the seed head was stable, so the grain did not get dispersed before being harvested. Around 8,000 years ago an einkorn wheat naturally hybridized, or crossed, with a species of wild grass to produce emmer wheat, which was gluten rich and made good flour. Another natural mutation produced durum wheat, in which the grain was easier to separate from the chaff by threshing. Wheat production was still inefficient, however. Farmers only reaped about six ears of wheat for every one they sowed. From about 7,000 years ago in the New World another cereal—corn (maize)—was far more productive. For every kernel planted, a farmer could harvest about 45 times as many.

Between 8,000 and 5,000 years ago came root crops and legumes, such as beets and beans. Later still were fruiting trees, leafy vegetables, and crops grown for feeding livestock.

EARLY HUMANS

THE STORY OF HUMAN EVOLUTION BEGAN more than 5 million years ago. The first hominids, or humanlike creatures, appeared about 2.4 million years ago in Africa. They learned to make fire and shaped tools, mainly as practical aids to survival but also for ceremonial use.

Human ancestors were making tools about 2.3 million years ago in Ethiopia and about 2.25 million years ago in China. Nearly 2 million years ago at Olduvai Gorge, Tanzania, "handy man" (*Homo habilis*) was making choppers by striking one stone against another. Choppers were used for cutting or sawing, and the blunt end of the stone would smash stone or bone.

Leaving Africa

Homo habilis lived only in Africa. A later species, *H. erectus*, migrated out of Africa and spread across Eurasia. *Homo erectus* lived from 1.85 million years ago until about 400,000 years ago and made tools that were more sophisticated than those of its predecessors. The manufacturing technique, however, was the same: striking one stone against another. The earliest tools associated with *H. erectus* were found in Olduvai Gorge and are about 1.4 million years old. Flint was the preferred stone of *H. erectus*, but flint is not found everywhere. When flint was not available, the toolmakers used other rocks, including quartz.

Instead of shaping one stone by striking identical stones together, *H. erectus* toolmakers used stone hammers to make cleavers and hand axes, with longer, straighter cutting edges than the old choppers. By about one million years ago they had discovered a new technique—using hammers made from deer antlers. This development allowed them to work with greater precision to make a much wider range of tools.

Neandertal people (*H. sapiens neanderthalensis*) lived in Europe, the Mediterranean region, and parts of the Middle East at the same time as modern humans, and in some places side by side with them. They first appeared about 100,000 years ago and became extinct about 30,000 years ago. Neandertals made a variety of simple stone tools.

Modern humans, *Homo sapiens*, were making much more efficient tools by 40,000 years ago. At two sites in France, they produced up to 80 different kinds of stone implements. People were also making tools with stone blades fixed to bone or antler handles. Cro-Magnon people living from 35,000 to 10,000 years ago made beautifully engraved bone tools that were probably used for ceremonial purposes. Among other things, they made chisels, awls, and tools with blades for scraping animal skins to make leather.

Stone tools survive indefinitely, allowing archaeologists to trace their development, but humans have also used other materials to make tools, such as wood and plant fibers, that decompose and disappear soon

KEY DATES

2,000,000 B.C.E.
Homo habilis makes stone tools

1,400,000 B.C.E.
Earliest-known *Homo erectus* tools

1,000,000 B.C.E.
H. erectus uses hammers made from deer antlers

20,000 B.C.E.
Leaf-shaped stone blades made in France

8000–7000 B.C.E.
European rock carving depicts a framed boat

5000 B.C.E.
Baskets made in Egypt

2700 B.C.E.
Silk woven in China

range of early hominids

range of *Homo erectus*, ca 500,000 years ago (y.a.)

range of modern humans by 10,000 y.a.

Selected fossil sites

Ardipithecus ramidus

Australopithecus

Homo habilis

Homo erectus

Homo sapiens neanderthalensis

anatomically modern humans, with date (y.a.)

other early modern human sites, with date (y.a.)

migration of modern humans, 100,000–18,000 y.a.

range of Neandertals, ca 100,000 y.a.

Limit of ice cap

18,000 y.a.

10,000 y.a.

ancient coastline 18,000 y.a.

Rift Valley

Map labels: Bluefish Cave 15–12,000; Laurentide Ice Sheet; Marmes 10,500; Folsom 9,000; Clovis 11,200; Little Salt Spring 12,000; Tepexpan 11–10,000; Pedra Pintada 11,200–10,500; Guitarrero Cave c.10,000; Monte Verde 12,500; Fell's Cave 11,000 after they are thrown away. Arrows and spears had wooden shafts, and arrows needed wooden bows to fire them. None of the wood survives.

People also began wearing clothes. The first garment may have been a woman's skirt made from cords hung from a belt. It is likely that people were twisting fibers into cord and ropes by 20,000 years ago. By that time they were also weaving willow stalks into baskets and fish traps and using twisted cords to make fishing nets. These techniques were adapted to making cloth. The earliest evidence of basket weaving, using palm leaves, split reeds, and other plant fibers, dates from

about 5000 B.C.E. at Fayoum, Egypt. By about 2700 B.C.E. silk was being woven into cloth in China.

Fish were an important part of the diet of most communities. In small rivers, hunters could wade across to set traps and spear fish. Wider rivers and lakes called for an alternative method. A rock carving from northern Europe, made between 9,000 and 10,000 years ago, shows a boat carrying hunters in pursuit of swimming reindeer. The boat seems to have a frame, in which case it would have resembled a kayak or coracle, which consists of a strong wooden frame covered in animal skin.

This map shows where early hominids lived and the migration of Homo sapiens around the world from about 100,000 years ago.

MAKING FIRE

CAPTURING AND MAKING FIRE CHANGED THE lifestyle of early humans. It gave them warmth and a means of defense and allowed them to settle in previously inhospitable areas. Cooking food enabled them to expand their diet and grow stronger. Sitting around the shared warmth of a fire, early humans were also able to develop communication skills that advanced their mental and social development.

Fire was essential for the growth of human civilization. People used it to cook their food, warm their homes, clear woodland or scrubland for cultivation, make pottery, and eventually smelt metals from ores. Historians usually give credit for the first use of fire, around 750,000 B.C.E., to *Homo erectus*, a race of early humans who lived between 1.85 million and 400,000 years ago, gradually spreading from Africa to areas of Asia and Europe.

Early humans likely saw how lightning set fire to dry trees and grass and, in some parts of the world, observed vegetation become ignited by molten lava or hot ashes from erupting volcanoes. At first people probably simply "captured" fire from these natural occurrences. They then kept a campfire burning nonstop, throughout day and night. They may have kept glowing coals or charcoal in a brazier; later, people would keep a lamp or a candle burning so that they were never without a source of fire. It was easier to keep a fire going than to start a new one.

Making fire from scratch is difficult, and all early methods relied on friction. When two surfaces rub together, they become hot. Early ways of making fire involved rubbing two pieces of wood together until they got hot enough to start a fire. The techniques—beginning about 7000 B.C.E.—included the use of fire sticks and fire drills. A fire stick is a stick of dry wood, one end of which has a blunt point that is turned in a small hollow dug in a larger piece of wood. The stick can be rotated between a person's hands by rubbing the palms together back and forth very rapidly. This method is still used by traditional peoples in Africa and Australia, and occasionally by hikers in wilderness areas. The friction between the pieces of wood gradually raises them to burning temperature, and the resulting heat ignites pieces of dry grass (tinder) in the hollow. The stick-and-groove method is a variation on the fire stick, in which a fire stick is rubbed hard back and forth along a groove in another piece of wood.

Alternatively, a bow can be used to rotate the fire stick more rapidly. Using a fire drill, the string of the bow makes a couple of turns around the fire stick, which spins first one way and then the other as the bow is pulled backward and forward.

Other Sources of Fire

Early humans also created fire by using sparks produced when a piece of flint strikes a piece of pyrite (a mineral form of iron sulfide). The sparks fall on tinder, such as dry grass or sawdust. Vigorous blowing then causes the smoldering tinder to burst into flame. A tinder box—which was in use for more than 2,000 years—holds all the necessary equipment to create a fire: flint, steel to strike it on, and tinder to get the fire going. Some later tinder boxes incorporated a candleholder to "capture" the new flame. Another method of making fire, apparently known to the ancient Greeks, used a lens or curved mirror to focus and concentrate the sun's rays—the idea of the burning glass. The final breakthrough in fire production came with the invention of friction matches in the 19th century.

KEY DATES

750,000 B.C.E.
Homo erectus uses fire

7,000 B.C.E.
Modern humans learn to make fire

1827 C.E.
Friction matches invented

The fire drill was probably one of the earliest human inventions. It uses a wooden bow to rotate a blunt-ended fire stick in a hollow in a piece of softer wood. The stick spins one way and then the other as the bow is pulled back and forth.

A tribesman from Kenya, Africa, builds up a fire, which he made with fire sticks, into a blaze by adding dried grass.

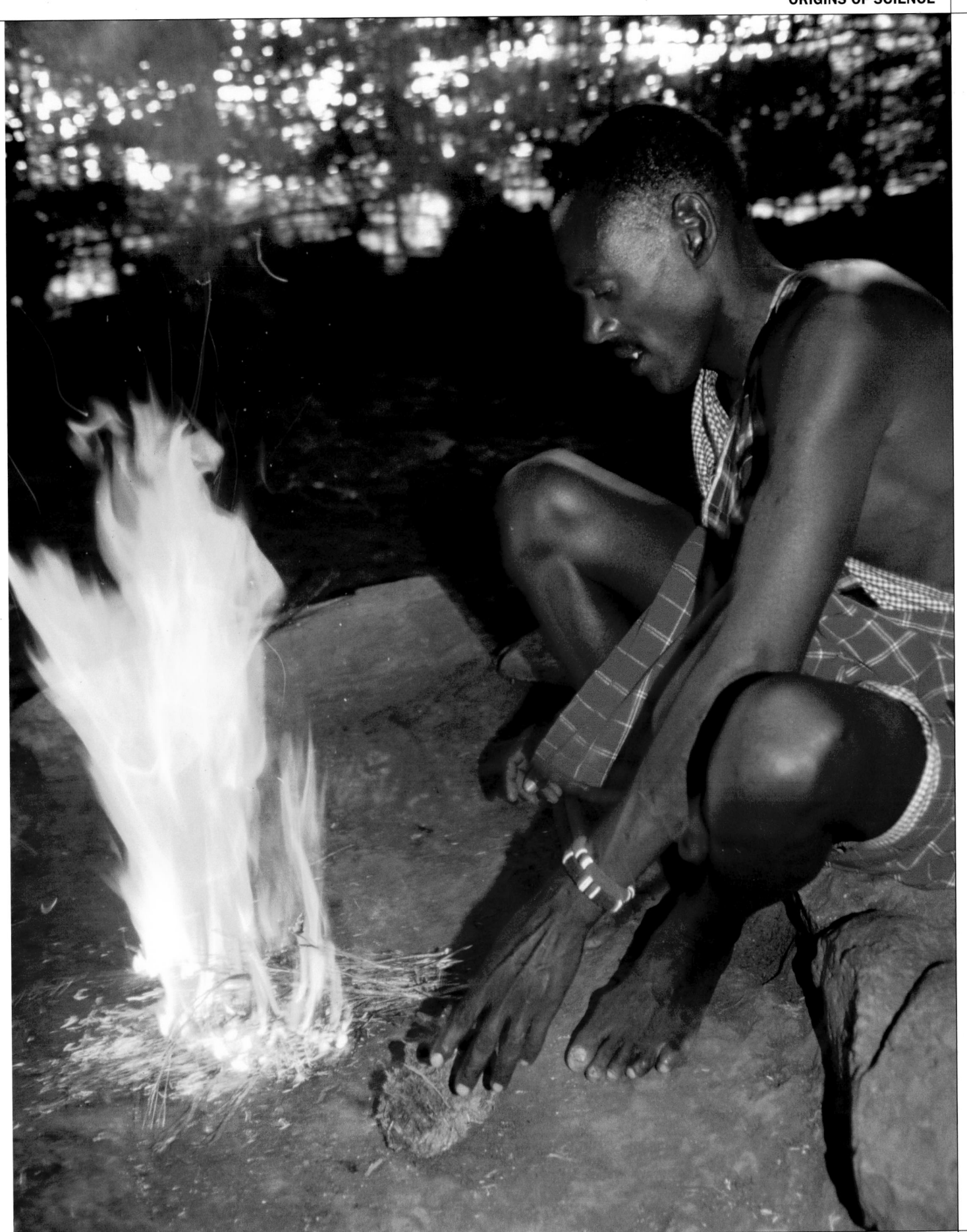

ASTRONOMY & MATH	BIOLOGY & MEDICINE	PHYSICAL SCIENCES

EUROPE

ca 4000 Domestication of horses occurs in Ukraine, for food, as beasts of burden, and also for riding.

INSIDE STORY

Dating the Past: Pottery

Because pottery lasts well, ceramic objects, such as pots and fragments of pottery, are common and valuable archaeological finds. The study of pottery artifacts helps archaeologists build up a picture of a culture, including its social organization, daily habits, diet, wealth, and religion.

For cultures that left no written records, pottery is one of the main ways of dating them. One technique is by comparison: Archaeologists can get a rough estimate of when a culture thrived from the style of its ceramics and how it compares with the style of other ancient cultures. A more accurate source of dating is known as thermoluminescence. It analyzes electrons to determine when the clay was fired. In addition, trace element analysis can be used to pinpoint the precise source of the clay, revealing whether it was local or had been transported over a distance.

THE AMERICAS

ca 5000 Arable farming begins in Mexico and Central America, with people growing an early type of corn.

ca 4500 In Central America avocados are grown, and cotton is cultivated.

Yangshao pot from China. The Yangshao culture flourished along the Yellow River from about 5000 to about 3000 B.C.E.

ASIA & OCEANIA

ca 5500 The jungle fowl is domesticated in Southeast Asia. The red jungle fowl of India is the ancestor of today's chicken.

ca 5200 People in northern Iran make wine from wild grapes. The fermentation process relies on natural yeasts.

ca 4000 The water buffalo is domesticated in China.

AFRICA & THE MIDDLE EAST

4236 Ancient Egyptians introduce a 365-day calendar (12 months of 30 days plus a 5-day holiday). This is the first precisely dated calendar until the Sumerian calendar of about 3000 B.C.E.

ca 6000 People in southwestern Asia cultivate flax to get fibers for making cloth.

ca 5000 Farmers in northern Africa and Ethiopia grow various types of millet as the principal grain crop.

ca 5000 People in settlements in the Middle East use cats for catching rats and mice.

If I die you will weep, but if the water buffalo dies, you will starve.

CHINESE PROVERB

ENGINEERING & INVENTION	WORLD EVENTS
ca 6000 In Scandinavia wooden sleds are used to travel over snow. Cave paintings from 1,000 years later show people on skis.	**ca 5400** Central European farmers begin the Bandkeramik culture, named for the linear patterns on their pottery.
ca 5000 People in Italy make mirrors out of the mineral obsidian, probably taken from the island of Melos.	**ca 4300** The first megalithic tombs are built of huge stones in western Europe.
ca 4300 People living near present-day Paris, France, make oak canoes up to 16 feet (5 m) long.	
ca 6000 The oldest-known pottery in the Americas is produced in Santarém on the Amazon River Basin in present-day Brazil.	
ca 5000 Permanent villages begin to spring up in Central America, following the development of corn as a crop.	
ca 4000 People in modern-day Thailand are the first in the world to make bronze, an alloy consisting of 90 percent copper and 10 percent tin.	**ca 6500** Farming begins in the Indus Valley in modern-day Pakistan and western India.
	ca 5000 In China the Yangshao culture produces pottery painted with images of people and animals or geometric patterns.
ca 6000 People in Asia Minor (present-day Turkey) produce clay pottery, weave cloth, and make rope.	**ca 5500** First archaeological evidence of Sumerians in Mesopotamia.
ca 6000 Palestinians start using mortar to bind together sun-dried bricks for construction.	**ca 4000** Village culture emerges in the Nile Valley.
ca 5000 Copper is smelted in Egypt and used to make weapons and other tools.	
ca 4400 Egyptians weave cloth on a loom, usually linen made from wild flax.	
ca 4000 The brick-built arch is used in construction in Egypt and Mesopotamia.	
ca 4000 The door lock is invented in Mesopotamia. People there employ a harness to use oxen as draft animals.	
ca 4000 Egyptians make boat hulls by joining planks of wood together, allowing them to make larger vessels.	

DOMESTICATION OF ANIMALS

Ancient humans hunted wild animals for thousands of years. As humans evolved, animals became a source not just of food, but also of fur, hide, sinew, horn, and bone.

The domestication of livestock probably began about 10,000 years ago (8000 B.C.E.), when wild goats and mouflon (sheep), followed by wild pigs (7000 B.C.E.), were captured in eastern Asia and Mesopotamia and kept close to settlements. As these animals bred, their descendants became more accustomed to human proximity.

By about 8,500 years ago (6500 B.C.E.) cattle were kept under domestication in Africa and India. Chickens were domesticated in Southeast Asia in about 5500 B.C.E. Evidence suggests that by about 4000 B.C.E., people in the Middle East were harnessing the strength of animals to drag heavy loads or pull plows. At the same time, Europeans began to keep horses, first for meat and milk, but soon also for riding: Some 6,000-year-old horse teeth found in Ukraine show signs of wear possibly caused by a bit.

By 2000 B.C.E. horses were animals of status, ridden by wealthy or important people. They were also used in war to intimidate the enemy, ridden by cavalry soldiers or used to pull chariots. Bactrian camels were domesticated in northern Afghanistan by about 2500 B.C.E. In the New World the llama was domesticated in about 3000 B.C.E. and the guinea pig (cavy) in 2000 B.C.E. The latter was bred for meat long before it became a pet.

Domesticated cattle in a 4,000-year-old cave painting in Algeria

THE COMING OF THE WHEEL

THE WHEEL HAS BEEN INVENTED AND reinvented several times throughout history. The details of its first appearance, at least 5,000 years ago, are lost in the distant past. About 6,000 years ago humans were already using drag technology such as plows and sledges. In some parts of the world, heavy objects such as rocks and boats were moved using log rollers. As the object moved forward, rollers were taken from behind and replaced in front. Rollers may have been the starting point for the invention of the cartwheel.

After a set of logs had been used for some time, they would become worn where they scraped against the sledge. Eventually the sledge would settle into the worn section of the rollers, and this may have given people the idea for the axle wheel. Because an axle has a small circumference, it takes less energy to turn than a whole wheel. However, there are some problems with the theory that the wheel evolved from rollers— whole logs split and fall apart quite easily when rolled under pressure, and the tall, straight trees that were needed to make rollers were not abundant in the Middle East, where the first solid evidence for vehicular wheels appears.

The development of a wheel constructed to rotate on a fixed axle is used by archaeologists as an indicator of relatively advanced civilization. The earliest evidence of axled wheels dates back to about 3200 B.C.E. The Sumerian people of Mesopotamia (modern-day Iraq) produced pictures of carts with solid wheels, apparently made from two pieces of plank bracketed together and cut into a circular shape. The axles went through the center of each wheel and were fixed in place by lynchpins. Similar wheels appeared on war chariots also built by the Sumerians in Mesopotamia in about 2500 B.C.E. By 2000 B.C.E. the Sumerians had developed spoked wheels, which made chariots much lighter and more maneuverable. The design later spread and was refined by other civilizations, including the Egyptians and the Romans. In China, the wheel appeared independently in about 2800 B.C.E.

Not Just Transportation

The first wheels were probably not intended for transportation. Evidence from around 3500 B.C.E. shows that potters were using simple turntables to help them create smooth, evenly shaped pots. These early potters' wheels were developed further by the Greeks and Egyptians into flywheels that could convert pulses of energy, such as the pressing of a treadle, into smooth, continuous motion. The flywheel was to become just as important as the vehicular wheel. The Greeks also came up with other variations on the wheel. The fourth and third centuries B.C.E. saw the development of cogs, gearwheels, and pulleys. The waterwheel was another important variation on the basic axled design. First developed around 85 B.C.E., waterwheels allowed humans to harness the power of water to drive millstones for grinding grain.

Since ancient times there have been several more wheel innovations. The Chinese began using spinning wheels for manufacturing yarn between 500 and 1000 C.E. The flywheel also played a key role in the Industrial Revolution. When connected to pistons driven by a steam engine, it converted pulses of raw power into smooth movement that could be used to drive machines and power locomotives. Later still came wheel-based innovations including turbines, gyroscopes, and castor wheels—all variations on an ancient piece of technology still going strong today.

OPPOSITE: *Inspiration for the vehicular wheel may have come from the potter's wheel, which was developed a few centuries earlier.*

KEY DATES

3500 B.C.E.
First potters' wheels appear in Mesopotamia

3200 B.C.E..
First axled vehicular wheel appears (also in Mesopotamia)

2800 B.C.E.
Chinese develop the wheel (probably independently)

85 B.C.E.
Waterwheel is developed in Greece

500–1000 B.C.E.
Spinning wheel is developed in China

War has long been a driving force of invention, and the wheel may be another example. The Sumerians were the first to develop wheeled chariots, closely followed by the ancient Egyptians.

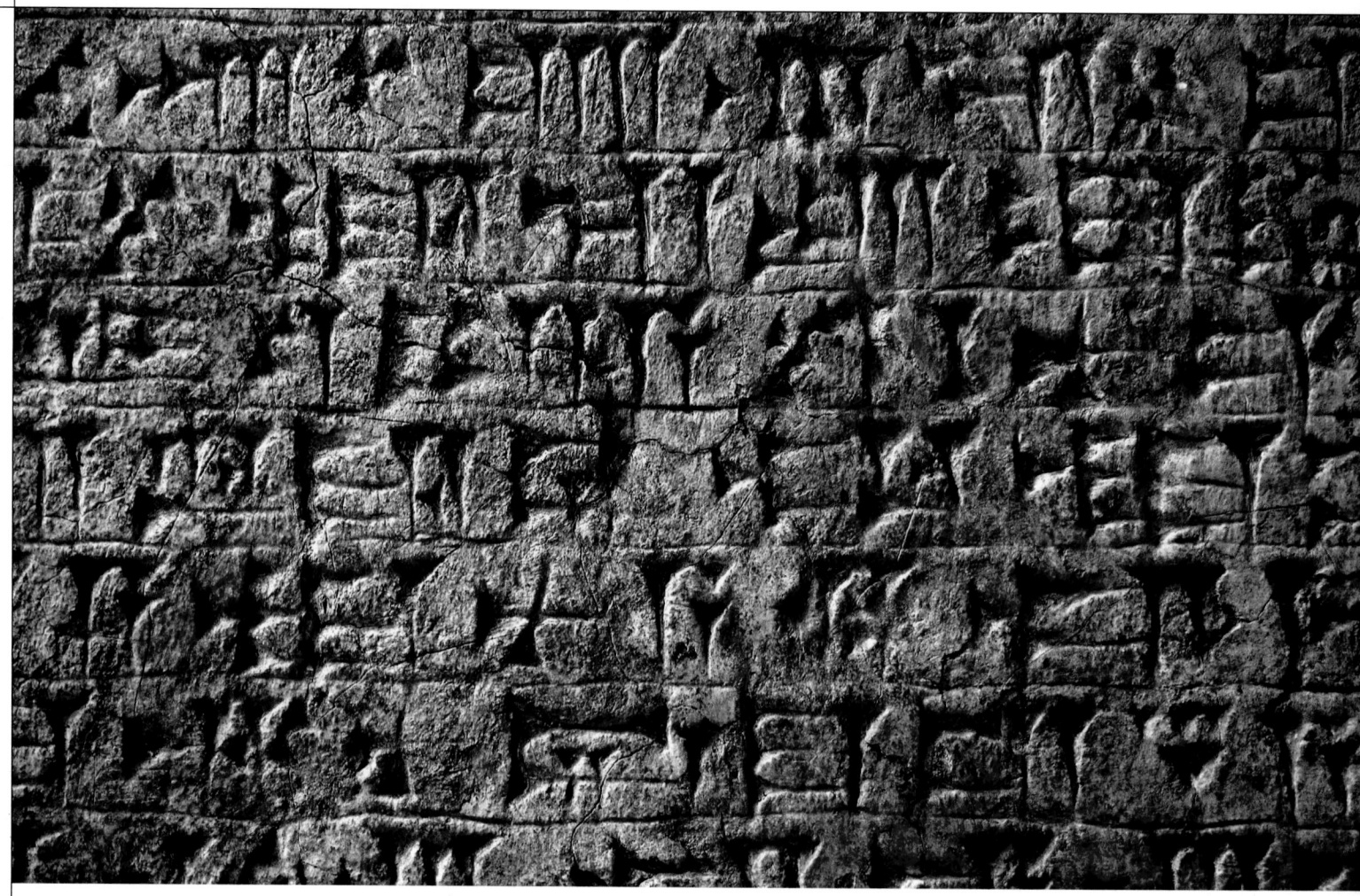

WRITING AND NUMBERS

PEOPLE HAVE ALWAYS NEEDED TO KEEP records of important events, goods stored or traded, and taxes collected. A drawing is the simplest type of record. Scientists believe that the cave paintings in the Lascaux Grotto in France, made between 17,000 and 15,000 years ago and depicting various animals and a man, record a religious ritual. Early drawings signified exactly what they represented—a picture of a deer meant "deer." Gradually, the symbols acquired more abstract meanings, and eventually they developed into writing.

Writing developed as a way of keeping records. At first, representational drawings became simpler in form. "Sun" might be a small circle inside a larger circle, and water might be depicted as a wavy line. Such simple signs could be drawn quickly and remained clearly recognizable even when they were made very small. In time they came to have more than one meaning. The sign for "sun" also meant "day," or in Egypt the sun-god Re (or Ra).

In the next stage each sign came to represent a sound as well as an object, or simply a sound. This type of writing, in which pictures represent sounds, is called "hieroglyphic," and the best-known type was developed in Egypt, where it first appeared around 3100 B.C.E. By about 2700 B.C.E. Egyptian hieroglyphic writing had been more or less standardized, and it remained in use for some 3,000 years.

At about the same time another system of writing was emerging in Mesopotamia, the region between the Euphrates and Tigris rivers, in what is present-day Iraq. It also began as a system of stylized pictures, but it developed very differently from Egyptian hieroglyphs because of the tools used to write it. Whereas

ABOVE: *Cuneiform script —seen here on a stone wall—fell into disuse around the beginning of the Common Era. It was deciphered by scholars in the 19th century.*

Egyptian scribes wrote on papyrus paper with reed pens and ink, Mesopotamian scribes pressed a writing tool called a stylus into a tablet of soft clay, making a wedge or round shape. This type of writing is called cuneiform. It came into use in about 2400 B.C.E. Cuneiform was the writing system used by the Sumerians, the Assyrians, and the Babylonians. It spread to Persia and remained in use for nearly 2,000 years. The first real alphabet (the Proto Canaanite) emerged in the Middle East in about 1700 B.C.E. It used 30 symbols to represent single sounds. From this the Phoenician alphabet of 22 letters developed by about 1000 B.C.E., eventually giving rise to Arabic, Hebrew, Latin, and Greek scripts.

Chinese writing also developed from pictures. They were inscribed on bones and seashells that were then thrown into the air. People believed that the pattern in which they fell conveyed messages from the gods or from ancestors. These symbols were in use from about 1700 B.C.E. They became more abstract during the Zhou Dynasty (ca 1122–256 B.C.E.).

Writing Numbers

Record keepers also needed a way to write numbers. A picture of one cow can represent one cow, but it would be impractical to represent 60 cows by drawing each one. In about 30,000 B.C.E. in what is now the Czech Republic someone carved 55 notches (11 groups of five) on a bone from the leg of a wolf. They may refer to the number of animals killed in a hunt, although no one really knows, but the bone is clearly a numerical record. A stick or bone used in this way is called a tally stick.

Numerals for quantities greater than ten were first used in Egypt in about 3400 B.C.E., Mesopotamia in about 3000 B.C.E., and in Crete in about 1200 B.C.E. Using ten as a base was an obvious choice because humans have ten fingers, and most cultures adopted this counting system. The Babylonians and Sumerians were the major exceptions: They calculated to base 60. Egyptian and cuneiform numbers used different symbols for 1; 10; 100; 1,000; 10,000; 100,000; and 1,000,000, and indicated higher values by repeating them, as in Roman numerals, where X is 10, XX is 20, and XXX is 30; C is 100, and CCC is 300. However, none of these systems had a symbol for zero.

Clay was plentiful, and cuneiform writing has survived on thousands of Babylonian tablets. As long as the clay was soft, a tablet could be smoothed and used again. Some of the tablets found were students' exercise books. They include multiplication tables and complex calculations. Egyptians, however, used only addition and the two times table. They performed multiplication by repeatedly doubling or halving and then adding the results. Nevertheless, surviving Egyptian papyri describe such tasks as dividing a given number of loaves among a given number of people and finding the area of a right-angled triangle.

Proto Canaanite	Early letter names and meanings	Phoenician	Early Greek	Early monumental Latin	Modern English
	alp oxhead				A
	bêt house			B	B
	gaml throwstick				C
	digg fish			D	D
	hô(?) man calling				E
	wô mace				F
	zê(n) ?				
	hê(t) fence?			H	H
	tê(t) spindle?				
	yad arm				I
	kapp palm			K	K
	lamd ox-goad				L
	mêm water				M
	nahs snake				N
	cên eye				O
	pi't corner?				P
	sa(d) plant				
	qu(p) ?				Q
	ra's head of man			R	R
	taan composite bow				S
	tô owner's mark			T	T

Most of the letters in our modern English alphabet can be traced back to the Phoenician alphabet, as shown here. However, the Phoenicians made no distinction between the letter J and the letter I.

KEY DATES

3400 B.C.E.
Numbers (base 10) used in Egypt

3100 B.C.E.
Egyptian hieroglyphs

2400 B.C.E.
Cuneiform writing

1700 B.C.E.
Early Chinese writing

1700 B.C.E.
Proto Canaanite alphabet

1000 B.C.E.
Phoenician alphabet

	ASTRONOMY & MATH	BIOLOGY & MEDICINE	PHYSICAL SCIENCES
EUROPE		**ca 3000** People establish towns in the Aegean region of Greece, based on the cultivation of olives and grapes.	**ca 3000** Copper ore deposits are found on the Mediterranean island of Cyprus, which soon becomes the major source of the metal in the ancient world.

South Americans have used the llama as a beast of burden and for meat and fiber production for about 5,000 years.

Acupuncture remains in regular use over 4,500 years since its invention in China.

THE AMERICAS		**ca 4000** Potatoes are cultivated in the Andes, where it is too cold to grow corn. **ca 3000** People in Peru domesticate the llama. **ca 2500** The peanut becomes a food crop.	
ASIA & OCEANIA	**2950** In China a lunar calendar is developed. **2637** According to later tradition, this is year 1 of the Chinese calendar.	**ca 2900** Cotton is cultivated in the valley of the Indus River to weave into cloth. **ca 2700** In China silkworms are cultured on mulberry leaves. Strands of silk are unwound from their cocoons to make cloth. **ca 2500** People in Iran and Afghanistan domesticate the Bactrian camel. **ca 2500** Chinese doctors use acupuncture to heal ailments.	
AFRICA & THE MIDDLE EAST	**ca 3500** The Egyptians use a simple shadow clock, or gnomon, a vertical stick or obelisk that casts a shadow. **ca 3400** The Egyptians adopt numerals for quantities greater than 10 (with base 10). **ca 3000** The Sumerians introduce a 360-day solar calendar with 12 months of 30 days. They add an extra month roughly every eight years to keep in step with the seasons. **ca 2500** Sumerian traders introduce a system of standard weights, including the shekel and the mina. **ca 2600** Egyptian builders use a set square for setting out right angles and a plumbline for checking verticals.	**ca 4000** In Egypt the donkey is domesticated as a beast of burden. **ca 3000** In West Africa yams are cultivated; palm trees are also grown for producing oil. **ca 2600** In Egypt priests begin the practice of embalming dead dignitaries such as pharaohs to create mummies. **ca 2500** Egyptian physicians begin practicing surgery and develop a range of surgical instruments for the purpose.	**ca 3200** Bronze, the copper–tin alloy, is first used in Mesopotamia (present-day Iraq). The use of bronze spreads throughout the Middle East and Europe. By 2500 B.C.E. the Sumerians cast ax heads out of copper and bronze. **ca 3200** The Egyptians use a "nilometer" to measure the annual Nile flood. **ca 3000** To create an artificial lake for water for irrigation, Egyptian engineers build a 328-foot (100-m) dam across the Garawi River Valley. **ca 2600** People in Mesopotamia make glass by melting together sand (silica) and soda (sodium carbonate). At first it is used for glazes on pots and vases; later they learn to shape molten glass and make bottles.

ENGINEERING & INVENTION	WORLD EVENTS
ca 3100 The first stage of construction of Stonehenge—an earth bank with a ring of holes—begins in southern England. **ca 3000** An industry making marble sculptures develops on the Greek islands in the Aegean Sea (the Cyclades).	**ca 3000** Megalithic tombs are built on the island of Malta. **ca 2500** The Beaker people spread from the Low Countries to France.
ca 3000 People in North America create rock shelters and produce items made of feathers, including blankets and baskets.	**ca 3500** The Haida culture begins in Canada. **3372** In the calendar of the later Maya, this year marks the beginning of time.
ca 3500 Farmers in Mesopotamia and China use a primitive plow. **ca 3000** Chinese and Egyptian sailors equip their boats with anchors. **ca 2500** Clay water pipes are used for drains at Mohenjo-Daro in Pakistan and in Knossos, Crete.	**ca 4000** Farmers begin to settle on the Indus Valley floodplain and build irrigation systems with dams and canals. **ca 2600** The first cities emerge in the Indus Valley.
ca 3500 River barges with sails are used in Mesopotamia and Egypt. **ca 3500** The wheel appears in Mesopotamia, first as a potter's wheel. **ca 3400** The Sumerians use simple picture writing that later develops into cuneiform. **ca 3200** Wheeled vehicles with axles are used in the Near and Middle East. **ca 3100** Egyptian scribes begin using hieroglyphs as a form of writing. **ca 2800** The Sumerians make soap. **2630** Work begins on the stepped pyramid of Djoser (r. ca 2630–ca 2611) at Saqqara in Egypt. **2550** The Great Pyramid of King Khufu (r. ca 2589–ca 2566) is completed at Giza in Egypt.	**ca 3500** The Sahara region suffers from prolonged desertification. **ca 3200** The first acknowledged civilization emerges between the Tigris and Euphrates Rivers, known in Greek as Mesopotamia or "land between the rivers." The Sumerians farm the fertile valley, build cities, and organize government and religion. **3100** Upper (southern) and Lower (northern) Egypt are united under the kings of the Predynastic period. **2950** The Dynastic Period begins in Egypt when the First Dynasty is formed by Pharaoh Menes.

ANCIENT MEDICINE

Throughout history, people have tried various ways to heal the sick. Some were not particularly medical: Healers, for example, often predicted the course of a disease by examining the liver of a sacrificed animal.

Seeking advice or using herbal remedies to treat minor complaints—"folk medicine"—was widespread. However, people believed that more serious illness was caused by angry gods or by demons entering the body. Treatments involved physical manipulation of the patient, herbal medicines, and incantations to drive the demons away. Drilling a hole in the top of the skull—a procedure called trepanning—was often used to allow whatever caused an illness to escape.

Chinese medicine, including acupuncture, began over 4,500 years ago. Chinese doctors believed that illness was caused by imbalances between the female (yin) and male (yang) cosmic principles, and they aimed to correct the imbalance with herbal remedies.

Ayurvedic medicine, based on religious writings, is still used in India, where it began about 3,000 years ago. It aims to prevent illness through lifestyle, hygiene, and yoga, and to cure complaints by diet and preparations of herbs and minerals. In ancient Greece, there were hundreds of temples to Asclepius, the god of healing. Sick people spent the night at the temple and described their dreams to the priests, who then advised them on a cure.

Ayurvedic yoga is still widely practiced today.

THE AGRICULTURAL REVOLUTION

THE HISTORY OF FARMING DATES FROM ABOUT 11,000 years ago, when people gradually gave up nomadic foraging—the hunter-gatherer way of life—and began to form more settled communities. At first using slash-and-burn techniques, people began to live in settlements where they could cultivate, or grow, crops and domesticate, or tame, animals. The need to store or prepare the food they grew or raised to survive times when food was hard to find also led to new discoveries, such as grinding grain to make flour or salting and curing meats. This shift, often called the agricultural revolution, occurred independently in West and East Asia, the Americas, and Africa.

In the fertile valley of the Nile River in Egypt and in Mesopotamia between the Tigris and Euphrates Rivers (in present-day Iraq) early farmers used digging sticks and hoes to prepare the soil for planting and sickles to harvest crops. The plow, invented in about 3500 B.C.E. by farmers in Mesopotamia and China, greatly extended the areas of land that could be prepared to cultivate crops.

Selective Breeding

Over years, selective breeding—choosing which plants or animals (usually the most useful) can reproduce—resulted in higher-yielding strains of cereal plants such as wheat and barley. People also began to domesticate useful animals and selectively bred them for certain characteristics, such as strength or docility. Beasts of burden, such as horses, oxen, camels, llamas, and buffalo, began to replace human muscle power to carry loads, draw plows, and pull carts. Other animals, such as sheep, goats, pigs, chickens, and other poultry, were also domesticated not only for their meat, milk, or eggs, but also for their skin, fiber (hair or wool), and feathers.

It was difficult to keep food over winter, although people did store dried grain. Stored grain became infested with rats and mice, which in turn attracted wildcats. Farmers in the Near East recognized the

usefulness of the cats in controlling the rodent pests, which led to the domestication of the cat. Pulses (edible seeds), such as lentils, peas, and beans, could also be dried and easily stored.

Farmers tended to slaughter many of their animals in late fall because they had insufficient food for the livestock to survive through winter. Because meat would spoil if not soon eaten, people in early settlements needed to find ways to preserve animal carcasses as a supply of meat into the following year. The initial methods for preserving meat included simply allowing the carcasses to dry in the wind or in cold climates storing them in caves—in a similar way as we now refrigerate meat. New technologies eventually arose to preserve food in other ways. One method involved smoking meat or fish over a wood fire, a method still widely used today (more often to improve flavor than out of necessity). Fish and meat were also salted. A combination of curing (smoking) and salting pig meat (pork) created ham and bacon.

People also began to use grindstones to make flour from harvested grains and to make clay pots to store food as well as for cooking. The earliest-known pottery dates from about 11,000 B.C.E. in Japan. It was invented independently in the Middle East about 5,000 years later. As the potters grew more skillful, they built ovens for baking the clay.

By about 5000 B.C.E. some communities were producing a food surplus that they could trade or barter for other goods, such as tools or pottery. Once they had reached that stage, people were poised to take the next leap forward: The urban revolution and the establishment of what we call civilization.

This painting from the tomb of an Egyptian artisan called Sennedjem shows him using a simple plow pulled by a pair of oxen. It dates from the reign of pharaoh Rameses II (ca 1303–1213 B.C.E.).

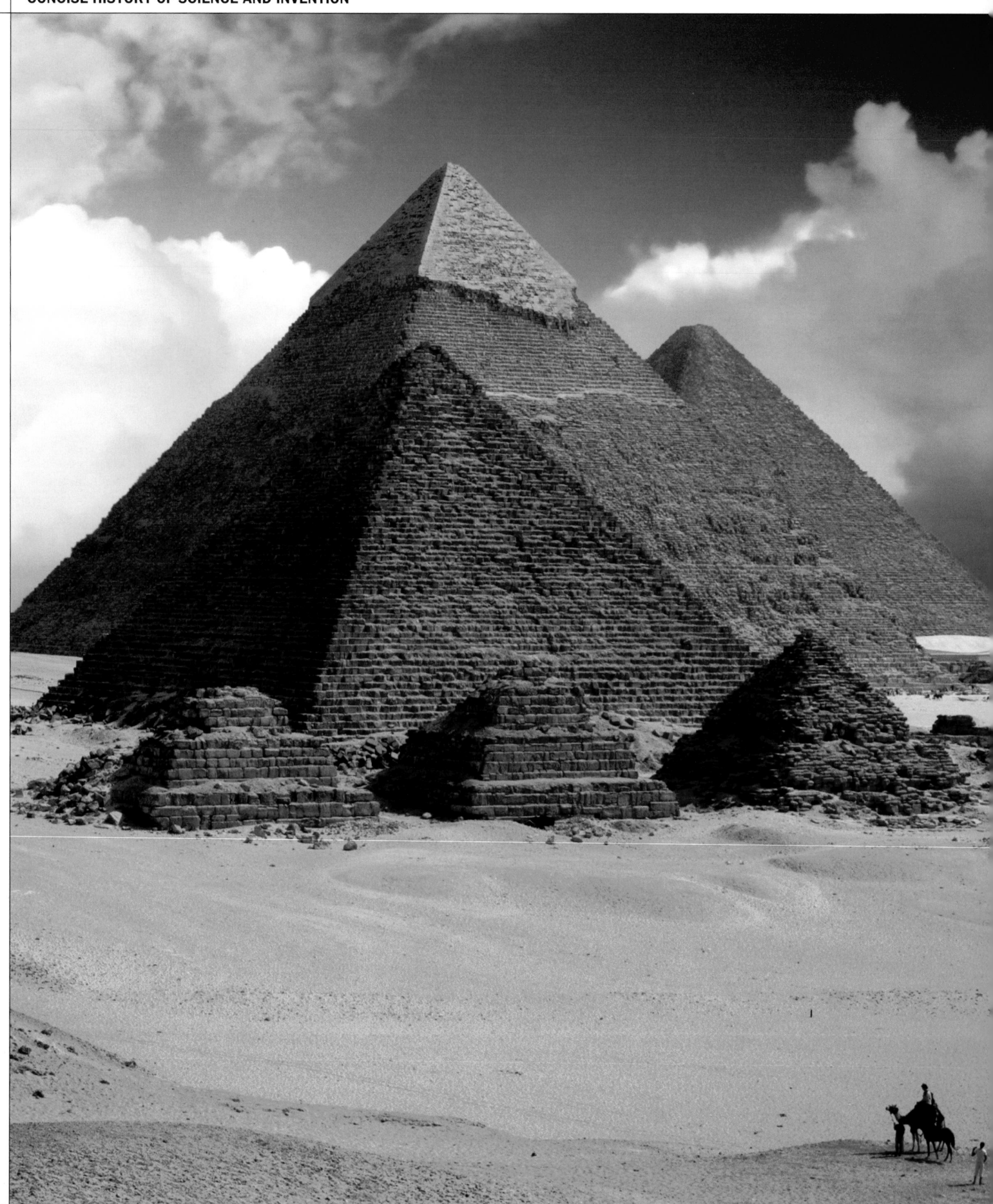

BUILDING THE PYRAMIDS

THE GREAT PYRAMID AT GIZA IS THE ONLY one of the Seven Wonders of the Ancient World to survive today. That it is still standing after 4,500 years is testament to the technological sophistication, ingenuity, and organizational skills of the ancient civilization that built it.

Humankind seems compelled to create tall buildings. Four thousand years ago the only shape for such a structure was a broad base tapering to the top—giving stability and a means of transporting building materials upward. Smooth-sided pyramids seem to have been a natural progression from another type of building, known as a ziggurat. Ziggurats were built by the ancient civilizations of Mesopotamia and Persia (Sumerians, Babylonians, and Assyrians) between 3000 and 500 B.C.E. A ziggurat was a sort of stepped temple-tower built in several levels, each smaller than the one below. Ziggurats were built with a core of unfired mud bricks and an outer covering of fired bricks, often glazed with elaborate colors. They had between two and seven tiers. Among the most famous are the beautifully preserved ziggurat at Ur in Iraq and the ziggurat of Marduk in Babylon.

Egypt's Pyramids

The first pyramid in Egypt was built at Saqqara starting in about 2630 B.C.E. to honor King Djoser (reigned 2630–2611 B.C.E.). It had a stepped structure not unlike that of a ziggurat, but it was made of stone rather than mud. Within 30 years the Egyptians had refined the design and were beginning to build smooth pyramids, such as the Red Pyramid at Dashur, generally taken as the first "true" pyramid. The core was still made of massive structural blocks, but they were cased in smaller blocks to smooth the outline into something more pleasing to the eye.

The pyramids were burial structures built to honor the kings (or pharaohs), who were regarded by their people as living gods. The site for a pyramid would have been chosen by the king himself. Detailed plans were drawn up by skilled draftsmen working on sheets of papyrus. Sometimes the pyramids were built over significant natural features such as rocky outcrops. This meant that fewer materials had to be imported, but it must have posed challenges for the architects, since uneven ground is much more difficult to survey and measure precisely, and precision was imperative.

All Egyptian pyramids are built along a precise north–south axis, but this was achieved thousands of years before the magnetic compass existed. Instead, the Egyptians used a surveying tool called a *bay* to determine the direction of true north from the stars. The perfection of symmetry in the finished pyramids shows that the Egyptians also had a firm grasp of geometry, allowing them to mark out the base of the pyramid as a perfect square. Anything less than perfect right angles would mean that the four sides would fail to form a neat point at the apex. The same perfection was required of the individual blocks, the shape of which was honed by skilled masons.

How Were the Pyramids Built?

For years the questions that have puzzled archaeologists most about the pyramids are: How did the builders transport the enormous blocks of stone used in construction and how did they raise them to such great heights? The blocks used to build the Great Pyramid at Giza weigh from 2.5 to 15 tons (2–14 tonnes) each, and those at the top have been lifted 480 feet (147 m) above ground level. The answer to the first question is that the stone was quarried as locally as possible. Anything brought from far away was carried by boat along the Nile River. To carry the stone to the top the builders used ramps—gentle gradients up which it would have been possible to drag the blocks on wooden sleds. Once at the top, it is assumed that wooden and bronze levers were used to maneuver the blocks into position.

While technology obviously played a key role in the construction of the pyramids, perhaps the real secret of the Egyptians' success was in organizing a vast workforce. Estimates of the numbers of people involved vary from 100,000 to just a few thousand. It seems unlikely that these people were slaves. There is archaeological evidence of thriving communities centered on the construction sites, providing accommodation and services for a huge workforce.

OPPOSITE: *The Giza pyramid complex includes the Great Pyramid (back), the Pyramid of Khafre (center), and the Pyramid of Menkaure, along with numerous temples, cemeteries, and the smaller "queens" pyramids (front).*

KEY DATES

2630 B.C.E.
First pyramid built in Egypt at Saqqara

2600 B.C.E.
First true pyramid built, the Red Pyramid at Dahshur

2550 B.C.E.
Great Pyramid at Giza completed

2250 B.C.E.
Last pyramid built for Pharaoh Pepi II at Saqqara

ASTRONOMY & MATH	BIOLOGY & MEDICINE	PHYSICAL SCIENCES

EUROPE

ca 2300 Work begins on the largest stone circle in Europe at Avebury in southern Britain. The precise alignment of its stones suggests that it may have had an astronomical purpose.

ca 1700 In central Europe, people trade widely in precious amber and metals such as copper and tin.

The large stones of Stonehenge were probably shaped before being dragged to the site on rollers. Using ropes, levers, and props, workers pulled each 28-ton (25-tonne) stone upright and rammed small stones around its base to make it stable.

THE AMERICAS

ca 2000 Copper is mined in the Great Lakes region of North America.

ASIA & OCEANIA

2296 Chinese astronomers record a sighting of a comet.

Stonehenge

Stonehenge is a megalithic (meaning made of large stones) monument on the Salisbury Plain in southern England. It was built in three phases from about 3100 B.C.E. The upright stones were erected in about 2300 B.C.E. and joined along their tops by lintels to form a circle 100 feet (30 m) across. It must have taken hundreds of people many years to drag the stones to the site. The purpose of the monument is not known, but it may have been a temple linked to the worship of the sun and the moon.

ca 2000 Chinese emperors establish an early zoo, called the Park of Intelligence.

AFRICA & THE MIDDLE EAST

ca 2300 Astronomers in Babylon study comets and observe the constellations.

ca 2000 Mathematicians in Babylon introduce a positional number system (in which the value of a digit depends on its position in a number) using base 60.

ca 1800 Mathematicians in Mesopotamia discover what is now called Pythagorean theorem (concerning the lengths of the sides of a right-angled triangle).

1750 King Hammurabi of Babylon authorizes astronomers to compile catalogs of stars and planets.

ca 1650 Egyptian mathematicians learn how to solve simple equations, as indicated in the Rhind Papyrus, which was written at about this time.

ca 1600 Astrologers in Babylon recognize the zodiac, the path that the sun, moon, and planets (except Pluto) appear to take as they move across the sky.

ca 2400 The Egyptians domesticate cats. Some cats are regarded as sacred and made into mummies.

ca 2300 People in the Middle East keep geese. They collect and eat the eggs.

ca 2300 The Egyptians make wine from cultivated grapes. They add resin to improve the taste.

ca 2000 In Syria and Babylon medicine (based largely on astrology) becomes an important science. Recipes for ointments and poultices are recorded on clay tablets.

ca 1550 A papyrus known as the Ebers Papyrus—named for 19th-century German Egyptologist Georg Ebers (1837–98)—describes Egyptian medical practices and gives details of 700 drugs and other medications.

ca 2500 Tin ore is mined and smelted in Göltepe (in present-day Turkey). It becomes a source of the metal for alloying with copper to make bronze.

ca 2400 People in Mesopotamia use naturally occurring tar, or bitumen, to waterproof buildings and boats.

ENGINEERING & INVENTION	WORLD EVENTS
ca 1600 Bellows are used in metal and glassmaking around the Mediterranean. **ca 1500** Interior bathrooms with running water are built in the palace of Minos on the Mediterranean island of Crete.	**ca 2000** The Minoan culture on Crete builds palaces at Knossos. **ca 1700** Trade routes across Europe carry luxury goods such as amber and raw materials such as copper and tin. **ca 1600** The Mycenaean culture emerges on Crete.
ca 2500 People in the Arctic begin to chip delicate tools from flint. **ca 1750** People living in the settlement of La Florida in the Rimac River Valley in Peru construct a long canal to irrigate their farmland.	**1600** The Poverty Point culture, named for a site in Louisiana, emerges in North America.
ca 1550 Farmers in Southeast Asia make plowshares with bronze.	**2333** A legendary ruler named Tangun forms the first Korean kingdom. **1766** The Shang Dynasty begins in China. **ca 2500** About 40,000 people live in the Indus Valley city of Harappa. **ca 2000** Austronesians, sailing on outrigger boats, reach and settle on various islands in the South Pacific.
ca 2400 The parasol or umbrella is invented in Mesopotamia. **ca 2300** The earliest known map is produced on a clay tablet in Mesopotamia. It probably shows a nobleman's estate. **ca 2300** King Sargon I of Akkad produces maps of his kingdom in Mesopotamia to calculate land taxes. **ca 2100** The Sumerians construct a ziggurat (temple) near Ur using mud bricks. **ca 2000** Egyptian military engineers develop a portable battering ram. **ca 2000** Spoked wheels are used in Egypt and Mesopotamia, and bridles on horses. **ca 1950** Farmers in Palestine make plows with iron plowshares. **ca 1500** The Egyptians invent the shaduf—a bucket counterbalanced on a lever—for raising water from a well, a ditch, or a river.	**ca 1950** Elamites seize Ur, ending the great period of Sumerian civilization. **ca 1792** Under Hammurabi I (ca 1792—50), Babylon becomes the center of an empire that stretches into Assyria and Persia. **ca 1750** The earliest literary classic—*The Epic of Gilgamesh*—is written down in Mesopotamia. **ca 1595** Hittites led by Mursilis I (r. ca 1556–26) sack Babylon and bring its power to an end. **ca 1550** The people of the city of Mittani, in Mesopotamia, begin to build an empire. **ca 1550** Ahmose (r. ca 1550–25) establishes the 18th Dynasty and begins Egypt's New Kingdom. **ca 1504** Amenhotep I (r. ca 1526–06) is the first pharaoh to be buried in the Valley of the Kings.

Egyptian king in a papyrus boat

THE FIRST BOATS

The dugout canoe was the first purpose-built boat. It was made from a hollowed-out log. The oldest-known dugout boat was found in the Netherlands and dates from 6300 B.C.E. Later canoes were made by stretching leather or bark over a wooden frame. Oars provided propulsion. The next development was the sail, invented by the Egyptians in about 3500 B.C.E.

At first Egyptian boats were made from woven papyrus reeds, but they later used wooden planks bound together with strips of leather or papyrus. The first sailboats were square-rigged, with a square sail set at more or less right angles to the direction of travel, which was with the wind. The boats were steered using oars. They were used for many centuries. Later Egyptian vessels abandoned sails and reverted to banks of oars for propulsion. By about 700 B.C.E., the Phoenicians were using biremes, which had two banks of oars; later they built triremes with three banks of oars.

In the first century C.E., the Chinese invented the rudder, a pivoted vertical plank that steers the boat. Another breakthrough was the triangular lateen sail, invented in about the third century C.E. by the Arabs. A lateen sail can be swung through an angle so that the wind does not have to come from behind for the ship to make progress.

Mediterranean vessels also used lateen sails in combination with square sails on the masts. The descendants of these craft were used by Spanish and Portuguese explorers on their voyages of discovery.

MAKING USE OF METALS

THE CLASSICAL POET HESIOD DIVIDED GREEK history into five ages. The first was a perfect "Golden Age." There followed Silver and Bronze Ages, then a Heroic Age, before the Iron Age, in which Hesiod himself lived. With each passing age, the lives of humans become harder and more miserable. Hesiod's choice of different metals to identify four of the five ages reflected the changing use of metals in ancient society.

The importance of gold and silver is well attested by finds buried in ancient graves. For example, at the prehistoric city of Mycenae in Greece, archaeologists found treasures including the gold Cup of Nestor, crafted sometime between 1600 and 1500 B.C.E., and a star-

tling death mask said to portray the Greek warrior king Agamemnon (although few historians take the claim seriously).

The Egyptians also produced gold ornaments. The mask of Tutankhamun, the boy king who reigned from 1333 to 1323 B.C.E., is made from gold inlaid with lapis lazuli. It was found in his tomb. Gold and silver vessels, masks, ceremonial weapons, and ornaments have been found in graves throughout the eastern Mediterranean region and Near East. Many are of a very high standard. By about 1600 B.C.E., Mycenaean metalworkers were producing daggers with bronze blades inlaid with gold, electrum (an alloy of silver and gold), silver, and niello (a black substance formed when sulfur is mixed with lead, silver, or cop-

This gold funeral mask was unearthed at Mycenae, Greece, in 1876 by German archaelogist Heinrich Schliemann (1882–90). It was made about 1500 B.C.E. and is known as the Mask of Agamemnon, although it predates the believed time of the Trojan War.

KEY DATES

ca 5000 B.C.E.
Egyptian weapons and tools made of copper

ca 3200 B.C.E.
Bronze produced in the Middle East

ca 2000 B.C.E.
Iron produced in southern India

ca 1600 B.C.E.
Mycenaean daggers with bronze, gold, and silver

ca 200 B.C.E.
Early steel production

per). Copper, silver, and gold occur naturally as nuggets. These can be pried from rocks or found lying on the surface or in the sand and gravel of riverbeds. Small nuggets of gold can be merged together by hammering; but on its own or alloyed with silver to make electrum, gold is too soft for making tools or weapons. Gold and silver were therefore purely decorative.

Copper was different. Hammering does not fuse copper nuggets. In order to make useful articles from copper, the lumps of metal must be melted and then cast in molds. Hammering then hardens the copper, allowing it to be used to make blades with a sharp edge. Weapons and tools were being made from copper in Egypt by 5000 B.C.E., and copper axes were being made and used in the Balkans before 3000 B.C.E. It was around then that people discovered, probably by accident, that they produced much more copper if they melted it in the presence of a particular kind of bright blue stone heated to red heat. They had begun to extract a metal from its ore, in this case azurite.

Bronze: The First Alloy

Many ore minerals contain more than one metal, and some time after 4000 B.C.E., people began to mix a little tin into the copper. At first it may have happened accidentally when metalworkers used stannite, a rare mineral that contains copper, tin, and iron. An alloy of copper and tin is called bronze. It is much harder than copper, and bronze implements retain a sharp edge much longer than those made of copper. Bronze was first made in what is now southern Iraq between 3200 and 2500 B.C.E. Its use spread throughout the Middle East and Europe and probably China. As it did, the Copper Age gave way to the Bronze Age.

Iron was also available. Certain meteorites are made mainly of iron, and melting them releases the metal. But meteorites are rare, and it is more difficult to obtain iron from hematite, its most widespread ore. Copper melts at 1,982.1°F (1,083.4°C), but iron only melts at 2,795°F (1,535°C)—a temperature that is much harder to achieve. Smelting hematite produces a spongy mass mixed with waste products, called slag. Changing this into workable iron requires repeated melting and hammering. Nevertheless, iron was being produced in southern India by about 2000 B.C.E. An iron dagger blade dating from about 2200 B.C.E. was found at Alaca Hüyük in Anatolia (present-day Turkey), although it was a precious and almost certainly ceremonial object. Iron was becoming important to the Hittites by 1400 B.C.E., and by 1000 B.C.E. its use had spread across Europe.

Iron is soft, and an iron blade has to be straightened after each blow struck with it, so iron could not compete against bronze. Then smiths discovered that iron becomes much stronger if it is kept for a long time at bright-red heat in a charcoal fire. By absorbing carbon from the charcoal, iron is converted into steel, and steel can be made stronger still if it is plunged into water while red hot. Steel was first made in India in about the third century B.C.E. and was exported widely. Stories about swords with special powers probably refer to steel blades that were tougher and sharper even than bronze.

Chinese craftsmen made complex shapes, such as bowls and bells, by casting them in molten bronze. The mold itself was made from fireclay in several pieces, which were assembled around a central core to make the mold and then carefully taken apart again after the casting process. In this way, the mold could be used again and again to produce a series of identical objects.

Lid

Mold piece

Mold piece

Central core inside

Base

Mold piece

ASTRONOMY & MATH	BIOLOGY & MEDICINE	PHYSICAL SCIENCES

EUROPE

When tillage begins, other arts follow. The farmers, therefore, are the founders of human civilization.

DANIEL WEBSTER

1000 Etruscan craftsmen in northern Italy make false teeth from gold, probably more for show than for function.

950 Farmers in northern and central Europe cultivate oats, a cereal crop better suited than wheat to the wetter, cooler climate of the region. It was soon grown in northern Britain and is still associated with Scotland, where people make it into porridge.

ca 1500 Copper from the Alps is imported to England and used to make jewelry.

ca 1050 Dorian invaders from Anatolia introduce ironworking into Greece.

ca 900 The Etruscans of central Italy prosper thanks to their rich supplies of copper and tin.

THE AMERICAS

1200 The Olmec develop a lunar calendar.

1400 South American farmers grow cassava (manioc).

1200 Offshore fisherman in Peru use rafts and boats (*cabalitos*) made from reeds.

ASIA & OCEANIA

1361 Chinese astronomers record the sighting of a solar eclipse.

1360 Chinese mathematicians introduce a nonpositional number system (with no zero). It was multiplicative (e.g., 300 was written as 3 together with the symbol for 100) and additive (1,975 was written as 1,000 + 900 + 70 + 5).

1000 The Hindu calendar of 360 days (12 lunar months of 27 or 28 days) is introduced in India.

1500 Chinese people make beer. Also people in various parts of Asia produce alcohol (for drinking) by distilling wine.

1450 People in Manchuria, China, cultivate soybeans. They eat the beans fresh or dry them and store them for use in the winter. They also let them germinate and eat the bean sprouts or allow them to ferment and make them into soy.

1350 Chinese farmers are growing more than one crop in the same year on the same land.

1000 People in Siberia in northern Russia keep herds of domestic reindeer.

The Chinese invented the kite about 1000 B.C.E., arguably the first heavier-than-air flying object made by humans.

AFRICA & THE MIDDLE EAST

1200 Astronomers in Babylon construct an instrument for determining when a star is due south of their observatory.

975 The Hebrews introduce the Gezer lunar calendar (with 12 months of 27 or 28 days).

1500 In Egypt, the first professional millers begin grinding wheat.

1450 Mesopotamian farmers use a single-tube seed drill, in which seeds trickle down a tube into a groove plowed in the soil.

1350 An Egyptian text describes the symptoms of leprosy.

1000 Farmers in Egypt and Mesopotamia fertilize their crops using animal dung.

900 Farmers in Mesopotamia (present-day Iraq) use irrigation systems to improve the yields of their crops.

1500 Egyptian engineers in Syria dam the Orontes River Valley to create a 19-square-mile (50-sq-km) lake.

1350 Egyptian workmen weld iron at about the same time as the Hittites begin working with iron. Ironworking spreads to India by 1200 B.C.E. and Europe by 1000 B.C.E.

1200 The Egyptians join the Nile River to the Red Sea with a canal at Lake Timsah.

ENGINEERING & INVENTION	WORLD EVENTS
1500 People in the Aegean, around Greece, invent the beam press, which uses a weighted lever to squeeze juice from grapes for wine-making or oil from olives.	**ca 1400** People begin to cremate rather than bury their dead.
ca 1400 The last stage of construction of Stonehenge is finished in southern England.	**ca 1200** Proto-Celtic people of Indo-European origin migrate to Central Europe.
1150 Craftsmen in Cyprus and Mycenae (in Greece) decorate objects with vitreous enamel (colored glass).	**ca 1100** Indo-Europeans settle in Italy.
	ca 900 Etruscan culture flourishes.
	ca 850 Greek epic poet Homer writes the Iliad and the Odyssey.
1200 From this time Olmec sculptors in Mesoamerica carve human–animal figurines and giant human heads at sites at La Venta and San Lorenzo near the Gulf coast. Many are ritually destroyed in 900 B.C.E.	**ca 1500** The Olmec culture develops in Central America.
	ca 1100 Andean society flourishes in South America.
	ca 1000 Aleuts and Inuits have now adapted to life in their Arctic environment.
1150 Chinese workmen cast bells in bronze.	**ca 1500** The Jomon period peaks in Japan.
1100 Chinese craftsmen introduce spinning to produce yarn from wool and cotton.	**1300** The Shang rulers of China make Anyang their capital.
1000 Chinese scribes use brushes and black ink made from soot and gum to write on bamboo strips or paper made from tree bark.	**ca 1000** Aryans in India settle between the Himalayas and the Ganges River.
900 Chinese people use cast metal coins in the shape of shovels or knives.	**ca 1000** The Hindu caste system organizes people into four varnas: Brahmins (priests), Kshatriyas (warriors and aristocrats), Vaishyas (farmers, craftsman, and merchants), and Shudras (peasants).
850 The Chinese use natural gas for lighting, conveying it along bamboo "pipes." The gas is probably methane from underground deposits of petroleum.	
1450 The Egyptians make a water clock that measures time by the rate at which water flows out of a hole in a vessel.	
1000 The Phoenicians of the Mediterranean develop a 22-letter alphabet.	
950 The Phoenicians make Tyrian purple dye from the *Murex* sea mollusk. It is so expensive that only kings and emperors have clothes dyed with it.	
850 Smyrna (now Izmir, Turkey) becomes the site of the first known arch bridge.	

EARLY CALENDARS

People have always needed to count the passage of time, partly to know when to sow and harvest crops. The Lebombo bone from Swaziland was marked with 29 notches about 35,000 years ago to record the passage of the lunar month.

All early calendars were based on the lunar cycle. The Egyptians developed a lunar calendar in about 4236 B.C.E. However, it could not predict the most important event in the Egyptian year—the annual flooding of the Nile. They later devised a calendar based on a solar year that could predict the flooding.

In about 1800 B.C.E., the Sumerians of modern-day Iraq produced a lunar calendar with a year that had 12 months alternating between 29 and 30 days. They inserted an extra month so that the calendar coincided with the seasons. The Babylonian and Assyrian empires later adopted the Sumerian calendar. The ancient Chinese, the Hindus in India, and the Hebrews developed their own lunar calendars too.

The zodiac—and the practice of casting horoscopes—originated in ancient Babylon.

THE FIRST PEOPLE WE IDENTIFY WITH SCIENCE AND WHOSE NAMES WE know for certain were Greek philosophers who lived in the fourth century B.C.E., such as Plato (ca 428–ca 348) and Aristotle (384–22). Euclid (fl. 300), their contemporary, and Archimedes (ca 287–12), who flourished about a century later, have become famous as early mathematicians, although Archimedes was also an accomplished engineer. In the second century C.E. Greek astronomer Ptolemy (90–168) established geography as a major scientific discipline. The word *philosopher* means "lover of wisdom," and the Greek philosophers attracted numbers of students to whom they passed on their wisdom. Their schools, or academies, were the first universities, where they also established libraries in which recorded knowledge could be stored and referred to.

The Greeks were also practical people, and they applied scientific principles to architecture, constructing great temples and other buildings in their homeland and the regions they settled, such as the Mediterranean island of Sicily. This tradition was continued by the Romans who became the Mediterranean region's next dominant power. The Romans built great aqueducts for water supply and a system of stone roads that extended for a total of 50,000 miles (80,000 km) across a vast empire that at its height

The first major source of mechanical power came from water. Huge wooden waterwheels named norias *were used throughout the Arab world to lift water from rivers to irrigate fields. Up to 40 feet (12 m) across, they were turned by the current of the river itself, making them the first machines that did not need to be driven by animal or human power.*

Throughout the classical world, astronomers studied and recorded the movements of the heavens in order to create accurate calendars. They could predict regular events such as equinoxes and eclipses. They often saw unexpected astronomical events, such as the appearance of a comet, as supernatural omens of events that might occur on Earth.

in the first century C.E. stretched from Scotland in the north to Syria in the south, and from Iberia in the west to the borders of modern Russia in the east. Like the Greeks, Roman engineers also constructed practical machines as diverse as clocks, cranes, catapults, and waterwheels.

At the same time, and independently of the Mediterranean countries, science and technology developed among civilizations elsewhere in the world. In Mesoamerica people built pyramids that rivaled those of the ancient Egyptians; in northern India complex canal systems served huge cities; and in China advances in astronomy and math were matched by technical developments such as improved plows and ships and the invention of paper and printing. The last, in particular, would have a profound impact on the history of science. From now on, knowledge could not just be passed on from one generation to the next; it could also be multiplied and widely shared.

The technique of glassblowing—heating glass until it is soft and then blowing in air to enlarge its shape—was discovered by craftsmen in Syria in about 30 C.E. and soon adopted by the Romans, who used it to make bottles and other glass objects.

	849 B.C.E.	500 B.C.E.	250 B.C.E.	0 C.E.	150 C.E.	
EUROPE	**ca 600** Greeks make the first solder. **ca 560** Xenophanes of Colophon deduces that land rises when he find fossils of seashells on mountaintops. **ca 550** Pythagoras observes mathematical relationships between the length of vibrating strings and the notes they produce. **ca 535** Greek physician Alcmaeon studies anatomy by dissecting animals. **ca 515** The sundial is introduced in Greece for telling time.	**424** The Greeks record the use of an early flamethrower in a war between Sparta and Athens. **ca 400** Hippocrates of Kos describes human anatomy. **387** Plato opens his Academy in Athens. **ca 350** Metalworkers in Greece and Italy use coal as a fuel. **330** Aristotle suggests that the sun and planets orbit the Earth. **300** Greek mathematician Euclid writes a book on geometry.	**ca 235** Eratosthenes calculates the circumference of Earth. **200** Greek astronomers in Alexandria invent the astrolabe. **ca 110** The Romans begin using nailed horseshoes. **ca 100** Roman builders use a type of concrete that sets underwater. **ca 80** Overshot waterwheels, more efficient than undershot wheels, are introduced in Mediterranean countries. **46** Julius Caesar introduces the Julian calendar.	**50** Farmers use watermills to grind grain in Italy. **77** Pliny the Elder summarizes natural history as known to the Romans. **80** The Colosseum—a four-story amphitheater—is built in Rome. **100** Roman physician Soranus writes a book on pregnancy and disorders that affect women. **128** The domed Pantheon is built in Rome. **150** Ptolemy writes the *Almagest*, a standard guide to astronomy for over a thousand years.	**226** The Romans build a 14-mile (22-km) aqueduct to carry water into Rome. **ca 250** Parchment replaces papyrus as the standard writing material around the Mediterranean. **250** Greek mathematician Diophantus invents algebra.	
THE AMERICAS	**ca 600** The Maya use cacao to make a chocolate drink.	**ca 400** Mayan mathematicians develop a number system, using base 20, that includes a symbol for zero. **ca 300** The Maya build pyramids in Mexico.	**ca 200** The Nazca Lines are drawn in the desert in southern Peru. **ca 200** South American furnaces produce alloys of gold and silver.	**ca 0** The Anasazi culture begins in the American Southwest.	**ca 200** The Moche civilization in Peru build huge terraced tombs from adobe mud bricks.	
ASIA & OCEANIA	**ca 733** Chinese astronomers record a solar eclipse.	**ca 400** The Chinese use a counting board with bamboo rods to do calculations and keep records.	**240** Chinese astronomers record an appearance of what is now called Halley's comet. **214** The main section of the Great Wall of China is completed. **ca 100** Chinese astronomers begin to use negative numbers. **ca 55** The Hindu Ayurveda appears; the medical treatise is still in use. **28** Chinese astronomers begin to keep a record of the appearance of sunspots.	**1** Chinese mathematician Liu Hsin introduces decimal fractions. **8** Horizontal waterwheels are recorded in China. **ca 100** The wheelbarrow is invented in China. **105** Chinese court official Ts'ai Lun invents a way to make paper. **105** The Chinese use powdered chrysanthemum flowers to kill insects. **132** In China, Zhang Hen invents the first seismograph.	**263** Mathematician Liu Hui correctly calculates the value of pi to five decimal places. **ca 265** Huang Fu-Mi writes a major treatise on acupuncture. **271** The compass is first used in China.	
AFRICA & THE MIDDLE EAST	**ca 800** Egyptians use incubators to hatch eggs. **763** Babylonian astronomers observe an eclipse of the sun. **700** Phoenicians develop biremes, warships with two rows of oars. **691** Assyrians build an aqueduct to carry water to their capital Nineveh.	**283** At Alexandria, in Egypt, Greeks build the 380-foot (115-m) Pharos lighthouse, one of the Seven Wonders of the Ancient World.	**ca 30** Ironworking reaches parts of sub-Saharan Africa. **ca 30** Craftsmen in Syria discover the technique of glassblowing, which soon spreads through the Roman empire. **ca 10** King Herod the Great builds a huge harbor of stone blocks at Caesarea in Palestine.	**100** Nichmachus of Gerasa writes *Introduction to Arithmetic*.	**190** Ironworking spreads as far south as the Limpopo Valley. **269** The library at Alexandria is partly destroyed by fire.	

300 C.E.	500	700	800	900–1000
ca 300 Roman emperor Diocletian builds a palace using arches supported by freestanding columns. **ca 300** The Romans begin burning coal as fuel. **350** A water-powered sawmill is built in France to cut marble. **365** Mechanical cranks are used to set broken bones in Greece. **410** Hypatia of Alexandria invents the hydrometer.	**ca 500** Silk production begins in Byzantium using silkworms smuggled from China. **520** Boethius translates the works of Aristotle into Latin. **532** The church of Hagia Sophia is designed. **537** Roman engineer Belisarius builds a floating watermill. **ca 680** Dutch farmers begin building dikes to protect land from the sea. **685** The *Ravenna Cosmography* lists all countries, rivers, and towns in Europe.	**ca 700** Europeans adopt the use of stirrups for riding horses. **750** Arab scholars begin to settle in Spain, bringing knowledge from the Islamic world. **789** Charlemagne, the Holy Roman emperor, introduces standard weights and measures.	**ca 800** The use of the blast furnace to produce cast iron spreads through Europe. **834** The use of a hand crank to turn a wheel is pictured in an illustrated manuscript. **860** Viking seafarers venture as far west as Iceland.	**975** Scholar Gerbert of Aurillac builds a hydraulic organ. **982** Viking longships cross the North Atlantic Ocean and reach Greenland.
ca 400 The wheel is introduced in Mesoamerica, but only for children's toys—the region has no beasts of burden for pulling wheeled vehicles.	**ca 500** Potters in Costa Rica and Panama produce vividly colored ceramics.	**ca 720** Mayan builders at Tikal construct Pyramid IV, one of the tallest buildings in the Americas.	**ca 800** Metalworking techniques from South America are adopted by peoples in Central America. **ca 800** The Hohokam of Arizona build canals to irrigate their fields.	**ca 900** The Mayan civilization collapses in the lowlands of the Yucatán.
304 The Chinese use ants to control other pest insects. **310** Chinese astronomers produce a comprehensive star map. **ca 400** The Chinese invent the umbrella. **405** Chinese craftsmen beat wrought iron and cast iron together to make steel. **415** Indians use iron chains to build suspension bridges. **497** Indian Aryabhata proposes that the Earth rotates on its axis.	**534** Chinese math is adopted in Japan. **535** Chinese engineers invent a device for sifting flour. **577** Chinese women invent matches. **610** In India, a number system is introduced using base ten. **628** *Brahmasphuta Siddhanta* is written by Indian astronomer Brahmagupta.	**725** Chinese engineers construct a water clock with an escapement mechanism.	**812** Bank drafts are introduced in China—the first form of paper money. **ca 855** A Chinese writer describes an early form of gunpowder, or "fire drug." **868** The earliest book is printed in China. **876** Mathematicians in India introduce a symbol for zero.	**960** Chinese authorities begin to print paper money as a means of exchange. **976** The Chinese invent a chain-drive mechanism for the astronomical clock.
ca 350 The world's first street lighting is introduced at Antioch in modern-day Turkey. **ca 400** Scholars at Alexandria, Egypt, use the Arabic term *al-kimiya* to describe a change of state in matter; it is the root of the English word *alchemy*.	**622** First year of the Muslim calendar, commemorating the flight of Mohammad to Medina. **674** Syrian-born Callinicus invents Greek fire, a burning substance used as a weapon. **685** The Dome of the Rock is begun in Jerusalem.	**760** The use of Arabic numerals reaches Baghdad. **780** Arabs in Baghdad begin making paper.	**ca 820** The House of Wisdom (Bayt al-Hikma) is founded in Baghdad to encourage scholarly research. **ca 820** An Arab writer describes an astrolabe. **850** An Arab physician writes a treatise about the eye, including eye disorders and treatments.	**ca 900** Arab scientists distill wine to make alcohol, mainly for use in medicine. **ca 900** Persian physicians use plaster of Paris to set broken bones. **972** A university is founded in Cairo.

ASTRONOMY & MATH	BIOLOGY & MEDICINE	PHYSICAL SCIENCES

EUROPE

550 Greek mathematician and philosopher Pythagoras (ca 580–ca 500) determines the relationship between the length of a vibrating string and the pitch of the note it produces.

434 Ionian philosopher Anaxagoras (ca 500–ca 428) postulates that the sun is a ball of hot rock.

430 Greek mathematician and philosopher Zeno of Elea (ca 490–ca 430) expresses four mathematical paradoxes.

387 In Athens Greek philosopher Plato (ca 428–ca 348) opens an academy for the pursuit of philosophical and scientific teaching and research.

330 Greek scientist and philosopher Aristotle (384–322) proposes that the Earth is at the center of the universe and that the sun, moon, planets, and stars orbit around it.

300 Greek mathematician Euclid (fl. 300) writes *Elements*, a geometry book.

560 Greek poet Xenophanes of Colophon (fl. sixth century) accounts for the presence of fossil seashells on mountaintops by deducing that the land surface must have risen from below sea level in the past.

535 Greek physician and philosopher Alcmaeon (fl. sixth century) uses dissection to study the anatomy of animals.

ca 400 Greek physician Hippocrates of Kos, traditionally thought to be the originator of the doctor's Hippocratic Oath, (ca 460–ca 377) describes human anatomy and various diseases.

350 Greek scientist and philosopher Aristotle draws up a classification scheme for animals and plants.

340 Greek physician Praxagoras of Kos (fl. fourth century) distinguishes between arteries and veins.

600 Greek artist and metalworker Glaucus of Chios (fl. fifth century) makes an alloy that melts easily and uses it to solder metals.

350 According to Greek philosopher Theophrastus of Eresus (ca 372–ca 287) metalworkers in Greece and Italy begin using coal as a fuel.

INSIDE STORY

Ancient Paradox

The classic version of Zeno's racecourse paradox involves a race between the Greek hero Achilles and a tortoise. Achilles can run ten times as fast as the tortoise so he gives the animal a 33-foot (10-m) head start. By the time Achilles reaches the 33-foot (10-m) mark, the tortoise has shuffled along to 36 feet (11 m). Then when Achilles reaches 36 feet (11 m), the tortoise is already at 36.5 feet (11.1 m). And so on, halving the remaining distance to be covered an infinite number of times. It seems to demonstrate that Achilles will never catch up with the tortoise.

THE AMERICAS

400 Mayan mathematicians use a place-value number system, to base 20, that includes a symbol for zero.

600 Mayan people of Central America make a chocolate drink using pods of the cacao plant.

ASIA & OCEANIA

400 Chinese people use a counting board with bamboo rods for calculations and record keeping.

One of the Seven Wonders of the Ancient World, the Pharos lighthouse at Alexandria was 380 feet (115 m) tall. This is a 19th-century artist's impression of the lighthouse.

AFRICA & THE MIDDLE EAST

763 Babylonian astronomers observe and record an eclipse of the sun. About 30 years later Chinese astronomers do the same.

800 Egyptians use artificially heated incubators to hatch eggs.

ENGINEERING & INVENTION	WORLD EVENTS

530 Greek engineer Eupalinus of Megara (fl. sixth century) builds a 3,600-foot (1,100-m) tunnel through a mountain on Samos to carry water across the island.

515 Ionian philosopher Anaximander of Miletus (ca 611–ca 547) introduces the sundial to Greece for telling time.

424 In the war between Athens and Sparta (in Greece), the attackers of Delion use a flamethrower consisting of a tube containing burning charcoal, sulfur, and tar, mounted on a wheeled carriage and "powered" by bellows to blow the flames forward.

312 Roman politician and general Appius Claudius Caecus (fl. fourth century) authorizes the building of the Aqua Appia aqueduct. He also commissions the Via Appia (Appian Way), the first of the great Roman roads.

283 The Greeks build the 380-foot (115-m) Pharos lighthouse at Alexandria (Egypt), one of the Seven Wonders of the Ancient World.

800 The Celts spread westward into central Europe.

800 The Greeks establish independent city states, including Athens and Sparta.

776 The first Olympic Games are held at Olympia, Greece.

ca 700 The Etruscans flourish in northern Italy and trade widely.

490 Greek forces halt a Persian incursion at the Battle of Marathon.

399 Greek philosopher Socrates is sentenced to death in Athens.

336 Alexander the Great (r. 336–323) becomes king of Macedon.

ca 300 Rome becomes the dominant power in modern-day Italy.

ca 300 Zapotec society develops in the Oaxaca Valley in Mexico.

ca 300 The Maya construct monumental pyramids in modern-day Mexico.

The chief forms of beauty are order and symmetry and definiteness, which the mathematical sciences demonstrate in a special degree.

ARISTOTLE, *METAPHYSICS*

ca 563 Siddhartha Gautama (ca 583–ca 483) is born in the foothills of the Himalaya. He is later known as Buddha.

ca 450 Confucianism spreads in China.

700 Phoenician sailors use biremes (boats with two rows of oars) as warships.

691 Assyrian King Sennacherib (r. 705–681) builds an aqueduct to carry water 50 miles (80 km) from a tributary of the Greater Zab River to supply his capital city Nineveh (present-day Mosul) with water.

513 Persian King Darius (r. ca 549–ca 486) builds a 2,000-foot (600-m) pontoon bridge to carry his invading army across the Bosporus (near present-day Istanbul).

750 The Phoenician city of Carthage flourishes in North Africa.

ca 300 Ptolemaic rule begins in Egypt and lasts nearly 300 years.

GREEK TEMPLES

In ancient Greece people believed in many gods. Each god possessed particular attributes, and worshippers approached whichever gods they thought most likely to answer their particular prayers.

When the Greeks began to represent their gods with large statues, the statues had to be protected from the weather. The buildings erected to house them were called *naoi*, literally "dwellings." At first these temples were made from wood and mud brick; but as the temples decayed, they were rebuilt with stone and brick. The buildings were rectangular and built on an east–west axis with an entrance porch at one end covered with a roof supported by columns. Later temples had a porch at either end and were surrounded by columns. The first-known example of a temple surrounded by columns is the Temple of Hera (Heraion) at Samos, built in 750 B.C.E.

The Parthenon, built of white marble on the hill of the Acropolis at Athens, is the largest and most famous of all Greek temples. It was built under the supervision of the Greek sculptor Phidias. Work began in 447 B.C.E., and the building was completed in 438 B.C.E., although the exterior decoration was not finished until 432 B.C.E. The Parthenon was dedicated to Athena Parthenos (Athena the Virgin).

The Parthenon was a temple dedicated to Athena. In ancient times, a huge gold and ivory statue of the goddess dominated the interior.

MESOAMERICAN PYRAMIDS

DESPITE THEIR APPARENT SIMILARITIES THE pyramids of Egypt and those in central America are not related. The Mesoamerican pyramids were constructed thousands of years later. Rather than serving as private tombs for rulers, like the Egyptian structures, they were used mainly as public temples for ritual and celebration.

In 1922 archaeologists in the Valley of Mexico found the ruins of Cuicuilco, a city buried by volcanic eruption in about 30 C.E. They discovered the lower part of a circular pyramid, built in four tiers with a core made from clay and rubble faced with blocks of volcanic rock. Ramps on opposite sides of the pyramid led to the temple that once stood on the top. Circular temples were usually dedicated to the Feathered Serpent god, known to many Mesoamerican peoples as Kukulkan and to the Aztec as Quetzalcóatl. He may have been the most important god in Cuicuilco.

A Tradition of Pyramids

Pyramid building had become widespread throughout Mesoamerica long before the Cuicuilco pyramid was built. The earliest pyramid known was built by the Olmec people near La Venta in the Mexican state of Tabasco some time around 900 B.C.E. The Olmec was the most prominent civilization of Mesoamerican culture until about 600 C.E. Olmec cities grew around a central mound where religious ceremonies were conducted. Pyramids replaced the mounds from about 900 B.C.E. There is no evidence of a ramp or stairway used to reach the top of the La Venta pyramid, so historians suspect it was more like a sculpture than a building. It may have represented the mountain that the Olmec believed reached to heaven and was the source of the corn on which agriculture depended.

After the Olmec, the Maya also built pyramids, usually from stone blocks bonded with lime mortar and with steep stairways that only priests were permitted to climb. Tikal, in Guatemala, is the largest and possibly oldest Mayan city. Occupied between about 800 B.C.E. and 900 C.E., at one time it was home to about 100,000 people. The center contained a number of small pyramids and six very large pyramids, each with a temple at the top. Archaeologists have numbered the pyramids from I to VI in the order they were built. Pyramid I, topped by the Temple of the Jaguar, was built in 695 C.E. and Pyramid VI was built in 766 C.E. The tallest structure, Pyramid IV, is approximately 230 feet (70 m) high and is topped by the Temple of the Two-Headed Serpent. A chamber in the temple was designed to amplify the voice of the priest standing in it, so the people in the square below could hear him.

Although prominent people were sometimes buried in them, Mesoamerican pyramids were not primarily tombs. They represented the three levels of

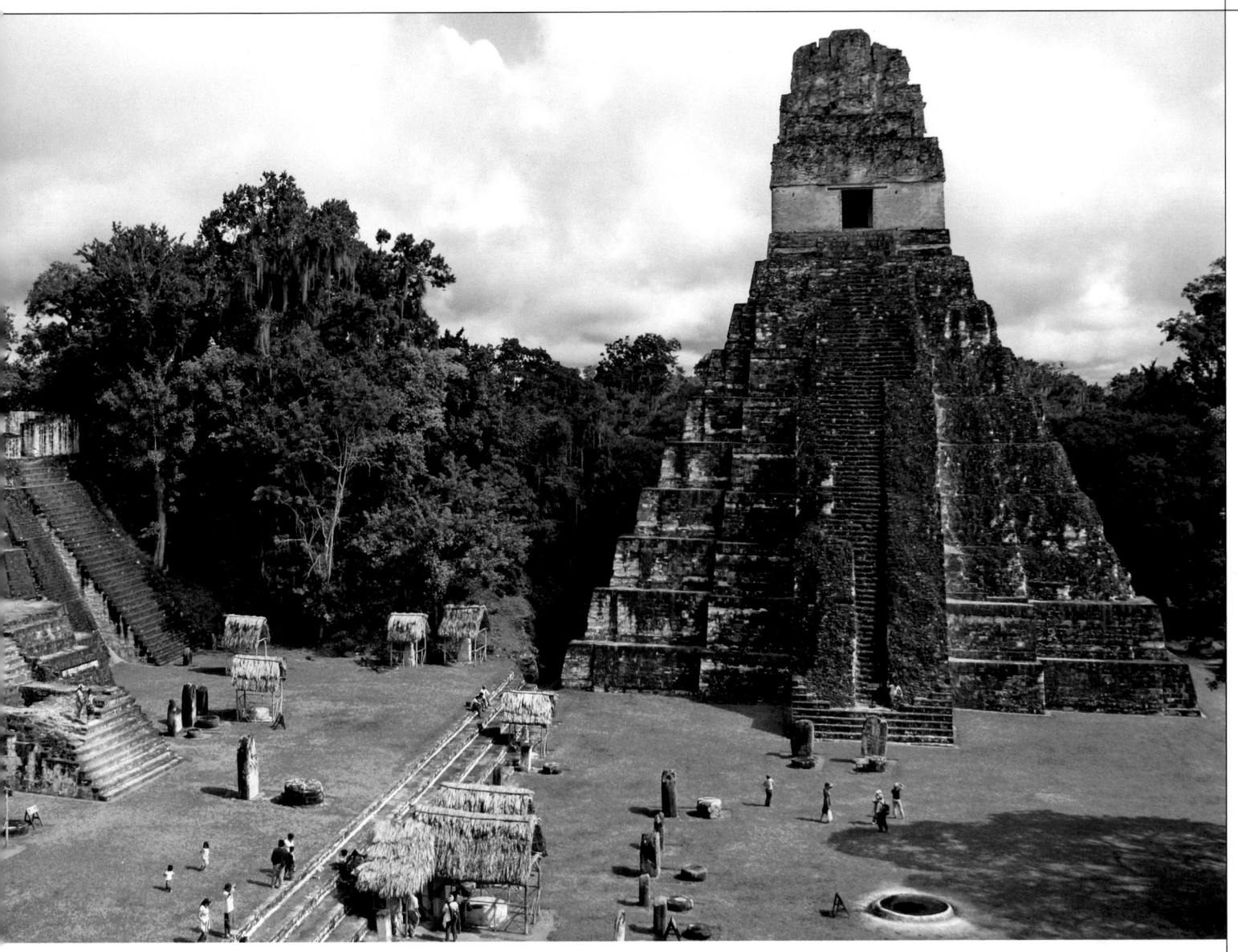

the universe: the subterranean, terrestrial, and celestial. The subterranean level is represented by buried shrines beneath some pyramids.

A New Center

The people who fled from Cuicuilco in about 30 C.E. settled in Teotihuacán, about 30 miles (50 km) northeast of modern Mexico City. The new arrivals stimulated rapid urban expansion. At its peak in about 500 C.E. Teotihuacán covered some 8 square miles (21 sq. km), and its population of up to 200,000 made it one of the world's largest cities. Teotihuacán was destroyed by fire in about 750 C.E. When the Aztec discovered the ruins centuries later, they believed the city had been built by supernatural beings. They named it Teotihuacán, meaning "Place of the Gods."

The ceremonial Street of the Dead runs through the center of the city. The Pyramid of the Moon sits at its northern end. The pyramid is 140 feet (43 m) tall and built with a core of rubble covered by a larger pyramid and with a third pyramid covering that. In 1998 archaeologists found burial pits with many rich burial goods deep inside the Pyramid of the Moon.

The Temple of the Feathered Serpent stands on top of another pyramid at the southern end of the street. It contained the remains of 18 men, apparently soldiers who had been ritually sacrificed.

The Pyramid of the Sun, standing on the eastern side of the street, is the biggest of all the pyramids, rising to 216 feet (66 m) and measuring about 720 by 760 feet (220 by 232 m) at its base. A cave beneath the pyramid was probably a shrine.

Pyramid I towers above the plaza at the Mayan city of Tikal, in present-day Guatemala. It has nine levels rising to the Temple of the Jaguar on top: Nine was a sacred number for the Maya.

ASTRONOMY & MATH	BIOLOGY & MEDICINE	PHYSICAL SCIENCES

EUROPE

235 Greek mathematician Eratosthenes of Cyrene (ca 276–ca 194) calculates the circumference of the Earth. Ten years later he devises the sieve of Eratosthenes as a method of finding prime numbers (numbers that can be divided only by 1 and themselves).

230 Greek mathematician Apollonius of Perga (ca 262–ca 190) writes his treatise *Conics*, dealing with conic sections (i.e., the circle, ellipse, parabola, etc.).

200 Astronomers of the Alexandrian school, founded by pharaoh Ptolemy I (r. 323–283), develop astronomical instruments, including the astrolabe.

150 Greek astronomer Hipparchus of Nicaea (ca 180–125) calculates the distance from the Earth to the moon and discovers the precession of the equinoxes.

100 Roman entrepreneur Gaius Sergius Orata develops a system for heating seawater in order to rear oysters to sell to wealthy people in Rome.

75 Greek physician Asclepiades of Bithynia (ca 120–ca 30) teaches that disease comes from discord in the corpuscles of the body.

There are hundreds of designs, or geoglyphs, of figures in the Nazca Desert, including this hummingbird. The largest geoglyphs are more than 650 feet (200 m) across.

THE AMERICAS

200 At about this time the Nazca people in southern Peru begin "drawing" huge outlines of animals and plants on the surface of the Pampa Colorada desert. Later they add lines and geometric shapes. The purpose of the figures is unknown but they are thought to have astronomical or religious significance.

ASIA & OCEANIA

240 Chinese astronomers make the first records of what becomes known as Halley's comet.

165 Chinese naked-eye astronomers record the existence of sunspots.

100 Chinese mathematicians begin to use negative numbers.

52 Chinese astronomer Ken Shou-Ch'ang makes a form of armillary ring (a metal ring representing the equator, used to observe the stars).

125 Chinese traveler Chang Ch'ien (ca 172–ca 114) introduces wine grapes into China from the West.

55 Hindu medical system the Ayurveda is developed at about this time and becomes the basis of medical teaching in India for centuries.

In Chinese the Great Wall of China is known as Wan-li Ch'ang-ch'eng, which means "10,000-li-long wall." One li equals about 1640 foot (500 m).

INSIDE STORY

Great Wall of China

One of the greatest surviving examples of ancient building construction, the main section of the Great Wall of China runs for 1,400 miles (2,250 km) along the crests of mountains and hills from the Shan-hai Pass (on the Gulf of Chihli) in the east to the Chia-yu Pass (in modern Gansu Province) in the west. Secondary branches add about another 2,600 miles (4,180 km) to the structure, which ranges in height from 20 to 50 feet (6–15 m). It had its origins in the seventh century B.C.E., and the main section was completed in 214 by emperor Shi Huang-di as a defense against northern invaders. It was added to and repaired many times, culminating in major restoration by the Ming emperors (1368–1644).

AFRICA & THE MIDDLE EAST

ENGINEERING & INVENTION	WORLD EVENTS
250 Greek scientist and mathematician Archimedes (ca 287–212) invents the screw pump (a coarse screw rotated inside a sloping tube) for raising water for irrigation. **150** Greeks and Romans use a screw press for crushing olives to make olive oil. **110** Romans begin to use nailed horseshoes. **100** Roman builders use concrete made from crushed stones and pozzolana (volcanic ash) cement, which sets underwater. **80** Vertical undershot waterwheels, used for grinding wheat, are introduced in eastern Mediterranean countries.	**218** Rome battles Carthage in the Second Punic War (ca 218–201). **216** Hannibal (247–183) defeats the Romans at the Battle of Cannae. **214** Rome goes to war against the Macedonians in the First Macedonian War (214–205). After winning the war, Rome dominates the western Mediterranean. **197** Hispania (Spain) becomes a province of the Roman Empire. **149** The Third Punic War (149–146) begins. **102** Uprisings by the Germanic Cimbri and Teutones tribes are ruthlessly put down by the Romans. **58** Julius Caesar (r. 49–44) begins a 10-year campaign to conquer Gaul (France). **55** Julius Caesar briefly invades Britain on what amounts to a military reconnaissance trip.
200 Metalworkers in South America use blowpipes to create the draft for furnaces to make alloys of gold and silver.	**ca 200** Development starts on the North Acropolis at Tikal, Guatemala, with the construction of a massive stone platform that will subsequently provide a foundation for several Mayan pyramid temples.
214 The main part of the Great Wall of China—a section 1,400 miles (2,250 km) long—is completed. **105** Traditional date for the invention of paper, made from scraps of cloth and wood chips, in China. For the next two centuries paper will only be used for wrapping and packing, not for writing.	**221** King Zheng of the Qin state conquers rival states and becomes emperor of unified China (r. 221–210). **206** The Han dynasty comes into power in China. **ca 150** Austronesians arrive and settle in Tahiti and the Marquesas Islands. **141** Han Wudi (r. 141–87) becomes emperor of China and expands Chinese influence abroad during his long reign. **ca 100** Buddhism begins to spread along the Silk Road into Central Asia.
ca 250 Ironworking reaches sub-Saharan Africa, probably brought across the desert from southern Mauritania to the Niger Valley. **250** Egyptian pharaoh Ptolemy II (r. 283–246) rebuilds the canal linking the Nile River to the Red Sea. **210** Egyptian pharaoh Ptolemy IV (r. ca 221–205) builds a huge galley that needs 4,000 oarsmen and a crew of 3,250 others. **ca 200** Glassblowing is refined in Syria.	**ca 200** The Nok Culture reaches its height in Central Nigeria. **ca 171** Mithridates I (r. ca 171–138) takes control of the Parthian Empire and eventually conquers much of the Seleucid Empire, including Mesopotamia. **104** Jugurtha, ruler of Numidia (in modern Algeria), dies in prison after an unsuccessful rebellion against Roman rule. **83** Syria becomes part of the Roman Empire.

GANGES VALLEY TECHNOLOGY

The Indian civilizations that developed along the valleys of the Ganga (formerly Ganges) and Indus Rivers were masters of the technologies involved in managing an erratic water supply and working with metals.

About 1500 B.C.E. Aryan people began migrating southwestward into the broad plain of the Ganga River, in what is now northern India. Rice was their staple food. In the hills rice is watered by the rain. In the lowlands it is raised in seedbeds then transplanted into flooded fields called paddies, which are drained before harvesting. Paddy rice produces bigger yields than upland rice, but successful cultivation depends on careful management of the water supply. Water management is especially important in India's monsoon climate, where nearly all the rain falls during the summer.

Dams, artificial lakes, and irrigation systems were being used by 300 B.C.E. Inundation canals were widely used in Bengal (also in northeastern India). Monsoon rainwater and meltwater from the mountains flowed along the canals and through openings in their sides into channels leading to the fields.

A tank built in the first century B.C.E. at Sringaverapura near Allahabad in northern India is a remarkable example of water harvesting. It is 800 feet (244 m) long, 60 feet (18 m) wide, and 12 feet (3.7 m) deep and lined with brick. Water from the Ganga River flowed downhill and through two deep earthen tanks, where silt settled at the bottom. Water left each of these tanks from outlets near the top, which fed into the main tank.

Indian metal working was advanced too. Beside the Quwwat-ul-Islam (Might of Islam) Mosque in Delhi stands a cast-iron pillar more than 23.5 feet (7 m) tall and 16 inches (40 cm) in diameter. It was commissioned by Kumara Gupta (r. 415-55 C.E.) in honor of his father Chandra Gupta II. Not until late in the 19th century were Europeans capable of casting a single piece of metal of that size.

ARCHIMEDES

ABOVE: *This 18th-century engraving is an artist's impression of the "claws," a famous weapon designed by Archimedes to sink Roman ships during the siege of Syracuse in 215 B.C.E.*

ARCHIMEDES IS CONSIDERED TO BE ONE OF THE greatest mathematicians not just of the Classical period but of all time. His theories and philosophies became known the world over, and his inventions brought him fame that lasts to this day.

Archimedes (ca 287–212 B.C.E.) was the greatest mathematician and physicist of the ancient world. He was born in Syracuse, Sicily (then a Greek colony), the son of an astronomer named Phydias. The family was friendly with Hieron II, king of Syracuse, and possibly related to him. Archimedes studied in Alexandria, Egypt, where his teacher was a former pupil of the Greek mathematician Euclid (fl. ca 300 B.C.E.). His studies completed, Archimedes returned to Syracuse, where he remained for the rest of his life.

Archimedes was the first person to work out the principle underlying levers, and how they were able to multiply force. He said that if he had somewhere to stand and a lever long and strong enough, he could move the world. The claim led King Hieron to challenge Archimedes to move a very heavy object. Archimedes is said to have assembled a system of levers and pulleys with which Hieron himself was able to pull the royal ship—loaded with passengers and cargo—out of the dry dock, across land, and into the harbor.

Archimedes is said to have designed a planetarium and also the screw pump to help with irrigation of crops (although the Egyptians may have had this much earlier). It is a spiral screw inside a cylinder which, when turned, raises water. It is still used today.

President Reagan taught us to always put freedom first. He stood squarely by his principles, strongly promoted his freedom philosophy, and made clear to all of us that every generation must defend freedom—or lose it.

Ronald Reagan On FREEDOM

"Freedom is one of the deepest and noblest aspirations of the human spirit."

"Freedom is the right to question and change the established way of doing things. It is the continuous revolution of the marketplace. It is the understanding that allows us to recognize shortcomings and seek solutions."

"Freedom is not something to be secured in any one moment of time. We must struggle to preserve it every day. And freedom is never more than one generation away from extinction."

...ns that are said to have ...of the Romans who laid ....C.E. Anticipating the ...Archimedes to design ...uilt the walls to accom- ...cranes that lifted large ...onto the troops below, ...ons. His weapons held ...years, turning the siege ...omans and Archimedes. ..es" were among the most ...s. It was said that they ...ssel that came close, and ...the soldiers were shaken ...ow the claws worked, but ...large grappling hook low- ...gripped the bow of a ship ...vessel until it was almost ...releasing it.

...ocusing mirror that worked ...s said that it set fire to the ...proached close enough for ...ange of the city wall, but it ...uch a weapon existed.

...de Archimedes famous and ...nds, but he seems to have ...l devices were unworthy of ...only his mathematical work. ...possible to say whether he ...ines credited to him.

...marily a mathematician. He ...r pi, the relation between ...radius of a circle, that is very ...lue, and also devised methods ...olume and surface area of ...d surface—anticipating in- ...000 years. He found a way to ...mbers, demonstrating it with a ...mber of grains of sand that ...exist in the u...

The Romans finally took Syracuse in about 212 B.C.E., and the general, Marcellus, ordered that Archimedes and his house should not be harmed. A Roman soldier found Archimedes working on a mathematical problem. When the soldier demanded that Archimedes accompany him, the mathematician told him not to disturb the circles he had drawn in the sand. Impatient, the soldier killed him.

Archimedes's Principle

One of the most famous stories about Archimedes concerns his principle. Hieron of Syracuse had commissioned a new crown of gold, but when it was delivered, he doubted its purity. He asked Archimedes to determine, without damaging the crown, whether the gold had been mixed with cheaper silver. Archimedes could think of no way of doing this until one day he overfilled his bath. When he stepped into it, it overflowed. He realized that when an object is immersed in water it displaces its own volume of water. He was so excited that he is said to have run naked through the town shouting "Eureka!" ("I've got it!"). He measured the precise volume of the crown by immersing it in water, and then borrowed a piece of gold weighing exactly the same as the crown and measured its volume the same way. Silver is less dense than gold and there- fore bulkier, so when Archimedes found that the crown displaced more water than the same weight of pure gold, he was able to tell the king that the goldsmith had cheated him.

Archimedes's principle can be demonstrated by immersing a heavy object in water. The water exerts an upward force (buoyancy) on the item, and the item's weight decreases. The water displaced by the item flows out of a spout into a bowl. The buoyancy is equal to the weight of the displaced water.

KEY DATES

287 B.C.E.
Archimedes born at Syracuse

ca 250 B.C.E.
Archimedes designs screw pump

ca 215 B.C.E.
Romans lay siege to Syracuse; Archimedes designs weapons

212 B.C.E.
Siege ends; Archimedes killed by a Roman soldier

ASTRONOMY & MATH	BIOLOGY & MEDICINE	PHYSICAL SCIENCES

EUROPE

46 B.C.E. Roman emperor Julius Caesar (r. 49–44 B.C.E.) introduces the Julian calendar.

ca 62 C.E. Greek mathematician Hero of Alexandria describes the calculation of various areas and volumes.

110 Greek mathematician and astronomer Menelaus of Alexandria introduces spherical geometry in his book *Spherica*.

150 Greek geographer Ptolemy (ca 100–ca 170) compiles a compendium of astronomy called the *Almagest*. It remains a standard textbook until the Renaissance.

250 Greek mathematician Diophantus (ca 200–284) invents algebra.

30 C.E. Roman physician Aulus Cornelius Celsus publishes *De Medicina*, the first Latin treatise on medicine.

77 Roman Pliny the Elder summarizes natural history as known to the Romans in *Historia Naturalis*. He is killed in 79 by the eruption of Vesuvius, which also destroys Pompeii.

77 Pedanius Dioscorides writes a guide to medicinal herbs and drugs that remains authoritative until the 17th century.

100 The Roman physician Soranus of Ephesus writes *Gynecology*, dealing with pregnancy and disorders that affect women.

27 B.C.E. Roman architect Marcus Vitruvius Pollio describes gold amalgam, a gold–mercury alloy.

THE AMERICAS

The Pantheon in Rome was begun in 27 C.E. and completed nearly 100 years later. Its 142-foot (43-m) concrete dome was the largest in the world; its thickness tapered to only about a foot at the top to keep it light.

ASIA & OCEANIA

28 B.C.E. Chinese astronomers begin keeping records of sunspots.

1 C.E. Chinese mathematician Liu Hsin introduces decimal fractions.

185 Chinese astronomers observe a supernova in the constellation Centaurus, which continues to shine for 20 months.

263 Chinese mathematician Liu Hui calculates the value of pi as 3.14159 (correct to five decimal places).

ca 50 B.C.E. The Ayurveda, a Hindu medical treatise, establishes a holistic medical system that is still in use today.

105 C.E. Chinese people use powdered chrysanthemum flowers to kill insects.

132 In China Zhang Heng (ca 78–ca 139) constructs a seismograph for detecting the direction of an earthquake.

AFRICA & THE MIDDLE EAST

100 C.E. Mathematician and philosopher Nicomachus of Gerasa (fl. ca 100) writes *Introduction to Arithmetic*, a collection of knowledge about number theory.

The brilliant glow of a supernova—the central ring in this image—is caused by the explosion of a dying star and can last for months. Chinese astronomers called the supernova a "guest star," because it appeared only temporarily.

ENGINEERING & INVENTION	WORLD EVENTS
50 C.E. Farmers use grain-grinding watermills in Italy.	**44 B.C.E.** Julius Caesar (r. 49–44 B.C.E.) is assassinated in Rome.
50 Hero of Alexandria describes a simple steam turbine built as a toy or novelty.	**31 B.C.E.** The Roman navy defeats the forces of Antony and Cleopatra at the Battle of Actium.
80 The Colosseum, a four-story amphitheater, is completed in Rome.	**27 B.C.E.** Octavian takes the title Augustus, marking the start of the Roman Empire.
128 The Pantheon—a Greek-style temple with a concrete dome—is completed in Rome.	**117 C.E.** Under Hadrian, the Roman Empire reaches its greatest extent.
226 The 14-mile (22-km) Aqua Alexandriana aqueduct is completed, carried mostly on arches into the city of Rome.	
ca 250 Parchment supersedes papyrus as a writing material in Mediterranean countries.	
ca 200 C.E. People of the Moche civilization on coastal Peru build two huge terraced platform tombs from molded adobe brick: one is dedicated to the sun, the other to the moon.	**ca 0** The first phase of Anasazi culture begins in the American Southwest. **ca 150** Tikal becomes the main lowland center of the Mayan empire.
8 C.E. Horizontal waterwheels are used in China. **ca 100** Chinese farmers sow seed using a multitube seed drill. At about this time they also introduce the tandem hitch so that two horses can pull plows and carts. **ca 100** The wheelbarrow appears in China and is used for carrying goods and people. **105** Chinese court official Ts'ai Lun (ca 50–ca 118) describes a technique for making paper using tree bark, rags, and other materials.	**ca 50** The Kushans of Central Asia gain control of northwestern India. **ca 100** Buddhism begins to spread in China. **184** The Yellow Turban rebellion seriously weakens the Han Dynasty of China. **ca 200** The Hinduized kingdom of Champa is founded in modern-day central Vietnam. **220** The last Han emperor is deposed in China, which splits into three kingdoms.
ca 30 B.C.E. Craftsmen in Syria discover the technique of glassblowing, which the Romans soon adopt for making bottles and other objects. **10 B.C.E.** King Herod the Great (r. 31–4) of Judea builds an open-sea harbor of concrete blocks to serve the city Caesarea of Palestine (in present-day Israel).	**ca 50** The Greek influenced Kingdom of Axum is founded in Ethiopia. **ca 190** Ironworking in Africa spreads as far south as the Limpopo Valley.

Carving of a Mayan god from Chichén Itzá

MAYAN SCIENCE

The Maya of Mexico and Central America appeared in about 300 B.C.E. and flourished until about 900 C.E. Mayan astronomers used observations to discern cycles in astronomical phenomena. They calculated the length of a lunar month as 29.5302 days. The length accepted today is 29.53059 days. The Maya could predict solar eclipses and calculated the movements of Venus with great accuracy. In the late Maya period, astronomers maintained an observatory in the great city of Chichén Itzá in the Yucatán.

To record dates and perform calculations, the Maya used a number system. They introduced two important concepts: Place values, which allowed them to write large numbers clearly, and a symbol for zero, represented by a picture of a shell. They were already using this notation by about 400 B.C.E.

The Mayan calendar was in fact three calendars. The first was based on a sacred year of 260 days arranged in two overlapping cycles. It was used to maintain ritual practices. For everyday use there was a calendar based on a solar year. It was divided into 18 months each of 20 days plus five extra "unlucky" days. People born on those days were considered cursed. The third calendar, used for "long counts," dated events from a zero date equivalent to August 13, 3114 B.C.E.

ROMAN ENGINEERING

FROM THE FOURTH CENTURY B.C.E. THE Romans built roads throughout their empire to replace the earlier tracks that consisted of clinging mud in winter and choking dust in summer.

At their peak Roman roads totaled over 50,000 miles (80,000 km)—enough to stretch twice around the world. There were 29 great military roads spreading out from Rome. A system ran from Carthage in North Africa along the southern coast of the Mediterranean; in Gaul (France) roads radiated from Lyon; and in Britain London was the hub of the road system.

The first Roman road was the Via Appia (Appian Way) built southward from Rome in 312 B.C.E. by Roman general Appius Claudius Caecus (fl. fourth century B.C.E.). It eventually ran to the coast at Brundisium (present-day Brindisi). Other roads soon followed in the Italian peninsula, such as the Via Aurelia to Genua (Genoa) and the Via Flaminia to the Adriatic coast, each named after a different Roman dignitary.

The Romans built roads mainly for couriers, merchants, and administrators such as tax collectors. They were also useful for moving troops rapidly. The army provided the labor to build many of the roads when there was no fighting. Wherever possible, the roads followed a straight line set out by surveyors using a sighting staff called a *groma*, and the roads tended to turn (if they had to turn at all) at high points with good visibility.

KEY DATES

312 B.C.E.
Via Appia begun

ca 20 B.C.E.
Pont du Gard built in France

ca 50 C.E.
Aqueduct built in Segovia, Spain

52 C.E.
Aqua Claudia completed, Rome

The layered structure of Roman roads gave them great stability, which is one reason why some are still in use today, some 2,000 years after they were built. The surface stones allowed rainwater to drain into ditches at either side of the roadway.

Curb stones

Large surface stones

Gravel

Bank

Ditch

Foundation of stone slabs

Structure of a Road

For a major highway engineers first dug parallel drainage ditches about 40 feet (12 m) apart, then excavated a shallow trench between them, which they filled with sand, mortar, and a succession of stone courses to form a foundation. They topped a watertight layer of crushed stone with a surface pavement of stone slabs or cobbles set in mortar. They made concrete from crushed stones, pozzolana (volcanic ash) cement if available, and lime. On marshy ground the whole road was raised above the surrounding land.

Some of the major roads in Italy had stone curbs 8 inches (20 cm) high and 2 feet (60 cm) wide on each side, with side lanes outside them that operated as one-way streets. Drivers of two-wheeled chariots could achieve 75 miles (120 km) a day, with eight-horse freight wagons covering a more modest 15 miles (25 km) a day. As the Roman Empire crumbled, so did its roads owing to a lack of maintenance. Later road builders sometimes followed Roman routes, as shown by the straight stretches on any road map of England.

Water Engineering

As Roman towns and cities increased in size, there was growing demand for water for the people to drink and to wash in—public baths and fountains were features of many Roman towns. To bring in the water, Roman engineers built aqueducts. An aqueduct is any permanent channel for carrying water. It may be an open or closed culvert, a tunnel through a hill, or—at its most spectacular—a bridge across a valley.

Between 312 and 200 B.C.E., engineers built 11 aqueducts to take water into Rome, some from more than 56 miles (90 km) away. They built them with a gentle downward slope, and the water flowed by gravity. Roman aqueducts in Italy, Greece, and Spain are still in use today. The aqueduct at Segovia, Spain, for example, was authorized by Roman emperor Trajan (53–117). It is made from 24,000 granite blocks that form a 2,400-foot (730-m) series of 165 arches.

The three-tiered Pont du Gard was built over the Gard River to carry water to the French city of Nîmes. It was built in about 20 B.C.E. by Roman general Marcus Agrippa (63–12 B.C.E.).

	ASTRONOMY & MATH	BIOLOGY & MEDICINE	PHYSICAL SCIENCES

EUROPE

340 Greek mathematician Pappus of Alexandria (fl. fourth century) publishes his *Synagoge*, a collection of geometry problems. It also includes commentaries on the *Elements* of Greek mathematician Euclid (fl 300 B.C.E.) and the *Almagest* of Greek astronomer and geographer Ptolemy (ca 100–ca 170).

460 Greek mathematician Proclus of Constantinople (ca 410–85) states that, through a given point, only one line can be drawn parallel to an existing line. This becomes known as Playfair's postulate after its rediscovery by Scottish mathematician John Playfair (1748–1819) in 1795.

520 Roman philosopher Boethius translates many of Aristotle's works into Latin, thus providing the main source of these works to later medieval scholars.

500 Cultivation of silkworms begins in Byzantium (present-day Istanbul), using silkworms smuggled from China by Christian monks.

300 At about this time Romans observe the British using coal as a fuel and soon adopt it for heating their villas.

TURNING POINTS

The Library at Alexandria

The greatest collection of documents in classical times was kept in a library in Alexandria, northern Egypt. The library was founded by pharaoh Ptolemy I Soter (r. 323–283 B.C.E.) at the beginning of the third century B.C.E. and built up by his son Ptolemy II Philadelphus (r. 283–46 B.C.E.). Established as part of the research "department" of the Alexandrian Museum, it had a smaller section, the Serapeum, located in the nearby Temple of Serapis that was established by Ptolemy III Euergetes (r. 246–22 B.C.E.). The hundreds of thousands of vellum and papyrus scrolls included nearly all the works of the Greek poets and dramatists, based originally on copies of the works in Aristotle's library in Athens. The large staff included translators, editors, and scribes, who kept adding texts to the collection. Fire damaged part of the library in 269 C.E., and rioting during a civil war led to its final destruction. The Serapeum was pillaged by a Christian mob in 391.

THE AMERICAS

ASIA & OCEANIA

310 Chinese astronomer Chen Zhuo combines the maps of earlier astronomers into a comprehensive star map.

ca 350 An Indian account of astronomy, the *Surya-Siddhanta*, is published with tables of trigonometrical sines.

369 Chinese astronomers observe a supernova (a so-called guest star) that remains bright for five months.

465 Chinese mathematician Tsu Ch'ung Chi (429–501) uses a circle three meters across to calculate π (pi) to ten decimal places.

497 Indian astronomer Aryabhata proposes that the Earth rotates on its axis.

265 Chinese physician Huang Fu-Mi writes a major treatise on acupuncture, a method of medical treatment that involves inserting fine needles through the skin.

304 Chinese writer Hsi Han describes the deliberate use of ants to control other insects that attack mandarin orange trees (the ants are sold at markets in woven straw baskets).

305 Chinese craftsmen use coal instead of wood in making cast iron.

405 Chinese craftsmen make steel by beating together wrought iron and cast iron.

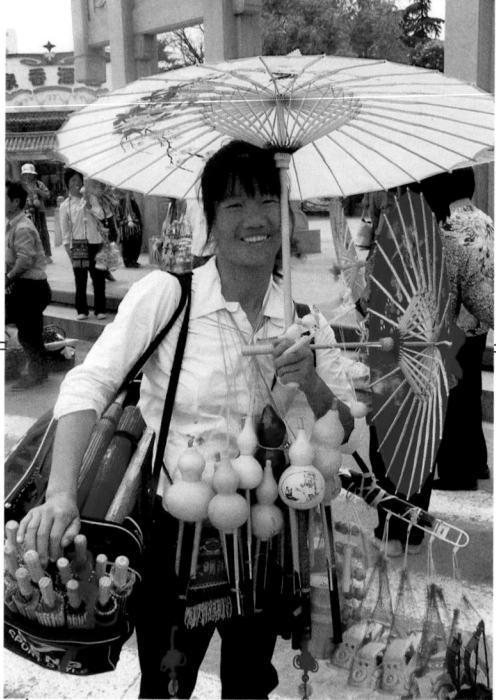

An umbrella seller in China sells paper parasols that are more protection against the sun than the rain.

AFRICA & THE MIDDLE EAST

400 Scholars in Alexandria use the Arabic term *al-kimiya* to describe what takes place when matter changes. The derived word "alchemy" did not enter English until the early 1600s.

Reserve your right to think, for even to think wrongly is better than not to think at all.

HYPATIA OF ALEXANDRIA

ENGINEERING & INVENTION	WORLD EVENTS
300 Roman emperor Diocletian (r. 284–305) builds a palace at modern-day Split in Croatia that employs the new technique of arches supported by freestanding columns.	**286** Troubled by barbarian attacks, the Emperor Diocletian (r. 284–305) divides the Roman Empire into western and eastern parts.
300 The Romans build a flour mill in France, driven by 16 overshot waterwheels.	**313** The Edict of Milan tolerates Christianity in the Roman Empire.
350 A water-powered sawmill is installed in France for cutting marble.	**402** Ravenna replaces Rome as capital of the western empire.
365 The first reference to mechanical cranks appears in a Greek text that describes their use to set broken bones.	**ca 450** Angles and Saxons from northern Germany and Denmark begin to settle in eastern and southern England.
410 Greek mathematician and philosopher Hypatia of Alexandria (d.415) invents a hydrometer for measuring the density of liquids, consisting of a sealed tube weighted at one end and graduated with densities. She calls it a hydroscope.	**476** Odoacer (r. 476–93) declares himself king of Italy, marking the end of the Roman empire in the west.
	486 Clovis (r. 481–511), king of the Franks, begins to expand his kingdom southward.
ca 500 Ceramics in vivid colors are produced in many parts of Costa Rica and Panama.	**ca 450** With an estimated population of 200,000, the city of Teotihuacán dominates central Mexico.
271 A compass is first used in China.	**ca 300** Yamato kings in Japan extend their power through Honshu island.
302 A Chinese pottery figure depicts a horseman using metal stirrups.	**320** Chandragupta I (r. ca 320–ca 335) creates a powerful Hindu kingdom on the Ganges plain and founds the Gupta Dynasty.
ca 400 The umbrella, for protection against the sun as well as the rain, is used in China.	**372** Buddhism reaches Korea.
415 Indian engineers use iron chains to build suspension bridges.	**ca 400** Indian traders spread Hinduism into Southeast Asia.
489 Chinese artists carve 165-foot (50-m) statues of Buddha into a rock face at Yungang.	**ca 400** Polynesian seafarers settle the Hawaiian Islands.
495 Chinese writer Zu Chong Zhi describes a paddleboat with several paddle wheels along each side.	**439** The state of Wei controls all of northern China.
350 Antioch becomes the world's first city to have a system of street lighting.	**ca 270** Saint Anthony becomes a hermit in the Egyptian desert.
510 In about this year craftsmen construct an elaborate chiming water clock at Gaza (in present-day Palestine).	**ca 303** Armenia becomes the first country to adopt Christianity as its official religion.
	439 Vandals from Spain make Carthage their capital.

KEEPING COUNT

As society and its economy grew more complex, traders needed to keep accurate records of transactions. Officials also had to keep records of such things as land holdings, stored foods, and the size of armies. Records had to be written down, and so ways were found to represent numbers.

The simplest way was to carve a series of notches on the edge of a stick or scratch marks onto a stone or piece of bone, but this was not practical for writing large numbers. Numerals came into use in Egypt in about 3400 B.C.E. They consisted of a straight vertical mark for 1 and different symbols for powers of 10 (100, 1,000, 10,000, and so on) and could be written on papyrus paper. At about the same time the Sumerians were using shapes that looked like arrowheads. By about 2400 B.C.E. this system had developed into cuneiform writing. The Cretans began to use numbers in about 1200 B.C.E., with a vertical line for one and a horizontal line for ten.

Systems of this type worked by grouping. If | means 1, then 2, 3, and 4 are ||, |||, and ||||. The alternative is to allocate individual symbols to all numerals up to a given value. The Chinese devised a system of this type in the fourth century B.C.E. with symbols from 1 to 9 and for 10, 100, and 1,000. Roman numerals were simple to use. Students needed to memorize only the symbols I (1), V (5), X (10), L (50), C (100), D (500), and M (1,000). I, V, X, and L were sufficient for most purposes. The Hindu-Arabic numerals we use today originated in India, probably in the fourth century B.C.E. Arab scholars began using them in the eighth century C.E.

Ancient mathematicians performed complex calculations using a counting board, or abacus, a device that was probably invented in Babylon. The Chinese had also invented the counting board by the fourth century B.C.E. and were using the familiar abacus with beads on wires by 1500 C.E. The lines, grooves, or rods represent values (tens, hundreds, thousands) or units of money or measure.

CHINESE SCIENCES

SOME OF THE WORLD'S MOST IMPORTANT early inventions originated in China, including the kite, the spinning wheel, the compass, the crossbow, gunpowder, and the wheelbarrow. The camel's-hair brush for writing appeared in about 250 B.C.E. At the time, people wrote on cloth, but the popularity of the brush led to a demand for a cheaper medium. In about 105 C.E. a court official made sheets of writing material from a mixture of tree bark, waste from hemp manufacture, rags, and worn-out fishnets: He had invented paper. The oldest-known printed book (a Chinese translation of the *Diamond Sutra*, a Buddhist text) is also Chinese, made in 868 C.E.

Chinese books on alchemy, also from the ninth century, contain formulas for making mixtures that burn with a flash—precursors of gunpowder. A text written in about 83 C.E. mentions a *sinan*, a magnetic ladle balanced so that its handle always points south. It is thought to have been used as a primitive compass from about 300 B.C.E. In 132 C.E. a scholar invented an "earthquake weathercock," or seismograph.

Chinese Astronomy

Astronomy was vital because the Chinese believed that the emperor must preserve harmony in the cosmic order by the correct performance of ritual. This required a reliable calendar. The present Chinese calendar emerged in the 14th century B.C.E. after a period of development that began 1,500 years earlier.

The calendar counted days, months, and years in cycles of 60. A year had 12 months of 29 or 30 days beginning at the new moon and an additional month every two or three years to reconcile the lunar year with the solar year. As well as marking the equinoxes, solstices, and agricultural seasons, the calendar noted the dates of predictable events such as lunar eclipses and the positions of the planets. Irregular and unpredictable heavenly events were seen as omens.

Chinese astronomers kept detailed records of eclipses, novas, comets, and sunspots. From as early as the fourth century B.C.E., they noted the positions

In the 12th century firework displays became popular in China. One witness recorded that they made "a noise like thunder."

of stars in star tables, and there is a continuous record from about 70 B.C.E. Not all records survive, but there exists a table of ephemerides—the positions of the sun, the moon, and planets—and a table of planetary motions from 244 to 177 B.C.E.

Chinese Math

Astronomy is a mathematical science, and the earliest-known Chinese mathematical text is the *Zhou Dynasty Canon of Gnomic Computations*, written sometime between 400 and 200 B.C.E. but based on earlier texts that are now lost. It deals mainly with astronomical calculations and also contains instructions in arithmetic and geometry, including a statement of the Pythagorean theorem.

Early Chinese mathematicians also noticed the relationship between the pitch of a sound and the physical processes producing it. This led to Chinese harmonics—used to tune stone chimes and bells employed in rituals—and then to the development of music performed at court. In 1978 archaeologists discovered 65 bronze bells with gold-inlaid inscriptions in a tomb from the fifth century B.C.E. Each bell makes two different tones, depending on where it is struck.

Chinese Medicine

Medicine based on the balance between the cosmic principles of yin and yang is said to have begun in about 2953 B.C.E. Much of Chinese medical literature is based on the text *Nei Ching*, traditionally attributed to the legendary Yellow Emperor, Huang Ti (ca 2698–2598 B.C.E.) but more probably written in the third century B.C.E. Doctors relied mainly on administering herbal, animal, and mineral substances. They also used massage, physical exercises, controlled breathing, and dietary adjustments. Acupuncture and moxibustion—burning cones of substances on the skin—were minor branches of therapy. Their studies of therapeutic materials covered thousands of ingredients and gave the people of China an extensive knowledge of natural history.

The crossbow was in use in China by the sixth century B.C.E. The mechanical trigger meant that, unlike other bows, the crossbow did not depend on the strength of the archer, so that many bolts could be fired in succession.

ASTRONOMY & MATH

EUROPE

685 The *Ravenna Cosmography* is published in Italy, an index of all known countries, rivers, and towns in the Roman Empire.

750 Knowledge from the Alexandrian school spreads to Europe as Arab scholars begin to settle in Spain.

As the sun eclipses the stars by its brilliancy, so the man of knowledge will eclipse the fame of others… if he proposes algebraic problems, and still more if he solves them.

BRAHMAGUPTA

ASIA & OCEANIA

534 Japanese mathematicians adopt Chinese math.

610 Indian mathematicians introduce a number system using base ten.

628 Indian astronomer Brahmagupta (598–ca 660) writes *Brahmasphuta Siddhanta*, a work about astronomy that also contains chapters on mathematics, including algebra and trigonometry.

680 The symbol 0 for zero appears in mathematical calculations in Cambodia and Sumatra, although not necessarily as a number but merely as a place holder.

AFRICA & THE MIDDLE EAST

540 Eutocius of Ascalon (ca 480–ca 540) writes commentaries on works by the Greek mathematicians Apollonius of Perga (ca 262–ca 190 B.C.E.) and Archimedes (ca 287–212 B.C.E.)

622 This year marks the start of the Muslim calendar, commemorating the flight of the prophet Muhammad from Mecca to Medina.

760 The use of Arabic numerals, which originated in India, spreads as far as the region of Baghdad in the Middle East.

BIOLOGY & MEDICINE

542 An epidemic of bubonic plague breaks out and eventually kills a quarter of the population of eastern Mediterranean countries.

640 Greek surgeon Paul of Aegina (fl. 640), who practiced in Alexandria, writes *Epitome Medicae Libri Septum* (Seven Books of Medicine).

In 635 Chinese astronomers observed that the tail of a comet always points away from the sun.

752 Chinese physician Wang Tao writes *Wai Tai Mi Yoo* (The Extra Important Secret), in which he describes various ailments and their remedies, including diabetes and goiter.

The Dome of the Rock in Jerusalem was begun in 685 and finished in 691. The Islamic shrine is built on land sacred to both Jews and Muslims.

PHYSICAL SCIENCES

700 About this time workers in Spain employ a blast furnace for iron smelting, using hand bellows to provide a draft of air to raise the temperature of the furnace.

750 Craftsmen in Italy cast large church bells out of bronze

ca 770 Arab scholar Abu Musa Jabir ibn-Hayyan (ca 721–815), also known as Geber, describes how to make ammonium chloride, white lead, nitric acid, and acetic acid.

ENGINEERING & INVENTION	WORLD EVENTS
532 On the orders of Emperor Justinian I (r. 527–565) Byzantine architect Isidorus of Miletus designs the church of Hagia Sophia in Byzantium (present-day Istanbul).	**561** Civil war erupts among the Merovingians in France.
537 Roman engineer Belisarius (ca 505–65) constructs a floating watermill.	**570** Byzantium and Persia agree to 50 years of peace.
680 Farmers in the Netherlands build dikes to protect their low-lying fields from the gradual rise in sea level.	**602** Vikings invade Ireland.
	675 Bulgars—originally from Asia—establish their first kingdom south of the Danube.
700 Riders in Europe adopt the use of stirrups for mounting and riding horses.	**ca 700** Vikings invade Britain.
	711 Muslim armies invade southern Spain.
720 The Mayan people of Tikal (Guatemala) build a huge pyramid, Pyramid IV, one of the tallest buildings in Mesoamerica.	**ca 700** The Moche and Nazca civilizations (based in present-day Peru) collapse.
535 Chinese engineers make a machine for sifting flour.	**535** The Gupta Empire in India collapses.
577 Chinese women invent a type of match for starting cooking fires.	**587** The Soja clan champions Buddhism in Japan.
610 Chinese engineer Li Ch'un constructs a segmented arch in the Great Stone Bridge over the Chiao Shui River; it still stands.	**607** Tibet is unified under king Songstan Gampoh (r. ca 605–ca 649).
618 Printed newspapers are reputed to have been produced in China.	**710** Nara is made capital of Japan.
725 Chinese engineer Liang Ling-Zan and Buddhist monk Yi-Xing construct a water clock with a proper escapement mechanism. The clock's purpose is to display various astronomical events (such as the phases of the moon) rather than tell the time.	
605 Farmers in Persia (modern Iran) use windmills with horizontal sails to grind cereal grains.	**550** Muhammad (500–632), the Prophet and future messiah of Islam, is born in Mecca.
674 Syrian-born Greek architect and chemist Callinicus, or Kallenikos (b. ca 620), invents Greek fire, a mixture of sulfur, resin, pitch, and saltpeter.	**622** Muhammad and followers flee from Mecca to Medina.
	630 Muhammad conquers Mecca.
685 The 525-foot- (160-m-) high Dome of the Rock is begun in Jerusalem, made of wood and brass and covered overall with gold.	**651** Muslim armies conquer Persia.

WATER POWER

Ancient machines worked by the muscle power of draft animals or people. The first major source of mechanical power came from water, which was harnessed by waterwheels from about 80 B.C.E.

A waterwheel is fitted with paddles that make the wheel turn when water flows past them. Early waterwheels were usually mounted horizontally; later waterwheels were mounted vertically. They used a gear arrangement to turn a horizontal shaft to perform tasks such as turning millstones.

An undershot wheel is a vertical wheel in which the water hits its base. In the more efficient overshot waterwheel, the water arrives at the top of the wheel; the paddles are angled to create small "buckets" to catch the water. The weight of falling water makes the wheel turn.

By 300 C.E. the Romans were building flour mills with several wheels that could process many tons of grain each day. Waterwheels were also used to drive saws for cutting stone and wood, and for lifting water for irrigation purposes.

This Roman flour mill near Arles in southeastern France had two sets of eight overshot wheels.

ARABIC SCIENCES

FROM ABOUT 750 C.E. SCIENCE FLOURISHED under the Abbasid caliphs of Baghdad. Drawing on Greek and Hindu texts, early Islamic scholars collected the greatest body of scientific knowledge in the world, to which they added their own important discoveries.

After the death of the prophet Muhammad in the seventh century, his followers spread his teachings throughout an empire that eventually extended from central Asia to Spain.

Damascus was the first Muslim capital, but in 750 the Abassid caliphs moved the capital Baghdad. The seventh caliph, Abdallah al-Ma'mun (786–833) was one of the greatest. In about 820 he ordered the establishment of an astronomical observatory and library as part of an academy called Bayt al-Hikma (The House of Wisdom). His astronomers calculated the inclination of the plane of the ecliptic—the angle between Earth's rotational axis and its orbital plane—to within a few minutes of the modern value. The caliph's geometers calculated the circumference and radius of Earth as 20,400 miles (32,824 km) and 6,500 miles (10,459 km) respectively. The correct values are 24,875 miles (40,030 km) and 3,959 miles (6,371 km).

Arabian alchemist Abu Musa Jabir Ibn-Hayyan (ca 721–815), known later in Europe as Geber, expanded the Greek idea that all matter is made from four elements: earth, air, fire, and water. He lived during the reign of the fifth Abassid caliph, Harun al-Rashid (786–809). Geber believed that the Greek elements combine to form sulfur and mercury. These two substances could be combined to make any metal, including gold, with the help of a substance called *al-iksir*, from which we derive the word "elixir."

Abu-Bakr Muhammad ibn-Zakariya al-Rhazi (ca 865–923), or Rhazes, became chief physician at the main hospital in Baghdad. Rhazes prepared plaster of Paris and described its use for making casts to hold broken limbs in place. He was possibly the first person to classify all substances as being animal, vegetable, or mineral.

Math and Astronomy

We owe our system of numerals to an Arabic mathematician, Abu Jafar Muhammad ibn-Musa al-Khwarizmi (ca 780–ca 850). Al-Khwarizmi studied Hindu and Greek sources and used Hindu numerals, including zero, in his own works, which were later translated from Arabic into Latin. He lived most of his life in Baghdad, where he was chief librarian at the House of Wisdom. In about 830 Al-Khwarizmi wrote *Hisab al-jabr w'al-muqabala* (Calculation by Restoration and Reduction), a treatise on mathematics. Translated into Latin, *al-jabr* ("restoration") became "algebra." Al-Khwarizmi's name gave us our word "algorithm."

Arabian astronomers preserved the ideas of the Greek astronomer Ptolemy (ca 100–170 C.E.), which Ptolemy expounded in a book written in 150 now known as the *Almagest*, from the Arabic phrase meaning "the greatest."

Most astronomers accepted Ptolemy's work, but in about 880 Abu-Abdullah Muhammad ibn-Jabir al-Battani (ca 850–929) observed that when the sun appeared at its smallest—when it is farthest from Earth—its position in the sky was not where Ptolemy said it was. He deduced that the position changes slowly and calculated fairly accurately the rate of its motion. This allowed him to measure the length of the year more accurately: Calendar makers were still using his measurement centuries later. Al-Battani calculated the time of the equinoxes to within an hour or two.

Arabian science depended heavily on scholars who translated works from Greek into Arabic. One of the greatest was a Christian living in Baghdad. Honain ben Isaac (809–873) was a physician as well as a translator. He translated the works of Greek physician Hippocrates of Kos (ca 460–ca 370 B.C.E.) and practiced medicine according to Hippocratic principles.

KEY DATES

622
Mohammad's flight from Mecca to Medina

630
Mohammad's return to Mecca

750
Umayyad Dynasty overthrown; capital moves from Damascus to Baghdad under Abassid caliphs

ca 820
Bayt al-Hikma (The House of Wisdom) established in Baghdad

ca 830
Hindu numerals introduced

ca 860
Medicine according to principles of Hippocrates practiced in Baghdad

ca 880
Al-Battani (Albategnius) calculates the length of the year and the times of the equinoxes

ca 900
Plaster of Paris used to support fractured bones

Algebra—the use of mathematical equations or relations to determine unknown quantities—probably had its roots in Hindu math. Its most important statement in the early medieval period, however, came in an Arabic text the title of which (al-Jahr wa'al-Muqabalah) *gave us the English word "algebra."*

This 16th-century manuscript illustration shows astronomers in Istanbul using different astronomical devices, including an astrolabe, telescope, and sextant. Many instruments developed by Arab astronomers were used in navigation until the 17th and 18th centuries.

| ASTRONOMY & MATH | BIOLOGY & MEDICINE | PHYSICAL SCIENCES |

EUROPE

975 French cleric, scholar, and natural scientist Gerbert of Aurillac (ca 945–1003) builds a hydraulic organ that produces a steady extended level of sound. Its pipes are matched mathematically, providing better harmonics. He also reintroduces Hindu-Arabic numerals and the abacus into Europe. In 999 he becomes Pope Sylvester II.

Astrolabes were used mainly for astronomical studies in medieval Islamic countries. They could measure the angular height and position of stars and tell local time.

THE AMERICAS

Gentility of character, friendliness, and purity of mind are found in those who are capable of thinking profoundly on abstruse matters and scientific minutiae.

RHAZES

ASIA & OCEANIA

876 People in Gwalior, India, use a place-value number system with a symbol for zero.

ca 855 In China the pamphlet *The Classified Essentials of the Mysterious Tao of the True Origin of Things*, attributed to Zheng Yin, describes a primitive form of gunpowder, called the "fire drug."

According to popular legend, a goatherd named Kaldi in East Africa discovered the coffee plant in about 850 C.E.

AFRICA & THE MIDDLE EAST

ca 820 In Baghdad Abdallah al-Ma'mun (786–833) founds Bayt al-Hikma (The House of Wisdom), in which scholars translate astronomical and other scientific texts into Arabic.

ca 820 Arab mathematician Abu Jafar Muhammad ibn-Musa al-Khwarizmi (ca 780–ca 850) describes the astrolabe.

880 Arab astronomer Abu Abdullah Muhammad ibn-Jabir al-Battani (850–929), also known as Albategnius, introduces trigonometry to Arab astronomy.

850 Arab physician Hunayn ibn-Ishaq (809–73) writes *The Book of the Ten Treatises on the Eye*, describing eye anatomy, disorders, and treatments.

ca 900 Persian-born Arab physician Rhazes (c.865–923) distinguishes between the diseases measles and smallpox. He also uses plaster of Paris to hold broken bones in place while they heal.

900 Arab chemists make alcohol by distilling wine, for use mainly in medicine.

ENGINEERING & INVENTION

789 In Europe Emperor Charlemagne (r. 764–814) introduces standard weights and measures.

800 The use of the blast furnace for producing cast iron spreads from Spain to Scandinavia.

834 The hand crank is first used in Europe to impart rotary motion to a wheel. It is pictured in the *Utrecht Psalter*, a graphic codex produced near Reims (in present-day France).

860 Viking longships from Norway and Sweden venture as far as Iceland. Norwegians make settlements there 14 years later.

982 Viking longships from Iceland under the command of Erik Thorvaldson (950–ca 1003), known as Erik the Red, cross the North Atlantic Ocean and discover Greenland. Four years later 400 Norse people establish a settlement there.

800 People in Central America adopt metalworking techniques from South America.

ca 800 The Hohokam people of Arizona construct an irrigation network of canals and dams. Bows and arrows are used for the first time by hunters in the Mississippi Valley.

812 In China paper bank drafts, or money certificates, are introduced for limited use.

868 The earliest surviving printed book (a scroll), called the *Diamond Sutra*, is made in China.

954 Chinese emperor Shih Tsung authorizes the creation of the Great Lion of Tsang-chou, a cast-iron statue weighing about 44 tons (40 tonnes). It is the largest single piece of cast iron ever made in ancient China.

960 Authorities in the Chinese province of Szechuan begin to print paper money as a means of exchange.

976 Chinese engineer Chang Ssu-Hsun invents a chain-drive mechanism for an astronomical clock.

780 Arabs in Baghdad begin making paper, using a method learned from Chinese craftsmen in Samarkand (present-day Uzbekistan).

800 Arab caliph Harun al-Rashid (ca 766–809) presents a water clock to Emperor Charlemagne.

820 The Moors (Arabs) in Spain produce copper by smelting sulfide ores.

WORLD EVENTS

795 Viking raiders attack the coast of Ireland.

799 First Viking raids along the coast of France.

800 Charlemagne, king of the Franks, is crowned Holy Roman Emperor by the pope in Rome on Christmas Day.

825 Arabs expelled from Spain conquer Crete.

840 Viking settlers in Ireland found Dublin as a trading center.

841 Viking raiders invade Normandy.

874 Danish Vikings settle in Iceland.

888 Charlemagne's empire breaks up on the death of Roman emperor Charles the Fat (r. 881–88).

930 Settlers in Iceland establish the Althing, the world's oldest parliament.

987 Hugh Capet (r. 987–96) is crowned king of France, founding the Capetian Dynasty.

ca 850 The Toltec people establish military supremacy in the Valley of Mexico.

ca 900 Mayan civilization finally collapses in the southern lowlands, and the surviving cities are abandoned.

780 The Chinese writer Yu Lu writes *The Classic of Tea*, describing the use of tea.

791 The Tibetans defeat the Chinese at the Battle of Tingzhou, forcing the Tang emperors to abandon their gains in Central Asia.

ca 800 The first Polynesian seafarers, perhaps from the Society Islands, arrive on Aotearor ("the Land of the Long White Cloud"), later to be known as New Zealand.

907 The last Tang emperor of China is deposed, and China splits into ten separate states (the Ten Kingdoms).

ca 800 Arab merchants found trading towns on the East African coast, including Kilwa Kisiwani (in present-day Tanzania).

ca 871 Ibn Abd al-Hakam writes the first known history of the Arab conquest of Egypt.

935 Algiers is founded by Arabs.

972 A university is founded in Cairo.

MAKING PAPER

As soon as people learned to write, they needed something to write on. Walls, pillars, and tablets were used but were not very portable. The Egyptians invented papyrus, but real progress was made when Chinese craftsmen invented paper.

From about 2800 B.C.E. the Egyptians made papyrus from reeds. They peeled the reeds and sliced the inner pith into strips, which they criss-crossed and pounded into a flat sheet. Other early writing materials included tree bark, cloth, and thin animal skins, the latter made into parchment or vellum.

The first Chinese reference to paper comes in about 105 C.E. It describes paper being made from rags and other materials, such as bark. Chinese craftsmen also made paper from leaves and other vegetable matter. One method involved taking young bamboo fibers and the inner bark of a mulberry tree and pounding them together in water. The resulting slurry was poured through a piece of coarse cloth stretched on a wooden frame to act as a kind of filter. The water trickled through, leaving the fibers on the cloth, which dried to form paper. They also used hemp fibers to make a fine paper, but the most expensive kind was made from silk. Coarse paper was used for wrapping and soft paper used as toilet paper.

Other cultures invented paper independently of the Chinese. Mesopotamians developed a reed paper resembling papyrus. In Central America by about the sixth century inhabitants in Teotihuacán, Mexico, were making paper from the fibers of fig bark.

Knowledge of Chinese papermaking spread across Asia, and by the eighth century had reached the Middle East. Arab traders spread the technique to Egypt by the tenth century. The first European papermaking plant was built in 1150 near Valencia, Spain. By then paper factories were called mills, either because waterwheels provided the power for the pulping machines or because they used grindstones to crush vegetable materials.

THE THOUSAND OR SO YEARS FOLLOWING THE FALL OF THE ROMAN EMPIRE in the West in 476 C.E. were once commonly referred to as the Dark Ages because of the perceived lack of learning during the period. To Europeans looking back from the Renaissance, it seemed that the great cultural and technological achievements of the classical Greeks and Romans had been lost. In fact, the period was marked by steady scientific development, artistic and architectural achievement, and the spread of literacy, particularly in Europe's monasteries. Supposedly "lost" knowledge was preserved in the libraries of the Islamic world. Technology advanced as it had for centuries, through a succession of small improvements. Windmills provided a new source of power to supplement the waterwheels that already existed, and the wind also powered a new generation of sailing ships. Together with the introduction of the magnetic compass from East Asia, such ocean-going ships enabled a host of European adventurers to travel the world, taking them to America and eventually around the entire globe.

Increased travel also led to the more rapid spread of ideas around the world. The compass originated in China, which was also a source of the secret of how to make gunpowder (although its manufacture may have been discovered independently in Europe). Printing with movable type, also first developed in the East, was reinvented in Europe, so books no longer had to be copied laboriously by hand. Books spread knowledge, leading to what contemporaries heralded as a renaissance—literally a "rebirth" —of learning in the 14th and 15th centuries. Many of the classical texts that fueled this rebirth of learning arrived in Europe from the Islamic world.

The typical Renaissance man was Leonardo da Vinci (1452–1519), the Italian artist, architect, and engineer, whose inventions anticipated technical developments that came three or four centuries later. Leonardo's contemporary Nicolaus Copernicus (1473–1543) suggested that the sun is at the center of the solar system, with the planets orbiting around it, laying the foundation of modern astronomy.

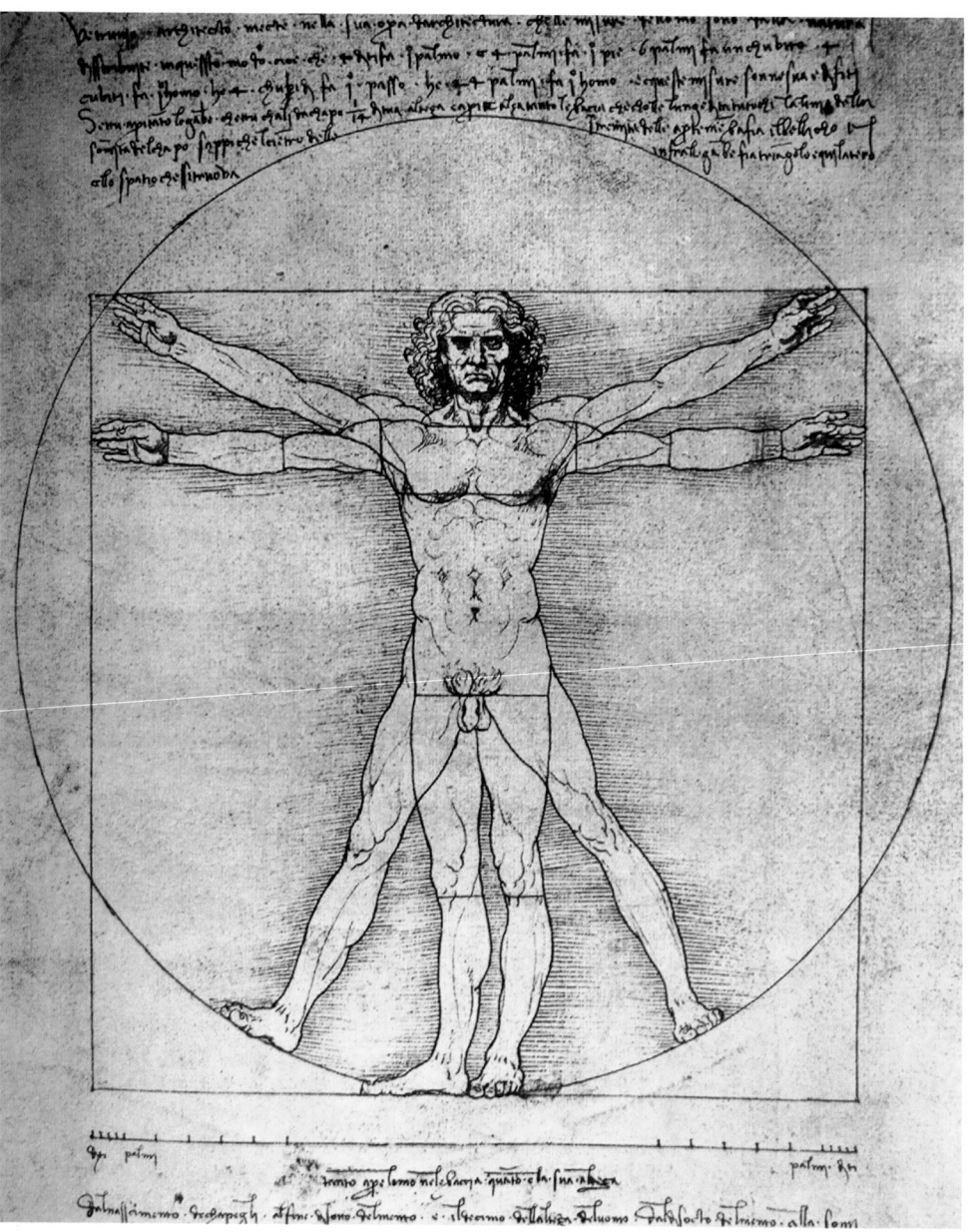

Leonardo da Vinci's "Vitruvian Man." This drawing, a sketch in one of his notebooks, is a study on the principles of ideal human proportions described by classical architect Marcus Vitruvius Pollio (ca 80–20 B.C.E.). This combination of old and new is characteristic of the Renaissance.

Outside Europe the so-called Dark Ages were not a time of intellectual stagnation; the Islamic world, which spread from from Cordoba in Spain to Bukhara in Uzbekistan, contained many great centers of learning. Islamic rulers encouraged intellectual activity. Many of them kept extensive libraries, built observatories for accurate astronomical studies, and offered their patronage to physicians, astronomers, mathematicians, and philosophers. In this climate great scientists such as Ibn Sina (980–1037), Ibn Rushd (1126–98), and Ibn al-Haytham (995–1039) had both access to existing scientific texts and the ability to test scientific knowledge through experimentation. In the West, they are known by their Latin pseudonyms: Avicenna, Averroës, and Alhazen, respectively.

One of the earliest figures who can be called a Renaissance man, the English theologian and scientist Roger Bacon (ca 1214–94), demonstrates the link between the rebirth of European science and its contact with the Islamic world. In his surviving works, such as the *Opus Majus* and the *Opus Tertium*, Bacon describes his extensive knowledge of the Arabic language and his study of the work of Islamic scientists and philosophers. He also asserts that without knowledge of Arabic no European intellectual could consider himself properly educated.

Windmills transform wind power into mechanical power, which is used to grind grain or, as in the case of this set of windmills in the Netherlands, to pump water into a drainage canal in order to reclaim low-lying land from the sea.

The magnifying-glass, made by grinding and shaping a piece of glass to form a convex lens, was first described by the 10th-century Arab physicist Alhazen in his Book of Optics, *which was translated into Latin in 12th-century Spain. Alhazen's work strongly influenced the later studies of English scientist Roger Bacon.*

CONCISE HISTORY OF SCIENCE AND INVENTION

	1000	1100	1200	1300	1350	
EUROPE	**1030** Italian Benedictine monk Guido d'Arezzo invents a form of musical notation (for writing down music). **1066** Halley's comet is sighted in England and is associated with the Norman Conquest of that year. **ca 1075** Female obstetrician Trotula of Salerno gives lectures on women's disorders.	**1135** Scholars in Toledo, Spain, translate the medical works of Persian scholar Avicenna into Latin. **1140** Construction begins on a new basilica at the Abbey of Saint-Denis, France, the first building to use flying buttresses in its structure. **1150** A papermill is built in Spain. **1180** European boatbuilders make ships steered by a rudder at the stern.	**1209** The 20-arch Old London Bridge over the Thames River is completed. It is lined with houses to provide rent for its upkeep. **1242** English scientist and philosopher Roger Bacon gives precise instructions on how to make gunpowder. **1286** Eyeglasses are invented in Italy.	**1316** Italian anatomist Mondino de' Luzzi publishes the first Western account of anatomy. It becomes a standard work until the writings of Belgian anatomist Andreas Vesalius become available. **1340** Avoirdupois weights are introduced in England and France. **1345** Dutch engineers use windmills to pump water when reclaiming land from the sea.	**1363** French physician Guy de Chauliac describes how to treat fractures and hernias in his book *Chirurgia Magna* (Great Surgery). **1364** Italian clockmaker Giovanni di Dondi makes an astronomical clock. **1380** Military rockets are fired in Europe for the first time at the Battle of Chioggia between Genoese and Venetian armies.	
THE AMERICAS	**1000** Viking longships commanded by Leif Eriksson cross the North Atlantic Ocean and reach North America, establishing a colony.	**1116** According to legend the Aztec leave their homeland, Aztlan, and begin to migrate south into Mexico.	**ca 1200** The Anasazi begin to use a sun calendar that divides the year into four seasons.	**ca 1325** The Hohokam begin to build Casa Grande, a large structure in modern-day Arizona.	**ca 1350** Aztec craftsman are renowned for their technological capability. **ca 1360** The Aztec divide their capital, Tenochtitlan, in quarters based on the four cardinal directions.	
ASIA & OCEANIA	**1000** Persian philosopher and physician Ibn Sina, also known by the Latin name Avicenna, writes his medical textbook *Canon of Medicine*. **1044** A Chinese military treatise describes the use and making of gunpowder. **1086** Chinese scientist Shen Kua describes a magnetic compass used for navigation.	**1105** Persian mathematician Omar Khayyam solves cubic equations. **ca 1105** Chinese potters make porcelain, a fine white ceramic that Europeans soon call "China." **1155** Chinese cartographers print maps of western China, the oldest known printed maps.	**ca 1200** Chinese mathematicians introduce a symbol for zero. **1220** The Chinese military use gunpowder bombs with outer cases that shatter on explosion, acting like a type of shrapnel. At about the same time they employ kites to carry messages across enemy lines.	**1313** Chinese printer Wang Chen produces *Nong Shu* (Treatise on Agriculture), using more than 50,000 movable type characters carved from hardwood. (Wooden type replaces the clay characters used previously.)	**1395** Chinese astronomers calculate the length of the solar year as 365.25 days. (A solar year is the time Earth takes to make a complete orbit of the sun, modern value 365.242 days.)	
AFRICA & THE MIDDLE EAST	**1013** Arab builders complete the large al-Hakim Mosque in Cairo, Egypt, with a courtyard big enough to hold half the city's male population. **1021** Arab mathematician Alhazen publishes a treatise on optics, describing lenses, curved mirrors, and the refraction of light.	**1150** Hebrew astronomer Solomon Jarchus compiles the first celestial almanac, giving details about the stars.	**1205** Arab scholar Abu al-Iz Ismail ibn al-Razaz Al-Jarzi gives instructions for building 50 machines in his *Book of Knowledge of Ingenious Mechanical Devices*. **1240** Arab physician Ibn al-Baytar lists 1,400 different medications in *The Comprehensive Book on Materia Medica and Foodstuffs*.	**1331** Arab traveler Ibn Battuta visits east Africa as part of a long voyage through the Islamic world.	**ca 1350** Muslim architects adopt the four-liwan style for mosques and schools of four vaulted halls around an open courtyard. **ca 1360** The Ottoman timar system establishes a degree of centralized control over agriculture and manufacture.	

1400	1450	1500	1550	1600–1625
1405 Triangular lateen sails come into use on Spanish ships and soon spread throughout the Mediterranean region.	**1450** European metalworkers devise a way of separating silver from lead ores such as galena (silver sulfide); some lead contains up to 10 percent silver.	**1502** German clockmaker Peter Henlein makes the first spring-driven pocket clock, or watch.	**1551** English mathematician Leonard Digges invents the theodolite for measuring angles during surveying.	**1608** Dutch eyeglass-maker Hans Lippershey makes a refracting telescope (using two lenses).
1407 In London, England, Bethlehem Hospital becomes an institution for the insane; it is popularly known as Bedlam.	**1457** The first four-wheel passenger coach is built in Hungary.	**1503** The Spanish begin using mines during warfare.	**1573** Danish astronomer Tycho Brahe publishes *De Nova Stella*, describing a new supernova in the constellation Cassiopeia (often called Tycho's Star at the time).	**1609** German Johannes Kepler draws up his first two laws of planetary motion.
1425 German philosopher Nicholas Krebs maintains that the Earth rotates on its axis once a day and orbits the sun once a year.	**1474** English printer William Caxton produces the first printed book in the English language, *Recuyell of the Historyes of Troye*.	**1513** Swiss artist Urs Graf invents metal etching.	**1590** Dutch optician Zacharias Jansen builds a compound microscope.	**1610** Italian scientist Galileo Galilei observes four of Jupiter's moons and craters on the moon.
1430 Germans use a flywheel to even out the motion of rotating machinery.		**1515** The wheel-lock pistol is introduced in Germany.	**1592** Italian scientist Galileo Galilei makes a thermometer.	**1622** English mathematician William Oughtred invents the slide rule.
		1517 Italian physician and poet Girolamo Fracastoro proposes that fossils are the petrified remains of once-living organisms.	**1595** Geraldus Mercator publishes the first atlas.	**1623** German mathematician Wilhelm Schickard makes a wooden adding machine.
ca 1400 The Inca use quipu, knotted strings, to keep trade records.	**ca 1450** The Inca construct a road system 20,000 miles (32,200 km) long to unite their empire.	**1520** Smallpox decimates the Aztecs.	**1555** Tobacco from the Americas is imported to Spain.	**1598** Spanish colonists begin to grow wheat, apricots, and peaches, north of El Paso.
ca 1400 The Mississippians build large earth mounds in North America.		**1520** Spanish voyagers take turkeys and corn from America to Europe.	**ca 1560** Mercury is discovered in Peru and used in a new process to refine silver ore.	**1607** The first American ship is constructed in Sagadahoc, Maine.
ca 1405 Improvement works begin on China's Grand Canal.	**1483** Russian pioneers begin to explore Siberia.	**1500** Chinese scientist Wan Hu attempts to make a flying machine by tying 45 rockets to the back of a chair. He is killed when the device explodes.	**1543** The Portuguese introduce firearms to Japan.	**ca 1600** The tradition of building huge stone statues dies out on Easter Island.
1408 *Yongle dadian*, a wide-ranging encyclopedia, is published under the patronage of the Chinese emperor Yongle.	**1495** The Chinese divert the Yellow River to a new course near the Shandong Peninsula.		**1574** *Taiping Guangzhi* is the first Chinese book printed with movable type.	**1602** Italian missionary Matteo Ricci publishes a Chinese atlas of the world.
1414 From this year Chinese trading fleets sail to India, the Middle East, and as far as Africa, using large oceangoing junks.		**1514** The Chinese open silver mines at Yunnan.		
		1520 The Chinese buy cannon from the Portuguese.		
1410 Hebrew astronomer Hasdai ben Abraham Crescas writes *Or Adonai* (The Light of the Lord). He disagrees with Aristotle that there are no worlds other than Earth.	**1453** At the siege of Constantinople (present-day Istanbul), Ottoman forces use a huge cannon that fires cannonballs weighing up to 1,345 pounds (610 kg).	**1511** The Ottomans begin providing gunpowder weapons to their allies such as Egypt and Mesopotamia. Ottoman gunmakers are in demand as far away as Delhi, in India.	**ca 1550** The Ottomans build aqueducts to carry water into their growing capital city at Istanbul.	**ca 1600** The Ottomans introduce tobacco from the Americas.
1420 Tartar prince, astronomer, and Turkish ruler of Maverannakhr (modern Uzbekistan) Ulugh Beg begins construction of a three-story observatory in Samarkand.	**1471** Portuguese navigator Fernão do Po discovers the island of Fernando Póo (now Bioko) in Equatorial Guinea, West Africa.	**1513** The Ottoman geographer Piri Reis draws a map of the world that includes what is then known of the Americas.	**1569** Ottoman engineers attempt to construct a canal between the Don and Volga Rivers.	

ASTRONOMY & MATH

EUROPE

1050 Arab astronomers and navigators introduce the astrolabe to Europe.

1066 Halley's comet is sighted in England and is associated with the Norman Conquest of that year.

1142 English philosopher Adelard of Bath (ca 1080–ca 1160) translates *Elements* (books about geometry) by Greek mathematician Euclid (ca 300 B.C.E.) from Arabic into Latin.

1145 English scholar Robert of Chester translates *Hisab al-jabr w'al-muqabala* (Calculation by Restoration and Reduction) by Arab mathematician Abu Jafar Muhammad ibn-Musa al-Khwarizmi (ca 780–ca 850) into Latin.

ASIA & OCEANIA

ca 1000 Indian astronomers introduce a calendar of 360 days with 12 months of 27 or 28 days; an extra month is added every five years to bring the calendar in step with the seasons.

1006 Astronomers in China, Egypt, Europe, and Japan record a supernova that remains visible for several months.

1105 Persian mathematician and poet Omar Khayyam (1048–1131) solves cubic equations (algebra equations of the degree 3).

1150 Hindu mathematician Bhaskara Acharya (1114–85) sums up Indian knowledge of algebra and math in *Siddhanta Siromani*.

AFRICA & THE MIDDLE EAST

1075 Arab astronomer al-Zarqali (1028–87), also known by the Latin name Arzachel, proposes that the orbits of the planets are ellipses rather than circles.

1150 Hebrew astronomer Solomon Jarchus compiles the first celestial almanac, giving details about the stars.

BIOLOGY & MEDICINE

ca 1075 Italian obstetrician Trotula of Salerno lectures at a university (unusual for a woman) and writes books on hygiene and women's disorders.

1135 Scholars in Toledo, Spain, translate the medical works of Persian scholar Ibn Sina (980–1037), also known as Avicenna, into Latin.

1140 King Roger II of Sicily (r. 1130–54) introduces government licenses for physicians; only those with licenses may practice medicine.

1150 In Spain Arab physician Avenzoar (ca 1091–1162) introduces blood-letting as a medical treatment.

A modern fireworks display. Fireworks were developed soon after the discovery of gunpowder, and became a popular entertainment in 12th century China.

1000 Avicenna writes his medical textbook *Canon of Medicine*, which remains a standard work for centuries.

The knowledge of anything, since all things have causes, is not acquired or complete unless it is known by its causes.

AVICENNA (IBN SINA), *CANON OF MEDICINE*

PHYSICAL SCIENCES

1120 French-born Prior Walcher of Malvern Abbey, England, begins using degrees to express latitude and longitude on maps.

ca 1000 The Chinese dig the first coal mines.

1086 Chinese scientist Shen Kua writes *Dream Pool Essays*, in which he anticipates earth science by discussing the principles of sedimentation, uplift, and erosion.

1155 Chinese cartographers create maps of western China, the oldest known printed maps.

1160 Persian mathematician Sharaf al-Din al-Tusi of Damascus invents the sighting rod or linear astrolabe, which is much easier to make and use than the regular astrolabe.

1021 Arab mathematician Alhazen (ca 965–ca 1040) publishes a treatise on optics, describing lenses, curved mirrors, and refraction of light.

THE AMERICAS

ENGINEERING & INVENTION	WORLD EVENTS
1030 Italian Benedictine monk Guido d'Arezzo (ca 991–1050) invents a form of musical notation (for writing down music). **1080** The swingletree allows two horses side by side to pull a plow or wagon. **1105** A major arsenal is established in Venice, Italy. **1110** European military engineers invent the gravity-powered catapult. **1140** Construction begins on a new basilica at the Abbey of Saint-Denis, France, the first building to use flying buttresses in its structure. **1150** The first European papermill is built in Valencia, Spain.	**1016** The Danish king Canute (r. 1016–35) becomes undisputed king of England. **1000** Bohemia and Moravia are united. **1066** William of Normandy (1066–87) invades England and becomes king. **1096** The first Crusade begins as European knights set out to expel Muslims from the Holy Land. **1149** Oxford University is founded. **1152** Frederick Barbarossa (r. 1155–90) becomes Holy Roman Emperor.
1000 Viking longships commanded by Leif Eriksson (ca 970–ca 1020) cross the North Atlantic Ocean and reach North America, establishing a colony there.	**1116** According to legend the Aztec leave their homeland, Aztlan, and begin to migrate south into Mexico.
1044 A Chinese military treatise describes the use and making of gunpowder. **1045** In China, Bi Sheng invents movable type made from baked clay. **1086** Chinese scientist Shen Kua describes a magnetic compass used for navigation. **ca 1100** Fireworks become popular in China. **ca 1105** Chinese potters make porcelain, a fine white ceramic that Europeans soon call "china."	**1115** The Jurchen from Manchuria found China's Jin dynasty. **1156** The Taira and Minamoto clans fight for control of Japan.
1013 Arab builders complete the large al-Hakim Mosque in Cairo, Egypt, with a courtyard big enough to hold half the city's male population. **1075** Arab astronomer al-Zarqali (1028–87), working in Spain, builds several complex astronomical water clocks in Toledo.	

On the coasts and islands of the Mediterranean, windmills could be built facing the direction of the prevailing wind, from the sea. Inland, more variable winds required windmills that could be moved.

WIND POWER

Windmills arrived in western Europe in the 12th century: Crusaders probably brought the idea from the Holy Land. But European windmills differed in one important respect: Instead of being mounted on a vertical axis, their sails radiated from a horizontal axis, supported on the side of a post or a stone tower. This design makes much more efficient use of available air currents.

Using an upright mill to turn millstones required the use of gears to move the turning force through 90 degrees. Windmills also had to be adjustable so that the sails faced into the wind. Inland mills, known as post mills, were small and mounted on a stout post that could be turned to face the wind. By the 15th century windmill sails were mounted in a free-rotating cap that was separate from the main tower. When the miller needed to change the direction of the sails, he only had to turn the cap, not the whole structure. This advance meant that the size of windmills was no longer restricted by the need to turn them around. Mill towers could be built of brick or stone, several stories high.

ASTRONOMY & MATH

EUROPE

1175 Italian scholar Gerard of Cremona (1114–1187) makes Latin translations of the Arabic versions of older texts, including the *Almagest* by Greek astronomer Ptolemy (ca 100–70 C.E.) and the works of the Persian physician Avicenna (980–1037).

1202 Italian mathematician Leonardo Fibonacci (ca 1170–1250) introduces the Fibonacci series, in which each number is the sum of the previous two.

1217 Scottish scholar Michael Scot (ca 1175–ca 1235) introduces the ideas of Greek philosopher Aristotle (384–322 B.C.E.) into European astronomy.

1225 Mathematician Jordanus Nemorarius, in his *Arithmetica*, uses letters to denote variable quantities (as in modern algebra).

1240 English mathematician Johannes de Sacrobosco publishes *De Sphaera Mundi* (On the Sphere of the World), a standard astronomical text for the next four centuries.

THE AMERICAS

ca 1200 The Anasazi begin to use a sun calendar that divides the year into four seasons, using patterns of sunlight falling on rock carvings to identify the first day of each season.

ca 1200 A Maya codex records information about the cycles of the planet Venus.

ASIA & OCEANIA

1181 Chinese and Japanese astronomers report a new supernova that stays visible for about 183 days.

ca 1200 Chinese mathematicians introduce a symbol for zero.

The Citadel at Aleppo, Syria, was constructed between 1193 and 1215 under the supervision of Saladin's son Malik az-Zahir.

BIOLOGY & MEDICINE

1180 Italian physician Roger of Salerno publishes *Practica Chirurgica* (Practice of Surgery), the first European book devoted entirely to surgery.

1193 Italian scholar Burgundo of Pisa translates the medical works of Greek physician Galen of Pergamum (ca 129–ca 216) from Greek into Latin. This has a profound effect on the teaching and practice of medicine for the next two centuries.

1205 European farmers begin to grow buckwheat as an alternative to emmer wheat, barley, and oats.

1240 Dissection of human corpses is permitted in a decree issued by the Holy Roman Empire.

AFRICA & THE MIDDLE EAST

1240 Arab physician Ibn al-Baytar (1179–1248) lists 1,400 different medications in *The Comprehensive Book on Materia Medica and Foodstuffs*.

PHYSICAL SCIENCES

1180 English scholar and cleric Alexander Neckam (1157–1217) writes *De Naturis Rerum* (Concerning Natural Things), which contains the first reference to the magnetic compass in Western writing.

1209 Italian engineers build a 31-mile (50-km) irrigation canal from the Ticino River near its outlet at Lake Maggiore to the suburbs of Milan. It is later (1269) enlarged into the Naviglio Grande (Grand Canal) for navigation.

1225 Scientist and mathematician Jordanus Nemorarius, in his book *Elementa super demonstrationem ponderis* (Elements for the Demonstration of Weights), includes laws for calculating the displacements produced by levers.

1242 English scientist and philosopher Roger Bacon (ca 1214–1292) gives precise instructions on how to make gunpowder.

1198 Arab scholar Ibn Rushd (1126–98), also known as Averroës, dies after becoming a world-renowned commentator on the works of Aristotle.

ca 1200 Arab geographer Abdallah al-Rumi writes his encyclopedia *Mu'jam ul-Buldan*, a survey of geographical knowledge.

ENGINEERING & INVENTION	WORLD EVENTS
1180 Western boatbuilders start making ships steered using a rudder at the stern instead of steering oars at the sides.	**1189** Richard I (r. 1189–99) becomes king of England.
1205 Ironworkers in Catalonia, Spain, improve the Catalan forge, which employs a draft of air in the smelting furnace (a forerunner of the blast furnace).	**1204** Amsterdam is founded in Holland.
1209 The 20-arch Old London Bridge over the Thames River is completed. It is lined with houses to provide rent for its upkeep.	**1215** King John of England (r. 1199–1216) signs Magna Carta, a document that grants English nobles certain rights in their dealings with the king; the document becomes a cornerstone of constitutional government.
ca 1220 The main structure of Chartres Cathedral, France, is rebuilt around this time following a fire of 1194 that destroyed all but the western front of the original building.	**1220** Several universities are founded in Europe at about this time, including Padua (1222), Naples (1224), Toulouse (1229), Cambridge (1231), and Rome (1244).
1225 French master mason Villard de Honnecourt makes detailed drawings of various mechanisms, including a water-powered machine for sawing timber.	
ca 1200 The Anasazi make sandals by weaving together the leaves of yucca plants.	**ca 1175** Toltec power fades in Mexico.
	ca 1200 Inca leader Manco Capac founds the city of Cuzco in Peru.
	ca 1200 Chichen Itza's dominance of the Yucatán is overtaken by that of Mayapán.
1185 Chinese craftsmen invent the rotary disk cutter (for cutting jade).	**1185** Minamoto Yoritomo (1147–99) sets up a military government in Japan, and later becomes shogun.
1189 Construction of the 770-foot (235-m) Marco Polo Bridge begins across the Yongding River in China; it survives today.	**ca 1200** While Islam spreads into India, Zen Buddhism begins to become popular in Japan.
1220 The Chinese military use gunpowder bombs with outer cases that shatter on explosion, acting like a type of shrapnel. At about the same time they employ kites to carry messages across enemy lines.	**1206** Genghis Khan (born ca 1162) becomes leader of the Mongols and begins an expansion of the Mongol Empire across Asia that ends with his death in 1227.
1227 Japanese artisan Kato Shirozaemon (1169–1249) returns from China with the secret for making porcelain.	**1220** The kingdom of Sukothai is established in Thailand.
1205 Arab scholar Abu al-Iz Ismail ibn al-Razaz Al-Jarzi gives instructions for building 50 machines in his *Book of Knowledge of Ingenious Mechanical Devices*.	
1209 The Persian Al-Razi dies after a lifetime of writing on philosophical subjects, including a compendium of science.	

CASTLES AND BRIDGES

In the Roman Empire, fortifications and bridges were common. After the empire's collapse it was not until the 11th century that they were again built on the same scale. They were simple structures—motte and bailey castles made from earthworks and wooden palisades, and bridges built from wooden piers and beams. Over the 11th and 12th centuries, however, engineers matched the work of their forbears.

Castles became massive, with high towers, secret tunnels, and walls up to 100 feet (30 m) thick. They were often built on steep hillsides or coastal cliffs and dominated the landscapes of Europe and the Middle East for centuries. Castles were continually upgraded to match the advances in weaponry. By the 15th century, however, artillery had become so powerful that no castle could defend itself adequately.

Bridges also grew more complex. Some, such as the Pont Valentré on the Lot River in France, were fortified. Others had stores, chapels, tollhouses, or homes all the way across. Old London Bridge was the first stone bridge with masonry foundations to be built across a swift-flowing tidal river—the Thames. Constructed between 1176 and 1209 and lined with houses and shops, it survived for more than 600 years.

An illustration of the Old London Bridge, which was continually in use as a major transport route until its demolition in the early 19th century.

ASTRONOMY & MATH	BIOLOGY & MEDICINE	PHYSICAL SCIENCES

EUROPE

1272 After 10 years' work, the Alfonsine Tables of astronomical data are completed, sponsored by King Alfonso X of Léon and Castile (ca 1221–84). The first set of astronomical tables prepared in Christian Europe, they are used for several centuries.

1275 William of Moerbeke (1215–86) translates works of Greek mathematician and philosopher Archimedes (ca 287–212 B.C.E.) from Greek into Latin. He also translates the medical works of Greek physician Galen of Pergamum (ca 129–ca 216).

1321 French–Hebrew mathematician and philosopher Levi ben Gershon (1288–1344) introduces the mathematics of permutations and combination.

1267 In his *Opus Majus* (Great Work) English scientist and philosopher Roger Bacon (ca 1214–92) describes the magnification of objects by convex lenses, and suggests that magnifying glasses could enhance "weak sight."

1276 Italian theologian Giles of Rome (d. 1316) writes *De Formatione Corporis in Utero* (On the Formation of the Body in the Uterus), in which he discusses the role of both parents in procreation.

1316 Italian anatomist Mondino de' Luzzi (ca 1275–1326) publishes his *Anatomia*, the first Western account of anatomy and a standard work until the writings of Belgian anatomist Andreas Vesalius (1514–64) become available.

1320 In his book *Chirurgia* (Surgery) French pioneer surgeon Henri de Mondeville (1260–1320) recommends the cleansing and stitching of wounds to aid healing.

1250 German Dominican monk, scholar, and alchemist Albertus Magnus (1193–1280) isolates arsenic.

1269 In *Epistola de Magnete* (Letter about Magnets) French soldier Petrus Peregrinus introduces the idea that a magnet has "poles" that influence a compass needle.

1300 Spanish alchemist known as False Geber (b. ca 1270), who took his name from the eighth-century Arab scholar Jabir ibn-Hayyan (ca 721–ca 803), describes sulfuric acid.

1304 German scientist Theodoric of Freibourg (d. 1310) investigates the role of raindrops in forming rainbows. He also discovers that refraction causes a colored spectrum, as he records in *De Iride* (Concerning the Rainbow).

1315 According to tradition, Spanish cleric and philosopher Ramón Llull (ca 1232–1315), also known as Raymond Lully and Doctor Illuminatus, discovers ammonia gas.

THE AMERICAS

ASIA & OCEANIA

1270 To observe the positions of the stars, Chinese astronomer Kuo Shou-Ching (1231–1316) constructs an armillary sphere on an equatorial mount, which he calls his "simplified instrument."

1276 Chinese astronomer Zhou Kung erects a 40-foot (12-m) gnomon (shadow clock) for accurate timekeeping.

ca 1300 Hawaiians begin to farm popular food fish in giant ponds.

INSIDE STORY

Roger Bacon

Englishman Roger Bacon (ca 1214–94) was not only a philosopher but also one of the first experimental scientists. Among his many interests he experimented with light and lenses, the branch of science now known as optics, building on the work of Islamic scientists such as Alhazen, whose *Book of Optics* had revolutionized the science of light and vision around 100 years earlier. Bacon is also occasionally credited with the invention of eyeglasses, although glasses were also invented independently in Italy at about this time. Among Bacon's other achievements was the first account in western Europe, in 1242, of the precise composition of gunpowder. Bacon did not suggest any uses for the explosive, however, and guns and cannon were not made in Europe until around 50 years later.

AFRICA & THE MIDDLE EAST

1262 Arab astronomer and mathematician Nasir al-Din al-Tusi (1201–74) designs and builds a well-equipped observatory at Maragheh (in present-day Iraq), which includes a quadrant 12 feet (3.6 m) across. Twelve years later he publishes a set of precise astronomical tables.

1255 Carrier pigeons are used to convey messages in the Middle East. The 400 miles (640 km) between Cairo and Damascus is covered in about a day (using relays of birds).

1260 Arab physician Ibn al-Nafis describes the pulmonary circulation of the blood (the loop of the main circulation that passes from the heart to the lungs and back).

1284 Mamluk Sultan Qala'un (r. 1279–90) builds the Mansuri Maristan in Cairo, Egypt, a hospital with separate wards for different medical disorders.

The workings of the magnifying lens were explained by the optical experiments of Roger Bacon and Alhazen.

1280 A book on warfare by Syrian al-Hassan al-Rammah refers to saltpeter and rockets, suggesting a knowledge of the composition of gunpowder.

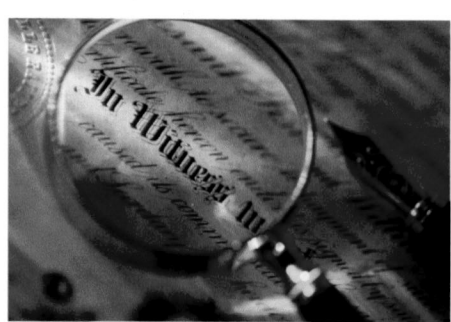

ENGINEERING & INVENTION

1250 Armorers in Bohemia (in present-day Czech Republic) make armor using tinplate (steel coated with a layer of tin) to prevent rust.

1250 In Paris the main part of Notre-Dame Cathedral is completed.

1272 Italian mechanic Borghesano of Bologna invents a machine for forming silk threads.

1286 Eyeglasses are invented in Italy at about this time. The invention is often attributed to physician Salvino degli Armati.

ca 1310 Portuguese sailors produce portolan charts to aid coastal navigation.

1315 Italian immigrants establish a silk industry in Lyons, France.

1323 Waterwheel-driven bellows are described for the first time in a French manuscript.

1290 South American people living in the Andes mountains build cable bridges to cross deep gorges.

ca 1325 The Hohokam begin to build Casa Grande, a large structure in present-day Arizona.

1288 Chinese military engineers make the first gunpowder cannon, which they call "erupters."

1313 Chinese printer Wang Chen produces *Nong Shu* (Treatise on Agriculture), using more than 50,000 movable type characters carved from hardwood. (Wooden type replaces the clay characters used previously.)

ca 1275 Building begins at Great Zimbabwe in southern Africa of a large ceremonial enclosure constructed of stone without the use of mortar.

Armillary sphere, similar to that constructed by Kuo Shou Ching in 1270

WORLD EVENTS

1271 Aged 17, Venetian Marco Polo (ca 1254–1324) sets off with his father and uncle on a four-year journey across Asia to China.

1283 The Teutonic Knights complete the conquest of Prussia.

1284 After destroying the Pisan navy at Meloria, Genoa emerges as the major Italian rival of Venice.

1291 The last Crusade ends when the Knights of Saint John of Jerusalem settle in Cyprus.

1306 Robert the Bruce (r. 1306–29) is crowned king of Scotland and leads attacks on the English.

ca 1315 The so-called Little Ice Age, a prolonged period of lower than normal average temperatures, leads to poor harvests and famine across Europe.

ca 1260 The Aztec settle in the Valley of Mexico.

ca 1275 Drought drives the Anasazi away from Mesa Verde in present-day Colorado.

ca 1300 The Toltec domination of Mesoamerica comes to an end.

1279 Kublai Khan (1215–94) reunites China under the Yuan dynasty.

1281 The Mongols launch an unsuccessful invasion of Japan.

1296 The Khalji dynasty of Delhi takes control of much of India.

1320 Tughlak leader Gharzi Khan becomes sultan of Delhi.

1250 Mamluks take power in Egypt after assassinating the Abuyyid caliph.

1291 The Mamluks seize Acre.

1301 Osman (r. 1299–1326), the first ruler of the Ottoman Turks, defeats the Byzantines in battle.

1312 Mansa Musa (r. 1312–37) comes to power in Mali, which he makes a center of Islamic culture.

THE MAGNETIC COMPASS

As compasses function using the Earth's magnetic field, the development of the compass is closely linked with the understanding of magnetism. People were aware of magnetism thousands of years ago, when they realized the unusual properties of rocks they called lodestones. Lodestones are rich in the mineral magnetite, a mixed iron oxide (Fe_3O_4) that is naturally magnetic.

Like a simple bar magnet, Earth's magnetic field has two poles: north and south. Place a bar magnet under a sheet of iron filings, and the filings line themselves up along the field lines that radiate from the poles. A magnetized object such as a lodestone or compass needle will try to align itself to the Earth's magnetic field lines in just the same way.

Compasses were first made in the first century C.E. by Chinese mystics but were not used for navigation until the 11th century. There is some evidence to suggest that the Vikings used compasses on their voyages around northern Europe in the 11th century, but the first clear reference to a magnetic compass in Europe comes from *De Naturis Rerum* (Concerning Natural Things), published in about 1180 by English scholar Alexander Neckam (1157–1217).

Early European compasses consisted of a magnetized needle thrust perpendicularly through a straw that was then floated upright in a dish of water. By 1250 the needle was mounted on a pivot so that it hovered beneath a circular card marked up with the cardinal directions. When the needle moved, so did the card. Further refinements in compass technology included mounting the needle and dial inside a box. Early compass cases were made of wood or ivory—materials that did not interfere with the magnetic forces acting on the needle. Later models used brass for the same reason. They were later mounted on gimbals so that the needle was not affected by the roll of a ship at sea.

ASTRONOMY & MATH	BIOLOGY & MEDICINE	PHYSICAL SCIENCES

EUROPE

1328 In an attempt to improve on the laws of motion proposed by Aristotle (384–322 B.C.E.), English theologian Thomas Bradwardine (ca 1290–1349) publishes his theory of proportions in *De Proportionibus Velocitatum in Motibus* (Dealing with Proportions), without great success.

1336 Authorities at the University of Paris make mathematics a compulsory subject for all students.

1355 French philosopher Jean Buridan (ca 1300–ca 58) comes up with the idea of "impetus," which keeps celestial bodies continuously in orbit. The idea is close to the modern concept of inertia, the property that makes an object resist a change in its motion.

1365 French cleric and philosopher Nicole d'Oresme (ca 1330–82) publishes a wide-ranging mathematical text, *Latitudes of Forms*, that anticipates ideas such as analytic geometry and calculus.

1333 Europe's first medieval botanical garden is opened in Venice.

1363 French physician Guy de Chauliac (ca 1300–68) describes how to treat fractures and hernias in his book *Chirurgia Magna* (Great Surgery).

1377 As a measure against the spread of plague, authorities at the port of Ragusa (present-day Dubrovnik, Croatia) establish a quarantine station on a nearby island. Suspected carriers of the disease have to stay there for 30 days.

1407 In London, England, Bethlehem Hospital becomes an institution for the insane; it is popularly known as Bedlam.

1410 Italian physician Benedetto Rinio writes *Liber de Simplicibus,* a catalog of more than 500 medicinal plants.

1340 Avoirdupois weights (using pounds and ounces) are introduced into England from France.

ca 1350 At about this time ironfounders at Liège, Belgium, build a blast furnace for extracting iron from its ores.

1398 A 7.2-mile (12-km) canal from Lake Mölln to the Delvenau River in Germany is built. It links with the Elbe River to provide a tortuous route between the Baltic and the North seas.

THE AMERICAS

ca 1360 The Aztec divide their capital, Tenochtitlan, in quarters based on the four cardinal directions.

ca 1400 The Aztec universe combines three types of time: two belong to the gods—transcendent time and active time; the remainder is the time of humans.

ASIA & OCEANIA

1395 Chinese astronomers calculate the length of the solar year as 365.25 days. (A solar year is the time it takes Earth to make a complete orbit of the sun, modern value 365.242 days.)

Architect Filippo Brunelleschi's great dome for Florence Cathedral was finished by 1434, but he continued to be involved with the building of the cathedral until his death in 1446.

HOW THINGS WORK

The Longbow

In 1415 the massively outnumbered English army of King Henry V defeated the French army at the Battle of Agincourt. One of the decisive factors in the English victory was the use of the English longbow, a weapon that allowed archers to fire arrows at high enough speeds to penetrate the thick armor of the French knights. The arrows the weapons fired had narrow barbed heads that were nearly impossible to remove without making a wound worse. The longbow, as the name suggests, was a huge weapon between 4 and 6 feet (1.2–1.8 m) in length. The weapon required around four times the strength as a normal bow to fire accurately. In order to be able to use the longbow effectively, archers had to be trained from a very young age and continue to practice throughout their lives. Archery practice became a standard part of English life. Examination of the skeletons of medieval English longbowmen reveals that they usually had one arm significantly longer than the other, caused by the massive compression of the bow's draw.

AFRICA & THE MIDDLE EAST

1410 Hebrew astronomer Hasdai ben Abraham Crescas (ca 1340–1412) writes *Or Adonai* (The Light of the Lord). He disagrees with Aristotle that there are no worlds other than Earth.

1420 Tartar prince, astronomer, and Turkish ruler of Maverannakhr (modern Uzbekistan) Ulugh Beg (1394–1449) begins construction of a three-story observatory at the new university in Samarkand. In 1437 he produces the *Zij-i Gurgani*, a catalog of 992 stars.

1410 People in Ethiopia make and drink coffee from the berries of the wild Ethiopian coffee plant. Coffee does not become a popular drink in Europe until about 200 years later.

ENGINEERING & INVENTION	WORLD EVENTS
1391 *A Treatise on the Astrolabe*, possibly by poet Geoffrey Chaucer (ca 1342–1400), is the first technology book in English.	**1333** Islamic culture reaches its height in Granada, Spain, under Caliph Yusuf I (1318–54).
1345 Dutch engineers use windmills to pump water in land reclamation projects.	**1337** Edward III of England (r. 1327–77) claims the French throne, sparking the Hundred Years' War.
1364 Italian clockmaker Giovanni di Dondi (1318–80) makes an astronomical clock.	**1346–50** The Black Death (plague) kills at least 25 million people, more than a quarter of Europe's population.
1380 Military rockets are fired in Europe for the first time at the Battle of Chioggia between Genoese and Venetian armies.	**1371** The Stewart dynasty comes to the Scottish throne.
1405 Triangular lateen sails come into use on Spanish ships and soon spread throughout the Mediterranean region.	**1381** Venice defeats Genoa and begins a golden age of commerce and culture.
1420 A manual for gunners, *The Book of Fireworks*, is published in Germany and becomes the standard work for 200 years.	**1415** Henry V of England (r. 1413–22) defeats the French at the Battle of Agincourt, part of the Hundred Years' War.
1420 Architect Filippo Brunelleschi (1337–1446) begins supervision of the building of the dome of the Florence Duomo, or cathedral, Italy.	
ca 1350 Aztec craftsman are renowned for their technological capability.	**ca 1350** The Aztec demand tribute from their subject peoples.
ca 1400 The Inca use quipu, knotted strings, to keep trade records and to preserve oral histories.	**1410** Viracocha Inca expands the Inca empire from its base at Cuzco, Peru.
ca 1400 The Mississippians build large earth mounds in North America.	
1395 Printers in Korea use metal type; in 1403 King Taejong (reigned 1400–18) orders type to be cast in bronze.	**1336** The Ashikaga shogunate is established in Japan.
ca 1405 Improvement works begin on China's Grand Canal.	**1368** The Ming dynasty is founded in China, with its capital at Nanjing.
1408 *Yongle dadian*, a wide-ranging encyclopedia, is published under the patronage of the Chinese emperor Yongle.	**1398** Tamerlane (r. 1370–1405) invades India and sacks the capital at Delhi.
1414 From this year Chinese trading fleets sail to India, the Middle East, and as far as Africa, using large oceangoing junks.	**ca 1405** Chinese admiral Zheng He (1371–1433) leads seven huge naval expeditions around the India Ocean.
	1420 Emperor Yongle (r. 1402–24) moves the Chinese capital to Beijing.
ca 1350 Muslim architects adopt the four-liwan style for mosques and schools of four vaulted halls around an open courtyard.	**1331** Arab traveler Ibn Battuta (1304–ca 1368) visits East Africa as part of a long voyage through the Islamic world.
ca 1360 The Ottoman timar system establishes a degree of centralized control over agriculture and manufacture.	**1354** The Ottoman empire reaches across the Bosporus to Europe.
ca 1390 Tamerlane reconstructs Samarkand as his capital.	**1396** An Ottoman army led by Sultan Bayezid (r. 1389–1402) defeats a Christian army led by Sigismund of Hungary (r. 1433–1437) at Nicopolis.
	1402 The Ottomans are defeated by the Mongols led by Tamerlane.
	1421 The Ottoman sultan Murat II (r. 1421–44) resumes a policy of expanding the empire.

THE BLACK DEATH

In the 1340s Europe and the Middle East were struck by an outbreak of the Black Death. The disease—most likely bubonic plague—spread rapidly around the trading centers of the medieval world, killing millions of people. The symptoms of the disease were black spots on the skin, fever, and swollen glands. It was spread by the bites of fleas carried by rats, although the people of the time did not know this.

The disease spread rapidly in the unsanitary conditions of the cities and merchant ships that traveled between them. People panicked, set fire to their homes, and fled, taking their animals—and often their animals' infected fleas—with them.

By the time the pandemic had run its course, the Black Death had killed more than one-quarter of the population of Europe. Across the continent, building projects and road construction came to a halt, and harvests failed for lack of workers. In the aftermath of the disease came social change, as workers who had been tied to the land could now hire themselves out to the highest payer.

A plague doctor. The beak at the front of the hood contained strong-smelling herbs that were believed to prevent infection.

CLOCKS AND WATCHES

THE SHADOW CLOCK, THE FIRST TIMEKEEPER, was in use in ancient Egypt by about 3500 B.C.E. The device consists of a vertical stick in the ground, and time is indicated by the position of its shadow, which changes during the day with the apparent movement of the sun across the heavens. By the eighth century B.C.E. the shadow clock had evolved into the sundial, in which a triangular "fin" (gnomon) replaced the stick. Sand clocks also date from ancient times. The most common type

was the hourglass, so called because it took exactly one hour for dry sand to run through a narrow neck from the upper section to the lower section. The British Royal Navy used hourglasses to keep time onboard ships at sea until the 1820s.

At night the ancient Egyptians used a water clock to tell the time. Called a *clepsydra*, the simplest type consisted of a vessel full of water with a graduated scale marked on the inside. Water dripped out of the vessel through a hole in the bottom, and the water level on

The ornate 24-hour clock (dating from 1344) at the Capitanio Palace in Padua, Italy, displays the date as well as the phases of the moon and the positions of the sun in the zodiac.

the scale inside indicated the time. The Greeks added a float mechanism that moved a pointer to show the time. Chinese inventors also made a version of the clepsydra, sometimes using mercury instead of water.

In 725 C.E. Chinese engineer Liang Ling-Zan and Buddhist monk Yi-Xing (683–727) made the first mechanical clock, based on the regular movement of a huge 33-foot (10-m) paddlewheel. Each "paddle" consisted of a cup and, as it filled with water, it rotated the wheel by exactly one thirty-sixth of a turn. A system of gears gave readings of the time of day, as well as the day of the year and the phase of the moon. In about 1090 Chinese imperial minister Su Sung (1020–1101) built a huge water-driven clock, or "Cosmic Engine," which indicated the apparent movement of the stars as well as the time.

Mechanical Clocks and Watches

The first mechanical clocks were driven by the action of a slowly falling weight at the end of a cord wrapped around a drum. A horizontally oscillating bar controlled the rotation of a cogwheel on the drum and slowed its rotation—this was the first example of a clock escapement. At hourly intervals a hammer rang a bell to indicate the passing of time (there were no hands or dials). The word *clock* comes from the German *glock*, meaning bell. This type of clock is said to have been invented by the French cleric and scholar Gerbert of Aurillac (ca 945–1003) in about 996, before he became Pope Sylvester II in 999. Similar clocks dating from the 1380s still exist in the cathedrals at Rouen, France, and Salisbury, England.

In 1502 German clockmaker Peter Henlein (1480–1542) invented a spring-driven clock, which had a horizontal face with a single hour hand. Then in 1656 Dutch scientist Christiaan Huygens (1629–95) designed the pendulum clock, the first of which was made a year later by a clockmaker in The Hague named Salomon Coster (1620–59). The anchor escapement was the next major improvement in the design, invented in 1660 by English scientist Robert Hooke (1635–1703). Since it was a regular timekeeper, the pendulum could be applied to both weight-driven and spring-driven clocks.

Henlein made the first portable timekeeper, or watch, a year or two before he died in 1542. Spring-

Anchor

Escape wheel

Main Wheel

Barrel

Driving weight

Pendulum bob

The mechanism that controls the speed at which a clock runs is the escapement. The anchor escapement was used in long-case clocks from about 1670. The swinging pendulum causes a horseshoe-shaped anchor to rock from side to side, allowing the escape wheel to make a fraction of a turn at each half-swing. This action allows the driving weight to fall slowly, rotating the barrel and turning the hands of the clock.

driven, it had a single hour hand that showed through holes in the front of the case. It was highly inaccurate, however. The oscillating balance wheel and hairspring regulator were invented in about 1675; they are still used in mechanical clocks and watches today. In 1680 English clockmaker Daniel Quare (1648–1724) invented a repeating watch that chimed the hours and repeated the last set of chimes when the owner pressed a lever at the side. That made it possible to find out at any time the last hour that had struck.

Verge

Foliot

Disengaged pallet

Engaged pallet

Crown wheel

Weight

The verge-and-foliot escapement was used on lantern clocks until about 1800. The verge was controlled by two teeth (pallets) that engaged a vertical crown wheel. As the foliot swung in one direction, a pallet disengaged the crown wheel, allowing the weight to fall and turn the hand. The foliot swung back, and a pallet engaged the crown wheel, stopping the fall of the weight. The foliot then swung in the other direction, allowing the weight to fall again.

ASTRONOMY & MATH

1425 German philosopher Nicholas Krebs (1401–64), known as Nicholas of Cusa, maintains that the Earth rotates on its axis once a day and orbits the sun once a year.

1435 Italian architect and artist Leon Alberti (1404–72) publishes a book that includes the scientific laws of perspective, which are the basis of projective geometry.

1460 Austrian astronomer Georg von Peuerbach (ca 1421–61) begins work on a version of Ptolemy's *Almagest*. After his death, it is finally published in 1496.

1464 German mathematician Regiomontanus (Johann Müller, 1436–76) writes *De Triangulis Omnimodis* (Concerning Triangles of All Kinds), an overview of trigonometry.

1472 Regiomontanus describes a comet, which we now know as Halley's comet. Two years later he publishes his *Ephemerides Astronomicae* (Astronomical Ephemeris), in which he gives the positions of the stars.

BIOLOGY & MEDICINE

1451 Nicholas of Cusa prescribes eyeglasses with concave lenses for nearsighted people.

1453 A professional association for midwives is established in Regensburg, Germany.

1460 German physician Heinrich von Pfolspeundt publishes *Bündt-Ertzney*, the first German book on surgery.

1473 In Italy the *Canon of Medicine* by Persian physician Avicenna (980–1037) is published. It is the first complete version available in Europe.

1474 *Da Buch der Natur* (The Book of Nature), written by Conrad von Megenburg in 1350, appears in print. It contains the first woodcut images of plants.

PHYSICAL SCIENCES

1450 European metalworkers devise a way of separating silver from lead ores such as galena (silver sulfide); some lead contains up to 10 percent silver. Miners from central Europe are encouraged to work in England to improve mining there.

1453 Pope Nicholas V (ca 1397–1455) authorizes major repairs to the Aqua Virgo aqueduct (destroyed in 537) so that it can once more be used to carry water into Rome.

1462 Italian writer Giovanni da Castro describes the alum mines at Tolfa, Italy, showing the increasing importance of the mineral.

TURNING POINTS

Avicenna

The first European printing of the *Canon of Medicine* was a milestone in the development of medicine. Its author, Ibn-Sina—whose name was Latinized for publication in a field still dominated by the ideas of ancient Roman and Greek physicians—was a Persian philosopher and physician. He was born in a village near Bokhara (now Bukhara in present-day Uzbekistan). He studied there and traveled widely. He learned all the classical Arab texts and mastered astronomy, Greek, mathematics, and all the available texts on medicine. At age 18 he became a court physician, then vizier (advisor) at the Buyid court in Hamadan, and from 1024 was physician to several sultans. As well as introducing the works of Aristotle to the Islamic world, Ibn-Sina also wrote more than 100 works on science, philosophy, and religion. His pioneering medical work, however, was his most important contribution to the spread of knowledge. The *Canon of Medicine*, written in 1000, remained a standard medical textbook for centuries. It contains instructions for testing medications, guidelines for diagnosing disease by examining the patient, and advice to surgeons to learn anatomy from observation and dissection, rather than from textbooks.

ca 1470 Inspired by Ali Kusai (ca 1400–74) and Ulugh Beg (ca 1390–1449), the Ottoman Empire is home to many advances in the field of mathematics.

A reconstructed Portuguese caravel. Based on an earlier Arabic design, the caravel was capable of performing long ocean crossings. As a result, it was the type of ship chosen by Christopher Columbus for his voyage to the Americas.

EUROPE

THE AMERICAS

ASIA & OCEANIA

AFRICA & THE MIDDLE EAST

ENGINEERING & INVENTION

1430 German mechanics use a flywheel to even out the motion of rotating machinery.

ca 1430 The matchlock is introduced as the firing mechanism for small arms.

1442 German inventor Johannes Gutenberg (ca 1400–68) sets up a printing press using movable type.

1445 Portuguese shipbuilders develop the caravel, a two- or three-masted ship that will be used by many navigators over the next two centuries.

1457 A four-wheeled wagon with strap suspension—the first passenger coach—is constructed at Kocs in Hungary.

1461 Breech-loading cannon are first made experimentally in Europe.

1474 English printer William Caxton (ca 1422–91) produces the first printed book in the English language, *Recuyell of the Historyes of Troye*.

---

ca 1450 The Inca construct a road system 20,000 miles (35,000 km) long to unite their empire.

1428 The Timurid ruler Ulugh-Beg builds an observatory at Samarkand to carry out astronomical observations.

---

ca 1430 The Ottomans become experts at making cannon.

1432 Portuguese navigator Gonzalo Cabral rediscovers the Azores islands in the Atlantic Ocean (probably first discovered in 1427 by Diogo de Sevilla).

1453 At the siege of Constantinople (present-day Istanbul), Ottoman forces employ a huge cannon that fires cannonballs weighing up to 1,345 pounds (610 kg).

1471 Portuguese navigator Fernão do Po discovers the island of Fernando Póo (now Bioko) in Equatorial Guinea, West Africa.

WORLD EVENTS

1428 Joan of Arc (1412–31) leads French armies against the English; she is executed in 1431.

1434 Cosimo de Medici (1389–1464) comes to power in Florence.

1453 The French defeat of the English at Castillon ends the Hundred Years' War.

1455 The families of Lancaster and York begin the Wars of the Roses, a struggle for the throne in England.

1477 The wedding of Maximilian of Austria (1459–1519) and Mary of Burgundy (1457–82) launches the Hapsburgs on their rise to dominate much of Europe.

1440 Moctezuma (1440–69) becomes ruler of the Aztec Empire.

1470 Cuzco defeats the coastal empire of Chimu and absorbs its territory into its growing empire.

1434 The Khmer of modern Cambodia move their capital from Angkor to Phnom Penh.

An engraving of a 16th-century printing shop. It shows the printing press (on the left), the proofreaders (bottom left), and the typesetters (right). Caxton's press concentrated on making books for the wealthy and powerful.

1433 Tuareg nomads occupy Timbuktu on the edge of the Sahara.

1453 Ottomans led by Mehmed II (r. 1444–46 and 1451–81) seize Constantinople, bringing the Byzantine empire to an end.

1464 Sonni Ali Ber (r. 1464–92) overthrows the Tuareg in Timbuktu on behalf of the empire of Songhai.

WILLIAM CAXTON

William Caxton was the first printer to produce a book in the English language. His work is credited with beginning the standardization of written and spoken English, changing it from a language composed of a large number of highly varied dialects. Caxton was born in southern England and took an apprenticeship with a London merchant whose business was the import and export of mainly woolen goods to continental Europe.

In about 1441 Caxton went to the Belgian city of Bruges, where he became prosperous. He made translations to produce fine manuscripts for noble patrons. After a change in the political climate he went to Köln in Germany to learn about printing, based on the kind of press first developed by Johannes Gutenberg (ca 1400–68). Caxton returned to Bruges and, with Flemish calligrapher Colard Mansion, set up a printing firm. In 1474 they produced the first printed book in the English language, *Recuyell of the Historyes of Troye* (which Caxton himself translated from French).

Two years later Caxton returned to England and established a printing shop with a wooden press near Westminster Abbey, London, in 1477. His first publication in England was *Dictes or Sayengis of the Philosophers*. Over the next 15 years he produced 73 books and 33 other printed works from what became known as the Caxton Press (a name that is still trading in Britain).

THE STORY OF PRINTING

PRINTING ORIGINATED IN CHINA. IN ABOUT the ninth century printers there made paper money and books, with each page of characters carved from a single block of wood to make a printing "plate." By 1045 Chinese printer Bi Sheng was making movable type of baked clay and within ten years was printing books with it.

Printing from cast-metal type began in Korea in the 1390s. In 1403 Korean King Taejong authorized the casting of metal type in bronze. Other printers adopted woodcuts for printing, often carving the type for whole pages out of a single piece of wood. There are thousands of different characters in the Chinese language, and in 1313 printer Wang Chen used more than 50,000 movable wooden characters to print *Treatise on Agriculture*. By 1438 Dutch printer Laurens Koster (ca 1370–1440) of Haarlem is thought to have used movable wooden blocks for printing.

Gutenberg's Bible

Metal type was reinvented in Europe by German inventor Johannes Gutenberg (ca 1400–68) in the 1440s. Gutenberg brought together the ideas of making copper molds in which to cast the type, a low-melting lead alloy to do the casting, a special oil-based printing ink, and a printing press to squeeze the paper against the inked plates. He adapted the screw press previously used for crushing grapes to make wine. (Asian printers did not use a printing press. Instead, they placed the paper on the inked type and used a brush or a roller to push the two into contact.)

Gutenberg set up his first press in about 1442 in Strasbourg, France, but in about 1450 he returned to his hometown of Mainz, Germany, and established a press. Gutenberg's first book—the world's first book to be printed using movable metal type—was a Latin Bible, which he produced in 1455. It is sometimes known as the Forty-Two Line Bible, because its Latin text was printed in 42-line columns. Like other publications of the time, Gutenberg's Bible had no page numbers, no title page, and nothing to indicate who had published it. The first printed book in Europe to carry the name of its printer was a book of psalms produced in 1457 by one of Gutenberg's backers, Peter Schöffer (ca 1425–1502). It was also the first book to be printed in two colors.

Printing Spreads

Printing presses soon began to appear in other parts of Europe. The first press in Italy, at Subiaco near Rome, was established in 1465, and by 1470 the university in Paris had its own press. In 1471 German astronomer and mathematician Regiomontanus (Johann Müller, 1436–76) set up a press at his Nuremberg observatory for printing astronomical tables.

Metal-type printing was introduced to England by William Caxton (ca 1422–91). In 1474 Caxton was the first person to print a book in English, while living in Belgium. Called *Recuyell of the Historyes of Troye*, it had been translated from French by Caxton himself. He printed his own translation from French of *The Game and Playe of the Chesse* a year later. Caxton returned to England in 1476 and established a printing press in London a year later. In 1481 he published the first illustrated book in English. The Caxton Press published more than 100 works over the next 15 years. Many of the books were translations, mainly from French, made by Caxton himself.

KEY DATES

1395
Cast metal type used in Korea

1403
Bronze type used in Korea

1438
Wooden blocks used by Koster for printing

1442
Printing press established by Gutenberg

1455
World's first book printed using movable type

1474
First book printed in the English language

A reproduction of Gutenberg's printing press shows how closely it was based on presses used to crush grapes for wine and olives for oil.

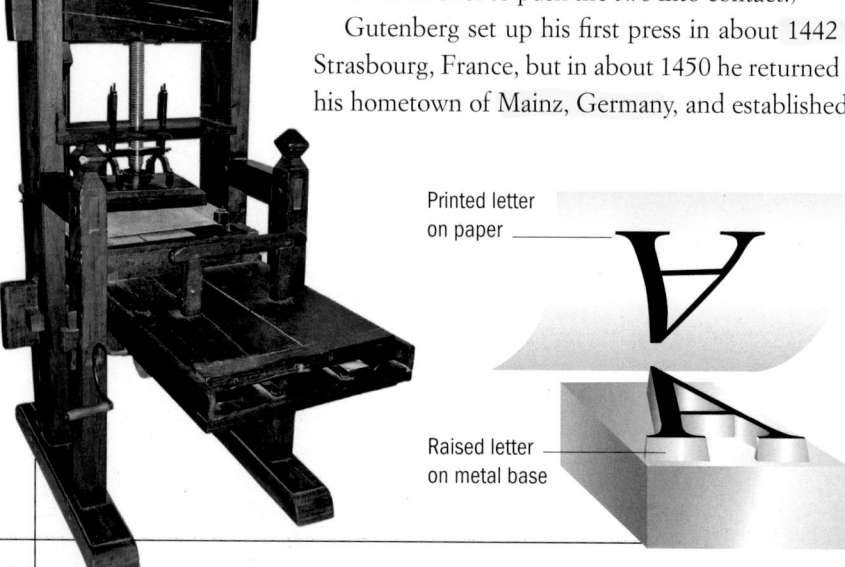

Printed letter on paper

Raised letter on metal base

Nearly all early printers used letterpress printing. The characters to be printed are carved or cast as raised, mirror-image letters. The letters are arranged as text and locked into a frame (called a chase). The printer applies ink to the type, usually with a roller, then places a sheet of paper on the inked type, and squeezes them together in a press. When the paper is peeled off the type surface, it retains the printed image. This method —called flatbed letterpress—remained the standard form of printing into the 19th century.

A page from the Gospel of Saint Paul in the Gutenberg Bible.

Incipit epistola sancti iheronimi ad paulinum presbiterum de omnibus diuine historie libris · capitulū pmū.

Frater ambrosius tua michi munuscula pferens detulit simul et suauissimas lras · q̃ a principio amiciciay fide pbate · iam fidei z veteris amicicie noua pferebant. Uera eñ illa necessitudo ẽ · z xp̃i glutino copulata · q̃m non utilitas rei familiaris · nõ p̃ncia tantum corpoy · nõ sbdola z palpãs adulaco · sed dei timor · et diuinay scripturay studia conciliant. Legim9 in veterib3 historijs · quosdã lustrasse puincias · nouos adijsse pfos · maria trãsisse · ut eos quos ex libris nouerant · corã q3 videret. Sicut pitagoras memphiticos vares · sic plato egiptū z architã tarentinū · eandemq3 oram ytalie · que quondã magna grecia dicebat · laboriosissime peragrauit · et ut qui athenis mgr erat z potens · cuiusq3 doctrinas achademie gignasia psonabant · fieret pegrinus atq3 discipulus · malẽs aliena verecude discere · q̃m sua ipudent ingerer. Deniq3 cũ lras quasi toto orbe fugientes psequit · capt9 a piratis z venudatus · tyrãno crudelissimo paruit · duct9 captiuus vinct9 z seruus. Tame quia phus maior emente se fuit · ad tytum liuium lacteo eloquencie fonte manante · de ultimis hispanie galliaruq3 finib3 · quosdam venisse nobiles legimus · z quos ad ctemplacionē sui roma nõ traxerat · uni9 hois fama pduxit. Habuit illa etas inauditū oĩb3 seculis · celebranduq3 miraclm · ut urbē tantã

ingressi · aliud extra urbem quererent. Appoloni9 siue ille mag9 ut vulgus loquitur · siue phus ut pitagorici tradunt · intrauit psas · ptrãsiuit caucalū · albanos · scithas · massagetas · opulẽtissima indie regna penetrauit · et ad extremum latissimo physon ampne trãsmisso puenit ad bragmanas · ut hyarcam in throno sedente aureo et de tantali fonte potantem · inter paucos discipulos · de natura · de morib3 · ac de cursu diey et sidey · audiret docentem. Inde p elamitas · babilonios · chaldeos · medos · assyrios · parthos · syros · phenices · arabes · palestinos · rsus ad allexandriā · perrexit ad ethiopiã · ut gignosophistas z famosissimam solis mensam videret in sabulo. Inuenit ille vir ubiq3 qd disceret · et semp proficiẽs · semp se melior fieret. Scripsit super hoc plenissime octo voluminibus · phylostratus.

Quid loquar de secli hominib3 · cũ apsus paulus · vas eleccois · z magister genciū · qui de consciencia tãti i se hospitis loquebat dicens. An experimentū queritis eius qui in me loquit xp̃c. Post damascū arabiãq3 lustratã · ascendit iherosolimā ut videret petrū z mãsit apud cũ dieb3 quindeci. Hoc eñ mistio ebdomadis et ogdoadis · futur9 genciū pdicator instruendus erat. Rursũq3 post ānos quatuordecim assumpto barnaba et tyto · exposuit cũ apsis euãgelm · ne forte in vacuum curreret aut cucurrisset. Habet nescio qd latentis energie · viue vocis actus · et in aures discipli de audoris ore transfusa · forcius sonãt. Unde et eschineus cũ rodi exularet · z legeretur

89

ASTRONOMY & MATH

EUROPE

1478 The first popular book on math, the *Treviso Arithmetic*, appears in Italy with rules for common types of calculations.

1482 Italian mathematician Johannes Campanus (1220–96) publishes his Latin translation from the Arabic of *Elements* by Greek mathematician Euclid (fl. 300 B.C.E.).

1494 Italian mathematician Luca Pacioli (1445–1517) describes double-entry bookkeeping in an early printed book on math, *Summa de Arithmetica, Geometrica, Proportioni, et Proportionalita* (Everything about Arithmetic, Geometry, and Proportion).

1497 Polish astronomer Nicolaus Copernicus (1473–1543) records a star being occluded by the moon (which occurs when the moon passes in front of the star).

1519 Portuguese navigator Ferdinand Magellan (ca 1480–1521) observes the Magellanic clouds, the two nearest galaxies to our own galaxy, the Milky Way.

THE AMERICAS

1515 German astronomer Johannes Schöner (1477–1547) makes the first globe to include the name America.

BIOLOGY & MEDICINE

1490 A temporary demonstration theater opens in Padua, Italy, where human dissections are performed.

1517 Italian physician and poet Girolamo Fracastoro (ca 1478–1553) proposes that fossils are the petrified remains of once-living organisms.

1518 English humanist and physician Thomas Linacre (ca 1460–1524) founds the Royal College of Physicians in London.

The origins of fossils were first correctly understood by Italian physician Girolamo Fracastoro.

1493 Italian explorer Christopher Columbus (1451–1506) observes that Native Americans use tobacco as a medicinal herb.

1518 Smallpox reaches the Americas with Europeans. In 1520 it decimates the Aztecs.

1520 Spanish voyagers take turkeys and corn from America to Europe.

PHYSICAL SCIENCES

1477 First recorded mention of a gun with a rifled, or grooved, barrel (with internal grooves to impart spin to the bullet), although rifling did not become standard until the 16th century.

1490 Italian artist and inventor Leonardo da Vinci (1452–1519) explains capillary action (the way in which a liquid rises up a very narrow tube, or capillary).

1492 In England graphite is used for the "lead" in pencils.

ASIA & OCEANIA

1495 The Chinese divert the Yellow River to a new course near the Shandong Peninsula.

1514 The Chinese open silver mines at Yunnan.

AFRICA & THE MIDDLE EAST

1513 The Ottoman geographer Piri Reis draws a map of the world that includes what is then known of the Americas.

An early map of the Americas, drawn using information gathered from the early voyages of Columbus and Magellan.

ENGINEERING & INVENTION	WORLD EVENTS
1495 French gunners begin using cast-iron cannonballs rather than stones.	**1485** Henry VII (r. 1485–1509) is victorious over Richard III (r. 1483–85) at Bosworth Field, marking the start of the Tudor dynasty in England.
1499 German abbot Johannes Trithemius (1462–1516) writes *Steganographia*, a major work on cryptography (codes).	**1492** The Spanish seize Granada, the last Muslim kingdom in Spain.
1502 German clockmaker Peter Henlein (1480–1542) makes the first spring-driven pocket clock.	**1508** Maximilian I (r. 1508–19) becomes Holy Roman Emperor.
1503 The Spanish successfully explode a series of mines under castles at Naples, establishing a new form of land warfare.	**1509** Henry VIII (1509–47) becomes king of England.
1513 Swiss artist Urs Graf (ca 1485–1527) introduces the technique of metal etching.	**1517** German monk Martin Luther (1483–1546) protests against practices of the Catholic Church, beginning the religious upheaval of the Reformation.
1515 The wheel-lock pistol is introduced in Germany.	**1522** The expedition of Portuguese navigator Ferdinand Magellan (ca 1480–1521) completes the circumnavigation of the globe, although Magellan himself was killed the year before in the Philippines.
	1492 Italian navigator Christopher Columbus (1451–1506) sails to islands in the Caribbean.
	1500 Portuguese navigator Pedro Cabral (ca 1467–ca 1520) claims Brazil for Portugal.
	1513 Spanish explorer Vasco Balboa (1475–1519) crosses the Isthmus of Panama and sees the Pacific Ocean.
1500 Chinese scientist Wan Hu attempts to make a flying machine by tying 45 rockets to the back of a chair. He is killed when the device explodes.	**1483** Russian pioneers begin to explore Siberia.
1520 The Chinese buy cannon from the Portuguese.	**1498** Portuguese navigator Vasco da Gama (1460–1524) sails around the Cape of Good Hope and crosses the Indian Ocean to reach India.
1522 Fine, pale blue porcelain is made in China during the Chia-Ching period.	**1511** The Portuguese conquer Malacca in Malaysia.
	1514 Portuguese travelers reach China.
	1523 The Chinese expel Portuguese traders.
1511 The Ottomans begin providing gunpowder weapons to their allies such as Egypt and Mesopotamia. Ottoman gunmakers are in demand as far away as Delhi, in India.	**1488** Portuguese navigator Bartholomew Diaz (ca 1450–1500) sails around the Cape of Good Hope at the southern tip of Africa. He calls it the Cape of Storms.
	1514 The Ottomans defeat the Persians at the Battle of Chaldiran.
	1515 The Songhai empire, based in Timbuktu, reaches the height of its power.
	1517 Ottoman Turks defeat the Mamluks of Egypt and take control of Egypt and the Arabian penisula.
	1520 Süleyman I (r. 1520–66), called the Magnificent, becomes Ottoman emperor.

Leonardo's design for a helicopter.

LEONARDO DA VINCI

Leonardo in many ways sums up the spirit of the Renaissance. Born in the small town of Vinci in 1452, at age 16 he was apprenticed to painter and sculptor Andrea del Verrochio (1435–88). Leonardo became well known not only as a painter and sculptor but also as an architect, engineer, and inventor. He worked for some of the most powerful rulers of the time, including Cesare Borgia (ca 1476–1507), the ruler of Florence, and the French kings Louis XII (r. 1498–1515) and Francis I (r. 1515–47).

Throughout his life Leonardo made sketches and plans of a range of fortifications, civil engineering schemes, and mechanisms. He described pulleys and belt drives to transmit power, a treadle-operated lathe, a paddlewheel boat, and a machine for grinding and polishing glass lenses. He designed pumps, mechanized vehicles, and a machine for digging canals. From the study of birds in flight, he designed a flying machine with flapping wings. (It could never work because a human could not produce enough power.) There were also impractical designs for a tank, a submarine, and a helicopter. His 1485 drawing of a parachute was more practical, and he is even thought to have made some small model parachutes and to have tested them.

When Leonardo died in 1519, his friend Francesco Melzi (1493–1570) gathered up his paintings, papers, and models. However, after Melzi's death many were lost or destroyed. Today only about 7,000 of the original 13,000 pages of notes have survived, but they are more than enough to testify to Leonardo's genius.

GUNS AND GUNPOWDER

This manuscript from the 15th century shows a soldier firing a "hand gonne." These early hand cannon were so heavy they had to be rested on a portable stand to be fired.

GUNPOWDER IS A CHINESE INVENTION dating from the 11th century. One or two Europeans also claimed to have invented gunpowder. They may have reinvented it, or they may have learned the secret of how to make it from travelers who had visited China. Either way, gunpowder and the firearms that used it changed the course of history.

The origins of gunpowder are shrouded in mystery, mainly because the people who invented it wanted to keep it a secret. The first written mention comes from Chinese writer Tseng Kung Liang in 1044 when he gives a formula for what he calls the "fire drug." Gunpowder is a mixture of charcoal, sulfur, and saltpeter (potassium nitrate). When mixed in the correct proportions it burns rapidly, with 40 percent of the products being gases and the rest solids that take the form of smoke. The hot gases produced expand; and if confined inside a container, explode with a loud bang. If burned at the closed end of an open-ended tube, the expanding hot gases will push out a ball or bullet, and this is the principle of the cannon and all firearms.

With the advent of gunpowder, fireworks became popular in China in the 1100s. A document from

about 1100 describes "a noise like thunder," although more often fireworks came in the form of strings of firecrackers. Gunpowder bombs were more dangerous. In about 1220 the Chinese military made bombs with outer casings that shattered on explosion, producing a kind of shrapnel to kill or maim the enemy. A Japanese woodcut of 1292 illustrates a bomb exploding, showing that gunpowder had reached Japan by this time. In 1126 Chinese soldiers used grenades and "fire arrows" in the defense of Kaifeng. The fire arrows were presumably rockets, made by packing gunpowder into bamboo cases. The packing had to be fairly loose or the rockets would have exploded. This knowledge spread abroad, and there is a reference to saltpeter and rockets in a 1280 book on warfare by Syrian writer al-Hassan al-Rammah.

Cannon

The gunpowder cannon first turns up in the late 1280s, when the Chinese military employed what they called "erupters" to fire stones at their enemies. By about 1300 Arab technicians made cannon barrels from bamboo tubes bound around with iron bands. Metal barrels were made from a bundle of wrought-iron rods bound with iron, rather like wooden barrels. In 1346 the English used these wrought-iron cannon against the French at the siege of Calais. A year later European gunsmiths made arrow-firing cannon. The first cannon barrels cast as a single piece in bronze can be dated to German gunsmiths in 1378. Bronze became the material of choice, especially for ships' cannon, because bronze does not corrode as readily as iron. Cast iron was not used for barrels because the castings were often flawed, resulting in bomblike explosions of the barrels themselves. When a bronze cannon barrel failed it usually tore or ruptured, with less tragic results. French gunners used cast iron to make cannonballs from about 1495, and safe cast-iron barrels were first made in England in 1543.

The first "small arm," as opposed to a cannon, was called variously arquebus, harquebus, or hackbut.

This gun was invented in Spain in the mid-1400s. The shooter propped its barrel on a support and fired the weapon from the shoulder. He inserted the gunpowder charge, dropped a ball down the barrel, and ignited the charge with a matchlock—a length of glowing wick on an S-shaped lever. The weapon was inaccurate, with a range of about 200 yards (200 m). It was used widely, including in the conquest of Mexico in the 1520s. Within a hundred years the musket replaced the arquebus, and the wheel lock and then the flintlock replaced the matchlock. The flintlock was more reliable and could be fired in the rain.

To fire a flintlock, the musketeer first poured a charge of gunpowder down the muzzle of the musket, followed by a lead ball and a felt wad that he rammed down to keep the ball and charge in place.

He then put some fine powder in the pan at the side of the lock, and cocked the weapon by pulling back the cock, which held a piece of flint. When he pulled the trigger, the flint sprang forward, hit the steel, and made sparks that ignited the powder in the pan. This action in turn lit the main charge, and the musket went off. If the main charge did not light, it was just a "flash in the pan."

The musket had a smooth bore and gradually gave way to the rifle, which had a spirally grooved barrel to give a spin to the ball or bullet. The final development was the breech-loading rifle and cartridges to go with it. Handguns also followed the same line of development from muzzle-loading flintlock pistols to cartridge weapons, with multishot revolvers being yet another advancement.

A contemporary illustration of the Siege of Calais in 1346. The cannon in the foreground are aimed at the city walls; the stone cannonballs they fired are lying on the ground beside them.

ASTRONOMY & MATH

EUROPE

1525 German mathematician Christoff Rudolf (1499–1545) introduces the mathematical sign for square root.

1541 German mathematician Rheticus (Georg von Lauchen, 1514–74) publishes a set of trigonometrical tables.

1543 Polish astronomer Nicolaus Copernicus (1473–1543) expounds his idea of a sun-centered universe in *De Revolutionibus Orbium Coelestium*.

1569 Flemish cartographer Gerardus Mercator (1512–94) introduces the Mercator map projection. Two years later his compatriot Abraham Ortelius (1527–98) publishes *Theatrum Orbis Terrarum*, the first compendium of maps, later called an atlas.

1573 Danish astronomer Tycho Brahe (1546–1601) publishes *De Nova Stella*, describing a new supernova in the constellation Cassiopeia (often called Tycho's Star at the time).

THE AMERICAS / ASIA & OCEANIA

Finally we shall place the sun himself at the center of the universe. All this is suggested by the systematic procession of events and the harmony of the whole universe, if only we face the facts, as they say, "with both eyes open."

NICOLAUS COPERNICUS

AFRICA & THE MIDDLE EAST

1543 Copernicus uses theorems in mathematical astronomy developed by Arabian scientists.

1554 Turkish admiral Sidi Ali Reis includes astronomy and mathematics in his writings about the Indian Ocean.

BIOLOGY & MEDICINE

EUROPE

1528 Swiss-born alchemist Paracelsus (1493–1541) writes the first modern book on surgery.

1530 Italian Girolamo Fracastoro (ca 1478–1553) describes syphilis, introduced to Spain by sailors returning from America.

1540 French surgeon Ambroise Paré (1510–90) makes jointed artificial limbs.

1542 French physician Jean Fernel (1497–1558) explains the condition appendicitis.

1543 Belgian anatomist Andreas Vesalius (1514–64) publishes his seven-volume *De Humani Corporis Fabrica* (On the Structure of the Human Body).

1551 Italian anatomist Gabriello Fallopio (1523–62) discovers the Fallopian tubes (from the ovaries to the womb).

1573 Italian anatomist Costanzo Varoli (ca 1543–75) describes the optic nerves.

THE AMERICAS

1532 Sugarcane is first grown in Brazil.

ca 1550 Spanish farmers import European cattle to the pampas or plains of Argentina.

1555 Tobacco from the Americas is exported to Spain.

ASIA & OCEANIA

1573 Crops from the Americas, including sweet potatoes, corn, and peanuts, are grown in China.

AFRICA & THE MIDDLE EAST

ca 1560 Crops including peanuts and manioc arrive in Africa from the Americas.

PHYSICAL SCIENCES

EUROPE

1531 German theologian and cosmographer Sebastian Münster (1488–1552) publishes *Horologiographia*, which describes the construction of sundials. In 1544 he publishes a book on world geography entitled *Cosmographia Universalis*.

1533 *De Principis Astonomiae et Cosmographie* by Dutch cosmographer Regnier Gemma Frisius (1508–55) gives the first published explanation of the use of triangulation in surveying and mapmaking. He also points out that latitude can be found by comparing the time given by a clock with that given by the sun.

1537 Italian mathematician Niccolò Tartaglia (1499–1557) invents the gunner's quadrant for aiming cannon.

1556 *De Re Metallica* by German mineralogist Georgius Agricola (1494–1555) is published after his death. It describes the formation of minerals and has information about mining and metal smelting.

THE AMERICAS

1545 The Spanish begin silver mining at Potosí in Peru and Zacatecas in Mexico.

1550s Gold is discovered in Chile and Colombia.

ca 1560 Mercury is discovered in Peru and used in a new process to refine silver ore.

ASIA & OCEANIA

1555 A huge earthquake in northern China kills more than 800,000 people.

1570 Silver from the Americas reaches China.

The Mercator projection, as devised by Gerardus Mercator, allows Earth's landmasses to be depicted on a flat map in a similar way to their appearance on a spherical globe.

AFRICA & THE MIDDLE EAST

ca 1530 Africa exports iron and steel to Portugal.

1539 The Ottoman architect Mimar Sinan builds the first of the 80 mosques, 34 palaces, and many other public buildings that establish him as the leading architect of the Islamic world.

ca 1535 The traveler Motrakci Nasru makes a survey of the route between Istanbul and Baghdad.

ENGINEERING & INVENTION	WORLD EVENTS
1525 The fusée comes into use for spring-powered clocks; it equalizes the pull of the clock's spring as it slowly runs down.	**1530** The Schmalkaldic League is formed by German princes to oppose the Holy Roman emperor Charles V (r. 1519–56) and promote Protestantism.
1535 The diving bell comes into use in Europe for working on bridge foundations.	**1547** Ivan IV (the Terrible; r. 1533–84) becomes tsar of Russia, having reigned as Grand Prince of Moscow since 1533.
1551 English mathematician Leonard Digges (1520–ca 1559) invents the theodolite for measuring angles during surveying.	**1555** Religious wars in Germany are ended for a time by the Peace of Augsburg.
ca 1555 Trucks running on rails, pushed by hand, come into use in mines in Germany.	**1556** Holy Roman Emperor Charles V abdicates in favor of his brother, Ferdinand I (r. 1558–64).
1567 The Santa Trinità Bridge, with an elliptical arch, is constructed over the Arno River in Florence, Italy.	**1558** Elizabeth I (r. 1558–1603) becomes queen of England.
1570 Italian architect Andrea Palladio (1508–80) publishes *Four Books on Architecture*.	**1572** As part of the French Wars of Religion, two thousand Protestant Huguenots are massacred on St. Bartholomew's Day.
1573 English sailor Humphrey Cole devises the ship's log for measuring a vessel's speed; it measures "knots" in a rope attached to a log.	**1572** Dutch nobles begin fighting for independence from Spain.
1556 The Spanish develop a more efficient process for separating silver from silver ore.	**1532** Spanish soldier Francisco Pizarro (ca 1475–1541) invades Peru and later kills the Inca leader Atahualpa (r. 1532–33).
	1536 French navigator Jacques Cartier (1491–1557) claims Canada for France.
	1565 The Spanish found St. Augustine in Florida.
1543 The Portuguese introduce firearms to Japan.	**1556** Akbar (r. 1556–1605) becomes emperor of India and begins a policy of unifying his Hindu and Muslim subjects.
1574 *Taiping Guangzhi* is the first Chinese book printed with movable type.	**1550** Mongols besiege Beijing.
	ca 1550 Conflict between warlords causes upheaval in Japan.
	1569 In Thailand, the kingdom of Ayutthaya is overthrown by the Burmese.
	1570 Japan allows Westerners to trade from the port of Nagasaki.
ca 1550 The Ottomans build aqueducts to carry water into their growing capital city at Istanbul.	
1569 Ottoman engineers attempt to construct a canal between the Don and Volga Rivers.	

VOYAGES OF DISCOVERY

Until the beginning of the Age of Exploration, the only way Europeans could make contact with India and China was overland by way of the Silk Road through the mountains and deserts of central Asia. The journey by sea was not possible in the small square-sailed ships of the time. In about 1445 Portuguese shipbuilders developed a new type of vessel called a caravel, capable of longer sea journeys. It had two or three masts with one square sail and a set of triangular sails similar to the lateen sails of an Arab *dhow*.

The map below shows the important voyages of the Age of Exploration. They began with an accidental voyage round the horn of Africa by Bartholomew Diaz (ca 1450–1500) after his ship was blown off course in a storm. This was followed by the voyage to the Caribbean made in 1492 by Christopher Columbus (1451–1506). After Columbus's expedition, Italian John Cabot (1450–98) became the first navigator to reach continental North America. In 1498 the Portuguese Vasco da Gama (1460–1524) followed Diaz's route, then crossed the Indian Ocean to reach India. Another voyage, led by Ferdinand Magellan (ca 1480–1521), set out to circumnavigate the globe in 1519. Although Magellan died during the voyage, one of his five ships, captained by Juan del Cano (1486–1526), successfully returned to Spain, completing the first circumnavigation of the globe.

Most of the early voyages of exploration were made in the 30 years between 1492 and 1522.

ASTRONOMY & MATH

1576 Danish astronomer Tycho Brahe (1546–1601) establishes a purpose-built observatory on the Baltic island of Hven.

1582 The Gregorian calendar replaces the Julian calendar; it has a more accurate year length.

1584 Italian philosopher and monk Giordano Bruno (1548–1600) posits his theory of an infinite universe.

1585 Flemish mathematician Simon Stevin (1548–1620), also known as Stevinus, introduces decimal fractions to common use.

1609 German Johannes Kepler draws up his first two laws of planetary motion.

1610 Italian scientist Galileo Galilei (1564–1642) observes craters on the moon and discovers four of Jupiter's moons.

1606 A Chinese version appears of *Elements* by the Greek mathematician Euclid.

1577 Turkish astronomer Takiyuddin founds an advanced observatory at Galatu and begins to correct existing astronomical tables.

BIOLOGY & MEDICINE

1580 Italian botanist and physician Prospero Alpini (1553–1617) distinguishes between male and female flowers.

1583 Italian botanist and physician Andrea Cesalpino (1519–1603) devises a system of classifying plants by their structure in his book *De Plantis*.

1597 Italian surgeon Gaspare Tagliacozzi (1545–99) practices rhinoplasty (skin grafting to reshape the nose).

1603 Italian anatomist Hieronymus Fabricius ab Aquapendente (1537–1619) gives the first clear description of the valves in veins.

1614 Italian physician Sanctorius (1561–1636) writes *De Statica Medicina* (On Medical Measurement) and founds the study of metabolism.

1598 Spanish colonists begin to grow wheat, apricots, and peaches, north of El Paso.

1612 Colonists in Virginia first grow tobacco to sell commercially.

1578 A treatise on pharmacology, *Bencao gangmu*, is published in China.

This engraving shows Danish astronomer Tycho Brahe and his assistants stargazing in Brahe's observatory on the island of Hven.

ca 1600 The Ottomans introduce tobacco from the Americas.

PHYSICAL SCIENCES

1581 Galileo Galilei begins to investigate the properties of the pendulum.

1592 Galileo Galilei makes an air-filled (open-ended) liquid-in-glass thermometer.

1595 Gerardus Mercator publishes the first atlas identified as such, from its cover image of the Greek deity Atlas carrying the globe on his shoulders.

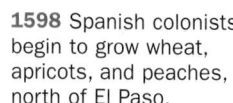

Named for the Italian scientist, a Galileo thermometer is a glass cylinder containing clear liquid and objects (such as liquid-filled glass bulbs) that sink in sequence as the clear liquid warms and decreases in density.

1584 China's tempered musical scale is defined.

ca 1590 With the development of an economy based on coinage, mining fever hits China.

1602 Italian missionary Matteo Ricci (1552–1610) publishes a Chinese atlas of the world.

It is a custom loathsome to the eye, hateful to the nose, harmful to the brain, dangerous to the lungs, and in the black stinking fumes, nearest resembling the horrible smoke of the pit that is bottomless.

JAMES I OF ENGLAND,
A COUNTERBLASTE TO TOBACCO (1604)

EUROPE

THE AMERICAS

ASIA & OCEANIA

AFRICA & THE MIDDLE EAST

LATE MEDIEVAL AND RENAISSANCE SCIENCE

ENGINEERING & INVENTION	WORLD EVENTS
1588 English cleric William Lee (ca 1550–ca 1615) invents a machine for knitting hosiery.	**1579** The English and Dutch form an alliance against Spain.
1590 Dutch optician Zacharias Jansen (1580–ca 1638) invents the compound microscope using two lenses.	**1588** England defeats the Spanish Armada.
1598 Dutch inventor Cornelis van Drebbel (1572–1633) patents a "self-winding" clock.	**1590** William Shakespeare (1564–1616) begins writing plays in London.
1608 German-born Dutch eyeglass-maker Hans Lippershey (ca 1570–ca 1619) makes a refracting telescope (using two lenses).	**1603** Queen Elizabeth (r. 1558–1603) of England dies.
1622 English mathematician William Oughtred (1574–1660) creates the slide rule, which uses logarithms to perform multiplication and division.	**1605** The Gunpowder Plot is uncovered in which Catholic plotters try to blow up the Houses of Parliament in London.
1623 German mathematician Wilhelm Schickard (1592–1635) builds a wooden adding machine ("calculating clock").	**1606** Italian opera becomes popular.
	1611 The King James Bible is published.
	1611 Germans plant potatoes—from the New World—as crops.
	1612 Miguel de Cervantes Saavedra (1547–1616) completes publication of *Don Quixote.*
ca 1570 People living in the Rimac River Valley in Peru construct a long canal to irrigate their farmland.	**1600** The Poverty Point culture, named for a site in Louisiana, emerges in North America.
1607 The first American ship is constructed in Sagadahoc, Maine.	**1575** Spanish America begins to import 1,250 African slaves each year.
1619 Virginia colonists fail in their attempt to build an ironworks in the colony.	**1616** Pocahontas (1595–1617) sails for England with English husband John Rolfe (ca 1585–1622).
ca 1575 In Japan, castle-building reaches a peak.	**1581** Under Akbar (1556–1605), India conquers neighboring Afghanistan.
1598 The Koreans invent the turtle ship, an iron-covered warship.	**1591** Territorial lord Toyotomi Hideyoshi (1537–1598) unites Japan.
ca 1600 The tradition of building huge stone statues dies out on Easter Island.	**1600** Ieyasu (r. 1603–05) becomes the undisputed ruler of Japan and founds the Tokugawa shogunate.
	1605 The Mughal emperor Jahangir (r. 1605–27) becomes ruler of India.
	1624 The English begin settling in eastern India.
ca 1590 The Royal Mosque becomes the centerpiece of urban planning in the rapidly growing Persian city of Isfahan.	**1588** Shah Abbas (r. 1588–1629) becomes ruler of Safavid Persia and begins reforming the empire.
	1591 The Songhai Empire is overthrown by Morocco.
	1598 Isfahan becomes the Safavid capital.
	1623 Queen Nzinga Nbandi drives the Portuguese from Ndongo, present-day Angola.

POTATOES AND TOBACCO

Natives of South America have been eating potatoes for at least 10,000 years. At first they were collected from the wild, but around 6,000 years ago people began to cultivate them as a staple crop. Potatoes can grow in high-altitude, cold environments in which other staple crops, such as wheat or corn, would not survive. Potatoes can be easily transported, stored for long periods of time, and are a rich, easily prepared, source of carbohydrate.

The first European to see a potato was probably the Spaniard Juan de Castellanos in about 1537, who described them as "truffles." The potato was first introduced to England in 1563. Across most of Europe it was met with suspicion and considered dirty and primitive. Ireland, however, quickly embraced the potato, which arrived there in about 1600, as it grew well in the country's cool, damp climate. By the early 1780s the population was almost entirely dependent on it. In 1845 the potato crop succumbed to a disease, known as potato blight, resulting in more than one million people starving to death.

Tobacco leaves have been chewed or smoked by Native Americans for at least 2,000 years. The Arawaks of the Bahamas gave Italian explorer Christopher Columbus tobacco leaves when he arrived in 1492. Columbus did not understand that the leaves should be smoked: He threw them away. When explorers later learned its use, tobacco was taken to Europe.

Europeans began cultivating tobacco in South America as early as 1531. Tobacco was introduced to much of Europe from the 1550s. By the late 16th century it was being grown extensively in South America and eastern North America and was regarded as something of a cure-all. The addictive nature of tobacco was recognized early. In the 17th century there was plenty of anti-tobacco feeling: Public smoking was banned in many places.

CHAPTER 4

THE SCIENTIFIC REVOLUTION

IN MANY WAYS, MODERN SCIENCE BEGAN IN THE 17TH AND 18TH CENTURIES. It was marked not only by a flood of discoveries and inventions, but also by the adoption of new methods of studying all aspects of the world and using rational analysis to draw conclusions from the available evidence. So great was the change in approach that the period is commonly described as the Scientific Revolution. The term is somewhat misleading. Knowledge still tended to advance in a series of gradual steps, and by trial and error, rather than in moments of dramatic revelation. Although reason became the universal basis for trying to understand the world, both superstition and religious faith persisted throughout the period. The period itself is difficult to define with a precise start and finish.

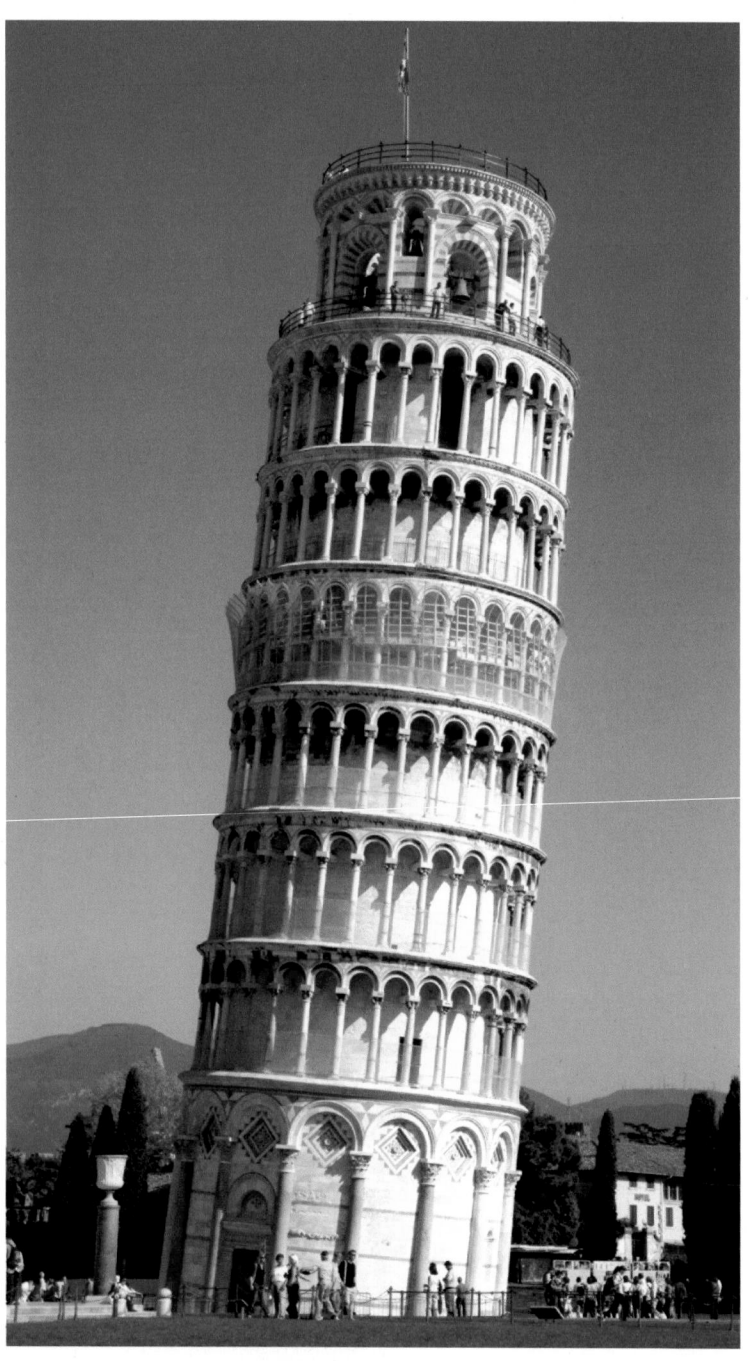

According to legend, Galileo dropped cannonballs of unequal sizes from the Leaning Tower of Pisa to demonstrate that their speed of descent is the same and independent of mass.

Nevertheless, over the space of only about a century and a half, a revolution of sorts in scientific knowledge did take place. Near the start of the period, in 1633, the pioneering Italian scientist Galileo Galilei (1564–1642) was put on trial by the Roman Catholic Church for supporting the idea that the sun lay at the center of the solar system, put forward in the previous century by Polish astronomer Nicolaus Copernicus (1473–1543). The church still maintained that the Earth lay at the center not only of the solar system but of the whole universe, a notion first proposed by Greek philosopher Aristotle (384–22 B.C.E.). At the Inquisition, the religious court established to enforce orthodox beliefs, Galileo was found guilty and sentenced to house arrest for the last eight years of his life. By the end of the period, in the 1660s, the English scientist and mathematician Isaac Newton (1642–1727) had explained the invisible force that attracted objects toward the Earth and kept the planets in their orbits around the sun. That force is called gravity.

Galileo and Newton—and many of their contemporaries—shared one essential quality: They were not just thinkers, but experimenters. They gathered information and tested their ideas by close observation, recording, and analysis. Galileo developed his ideas about pendulums by using his pulse rate to time the swings of a chandelier in Pisa Cathedral. The story goes that Galileo tested his theory about falling weights by dropping cannonballs from the Leaning Tower of Pisa. Newton used a glass prism to split white sunlight into a spectrum when formulating his ideas about light.

Accurate observation required the development of accurate instruments. Dutchman Antonie van Leeuwenhoek (1632–1723) invented the microscope, while Galileo himself made significant improvements to the telescope and was the first person to use it to observe heavenly bodies. He identified spots on the sun, hills and craters on the moon, and four satellites of Jupiter. Enthusiastic astron-

Isaac Newton made many breakthroughs in the understanding of mathematics, astronomy, and physics. In the engraving above, he demonstrates that a beam of white light from the sun can be split by a glass prism into the colors of the rainbow.

omers throughout Europe recorded a wealth of new observations: A transit of Mercury across the sun, Saturn's rings, and the regular return, or periodicity, of comets. Meanwhile, van Leeuwenhoek's invention allowed the study of another previously invisible world: the internal structure of matter. Newton's contemporary Robert Hooke (1635–1703) coined the word *cell* to describe the "little boxes" he saw when looking at plant tissue under a microscope.

Science did not solely belong to Europeans. The American tradition of practical ingenuity, which continues at the start of the 21st century, began with the towering figure of Benjamin Franklin (1706–90). Franklin combined a career as a printer with politics—he was America's ambassador in France during the American Revolution—and a series of scientific discoveries and inventions. He showed that lightning was a discharge of static electricity and invented bifocal eyeglasses and a nonsmoking woodburner. Franklin's friend Thomas Jefferson (1743–1826) also displayed a flair for practical problem solving, inventing the dumbwaiter to get easy access to his wine cellar.

By the end of the Scientific Revolution, many of the principles of modern science had been explained. Natural philosophers, as these amateur enthusiasts were known, had made huge strides in all areas of science. In biology, for example, they had learned about the circulation of the blood; in physics, they formulated laws about the behavior of gases; and in chemistry, they identified the first elements, the chemical building blocks of the universe. In mathematics, French philosopher René Descartes (1596–1650) invented coordinate geometry, and German philosopher Gottfried Leibniz (1646–1716) introduced binary arithmetic.

THE WORLD AT A GLANCE

CONCISE HISTORY OF SCIENCE AND INVENTION

	1625	1645	1660	1675	1690
EUROPE	**1626** Saint Peter's Basilica in Rome is completed after 120 years. **1628** English physician William Harvey explains the circulation of blood in the body. **1632** The first modern observatory is built in Germany. **1633** Italian scientist Galileo Galilei is condemned by the Roman Catholic Church for his theories. **1633** French mathematician Pierre de Fermat proposes that light always travels in straight lines. **1642** French scientist Blaise Pascal constructs a wooden calculating machine.	**1645** Flemish cartographer Michael Langrenus publishes the first map of the moon. **1645** Italian physicist Evangelista Torricelli makes a mercury barometer. **1649** English physician Henry Power discovers capillary blood vessels. **1654** German physicist Otto von Guericke invents an air pump. **1655** Dutch scientist Christiaan Huygens observes the rings around Saturn with a homemade telescope. **1656** Christiaan Huygens designs a pendulum clock. **1658** Dutch naturalist Jan Swammerdam describes red blood cells.	**1663** Scottish mathematician James Gregory designs a reflecting telescope. **1664** English scientist Robert Hooke describes Jupiter's giant red spot. **1665** Robert Hooke coins the word *cell* after studying plant tissues. He also proposes the wave theory of light. **1666** French engineer Melchisedech Thévenot invents the spirit level. **1669** Jan Swammerdam describes metamorphosis in insects. **1671** English scientist Isaac Newton discovers that a prism splits white light into a spectrum of rainbow colors.	**1675** Royal Greenwich Observatory is completed near London, England. **1675** Isaac Newton theorizes that light travels in particles. **1676** Dutch scientist Antonie van Leeuwenhoek observes bacteria, using a simple microscope. **1676** Robert Hooke invents the universal joint for connect two shafts. **1679** German mathematician Gottfried Leibnitz devises binary arithmetic, which is now used by all computers. **1679** English botanist Nehemiah Grew describes the male and female parts of flowers. **1687** Isaac Newton publishes his major work *Principia*.	**1690** French engineer Denis Papin builds a basic steam engine. **1691** English naturalist John Ray suggests fossils are ancient life-forms. **1698** English engineer Thomas Savery invents a steam pump, a forerunner of the atmospheric steam engine. **1701** English astronomer Edmond Halley publishes a map showing the magnetic variations of Earth. **1701** English agriculturalist Jethro Tull makes a seed drill. **1704** Isaac Newton publishes his theories on light in *Optiks*. **1704** Italian clockmaker Nicolas Fatio de Duiller makes a clock with jewel bearings.
THE AMERICAS	**1630** The bark of the South American cinchona tree is brought to Europe to treat malaria. **1630** Glassworks are built in Massachusetts. **1644** Ironworks are built in New England.	**1645** The first hospital in North America is founded in Montreal, Canada.	**ca 1670** New Spain takes over from Peru as the major source of silver. **1672** North American wildlife is described in *New England's Rarities Discovered.* **1673** A road is laid between Boston and Philadelphia.	**ca 1680** Rice fields are planted in South Carolina.	**1690** A paper mill is established in Pennsylvania. **1690** North Americans begin making paper money. **1700** Making liquor becomes a significant part of the New England economy.
ASIA & OCEANIA	**1637** An encyclopedia of Chinese technology is published. **1644** Western telescopes are used by Chinese astronomers.	**1653** The Taj Mahal—a gigantic marble mausoleum—is completed in India.		**1678** Japanese chrysanthemums are brought to the Netherlands. **1681** The Chinese adopt Western farming practices. **1681** The use of determinants is introduced in Japanese mathematics.	**1699** The Russians adopt the same calendar used in the West, starting the year on January 1.
AFRICA & THE MIDDLE EAST	**1630s** Large areas of Africa are deforested to provide fuel for iron smelting. **1641** A chimpanzee is transported to the Netherlands. It is the first great ape seen in Europe.	**1652** The Dutch plant gardens near the Cape of Good Hope to provide food for passing sailors.			**1702** Islamic observatories begin using European telescopes.

1705	1720	1735	1750	1765–1774
1709 English physicist Francis Hawksbee describes capillary action. **1712** English engineer Thomas Newcomen invents an atmospheric steam engine that uses a piston. **1712** English astronomer John Flamsteed publishes a catalog of the positions of 3,000 stars. **1714** Dutch physicist Gabriel Fahrenheit makes a mercury thermometer. **1717** English astronomer Abraham Sharp calculates π (pi) to 72 decimal places. **1717** Italian physician Giovanni Lancisi correctly links malaria to mosquito bites. **1719** German printer Jakob Le Blon invents four-color printing.	**1728** French dentist Pierre Fauchard invents the dental drill. **1729** English physicist Stephen Gray distinguishes between electrical conductors and insulators. **1730** English mathematician John Hadley invents the quadrant as a navigational aid. **1730** French surgeon George Martine performs the first tracheostomy. **1731** English astronomer John Bevis discovers the Crab Nebula. **1733** French mathematician Abraham de Moivre discovers the normal distribution. **1733** English engineer John Kay patents the flying shuttle.	**1735** Swedish naturalist Carolus Linnaeus introduces the binomial system of naming of plants and animals. **1738** Swiss scientist Daniel Bernoulli proposes a kinetic theory of gases. **1735** English clockmaker John Harrison unveils his chronometer. **1737** Swedish chemist Georg Brandt discovers cobalt. **1742** Swedish astronomer Anders Celsius devises the 100-degree Celsius scale. **1743** French mathematician Jean d'Alembert establishes mathematical dynamics. **1745** French surgeon Jacques Daviel successfully removes a cataract from a patient's eye.	**1753** Scottish engineer Charles Morrison invents a 26-wire telegraph. **1756** English engineer John Smeaton invents cement that can set underwater. **1760s** English agriculturalist Robert Bakewell uses selective breeding to improve farmstock. **1761** Scottish chemist Joseph Black introduces the concept of latent heat. **1762** English astronomer James Bradley publishes a catalog containing the positions of 60,000 stars. **1763** German botanist Josef Kölreuter discovers the role insects play in pollination. **1764** English mechanic James Hargreaves invents the spinning jenny.	**1765** Scottish engineer James Watt builds a steam engine with a separate condenser. **1766** English scientist Henry Cavendish identifies hydrogen. **1767** Swiss mathematician Leonhard Euler establishes the rules of algebra. **1772** Scottish chemist Daniel Rutherford discovers nitrogen. **1773** English astronomer William Herschel figures out that the sun is moving through space. **1774** English chemist Joseph Priestley identifies oxygen. **1774** Swedish chemist Karl Scheele discovers barium, chlorine, and manganese.
1709 A model hot-air balloon is made in Brazil. **1716** The first lighthouse in North America is built in Boston Harbor.	**1721** Smallpox inoculation is carried out in North America. **1728** The first botanical garden in North America is opened near Philadelphia. **1723** A house in Rhode Island is built with indoor plumbing.	**1740** The drug curare is discovered by French explorer Charles-Marie de la Condamine in South America. **1742** American inventor Benjamin Franklin invents a wood-burning stove.	**1751** Cartographers begin to make accurate maps of the frontiers of North America. **1752** Benjamin Franklin demonstrates the electrical nature of lightning. **1760** Threshing machines are used in rice production.	**1765** The first medical school in the United States is established at the College of Pennsylvania. **1769** American astronomer David Rittenhouse builds the United State's first astronomical telescope.
1709 Magnolias are brought to England from Japan.	**1720s** Jaipur City in India is built on a grid system. **1729** Movable type is used to print an encyclopedia in China.	**1736** India rubber is discovered by Charles-Marie de la Condamine. **1747** Jesuit missionaries design a summer palace for the Chinese emperors.	**1762** A flightless bird called the solitaire becomes extinct on Rodriguez Island in the Indian Ocean.	**1769** Captain James Cook observes a transit of Venus—when the planet passes in front of the sun—in Tahiti.
1717 Smallpox inoculation is witnessed in Turkey and the idea is brought to Britain.	**1729** Ottoman printer Ibrahim Müteferrika publishes descriptions of European life. **1732** The Ottomans build an aqueduct to supply Istanbul with water.	**1730s** A school of military engineering is established by a French aristocrat in Turkey.	**1750** French astronomer Nicolas de Lacaille travels to the Cape of Good Hope to study parallax—the relative position of celestial bodies as seen from different parts of Earth.	**1767** The Ottoman army establishes a cannon foundry and a military school.

ASTRONOMY & MATH

1627 German astronomer Johannes Kepler (1571–1630) publishes tables describing the motions of the planets; they become known as the Rudolphine Tables.

1631 French mathematician and astronomer Pierre Gassendi (1592–1655) makes the first observation of the transit of the planet Mercury across the sun's disk.

1632 The first modern astronomical observatory is built at Leyden (now spelled Leiden) in the Netherlands.

1633 Italian scientist Galileo Galilei (1564–1642) is condemned by the Roman Catholic Inquisition for refusing to withdraw his statement that the sun—and not the Earth—is at the center of the universe.

1639 English astronomers William Crabtree (1610–44) and Jeremiah Horrocks (1617–41) make the first observation of the transit of the planet Venus across the sun's disk.

1642 French scientist Blaise Pascal (1623–62) builds a wooden mechanical calculating machine.

1644 Polish scientist and astronomer Johannes Hevelius (1611–87) observes that Mercury shows phases, like the moon.

BIOLOGY & MEDICINE

1628 English physician William Harvey (1578–1657) explains the circulation of blood—the way in which blood is pumped by the heart through the lungs and around the body.

1641 German anatomist Franciscus Sylvius (1614–72) identifies the Sylvian fissure in the brain, which separates the temporal lobe (at the side) from the rest of the brain.

1642 German anatomist Johann Wirsung (1600–43) discovers the pancreatic duct, which carries digestive juices from the pancreas to the small intestine.

PHYSICAL SCIENCES

1640 French mathematician Pierre de Fermat (1601–65) proposes that light always travels in straight lines.

1642 French scientist Blaise Pascal (1623–62) puts forward Pascal's law, which states that the pressure within a liquid is the same everywhere. The principle underlies the working of all hydraulic machinery.

1644 German chemist Johann Glauber (1604–68) makes impure water glass (sodium silicate), a chemical later found to have many uses (including the preservation of eggs).

Consecrated in 1626, St. Peter's Basilica in Rome stood as the world's largest Christian church for more than 250 years.

1630 The bark from the South American cinchona tree is introduced to Europe by Jesuit priests. It contains the drug quinine, used to treat malaria.

1644 Jesuits in China reform the Chinese calendar on Western lines and introduce Western telescopes to Chinese astronomy.

1631 Persian metaphysician Mir Damed dies, leaving pioneering works that will later influence the development of psychology.

1630s Cutting trees to burn in furnaces for iron smelting causes deforestation in Africa.

1641 Dutch naturalist Nicolaas Tulp (ca 1593–ca 1674) describes the first chimpanzee (*Pan troglodytes*) brought to the Netherlands.

HOW THINGS WORK

Pascal's Law

A hydraulic press works according to the principles of Pascal's law of 1642. A large piston is connected to a small piston, and the setup is filled with an oily liquid. Because pressure is transmitted equally throughout a liquid, a small force on the small piston creates a greater force on the large piston. However, the larger piston will only move a fraction of the distance of the smaller one.

Small force

Large force

EUROPE

THE AMERICAS

ASIA & OCEANIA

AFRICA & THE MIDDLE EAST

ENGINEERING & INVENTION

1626 St. Peter's Basilica in Rome is finally consecrated, having taken 120 years to build.

1629 Italian engineer Giovanni Branca (1571–1640) manufactures a primitive steam turbine.

1631 French mathematician Pierre Vernier (1580–1637) invents the vernier measuring scale, which allows precise measurements to be made.

1638 English astronomer William Gascoigne (ca 1612–44) and Frenchman Adrien Auzout (1622–91) invent the eyepiece micrometer independently, which enables accurate measurements to be made with telescopes and microscopes.

1640 French coachbuilder Nicolas Sauvage introduces the horse-drawn cab in Paris.

1641 Italian inventor Vincenzo Galilei (1606–49) tries (but fails) to make a pendulum clock, using a design produced by his father, Galileo Galilei (1564–1642).

1642 German engraver Ludwig von Siegen (1609–ca 1680) devises the mezzotint process, in which effects of light and shade are produced by scraping away parts of a roughened metal printing plate.

1639 A glassworks built in Plymouth, Maryland, is one of the first "factories" in the American colonies.

1639 North America's first printing press is opened.

1644 Ironworks are constructed in American colonies, including Massachusetts, Connecticut, and Rhode Island.

1635 Jesuit missionaries collaborate with the Chinese to publish a collection of scientific works called *Ch'ung-chen Li-shu*.

1637 An encyclopedia of Chinese technology, the *Tiangong Kaiwu*, is published.

WORLD EVENTS

1625 Vincent de Paul (1581–1660) sets up the religious order of the Sisters of Mercy.

1626 The French impose the death penalty for duelists who kill their opponents.

1627 Heinrich Schütz (1585–1672) composes *Dafne*, the first German opera.

1629 Charles I (r. 1625–49) dissolves the English Parliament.

1630 Public advertisements of goods is first used in France.

1630 Sweden becomes involved in the Thirty Years' War (1618–48).

1636 Tea drinking arrives in Paris.

1639 The Académie Française compiles a dictionary to try to standardize French spelling and language.

1640 Frederick William (1620–88), the Great Elector, becomes elector of Brandenburg.

1642 Puritans shut down the theaters in London.

1642 Charles I begins fighting against Parliamentary forces led by Oliver Cromwell (1599–1658).

1630 English Puritans colonize Massachusetts Bay.

1636 Harvard College is established in Massachusetts.

1643 New Sweden (present-day Delaware) is founded.

1628 Dutch settlers occupy the renowned "Spice Islands," Java and the Moluccas.

1642 Dutch navigator Abel Tasman discovers Tasmania, New Zealand, and Fiji.

1644 Invaders from the northern region of Manchuria conquer China and overthrow the Ming dynasty. The Manchus establish the Qing dynasty.

1625 The kingdom of Dahomey is created in the region that is now southern Benin.

1626 The French begin to colonize the Senegal River.

BLOOD CIRCULATION

While studying animals, English physician William Harvey (1578–1657) began thinking about the circulation of blood around the body. He noticed that in a single hour the heart forces out far more blood than the total amount that is in an animal's body. The blood must, Harvey reasoned, be going around in a continuous loop in what he referred to as "a circle of ceaseless motion."

Harvey announced his discovery in 1628 and published diagrams (below) in order to prove his point. He tied a ribbon around the upper arm—which modern doctors call a tourniquet—to make the veins stand out, with the valves showing up as swellings. They are one-way valves that allow the blood to flow back to the heart but not in the other direction. Harvey demonstrated that pressing one of the valves stops the blood flowing along a vein until the pressure is released.

In these woodcuts from William Harvey's book Exercitatio Anatomica de Motu Cordis et Sanguinis in Animalibus (On the Motions of the Heart and Blood)*, published in 1628, he shows the one-way system of valves in the veins.*

GALILEO GALILEI

GALILEO GALILEI (1564–1642), GENERALLY known as Galileo, was an Italian scientist who made important advances in astronomy, mathematics, and physics. Galileo's work is important both for his discoveries and for the methods that he used to prove they were right. He was different from most previous scientists because he based his theories on his observations of natural phenomena and confirmed them using carefully arranged experiments. This is known today as the scientific method, and Galileo was one of the first in the Western World to practice it.

Galileo was born in Pisa in northern Italy and educated at a monastery school in Florence. At age 17, he began attending the University of Pisa to study medicine. He soon switched to mathematics and philosophy but left school in 1585 without a degree and began working as a teacher. His reputation spread, and in 1589 he became professor of mathematics at Pisa despite his lack of formal qualifications. He moved to Padua in 1592 and taught there until 1610.

Galileo demonstrated that objects of different weight fall at the same speed. He also tried to show that they fall at a constant acceleration. As an object falls farther, it moves faster, but the acceleration is constant —the rate of acceleration increases 32 feet (9.8 m) per second every second.

Pendulums and Cannonballs

While attending a service in Pisa Cathedral in 1582, Galileo noticed the regular movements of a lamp swinging above his head. From his observations of the lamp, he created his own simple pendulum, consisting of a weight at the end of a length of string, and then timed its swings. At the time accurate clocks did not exist, so he used his heartbeat to time the swings. He found that the time of each swing depended only on the length of the pendulum and was independent of the mass of the weight. He realised that a pendulum could be used to measure time accurately but did not make a clock himself.

Since the time of the Greek philosopher Aristotle (384–322 B.C.E.) people thought that the speed at which an object fell depended on its weight. Galileo tested this idea in about 1602. According to legend, he dropped two cannonballs of different weights from the Leaning Tower of Pisa and showed that they hit the ground at the same time.

The invention of the telescope in the early 1600s stimulated Galileo's interest in astronomy. He observed the moon, recording in numerous drawings its mountains and craters at different times during the month. He then turned his attention to Jupiter and in 1610 announced that the planet had four moons of its own. A year later he studied the sun and noted that sometimes black spots moved slowly across its surface. The movement of these spots convinced him that the sun was rotating slowly on its axis.

Galileo's discoveries about the celestial bodies finally convinced him that the sun was at the center of the solar system, a theory that had first been published in 1543 by Polish astronomer Nicolaus Copernicus (1473–1543). The idea was contrary to the teachings of the Roman Catholic Church, which postulated an Earth-centered universe. The Church asked Galileo not to spread the idea, but in 1632 he published it in a book, called *Dialogo sopra i due massimi sistimi del*

KEY DATES

1582
Constancy of pendulum's swing

1602
Law of falling bodies

1610
Observes four of Jupiter's moons

1611
First views sunspots

1633
Condemned by the Inquisition

Object falls from here

16 feet (4.9 m)

48 feet (14.7 m)

80 feet (24.5 m)

After 1 second

After 2 seconds

After 3 seconds

0 feet (0 m) per second

32 feet (9.8 m) per second

64 feet (19.6 m) per second

96 feet (29.4 m) per second

mondo, tolemaico e copernico (Dialogue Concerning the Two Chief World Systems—Ptolemaic and Copernican). The book was banned because it was seen as a personal insult to Pope Urban VIII (1568–1644), who up to that point had been one of Galileo's supporters. In 1633 Galileo was arrested by the Inquisition and, under threat of torture, made to recant his views.

Old and in failing health, Galileo spent the rest of his life under house arrest in Florence. He became blind in 1637, possibly because of eye damage caused by looking at the sun. When he died in 1642, Pope Urban VIII refused to forget his feud with Galileo, and he was buried unceremoniously in the Church of Sante Croce in Florence.

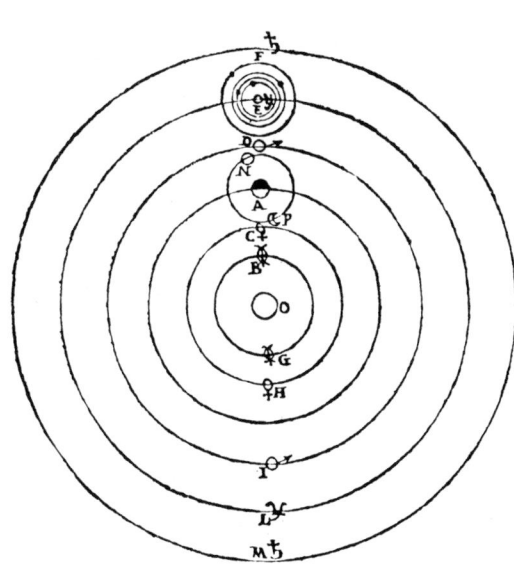

An artist's depiction of Galileo's appearance before the Inquisition.

Galileo made his own diagram of the sun-centered universe proposed by Copernicus (left). He also included his own discovery: the four moons of Jupiter.

CONCISE HISTORY OF SCIENCE AND INVENTION

ASTRONOMY & MATH

EUROPE

1645 Flemish cartographer Michael Langrenus (1600–75) publishes the first map of the moon.

1650 Italian astronomer Giovanni Riccioli (1598–1671) identifies the first binary (double) star, Mizar, in the constellation Ursa Major (Great Bear).

1653 French scientist Blaise Pascal (1623–62) devises Pascal's triangle of numbers, in which each number is the sum of the two numbers above it. It is later to have important applications in mathematics, such as the binomial theorem.

1655 Dutch scientist Christiaan Huygens (1629–95) uses a homemade telescope to observe the rings around the planet Saturn. He also discovers Titan, the largest of Saturn's moons.

1657 Christiaan Huygens writes the first book on mathematical probability theory.

1659 German mathematician Johann Rahn (1622–76) introduces the division sign (÷) to mathematics.

BIOLOGY & MEDICINE

1645 English physician Daniel Whistler (1619–84) first diagnoses the childhood disease rickets. It is later (1651) also independently described by his compatriot Francis Glisson (1597–1677).

1647 French anatomist Jean Pequet (1622–74) describes the thoracic duct in animals. This duct carries the fluid lymph from the lower body to a vein in the neck. In 1653 Swedish scientist Olof Rudbeck (1630–1702) discovers the lymphatic vessels in humans.

1649 English physician Henry Power (1623–68) discovers the extremely narrow capillary blood vessels.

1658 Dutch naturalist Jan Swammerdam (1637–80) describes red blood cells (erythrocytes).

1659 English physician Thomas Willis (1621–75) first describes typhoid fever.

1659 Italian anatomist Marcello Malpighi (1628–94) discovers the lymph nodes, enlarged structures where lymph vessels come together. Two years later he confirms the existence of capillary blood vessels.

PHYSICAL SCIENCES

1645 Italian physicist Evangelista Torricelli (1608–47) constructs the first mercury barometer. He also discovers the Torricellian vacuum, produced by inverting a tube full of mercury into a dish (the vacuum forms in the space at the closed top end of the inverted tube).

1646 English scientist Thomas Browne (1605–82) coins the word *electricity* (which at that time was limited to static electricity).

1646 Blaise Pascal demonstrates the existence of atmospheric pressure and confirms that it varies with altitude.

1649 French mathematician and philosopher Pierre Gassendi (1592–1655) publishes *Syntagma Philosophiae Epicuri*, a study of Greek philosopher Epicurus (ca 342–270 B.C.E.), who holds that all matter is made up of atoms.

1650 German scholar and inventor Athanasius Kircher (1601–80) demonstrates that sound will not travel in a vacuum.

1650 The first properly equipped chemistry laboratory is established at the University of Leyden in the Netherlands.

THE AMERICAS

1645 The Hôtel-Dieu de Montreal, the first hospital in North America, is founded by French nurse Jeanne Mance (1606–73).

ASIA & OCEANIA

The planet Saturn surrounded by its rings. These were first observed by Dutch astronomer Christiaan Huygens.

People almost invariably arrive at their beliefs not on the basis of proof but on the basis of what they find attractive.

BLAISE PASCAL, THE ART OF PERSUASION

AFRICA & THE MIDDLE EAST

1652 The Dutch East India Company begins planting gardens near the Cape of Good Hope to provide fresh fruit and vegetables for sailors on routes to and from the East Indies.

ENGINEERING & INVENTION	WORLD EVENTS

1647 Blaise Pascal invents a primitive roulette wheel to test his ideas on probability.

1652 Dutch engineer Cornelius Vermuyden (1595–ca 1683) completes the drainage of a large area of the Fens—marshy lands in the east of England—for farmland.

1654 Polish scientist Johannes Hevelius (1611–87) makes a closed-ended thermometer.

1654 German physicist Otto von Guericke (1602–86) of Magdeburg invents an air pump. As a demonstration, he removes the air from between two copper hemispheres. Two teams of horses fail to pull them apart, because of the force of atmospheric pressure.

1656 Christiaan Huygens designs a pendulum clock.

1658 English scientist Robert Hooke (1635–1703) has the idea for a watch regulated by a hairspring (the power from the main spring is released very gradually, controlled by the oscillations of the hairspring).

1648 Dissenting preacher George Fox (1624–91) founds the Society of Friends, also known as the Quakers.

1652 War begins between Britain and the Netherlands with a series of naval battles off the British coast.

1653 Puritan leader Oliver Cromwell (1599–1658) becomes the Lord Protector of the English commonwealth. During this time the nation is ruled by military governors.

1655 Pope Innocent X (1574–1655) dies in Rome. During his tenure as pope, Innocent involved the Catholic Church directly in a number of wars and diplomatic disputes. He also attacked those whom he considered heretics or political enemies.

The Taj Mahal in Agra, India, was built as a mausoleum for a Muslim princess.

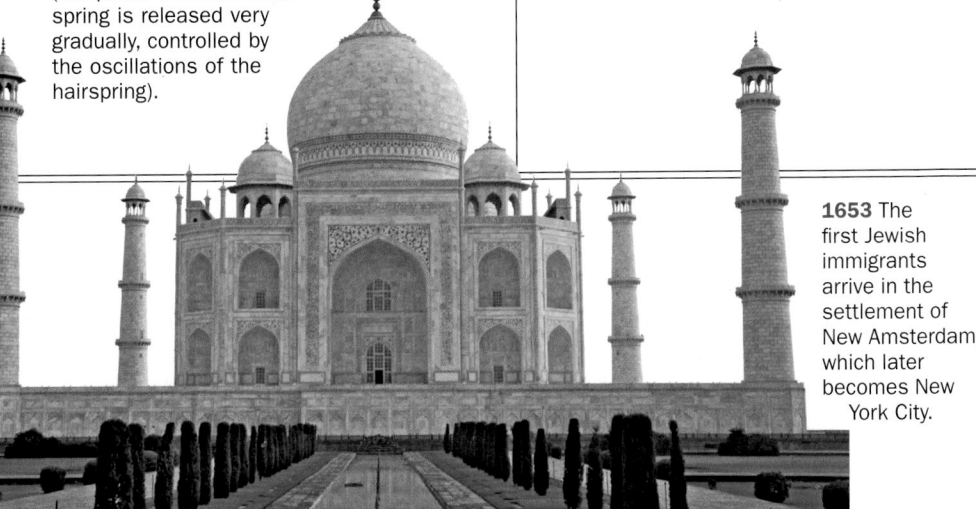

1653 The first Jewish immigrants arrive in the settlement of New Amsterdam, which later becomes New York City.

1653 The Taj Mahal, a gigantic and complex marble mausoleum, is completed in Agra, India. The structure took 22 years to complete.

1656 A devastating fire destroys most of the Japanese city of Edo, as well as its castle, and kills tens of thousands of people.

1650 A Venetian blockade halts Ottoman sea trade for four years.

1657 The Dutch defeat the local Khoikhoi population for control of territory in southern Africa.

THE PENDULUM CLOCK

The Chinese constructed the first mechanical clocks, which were in effect large, slowly turning waterwheels made of wood. Metal clocks powered by falling weights date from the 1300s, but they were unreliable and inaccurate. In 1582 Italian scientist Galileo Galilei (1564–1642) demonstrated that a pendulum always swings at a constant rate. He also proved that the rate of swing depends only on the length of the pendulum and not on the mass of the weight swinging at its end. A pendulum 39 inches (99 cm) long takes one second to complete one swing (forward and back), and so can be used to mark the passage of time.

In 1641 Galileo instructed his son Vincenzo (1606–49) how to make a clock regulated by a pendulum. Vincenzo did not complete the job, and it was not until 1657 that the first pendulum clock appeared. It was designed by the Dutch scientist Christiaan Huygens and assembled by clockmaker Salomon Coster (ca 1620–59) in The Hague. It kept time to within five minutes a day and was much more accurate than any earlier clocks.

The metal rod of a pendulum expands and contracts with changes in temperature, which changes the speed at which it swings and causes inaccuracy. Various methods were devised to overcome this problem. In 1722 English inventor George Graham (1673–1751) designed the mercury pendulum, which had a glass jar of mercury as the pendulum's weight. When the pendulum expanded downward because of a rise in temperature, the change was counterbalanced by the upward expansion of the mercury in the jar. Another solution, the gridiron pendulum, was invented by English clockmaker John Harrison (1693–1776) in 1728. Harrison's design had a grid of alternate brass and steel rods. Brass expands more than steel, so the expansion of the brass compensated for the lesser expansion of the steel.

ASTRONOMY & MATH

1664 English scientist Robert Hooke (1635–1703) describes Jupiter's Great Red Spot (now known to be due to a gigantic storm in the planet's atmosphere). In the same year Hooke proposes that the planets are held in their orbits by their own gravity and the gravity of the sun.

1665 English scientist and mathematician Isaac Newton (1642–1727) introduces the binomial theorem—a key concept in algebra that allows the expansion of the expression $(x + y)^n$. This was only one of many advances in math made by Newton at about this time.

1666 Italian astronomer Giovanni Cassini (1625–1712) observes the polar ice caps on Mars. (We now know that the "ice" is mainly frozen carbon dioxide.)

1670 French astronomer Jean Picard (1620–82) measures the length of part of the meridian (a line of longitude), thus allowing accurate calculation of the circumference of the Earth.

1671 Giovanni Cassini discovers Iapetus, Saturn's third-largest moon (after Titan and Rhea).

BIOLOGY & MEDICINE

1660 French physicist Edmé Mariotte (1620–84) discovers the blind spot on the retina of the eye (at the place where the optic nerve joins the retina).

1665 Robert Hooke coins the word *cell* to describe the "little boxes" he observes in plant tissues using a compound microscope of his own invention.

1669 Dutch naturalist Jan Swammerdam (1637–80) describes metamorphosis in insects—the sequence of changes from egg to larva to pupa to adult or imago (as in butterflies).

1670 English physician Thomas Willis (1621–75) detects the presence of sugar in the urine of patients with diabetes.

1672 Jan Swammerdam identifies the human ovaries. In the same year anatomist Regnier de Graaf (1641–73) uncovers egg-containing follicles (known as Graafian follicles) in the ovaries.

1673 Dutch scientist Antonie van Leeuwenhoek (1632–1723) begins writing letters to the newly formed Royal Society of London describing what he has observed under a microscope.

PHYSICAL SCIENCES

1661 Irish scientist Robert Boyle (1627–91) defines chemical elements for the first time. A year later he formulates Boyle's law: that at a fixed temperature the pressure of a gas is inversely proportional to its volume.

1665 Robert Hooke proposes the wave theory of light, but his proposal is largely ignored until championed by Dutch scientist Christiaan Huygens (1629–95) in 1678.

1668 English mathematician John Wallis (1616–1703) proposes the law of conservation of momentum: The momentum (mass x velocity) of objects before a collision equals their combined momentum afterward.

1669 German alchemist Hennig Brand (ca 1630–92) discovers phosphorus (in urine). This was the first discovery of a new element since prehistoric times.

1669 German chemist Johann Becher (1635–82) proposes the (incorrect) phlogiston theory of combustion (which states that materials get lighter in weight by releasing "phlogiston" when they burn).

1671 Isaac Newton demonstrates that a glass prism splits, or disperses, white light into a spectrum of rainbow colors.

1672 John Josselyn describes North American wildlife and plants in *New England's Rarities Discovered*.

ca 1670 New Spain surpasses Peru as the major producer of silver in the Spanish Empire.

INSIDE STORY

Champagne

Dom Pierre Perignon ("Dom" is a title given by the Roman Catholic Church) was a French Benedictine monk who developed the process for making champagne wine. He entered the Benedictine order when we was 19, and within ten years he became cellarmaster at the Abbey of Hautvillers. People in southern Europe have made wine since the time of the ancient Greeks and Romans, and the district along the valley of the Marne River became famous for its chardonnay grapes that result in a fine white wine. To make champagne, the winemakers allow chardonnay to ferment in large vats. Then they usually blend it with wines from previous years and add sugar and yeast before putting it in bottles made from thick, dark-green glass. The wine ferments for a second time in the bottles, and the gas (carbon dioxide) produced results in an effervescence that gives champagne its famous bubbles.

Jan Swammerdam demonstrated that insects have four different life stages: egg, larva, pupa, and adult. In butterflies and moths, such as the monarch butterfly shown above, the larval stage is known as a caterpillar.

Side labels: EUROPE · THE AMERICAS · ASIA & OCEANIA · AFRICA & THE MIDDLE EAST

ENGINEERING & INVENTION

1660 Robert Hooke devises the anchor escapement to regulate a pendulum-driven clock.

1661 Christiaan Huygens invents the manometer, a device for measuring gas pressure.

1663 Scottish mathematician and inventor James Gregory (1638–75) proposes a design for a reflecting telescope.

1664 Italian engineer Giuseppe Campani (1635–1715) creates a lens-grinding lathe (for making lenses for optical instruments).

1666 French engineer Melchisedech Thevenot (ca 1620–92) makes the spirit level.

1667 Robert Hooke (1635–1703) invents the anemometer to measure wind speed.

1668 Isaac Newton builds a reflecting telescope.

1670 French winemaker Dom Pérignon (1638–1715) creates champagne.

1674 English glassmaker George Ravenscroft (1618–81) develops lead crystal glass.

1674 Dutch engineer Menno von Coehoorn (1641–1704) invents the trench mortar.

WORLD EVENTS

1660 Charles II (r. 1660–81) is crowned king of England. His restoration marks the end of Oliver Cromwell's (1599–1658) puritan protectorate.

1662 The scientist, architect, and astronomer Christopher Wren (1632–1723) designs his first major building: the Sheldonian Theater in Oxford.

1663 The second Navigation Act is passed by the British Parliament. This act places restrictions on trade between the American colonies and any nation other than Britain, causing significant resentment and unrest in the American colonies.

1665 Bubonic plague strikes London. Many flee the city, but around 80,000 (a fifth of the city's population) die of the disease. The following year sees the city decimated by a massive fire that destroys around 13,000 houses and many public buildings.

1673 The Test Act is passed by the British Parliament, banning catholics and religious dissenters from holding any public office.

1673 American colonials build the Boston Post Road, a major route linking Boston and Philadelphia.

Isaac Newton's reflecting telescope. Scottish mathematician James Gregory designed the first reflecting telescope in 1663, and Isaac Newton built his own version in 1668.

THE BAROMETER AND VACUUMS

It is now common knowledge that air has mass, and that atmospheric pressure results from the weight of the atmosphere pressing down on Earth. In the 1640s an Italian scientist set out to measure air pressure; in doing so, he proved the existence of the vacuum and invented the barometer. Evangelista Torricelli (1608–47) trained as a mathematician and in 1641 went to work as an assistant to the aged Galileo (1564–1642), who always maintained that there was no such thing as a vacuum.

In 1645, aided by his assistant Vincenzo Viviani (1622–1703), Torricelli took a 6.6-foot (2-m) glass tube, sealed at one end, and filled it with mercury. Keeping his thumb over the open end, he upended the tube in a dish full of mercury and removed his thumb, while keeping the end of the tube below the surface of the mercury in the dish. Some of the mercury ran out into the dish, and the mercury level in the tube dropped to a height of about 30 inches (76 cm).

Torricelli reasoned that the weight of the atmosphere (air) pressing on the surface of the mercury in the dish equaled the weight of the mercury left in the tube. The height of the mercury column above the mercury in the dish was therefore a measure of air pressure. The whole device is known as a barometer. Torricelli also noticed that the height of the column varied from day to day depending on the weather and deduced that atmospheric pressure must also vary daily. In 1647 French thinker René Descartes (1596–1650) added a vertical scale to a Torricelli barometer and used it to record weather observations.

The space above the mercury in Torricelli's experiment was a vacuum, a volume of space without matter. In modern terminology it would be referred to as a partial vacuum, filled with extremely low-pressure gas, as a perfect vacuum with a gaseous pressure of zero is now understood to be an impossibility.

	ASTRONOMY & MATH	BIOLOGY & MEDICINE	PHYSICAL SCIENCES

EUROPE

1675 Italian astronomer Giovanni Cassini (1625–1712) discovers the major gap in Saturn's rings, now known as the Cassini division.

1675 The Royal Greenwich Observatory is completed near London and gives its name to the Greenwich Meridian (at longitude 0°).

1679 German mathematician Gottfried Leibniz (1646–1716) introduces binary arithmetic, which uses only two digits. Today it is employed by all computers.

1682 English astronomer Edmond Halley (1656–1742) plots the course of Halley's comet. In 1705 he correctly predicts that it will return in 1758.

1684 Giovanni Cassini discovers Dione and Thetys, two of Saturn's moons.

1676 Dutch scientist Antonie van Leeuwenhoek (1632–1723) reports his observations of bacteria, using a simple microscope made with lenses that he ground himself. A year later he observes human sperm.

1682 English botanist Nehemiah Grew (1641–1712) describes the male and female parts of flowers.

1683 English physician Thomas Sydenham (1624–89) gives the first full description of the disorder gout.

1683 The wild boar (*Sus scrofa*) becomes extinct in the British Isles.

1675 English scientist and mathematician Isaac Newton (1642–1727) proposes that light travels as a series of minute particles. He does not publish his theory until 1704.

1676 English scientist Robert Hooke (1635–1703) proposes Hooke's law, which states that when an elastic object stretches, the stress (force per unit area) in it is proportional to the strain (change in dimensions).

1678 Dutch scientist Christiaan Huygens (1629–95) takes up the wave theory of light proposed by English scientist Robert Hooke (1635–1703) in 1665.

1679 Robert Hooke proposes the inverse square law of gravity.

1687 Isaac Newton publishes his major work *Principia*, in which he sets out his various theories in astronomy, mathematics, and physics.

HOW THINGS WORK

Hooke's Law and Metals

Robert Hooke's law of elasticity, which was first proposed in 1676, states that stress is proportional to strain. When a piece of metal is stretched, the elongation (strain) is at first proportional to the load applied (stress)—in this phase the metal obeys Hooke's law. But beyond a certain point—called the elastic limit—the metal is permanently stretched and cannot return to its original length. With more stress, the metal reaches its yield point, when it yields and stretches rapidly with very little extra load until it breaks.

THE AMERICAS

1678 Thomas Thatcher publishes the first American medical treatise, *A Brief Rule in Small Pocks or Measles*.

ca 1680 Rice fields are planted in coastal areas of South Carolina.

ASIA & OCEANIA

1683 Japanese mathematician Seki Kowa (1642–1708) introduces the use of determinants into mathematics. A determinant is a square array of numbers (elements) useful in solving simultaneous equations and other mathematical problems.

1678 Japanese chrysanthemums are exported to the Netherlands.

1681 On the Indian Ocean island of Mauritius the dodo (*Raphus cucullatus*), a large flightless bird of the pigeon family, becomes extinct.

1681 Jesuits bring Western farming practices to China, including irrigation, and make three, rather than two, crops of rice each year possible.

AFRICA & THE MIDDLE EAST

THE SCIENTIFIC REVOLUTION

ENGINEERING & INVENTION	WORLD EVENTS
1675 Christiaan Huygens makes an oscillating balance and hairspring regulator for clocks.	**1675** Frederick William (r. 1640–88), Elector of Brandenburg, goes to war against the Swedish in Germany.
1675 Irish scientist Robert Boyle (1627–91) devises a hydrometer (an instrument for measuring the relative density of a liquid).	**1678** English writer and preacher John Bunyan (1628–88) finishes the first part of *The Pilgrim's Progress*.
1676 Robert Hooke invents the universal joint (for connecting two driven shafts joined at an angle).	**1680** Crops begin failing in many parts of Europe, causing widespread famine.
1679 French physicist Denis Papin (1647–1712) produces a steam digester, the forerunner of the pressure cooker.	**1682** Peter the Great (r. 1682–1725) becomes the tsar of Russia.
1680 Robert Boyle invents a match that uses a mixture of sulfur and phosphorus.	**1683** Englishman William Dampier (ca 1651–1715) begins a circumnavigation around the world.
1687 French physicist Guillaume Amontons (1663–1705) invents a hygrometer (an instrument for measuring the humidity of the atmosphere).	**1684** Street lighting is installed in parts of London.
1689 German musical instrument maker Johann Denner (1655–1707) develops the clarinet (as a single-reed instrument with no keys).	**1685** James II (r. 1685–88) succeeds his brother Charles II (r. 1660–85) as king of England. James II is deposed in 1688.
	1685 Huguenots are exiled from France.
	1675 King Philip's War breaks out between Native Americans and English Colonists in New England.
	1680 Spaniards are driven from New Mexico by Pueblo tribes in the Pueblo Revolt.
	1679 The Cambodians and Vietnamese go to war, with Cambodia losing the Mekong delta.
	1680 The French set up a trading station at Pondicherry, southern India.
	1683 The Qing—the last ruling dynasty of China—occupy Taiwan.
	1685 China opens ports to Europeans.
	1689 The Treaty of Nerchinsk between China and Russia defines borders and trading.
	1683 The Ottomans unsuccessfully besiege Vienna but are defeated by the Austrians.
	1689 Natal is made a Dutch colony.

Antonie van Leeuwenhoek's early microscopes, such as this one in which a single lens is mounted on a flat sheet of metal, could magnify objects up to x200. This allowed Leeuwenhoek to see microorganisms for the first time, which he named "animalcules."

ROYAL GREENWICH OBSERVATORY

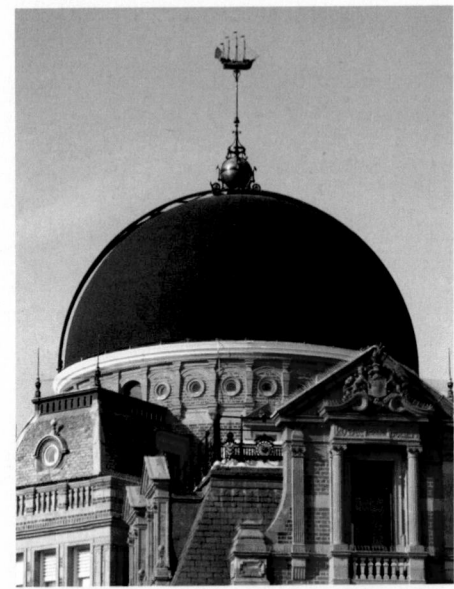

Founded in 1675 by King Charles II, England's Royal Greenwich Observatory was built primarily to help navigation at sea by fixing longitude and improving the determination of star positions. It was also charged with the improvement of timekeeping. The observatory was built on a hill overlooking the Thames River and designed by Sir Christopher Wren (1632–1723), himself an astronomer as well as an architect.

In 1766 the observatory published its first Nautical Almanac, which predicted the position of celestial bodies for the year ahead to allow sailors to fix their position. While this made it easy to determine latitude, or how far north or south a vessel was, calculating longitude remained open to error, which often led to ship wrecks. Finding longitude requires knowing the difference between local time and a reference time. It was not until the latter half of the 18th century that an effective timekeeper was invented by English clockmaker John Harrison (1693–1776) and enabled sailors to measure longitude at sea. In 1884, the Greenwich meridian—a line of longitude passing through Greenwich—was adopted as the Earth's prime meridian, with a longitude of 0°, and the starting point for the international time zones.

ISAAC NEWTON

ABOVE: *William Blake's depiction of Newton (1795)*

ONE OF THE FIRST SCIENTISTS WHOSE achievements brought him widespread recognition was Isaac Newton (1642–1727). He made fundamental breakthroughs in mathematics and established the basic laws that became the cornerstones of modern astronomy and physics. The first scientist to receive a knighthood, his name lives on as the newton, the modern International System of Units (SI) unit of force.

Isaac Newton was born in eastern England. He was brought up by his grandmother and educated at a local school before going to Trinity College (Cambridge University). He received his bachelor's degree in 1665 and was forced to remain in the countryside because of the plague that raged in London at that time. At first he concentrated on mathematics, working out the principles of "fluxions," which were to lead to differential calculus.

In 1667 Newton received a fellowship of Trinity College and became professor of mathematics in 1669. He turned his attention to what happens when objects move—what makes them start moving and what stops them. His conclusions are summed up in Newton's three laws of motion. All of the laws can be observed by watching a game of pool, although you do not have to be a physicist to play it!

Newton's next contribution was to have a profound effect on astronomy. According to the well-known story, he was sitting in an orchard when he saw an apple fall. Why did it fall? Newton concluded that it was attracted toward the Earth by a force, which we now call gravity. He also deduced that every object behaves as if its mass were concentrated in one place, its center of gravity (now called the center of mass). Applying his own laws of motion, he figured out that all objects in the universe are affected by such gravitational forces—it is gravity that keeps the moon in orbit around the Earth and the Earth in orbit around the sun. He produced a formula, the universal law of gravitation, that states the gravitational force between any two objects—two pool balls or even two stars—is equal to the product of their masses and inversely proportional to the distance between them.

The English scientist Robert Hooke (1635–1703) also devised a law of gravity in about 1678 and published his ideas a few years later. This led to a bitter dispute between the two great men.

In the branch of physics we now call optics, Newton's main studies concerned the nature of light. By allowing a narrow beam of white light from the sun to pass through a glass prism, Newton split the light into a multicolored spectrum, the sequence of colors seen in a rainbow. He showed that white light is made up of a variety of colors. (Today we say that it is made up of many different wavelengths.) Telescopes of the day produced images that were surrounded by a spectrum of colors because the poor-quality lenses brought dif-

ferent colors into focus in different places. Newton overcame the problem by using mirrors instead of lenses and in 1668 produced one of the first reflecting telescopes with mirrors he made himself.

Newton was convinced that light is composed of a "flux" of minute particles, which he called "corpuscles." The theory was soon challenged by Dutch Scientist Christiaan Huygens (1629–95) and others, who postulated that light travels as waves. The argument raged until the 20th century, when physicists finally concluded that light has properties of both particles and waves; but this had to await the development of quantum theory.

In 1703 Newton was elected president of the Royal Society, and two years later he was knighted. As Sir Isaac Newton he continued to be showered with honors. His final tribute was a state funeral and burial in Westminster Abbey, London. His name lives on in the SI unit of force, which is called the newton (the force that gives 1 kilogram an acceleration of 1 meter per second per second).

Newton's second major work Opticks, *published in 1704, outlined his theories on optics and the refraction of light.*

NEWTON'S LAWS

Newton formulated laws about two major topics in physics: gravity and motion. His law of gravity deals with the attractive force (gravitation) that exists between any two objects that have mass. The strength of the force depends on how close they are (illustrated below; the nearer they are, the stronger the force

pulling them together) and how massive they are (illustrated below; the more massive they are, the stronger the force between them). In mathematical terms the gravitational force is proportional to the product of the masses and inversely proportional to the distance between them.

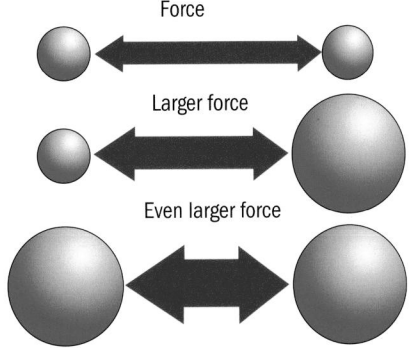

ASTRONOMY & MATH	BIOLOGY & MEDICINE	PHYSICAL SCIENCES

EUROPE

ca 1690 English naturalist John Ray (1627–1705) distinguishes between monocotyledons (plants with one seed leaf) and dicotyledons (plants with two seed leaves).

1691 John Ray suggests that fossils are the remains of creatures from the distant past.

1694 German botanist Rudolf Camerarius (1665–1721) establishes that plants have male and female parts.

1696 Dutch scientist Antonie van Leeuwenhoek (1632–1723) describes microorganisms.

1699 English botanist John Woodward (1665–1728) shows that plants grow best if other substances are added to their water.

1701 Italian physician Giacomo Pylarini (1659–1715) inoculates three children with smallpox to prevent more serious disease when they are older.

1694 Italian scientist Carlo Renaldini (1615–98) suggests that both the freezing point and boiling point of water should be used as "fixed points" on thermometers.

1697 German chemist Georg Stahl (1660–1734) champions the (incorrect) phlogiston theory of combustion devised by Johann Becher (1635–82) in 1669.

1700 German mathematician Gottfried Leibniz (1646–1716) founds the Berlin Academy, the first major national academy of science.

1701 Dutch chemist Wilhelm Homburg (1652–1715) discovers boric acid (sometimes called boracic acid).

1701 English astronomer Edmond Halley (1656–1742) publishes a map showing the magnetic variations of Earth.

1704 English scientist and mathematician Isaac Newton (1642–1727) publishes his book *Opticks*, in which he champions the corpuscular (particle) theory of light and explains the actions of lenses and prisms.

INSIDE STORY

The Sex Life of Flowers

Rudolf Camerarius was a German botanist who identified the reproductive parts of flowering plants. Camerarius described the function of the male and female parts of flowers in fertilization in 1694. The male organ—the stamen—consists of a pollen-filled anther at the end of a stalk, or filament. The female organ—the carpel—is made up of a stigma, style, and ovary, which contains the egg cells, or ovules.

Anther
Petal
Style
Ovary
Ovule
Stigma
Sepal

THE AMERICAS

ASIA & OCEANIA

1699 As part of his program to modernize Russia, Tsar Peter the Great changes the Russian calendar so that the year begins on January 1, as in the West, and not September 1 as previously.

AFRICA & THE MIDDLE EAST

1702 Observatories in Islamic countries begin using European scientific instruments, including telescopes.

This 17th-century watercolor depicts a lock on the Canal du Midi in southern France. The canal, completed in 1692, connected the Mediterranean Sea with the Atlantic Ocean.

ENGINEERING & INVENTION

1690 French engineer Denis Papin (1647–1712) constructs a primitive steam engine.

1692 In France the 46-mile (74-km) Orléans Canal from Orléans to Paris is completed, as is the 32-mile (51.5-km) Canal du Midi, linking the Mediterranean Sea with the Atlantic Ocean.

1694 English clockmaker Daniel Quare (1648–1724) makes a portable barometer.

1698 English engineer Henry Winstanley (1644–1703) completes the first lighthouse at Eddystone Rocks in the English Channel.

1698 English mining engineer Thomas Savery (ca 1650–1715) invents a steam pump, which becomes the forerunner of the atmospheric steam engine.

1701 French mechanic Charles Plumier (1646–1704) publishes his book *L'Art de Tourner* (The Art of Turning), in which he describes a lathe for turning iron.

1701 English agriculturist Jethro Tull (1674–1741) invents a mechanical seed drill for sowing seeds.

1704 Italian clockmaker Nicolas Fatio de Duiller (1664–1753) makes a clock with jewel bearings.

1690 A paper mill is set up in Pennsylvania.

1690 North American colonies begin printing paper money and bills of credit because of a scarcity of coins.

1700 Liquor distilling becomes a significant part of the economy in New England.

WORLD EVENTS

1690 William III of England (r. 1689–1702) invades Ireland to stifle a rebellion led by supporters of the deposed James II (r. 1685–88).

1697 Tsar of Russia Peter the Great (r. 1682–1725) travels around western Europe—often incognito—to study.

1699 English explorers travel to the South Seas and scout Australia.

1700 Peter the Great begins a campaign to westernize Russia.

1702 The English go to war against the French and their Habsburg allies in the War of the Spanish Succession (1701–14).

1702 Street lighting is provided in many German cities.

1704 German composer and organist Johann Sebastian Bach (1685–1750) writes his first cantata.

1692 The Witch trials in Salem, Massachusetts, convict and execute 19 people.

1693 The College of William and Mary is founded by royal charter.

1701 Yale University is established in New Haven, Connecticut.

1696 The Ashante kingdom spreads in West Africa.

1700 The Ethiopian Empire breaks up into feudal states.

Jethro Tull's seed drill allowed farmers to sow their crops evenly with little wastage of seeds.

THE TELESCOPE

Hans Lippershey (ca 1570–ca 1619), a Dutch eyeglass maker, made a refracting telescope in 1608. Other scientists, including Italian Galileo Galilei (1564–1642), refined the design. Among Galileo's discoveries were sunspots, craters on the moon, and four moons of Jupiter. Lenses of the time had various defects, such as chromatic aberration, which occurs because a lens cannot focus all colors to the same point and results in colored fringes around images. In 1655 an improved lens allowed Dutch scientist Christiaan Huygens (1629–95) to see the rings of Saturn. A century later optical instrument makers learned to make achromatic lenses by sticking together two lenses of different types of glass—flint glass and crown glass.

Another method of avoiding chromatic aberration involved using lenses with only slight curvature and therefore a long focal length (meaning the length of the telescope's light path from the main mirror or object lens to the focal point—the location of the eyepiece). This meant making telescopes very long. Telescopes measuring 33 feet (10 m) long were common.

A better way to view images is with a reflecting telescope, which uses mirrors instead of lenses, because mirrors do not cause chromatic aberration. James Gregory (1638–75), a Scottish mathematician, realized this in 1663 when he published a design for a telescope that had a small, curved secondary mirror to reflect the light back through a hole in the primary mirror to an eyepiece. English scientist Robert Hooke (1635–1703) later improved the design. In 1857 French physicist Léon Foucault (1819–68) devised a method of silvering glass to make curved mirrors. They were easier to manufacture, and could be resilvered if accidentally damaged. Since then telescopes have been made larger and more powerful. Most modern telescopes are reflecting telescopes since it is easier to make a big mirror than it is to make a big lens.

ASTRONOMY & MATH

1706 Welsh mathematician William Jones (1675–1749) introduces the symbol π (Greek letter pi) for the ratio of the circumference of a circle to its diameter (π = ca 3.1416).

1712 First volume of *Historia Coelestis Britannica* (cataloguing the position of 3,000 stars) by English astronomer John Flamsteed (1646–1719) is published.

1712 Italian mathematician Giovanni Ceva (ca 1647–ca 1734) publishes *De Re Numeraria* (Concerning Money Matters), the first clear application of math to economics.

1717 English astronomer Abraham Sharp (1651–1742) calculates the value of π (pi) to 72 decimal places.

1718 English astronomer Edmond Halley (1656–1742) identifies stellar proper motion, the apparent movement of a star that results from the star's very gradual movement relative to the sun (not relative to the Earth).

1718 French mathematician Abraham de Moivre (1667–1754) produces *The Doctrine of Chances*, his first book on probability.

1719 English mathematician Brook Taylor (1685–1731) demonstrates the principle of the vanishing point in perspective.

BIOLOGY & MEDICINE

1707 English physician John Floyer (1649–1734) produces a special watch for counting patients' pulse rates.

1711 Italian naturalist Luigi Marsigli (1658–1730) shows the animal nature of corals (formerly held to be plants).

1714 French physician Dominique Anel (1679–1730) invents a fine-point syringe for use in treating fistula lacrymalis (an abnormal opening in the cheekbone near the eye).

1717 Italian physician Giovanni Lancisi (1654–1720) blames malaria on the bite of the mosquito in his book *De Noxiis Paludum Effluviis* (Concerning the Noxious Effluvia of Marches).

PHYSICAL SCIENCES

1709 English physicist Francis Hawksbee (ca 1666–1713) describes capillary action, the phenomenon that causes a liquid to rise up a very narrow tube and a sponge or blotting paper to soak up liquids.

1710 French chemist René-Antoine Ferchault de Réaumur (1683–1757) presents a material completely woven from glass fiber to the Academy of Sciences in Paris.

Thomas Newcomen's atmospheric steam engine was the first practical steam-driven device to produce mechanical work. The engines were widely used for pumping water out of mines.

In 1712 English inventor George Graham built an orrery—a clockwork model of the solar system.

1709 Magnolias from Japan are introduced into England.

1707 Mount Fuji in Japan erupts.

1717 The use of inoculation against smallpox in Turkey is witnessed by Lady Mary Wortley Montague, who introduces it to Britain.

EUROPE

THE AMERICAS

ASIA & OCEANIA

AFRICA & THE MIDDLE EAST

ENGINEERING & INVENTION	WORLD EVENTS

1709 English iron founder Abraham Darby (ca 1678–1717) introduces the use of coke for iron smelting.

1709 Polish-born Dutch physicist Gabriel Fahrenheit (1686–1736) invents the Fahrenheit temperature scale.

1712 English engineer Thomas Newcomen (1663–1729) invents an atmospheric steam engine that employs a piston.

1712 English inventor George Graham (1673–1751) constructs an orrery, which is a working clockwork model of the solar system.

1714 Gabriel Fahrenheit makes a mercury thermometer.

1714 The British government offers £20,000 reward for a method to determine longitude at sea. In 1759 clockmaker John Harrison (1693–1776) claims the prize but has to wait 14 years to be paid in full.

1716 French engineer Hubert Gautier (1660–1737) publishes *Treatise on Bridges*, which has a lasting influence on bridge design.

1719 German printer Jakob Le Blon (1667–1741) develops a four-color printing process based on superimposing the primary colors blue, yellow, and red plus black.

1709 Brazilian Jesuit priest Bartholomeu de Gusmao (1685–1724) makes a model hot-air balloon.

1715 Sybilla Masters (d. 1720) of Pennsylvania invents a corn mill and a new process for weaving hats.

1716 A lighthouse in Boston Harbor is the first to be constructed in North America.

1707 England and Scotland unite to create Great Britain.

1713 Britain and France sign the Treaty of Utrecht, which ends the War of the Spanish Succession and leads to an exchange of territory in Europe and North America.

1715 Prince James the Younger arrives in Scotland as part of a failed campaign to win back the British throne for the Stuart dynasty.

1710 Mohawk leaders travel to England to ask Queen Anne (r. 1702–14) for help.

1710 The British take Acadia in modern Canada from the French.

1713 The Treaty of Utrecht cedes Acadia, Newfoundland, and other French colonies to Britain. Britain now has exclusive rights in supplying the Spanish colonies with slaves.

1715 30,000 slaves are used to work the gold fields of Minas Gerais in Brazil.

1708 The British East India Company and the New East India Company merge as the East India Company.

1712 India is split by a war of succession after the death of Shah Bahadur.

1714 Burma begins a 20-year period of economic and cultural development.

In the year 1456, a comet was seen passing retrograde between the Earth and the sun. Hence I dare venture to foretell, that it will return again in the year 1758.

EDMOND HALLEY, *A SYNOPSIS OF THE ASTRONOMY OF COMETS*, 1705

Scientists generally use the Celsius scale—as on this thermometer—to measure temperature.

GABRIEL FAHRENHEIT

Gabriel Fahrenheit was born in 1686 in the seaport of Danzig (Gdansk), Poland, of German descent. He is known for making the first reliable thermometers and devising the temperature scale named for him.

After both of his parents died from mushroom poisoning in 1701, the young Fahrenheit was apprenticed to a shopkeeper in Amsterdam, in the Netherlands. Four years later, he turned his interests to physics and became a meteorological instrument maker and glassblower. In 1709 Fahrenheit made an alcohol thermometer and also devised the Fahrenheit temperature scale, based on 32°F for the freezing point of water and 212°F for the boiling point of water.

In 1714 Fahrenheit invented the mercury thermometer, which gave more accurate readings than an alcohol thermometer. His scientific experiments led to the discovery that the boiling point of water varies with atmospheric pressure. He also discovered supercooling—the phenomenon in which water can remain liquid below its usual freezing point.

Other precision instruments Fahrenheit devised included a constant-weight hydrometer for measuring the density of liquids and a thermobarometer for reading barometric pressure by determining the boiling point of water.

Fahrenheit spent most of his life in the Netherlands but traveled widely in Europe. He gave lectures in chemistry in Amsterdam beginning in 1718 and also spent much of his time in London, where he became a member of the Royal Society.

Mercury thermometers are still commonly used in meteorology, but their use in medicine is now being phased out. The Fahrenheit temperature scale is still widely used in the United States, although the Celsius—also known as centigrade—scale, which is named for the Swedish astronomer Anders Celsius (1701–1744), is generally used by scientists worldwide.

THE NATURE OF LIGHT

EARLY SCIENTIFIC INVESTIGATIONS REVEALED various properties of light—how it is bent by lenses, how it casts shadows, even how fast it travels—but fundamental to understanding those properties is a knowledge of the nature of light itself. In particular, does light consist of a stream of minute particles, like bullets being fired from a machine gun? Or does light consist of waves that are capable of rippling across the endless vacuum of outer space?

It is clear that parallel rays of light bend as they go through a lens and come to a focus. The concentration of the rays allows a magnifying glass to be used as a burning glass, an application known since ancient times. In 212 B.C.E. Greek scientist Archimedes (ca 287–212) is said to have used a burning glass to destroy ships of the Roman fleet at Syracuse, on the island of Sicily. The first person to measure the bending of light in this way was the Dutch mathematician Willebrord Snell (1580–1626). In 1621 he found that when a ray of light passes through a piece of glass, the angle of incidence (at which the ray enters the glass) is related to the angle of refraction (the angle through which the ray is bent) by a property of the glass now known as the refractive index.

Fermat's Principle

It was another mathematician, the Frenchman Pierre de Fermat (1601–65), who figured out how light casts shadows. Fermat stated that it is because light always travels in straight lines—it will not "go around corners" to illuminate a shadow. Known as Fermat's principle, it was proposed in 1640. He also observed that light travels slower in a denser medium such as water or glass.

Snell's law is named for the Dutch mathematician Willebrord Snell (1580–1626), who discovered it in 1621 when he was professor of mathematics at Leyden (now Leiden) University. It concerns refraction of light, which is the way a ray of light changes direction when it goes from one transparent medium to another—for example, moving from air into a block of glass. The amount of refraction depends on an optical property of the denser medium, called its refractive index. The law says that the sine of the angle of incidence divided by the sine of the angle of refraction equals the refractive index.

The first attempt to measure the speed of light was made in 1676 by Danish astronomer Ole Rømer (1644–1710). He was checking the predictions made by Italian astronomer Giovanni Cassini (1625–1712) about the timing of eclipses of Jupiter's moons (when they move out of sight behind the planet). He discovered that the eclipses seemed to happen earlier than predicted when the Earth was moving toward Jupiter and later when the Earth was moving away. Rømer accounted for the differences by assuming that the light had to travel a shorter or longer distance, and that light must therefore have a finite speed, which he calculated as 140,000 miles (225,000 km) per second—75 percent of the actual value. It was nearly 200 years before French physicist Armand Fizeau (1819–96) obtained a more accurate value—5 percent too high —of 195,737 miles (315,000 km) per second. This in turn was improved on by American physicist Albert Michelson (1852–1931) in 1882, who calculated it as 186,325 miles (299,853 km) per second. The value that is used today is 186,288 miles (299,793 km) per second.

In 1675 English scientist Isaac Newton (1642–1727) postulated that light travels as a stream of minute particles ("corpuscles"). Over the years various physicists challenged this idea, the first being his great rival Robert Hooke (1635–1703), who had already proposed the wave theory of light in 1665. The fact that light is refracted by glass and that it travels more slowly in water than it does in air, for example, were cited as evidence that light travels as waves.

KEY DATES

1621
Snell's law (refraction of light)

1640
Fermat's principle

1665
Wave theory (Hooke)

1675
Corpuscular theory (Newton)

1676
Speed of light (Rømer)

1801
Interference of light

1900
Quantum theory (Planck)

1924
Wave-particle duality

Incident ray — Normal — Glass block — Angle of refraction — Refracted ray

In about 212 B.C.E. Greek scientist Archimedes is said to have used a giant lens as a burning glass to defend Syracuse against attacking Roman ships.

The final nail in the coffin of Newton's corpuscular theory came in 1801, when English physicist Thomas Young (1773–1829) discovered the interference of light, a phenomenon in which white light shining through a narrow slit is split into the colors of the rainbow. At that time it could only be explained if light was assumed to travel as waves. Young published his findings in 1804. That is how the argument on the nature of light remained until the beginning of the 20th century, when German physicist Max Planck (1858–1947) put forward his quantum theory. It postulated that all forms of energy, including light, travel in finite "packets," or quanta, similar in fact to Newton's corpuscles. But as modern physics continued to develop, French physicist Louis de Broglie (1892–1987) suggested in 1924 that moving particles can also behave like waves, and this was soon proved to be the case.

So Newton, Hooke, and the others were all correct, and one of the great arguments in the history of science melted away.

In 1849 French physicist Armand Fizeau made the first fairly accurate measurement of the speed of light.

He bounced a light ray between two mirrors 5.6 miles (9 km) apart, directing the ray between the teeth of a fast-rotating cogwheel. The returning ray went between the next pair of teeth and then through a semi-silvered mirror to the observer.

Fizeau adjusted the speed of the cogwheel so that there was no flicker as the light traveled to the mirror and back. Using the wheel's speed and the distance traveled by the light, Fizeau was able to calculate the speed of light.

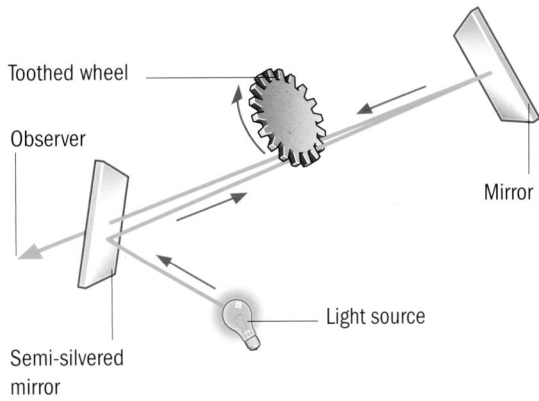

ASTRONOMY & MATH

1729 English astronomer James Bradley (1693–1762) discovers the aberration of starlight, an apparent shift in a star's position that results from a combination of the motion of the Earth and the fact that light travels at a finite speed.

1731 English astronomer John Bevis (1695–1771) discovers the Crab Nebula. In 1758 it is rediscovered by French astronomer Charles Messier, who catalogues it as M1. Most known nebulae have Messier numbers.

1733 French mathematician Abraham de Moivre (1667–1754) discovers the normal (bell-shaped) distribution curve, soon to become of major importance in statistical studies.

The Crab Nebula was first seen by English astronomer John Bevis in 1731. The nebula (Latin for "cloud") is a remnant of a supernova—the gigantic explosion of a star.

BIOLOGY & MEDICINE

1727 English botanist Stephen Hales (1677–1761) writes *Vegetable Staticks*, the first book on plant physiology.

1730 French surgeon George Martine (1702–41) performs the first tracheostomy, an operation to make an opening in the trachea (windpipe) to help a patient with life-threatening breathing difficulties.

1731 English agriculturist Jethro Tull (1674–1741) publishes *The New Horse-Hoeing Husbandry*, a book that recommends harrowing the soil, growing crops in rows, removing weeds by hoeing, and using manure as fertilizer.

1734 French chemist René-Antoine Ferchault de Réaumur (1683–1757) founds the science of entomology with his book *Mémoires pour Servir à l'Histoire des Insectes* (Memoirs Serving as a Natural History of Insects).

1721 American physician Zabdiel Boylston (1676–1766) carries out the first smallpox inoculation in North America.

1728 The first botanical garden in North America is opened by naturalist and explorer John Bartram (1699–1777) at his home near Philadelphia.

PHYSICAL SCIENCES

1724 Dutch scientist Hermann Boerhaave (1668–1738) publishes his book *Elementa Chemiae* (Elements of Chemistry), the first major chemistry textbook.

1725 The St. Petersburg Academy of Sciences is founded in Russia by Peter the Great (r. 1682–1725).

1725 German physician Johann Schulze (1684–1744) observes that daylight turns certain silver salts dark (later to have significance in photography).

1729 English physicist Stephen Gray (1666–1736) distinguishes between electrical insulators and conductors.

1730 French scientist Pierre Bouguer (1698–1758) demonstrates the Bouguer anomaly: that gravitational attraction decreases with altitude.

1733 French chemist Charles du Fay (1698–1739) distinguishes two types of static electricity: "vitreous" (positive) and "resinous" (negative).

HOW THINGS WORK

The First Piano

The pianoforte (meaning "soft–loud") was a development of the harpsichord. Both instruments were based on a harp lying on its side. In a harpsichord the string is plucked by a small plectrum (originally made of quill), but the instrument lacks the ability to provide contrast between loud and soft notes. However, the strings of a piano are struck by a felt-covered hammer, producing a very different sound and giving performers control over both the volume and length of a given note.

Since we are assured that the all-wise Creator has observed the most exact proportions, of number, weight, and measure, in the make of all things; the most likely way therefore, to get any insight into the nature of those parts of the creation, which come within our observation, must in all reason be to number, weigh, and measure. And we have much encouragement to pursue this method, of searching into the nature of things, from the great success that has attended any attempts of this kind.

STEPHEN HALES, *VEGETABLE STATICKS*

EUROPE

THE AMERICAS

ASIA & OCEANIA

AFRICA & THE MIDDLE EAST

ENGINEERING & INVENTION	WORLD EVENTS
1720 Italian harpsichord maker Bartolomeo Cristofori (1655–1731) invents the pianoforte.	**1721** Bubonic plague breaks out for the last time in Europe.
1725 French clockmaker Antoine Thiout (b. 1692) constructs a clock that displays solar time.	**1721** Robert Walpole (1676–1745) becomes the first British prime minister.
1726 English inventor George Graham (1673–1751) invents the mercury pendulum for clocks, which does not change in length with changes in temperature.	**1721** A regular mail service is set up between London and New England.
1728 English clockmaker John Harrison (1693–1776) creates the gridiron pendulum for clocks.	**1727** The Society of Friends—also known as the Quakers—in England advocates the abolition of slavery.
1728 French dentist Pierre Fauchard (1678–1761) invents the first dental drill and introduces fillings.	**1730** John Wesley (1703–91) and Charles Wesley (1707–88) form the Methodist Church at Oxford, England.
1730 English mathematician John Hadley (1682–1744) devises the quadrant, a navigational instrument that was the forerunner of the sextant.	**1730** Russia, Persia, and the Holy Roman Empire go to war against the Ottomans.
1730 René-Antoine Ferchault de Réaumur makes an alcohol thermometer and devises the Réaumur temperature scale.	**1733** The War of the Polish Succession begins when France and Spain reject the claimant to the Polish throne backed by Austria and Russia. Most fighting takes place in the Hapsburg lands in Italy.
1733 English engineer John Kay (1704–64) patents the flying shuttle, which increases the speed at which a loom makes cloth.	**1734** The Koran is translated into English by English Orientalist George Sale (1697–1736).
1723 A house in Newport, Rhode Island, is built with indoor plumbing.	**1730** English colonies begin to experience a religious revival known as the Great Awakening.
1724 Levees are built along the Mississippi River in Louisiana to protect against floods.	**1732** George II of Great Britain (r. 1727–60) grants a charter to British general James Oglethorpe (1696–1785) to found the colony of Georgia.
1725 The Principio Company constructs Accokeek Furnace in Virginia. The company exports its iron to England.	
1720s In India, Jaipur City is built on a geometric grid.	**1720** The Chinese expel the Dzungars from Tibet, and it becomes a Chinese protectorate.
1729 *T'ushu ji cheng*, a 1,000-page encyclopedia printed in movable type, is published in China.	**1722** Dutch explorers arrive on Easter Island.
	1729 Opium smoking is prohibited in China by Emperor Yongzheng (r. 1722–35).
1729 Transylvanian-born Ottoman printer Ibrahim Müteferrika (1674–1745) publishes descriptions of European governments, military, and geography.	**1720** The Ottomans begin sending ambassadors to Europe to learn about European culture.
1732 The Ottomans build a new system of aqueducts to bring water into Istanbul.	**1729** The Ottomans end the ban on printing books in Turkish or Arabic.
	1729 Arabs drive the Portuguese out of Dahomey.

IRON SMELTING

Iron is made in a blast furnace—a furnace in which combustion is forced by a current of air. Early blast furnaces were holes in the ground covered with a chimney. The furnace was filled with a mixture of iron ore, limestone, and charcoal, and set on fire. Bellows forced a blast of air through the furnace. Impurities rose to the top and molten iron was tapped through a hole at the bottom.

By the 14th century England was Europe's main iron-producing country. With bellows driven by waterwheels, blast furnaces could produce up to 3.3 tons (3 tonnes) of iron a day. This output required large amounts of charcoal, produced by burning wood. As a result, most of Britain's forests were destroyed.

In 1709 English iron-founder Abraham Darby (ca 1678–1717) began using coke (derived from coal) instead of charcoal. Darby's development had a dramatic effect on production. Cast-iron pans, kettles, and other utensils became commonplace in homes.

Darby built his furnaces at Coalbrookdale on the banks of the Severn River. His grandson Abraham Darby III (1750–91) built a lasting memorial to the family. In 1779, using prefabricated cast-iron sections, he completed a bridge across the river. It is 98 feet (30 m) long and stands 39 feet (12 m) above the water. It still carries foot passengers, but it was closed to traffic in 1934.

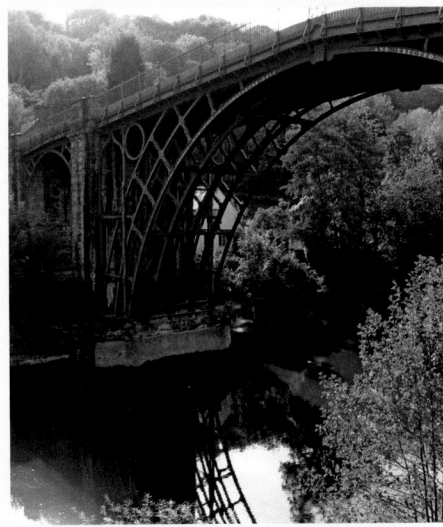

The iron bridge built by Abraham Darby III

ASTRONOMY & MATH

EUROPE

1735 English scientist George Hadley (1685–1768) proposes that the overall circulation of air in the atmosphere is due to convection currents.

1736 French mathematician Pierre de Maupertuis (1698–1759) states correctly that the Earth is an oblate spheroid (a sphere flattened slightly at the poles).

1736 French surveyor Alexis Clairaut (1713–65) measures the length of 1 degree of meridian (longitude), thus enabling accurate calculation of the size of the Earth.

1743 French mathematician Jean d'Alembert (1717–83) establishes mathematical dynamics (a branch of mechanics) with his book *Traité de Dynamique* (Treatise on Dynamics). Three years later he advances the theory of complex numbers.

1743 English mathematician Thomas Simpson (1710–61) devises Simpson's rules, a systematic approach to finding the area bounded by a curve.

1748 English astronomer James Bradley (1693–1762) discovers the nutation of the Earth, which is the slight "nodding" of the Earth's axis as it describes a very slow circle in space.

BIOLOGY & MEDICINE

1735 Swedish naturalist Carolus Linnaeus (1707–78) publishes *Systema Naturae*, in which he classifies objects into three kingdoms: animal, plant, or mineral. Later (1749) he introduces binomial naming (genus and species names).

1737 Swedish chemist Georg Brandt (1694–1768) discovers cobalt, the first discovery of a completely new metal since ancient times.

1740 Swiss naturalist Charles Bonnet (1720–93) observes parthenogenesis in aphids. (Parthenogenesis is the phenomenon in which unfertilized female animals give birth to young.)

1745 French surgeon Jacques Daviel (1693–1762) successfully performs an operation for the removal of a cataract from a patient's eye.

1747 Scottish physician James Lind (1716–94) experiments with citrus fruits to prevent scurvy among British sailors. (Citrus fruits are rich in vitamin C, the lack of which is now known to cause scurvy.)

1748 Scottish physician John Fothergill (1712–80) gives the first description of diphtheria.

PHYSICAL SCIENCES

1735 English physicist Stephen Gray (1666–1736) postulates that lightning is an electrical phenomenon.

1738 Swiss scientist Daniel Bernoulli (1700–82) becomes the first to put forward a kinetic theory of gases—that their properties can be explained by considering gases to be composed of rapidly moving small particles of matter.

1742 Swedish astronomer Anders Celsius (1701–44) devises the 100-degree Celsius temperature scale (later known as the centigrade scale but now called by its original name).

1745 Russian scientist Mikhail Lomonosov (1711–65) compiles a catalog of more than 300 minerals.

1747 German chemist Andreas Marggraf (1709–82) discovers sugar in beets.

THE AMERICAS

HOW THINGS WORK

The Leyden Jar

The Leyden jar is named for the Dutch University of Leyden (now spelled Leiden) where it was invented in 1745 by Pieter van Musschenbroek. It is a type of condenser used for storing electrical charge. It has plates of metal foil glued inside and outside a glass jar. A brass rod running through an insulating stopper has at its end a short length of metal chain that makes contact with the inner foil. An electrostatic charge, produced by rubbing an insulating rod or by an electrostatic generator, can be brought up to the brass rod to charge up the condenser. A person who touches the brass knob receives a powerful electric shock. According to one account, French cleric and physicist Jean-Antoine Nollet connected a charged Leyden jar to a row of monks holding hands and watched them all leap into the air with the shock.

Brass rod joined to chain, touching the inner foil

Rubber stopper

Glass jar

Inner foil

Outer foil

Chain

1738 Introduced by Eliza Lucas Pinckney, indigo becomes an important crop in the South; it is grown for its blue dye.

1740 French explorer Charles-Marie de la Condamine (1701–74) discovers the powerful paralyzing drug curare (used as an arrow poison by South American Indians).

1736 Charles-Marie de la Condamine discovers India rubber (then called *caoutchouc*).

1735 Spanish scientist and naval officer Antonio de Ulloa (1716–95) rediscovers platinum in South America. It had been used by local people for centuries and was found in Central America by Spanish explorers, but its discovery had not been announced.

1743 The American Philosophical Society is founded.

The "Franklin stove," invented by Benjamin Franklin in 1742, became very popular and gradually replaced open fires to heat rooms in North America.

ASIA & OCEANIA

AFRICA & THE MIDDLE EAST

ENGINEERING & INVENTION

1735 English clockmaker John Harrison (1693–1776) unveils his first chronometer, a clock so accurate it can be used to calculate longitude at sea.

1738 English inventor Lewis Paul (d. 1759) produces a machine for carding wool. (Carding is the process of combing out woolen fleeces into parallel fibers.)

1738 English metallurgist William Champion (1710–89) devises a new industrial process for the large-scale production of zinc from its ores.

1740 English metallurgist Benjamin Huntsman (1704–76) invents the crucible process for making steel in batches.

1742 French metallurgist Jean-Paul Malouin (1701–78) creates a process for covering steel with a layer of zinc (later to be called galvanizing).

1743 English metalworker Thomas Boulsover (1706–88) produces "Sheffield plate," metalware consisting of copper coated with a thin layer of silver.

1745 Dutch physicist Pieter van Musschenbroek (1692–1761) invents the Leyden jar, a simple form of electrical condenser.

1739 German-born Caspar Wistar (1696–1752) opens a glassworks in New Jersey.

1741 Porcelain production begins in Savannah, Georgia.

1742 American scientist and politician Benjamin Franklin (1706–90) invents a wood-burning stove. The design is patented, and later stoves of the same design come to be known as "Franklin stoves."

1747 Jesuit missionaries design a Summer Palace for the Chinese emperors outside of Beijing.

1730s Ottoman artillery officers enlist the help of the French aristocrat Count Bonnerai to teach Turkish gunners and to found a school of military engineering.

1740 Frederick II, known as Frederick the Great, of Prussia (r. 1740–86) succeeds to the throne after the death of his father Frederick William I (r. 1713–40).

1741 An outbreak of yellow fever in Cádiz, Spain, kills 10,000 people.

1741 German composer George Frederick Handel (1685–1759) premieres his oratorio *The Messiah.*

1745 Charles Stuart, known as Bonnie Prince Charlie, the grandson of deposed king of England James II (r. 1685–88) fails to regain the English throne.

1746 The feudal clan system declines in Scotland, and Celtic culture is suppressed after the rebellion of 1745. Many Scots emigrate to America.

1748 Excavations begin on the site of the rediscovered ancient city of Pompeii, Italy, buried by an eruption of Mt. Vesuvius in 79 C.E.

1740 Smallpox kills many Lakota of the northern plains.

1742 The Moravian College for Women is established in Pennsylvania.

1743 Russians explore Alaska.

1744 King George's War (1744–48) breaks out in New England.

1739 Persian troops led by Nadir Shah invade India and loot many of the finest Mughal palaces.

1746 In the French and British struggle for control in India, the French conquer Madras.

Carolus Linnaeus

Carolus Linnaeus was a Swedish naturalist who devised the binomial (two-name) system of classifying plants and animals and founded the science of taxonomy. Born Carl von Linné in Råshult, southern Sweden, in 1707, he was the son of a pastor. He studied medicine and then botany at universities in Lund and Uppsala.

Between 1732 and 1735 Linnaeus traveled around Lapland and several European countries and found 100 new species of plants. He settled in Holland and qualified as a doctor of medicine. In 1735 he published *Systema Naturae* (Systems of Nature), in which he classified objects into three kingdoms: animals, plants, and minerals.

Linnaeus introduced binomial naming in 1749, and in his book *Species Plantarum* (Species of Plants) of 1753 he gave each plant a Latinized genus name and a species name. For example, using his system, the American beech tree is *Fagus grandifolia* (genus *Fagus*, species *grandifolia*). The modern convention is for the names to be printed in italic letters with a capital letter for only the genus. The names of orders and classes are not printed in italics.

In 1738 Linnaeus returned to Sweden, where he practiced as a physician. In 1741 he became a professor of medicine and botany at Uppsala University.

Swedish naturalist Carolus Linnaeus is considered the founder of modern taxonomy.

NAVIGATION AT SEA

THE CREW OF A SHIP IN THE MIDDLE OF AN open ocean needs to know in what direction the ship is going and exactly where it is. A compass can indicate direction, and the magnetic compass was in regular use by the 1100s. But accurate positioning needs a knowledge of latitude and longitude, which proved to be much more difficult to determine.

Latitude indicates a position in terms of its distance north or south of the equator. It is measured in degrees. For example, Philadelphia is at a latitude of 40° north. Latitude can be found by measuring the angle of a particular heavenly body above the horizon and consulting books of tables or almanacs. At night the angle of the polestar or during the day the angle of the sun at noon can be measured and compared with tables. Early sailors had various instruments for measuring these angles. Using a cross-staff, a sailor sighted along a 3-foot- (1-m-) long staff while moving a crosspiece until the lower end lined up with the horizon and the upper end coincided with the star or the sun. The staff was calibrated in degrees from which the sailor could read off the angle. It was first described in about 1330 by French astronomer Levi ben Gershon (1288–1344) and used in Europe until as late as the 18th century.

In 1594 English sailor John Davis (ca 1550–1605) invented the backstaff. It was pointed in the opposite direction, and the operator did not need to look directly into the sun. The quadrant was a similar

This illustration shows a ship's navigator taking a reading of latitude from the shore using a variant of the cross-staff.

KEY DATES

1594
Backstaff

1731
Octant

1735
Harrison's early chronometers

1757
Sextant

1759
Harrison's prize-winning chronometer

instrument, also used by astronomers and by gunners to set the correct angles for aiming artillery pieces.

Then in 1731 English mathematician John Hadley (1682–1744) invented the octant, incorrectly named Hadley's quadrant at the time. Anglo-American inventor Thomas Godfrey (1704–49) of Philadelphia invented an almost identical instrument independently. In the octant a pivoted arm carries a mirror that can be moved to bring an image of the sun in line with another mirror. The second mirror also gives a view of the horizon. The maximum angle it could measure was 45°. From there it was a simple step to the sextant (which measured up to 60°), introduced by Scottish naval officer John Campbell (ca 1720–90) in 1757. It remained the standard navigational instrument for 250 years. It was even used on aircraft until it was finally supplanted by radio beacons and the satellite-based GPS (global positioning system).

The Search for Longitude

Finding the longitude of a ship's location—its position east or west of the Greenwich meridian (longitude 0°) —proved to be far more difficult than calculating latitude. For centuries sailors measured the angle between the moon and another heavenly body, and consulted tables called ephemerides that gave the day-to-day positions of the moon. German astronomer Johann Müller (1436–76), also known as Regiomontanus, drew up the first tables in 1474. They were published in 1766 in the *Nautical Almanac* by English astronomer Nevil Maskelyne (1732–1811) and revised every year.

The solution to the longitude problem lay in finding an accurate way of measuring time, which varies locally depending on longitude. For example, at 12 noon in London, England, it is 7.00 A.M. in Philadelphia (longitude about 75° west). If we know the exact time at a given place when it is noon in London,

we can calculate its longitude. To do this we need a chronometer, or very accurate clock. In 1714 the British government offered a prize of £20,000 to anyone who could produce such an instrument. A condition of the competition was that the "sea clock" had to gain or lose no more than two minutes after a six-week voyage to the West Indies and back.

English clockmaker John Harrison (1693–1776) took up the challenge and in 1735 introduced his first chronometer. But it was his fourth instrument of 1759 that won the prize (or half of it, since the government retained half the money until Harrison could prove that the chronometer could be duplicated). He did not receive the remainder until 1773, and then only after King George III intervened on Harrison's behalf. Chronometers based on Harrison's H4 were rarely used at first as they were very expensive, costing about a third of the price of a new warship.

Chronometers are precision timepieces used to keep accurate time and help calculate longitude at sea.

A sextant measures the angle of the sun or a star above the horizon. Special tables convert the angle into the navigator's latitude, the angular distance north or south of the equator.

The index glass (in fact, a mirror) reflects the sun's rays onto a second mirror called the horizon glass. It is a half-mirror that reflects the rays along a telescope to the navigator's eye. A shade glass cuts down the brightness and prevents eye damage. The navigator also looks through the plain (unsilvered) half of the horizon glass at the horizon and adjusts the angle of the index glass until the sun's image appears to be on the horizon. The graduated scale on the limb of the sextant then indicates the angle of the sun above the horizon.

Rays from the sun
Index glass
Shade glass
Index arm
Telescope
Rays from horizon
Shade glass
Viewer
Horizon glass
Limb (graduated scale)
Index-arm adjuster

ASTRONOMY & MATH

EUROPE

1750 French astronomer Guillaume Legentil de la Galaisière (1725–92) discovers the Trifid Nebula (M20) in the constellation Sagittarius. It is named by English astronomer John Herschel (1792–1871) for the three dark rifts that appear to divide the nebula and join at its center.

1755 German philosopher Immanuel Kant (1724–1804) explains his theory for the formation of the solar system in his *Universal Natural History and Theory of the Heavens*. He postulates that it is created from a spinning gaseous nebula and that our galaxy is just one of many in the universe.

1758 German astronomer Johann Palitzsch (1723–88) observes Halley's comet when it returns as predicted by English astronomer Edmond Halley (1656–1742) in 1682.

1761 Russian scientist Mikhail Lomonosov (1711–65) observes a transit of Venus across the sun's disk and deduces that Venus has an atmosphere.

1762 English astronomer James Bradley (1693–1762) produces a star catalog with measured positions of 60,000 stars.

A single worker could spin many threads at the same time with James Hargreaves's spinning jenny, invented in 1764.

AFRICA & THE MIDDLE EAST

1750 French astronomer Nicolas de Lacaille (1713–1762) leads an astronomical expedition to the Cape of Good Hope to study parallax, or the relative position of celestial objects seen from different points on Earth.

BIOLOGY & MEDICINE

EUROPE

1752 French chemist René-Antoine Ferchault de Réaumur (1683–1757) discovers the part played by gastric juices in the digestion of foods.

1760s English agriculturist Robert Bakewell (1725–95) uses selective breeding to produce improved varieties of farm animals.

1761 Austrian physician Leopold Auenbrugger (1722–1809) introduces the diagnostic technique of percussion, which involves tapping the patient's chest and listening to the quality of the sound produced.

1761 Italian physician Giovanni Morgagni (1682–1771) founds the science of pathology with his book *On the Seats and Causes of Disease*.

1762 The École Nationale Vétérinaire is established in Lyons, France, the world's first national veterinary college.

1763 German botanist Josef Kölreuter (1733–1806) discovers the role of insects in the pollination of flowers.

ASIA & OCEANIA

1762 The flightless dodo-like bird called the solitaire (*Pezophaps solitaria*) becomes extinct (on the Indian Ocean's Rodriguez Island).

AFRICA & THE MIDDLE EAST

ca 1750 Zahn al-Umar plants cotton and exports the product, marking the start of the cotton industry in Palestine.

PHYSICAL SCIENCES

EUROPE

1751 Swedish chemist Axel Cronstedt (1722–65) discovers nickel.

1758 German chemist Andreas Marggraf (1709–82) introduces flame tests as a method of chemical analysis. (Various metallic elements burn with a characteristic color in a gas flame.)

1760 German physicist Johann Lambert (1728–77) formulates Lambert's law, which states that the illuminance provided by light striking a surface at right angles is inversely proportional to the square of the distance between the surface and the light source.

1761 Scottish chemist Joseph Black (1728–99) introduces the concept of latent heat. Latent heat is the "extra" heat that must be added to an object at its melting point before it actually melts (or to a liquid at its boiling point before it boils).

1762 English physicist John Canton (1718–72) demonstrates that contrary to previous beliefs, water is a compressible liquid.

THE AMERICAS

1751 English surveyors Charles Mason and Jeremiah Dixon begin to accurately map the frontiers of North America.

1752 American scientist and politician Benjamin Franklin (1706–90) demonstrates the electrical nature of lightning in his famous kite-flying experiment.

This hand-colored engraving depicts a stretch of the Bridgewater Canal, in England, crossing the River Irwell in an aqueduct. The canal, completed in 1761, carried coal from the duke of Bridgewater's mines to Manchester.

ENGINEERING & INVENTION

1753 Scottish engineer Charles Morrison invents a 26-wire telegraph (one wire for each letter of the alphabet).

1756 English engineer John Smeaton (1724–92) invents cement that sets underwater (for building lighthouses).

1757 English clockmaker Thomas Mudge (1715–94) devises a lever escapement for a watch, although it is not used until 1770.

1758 English cotton weaver Jedediah Strutt (1726–97) invents the stocking frame, a machine for making ribbed hosiery.

1758 English optician John Dollond (1706–61) makes achromatic lenses that consist of two pieces of different glass types.

1761 English engineer James Brindley (1716–72) completes the Bridgewater Canal.

1762 English nobleman John Montagu, earl of Sandwich (1718–92), invents the sandwich (so that he did not have to leave the gambling tables to take his meals).

1764 English mechanic James Hargreaves (d. 1778) invents the spinning jenny for spinning many cotton or woolen threads at the same time.

ca 1760 About this time, rice planters in the American South start using threshing machines in rice production.

Science is organized knowledge. Wisdom is organized life.

IMMANUEL KANT

WORLD EVENTS

1751 In France, Denis Diderot begins to publish the multivolume *Encyclopédia*, a key work of the Scientific Revolution.

1755 An earthquake in Lisbon, Portugal, kills more than 60,000 people.

1755 Russia's first university, the University of Moscow, is founded.

1756 The Seven Years' War (1756–63) breaks out between Britain and France.

1759 Jesuits are expelled from Portugal and its colonies.

1759 King Ferdinand of Spain (r. 1746–59) dies and is succeeded by his half-brother Charles III (r. 1759–88).

1759 Voltaire publishes *Candide*.

1760 George II of England (r. 1727–60) dies and is succeeded by his grandson George III (r. 1760–1820).

1754 The French and Indian War (1754–63) breaks out between Britain and France, resulting in the British conquest of Canada.

1763 Chief Pontiac (1720–69) of the Ottawa leads a rebellion against British settlers.

ca 1750 About this time, the Dutch begin spreading Western learning in Japan.

1760 Canton becomes the only Chinese port allowed to trade with foreigners.

SELECTIVE BREEDING

Choosing which animals can breed together in order to improve the quality of cattle, sheep, and other types of livestock is called selective breeding. The technique was pioneered by Robert Bakewell (1725–95), who ran his own farm in Leicestershire, England.

Previously, farm animals of both sexes were kept in the same enclosures and allowed to breed randomly. This resulted in offspring with random characteristics. Bakewell separated the sexes and only allowed animals with specific characteristics to breed. This inbreeding resulted in exaggerated traits.

Bakewell created a breed of sheep with fatty meat—popular in those days—and a quality fleece called the New Leicester from the Lincolnshire breed. He hired out his best rams to neighboring farmers so that they could improve their stock, too. Bakewell also improved the Longhorn cattle breed, making it more meat productive.

With changes in taste, Bakewell's New Leicester breed of sheep eventually declined in popularity, and Longhorn cattle were superseded by Shorthorn breeds. However, Bakewell's selective breeding methods became widespread across the world in creating not only hundreds of productive breeds of sheep, cattle, goats, pigs, poultry, and other farm animals but also other domestic animals, such as pet cats and dogs.

The New Leicester breed of sheep was created by Robert Bakewell by selectively breeding sheep with fatty meat and long wool.

Benjamin Franklin

Benjamin Franklin (1706–90) was a complex character, an unusual combination of statesman and scientist. He played an important part in the development of the United States and made major discoveries in physics. He also was a talented inventor, and some of his inventions are still in use throughout the world today.

Born in Boston into a family of 17 children, Benjamin Franklin left school at the age of ten. Two years later he was apprenticed to his older brother James, a printer. When he was just 18, he took over publication of the *New England Courant*, a weekly newspaper founded by his brother. Franklin did not stay for long; instead, he went to Philadelphia and worked as a printer himself. In 1724 he set sail for England. He returned home two years later and published the first volume of *Poor Richard's Almanac* in 1733, a collection of articles on a wide range of subjects to "convey instruction among the common people." Franklin held various public offices and helped draft the Declaration of Independence in 1776. He traveled to France to raise help for the American cause in the War of Independence (1775–82). He was also a staunch supporter of the abolition of slavery. Franklin retired from public life in 1788.

Electrical Nature of Lightning

During his lifetime Franklin also conducted scientific experiments. The best known, in 1752, was one of the most dangerous experiments ever undertaken. He attached a metal key to the moistened string of a kite, which he flew during a thunderstorm. Electric "fluid" flowing down the string caused sparks to jump between the key and a Leyden jar (a primitive electrical condenser). Franklin had established the electrical nature of lightning and coined the words *positive* and *negative* to describe the two types of static electricity. Several European scientists who tried to repeat the experiment were struck by lightning and killed. As a result of his discovery Franklin invented the lightning rod—sometimes still called a Franklin rod—a pointed conductor located at the top of a building and connected to the ground by a thick wire attached to a plate buried in the soil.

Franklin made many scientific discoveries, wrote a number of bestselling books, and was a key figure in the formation of the United States.

BENJAMIN FRANKLIN.

KEY DATES
1733 Poor Richard's Almanac first published
1742 Franklin stove
1752 Kite experiment and lightning rod
1784 Bifocal eyeglasses

In 1742 Franklin invented the so-called "Franklin stove" designed to make more efficient use of fuel. In later life, Franklin, who was nearsighted, had the first pair of bifocal eyeglasses made for him. They had split lenses—the upper half for distance vision and the lower half for near vision. Franklin chose not to patent any of his inventions, believing that ideas should be exchanged freely.

Franklin had many other scientific interests. Unlike most of his contemporaries, he rejected Isaac Newton's corpuscular theory of light (that light travels as particles), favoring the wave theories of Robert Hooke and others. He suggested that the rapid heating of air near warm ground causes it to expand and spiral upward, producing tornadoes and waterspouts. He investigated the course of the Gulf Stream, the current of warm water that flows across the Atlantic Ocean, and he suggested that ships' captains should use a thermometer to locate and benefit from the current (or avoid it, depending on the direction in which they were sailing). In 1824 the Franklin Institute was founded in Philadelphia in his honor.

Opposite: *An artist's romantic depiction of Franklin's famous experiment. He flew a kite in a thunderstorm and found that electricity from the storm was conducted along the kite's wet string. During the experiment Franklin charged a Leyden jar, which was connected to the string by a thin wire and a key.*

ASTRONOMY & MATH	BIOLOGY & MEDICINE	PHYSICAL SCIENCES

EUROPE

1767 English astronomer Nevil Maskelyne (1732–1811) edits the *Nautical Almanac*, a book of astronomical and other tables.

1767 Swiss mathematician Leonhard Euler (1707–83) sets out the rules of algebra in his book *Vollständige Anleitung zur Algebra* (Complete Instruction in Algebra).

1773 French mathematician Pierre-Simon de Laplace (1749–1827) uses Newton's law of gravity to show that the solar system is inherently stable.

1773 German-born English astronomer William Herschel (1738–1822) studies the motions of distant stars and figures out that the sun is gradually moving through space.

1774 German astronomer Johann Bode (1747–1826) founds *Astronomisches Jahrbuch* (Astronomical Yearbook).

1774 Nevil Maskelyne determines the gravitational constant (the constant that appears in Newton's law of gravitation) and is thus able to calculate the average density of the Earth.

Luigi Galvani used animals such as frogs and sheep in his experiments with electricity in 1771.

1766 English scientist Henry Cavendish (1731–1810) identifies hydrogen, calling it "inflammable air."

1769 English chemist Joseph Priestley (1733–1804) suggests that electrical forces follow an inverse square law.

1771 Swiss geologist Jean Deluc (1727–1817) uses a barometer to find the heights of mountains (atmospheric pressure decreases with altitude).

1771 Italian physician and physicist Luigi Galvani (1737–98) shows that the muscles of a dissected frog twitch when they are stimulated by electricity.

1772 Scottish chemist Daniel Rutherford (1749–1819) discovers nitrogen.

1774 Joseph Priestley identifies oxygen.

1774 Swedish chemist Karl Scheele (1742–86) discovers barium, chlorine, and manganese.

1774 French chemist Antoine Lavoisier (1743–94) demonstrates the law of conservation of mass (in a chemical reaction).

THE AMERICAS

1765 Colonial American scientist John Winthrop (1714–79) includes calculations of comet masses in his book *Account of Some Fiery Meteors*. In 1772 he presents Harvard University with its first telescope.

1773 In Colombia, botanist Mutis is put on trial for heresy after giving a series of lectures about Copernicus's theory of the sun-centered universe.

ca 1765 Planters in the southern colonies of North America begin rice cultivation, which forms the basis of a period of economic growth.

ASIA & OCEANIA

1769 English explorer James Cook visits Tahiti to observe a transit of Venus (when the planet Venus passes in front of the sun's disk); German naturalist Peter Pallas (1741–1811) travels to the border between China and Russia for the same purpose.

INSIDE SCIENCE

Manganese

Manganese is a gray-white, hard but brittle metal. It occurs as a free element and as a part of many minerals. Swedish chemist Karl Scheele first recognized manganese as an element in 1774. Later that year, Scheele's colleague Johann Gottlieb Gahn (1745–1818) isolated the metal from manganese dioxide. Not long after its discovery, manganese became a key ingredient in iron and steel production because it produced harder alloys. Manganese and its compounds have many other industrial uses, including in batteries, as oxidizers, as pigments, and as an additive in gasoline to boost octane rating and reduce engine knocking. The metal is also essential to all forms of life, as a cofactor of a broad range of enzymes.

AFRICA & THE MIDDLE EAST

ENGINEERING & INVENTION

1765 Italian naturalist Lazzaro Spallanzi (1729–99) devises a method of preserving food using hermetically sealed containers.

1765 Scottish engineer James Watt (1736–1819) builds a steam engine with a separate condenser.

1768 French chemist Antoine Baumé (1728–1804) invents a hydrometer (which he calls an aerometer) and a new density scale for graduating it.

1769 English manufacturer Richard Arkwright (1732–92) produces the spinning frame for spinning strong cotton thread.

1770 Joseph Priestley invents the pencil eraser.

1770 French inventor Jacques de Vaucanson (1709–82) constructs textile machinery that incorporates a chain drive.

1770 French watchmaker Abraham-Louis Perrelet (1729–1826) develops a watch with automatic winding.

1774 English engineer John Wilkinson (1728–1808) patents a precision cannon-boring machine, also used for making cylinders for steam engines.

1765 The first medical school in the United States is established at the College of Pennsylvania.

1769 American astronomer David Rittenhouse (1732–96) constructs the first astronomical telescope in the United States.

1767 Hungarian Baron do Tott (1733–93) is placed in charge of the Ottoman Army. He builds a modern cannon foundry and a new military school and introduces a rapid-fire artillery corps.

WORLD EVENTS

1767 Catherine II of Russia, also called Catherine the Great (r. 1762–96), commissions a new code of laws.

1767 The Russians go to war against Ottoman Turks.

1770 Fifteen-year-old Marie Antoinette (1755–93), daughter of the Austrian Empress Maria Theresa, marries Prince Louis, later Louis XVI of France (r. 1774–93).

1771 Plague kills more than 50,000 people in Moscow, Russia.

1772 Poland is partitioned by Russia, Prussia, and Austria.

1772 Pope Clement XIV (1705–74) dissolves the Jesuit order.

1773 A Cossack soldier, Yemelyan Pugachev (ca 174–75), declares himself to be Peter III (r. 1762), Catherine the Great's assassinated husband, and leads a popular uprising in southern Russia.

1774 Louis XVI becomes king of France after the death of his grandfather, Louis XV (r. 1715–74).

1765 The Spanish begin loosening restrictions on American trade.

1773 Guatemala City becomes the capital of Guatemala after the former capital, Antigua, is destroyed by an earthquake.

Theologian and scientist Joseph Priestley is credited with the discovery of oxygen, which he called "dephlogisticated air."

1765 The Chinese invade Burma.

1768 English explorer Captain James Cook (1728–79) begins exploring the Pacific.

1771 The Tay Son Rebellion begins in Vietnam.

1769 Egyptians revolt against Ottoman rule.

1772 Scottish explorer James Bruce (1730–94) finds the source of the Blue Nile.

INVESTIGATING THE AIR

In the 1760s and 1770s scientists discovered several new elements. Among them were the gas hydrogen and the two most common atmospheric gases, oxygen and nitrogen.

English scientist Henry Cavendish identified hydrogen from a metal–acid reaction in 1766. He called the gas "inflammable air" and later discovered that, on burning, hydrogen produces water. The gas was not named until 1783. French chemist Antoine Lavoisier called it hydrogen, which is Greek for "water producer."

Scottish chemist Daniel Rutherford discovered nitrogen, which makes up about 78 percent of the air, in 1772. Scientists had long suspected that a large portion of the air did not support combustion. For that reason, scientists at first referred to nitrogen as burnt, fixed, noxious, or mephitic (meaning "lifeless") air. The name *nitrogen* means "saltpeter producer."

In 1774 English chemist Joseph Priestley identified oxygen, which makes up almost 21 percent of the volume of air. The gas had been discovered by Swedish chemist Karl Scheele in 1772, but since he did not publish his findings until 1777 Priestley is usually credited with its discovery. Lavoisier further characterized the gas and gave oxygen its name, which means "acid producer," because he mistakenly believed that all acids contained oxygen.

The understanding of carbon dioxide (about 0.04 percent of the air) also improved in the 1700s. Flemish chemist Jan Baptist van Helmont (1580–1644) had recognized carbon dioxide in the 1600s and coined the word *gas*. Scottish scientist Joseph Black (1728–99) further studied the properties of carbon dioxide in the 1750s, and Joseph Priestley also added to its understanding.

THE STEAM ENGINE

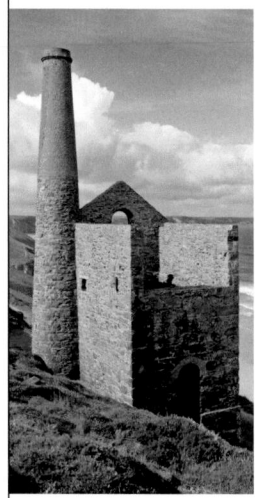

An old pumphouse above a disused mine in Cornwall, southwestern England. Steam engines were first used to pump water out of these coastal mines.

FROM THE TIME OF THE ANCIENT EGYPTIANS until the end of the 17th century only wind and water power provided an alternative to the muscles of animals and humans. But the situation changed dramatically with the invention of the steam engine, which involved a sequence of events beginning in 1690 and culminating in 1765 with the work of James Watt (1736–1819).

The earliest steam engines did not use the pressure of steam to provide power. Instead, they used the pressure of the air. For that reason they are more accurately called atmospheric engines. The first was devised by Denis Papin (1647–1712), a French physicist working in England. A vertical, open-ended cylinder with a close-fitting piston had water inside its base. A fire heated the base of the cylinder, causing the water to boil and turn into steam. Steam pressure lifted the piston, which remained raised while the cylinder cooled. The steam condensed back to liquid water, creating a partial vacuum in the cylinder. Then atmospheric pressure on the upper end of the piston pushed it down again. A rope connected to the piston and moving over a pulley could be used to lift a load or work a pump.

A similar arrangement, patented in 1698 by English mining engineer Thomas Savery (ca 1650–1715), made the atmospheric engine into a practical steam pump. It had no piston or other moving parts, just hand-operated valves to provide continuous operation. Steam from a boiler passed into a working chamber that was sprayed with cold water to condense the steam. The partial vacuum that was created as a result lifted water through a one-way valve into the chamber. Steam was then let in again, which forced the water out and up through another one-way valve.

Beam Engines

In 1712 English engineer Thomas Newcomen (1663–1729) perfected the first engine to use steam pressure to work a piston. Because of the way they were constructed, people generally referred to Newcomen's engines as "beam engines." Newcomen could not patent his engine because its principle was too close to that of Thomas Savery's, so the two men went into partnership and built engines together. This was the stage that steam power had reached in 1764, when Scottish engineer James Watt received a model of a Newcomen engine to repair. He realized how much energy is wasted by first heating the cylinder and then cooling it. In 1765 he hit on the idea of adding a separate external condenser. In addition he used steam to push up the piston and then—by admitting low-pressure steam on the other side—to push it down again. This double action greatly improved the efficiency of the machine.

By their very action early steam engines produced an up-and-down motion, but most machines of the time, except pumps, required rotary motion and most were driven by waterwheels. Then in 1781 James Watt invented the sun-and-planet gear to make his engines provide a rotary final drive. The steam engine became a vital part of most industrial facilities.

In a Newcomen engine, steam from a boiler (1) forced a piston up an open-ended cylinder (2). Cold water was sprayed into the cylinder to condense the steam (3). The water then ran out of the cylinder (4). That created a partial vacuum, which sucked the piston down again (5) and also pulled down one end of a long beam connected to the piston rod (6). The other end of the beam was connected to a pump. As the piston went up and down, the beam rocked and worked the pump continuously. A Newcomen engine could produce about 12 strokes a minute.

6. Action pulls down rocking beam on piston side and works pump on the other side

5. Piston drops down as partial vacuum is created

2. Steam pushes piston up

3. Cold water is injected to condense the steam

4. Water runs out

1. Water is heated and the boiler produces steam

113

This colored engraving shows the various parts of a Newcomen's engine, including the boiler (A), piston (P), cylinder (C), and beam (O).

High-pressure Engines

The next development was an increase in the pressure of steam in the engine—in the terminology of the day, "strong steam." This had to await the introduction of improved cylinders with better-fitting pistons and boilers that were safe at high steam pressures. They became available by 1800, when Watt's master patent expired. The following year English inventor Richard Trevithick (1771–1833) started building his own double-action, high-pressure engines. Trevithick removed the separate condenser and used the waste steam to preheat the water entering the boiler. Within four years he built nearly 50 engines that were used mainly in mines in many parts of Britain and South America. It was the high-pressure engines pioneered by Trevithick that made the steam engine a viable source or power for an even greater number of purposes. Although Trevithick's own experiments with locomotives were not successful, engines based on his designs were used in the earliest successful locomotives.

KEY DATES

1690
Papin's primitive engine

1698
Savery's atmospheric steam pump

1712
Newcomen's atmospheric steam engine

1765
Watt's engine with external condenser

1801
Trevithick's high-pressure engine

J. M W. Turner's landscape "Rain, Steam and Speed," painted in the mid-1800s, shows a locomotive crossing the Thames River in England above a barge, a symbol of the previous age of transportation. First built in 1803, steam locomotives—and the railroads they chugged along— soon became a common sight across the Western world and a symbol of the industrial revolution.

THE BEGINNING OF THE PERIOD COVERED BY THIS CHAPTER WAS A TIME of widespread political revolution, with major social upheavals in America—the Revolutionary War (1775–83)—and France—the French Revolution (1789–99). Just as influential on the course of history was the industrial revolution that followed the development of the steam engine by Scottish inventor and mechanical engineer James Watt (1736–1819). It opened the way to large-scale manufacture, freed transportation from its dependence on animal and wind power, and heralded significant social changes. The industrial world had begun.

Steam engines evolved from steam pumps, and the first applications of the new engines continued to be in mines, where they were employed to pump out water. They were then used in factories to drive textile machinery and other machines. In 1785 English inventor Edmund Cartwright made the first steam-powered loom. But the steam engine came into its own when it was applied to transportation. Various inventors tried fitting a steam engine to a road vehicle to create a "horseless carriage." English engineer Richard Trevithick (1771–1833) constructed in 1803 the first successful steam locomotive to run on rails. The first railroad to carry passengers and freight was the Stockton & Darlington Railway, which opened in 1825. It used steam locomotives built by English engineer George Stephenson (1781–1848). By 1840 there were railroads in England, Ireland, France, Germany, the Netherlands, and the United States.

In the early days of the industrial revolution—before the spread of the railroads—canals were used to transport raw materials, such as coal, iron ore, and timber, to the factories and also to carry finished products. Horses towed the barges along the canals. When the railroads took off, the canals fell into disrepair.

While people flocked to the towns and cities to work in the factories, advances in farming helped cope with the shortage of workers in the countryside. Cast-iron was used to make better plows. Machines were invented to reap and thresh (separate the seeds from the harvested crop). The combine harvester—invented in 1838—reaped, threshed, and bundled straw into sheaves.

In science a different kind of revolution took place in the field of biology. Scientists had come to recognize that fossils are the remains of long-dead plants and animals. The ages of the fossils correspond to the ages of the rocks in which they are found. But why did fossil animals become extinct? Based on observations made during his voyage on H.M.S. *Beagle*, English naturalist Charles Darwin (1809–82) came up with the theory that animal life is not static but gradually evolves into new forms. The dominant species are those that are best equipped—the fittest—to cope with their environment. Those that cannot adapt to environmental changes become extinct.

Another key development toward the end of this period was the birth of photography. Experiments with light-sensitive chemicals enabled Frenchman Joseph Niépce (1765–1833) to take the first photograph, in 1826. Another Frenchman, Louis Daguerre (1787–1851) improved on Niépce's techniques to make his own photographs, known as daguerrotypes. Electricity was sparking other scientists. English chemist Humphry Davy (1778–1829), English physicist and chemist Michael Faraday (1791–1867), and French physicist, chemist, and mathematician André-Marie Ampère (1775–1836) all improved our understanding of electricity and magnetism.

Steam engines powered the industrial revolution. James Watt's steam engine was first used to pump water out of mines. Watt later modified it to drive machinery in factories. Further improvements, notably by Richard Trevithick, led to the steam engines that powered locomotives.

Charles Darwin's voyage on H.M.S. Beagle *in the 1830s took him to many far-flung places, including South America and Australia. In the Galápagos Islands, off the coast of Ecuador, his study of similar species, including tortoises, on the different islands helped him formulate his groundbreaking theory of evolution.*

THE WORLD AT A GLANCE

CONCISE HISTORY OF SCIENCE AND INVENTION

	1775	1785	1795	1800	1810
EUROPE	**1778** English inventor Joseph Bramah patents a flushing toilet. **1778** Italian physicist Alessandro Volta discovers methane. **1779** French astronomer Antoine Darquier discovers the Ring Nebula. **1779** British scientist Jan Ingenhousz describes photosynthesis. **1781** British astronomer William Herschel discovers the planet Uranus. **1782** Scottish engineer James Watt invents a steam engine in which steam enters each side of the piston alternately. **1783** French brothers Joseph and Jacques Montgolfier, invent the hot-air balloon. **1783** English physicist John Mitchell predicts the existence of black holes.	**1785** French balloonist Jean-Pierre Blanchard invents the parachute. **1785** English physician William Withering introduces the use of the drug digitalis. **1785** English inventor Edmond Cartwright invents a steam-powered loom. **ca 1787** French physicist Jacques Charles proposes Charles's law: that, at constant pressure, the volume of a gas is proportional to its absolute temperature. **1789** German chemist Martin Klaproth discovers uranium and zirconium. **1789** French physician Joseph Guillotin invents the guillotine.	**1795** French chemist Nicolas Conté invents a pencil with a graphite "lead." Pencils of this type have remained in use ever since. **1795** The French adopt the metric system. **1795** English inventor Joseph Bramah devises a hydraulic press. **1796** English physician Edward Jenner introduces the smallpox vaccination into Europe. **1796** German printer Aloys Senefelder invents lithographic printing. **1798** English economist Thomas Malthus discovers a relationship between the size of a population and the available food supply.	**1800** Italian physicist Alessandro Volta invents the voltaic pile battery for producing a continuous electric current. **1805** French inventor Joseph Jacquard constructs a loom that is controlled by punched cards. **1806** English engineer William Congreve builds solid-fuel rockets. **1807** English chemist Humphry Davy uses electrolysis to isolate sodium and potassium. **1808** Humphry Davy invents the arc lamp. **1809** French naturalist Jean-Baptiste Lamarck proposes that characteristics acquired during life are inherited by offspring—a now discredited theory known as Lamarckism. **1809** French chemist Nicholas Vauquelin discovers nicotine in tobacco.	**1810** French chef Nicolas Appert invents food canning (originally for Napoleon's army). **1810** German engineer Friedrich König invents a steam-powered printing press. **1811** Schoolgirl Mary Anning discovers the first fossil of an ichthyosaur (a prehistoric fishlike marine reptile). **1811** Scottish anatomist Charles Bell distinguishes between motor and sensory nerves. **1811** English scientist William Wollaston invents the camera lucida. **1811** English engineer John Blenkinsop invents a steam rack locomotive that uses toothed wheels and track. **1813** English engineer Bryan Donkin begins producing canned meat.
THE AMERICAS	**1776** American inventor David Bushnell builds the *Turtle*, one of the first submarines. **1780** American physician Benjamin Rush describes dengue fever.	**1786** Long-fibered sea-island cotton is planted in the United States for the first time. **1793** American engineer Eli Whitney invents the cotton gin, a machine that automates the separation of cottonseed from cotton fibers.	**1799** A 12-year-old boy, Conrad Reed, finds a 17-pound (7.7-kg) gold nugget near his home in North Carolina, beginning the first gold rush in the United States.	**1807** American engineer Robert Fulton builds a successful paddle steamer, *Clermont* (originally named the *North River Steam Boat*). **1809** American surgeon Ephraim McDowell performs the first successful ovariotomy (removal of an ovary) to treat a tumor.	**1812** Russian explorers moving south from Alaska establish the town of Fort Ross in Northern California.
ASIA & OCEANIA	**1779** English explorer James Cook is killed by local people in Hawaii in the course of his exploration of the Pacific Ocean.	**1793** The remains of a mammoth are discovered preserved in the permafrost in Siberia.	**1797** Explorer George Bass leads an expedition along the coast of eastern Australia, recording the geographic and geological features he encounters.	**1805** Japanese physician Seishu Hoanoka performs the first surgery on a patient using general anesthesia.	**1813** European explorers first cross the Blue Mountains in Australia, an area that is home to many unique and ancient species of animals and plants.
AFRICA & THE MIDDLE EAST	**1775** Scottish explorer James Bruce returns to England having become the first European to discover the source of the Blue Nile.	**1794** The explorer Mungo Park embarks on an expedition to discover the source of the Niger River in central Africa.	**ca 1799** West African cultures begin to manufacture gunpowder, as well as repairing and replicating weapons obtained from European merchants and explorers.	**1807** It is estimated that there are about 20 million guns in use in Africa, fueling a number of wars and uprisings.	**1811** Construction begins on a water supply and sewer system in Cape Town, South Africa.

1815	1820	1825	1830	1835–1839
1815 Humphry Davy invents the miner's safety lamp.	**1820** Danish physicist Hans Ørsted discovers electromagnetism.	**1825** English chemist and physicist Michael Faraday discovers benzene.	**1831** Scottish botanist Robert Brown describes the nucleus of a cell.	**1836** English naturalist Charles Darwin completes his five-year voyage on H.M.S. *Beagle*.
1815 English scholar Peter Roget devises a slide rule with two logarithmic scales.	**1821** Swedish botanist Elias Fries draws up a systematic classification of fungi.	**1825** The Stockton & Darlington Railway, the first steam railroad to offer a regular service, opens in northern England.	**1831** Michael Faraday makes a simple dynamo.	**1836** Swedish chemist Jöns Berzelius discovers catalysts.
1815 French physicist Augustin-Jean Fresnel demonstrates that light consists of transverse waves.	**1822** Englishwoman Mary Ann Mantell discovers teeth from one of the first fossils later to be recognized as a dinosaur.	**1826** French chemist Joseph Niépce takes the first photograph.	**1831** English explorer James Ross locates the position of the north magnetic pole.	**1837** French mathematician Simon Poisson discovers the Poisson distribution curve.
1815 Scottish engineer John McAdam devises a method of making paved roads using crushed rock.	**1822** English mathematician Charles Babbage makes his "Difference Engine," a type of mechanical adding machine.	**1827** French mathematician Joseph Fourier suggests that world climate is affected by human activities.	**1832** French chemist Pierre Robiquet discovers codeine.	**1837** French physiologist René Dutrochet describes the role of chlorophyll in photosynthesis.
1816 Scottish engineer Robert Stirling invents a two-cylinder external combustion engine that makes use of the expansion of hot gas.	**1822** Jean-Baptiste Lamarck distinguishes between vertebrates and invertebrates.	**1828** French physiologist Pierre Flourens explains how the semicircular canals in the inner ear control balance.	**1833** English mathematician Charles Babbage begins work on his "Analytical Engine," a mechanical computer, but the work is never finished.	**1838** The paddle steamer *Sirius* becomes the first steamship to cross the Atlantic Ocean under steam power alone.
1819 French physicist Jean-Louis Poiseuille invents a mercury manometer for measuring blood pressure.	**1822** French physicist André-Marie Ampère formulates the laws of electrodynamics.	**1829** French teacher Louis Braille, blind himself from the age of three, invents the Braille alphabet to enable blind people to read using touch.	**1834** Michael Faraday formulates the laws of electrolysis.	**1839** French painter and physicist Louis Daguerre invents the daguerreotype, a type of photograph taken on metal plates.
			1834 English architect Joseph Hansom designs the Hansom cab.	
			1832 English physician Marshall Hall discovers the reflex action of certain nerves.	
1819 The SS *Savannah* becomes the first steamship to cross the Atlantic Ocean. The *Savannah* travels under sail for most of the journey, however, only using steam power for the last days of the voyage.	**1821** American engineer Zachariah Allen installs the first hot-air central heating system.	**1825** Scottish botanist David Douglas discovers the Douglas fir in North America.	**1833** American engineer Obed Hussey invents a reaping machine.	**1835** Swedish-born American engineer John Ericsson invents the screw propeller for ships.
	1822 American engineer William Church patents a typesetting machine in England.	**1825** The Erie Canal, which links the Great Lakes with ports of New York and New Jersey, is opened.	**1833** American army surgeon William Beaumont explains the role of gastric juices in digestion (he had studied a patient with a gunshot wound to the stomach in 1822).	**1835** American manufacturer Samuel Colt produces a revolver with interchangeable parts.
		1828 Work begins on the Baltimore & Ohio Railroad.		**1838** American inventor Samuel Morse invents the electric telegraph.
1815 The explosion of Mount Tambora in Indonesia throws enough volcanic ash and dust into the atmosphere to temporarily modify climates throughout the world.				**1837** A whaling station is established in New Zealand.
1816 Factories and other industrial structures are constructed in Egypt. They include lumber mills, sugar refineries, and glass-making factories.				

ASTRONOMY & MATH

1777 Swiss mathematician Leonhard Euler (1707–83) introduces the symbol i for the square root of -1. In mathematical terms i is an imaginary number.

1779 French astronomer Antoine Darquier (1718–1802) discovers the Ring Nebula (which formed 5,500 years ago).

1779 German astronomer Heinrich Olbers (1758–1840) publishes a method of calculating the orbits of comets.

1781 British astronomer William Herschel (1738–1822) discovers the planet Uranus.

1781 French astronomer Charles Messier (1730–1817) publishes the *Catalogue des Nébuleuses et des Amas d'Étoiles* (Catalog of Nebulae and Star Clusters), which gives details of the location in the night sky of 103 visible astronomical objects.

1783 English physicist John Michell (1724–93) predicts the existence of black holes, which he calls "dark stars."

BIOLOGY & MEDICINE

1775 Danish naturalist Johann Fabricius (1745–1808) draws up a classification system for insects in his epic work *Systema Entomologiae*.

1776 Scottish physician John Fothergill (1712–80) describes trigeminal neuralgia (a disorder that causes nerve pain in the face).

1778 German-born physician Friedrich (or Franz) Mesmer (1734–1815) first practices in Paris a form of hypnotism that becomes known as mesmerism. Later (1785) he is denounced as a charlatan and is unable to demonstrate any scientific basis for his technique.

1779 Dutch-born British scientist Jan Ingenhousz (1730–99) describes the process of photosynthesis in plants.

1780 Italian naturalist Lazzaro Spallanzi (1729–99) carries out artificial insemination (in dogs).

1780 American physician Benjamin Rush (1745–1813) describes dengue fever (then also known as breakbone fever).

PHYSICAL SCIENCES

1775 German geologist Abraham Werner (1749–1817) proposes the Neptunist theory of the origin of rocks—the now rejected idea that all rocks in the Earth's crust were created by the action of water.

1776 English chemist Joseph Priestley (1733–1804) synthesizes nitrous oxide ("laughing gas"), later to be employed as an anesthetic in dentistry.

1776 Swedish chemist Karl Scheele (1742–86) discovers uric acid.

1776 French chemist Antoine Lavoisier (1743–94) makes three contributions to chemistry: the (incorrect) proposal that all acids contain oxygen; the fact that air is a mixture of gases; and the idea that respiration (breathing) can be regarded as a form of combustion.

1778 Italian physicist Alessandro Volta (1745–1827) discovers methane.

1779 Swiss scientist Horace de Saussure (1740–99) coins the term *geology*.

1781 French mineralogist René Haüy (1743–1822) proposes the existence of "unit cells" in crystals, leading to his theory of crystal structure.

1779 English explorer James Cook (1728–79) is killed by local people in Hawaii in the course of his exploration of the Pacific Ocean.

The one-person submarine Turtle *carried enough air to last for 30 minutes and was powered by two hand-driven propellers.*

EUROPE

THE AMERICAS

ASIA & OCEANIA

AFRICA & THE MIDDLE EAST

ENGINEERING & INVENTION

1775 English engineer John Wilkinson (1728–1828) produces a machine for boring cannon—and later cylinders for steam engines.

1777 French physicist Charles Coulomb (1736–1806) invents the torsion balance to measure electrical, magnetic, and gravitational forces.

1778 English inventor Joseph Bramah (1748–1814) patents a flushing toilet.

1779 English weaver Samuel Crompton (1753–1827) builds the spinning mule, which twists strands of fibers into single lengths of yarn and winds them onto bobbins.

1782 Scottish engineer James Watt (1736–1819) invents a steam engine in which steam enters each side of the piston alternately.

1783 Swiss scientist François-Pierre Argand (1750–1803) patents the Argand burner, an oil lamp with an air supply. It burns ten times brighter than an ordinary lamp.

1783 French brothers Joseph (1740–1810) and Jacques (1745–99) Montgolfier invent the hot-air balloon.

The Montgolfier brothers' balloon flew 5.5 miles (8.8 km) on its first crewed flight.

1776 American inventor David Bushnell (ca 1742–1824) builds the *Turtle*, one of the first submarines.

WORLD EVENTS

1772 The first partition of Poland divides Polish territory between Russia, Prussia, and Austria. Further partitions will mean Poland ceases to exist by the end of the century.

1781 Serfdom is abolished in Austria.

1783 Russia annexes the Crimean Peninsula, which gives it access to the Black Sea and thus to the Mediterranean.

1775 The American Revolution begins at Concord and Lexington.

INSIDE STORY

James Cook

The three voyages of exploration conducted by British seaman and navigator James Cook between 1766 and 1779 were important to many branches of science and technology. The first voyage left Britain in 1766 and traveled to Tahiti in order to observe the transit of Venus—an important astronomical event—before mapping New Zealand and eastern Australia. On the second voyage in 1772, Cook's ship was equipped with the *K1*, a copy of John Harrison's revolutionary marine chronometer the *H4*. Accurate clocks allowed precise and reliable calculations of longitude, essential for navigation. The charts Cook drew using the *K1* were so accurate that they were still in use in the early 20th century. On all three of Cook's voyages the ship carried biologists who discovered countless species of previously unknown plants and animals.

JAMES WATT

James Watt was born in Scotland at Greenock on the Clyde River. He was the sixth son of a carpenter and merchant. He was educated at the local school and at Greenock Grammar School, and learned technical skills in his father's workshop. In 1755 Watt went to London and worked as an apprentice to a maker of mathematical instruments. Two years later he was appointed instrument maker at Glasgow University and had his own workshop.

The university had a model of a Newcomen steam engine, and in 1764 Watt was asked to repair it. The engine was heated by steam and then cooled by cold water sprayed into the cylinder to condense the steam. Watt realized that the alternate heating and cooling processes of the cylinder wasted a lot of energy.

In 1765 Watt made an engine that overcame the energy loss by leading the steam into a separate condenser so that the cylinder could remain hot all the time, making the engine three times more efficient. The project was financed by Scottish chemist Joseph Black (1728–99), who taught at the university.

In 1775 Watt went into business manufacturing his new engine, which he had patented in 1769. The first machine needed five years of development before it was reliable enough for quantity production. Most of the engines produced were used as pumps to replace the ageing Newcomen engines in the mines of Cornwall in southwestern England.

EUROPE

ASTRONOMY & MATH

1784 Dutch-born English astronomer John Goodricke (1764–86) observes a new type of pulsating variable star (Delta Cephei), the second of the so-called Cepheid variables. Earlier the same year the first—Eta Aquilae—was found by English amateur astronomer Edward Pigott (ca 1753–1825).

1784 French mathematician Adrien-Marie Legendre (1752–1833) determines Legendre polynomials, mathematical functions that arise as solutions to differential equations that relate to various problems in physics.

1786 French astronomer Pierre Méchain (1744–1804) discovers Encke's comet, which was later named for Johann Encke (1791–1865), who studied it in detail in 1819. It has the shortest-known orbital period of all comets—3.3 years—and has been seen about 60 times since its discovery.

1787 German-born English astronomer William Herschel (1738–1822) observes Oberon and Titania, two moons of the planet Uranus (which he had discovered in 1781). Two years later he discovers Saturn's moons Enceladus and Mimas, and in 1790 he identifies the first planetary nebula.

1788 French mathematician Joseph Lagrange (1736–1813) publishes his book *Mécanique Analytique*, which deals with the calculus of mechanics.

BIOLOGY & MEDICINE

1785 English physician William Withering (1741–99) introduces the use of the drug digitalis, made from the foxglove plant, to treat dropsy (fluid retention due to heart disease). The drug is still used to treat certain heart disorders.

1789 English naturalist Gilbert White (1720–93) publishes *The Natural History and Antiquities of Selborne*, a detailed year-long study of the habits of local animals, which is read by naturalists to this day.

INSIDE STORY

Glacier Tables

Early travelers to the Alps were often puzzled by great slabs of rock balanced on top of stems of ice like huge mushrooms. They persist because the rock casts a shadow that keeps the sun's warmth from melting the ice. Swiss geologist Bernard Kuhn figured out in 1787 that they had been slowly moved to their improbable locations by glaciers, most of which had subsequently melted away. They were known as "glacier tables," but modern geologists refer to them as "erratics." The largest known erratic is the Big Rock, a vast 16,000-ton (14,500-tonne), 30-foot (9-m) tall quartzite boulder located in Alberta, Canada.

PHYSICAL SCIENCES

1784 French chemist Antoine Lavoisier (1743–94) shows that matter can be neither created nor destroyed.

1784 English scientist Henry Cavendish (1731–1810) finds that water is a compound (of hydrogen and oxygen, H_2O) and not an element. A year later he determines the composition of nitric acid (HNO_3).

1784 French mathematician and physicist Gaspard Monge (1746–1818) is the first person to liquefy a substance that is a gas in its normal state—in this case sulfur dioxide.

ca 1787 French physicist Jacques Charles (1746–1823) postulates Charles's law: that, at constant pressure, the volume of a gas is proportional to its absolute temperature.

1788 English physicist Charles Blagden (1748–1820) puts forward Blagden's law: that, for a solution, the lowering of the freezing point of the solvent is proportional to the concentration of the substance dissolved in it.

1789 German chemist Martin Klaproth (1743–1817) discovers uranium and zirconium.

1791 English chemist and clergyman William Gregor (1761–1817) discovers titanium.

THE AMERICAS

1786 Long-fibered sea-island cotton is planted in the United States for the first time. In the next 50 years "King Cotton" becomes the most important crop in the American economy.

ASIA & OCEANIA

AFRICA & THE MIDDLE EAST

The flowers of the foxglove plant. Drugs derived from foxgloves are known as digitalins; they are used to treat arrhythmia and other heart problems.

As we enjoy great advantages from the inventions of others, we should be glad of an opportunity to serve others by any invention of ours; and this we should do freely and generously.

BENJAMIN FRANKLIN,
THE AUTOBIOGRAPHY OF BENJAMIN FRANKLIN (1791)

ENGINEERING & INVENTION	WORLD EVENTS

1784 Scottish engineer William Murdock (1754–1839) constructs a model steam-powered road vehicle.

1785 English inventor Edmund Cartwright (1743–1823) makes a steam-powered loom.

1785 English inventor Lionel Lukin (1742–1834) patents a noncapsizing lifeboat.

1785 French balloonist Jean-Pierre Blanchard (1753–1809) invents the parachute.

1786 Scottish millwright and inventor Andrew Meikle (1719–1811) makes a threshing machine (patented 1788).

1787 English engineer John Wilkinson (1728–1808) builds an iron-hulled boat.

1788 Scottish banker Patrick Miller (1731–1815) and Scottish engineer William Symington (1763–1831) build a steam paddleboat.

1789 French physician Joseph Guillotin (1738–1814) invents the guillotine. It is not used for executions until 1792, during the French Revolution.

1784 English minister John Wesley (1703–91) founds the Methodist Church in England.

1785 The first edition of the *Times* newspaper is printed in London.

1787 A group of ministers, politicians, and industrialists found the *Society for the Abolition of the Slave Trade* in London, one of the first organized abolitionist groups.

1789 Large crowds storm the Bastille prison in Paris, marking the beginning of the French Revolution.

1790 The population of Europe reaches an estimated 190 million people. Many of them live in the new cities and towns of the industrial revolution.

1784 American scientist and politician Benjamin Franklin (1706–90) invents bifocal eyeglasses.

1786 Revolutionary War veteran Daniel Shays (ca 1741–1825) leads an armed uprising against high taxes in Massachusetts, known as Shay's Rebellion.

1787 The United States Constitution is adopted by the Constitutional Convention.

A modern replica of a guillotine, the execution machine invented by Joseph Guillotin in 1789.

1786 The pirate states of North Africa sign treaties with the United States, agreeing to cease disruption of U.S. merchant shipping in exchange for large sums of money.

1787 A group of freed slaves from the United States settle in Freetown, Sierra Leone.

TEXTILE MACHINES

The development of the textile industry was at the forefront of the industrial revolution. During this period, many new technologies were developed to turn raw materials such as wool into yarn and then fabric.

The first aid to spinning was the distaff—a long stick onto which wool is loosely wound. The spinner held it under his or her arm and teased out a continuous strand of wool, which was spun between the fingers of the other hand. The spun thread wound itself around a rotating spindle at its end. Mesopotamians first used the distaff 7,500 years ago.

The spinning wheel was in use in Europe from the 1200s. It simplified the task by using a large vertical wheel. A belt drive spun the spindle, while the spinner pulled a strand of wool from a vertical distaff. With the other hand he or she turned the wheel.

In the 18th century, spinning became mechanized and mass production was possible. English mechanic James Hargreaves (ca 1720–78) invented the spinning jenny in 1764, and the spinning frame was invented by his compatriot Richard Arkwright (1732–92) in 1769. The spinning jenny allowed one operator to produce eight strands of yarn simultaneously. The spinning frame—powered by a waterwheel—made strong cotton yarn. The two were combined by English weaver Samuel Crompton (1753–1827), whose spinning mule produced 48 strands of fine yarn at the same time.

Once spun, yarn was made into cloth on a loom. A simple loom is a frame that holds a set of parallel threads called the warp. The weaver interweaves them at right angles with another thread—the weft—that is carried in a holder known as a shuttle. In 1733 English engineer John Kay (1704–ca 1780) invented the flying shuttle, a mechanism that enables the weaver to "throw" the shuttle rapidly from side to side. Mechanized looms came next, driven by water power until 1785, when English inventor Edmund Cartwright (1743–1823) made the first steam-powered loom.

ASTRONOMY & MATH	BIOLOGY & MEDICINE	PHYSICAL SCIENCES

EUROPE

1795 French astronomer Joseph de Lalande (1732–1807) records observations of Neptune, but he does not recognize it as a new planet.

1795 France adopts the metric system.

1796 French astronomer Pierre-Simon de Laplace (1749–1827) proposes his nebular hypothesis for the origin of the solar system. It states that the sun condensed out of a whirling mass of gas that threw off rings that in turn condensed into the planets. Modern theories retain some of these ideas.

1796 German physicist Karl Gauss (1777–1855) proposes the method of least squares for fitting a line or curve to a set of points on a graph. He does not publish it until 1806, when it is independently suggested by French mathematician Adrien-Marie Legendre (1752–1833).

1798 Danish mathematician Caspar Wessel (1745–1818) represents complex numbers as vectors (quantities with magnitude and direction).

1794 English chemist John Dalton (1766–1844) describes color blindness, a condition from which he and his brother both suffer.

1796 English physician Edward Jenner (1749– 1823) introduces smallpox vaccination into Europe.

1796 German physician Samuel Hahnemann (1755–1843) founds homeopathy, a form of unconventional therapeutic medicine. It involves giving a patient minute doses of a drug that produces similar symptoms in a healthy person. It is still practiced today.

1796 German physician Franz Gall (1758–1828) introduces the "science" of phrenology, in which mental ability is purported to be related to the shape of the head.

1798 English economist Thomas Malthus (1766–1834) discovers a correlation between population size and the available food supply—the former always increases faster than the latter.

1794 Finnish chemist Johan Gadolin (1760–1852) discovers yttrium.

1794 French chemist Joseph Proust (1754–1826) publishes Proust's law, also known as the law of definite proportions. It states that in any chemical compound the proportions of the components are always the same no matter how it is made.

1797 German chemist Martin Klaproth (1743–1817) and French chemist Nicolas Vauquelin (1763–1829) independently discover chromium. In 1798 Klaproth and Scottish chemist Thomas Hope (1766–1844) independently discover strontium.

1798 French chemist Nicolas Vauquelin (1763–1829) discovers the element beryllium, the lightest metal known.

1793 French naturalist Jean-Baptiste Lamarck (1744–1829) reintroduces the theory that fossils are the remains of extinct plants and animals.

INSIDE STORY

The Metric System

The idea of a system of weights and measures was first proposed by English scientist John Wilkins (1614–72). It was after the French Revolution in 1783 that the system was first worked out and promoted, becoming the official system of France and its colonies. Other countries adopted it, and by the end of the 19th century most of the world's nations were using the system. In 1960 it was adapted to become the *Systèm Internationale d'Unités* (International System of Units), usually abbreviated to SI, the system used in science, engineering, and commerce worldwide. Today only three countries in the world do not use SI units officially: Myanmar, Liberia, and the United States.

THE AMERICAS

ASIA & OCEANIA

Edward Jenner is depicted here vaccinating women and children against smallpox.

1793 The remains of a mammoth are discovered preserved in the permafrost in Siberia.

1797 Explorer George Bass (1771–ca 1803) leads an expedition along the coast of eastern Australia, recording the geographic and geological features he encounters.

AFRICA & THE MIDDLE EAST

The perpetual tendency of the race of man to increase beyond the means of subsistence is one of the general laws of animated nature, which we can have no reason to expect to change.

THOMAS MALTHUS, *AN ESSAY ON THE PRINCIPLE OF POPULATION* (1798)

ca 1799 West African cultures begin to manufacture gunpowder, as well as repair and replicate weapons obtained from European merchants and explorers.

ENGINEERING & INVENTION	WORLD EVENTS

1792 Scottish engineer William Murdock (1754–1839) introduces domestic lighting using coal gas.

1795 French chemist Nicolas Conté (1755–1805) invents a pencil with a graphite "lead." Pencils of this type have remained in use ever since.

1795 English inventor Joseph Bramah (1748–1814) invents a hydraulic press.

1796 German printer Aloys Senefelder (1771–1834) develops lithographic printing using sheets of flat stone as printing "plates."

1797 French aeronaut André Garnerin (1769–1823) produces an improved parachute and demonstrates it by jumping from a balloon.

1797 French physicist Jean Fortin (1750–1831) invents a portable mercury barometer.

1799 Scottish chemists Charles Tennant (1768–1838) and Charles Macintosh (1766–1843) develop a process for the large-scale manufacture of bleaching powder.

1799 French chemist Philippe Lebon (1767–1804) patents a light that burns gas made by heating sawdust at a very high temperature.

1792 France officially becomes a Republic.

1792 English radical and feminist Mary Wollstonecraft (1759–97) publishes the *Vindication of the Rights of Woman*.

1793 The execution of King Louis XVI (r. 1774–93) takes place in Paris.

1793 One of the leaders of the French Revolution, Maximillien Robespierre (1758–94), begins a series of public executions and persecutions known as the "Reign of Terror" in order to suppress counter-revolutionary plots.

1798 Economist Thomas Malthus (1766–1834) publishes *An Essay on the Principle of Population*, which argues that poverty is caused by the world's population growing at a consistently faster rate than the supply of food and natural resources.

1793 American engineer Eli Whitney (1765–1825) invents the cotton gin, a machine that automates the separation of cottonseed from cotton fibers.

1793 French balloonist Jean-Pierre Blanchard (1753–1809) makes the first untethered hot-air balloon flight to take place in the United States.

A cotton gin processing raw cotton

1792 The Coinage Act establishes the United States Mint and the dollar as the only legal currency in the United States.

1799 A 12-year-old boy, Conrad Reed, finds a 17-pound (7.7-kg) gold nugget near his home in North Carolina, beginning the first gold rush in the United States.

1798 Ranjit Singh (r. 1792–1839), ruler of the Punjab, founds the Sikh kingdom between regions that are predominantly Muslim on one side and Hindu on the other.

1798 Followers of the strict Wahhabi interpretation of Islam seize control of the city of Riyadh.

1799 The Rosetta Stone is found. Its inscription is written in three languages, allowing historians to translate ancient Egyptian hieroglyphs for the first time.

FARM MACHINERY

The earliest known agricultural inventions are the plow—used to prepare the earth for sowing seeds—and the sickle—used to cut down mature plants at harvest time. Although Middle Eastern farmers were using plows with forged iron plowshares as far back as 1900 B.C.E., it was not until the end of the 18th century that similar inventions began to change farming in Europe and the Americas.

In 1785 the English engineer Robert Ransome (1753–1830) invented a cast-iron plowshare. It was first mass produced in 1839 by the U.S. industrialist John Deere (1804–86). Like the wooden plowshare it replaced, it was pulled by oxen or horses, but it was able cut through the soil deeper and faster. Plowing was speeded up by the invention of the steam plow, which used a stationary traction engine to winch a plow from one side of a field to the other. Steam tractors were later used to pull standard plows; they were replaced in turn by gasoline-powered tractors.

In addition to plowing, other labor-intensive or time-consuming processes to be mechanized included sowing seeds, harvesting crops, and threshing the harvest to separate the grain. Sowing was revolutionized by the invention of the mechanical seed drill by Jethro Tull (1674–1741). This machine allowed farmers to sow seeds in parallel rows quickly, which also made harvesting easier. Threshing was a labor-intensive operation until Scottish millwright Andrew Meikle (1719–1811) invented the horse-driven threshing machine in 1786.

Reaping the harvest was the last part of the agricultural process to be mechanized. The first horse-drawn reaper was made in 1831 by U.S. inventor Cyrus McCormick (1809–11) and began mass production around 1879. Subsequent advances in farming technology involved the creation of combine harvesters that could reap and thresh grain as they worked. Early examples were extremely heavy and required dozens of horses to pull.

EUROPE

ASTRONOMY & MATH

1800 Italian astronomer Giuseppe Piazzi (1746–1826) locates Ceres, the first asteroid (minor planet) to be discovered.

1802 German astronomer Heinrich Olbers (1758–1840) discovers Pallas, the second asteroid to be recorded. Juno, the third asteroid, was located in 1804 by his compatriot Karl Harding (1765–1834). To date, more than 25,000 asteroids have been identified.

1802 English scientist William Wollaston (1766–1828) observes dark lines in the sun's spectrum. The discovery went unnoticed until reported again in 1814 by German astronomer Joseph von Fraunhofer (1787–1826). Since then they have been known as Fraunhofer lines.

1806 Swiss mathematician Jean-Robert Argand (1768–1822) devises the Argand diagram for representing a complex number, $z = x + y$, as points on a coordinate plane. The horizontal (x) axis represents the real part of the number, and the vertical (y) axis denotes the imaginary part.

BIOLOGY & MEDICINE

1800 The Royal College of Surgeons is established in London.

1801 English scientist Thomas Young (1773–1829) explains the eye disorder astigmatism.

1802 French naturalist Jean-Baptiste Lamarck (1744–1829) introduces the word "biology" for the study of living things and life processes.

1803 German physician John Otto (1774–1844) describes the inherited blood disorder hemophilia.

1805 French naturalist Georges Cuvier (1769–1832) founds the science of comparative anatomy.

1806 French chemists Nicolas Vauquelin (1763–1829) and Pierre Robiquet (1780–1840) identify the first amino acid: asparagine (in asparagus).

PHYSICAL SCIENCES

1800 English astronomer William Herschel (1738–1822) discovers infrared radiation.

1800 English chemists William Nicholson (1753–1815) and Anthony Carlisle (1768–1840) perform electrolysis for the first time.

1801 German physicist Johann Ritter (1776–1810) discovers ultraviolet light.

1801 French chemist Charles Désormes (1777–1862) establishes the formula for carbon dioxide (CO_2). It had been discovered by Scottish chemist Joseph Black (1728–99) in 1754, but its composition was unknown.

1803 English chemist William Henry (1774–1836) formulates Henry's law: at a constant temperature the amount of gas absorbed by a liquid is in proportion to the pressure of the gas.

1802 English scientist Edward Howard (1774–1816) postulates that meteorites originate outside the Earth (previously they were thought to be terrestrial phenomena).

1804 Two French scientists, Jean-Baptiste Biot (1774–1862) and Joseph Gay-Lussac (1778–1850), study the Earth's atmosphere by ascending in a balloon.

1805 English naval officer Francis Beaufort (1774–1857) devises the Beaufort wind scale for classifying winds in terms of their speed and effects on objects.

THE AMERICAS

INSIDE STORY

Dalton's Elements

English chemist John Dalton (1766–1844) put forward his atomic theory in 1803. He stated that chemical elements are made up of indivisible atoms that combine to form compounds. He also devised a set of symbols to represent the known elements. But his "elements" included several substances that are, in fact, compounds, such as magnesia and lime. We now know them as magnesium oxide and calcium oxide, but it was many years before other chemists separated these metals from their compounds.

A modern reconstruction of the earliest experiments with electrolysis. In the 19th century electrolysis was used to isolate large numbers of new metallic elements.

ASIA & OCEANIA

1805 Japanese physician Seishu Hoanoka performs the first surgery on a patient using general anesthesia. Due to the isolationist policies of the Japanese government at the time his achievements were not known to the Western World until 1854.

AFRICA & THE MIDDLE EAST

ELEMENTS

	wt.		wt.
⊙ Hydrogen.	1	⊕ Strontian	46
◑ Azote	5	⊛ Barytes	68
● Carbon	54	Ⓘ Iron	50
○ Oxygen	7	Ⓩ Zinc	56
☢ Phosphorus	9	Ⓒ Copper	56
⊕ Sulphur	13	Ⓛ Lead	90
◔ Magnesia	20	Ⓢ Silver	190
⊖ Lime	24	Ⓓ Gold	190
⦷ Soda	28	Ⓟ Platina	190
⦿ Potash	42	⊛ Mercury	167

John Dalton's table of elements from 1803

ENGINEERING & INVENTION

1800 English scientist and politician Charles Stanhope (1753–1816) invents an iron printing press.

1800 Italian physicist Alessandro Volta (1745–1827) invents the voltaic pile battery for producing a continuous electric current.

1801 English engineer Richard Trevithick (1771–1833) constructs a steam-powered road "locomotive." In 1803 he builds the first successful steam railroad locomotive.

1802 Scottish engineer William Symington (1763–1831) builds one of the most successful early steamboats, *Charlotte Dundas*.

1804 English inventor George Cayley (1773–1857) builds and flies a model glider.

1805 French inventor Joseph Jacquard (1752–1834) constructs a loom that is controlled by a "chain" of punched cards.

1805 Scottish clergyman Alexander Forsyth (1769–1843) develops detonating powder for use in firearms. Two years later he patents the percussion cap for muzzle-loading firearms.

1806 English military engineer William Congreve (1772–1828) constructs solid-fuel rockets.

1801 American chemist Robert Hare (1781–1858) invents an oxyhydrogen blowpipe that can produce flames of extremely high temperature.

1804 American engineer Oliver Evans (1755–1819) constructs an amphibious steam dredger.

After passing through

a narrow strip of woodland,

I came suddenly into an

open and boundless prairie.

I say boundless because

I couldn't see the edge of

the plain in any direction.

WILLIAM CLARK,
EXPEDITION JOURNAL, JUNE 19, 1804

WORLD EVENTS

1800 The Act of Union is passed, combining Great Britain and Ireland into the United Kingdom.

1805 After his defeat of the Russians at the Battle of Austerlitz, Napoleon (r. 1804–14 and 1815) dominates continental Europe.

1805 The Royal Navy led by Lord Horatio Nelson (1758–1805) defeats the French and Spanish fleets at the Battle of Trafalgar, ending Napoleon's hopes of invading Britain.

⊕

Zinc

Copper

Cloth soaked in salt solution

⊖

Alessandro Volta's voltaic pile battery, invented in 1800, consisted of a stack of alternate copper and zinc disks. They were separated by disks of cloth soaked in salt solution.

1803 The Louisiana Purchase doubles the size of the United States.

1804 The Lewis and Clark expedition sets out to explore the interior of the United States.

1803 The first penal colony is established in Van Diemen's Land (now Tasmania).

1803 Ranjit Singh (1780–1839), founder of the Sikh kingdom of the Punjab, declares himself maharaja ("great ruler") at the age of 21.

1805 United States Marines and their Berber allies attack the pirate stronghold of Tripoli, Libya.

CANAL TRANSPORTATION

The main method of moving heavy goods before the coming of the railroads was by canal. By the end of the 18th century timber, coal, and iron ore—all the raw materials needed for the emerging industrial revolution—as well as finished goods were towed on barges along the canals, with horses used as the motive power. The long narrow boats, which were designed specifically for use on canals, could carry a load of 33 tons (30 tonnes), while a wagon could carry just 2.2 tons (2 tonnes).

Chinese engineers built the first canals for transportation more than 2,000 years ago. Extensive canal systems were used for drainage and irrigation in northern India and by the Middle Ages in the Netherlands. Canals for industrial transportation were first used in England in 1757, after the engineer Henry Berry (1720–1812) completed the Sankey Brook Navigation near St. Helens in the north of England.

The first canal of economic importance was the Bridgewater Canal near Manchester, England. It was designed by engineer James Brindley (1716–72) and completed in 1761. The canal followed the contours of the land. A canal that takes a more direct route needs locks for coping with inclines, tunnels for going through hills, and aqueducts for crossing valleys.

In North America the first canal with locks was probably the short waterway at Coteau-du-Lac, Quebec, built in 1779 by English engineer William Twiss (1745–1827) to bypass a stretch of rough water on the St. Lawrence River. In 1825 the Erie Canal was completed to carry grain from the Great Lakes to New York City via the Hudson River. The 362-mile (583-km) canal was 39 feet (12 m) wide and 4 feet (1.2 m) deep, and it needed 83 locks to cross the high ground west of Troy. The enlarged modern canal, now part of the New York State canal system, can carry barges of up to 2,204 tons (2,000 tonnes).

ASTRONOMY & MATH

1807 German astronomer Heinrich Olbers (1758–1840) discovers Vesta, the fourth asteroid to be found.

1808 French mathematical physicist Siméon Poisson (1781–1840) puts forward a theory to account for irregularities in the orbits of the planets.

1810 French mathematician Joseph Gergonne (1771–1859) establishes the first privately owned mathematics journal, *Annales de Mathématiques Pures et Appliquées*.

1811 German-born English astronomer William Herschel (1738–1822) proposes a theory that stars develop from nebulae as clouds of gas condense into star clusters.

1812 French mathematician Pierre-Simon de Laplace (1749–1827) publishes *Théorie Analytique des Probabilités*, an exposition of probability theory, which greatly influences the development of the subject.

BIOLOGY & MEDICINE

1809 French naturalist Jean-Baptiste Lamarck (1744–1829) postulates that acquired characteristics (for example, a weightlifter's muscles) are inherited by offspring—a now discredited theory known as Lamarckism.

1811 Scottish anatomist Charles Bell (1774–1842) distinguishes between motor nerves (which are concerned with movement) and sensory nerves (which are concerned with sensations such as touch).

1813 Swiss botanist Augustin de Candolle (1778–1841) devises a plant classification system and describes it as a "taxonomy."

PHYSICAL SCIENCES

1807 English chemist Humphry Davy (1778–1829) uses electrolysis to prepare the first samples of sodium and potassium. A year later, using the same technique, he isolates barium, calcium, magnesium, boron, and strontium.

1807 Swedish chemist Jöns Berzelius (1779–1848) coins the term *organic* to describe chemicals that are derived from living things. Eleven years later he devises the modern system of chemical symbols for the elements.

1808 Swiss chemist Nicolas de Saussure (1767–1845) determines the composition of ethanol (ethyl alcohol).

1808 French scientist Joseph Gay-Lussac (1778–1850) formulates Gay-Lussac's law: that at the same temperature and pressure combining volumes of gases are in a simple relationship to the volume of the product.

1809 French chemist Nicolas Vauquelin (1763–1829) discovers nicotine in tobacco, which was first taken to France in 1561 by the diplomat Jean Nicot (1530–1600).

1811 Schoolgirl Mary Anning (1799–1847) discovers the first fossil of an ichthyosaur (a prehistoric fishlike marine reptile).

1807 A meteor explodes and falls over Weston, Connecticut. Later American scientist Nathaniel Bowditch (1773–1838) estimates that it originally weighed 6.6 million tons (6 million tonnes).

1809 American surgeon Ephraim McDowell (1771–1830) performs the first successful ovariotomy (removal of an ovary) to treat a tumor.

Lamarck contended that to feed in the trees, giraffes stretched their necks, which made them longer. Parents then passed this acquired trait to their offspring until over many generations very long necks developed. Lamarck's ideas are now discredited.

INSIDE STORY

Lamarckism

The theory of evolution promoted by Jean-Baptiste Lamarck became known as Lamarckism. It suggested that physical and behavioral characteristics acquired during an animal's lifetime could be passed on to its offspring. The giraffe was often used as an example of the hypothetical mechanism of the theory. As giraffes reach up for high leaves, the theory contends, they stretch their necks, which become longer. The longer neck is inherited by the giraffe's offspring, and over several generations giraffes acquire longer and longer necks. Lamarck's theory was not the first to suggest the evolution of species through acquired traits, but it was the most comprehensive. Although now discredited, it remained popular until the explanation of evolution by natural selection was proposed in the book *On the Origin of Species* by the English naturalist Charles Darwin (1809–82)—who studied Lamarck's theories as a young man—gained widespread public and scientific acceptance. Darwin was not willing to discount entirely the possibility that acquired characteristics could be inherited, however, and some research into Lamarck's ideas continued into the 1920s.

EUROPE

THE AMERICAS

ASIA & OCEANIA

AFRICA & THE MIDDLE EAST

ENGINEERING & INVENTION

1807 Two French-born brothers, Henry (1766–1854) and Sealy (1774–1847) Fourdrinier, patent a continuous paper-making machine.

1808 Humphry Davy invents the arc lamp.

1808 English inventor George Cayley (1773–1857) builds a full-sized (unpiloted) glider.

1810 French chef Nicolas Appert (ca 1750–1841) invents food canning (originally for Napoleon's army).

1810 German engineer Friedrich König (1774–1833) invents a steam-powered printing press.

1811 English engineer John Blenkinsop (1783–1831) invents a steam rack locomotive that uses toothed wheels and track.

1812 English scientist William Wollaston (1766–1828) invents the camera lucida, which attaches to a microscope so that the viewer can see at the same time an object and a paper surface on which to draw it.

1813 English engineer Bryan Donkin (1768–1855) begins producing canned meat.

1813 Swiss engineer Johann Bodmer (1786–1864) invents a breech-loading cannon.

1807 American engineer Oliver Evans (1755–1819) invents the conveyor belt.

1807 American engineer Robert Fulton (1765–1815) builds a successful paddle steamer, *Clermont* (originally named the *North River Steam Boat*).

1808 American engineer John Stevens (1749–1838) builds the first steamboat to go to sea, called the *Phoenix*.

WORLD EVENTS

1807 The British Parliament passes the Slave Trade Act, which abolishes the slave trade within the British Empire. This act only covered the trade in slaves however. It was not until the passing of the Slavery Abolition Act in 1833 that slavery itself was abolished.

1807 The system of serfdom, in which farmers were considered part of their landlord's property, is abolished in Prussia.

1811 Britain's King George III (r. 1760–1820) is declared insane; his son the Prince of Wales becomes prince regent.

1812 Napoleon Bonaparte (r. 1804–14 and 1815) invades Russia and advances as far as Moscow before being driven back by a lack of supplies and the fierce Russian winter.

1811 Paraguay declares its independence from Spain.

1812 The United States declares war on Britain (the war of 1812), citing as the cause the continued blockading of its ports and attacks on its commerce. U.S. forces also invade Canada.

The fossilized remains of an icthyosaur, a fishlike reptile that lived in the prehistoric oceans.

1811 Construction begins on a water supply and sewer system in Cape Town, South Africa.

HUMPHRY DAVY

Humphry Davy was an English chemist whose pioneering work using electrolysis led to the isolation of seven chemical elements. After basic education in southwestern England, Davy became apprenticed to an apothecary and surgeon. In 1797 he began to teach himself chemistry. A year later Davy became an assistant at the Pneumatic Institute in Bristol. In 1799 he discovered the anaesthetic effect of nitrous oxide. Two years later he became a chemistry lecturer at the Royal Institution in London.

He began experiments in electrolysis, using the new electric battery invented by Alessandro Volta (1745–1827). Davy broke water down into its component elements, and in 1807 extracted the metals sodium and potassium. The following year, Davy isolated barium, boron, calcium, magnesium, and strontium.

In addition to discovering new chemicals, Davy invented the arc lamp in 1808. He also found that the gas methane caused explosions in coal mines. This led him to invent the miner's safety lamp in 1815. It had a flame surrounded by a gauze that conducted the heat away, keeping the temperature from getting high enough to ignite methane.

THE BEGINNING OF RAILROADS

RAILROADS HAD THEIR ORIGINS IN ANCIENT Greece, where a stone trackway for transporting ships was carved across a narrow strip of land separating two seas. Later, in the 16th century, miners in various European countries used horses to pull wagons along "roads" made from beams of timber, and later iron, laid lengthwise along the ground. Using rails provides a smooth, even surface for the wheels to move along, reducing friction. The sleepers evenly distribute the weight on the rails and allow very heavy loads to be carried.

In the coal mines of the English Midlands at the end of the 17th century, horses pulled the empty trucks up the inclines to the mines; then the loaded trucks took themselves down again under the force of gravity. Stronger cast-iron rails became available in the early 1700s, allowing heavier loads to be carried by the trucks.

The first steam locomotive was built in 1803 by English engineer Richard Trevithick (1771–1833). He ran it along 10 miles (16 km) of cast-iron track from the Pen-y-Darren Ironworks to the Glamorganshire Canal in South Wales. The locomotive and rolling stock had smooth, unflanged wheels, and there was a lip on the outer edge of the track. Four years later he built a circular track in Euston, London, and charged people a shilling to chase their tails on his train— called *Catch Me Who Can*.

RIGHT: *Horse-drawn coaches were common on railroads until public confidence in steam locomotives grew.*

KEY DATES

1803
Trevithick's locomotive

1825
Stockton & Darlington Railway

1830
Liverpool & Manchester Railway

1830
Baltimore & Ohio Railroad

1831
South Carolina Railroad

The First Passenger Railroads

The first railroad to carry passengers regularly as well as freight opened in 1825. With locomotives built by English engineer George Stephenson (1781–1848) the Stockton & Darlington Railway ran for 26 miles (42 km); but until 1833 passengers traveled in horse-drawn coaches, and only freight was steam hauled. The first intercity line, the Liverpool & Manchester Railway, opened in 1830, and the first train was hauled by Stephenson's *Rocket*. The line was constructed to carry cotton from the port of Liverpool to the mills in Manchester in northwestern England.

Railroads also sprang up in other countries. The year 1830 saw the inauguration of the Baltimore & Ohio Railroad, which initially ran for 13 miles (21 km) from Baltimore to Ellicott's Mills. To operate it, U.S.

engineer Peter Cooper (1791–1883) built *Tom Thumb*, the first locomotive to be made in the United States. The Philadelphia & Columbia Railroad opened with horse-drawn vehicles in 1831, but within three years it had steam locomotives. The longest railroad in the world at the time, the South Carolina Railroad, also started operations in 1831. It ran for 154 miles (248 km) from Charleston to Hamburg.

In 1832 the first steam-hauled line in France opened between St. Étienne and Lyons; and in 1835 Germany's first railroad opened between Nürnberg and Fürth with a locomotive called *Der Adler* (The Eagle), built by English engineer Robert Stephenson (1803–59). By 1840 there were railroads in Austria, Ireland, and the Netherlands. As the new railroads appeared, the old barges disappeared and canals fell into disrepair.

Railway Technology

As well as locomotives and rolling stock, railroads need other equipment. The "road" of the original railroads were rails made of cast iron, at first with a right-angled section to keep the wheels on the track. Soon these flanged rails were replaced. The flanges were put on the wheels of the vehicles, which ran on short "fish-bellied" rails that were straight on top but curved beneath to make them thicker (and stronger) in the center. But cast-iron rails were brittle and often broke. From 1858 they were replaced by steel rails, introduced by English steelmaker Henry Bessemer (1813–98).

To enter sidings and branch lines, railroads need switches (known as "points" in Europe). They were invented as early as 1789 by English engineer William Jessop (1745–1814) for primitive tramway systems. As the traffic on railroads increased so did the risk of collisions. Signals were invented to direct drivers and warn them of hazards. At first they took the form of disks or arms that rotated or pivoted like semaphore signals. In 1849 the New York and Erie Company introduced block signaling, which does not allow a train to enter a section of track until the previous train has left it. Soon block signals were linked electrically.

To drum up interest in his new railroad, Richard Trevithick built a circular track on an open space in London. People paid a shilling to ride around in circles on the aptly named Catch Me Who Can.

Passengers ride a steam train on the opening day of the Stockton & Darlington Railway.

EUROPE

THE AMERICAS

ASIA & OCEANIA

AFRICA & THE MIDDLE EAST

ASTRONOMY & MATH

1815 German astronomer Heinrich Olbers (1758–1840) discovers Olbers' comet, which has the comparatively short orbit period of 74.1 years.

1815 German astronomer Joseph von Fraunhofer (1787–1826) makes a detailed map of the solar spectrum first seen by English scientist William Wollaston (1766–1828) in 1802.

1815 English scholar Peter Roget (1779–1869) devises a slide rule with two logarithmic scales, which greatly simplifies multiplication and division.

BIOLOGY & MEDICINE

1814 English surgeon Joseph Carpue (1764–1846) pioneers plastic surgery with the operation known as rhinoplasty (to restructure a patient's nose).

1817 French physician René Laennec (1781–1826) uses a stethoscope—a single-tube device of his own design—to listen to a patient's heartbeat.

1817 English surgeon James Parkinson (1755–1824) describes parkinsonism. At the time it is called "paralysis agitans," or Parkinson's disease.

1817 French chemists Pierre Pelletier (1788–1842) and Joseph Caventou (1795–1877) discover chlorophyll (the light-absorbing pigment in plants) and a year later discover the poisonous alkaloid strychnine.

1818 French chemist Jean Dumas (1800–1884) introduces the use of iodine to treat patients with the thyroid disorder goiter (which is often caused by iodine deficiency).

1819 French physicist Jean-Louis Poiseuille (1799–1869) invents a mercury manometer (pressure gauge) to measure blood pressure.

PHYSICAL SCIENCES

1814 Spanish-born physician Matthieu Orfila (1787–1853) publishes his book *Traité des Poisons* (Treatise of General Toxicology) in Paris and founds the science of toxicology.

1815 French physicist Augustin-Jean Fresnel (1788–1827) discovers the diffraction of light as it passes through small apertures. He also demonstrates that light consists of transverse waves.

1815 English geologist William Smith (1769–1839) publishes a geologic map of England and Wales. He observes that different rock layers contain different fossils and postulates that a fossil must be the same age as the rock in which it is found.

1817 Two new elements are found: cadmium by German chemist Friedrich Strohmeyer (1776–1835) and lithium by Swedish chemist Johan Arfwedson (1792–1841). A year later (1818) selenium is discovered by Swedish chemist Jöns Berzelius (1779–1848).

1819 British astronomer and photographer John Herschel (1792–1871) discovers that sodium thiosulfate can "fix" a newly developed photographic image.

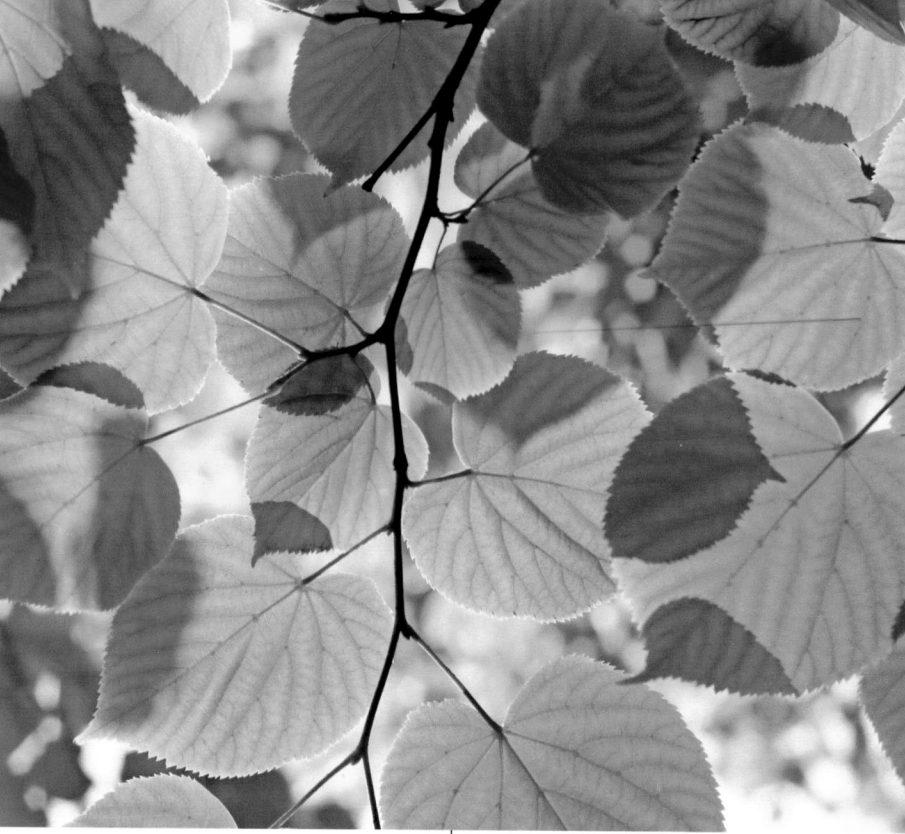

The green leaves of plants get their color from chlorophyll, discovered in 1817.

1815 The explosion of Mount Tambora on the island of Sumbawa in Indonesia throws enough volcanic ash and dust into the atmosphere to temporarily modify climates throughout the world.

ENGINEERING & INVENTION

1815 Scottish engineer John McAdam (1756–1836) devises a method of making paved roads using crushed rock.

1815 French-born engineer Marc Brunel (1769–1849) creates a tunneling shield (for making the first tunnel under the Thames River in London).

1815 English chemist Humphry Davy (1778–1829) and English engineer George Stephenson (1781–1848) independently invent the miner's safety lamp.

1816 Scottish physicist David Brewster (1781–1868) invents the kaleidoscope.

1816 German musician Johann Maelzel (1772–1838) patents the metronome, a clockwork upside-down pendulum that ticks to help students keep time with the music.

1816 Scottish engineer Robert Stirling (1790–1878) invents a two-cylinder external combustion engine that makes use of the expansion of hot gas.

1818 German-born English engineer Rudolph Ackermann (1764–1834) devises a steering mechanism for horse-drawn carriages. Ackermann steering is still the main type used by modern road vehicles.

1819 German inventor Augustus Siebe (1788–1872) develops a pressurized diving suit complete with helmet.

1819 American engineers Stephen McCormick (1784–1875) and Jethro Wood (1774–1834) independently produce a cast-iron plow.

1819 The SS *Savannah* becomes the first steamship to cross the Atlantic. The *Savannah* travels under sail for most of the journey, however, only using steam power for the last days of the voyage.

1819 European and American companies establish industrial-scale whaling around the islands of the Pacific.

1816 Factories and other industrial facilities are constructed in Egypt. They include lumber mills, sugar refineries, and glass-making factories.

WORLD EVENTS

1814 Napoleon Bonaparte (r. 1804–14 and 1815) abdicates and is exiled to the Mediterranean island of Elba. A year later he returns and raises a new army, only to be decisively defeated at the Battle of Waterloo.

1818 Mary Shelley (1797–1851) publishes her novel *Frankenstein*. Written during the cold, dismal summer caused by the eruption of Mount Tambora, the novel explored the ethical issues raised by advances in science and changing social attitudes.

1819 Eleven people are killed when calvary soldiers charge a crowd of protesters in St. Peter's Field, Manchester, England. The event becomes known as the Peterloo Massacre. The protest was calling for greater representation and voting rights for working people.

This miner's safety lamp is based on Humphry Davy's original design but with added improvements.

1814 British troops burn Washington D.C., during the War of 1812 (1812–15), which is ended by the Treaty of Ghent, signed in December 1814. (Although fighting continued into 1815 until news of the treaty reached America.)

1819 The British establish the port of Singapore in Southeast Asia. By allowing unregulated free trade in the port, the Dutch control over trade in the region is broken.

1817 Usman dan Fodio (1754–1817) establishes the Sokoto Caliphate in the Hausa lands of northern Nigeria and southern Niger.

EVIDENCE IN FOSSILS

Fossils are the remains of plants and animals that lived millions of years ago. Most are the hard parts of animals—bones, teeth, or shells—that have changed to rock. Some, such as the outlines of plants in coal or sedimentary rocks, are impressions.

The scientists who study fossils, paleontologists, recognize several ways in which fossils can form. One requirement for fossil formation is quick burial before the carcass can decompose or be eaten by scavengers. The best place for that to happen is in the mud or sediment at the bottom of a lake or sea. Remains embedded in sediment may be dissolved by water, leaving behind a perfect mold. Minerals may be deposited in the mold, forming a cast often made from a totally different type of rock from the sediment. Footprints or animal tracks in mud can be preserved in a similar way. Whole animals are preserved only occasionally, as with insects trapped in amber (fossilized tree resin) or mammoths buried in the frozen ground, called permafrost.

In 1517 the Italian physician and poet Girolamo Fracastoro (1478–1553) was probably the first person to suggest that fossils are animal remains. But it was not until the fossil finds in Europe of the late 18th century that scientists began to realize that fossils can tell us a great deal about the history of living things. In 1793 French naturalist Jean-Baptiste Lamarck (1744–1829) revived the idea that fossils represent ancient organisms.

ASTRONOMY & MATH

1820 English astronomer John Herschel (1792–1871), mathematician Charles Babbage (1791–1871), and others establish the Royal Astronomical Society in London.

1821 French astronomer Alexis Bouvard (1767–1843) observes irregularities in the orbit of Uranus. He hypothesizes that they are caused by a celestial body, later identified as Neptune.

1822 French mathematician Joseph Fourier (1768–1830) proposes the Fourier analysis, a method of analyzing continuous functions in terms of sine and cosine curves.

1824 German astronomer and mathematician Friedrich Bessel (1784–1846) publishes a treatise on the study of planetary perturbations, in which he develops Bessel functions (originally proposed in 1817). Bessel functions form an infinite series useful in solving partial differential equations that occur in astronomy and physics.

BIOLOGY & MEDICINE

1821 Swedish botanist Elias Fries (1794–1878) draws up a systematic classification of fungi. Published as *Systema Mycologicum* (System of Mycology), it takes 11 years to complete.

1821 English naturalist and botanist Joseph Banks (born 1743) dies. During his voyages with the explorer Captain James Cook he was the first to catalog many of the plants and animals of Oceania and South America.

1822 French naturalist Jean-Baptiste Lamarck (1744–1829) distinguishes between vertebrates (animals with backbones) and invertebrates (animals lacking backbones).

1823 English chemist and physician William Prout (1785–1850) identifies free hydrochloric acid in the stomach. Four years later he classifies foods into fats, carbohydrates, and proteins.

1823 The medical journal *The Lancet* is published for the first time in London.

1825 French naturalist Georges Cuvier (1769–1832) puts forward his catastrophe theory of extinction: that sudden worldwide events, such as land upheavals and floods, caused species to become extinct and new ones to appear abruptly to replace them. In keeping with religious doctrines of the time, Cuvier attributed the most recent changes to the great biblical flood.

1825 Scottish botanist David Douglas (1798–1834) discovers the Douglas fir in North America.

PHYSICAL SCIENCES

1820 Danish physicist Hans Ørsted (1777–1851) discovers electromagnetism by noticing the deflection of a compass needle in the magnetic field caused by an electric current flowing along a nearby wire.

1820 French chemists Joseph Caventou (1795–1877) and Pierre Pelletier (1788–1842) discover the alkaloid quinine, soon to be used to treat malaria. Two years later they discover caffeine (in coffee).

1822 Englishwoman Mary Ann Mantell discovers teeth from one of the first fossils later to be recognized as a dinosaur; her husband, paleontologist Gideon Mantell (1790–1852), names it *Iguanodon*.

1822 French physicist André-Marie Ampère (1775–1836) formulates the laws of electrodynamics that deal with electricity and magnetism.

1824 French physicist Dominique Arago (1786–1853) discovers magnetic induction —the production of an electric field by a changing magnetic field.

1824 Swedish chemist Jöns Berzelius (1779–1848) discovers silicon; a year later Danish physicist Hans Ørsted (1777–1851) prepares an impure form of aluminum.

1825 English chemist and physicist Michael Faraday (1791–1867) discovers benzene and several of its compounds.

The existence of the planet Neptune was deduced—before any astronomer had seen it—from the effects of its gravitational pull on the orbit of its neighbor Uranus.

EUROPE

THE AMERICAS

ASIA & OCEANIA

AFRICA & THE MIDDLE EAST

TURNING POINTS

Quinine

The isolation of the chemical compound quinine by French chemists Pierre Pelletier and Joseph Caventou in 1820 was a breakthrough with wide-reaching consequences in medicine and politics. Quinine is a compound found in the bark of the cinchona tree in South America. For centuries it was used by the Quecha peoples of Peru as a muscle relaxant to suppress shivering, and missionaries who saw this use brought the bark back to Europe in the 17th century, believing it would relieve the shivering associated with malarial fevers. It proved highly effective, not only stopping the shivering but also halting the advance of the disease. With the isolation of the active chemical component in 1820 quinine could be produced in large quantities and more easily administered. Tropical regions in which malaria was prevalent and therefore inhabitable to Europeans, who have no natural immunity, were now open for colonization, starting the "scramble for Africa" as European powers fought to take control of sub-Saharan Africa.

ENGINEERING & INVENTION

1821 German physicist Karl Gauss (1777–1855) invents the heliograph, which uses an adjustable mirror to reflect sunlight and send messages over a distance.

1822 English mathematician Charles Babbage (1792–1871) makes his "Difference Engine," a type of mechanical adding machine. In 1833 he devises an improved machine, the "Analytical Engine."

1823 Scottish chemist Charles Macintosh (1766–1843) patents waterproof fabric made by impregnating cloth with rubber.

1824 English mason Joseph Aspdin (1778–1855) patents Portland cement, made from a mixture of limestone and clay or limestone and shale.

1825 English physicist William Sturgeon (1783–1850) makes the first electromagnet.

1825 Scottish engineer Thomas Drummond (1797–1840) creates limelight (also called Drummond light), in which a piece of lime is heated to incandescence in an oil or gas flame.

1825 The Stockton & Darlington Railway, the first steam railroad to offer a regular service, opens in northern England. Its engineers are George Stephenson (1781–1848) and his son Robert (1803–59).

1821 American engineer Zachariah Allen (1795–1882) installs the first hot-air central heating system.

1822 American engineer William Church (ca 1778–1863) patents a typesetting machine in England.

1825 The Erie Canal, which links the Great Lakes with ports of New York and New Jersey, as well as the open sea, is formally opened to commercial traffic.

WORLD EVENTS

1821 Greece begins a war to win independence from the Ottoman Empire.

1823 French troops invade Spain to support King Ferdinand VII (r. 1808 and 1813–33) in quelling a rebellion in his country.

1824 Louis XVIII (r. 1814–24), who became king of France on the restoration of the monarchy following the death of Napoleon (r. 1804–14 and 1815), dies. He is succeeded by his brother, Charles X (r. 1824–30). The monarchy continues to rule in France until the beginning of the Second Republic in 1848.

1825 The "Decemberists"—progressive army officers seeking to reform autocratic rules in Russia—stage an unsuccessful uprising.

Charles Babbage's Difference Engine was designed to calculate logarithms and other mathematical functions using a system of cogs and gear wheels.

THE STOCKTON & DARLINGTON RAILWAY

Opened on September 27, 1825, the line between Stockton and Darlington in County Durham, in the northeast of England, was the world's first steam railroad. Thousands of people attended the opening ceremony out of curiosity, most believing that this form of transport would be a passing fad. However, the Stockton & Darlington Railway inspired the construction of railroads all over the world.

The track was the idea of the English businessman Edward Pease (1767–1858) who wanted to build an 8-mile (13-km) line to transport coal from Darlington to the port of Stockton. Pease planned to use horses to pull trucks along a fixed railway. But English engineer George Stephenson took an interest and convinced Pease that he would be better served by a steam engine, which could pull 50 times as much weight as a horse. Steam locomotives had been built before, but the Stockton & Darlington Railway was the first major commercial use.

More than 40,000 spectators lined the route on the day the Stockton & Darlington Railway opened. The train, pulled by a steam engine built by George Stephenson's son Robert in nearby Newcastle, left Darlington at 12.20 p.m. The engine pulled about 38 open wagons weighing a total of 90 tons (90 tonnes) and carrying about 600 passengers. The train reached a speed of 15 miles (24 km) per hour. All did not run smoothly, however. The train broke down three times on its journey, arriving in Stockton at 3.45 p.m.

Although the inaugural Stockton and Darlington train was full of people, the line was not primarily intended as a passenger railroad. Its main function was to bring coal from the pits to the port, where it was was loaded onto barges. Records show that 19,448 tons of coal were carried in 1828.

THE BIRTH OF PHOTOGRAPHY

THE CAMERA AS IT IS KNOWN TODAY IS made from two essential components. The first is the lens or aperture through which the light is focused. The second is a way of capturing the image viewed through this aperture, either with light sensitive chemicals or, as in many modern cameras, with digital image sensors.

The origin of the camera was the camera obscura (Latin for "dark room"), a windowless room with a small hole in one wall. Light entering the hole forms an upside-down image of the scene outside on the opposite wall. Artists used the device as an aid to trace an image, and later it became portable in the form of a large light-excluding box.

In 1725 the German physician Johann Schulze (1684–1744) found that certain silver salts turn dark when exposed to daylight. Fifty years later Swedish chemist Karl Scheele (1742–86) discovered that the darkening effect is due to the presence of grains of metallic silver. As a result, silver salts were to become standard ingredients in photographic emulsions (light-sensitive coatings) for films, paper, and even leather—as tried in the late 1790s by Englishman Thomas Wedgwood (1771–1805). However, a number of other processes were tested before Scheele's method was generally accepted.

The First Successful Photographs

In France, beginning in 1816, Joseph Niépce (1765–1833) also experimented with fleeting silver images. His first successful photograph in 1826 used a polished pewter plate coated with bitumen as the light-sensitive substance. During a long exposure the bitumen turned white. Niépce then removed the bitu-

In 1843 William Fox Talbot set up a professional photogaphic "factory" in Reading, England. The greenhouse shown here was a portrait studio, although there was often much more light available outside.

men from the unexposed areas using a solvent and darkened the metal by exposing it to iodine vapor.

Iodine also figured in the photographic process perfected by Frenchman Louis Daguerre (1787–1851) in 1839. To make his photographic plates, he coated a sheet of copper with silver and left it for a while (in the dark) exposed to iodine vapor; this process created light-sensitive silver iodide. He exposed the plate in a camera and "developed" it in mercury vapor. The resulting image was made permanent, or "fixed," in a solution of common salt. These daguerreotypes, as they came to be called, were mirror images and could not be used to make further copies.

Film and Multiple Prints

Although the discoveries of Daguerre and Niépce allowed images to be taken relatively quickly, the resulting images were as unique and hard to copy as paintings. In 1841 this changed when English chemist William Fox Talbot (1800–77) patented his calotype process, which he had devised six years earlier. It used paper film impregnated with silver nitrate and common salt or potassium iodide. After exposure to light in a camera, the film was developed in a solution of gallic acid and fixed in sodium thiosulfate solution, known as "hypo." The resulting "negative" image (with black and white reversed) was placed in contact with a sheet of light-sensitive paper and changed back to positive. This stage could be repeated to make many positive paper copies of the image.

Frenchman Louis-Désiré Blanquart-Evrard (1802–72) made improvements in 1850 by coating the printing paper with albumen (egg white), which allowed better quality and cheaper prints to be made. Fox Talbot accused him of "scientific piracy" and of stealing his patent.

As soon as the calotypes pioneered by Fox Talbot became popular, Englishman Frederick Archer (1813–57) hit on the idea of making a photosensitive emulsion of silver salts in collodion (a sticky solution of guncotton in ether) and coating it onto glass plates. His wet-collodion process of 1851 soon became paramount until it was superseded by the use of dry plates

by the late 1870s. The dry-plate process used gelatin emulsions, as invented by British physician Richard Maddox (1816–1902) in 1871. American George Eastman (1854–1932) used a dry gelatin emulsion for his first Kodak camera of 1888, initially on paper film and a year later on transparent celluloid. This film was sold in rolls, which greatly simplified the process of photography and turned it into a popular pastime.

The long exposure times of 19th-century photography meant that photographs were generally restricted to posed portraits taken in well-lit studios.

In a portable camera obscura a lens focuses light from a distant scene onto a mirror. The mirror, angled at 45 degrees, reflects the image upward onto a ground-glass screen. An artist can then trace over the image with perfect accuracy. This method is thought to have been used by Italian artist Canaletto (1697–1768) when he made his detailed views of cities. The camera obscura continued as an artist's aid until it was replaced by photographic cameras after the 1850s.

Lens

Ground-glass screen

Mirror

ASTRONOMY & MATH	BIOLOGY & MEDICINE	PHYSICAL SCIENCES

EUROPE

1826 German astronomer Heinrich Olbers (1758–1840) puts forward Olbers' paradox: Why is the sky dark at night (when the universe is full of stars)? One answer is that light from the most distant objects in the universe has not yet reached Earth.

1827 German physicist Karl Gauss (1777–1855) develops differential geometry.

1830 English mathematician George Peacock (1791–1858) first puts forward the laws of numbers in his book *Treatise on Algebra*.

1830 Scottish writer Mary Somerville (1780–1872) publishes *The Mechanism of the Heavens*, a popularization of *La Mécanique Céleste* by French astronomer Pierre-Simon de Laplace (1749–1827).

1827 Scottish botanist Robert Brown (1773–1858) distinguishes between angiosperms—flowering plants with enclosed seeds—and gymnosperms, which have naked seeds, often in cones.

1828 French physiologist Pierre Flourens (1794–1867) explains how the semicircular canals in the inner ear control the sense of balance.

1829 German anatomist Martin Rathke (1793–1860) finds evidence of gill structures in the embryos of birds and mammals.

1826 French physiologist René Dutrochet (1776–1847) describes the phenomenon of osmosis, in which a solvent passes through a semipermeable membrane separating solutions of different concentrations.

1827 German physicist Georg Ohm (1789–1854) publishes Ohm's law, which states that the voltage across a conductor divided by the current flowing through it is a constant, called the resistance.

1827 Scottish botanist Robert Brown (1773–1858) discovers Brownian motion, the random motion of microscopic particles suspended in a liquid.

1827 French mathematician Joseph Fourier (1768–1830) suggests that world climate is affected by human activities.

1828 German chemist Friedrich Wöhler (1800–82) synthesizes an organic compound from an inorganic compound. This proves that organic compounds are not limited to living things and causes a major rethink among chemists.

1830 Scottish geologist Charles Lyell (1797–1875) begins publication of his most influential book, *The Principles of Geology*.

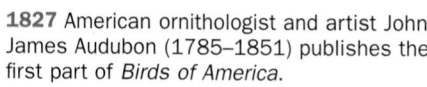

Why isn't a starry night full of light?

THE AMERICAS

1827 American ornithologist and artist John James Audubon (1785–1851) publishes the first part of *Birds of America*.

ASIA & OCEANIA

An engraving of Robert Stephenson's locomotive, Rocket. *Stephenson soon modified his design, decreasing the angle of the cylinders to improve the locomotive's stability.*

AFRICA & THE MIDDLE EAST

INSIDE STORY

The Principles of Geology

Between 1830 and 1833 English geologist Charles Lyell published the three volumes of his influential book *The Principles of Geology*, an explanation of Lyell's theories, backed up with his own observations. In this work, Lyell outlined his controversial theory of uniformity. This essentially argued that the world was formed by the same geological processes that can be observed in action today. The consequence of this new theory was that it placed estimates of the Earth's age in hundreds of millions of years, rather than the thousands suggested by biblical chronologies. Naturalist Charles Darwin (1809–82) was given a copy to help him with geological observations in his voyage on the H.M.S. *Beagle*. He was very impressed by Lyell's ideas, and considered them an important influence on his theory of natural selection.

ENGINEERING & INVENTION

1826 French chemist Joseph Niépce (1765–1833) takes the first photograph on a metal plate.

1827 Two French engineers, Claude Burdin (1790–1873) and Benoît Fourneyron (1802–67), begin work on a design for a practical outward-flow water turbine. It is completed in 1833.

1827 English chemist John Walker (ca 1781–1859) invents the friction match.

1828 Scottish engineer James Neilson (1792–1865) invents the hot-air process for smelting iron.

1829 The *Rocket* steam locomotive built by English engineer George Stephenson (1781–1848) wins the Rainhill Trials, a competition to find a locomotive for the new Liverpool & Manchester Railway.

1829 French teacher Louis Braille (1809–52), blind himself from the age of three, invents the Braille alphabet to enable blind people to read using touch.

1830 French engineer Barthélemy Thimonnier (1793–1857) patents a single-thread stitching machine.

1830 Scottish chemist Andrew Ure (1778–1857) invents the bimetallic strip thermostat.

1828 Work begins on the Baltimore & Ohio Railroad, the first steam-powered railroad in the United States.

1829 American William Burt (1792–1858) patents the first typewriter.

1830 American engineer Peter Cooper (1791–1883) builds *Tom Thumb*, the first railroad locomotive to be made in the United States.

Braille has been a most precious aid to me in many ways. I use Braille as a spider uses its web—to catch thoughts that flit across my mind for speeches, messages, and manuscripts.

HELEN KELLER, 1929

WORLD EVENTS

1829 Greece gains independence from Turkey.

1829 Sir Robert Peel (1788–1850) forms Britain's first official police force.

1830 Revolutions calling for political reform break out in France, Italy, Poland, and Germany.

1830 Belgium breaks away from the Netherlands and proclaims independence.

1828 Uruguay becomes an independent country.

1830 The first wagon trains cross the Rocky Mountains and arrive in California.

1830 The U.S. Congress passes the Indian Removal Act, enabling President Andrew Jackson (1767–1845) to relocate Native Americans from the eastern to the western part of the continent.

1828 Russia declares war on the Ottoman Empire, which is already fighting the revolutionary armies in Greece.

1828 The Dutch claim possession of the western half of New Guinea.

1828 The Zulu leader Shaka (ca 1787–1828), who is showing growing signs of insanity, is assassinated. During his reign Shaka's military leadership greatly expanded the power and influence of the Zulu nation.

MICHAEL FARADAY

Michael Faraday (1791–1867) was a highly influential chemist and physicist whose research into electricity and magnetism were important in the transformation of electricity from a scientific curiosity to a practical technological advance. His experiments founded the sciences of electrochemistry and electromagnetism. Faraday had little formal education and, unlike many of the scientists of his time, had only a limited understanding of higher mathematics. Faraday's success and importance lies in his skill as an empirical experimenter rather than in abstract theorizing.

Michael Faraday, the son of a blacksmith, was born in Newington Butts outside London. He left school at 13 to be apprenticed to a bookbinder. The books he read during this time aroused an interest in science, and in 1813 he left to work as assistant to English chemist Humphry Davy (1778–1829), where part of his job was to set up experiments for Davy's lectures. As Davy's assistant he met many famous scientists, and in 1827 he took over Davy's post of lecturer at the Royal Institution.

Faraday made a number of contributions to the field of chemistry before turning his attention to electricity. He liquified chlorine by heating it in a sealed tube and discovered the flammable hydrocarbon benzene (C_6H_6). His pioneering work with electrolysis established the fundamental laws and principles of the technique. It is his work with electricity and magnetism, however, that has had the greatest influence on everyday life. Faraday made the first primitive electric motor in 1821. He suspended a length of stiff wire alongside a bar magnet that projected vertically from a dish of mercury. When he connected a battery between the mercury and the top of the wire, the lower end of the wire rotated around the magnet. He discovered in 1831 that a moving magnet could induce a current in a coil of wire, a discovery that led to the development of electrical generators.

ASTRONOMY & MATH	BIOLOGY & MEDICINE	PHYSICAL SCIENCES

EUROPE

A screw propeller on a modern merchant ship. The first successful propeller was invented by Swedish–American engineer John Ericsson for use on the U.S.S. Princeton.

1831 French surgeon Guillaume Dupuytren (1777–1835) describes Dupuytren's contracture, an arthritic condition that affects a patient's fingers.

1831 Scottish botanist Robert Brown (1773–1858) describes the nucleus of a cell (in this case a plant cell).

1832 English physician Marshall Hall (1790–1857) discovers the reflex action of certain nerves (such as those involved in the knee-jerk reflex).

1833 Czech physiologist Jan Purkinje (1787–1869) discovers sweat glands in the skin.

1834 French agricultural chemist Jean Boussingault (1802–87) discovers nitrogen fixation—the ability of some plants (such as beans and other legumes) to convert nitrogen from the air into chemicals that the plant can absorb.

1831 English explorer and naval officer James Ross (1800–62) locates the position of the north magnetic pole (which changes continuously).

1832 French chemist Pierre Robiquet (1780–1840) discovers codeine (in opium from poppies).

1833 French chemist Jean Dumas (1800–84) develops a method of determining the nitrogen content in organic compounds. The method is still used today.

1833 French chemist Anselme Payen (1795–1871) discovers diastase, the first enzyme to be identified.

1834 German chemist Justus von Liebig (1803–73) synthesizes melamine, the basis of a range of modern plastics.

1834 English scientist Michael Faraday (1791–1867) formulates the laws of electrolysis.

1835 English geologist Adam Sedgwick (1785–1873) establishes the geology of the Cambrian system of rocks (which were laid down between 540 million and 505 million years ago).

1835 Scottish geologist Roderick Murchison (1792–1871) establishes the geology of the Silurian system of rocks (which were laid down between 439 million and 409 million years ago).

THE AMERICAS

INSIDE STORY

Ada Lovelace

Ada Lovelace (1815–52) was a British mathematician, regarded by many as the first computer programmer. She was born Augusta Byron, the only legitimate child of the aristocratic English poet Lord Byron. Her childhood was dominated by illness, and as a teenager she was left partially paralyzed by a bout of measles. She continued with her education, however, and as a young woman corresponded with many prominent scientists and mathematicians. Through her correspondence with Charles Babbage, she learned of his designs for the "Difference Engine" and later his "Analytical Engine." She was one of the few of Babbage's contemporaries who properly understood the ideas and intentions behind Babbage's designs. In an article discussing the Analytical Engine she wrote a program for the unbuilt device that would allow it to generate a sequence of Bernoulli numbers, which are used in pure mathematics.

1833 American army surgeon William Beaumont (1785–1853) explains the role of gastric juices in digestion (he had studied a patient with a gunshot wound to the stomach in 1822).

ASIA & OCEANIA

AFRICA & THE MIDDLE EAST

The Hansom cab was a one-horse cab with a low center of gravity that allowed safe cornering at high speeds.

ENGINEERING & INVENTION

1831 English scientist Michael Faraday (1791–1867) makes a simple dynamo.

1832 English physicist Charles Wheatstone (1802–75) invents the stereoscope, which produces an image in three dimensions from a pair of stereo photographs.

1832 Belgian physicist Joseph Plateau (1801–83) invents the stroboscope— a rapidly flashing light that can make rotating machinery appear stationary.

1832 The 61-mile (98-km) artificial section of the Gotha (Göta) Canal, which crosses Sweden from west to east, is completed.

1833 English mathematician Charles Babbage (1792–1871) begins work on his "Analytical Engine," a type of mechanical computer, but it is never completed.

1834 English architect Joseph Hansom (1803–82) designs the Hansom cab ("Patent Safety Cab"), a one-horse cab that soon appears in large numbers on the streets of Victorian London.

1834 English phonographer Isaac Pitman (1813–97) invents the system of shorthand writing that bears his name. It is soon adopted throughout the English-speaking world.

1833 American engineer Obed Hussey (1792–1860) invents a reaping machine.

1835 American physicist Joseph Henry (1797–1878) invents the electromagnetic relay.

1835 Swedish-born American engineer John Ericsson (1803–89) invents the screw propeller for ships.

1835 American manufacturer Samuel Colt (1814–62) produces a revolver with interchangeable parts.

Revolvers like this early Colt were used by the U.S. Army between 1873 and 1892. Similar models were popular with lawmen and civilians in the frontier towns of the Wild West.

WORLD EVENTS

1831 The Polish Diet (parliament) declares the nation's independence from Russia; Russian forces put down the revolt at the Battle of Ostrolenka.

1832 The Reform Act gives the vote in Britain to all wealthy men, rather than just those who own significant amounts of land.

1833 After a long campaign by anti-slavery activists and politicians like William Wilberforce (1759–1833), a law is passed abolishing slavery in the British Empire. It comes into effect at the beginning of 1834.

1834 The Spanish Inquisition, which had enforced Roman Catholic orthodoxy in Spain since 1478, was ended by royal decree.

1831 Nat Turner (1800–31) leads a slave revolt in Southampton, Virginia, that leaves 55 whites dead. In the aftermath the state executed 55 slaves believed to be involved with the rebellion; approximately 200 more slaves and former slaves were killed in the mob violence that followed.

1835 Texans declare independence, creating the Republic of Texas—a sovereign state that lasted until 1846, when it joined the United States.

1834 The South Australia Act is passed in the British Parliament, allowing the establishment of a colony there.

1831 The French Foreign Legion is founded in Algeria.

1831 Muhammad Ali (1769–1849), viceroy of Egypt, begins a revolt against his Turkish overlords that will see Egypt become an autonomous entity within the Ottoman Empire.

THE REVOLVER

The first pistols—the original "handguns"—were made in the 1400s. They were muzzle-loading weapons that fired a lead ball or bullet using black powder (gunpowder) as the propellant charge. The means of igniting the charge, called the lock, improved over time from the original matchlock through the wheel lock and the snaphaunce to the flintlock pistols of the late 1700s.

Most of the early pistols could fire only one shot. There were some double-barreled flintlocks, but the only effective way of ensuring more than one shot was to carry more than one loaded pistol. One attempt at increasing the number of shots was the invention of the pepper-box pistol, which had several barrels. They were rotated by hand to bring a new loaded barrel in front of the firing mechanism each time. But these weapons were heavy and poorly balanced, which made them difficult to aim.

Another solution was the revolving pistol, or revolver, which has a cylinder with a number of loaded chambers that can be fired in turn as they align with a single barrel. There are examples of flintlock revolvers (in which the spark from a flint ignites the charge), but the revolver only became a practical weapon when the percussion cap became available after 1807. In this type of weapon each chamber in the cylinder has a narrow hole at the back that holds a tight-fitting percussion cap. When the pistol is fired, the hammer strikes the cap, which explodes and fires the charge.

The first percussion revolvers were made in England after about 1820 by American gunsmith Elisha Collier of Boston. But the first manufacturer to make reliable revolvers in quantity was American Samuel Colt (1814–62), who obtained his first patent in England in 1835. The design was further improved by the invention of metal-cased cartridges, which allowed faster reloading. The first mass-produced cartridge revolvers were made by the Smith and Wesson company in 1857.

ASTRONOMY & MATH	BIOLOGY & MEDICINE	PHYSICAL SCIENCES

EUROPE

ASTRONOMY & MATH

1836 English astronomer Francis Baily (1774–1844) describes Baily's beads, a phenomenon during an eclipse when beads of light appear around the moon's rim (caused by the sun shining between mountain peaks).

1837 French mathematical physicist Siméon Poisson (1781–1840) discovers the Poisson distribution curve, a "normal" distribution important in statistical studies.

1838 German astronomer and mathematician Friedrich Bessel (1784–1846) for the first time determines the distance between the Earth and a star (other than the sun), finding that 61-Cygni is about 11.4 light-years from Earth.

1839 French painter and physicist Louis Daguerre (1787–1851) takes the first photograph of the moon.

1839 German astronomer Johann Encke (1791–1865) finds Encke's gap, a division in Saturn's "A" ring.

BIOLOGY & MEDICINE

1836 Czech physiologist Jan Purkinje (1787–1869) discovers the protein-digesting action of juices from the pancreas. A year later he identifies Purkinje cells in the brain (large branched nerve cells in the cerebellum), and in 1839 he coins the word *protoplasm* to describe the viscous fluid within cells.

1836 English naturalist Charles Darwin (1809–82) completes his epic voyage on H.M.S. *Beagle*; his observations during the voyage eventually enable him to propose his theory of evolution by natural selection.

1837 Estonian naturalist Karl von Baer (1792–1876) proposes an early form of the law of biogenesis, which states that a living thing can arise only from other similar organisms ("like gives rise to like") and never from anything nonliving.

1837 French physiologist René Dutrochet (1776–1847) describes the role of chlorophyll in photosynthesis—as the substance that absorbs sunlight and converts its energy to food.

1837 Three scientists independently discover the role of yeast in fermentation: in France Charles Cagniard de la Tour (1777–1859) and in Germany Theodor Schwann (1810–82) and Friedrich Kützing (1807–93).

1839 German biologist Theodor Schwann postulates that all living matter is made up of cells.

PHYSICAL SCIENCES

1836 English chemist James Marsh (1794–1846) devises the Marsh test for detecting arsenic.

1836 English chemist John Daniell (1790–1845) invents the Daniell cell, a primary cell (battery) with zinc and copper electrodes.

1836 French chemist Alexandre Becquerel (1820–91) identifies the photovoltaic effect (whereby light produces an electric current), the principle of most modern photocells.

1836 Swedish chemist Jöns Berzelius (1779–1848) discovers catalysts—substances that accelerate or slow down chemical reactions without taking part in them. Much of modern industrial chemistry and most natural biochemical processes depend on the action of catalysts.

1836 English chemist Edward Davy (1806–85) discovers acetylene (ethyne). It soon becomes an important gas for fuel and lighting.

1838 French chemist Anselme Payen (1795–1871) identifies cellulose, the basic material of all plants.

1839 Swedish chemist Carl Mosander (1797–1858) discovers lanthanum, one of a series of very similar "rare-earth" elements that are to puzzle chemists for many years.

THE AMERICAS

1839 American astronomer William Bond (1789–1859) becomes the first astronomical observer at the new Harvard College Observatory. Eight years later he installs the world's largest refracting telescope, the 15-inch (38-cm) "great refractor."

1836 American botanist Asa Gray (1810–88) draws up a method for classifying plants based on their fruits and seeds.

1837 American physician William Gerhard (1809–72) distinguishes between typhus and typhoid fever.

1839 American inventor Charles Goodyear (1800–60) develops the process of vulcanizing rubber to harden it (by heating raw rubber with sulfur).

ASIA & OCEANIA

AFRICA & THE MIDDLE EAST

Designed by Isambard Brunel, the S.S. Great Britain was the first successful seagoing steamship to use a propeller. The original version still carried sails in case of emergency.

A	B	C	D	E
F	G	H	I	J
K	L	M	N	O
P	Q	R	S	T
U	V	W	X	Y
Z				

ENGINEERING & INVENTION

1836 English physicist William Sturgeon (1783–1850) invents the moving-coil galvanometer, a sensitive instrument for detecting electric currents.

1837 German-born Russian printer Moritz von Jacobi (1801–74) invents a form of electrotyping in which a whole page of type is made by electroplating a mold taken from a page of type set in the usual way.

1837 English physicists William Cooke (1806–79) and Charles Wheatstone (1802–75) patent a five-needle electric telegraph.

1838 The paddle steamer *Sirius* is the first steamship to cross the Atlantic Ocean under steam power alone (taking 18 days). Only hours later S.S. *Great Western* arrives, having taken four days fewer. Seven years later (in 1845) the S.S. *Great Britain* becomes the first ship driven by a screw propeller to make the crossing.

1839 Scottish engineer Kirkpatrick Macmillan (1812–78) invents a bicycle powered by treadles.

1839 Louis Daguerre invents the daguerreotype, a type of photograph taken on metal plates (with the image reversed left to right).

1837 American industrialist John Deere (1804–86) invents a steel plow.

1838 American inventor Samuel Morse (1791–1872) demonstrates a single-wire electric telegraph over a 10-mile (16-km) circuit at New York University. The electromagnetic receiver "clicks" when telegraph signals arrive.

1838 American engineer Charles Page (1812–68) invents an electric generator with soft-iron electromagnets as field magnets instead of permanent magnets.

The natural history of the Galápagos Islands is eminently curious, and deserves attention. Most of the organic productions are aboriginal creations, found nowhere else.

CHARLES DARWIN,
THE VOYAGE OF THE BEAGLE (1837)

WORLD EVENTS

1836 In Britain the Chartists (backers of the People's Charter calling for the universal right to vote) found the first national movement representing working people.

1837 Victoria (r. 1837–1901) becomes queen of Great Britain.

A portrait of Charles Darwin around the time of his voyage on the H.M.S. Beagle

1838 Nicaragua declares its independence from Spain.

1839 Slaves being transported onboard the schooner *Amistad* rebel off the coast of Cuba, seizing control of the ship.

1837 The first whaling station is established in New Zealand, on a site near what is now the city of Christchurch.

MORSE CODE

Samuel Morse (1791–1872) was an American painter and inventor who made the first electric telegraph in the United States. His name is also remembered in the Morse code, which he helped invent. Morse was born in Charlestown, Massachusetts, the son of a minister. After graduating from Yale in 1810, he became a clerk for a Boston publisher. He traveled to England in 1815 and became a successful portrait artist.

Morse's interest turned to electricity in the 1830s. It was known by this time that the presence of an electric current in a wire could be detected by making it work as an electromagnet. This was the phenomenon that Morse decided to use in an electric telegraph.

Morse applied for a patent for his new telegraph in 1837. In 1843 Congress awarded him a grant for $30,000 to build a 37-mile (60-km) telegraph line between Washington and Baltimore. Morse sent his first message in May 1844.

The Morse code was essential for the success of the telegraph. It is a system of short and long electrical pulses ("dots" and "dashes") that encode the letters of the alphabet. The code was the work of Morse's financial backer Alfred Vail (1807–59), who is said to have consulted a newspaper printer to find out which letters are used most in the English language. Vail assigned the shortest codes to the most common letters.

CHARLES DARWIN

A newspaper cartoon depicts Charles Darwin as an ape, published during the controversy surrounding the publication of On the Origin of Species.

KEY DATES

1831–1836
Voyage of the *Beagle*

1838
Reads Malthus (book of 1803)

1858
Joint paper with Wallace

1859
On the Origin of Species

IN 1831 CHARLES DARWIN (1809–82) set sail around the world on H.M.S. *Beagle*; during the voyage he made observations that would eventually prompt him to propose the theory of evolution through natural selection. However, he sailed not as a naturalist or biologist but as a dinner companion for the captain.

Charles Darwin was the grandson of English physician Erasmus Darwin (1731–1802), whose writings contained speculations on the nature of familial inheritance and expressed his support for the now discredited ideas of French naturalist Jean-Baptiste Lamarck (1744–1829). When he was 22 years old and had recently finished his university degree, Charles Darwin joined H.M.S. *Beagle* as company for the captain, Robert Fitzroy. At the time naval captains were forbidden to socialize with their officers or crew, a situation that was believed to be the reason for the suicide of the *Beagle*'s previous captain on another voyage two years earlier.

Observation and Exploration

In addition to his desire for adventure, Darwin also wanted to be a naturalist, and he used the five-year voyage as a unique opportunity to study the plants and animals from the far-flung places he saw. The ship visited Tenerife and the Cape Verde Islands off the western coast of Africa before sailing around Cape Horn and up the western coast of South America. It then called at Patagonia, Chile, Peru, and the Galápagos Islands before sailing across the

Pacific to Tahiti and New Zealand, returning to England by way of South Africa. At each port of call Darwin went ashore to make observations and collect specimens of rocks, plants, and animals.

Darwin made more trips ashore in South America than anywhere else on the five-year voyage—in fact, he spent more time on land than on the ship. In addition to exotic plants and animals, he also studied the rocks and geology of the places he visited. In Patagonia he came upon a shore with a 19.6-foot- (6-m-) high gravel cliff containing some huge bones. They were too large to belong to any living creature, including the new ones he had already discovered. He observed that—apart from size—they resembled those of South American armadillos and sloths. He realized that their giant ancestors had become extinct but was unable to find a satisfactory explanation at the time for why this had happened.

Development of the Theory

H.M.S. *Beagle* returned to England in the fall of 1836, and Darwin went to live in London. He studied geology and was convinced by the uniformitarian

This map shows the route of the H.M.S. Beagle *around South America and the Galápagos Islands.*

ideas of Scottish geologist Charles Lyell (1797–1875), who argued that the world was shaped—and was still being shaped—by the same geological and environmental processes that could be observed in the present. Importantly for the development of Darwin's ideas, this hypothesis suggested that the age of the Earth should be measured in hundreds of millions of years rather than the thousands suggested by biblical chronologies. Darwin also read the works of English economist Thomas Malthus (1766–1834), who described history as a "struggle for existence" in which animal and human populations grow or contract in proportion to variations in available food.

Darwin recognized a similar state among animal species—why do some fish, for example, produce so many offspring when there is insufficient food for all of them? Darwin theorized that in a competitive environment, animals with traits that allow them to take full advantage of available food resources have a better chance of surviving and pass on these beneficial traits to their offspring.

Once Darwin had formulated his theory he set about gathering evidence to support it. In addition to his own observations on the *Beagle*, he consulted with hundreds of individuals—from his fellow zoologists to dog breeders, pigeon keepers, and gardeners—collecting their observations of species variation.

Publication and Further Development

At the same time as Darwin was putting together these ideas on evolution, Welsh naturalist Alfred Russel Wallace (1823–1913) came to very similar conclusions based on his observations of Asian and Australasian animals. He wrote of his theories in 1858 and sent a copy to Darwin. Darwin passed the paper to his friend, the geologist Charles Lyell, who decided to present both Darwin's and Wallace's papers to the Linnean Society at its next meeting. Darwin finally finished his epic work *On the Origin of Species by Means of Natural Selection*, which was published in 1859.

Darwin's theory was that evolution takes place in stages by chance mutations. Favorable mutations are inherited and passed on to offspring, so producing a gradual change in a whole species. Eventually new, fitter species come into existence and old, less fit ones become extinct. Darwin and his contemporaries

Darwin deduced that several species of finches in the Galápagos Islands had a common mainland ancestor. They evolved different beaks to suit their island diet. Finches 1, 3, and 4 have long beaks adapted for eating insects; finch 2 is a fruit-eating species; and the slightly crossed stubby beaks of finches 5 and 6 are best for tackling seeds.

had no idea of exactly how mutations take place. Unknown to them, however, heredity was being studied in the garden of a monastery in Austria by the monk Gregor Mendel (1822–84). He grew successive generations of pea plants and figured out the basic laws of heredity—that offspring receive sets of inherited "factors" that we now call genes. As scientific knowledge has advanced further, Darwin's theories have been vindicated and clarified by more discoveries, such as the discovery of DNA in 1953 and more recently the mapping of the human genome, completed in 2003.

W ITH NEW RAILROADS SPREADING ACROSS EUROPE AND THE United States (and at the same time putting most of the canal companies out of business), engineers began to find even more applications for the steam engine. The most important involved shipping. At first the steam engine drove paddlewheels, and paddle steamers could be seen plying their trade up and down rivers as far apart as the Danube in Europe and the Mississippi in the United States, where they helped transport settlers to the Midwest. Attempts at building paddle-driven oceangoing vessels met with little success, however, until the new power source was used to drive a propeller. Soon propeller-driven steamships replaced sailing ships on many of the world's oceans. The steam engine also came to displace the waterwheel as a source of power. However, the ancient device received a new lease on life with the invention of high-speed water turbines in the middle of the 19th century. Turbines are still used in hydroelectric power plants throughout the world.

The proliferation of advances in science and technology was celebrated in a number of international exhibitions, beginning with the Great Exhibition of 1851 in the remarkable iron-and-glass structure of the Crystal Palace in London. The electric telegraph carried the good news by way of cables across continents and under the oceans. On the theoretical side, Russian chemist Dmitri Mendeleev (1834–1907) brought

The steam engine was a versatile invention and was soon adapted to power ships. This lithograph depicts a celebrated race between two steamers, the Robert E. Lee *and the* Natchez, *on the Mississippi from St. Louis to New Orleans in 1870. The victorious* Robert E. Lee *made the trip in 3 days, 18 hours, 14 minutes, a record that still stands for a commercial vessel.*

order to chemistry with his development of the periodic table, and Austrian monk Gregor Mendel (1822–84) laid the foundation for the science of genetics when he revealed the laws of inheritance from his studies of garden pea plants. Atomic theory —that everything consists of atoms—became widely accepted, although at first atoms were thought to be just tiny indivisible particles of matter. Further investigation was needed to prove that atoms themselves are made up of even smaller particles.

A major medical breakthrough came with the understanding that infections are caused by parasitic organisms. With the aid of microscopes, scientists such as German doctor Robert Koch (1843–1910) and French chemist Louis Pasteur (1822–95) isolated the bacterial causes of infectious diseases such as typhoid and tuberculosis. Now doctors knew exactly what they were fighting, although it would be many years before the advent of effective drugs—antibiotics—that could kill bacteria.

The invention of the internal combustion engine in the late 19th century heralded the end of the age of steam. Much more efficient than a steam engine and more compact, the internal combustion engine could be adapted to smaller vehicles, including the newly invented automobiles, as well as boats and eventually airplanes.

Russian scientist Dmitri Mendeleev made sense of the known chemical elements by arranging them by atomic weight in his periodic table, as shown above on the wall of a technical school in Moscow. He arranged the table so that elements with similar properties fell in columns, and this allowed him to predict the existence of elements that were still undiscovered.

THE WORLD AT A GLANCE

CONCISE HISTORY OF SCIENCE AND INVENTION

	1840	1845	1850	1855	1860	
EUROPE	**1840** German pathologist Jacob Henle puts forward his germ theory of disease: that infection is caused by parasitic organisms. **1842** English zoologist Richard Owen coins the word *dinosaur* to describe certain prehistoric reptiles. **1842** German physicist Julius von Mayer first states that energy can neither be created nor destroyed. **1843** The first underwater tunnel is completed under the Thames River at Rotherhithe in London. **1843** German physiologist Emil du Bois-Reymond recognizes the electrical nature of nerve impulses.	**1845** Designed by engineer Isambard Brunel, S.S. *Great Britain*, the first successful propeller-driven ship, makes its maiden voyage. **1846** German astronomer Johann Galle is the first person to observe the planet Neptune. **1846** Italian chemist Ascanio Sobrero discovers the explosive nitroglycerin. **1848** Scottish physicist William Thomson, Lord Kelvin, introduces the absolute temperature scale. **1849** French gardener Joseph Monier invents reinforced concrete.	**1850** German chemist Robert Bunsen begins using the Bunsen burner, designed by his assistant Peter Desaga. **1851** French physicist Léon Foucault constructs Foucault's pendulum and uses it to show the Earth's rotation. **1852** English astronomer Edward Sabine establishes the connection between sunspot activity and magnetic storms on Earth. **1853** French chemist Charles Gerhardt derives acetylsalicylic acid (the basis of aspirin) from plants. **1854** English physician John Snow pinpoints a link between cholera and contaminated water.	**1855** Italian physicist Luigi Palmieri designs a seismograph, an instrument that detects and measures the strength of earthquakes. **1856** Workmen digging in the valley of the Neander River near Düsseldorf, Germany, discover remains of Neandertal man. **1857** Léon Foucault devises a method of silver-coating glass for use as mirrors in telescopes. **1858** English engineer Charles Bright organizes the laying of the first transatlantic submarine telegraph cable. **1859** English naturalist Charles Darwin publishes *On the Origin of Species*, the book in which he puts forward his theory of evolution.	**1860** The first fossil of *Archaeopteryx*, a birdlike prehistoric flying reptile, is found. **1860** English nurse Florence Nightingale establishes the world's first nursing college in London. **1860** Robert Bunsen and German physicist Gustav Kirchhoff develop a technique for analyzing substances by their spectra. **1862** German physician Felix Hoppe-Seyler establishes the presence of hemoglobin in blood. **1863** French chemist Louis Pasteur introduces pasteurization. **1864** French engineer Pierre Michaux makes the first pedal bicycle.	
THE AMERICAS	**1842** The first U.S. suspension bridge (designed by Charles Ellet) opens over the Schuylkill River in Fairmount, Philadelphia. **1842** American surgeon Crawford Long uses ether as an anesthetic. **1844** American dentist Horace Wells introduces nitrous oxide ("laughing gas") as an anesthetic. **1844** American inventor Samuel Morse sends the first telegraph message in the United States.	**1845** The first clipper ship, the *Rainbow*, is launched in the United States. **1846** American inventor Elias Howe patents a lock-stitch sewing machine. **1846** American John Deere (1804–86) markets a plow with a steel moldboard. **1849** Anglo-American engineer James Francis makes an improved reaction water turbine, in which a jet of water is directed at cup-shaped "paddles."	**1850** American engineer Charles Page builds the first electric locomotive in the United States. **1851** American inventor Isaac Singer patents a single-thread sewing machine that produces continuous and curved stitching. **1852** American inventor Elisha Otis patents the safety elevator. **1854** American chemist David Alter uses atomic spectra as a method of chemical analysis.	**1859** American industrialist George Pullman develops the Pullman sleeping car for use on railroads. **1859** American oil pioneer Edwin Drake drills the world's first productive oil well in Pennsylvania.	**1861** A telegraph line is built in the United States from Omaha, Nebraska, to Carson City, Nevada. **1862** American astronomers Lewis Swift and Horace Tuttle discover comet Swift–Tuttle, which causes the annual Perseid meteor shower. **1862** American inventor and gunsmith Richard Gatling patents a rapid-fire, ten-barrel machine gun.	
ASIA & OCEANIA					**1861** Australian astronomer John Tebbutt discovers the long-period Tebbutt's comet. The Earth passes through the comet's tail.	
AFRICA & THE MIDDLE EAST						

1865	1870	1875	1880	1882–1884
1865 Austrian monk Gregor Mendel formulates his laws of inheritance. **1865** German botanist Julius von Sachs identifies chloroplasts. **1867** Swedish chemist Alfred Nobel patents dynamite in Britain. **1868** English astronomer William Huggins detects a Doppler shift in the spectrum of the star Sirius and demonstrates that the star is receding from Earth. **1869** Russian chemist Dmitri Mendeleev compiles the first Periodic Table of the elements. **1869** Swiss pathologist Johann Miescher isolates deoxyribonucleic acid (DNA), which he calls *nuclein*.	**1871** Irish physicist George Stoney observes that three lines in the hydrogen spectrum have wavelengths in a simple ratio to one another. **1872** English-born chemist Robert Chesebrough patents the process of making petroleum jelly. **1873** Austrian physician Josef Breuer discovers the sensory function of the semicircular canals in the ear, which help maintain balance. **1873** English mathematician William Shanks calculates π (pi) to 707 decimal places.	**1876** German engineer Nikolaus Otto builds a four-stroke internal combustion engine fueled by coal gas. **1876** Polish-born German botanist Eduard Strasburger describes mitosis. **1877** English physicist Joseph Swan develops the first electric light bulb. **1877** German physiologist Wilhelm Kühne suggests the name *enzyme* for a protein that acts as a catalyst. **1879** English inventor Henry Lawson invents a chain-driven bicycle, which he calls the bicyclette.	**1880** French physical chemist Pierre Curie discovers the piezoelectric effect, which is the production of a voltage in a crystal that is under a mechanical stress. **1880** Louis Pasteur identifies the bacterium *Streptococcus*. **1880** Scottish astronomer George Forbes predicts the existence of "Planet X" orbiting beyond Uranus. **1881** German scientist Hermann von Helmholtz demonstrates that the electric charges of hydrogen atoms occur in whole-number portions.	**1882** German bacteriologist Robert Koch discovers the bacterium that causes tuberculosis. A year later he discovers the bacterium that causes cholera. **1883** Belgian engineer Étienne Lenoir invents the spark plug (for internal combustion engines). **1884** American-born English inventor Hiram Maxim makes the first fully automatic machine gun. **1884** Danish physician Hans Gram introduces a method of classifying bacteria by staining. **1884** Swedish chemist Svante Arrhenius begins to study the dissociation of electrolytes into ions in solution.
1865 A meteorite explodes just before reaching the ground in Vernon County, Wisconsin. **1866** The metric system is introduced in the United States but is largely ignored. **1867** English-born American engineer Andrew Hallidie invents the cable car. **1869** The Union Pacific transcontinental railroad is completed.	**1870** American engineer Lester Pelton designs a new form of water turbine—the Pelton wheel impulse water turbine. **1872** American astronomer Henry Draper photographs Vega's spectrum, creating the first photograph of the spectrum of a star.	**1876** American librarian Melvil Dewey introduces the Dewey Decimal Classification system for cataloging library books. **1876** Scottish-born American engineer Alexander Graham Bell patents the telephone. **1877** American engineer Thomas Edison invents the phonograph. **1877** American astronomer Asaph Hall discovers Phobos and Deimos, the two moons of Mars.	**1881** American astronomer Henry Draper takes the first photographs of comets. **1881** American astronomer Samuel Langley makes a bolometer, a sensitive temperature-measuring device with which he measures the sun's radiation. **1882** American physicist Albert Michelson publishes his first calculation of the speed of light. It is within 0.02 percent of the correct value.	**1882** The first steam-powered electricity-generating plant in the United States, designed by Thomas Edison, opens in New York City. **1884** German-born American inventor Ottmar Mergenthaler invents the linotype machine.
		1879 The first shipment of frozen meat is sent to England from Australia.		**1883** Mount Krakatoa, an active volcano in Indonesia, erupts. The explosion is heard as far away as Perth, western Australia.
1869 The Suez Canal is completed under the supervision of French engineer Ferdinand de Lesseps.				**1883** The world's last quagga (an African animal resembling a zebra) dies in the Amsterdam Zoo.

ASTRONOMY & MATH

1843 German astronomer Heinrich Schwabe (1789–1875) declares that sunspots have a cycle of about ten years (they reach a maximum number every ten years). Later Swiss astronomer Rudolf Wolf (1816–93) defines the period as 11 years.

1843 French amateur astronomer Hervé-Auguste Faye (1814–1902) discovers Faye's comet. It has a period of 7.3 years.

1843 Irish mathematician William Hamilton (1805–65) devises quaternions, a system of complex numbers that are not commutative (in which *ab* does not necessarily equal *ba*). They later find use in both theoretical and applied mathematics.

1840 English-born American scientist John Draper (1811–82) takes the first celestial photographs, daguerreotypes of the moon.

BIOLOGY & MEDICINE

1840 German pathologist Jacob Henle (1809–85) proposes his germ theory of disease: that infection is caused by parasitic organisms invading the body.

1840 Swiss embryologist Rudolf von Kölliker (1817–1905) describes spermatozoa as being cellular in origin and nature.

1842 English zoologist Richard Owen (1804–92) coins the word *dinosaur* (meaning "terrible lizard" in Greek) to describe certain prehistoric reptiles.

1842 Danish zoologist Johann Steenstrup (1813–97) first explains the alternation of sexual and asexual generations that takes place in plants such as mosses.

> **1842** Scottish anatomist Charles Bell (1774–1842) describes Bell's palsy, a type of facial paralysis.
>
> **1843** German physiologist Emil du Bois-Reymond (1818–96) recognizes the electrical nature of nerve impulses.

The dark spots visible on the surface of the sun are sunspots—areas of reduced temperature caused by magnetic anomalies.

1842 American surgeon Crawford Long (1815–78) uses ether as an anesthetic. American dentist William Morton (1819–68) patents it in 1846, and it is used by Scottish obstetrician James Simpson (1811–70) in 1847.

1844 American dentist Horace Wells (1815–48) introduces nitrous oxide ("laughing gas") as an anesthetic.

PHYSICAL SCIENCES

1840 French chemist Henri Regnault (1810–78) discovers dichloroethylene (dichloroethene), which soon becomes an important industrial solvent.

1840 Swiss-born Russian chemist Germain Hess (1802–50) formulates Hess's law, concerning the heats of reaction of chemical processes.

1840 English physicist James Joule (1818–89) proposes Joule's law, which states that the amount of heat per second that develops in a wire carrying a current is proportional to the electrical resistance of the wire and the square of the current.

1842 German physicist Julius von Mayer (1814–78) first states the principle of conservation of energy (that energy can neither be created nor destroyed, merely changed from one form into another form).

1842 Austrian physicist Christian Doppler (1803–53) describes the Doppler effect—the change in frequency (or wavelength) of a wave motion when the source and the observer move closer to or farther away from each other. Applied originally to sound waves, the effect also relates to any form of wave motion, such as light.

1841 English-born American scientist John Draper (1811–82) creates Draper's law: that only the radiation that is absorbed by a substance will produce a chemical change in it.

TURNING POINTS

Safe Anesthetics

For many centuries a major impediment to safe surgical procedures was the problem of pain. The intense pain that accompanied surgery before the introduction of reliable anesthetics not only caused considerable distress to the patient, but also made the surgery more dangerous. The patient's involuntary movements and the need to finish the surgery quickly increased the likelihood of potentially fatal mistakes. Anesthetics such as opium, cocaine, and mandrake had always been available but were not reliable: an underdose or overdose was too easily administered. Sometimes the anesthetic would be insufficient to dull pain; at other times it would kill the patient. The discovery of new anesthetics—including ether, chloroform, and nitrous oxide—in the mid-19th century improved the situation, but almost as important was the methodical research into anesthetic techniques and dosages conducted during this time. Physicians such as John Snow (1813–1858)—better known for identifying the cause of cholera—published dosage advice and designed apparatus for administering these new anesthetics safely to patients of all ages and body sizes.

Side labels: EUROPE · THE AMERICAS · ASIA & OCEANIA · AFRICA & THE MIDDLE EAST

ENGINEERING & INVENTION

1841 English engineer Joseph Whitworth (1803–87) introduces a system of standard screw threads.

1841 English chemist Alexander Parkes (1813–90) invents a process for cold vulcanizing rubber (using carbon disulfide and no heat).

1843 English engineer Thomas Crampton (1816–88) invents the Crampton railroad locomotive. It has a single pair of large driving wheels located behind the firebox.

1843 The first underwater tunnel is completed under the Thames River at Rotherhithe in London. It is designed by French-born engineer Marc Brunel (1769–1849) and constructed under the supervision of his son Isambard (1806–1859). Although intended for use by pedestrians, it is not a financial success and later (1865) it is acquired for use by railroad trains.

1844 Belgian engineer Égide Walschaert (1820–1901) invents the Walschaert's valve gear. It is used on the majority of steam railroad locomotives until the end of the steam era.

1841 German-born American engineer John Roebling (1806–69) invents a machine for making wire rope (cable). It becomes important in constructing suspension bridges.

1842 The first suspension bridge in the United States opens over the Schuylkill River in Fairmount, Philadelphia, designed by Charles Ellet (1810–62).

1843 African-American inventor Norbert Rillieux (1806–94) designs a vacuum evaporator for extracting sugar from sugarcane (patented 1846).

1844 American inventor Samuel Morse (1791–1872) sends the first message on a telegraph line in the United States (Washington to Baltimore).

WORLD EVENTS

1840 The world's first postage stamp comes into circulation in Great Britain.

1840 Queen Victoria of Great Britain (r. 1837–1901) marries the German Prince Albert (1819–61).

1844 A weavers' uprising in Silesia (now southern Poland) is put down by Prussian troops.

This skeleton is the fossilized remains of a Tyrannosaurus rex, *first discovered in 1874. The dinosaur stood up to 13 feet (4 m) tall.*

1840 A report prepared by Canada's Governor General Lord Durham (1792–1840) recommends the union of Upper and Lower Canada into a single state.

1844 The eastern part of the island of Hispaniola wins independence as Santo Domingo (now the Dominican Republic).

The two passages of the Thames Tunnel at Rotherhithe in London—depicted in this contemporary illustration—were completed by Marc Brunel and his son Isambard in 1844.

DISCOVERING THE DINOSAURS

The bones of the creatures now known as dinosaurs have been unearthed throughout history. In China the bones were thought to be the remains of dragons, while in Europe they were believed to be those of giants.

The first dinosaur to be scientifically described was *Megalosaurus*, following the discovery of a partial skeleton in Oxfordshire, England, in 1677. By the mid-19th century another two species had been identifed: *Hylaeosaurus* and *Iguanadon*. The term *dinosaur* was coined by paleontologist Robert Owen in 1842.

Public interest quickly grew in these vast ancient creatures, and some fossil hunters became famous for their discoveries. They often used reckless and unscientific techniques, such as blasting fossil beds with explosives. The late 19th-century rivalries among fossil hunters in the United States were dubbed the "Bone Wars." Since then the search for new fossils has expanded to include every continent, including Antarctica. This has led to the discovery of many new species, as well as a far greater understanding of the ecological roles and possible behaviors of these creatures.

ASTRONOMY & MATH

1845 Two French physicists—Armand Fizeau (1819–96) and Léon Foucault (1819–68)—take detailed photographs of the sun.

1846 German astronomer Johann Galle (1812–1910) is the first person to observe the planet Neptune. A few months later English astronomer William Lassell (1799–1880) discovers Triton, Neptune's moon.

1847 English mathematician Augustus de Morgan (1806–71) formulates de Morgan's laws, which are fundamental to the science of logic.

1848 English astronomer William Lassell (1799–1880) and, independently, American astronomers William (1789–1859) and George Bond (1825–65) discover Hyperion, one of Saturn's moons.

1848 French astronomer Édouard Roche (1820–83) calculates the Roche limit—the closest distance to a planet that one of its moons can approach without being torn apart by gravitational forces.

BIOLOGY & MEDICINE

1845 German zoologist Karl Siebold (1804–85) demonstrates that protozoa (protists) are single-celled organisms.

1845 English clergyman and amateur biologist Miles Berkeley (1803–89) shows that the disease potato blight is caused by a fungus. By 1848 the potato famine has killed more than one million people in Ireland.

1845 German pathologist Rudolph Virchow (1821–1902) and English physician John Bennett (1812–75) independently describe the disorder leukemia.

1846 French physiologist Claude Bernard (1813–78) describes the role of the pancreas in digestion.

1846 Italian astronomer and microscopist Giovanni Amici (1786–1863) discovers the circulation of sap in plants.

1847 French physiologist Pierre Flourens (1794–1867) first uses chloroform (trichloromethane) as an anesthetic on small animals. In the same year Scottish obstetrician James Simpson (1811–70) uses it on humans.

1846 American physician Oliver Wendell Holmes (1809–94) coins the term *anesthetic*, meaning "without feeling."

1847 The American Medical Association is founded in Philadelphia.

PHYSICAL SCIENCES

1845 German chemist Christian Schönbein (1799–1868) discovers the explosive properties of nitrocellulose (guncotton), which was first prepared by French chemist Théophile Pelouze (1807–67).

1845 German physicist Franz Neumann (1798–1895) publishes his first paper outlining his theory of electromagnetic induction, based on the experiments of Michael Faraday (1791–1867) and Joseph Henry (1797–1878).

1846 Italian chemist Ascanio Sobrero (1812–88) discovers nitroglycerin (trinitroglycerol), a powerful but unstable explosive, which is later found to be useful in the treatment of certain heart disorders.

1847 German scientist Hermann von Helmholtz (1821–94) and English physicist James Joule (1818–89) establish the principle of the conservation of energy, first proposed in 1842 by German physicist Julius von Mayer (1814–78).

1848 Scottish physicist William Thomson, Lord Kelvin (1824–1907), introduces the absolute temperature scale. Now known as the Kelvin scale, it is the SI unit of temperature.

The Smithsonian Institution in Washington, D.C. The institution was founded with the goal of advancing science and public knowledge in the United States.

INSIDE STORY

Temperature

The Kelvin temperature scale, devised in 1848 by William Thomson, Lord Kelvin, is based on absolute zero. The kelvin is the international standard (SI) unit of temperature.

Fahrenheit	Celsius	Kelvin	
212°	100°	373°	Water boils
176°	80°	353°	
140°	60°	333°	
104°	40°	313°	
68°	20°	293°	Average room temperature
32°	0°	273°	Water freezes
4°	-20°	253°	
-40°	-40°	233°	Mercury freezes
-76°	-60°	213°	
-112°	-80°	193°	
-148°	-100°	173°	
-184°	-120°	153°	Alcohol freezes
-220°	-140°	133°	
-256°	-160°	113°	
-292°	-180°	93°	Oxygen boils
-328°	-200°	73°	
-364°	-220°	53°	Oxygen freezes
-400°	-240°	33°	
-436°	-260°	13°	
-459.4°	-273°	0°	Absolute zero

EUROPE

THE AMERICAS

ASIA & OCEANIA

AFRICA & THE MIDDLE EAST

ENGINEERING & INVENTION	WORLD EVENTS
1845 Scottish engineer Robert Thomson (1822–73) patents a pneumatic tire made of vulcanized rubber for horse-drawn vehicles.	**1845** Potato blight causes a terrible famine in Ireland that will claim the lives of about a million people and drive many more into exile before its end in 1851.
1845 Designed by engineer Isambard Brunel (1806–59), S.S. *Great Britain*, the first successful propeller-driven ship, makes its maiden voyage.	**1846** The Corn Laws, which placed high tariffs on imports of grain to Britain, are repealed, ostensibly to ease the famine in Ireland. Repeal will be significant step in the development of international free trade.
1846 Belgian-born French musician Adolphe Sax (1814–94) patents the saxophone.	**1847** The ongoing famine in Ireland causes an estimated 200,000 people to emigrate in just one year, mostly to the United States.
1848 English inventor John Stringfellow (1799–1883) builds a model steam-driven airplane.	**1848** German political thinkers Karl Marx (1818–83) and Freidrich Engels (1820–95) publish the *Communist Manifesto*, a blueprint for a socialist state created through a revolution of the workers.
1848 English engineer William Adams (1797–1872) constructs a steam-powered railcar.	**1848** Pro-democracy uprisings take place across Europe, including in Italy, France, Germany, Austria, and Hungary. Unrest in France forces King Louis-Phillipe (r. 1830–48) to hand power to the Second Republic.
1849 French gardener Joseph Monier (1823–1906) invents reinforced concrete (concrete cast around iron or steel reinforcing rods).	**1849** Pope Pius IX (1792–1878) is returned to power in Italy, forcing revolutionary leader Giuseppe Garibaldi (1807–82) to return to exile in America.
1845 The first clipper ship, the *Rainbow*, is launched in the United States.	**1846** Oregon Territory (Washington, Oregon, and Idaho, with parts of British Columbia) is divided between the United States and Canada, with the border at the 49th parallel.
1846 American inventor Elias Howe (1819–67) patents a lock-stitch sewing machine.	**1846** Hostilities break out between the United States and Mexico when the two nations cannot agree terms on the sale of New Mexico. Mexican forces suffer heavy losses at the battles of Palo Alto and Resaca.
1846 American industrialist John Deere (1804–86) markets a plow with a steel moldboard.	**1848** Thousands of prospectors swarm to the California gold rush. Few of them succeed in making a living from the mining, but the influx of people accelerates the growth of the state of California.
1848 American inventor James Bogardus (1800–74) introduces a method of making cast-iron buildings.	
1849 Anglo-American engineer James Francis (1815–92) makes an improved reaction water turbine, in which a jet of water is directed at cup-shaped "paddles."	*A contemporary engraving of the steamship* Clermont *in New York Harbor*

STEAMSHIPS

Before the improvements made by James Watt (1736–1819), the steam engine was essentially a piece of specialized mining equipment. The utility of Watt's steam engine made it a vital part of any industrial enterprise. Its popularity brought it to the attention of many engineers and inventors, who modified the design and adapted it to different uses. The early development of locomotives was hindered by the size and weight of steam engines, but this was not a problem for steamships.

Attempts were made to build a steamboat in the late 18th century by inventors in Britain, France, and the United States. These early ships used a variety of methods of propulsion—including paddlewheels, mechanical oars, and suction pumps—but met with only limited success. Some later designs, such as the *Charlotte Dundas*, designed by William Symington (1763–1831), were technical successes but not commercial ones.

It was the U.S. engineer Robert Fulton (1765–1815) who built the first practical steamship—*Clermont*—in 1806. The *Clermont* made the trip up the Hudson River from New York to Albany at a speed of 5 miles (8 km) per hour and went into regular passenger service.

Although they were successful on rivers, and some operated in coastal waters, steamships did not cross the open sea until 1838, when two British steamships crossed the Atlantic. The S.S. *Great Britain*, launched in 1845, was the first transatlantic ship to be powered by an efficient screw propeller.

The total quantity of all the forces capable of work in the whole universe remains eternal and unchanged throughout all their changes.

HERMANN VON HELMHOLTZ

ASTRONOMY & MATH

1851 French mathematician Joseph Liouville (1809–82) publishes his work establishing the existence of transcendental numbers (numbers that are not algebraic).

1851 English astronomer William Lassell (1799–1880) discovers Ariel and Umbriel, two moons of Uranus.

1852 English physicist and astronomer Edward Sabine (1788–1883) establishes the connection between sunspot activity and magnetic storms on Earth.

1854 English mathematician George Boole (1815–64) introduces Boolean algebra, which is later important in the development of computer logic circuits.

1854 German mathematician Bernhard Riemann (1826–66) develops a type of non-Euclidean geometry later to find applications in relativity theory.

1850 American astronomer William Bond (1789–1859) and English astronomer William Lassell (1799–1880) independently observe Saturn's dark inner ring: the crepe ring, or C ring.

BIOLOGY & MEDICINE

1850 German scientist Hermann von Helmholtz (1821–94) measures the speed of a nerve impulse.

1850 English physician Alfred Higginson (1808–84) invents the hypodermic needle. It is used initially for extracting samples of blood or other fluid.

1851 Hermann von Helmholtz devises the ophthalmoscope, which enables physicians to look inside a patient's eye.

1851 French physiologist Claude Bernard (1813–78) discovers vasomotor nerves, which regulate the diameter of blood vessels.

1852 English zoologist Richard Owen (1804–92) identifies the parathyroid glands in the neck of a rhinoceros.

1852 German physiologists Georg Meissner (1829–1905) and Rudolf Wagner (1805–64) describe Meissner's corpuscles, which are receptors in the skin that detect slight pressure.

1854 English physician John Snow (1813–58) pinpoints a link between cholera and contaminated drinking water during an epidemic in London.

A contemporary engraving shows the figure of death working a water pump, reflecting John Snow's discovery of the cause of cholera.

1853 The world's largest tree, a giant sequoia, is found in California and named *Wellingtonia gigantea* (now *Sequoiadendron giganteum*).

Giant sequoias grow naturally only in the western Sierra Nevada, in California.

PHYSICAL SCIENCES

1850 French chemist Auguste Bravais (1811–63) publishes his analysis of crystal lattice structure, in which he identifies 14 different types of lattice.

1850 German physicist Rudolf Clausius (1822–88) formulates the second law of thermodynamics. It states that heat will not, on its own, move from a hot object to a hotter object.

1851 French physicist Léon Foucault (1819–68) constructs Foucault's pendulum and uses it to demonstrate the rotation of the Earth.

1851 Irish-born physicist George Stokes (1819–1903) proposes Stokes's law, an expression for the force acting on a small sphere falling through a liquid.

1853 French chemist Charles Gerhardt (1816–56) derives acetylsalicylic acid (the basis of aspirin) from plants. In the same year, together with his compatriot Auguste Laurent (1807–53), he introduces to organic chemistry the theory of "types"—the idea that certain characteristic groupings always behave in a similar way, even when they occur in different kinds of compounds.

1854 American chemist David Alter (1807–81) studies atomic spectra, the light given off by elements when heated to incandescence, and uses them as a method of chemical analysis.

HOW IT WORKS

Foucault's Pendulum

In 1851 the French physicist Léon Foucault devised an experiment to simply demonstrate the rotation of the Earth. In Foucault's experiment a steel ball, weighing 61 pounds (28 kg), was suspended from a 197-foot (60-m) steel wire in a large indoor space. The weight was drawn back and allowed to swing like a pendulum. The direction of the swing altered gradually, at a rate of around 11° per hour, so that it eventually completed a full rotation. The rotation of the swing around its center is caused by the rotation of the Earth on its axis and shows that the Earth makes one complete rotation every 24 hours. The experiment was soon replicated in locations around the world.

ENGINEERING & INVENTION

1850 German chemist Robert Bunsen (1811–99) begins using the Bunsen burner, which was probably designed by his assistant Peter Desaga.

1850 The French battleship *Napoléon* is launched. It is the first purpose built steam-battleship and the first to be driven by a screw propeller.

1850 A tubular railroad bridge is opened across the Menai Strait, North Wales, designed by English engineer Robert Stephenson (1803–59).

1851 The Crystal Palace, a cast-iron and glass building designed by English architect Joseph Paxton (1801–65), is put up in Hyde Park, London, for the Great Exhibition.

1852 French engineer Henri Giffard (1825–82) builds a steerable, hydrogen-filled nonrigid airship called a dirigible.

1853 English inventor George Cayley (1773–1857) constructs a glider capable of carrying a person.

1850 American engineer Charles Page (1812–68) builds the first electric locomotive in the United States.

1851 American inventor Isaac Singer (1811–75) patents a single-thread sewing machine that produces continuous and curved stitching.

1851 American dentist John Allen (1810–92) produces false teeth consisting of porcelain teeth on a platinum plate.

1852 American inventor Elisha Otis (1811–61) patents the safety elevator; the first is installed in Yonkers, New York, in 1857.

1854 American gunsmiths Horace Smith (1808–93) and Daniel Wesson (1825–1906) produce a single-action cartridge revolver (patented 1856).

WORLD EVENTS

1851 Louis Napoleon, nephew of Napoleon Bonaparte (r. 1804–14 and 1825) and president of France's Second Republic, creates the Second Empire, with himself as Emperor Napoleon III (r. 1852–70).

1854 The United Kingdom declares war on Russia, marking the beginning of the Crimean War (1854–56). Later in the year a misunderstood order costs the lives of 150 British soldiers in the infamous "Charge of the Light Brigade."

1854 British nurse Florence Nightingale (1820–1910) leaves for the Crimea with a group of 38 nurses she has trained. Her examination of mortality rates and causes—through first hand experience and statistical analysis—leads to revolutionary changes in hospital design and management.

1850 The Fugitive Slave Act requires all states to return slaves to their former masters, increasing tension between the Northern and Southern states.

1852 Harriet Beecher Stowe (1811–96) publishes the antislavery novel *Uncle Tom's Cabin.*

1854 The Kansas-Nebraska Act destroys the 1820 Missouri Compromise over the creation of new slave states. Fighting breaks out in Kansas territory between supporters and opponents of slavery.

The Menai Bridge in North Wales was one of the first modern suspension bridges.

THE GREAT EXHIBITION

Staged in London in 1851, the first Great Exhibition was a world fair of exhibits designed to celebrate the extent of human achievement. The emphasis was on practical science and technology, and more than half of the exhibits came from Britain or the British Empire.

The exhibition was devised by Queen Victoria's husband, Prince Albert (1819–61), who was at the time president of Britain's Royal Society of Arts. The idea was to mount an exhibition showcasing the "industries of all nations." The exhibition was funded partly by Queen Victoria herself and partly by British manufacturers.

The exhibition was staged in a vast glass-and-iron structure known as the Crystal Palace, designed by architect Joseph Paxton (1801–65). There were about 14,000 exhibitors showing more than 100,000 examples of manufactured goods. They included everything from printing presses, railroad locomotives, and hydraulic machinery, to items as small as cutlery and jewelry. The 560 exhibits from the United States included Cyrus McCormick's reaper and Samuel Colt's repeating revolver. The exhibition remained open for 23 weeks, during which time it received more than 6 million visitors (equivalent to about a third of the population of the United Kingdom at the time).

The profits made by the exhibition were used to found the Victoria and Albert Museum, the Science Museum, and the Natural History Museum in London—which collect and exhibit significant examples of design, technology, and biological and geological specimens respectively.

The original Crystal Palace was taken down in 1852 and rebuilt on a hill at Sydenham, south of London, where it remained in use by the public until it was destroyed by fire in 1936. The London district where it once stood is still known as Crystal Palace.

EUROPE

ASTRONOMY & MATH

1857 Scottish physicist James Clerk Maxwell (1831–79) suggests the true nature of Saturn's rings (that they consist of millions of small orbiting particles).

1857 French physicist Léon Foucault (1819–68) devises a method of silver-coating glass for use as mirrors in telescopes. Glass mirrors will replace the metal mirrors used in earlier reflecting telescopes.

1858 Italian astronomer Giambattista Donati (1826–73) discovers Donati's comet, which has a period of about 2,000 years. It is the first comet to be photographed (by English astronomer William Usherwood).

1859 German astronomer Gustav Spörer (1822–95) establishes Spörer's law. It states that during the course of the sunspot cycle sunspots gradually move toward lower latitudes (nearer the sun's equator).

1859 English astronomer Richard Carrington (1826–75) observes flares in the chromosphere (outer layer) of the sun.

BIOLOGY & MEDICINE

1855 German pathologist Rudolph Virchow (1821–1902) observes that cells originate from the division of other cells.

1855 English physician Thomas Addison (1793–1860) describes the disease of the adrenal glands, which later becomes known as Addison's disease.

1856 German physician Carl Ludwig (1816–95) is the first to keep animal organs alive outside the body by pumping blood through them.

1856 Workmen digging in the valley of the Neander River near Düsseldorf, Germany, discover remains of Neandertal man.

1857 French chemist Louis Pasteur (1822–95) observes that microorganisms cause fermentation.

1858 English anatomist Henry Gray (1825–61) publishes *Anatomy of the Human Body*, commonly known as *Gray's Anatomy*.

1859 English naturalist Charles Darwin (1809–82) publishes *On the Origin of Species*, the book in which he puts forward his theory of evolution.

PHYSICAL SCIENCES

1855 English geophysicist John Pratt (1809–71) demonstrates that gravity remains constant everywhere at sea level (whereas it varies over different altitudes on land).

1855 Northern Irish chemist and physicist Thomas Andrews (1813–85) proves that ozone is an allotrope (molecular compound) of oxygen with three atoms per molecule (O_3).

1856 Scottish physicist William Thomson, Lord Kelvin (1824–1907), coins the term *kinetic energy* to describe energy associated with movement.

1858 Italian chemist Stanislao Cannizzaro (1826–1910) distinguishes between atomic weights and molecular weights, thereby establishing atomic and molecular weights as the basis of chemical calculations.

1859 German chemist Hermann Kolbe (1818–84) synthesizes salicylic acid, leading to the mass production of aspirin, the first synthetic drug.

1859 Scottish physicist and engineer William Rankine (1820–72) devises the Rankine cycle to measure the efficiency of steam engines.

THE AMERICAS

ASIA & OCEANIA

AFRICA & THE MIDDLE EAST

HOW IT WORKS

Cell Division

All cells originate from the division of other cells, as first observed by German pathologist Rudolph Virchow in 1855. There are three different types of cell division: binary fission, mitosis, and meiosis. Binary fission is the type of cell division that single-celled organisms such as bacteria use to reproduce. Mitosis is the process by which a cell divides so that two identical sets of chromosomes appear in the daughter cells. In meiosis, new cells are created with half the chromosomes of their parent cells. This process creates the gametes used in sexual reproduction. Rapid and uncontrolled cell division is the defining characteristic of cancers.

This micrograph shows cancer cells at various stages of division. The image has been enhanced by using antibodies that attach fluorescent dyes to specific structures, thereby illuminating the cells.

ENGINEERING & INVENTION

1855 Swedish chemist Johan Lundström (1815–88) patents the safety match.

1855 Italian physicist Luigi Palmieri (1807–96) designs a seismograph, an instrument that detects and measures the strength of earthquakes.

1856 English steelmaker Henry Bessemer (1813–98) develops the Bessemer converter for making steel out of iron.

1857 English inventor Edward Cowper (1819–93) creates the hot-blast stove for blast furnaces and improves the steelmaking process.

1858 English engineer Charles Bright (1832–88) organizes the laying of the first transatlantic submarine telegraph cable.

1858 The S.S. *Great Eastern*, designed by English engineer Isambard Brunel (1806–59), is launched in England. At the time it is the world's largest ship.

1859 The first ironclad (wooden-hulled) warship, *La Gloire*, is built in France.

1859 Belgian engineer Étienne Lenoir (1822–1900) devises a gas-burning internal combustion engine.

1859 American industrialist George Pullman (1831–97) develops the Pullman sleeping car for use on railroads.

1859 American oil pioneer Edwin Drake (1819–80) drills the world's first productive oil well in Pennsylvania.

WORLD EVENTS

1857 An earthquake measuring an estimated 7 on the Richter scale partially destroys the city of Naples in Italy, killing thousands.

1859 The Battle of Solferino is fought between the Austrian Empire and an alliance of France and Italy. The aftermath of the bloody battle is witnessed by Swiss businessman Henri Dunant (1828–1910), who is inspired to found the International Red Cross. Dunant was later an important figure in the drafting of the first Geneva Convention.

1856 The worst railroad accident in the world to date occurs in Fort Washington, Pennsylvania. Around 60 passengers are killed when two trains collide on a single track line.

1858 In the *Dred Scott vs Sandford* case, the United States Supreme Court rules that Dred Scott (1799–1858), a slave, was not a citizen of the United States and that freeing him without the consent of his owner would be an unconstitutional confiscation of property.

1859 Abolitionist John Brown (1800–59) raids the armory at Harper's Ferry, Virginia, to arm a slave revolt; he is captured and hanged.

I often say that when you can measure what you are speaking about, and express it in numbers, you know something about it; but when you cannot express it in numbers, your knowledge is of a meagre and unsatisfactory kind; it may be the beginning of knowledge, but you have scarcely, in your thoughts, advanced to the stage of science, whatever the matter may be.

WILLIAM THOMSON, FIRST LORD KELVIN

NEANDERTAL MAN

Neandertals, also spelled Neanderthals, are an extinct type of hominid that lived about 130,000 to 30,000 years ago in Europe and Asia. In 1856 Neandertal remains were unearthed by quarrymen in a cave in the Neander Valley near Düsseldorf, Germany. Amateur naturalist Johann Carl Fuhlrott (1803–77) took the bones to Herman Schaaffhausen (1816–93), professor of anatomy at the University of Bonn. Together they announced their discovery in 1857. The term *Neandertal Man* was coined in 1863 by Anglo-Irish geologist William King (1809–86).

Early reconstructions of Neandertals portrayed them as stooping and apelike. It is now thought that their posture was upright and similar to modern humans. They did, however, have many anatomical differences from modern humans, such as larger skulls, sharper teeth, and stronger but not very dextrous hands.

Neandertals used fire, made wood, bone, and stone tools, and wore ornaments. They buried their dead in simple graves. Their diet was mainly carnivorous, and they lived in small groups.

A modern facial reconstruction based on a Neandertal skull

MENDEL AND GENETICS

A portrait of Mendel as Abbot of St. Thomas's Abbey, Brno. During his lifetime Mendel was known for his long-standing political disputes with the Austrian government, rather than his work on genetics.

TODAY GENETICS IS ONE OF THE MAJOR scientific disciplines. It has applications in agriculture, biology, medicine, and even law enforcement. But it had very humble beginnings in the garden of a remote monastery in Austria, where a monk named Gregor Mendel (1822–84) experimented by growing pea plants.

Gregor Mendel was born in Heinzendorf in Austrian Silesia (now Hyncice in the Czech Republic). He studied in college before entering the Augustinian order in 1843. By 1868 he was abbot of the monastery at Brünn (now Brno). He became interested in hybrids and began to breed pea plants in 1856. In the next six years he grew 30,000 plants, which he fertilized artificially by manually transferring pollen between flowers. For example, he crossed tall plants with short plants. He then counted the number of tall and short plants in the next and later generations. He found that all first-generation plants were tall, but that the second generation contained tall plants and short plants in the ratio of 3 to 1.

Mendel concluded that every plant receives two "factors" of inheritance, one from each parent. In the first generation of peas each plant receives one factor for tallness from the tall parent and one factor for shortness from the short parent. All the offspring are tall, since the tallness factor is dominant over the shortness factor (which is described as recessive). Recessive factors can, however, make themselves apparent when two occur in a single individual.

Mendel's Laws

These observations led Mendel to propose two laws. The law of segregation states that the two factors controlling each hereditary characteristic segregate and pass into separate germ cells (egg and sperm). The law of independent assortment states that the pairs of factors segregate independently of each other during the formation of germ cells. In 1865 Mendel reported his results to the Brünn Natural History Society and published them a year later in the society's journal. Nobody took much notice, but Mendel's interest continued. However, an increase in monasterial duties meant that science ceased to occupy the central position in his life.

Mendel's "factors" are now called alleles, which are alternative forms of a gene. In any one body cell of an organism there are two alleles of each gene, one inherited from each parent, which occupy the same place on a chromosome. Usually one allele is dominant and the other is recessive. A germ cell (gamete) —egg or sperm—has only one allele. When egg and sperm combine at fertilization, the two alleles come together in a new individual that inherits characteristics from each parent. The appearance of the new individual, however, depends on which characteristic (if any) is dominant.

In the 1890s, after Mendel's death, several European biologists independently studied inheritance in plants. In the Netherlands Dutch botanist Hugo de

The diagram shows how Mendel's laws predict the colors produced by crossing purple-flowered peas with white-flowered peas. Purple is dominant, and the first generation (known as F_1 phenotypes) produced by planting seeds from the cross are all purple. But when this generation is interbred, the second generation (F_2 phenotypes) has purple or white flowers in the ratio 3 to 1.

Vries (1848–1935) came up with results identical to Mendel's, and his accidental discovery of Mendel's obscure publication prompted him to announce his results in 1900. De Vries's publication in turn led German botanist Karl Correns (1864–1933) and Austrian botanist Erich von Tschermak-Seysenegg (1871–1962) to publish their observations, which also confirmed that Mendel's theories had been correct all those years before.

Heredity in Practice

The diagram on the opposite page shows the principles of heredity using pea plants (as Mendel did). Initially, a purple-flowered pea is crossed with a white-flowered pea. The seeds resulting from this cross are sown to produce first-generation hybrids, which have what biologists call the F_1 phenotype. (The phenotype is the appearance of a plant or animal that results from its genetic makeup, known as its genotype.) All of these plants have purple flowers.

This can be explained if it is assumed that the allele for purple (A) is dominant over the allele for white (a). If the F_1 generation is allowed to self-fertilize, and their seeds are planted, flowers of both colors are produced. But purple outnumbers white in the ratio of 3 to 1. This is because among the F_2 phenotypes one-quarter is AA and purple in color, two-quarters (one-half) are Aa and also purple (since A is dominant), and one-quarter is white (aa). White turns up only when two a recessives occur together.

Sometimes the gene for a characteristic is located on one of the sex chromosomes (in mammals they are X and Y). For example, a gene on the X chromosome prevents color blindness when functioning properly. If one allele is defective, the condition can develop. More males than females have this disorder, since they have only one X chromosome. In females, however, both alleles—one on each X chromosome—would need to malfunction before they developed the condition. The same applies with hemophilia.

This early photograph of a large 19th century family group shows the clear similarities between parents and children as well as the variation in appearance among the children.

KEY DATES

1856
Mendel begins experiments with pea plants

1865
Mendel reports to Brünn Natural History Society

1866
Mendel publishes his results

1900
De Vries, Correns, and Tschermak-Seysenegg confirm Mendel's findings

ASTRONOMY & MATH

EUROPE

1860 English astronomer and inventor Warren de la Rue (1815–89) shows that prominences visible during a solar eclipse are a feature of the surface of the sun.

1862 Swedish astronomer and physicist Anders Ångström (1814–74) identifies hydrogen in the sun's atmosphere (using a spectroscope).

1862 German astronomer Friedrich Argelander (1799–1875) publishes *Bonner Durchmusterung* (Bonn Survey), a catalog of more than 324,000 stars.

1863 Italian Jesuit priest and astronomer Angelo Secchi (1818–78) begins a four-year study of the stars, leading to a system of classifying stars according to their spectral type that is still used today.

The eyelike markings on the wings of Caligo eurilochus *butterflies—here on a piece of lemon—are an example of Batesian mimicry, in which harmless animals adopt the markings of harmful ones.*

THE AMERICAS

1862 American astronomers Lewis Swift (1820–1913) and Horace Tuttle (1837–1923) discover comet Swift–Tuttle, which causes the annual Perseid meteor shower.

ASIA & OCEANIA

1861 Australian astronomer John Tebbutt (1834–1916) discovers the long-period Tebbutt's comet. The Earth passes through the comet's tail—the first time this has been observed.

AFRICA & THE MIDDLE EAST

BIOLOGY & MEDICINE

1860 The first fossil of *Archaeopteryx* (a prehistoric flying reptile with some birdlike features) is found in a German quarry.

1860 English nurse Florence Nightingale (1820–1910) establishes the world's first training school for nurses in London.

1861 German anatomist Max Schultze (1825–74) defines a cell as a nucleus surrounded by living protoplasm.

1862 English naturalist Henry Bates (1825–92) defines Batesian mimicry, in which a harmless animal gains protection from predators by mimicking the coloration of an animal that is dangerous.

1862 German physician Felix Hoppe-Seyler (1825–95) establishes the presence of hemoglobin, the red oxygen-carrying pigment in the blood.

1862 German botanist Julius von Sachs (1832–97) establishes that starch is produced in plants by photosynthesis.

1863 French physician Casimir-Joseph Davaine (1812–82) identifies the bacterium that causes anthrax.

PHYSICAL SCIENCES

1860 English chemist and physicist Michael Faraday (1791–1867) presents his paper "Pressure Melting Effect" to the Royal Society, describing an experiment in which he lowers the freezing point of water by applying pressure.

1860 German chemist Robert Bunsen (1811–99) and German physicist Gustav Kirchhoff (1824–87) develop a technique for analyzing substances by their spectra. Using the new technique, they discover the elements cesium and, a year later, rubidium.

1860 German chemist Johann Greiss (1829–88) identifies diazo compounds. He later develops synthetic azo dyes.

1861 Scottish chemist Thomas Graham (1805–69) coins the term *colloid* to distinguish those materials in aqueous solution that will not diffuse through a parchment membrane (e.g., starch) from those that will (crystalloids, such as salt).

1862 Belgian chemist Ernest Solvay (1838–1922) patents an industrial process for making soda (sodium carbonate) from chalk (calcium carbonate) and common salt (sodium chloride).

HOW IT WORKS

Spectral Analysis

Robert Bunsen and Gustav Kirchhoff discovered new elements by analyzing their spectra. When a chemical element is heated strongly, electrons in its atoms "jump" to higher energy levels. When they fall back to their original levels, they give off light with characteristic wavelengths. In a spectrograph the wavelengths appear as colored lines (line spectra). Each spectrum has a unique pattern, like a fingerprint, and can be used to identify different elements.

Incandescent specimen

Lens

Slit

Second prism

First prism

Spectrum

LINE SPECTRA

Mercury

Potassium

Sodium

Lithium

ENGINEERING & INVENTION	WORLD EVENTS
1860 H.M.S. *Warrior*, the world's first iron-hulled warship, is launched in England. It is designed by Scottish engineer John Russell (1808–82).	**1860** Italian patriot Giuseppe Garibaldi (1807–82) leads an uprising in southern Italy, initiating unification of the country in 1861.
1860 German botanist Julius von Sachs (1832–97) introduces hydroponics, a method of growing plants without soil but using water and chemical fertilizers.	**1861** The Russian serfs are emancipated.
1863 French chemist Louis Pasteur (1822–95) introduces pasteurization, a process that kills bacteria with heat. At first it is used for treating wine.	**1862** Otto von Bismarck (1815–98) becomes prime minister of Prussia.
1863 Scottish engineer Robert Fairlie (1831–85) invents the Fairlie articulated locomotive, designed specifically for narrow-gauge railroads with tight curves.	**1863** Britain and other European countries adopt a gold standard for their currencies.
1863 The world's first underground railroad, the Metropolitan Line, opens in London using steam-hauled trains.	**1864** Henri Dunant (1828–1910) establishes the Red Cross in Switzerland.
1863 Built by French engineer Simon Bourgeois, *Le Plongeur*, a 140-foot (42.6-m) compressed air-driven submarine, is launched in France.	
1864 French engineer Pierre Michaux (1813–83) makes the first pedal bicycle.	
1860 Designed by American engineer Montgomery Meigs (1816–92), the Cabin John Bridge, the world's longest masonry arch, is completed.	**1860** The Pony Express is established, delivering mail across the western United States.
1861 A telegraph line is built in the United States from Omaha, Nebraska, to Carson City, Nevada. It links to local networks, giving transcontinental coverage.	**1861** The American Civil War (1861–65) starts when Confederate forces attack Fort Sumter, South Carolina.
1862 American inventor and gunsmith Richard Gatling (1818–1903) patents a rapid-fire, ten-barrel machine gun.	**1862** The French try to set up a puppet empire in Mexico.
	1864 Paraguay goes to war against Argentina, Brazil, and Uruguay in the War of the Triple Alliance (1864–70).
1861 Scottish-born Australian James Harrison (1816–93) builds the world's first large-scale meat-freezing plant, in which meat is prepared for export to Britain.	**1860** Robert O'Hare Burke (ca 1820–61) and William John Wills (1834–61) finish the first overland crossing of Australia; however, both die on the return journey.

ALFRED NOBEL

Alfred Bernhard Nobel (1833–96) was a Swedish chemist remembered for the invention of dynamite and for endowing the funds to pay for the annual Nobel prizes. He was born near Stockholm, the son of an inventor and industrialist, and taught mainly by his father after the family moved to St. Petersburg, Russia, in 1842. From 1852 Nobel worked for his father, but bankruptcy forced them to move back to Sweden in 1863.

Nobel soon built a factory in Stockholm. He experimented with producing nitroglycerin—a powerful but volatile explosive, which could be detonated by mild physical shock—but the factory exploded in 1864, killing his brother Emil. He was ordered to move his factory to a more isolated location. The explosives were still highly unstable, and his new factory in Krümmel, Germany, was twice destroyed by explosions.

In 1867 Nobel patented dynamite, which he created by mixing inert absorbent powder with nitroglycerin. Dynamite was relatively safe to manufacture and use. It soon replaced unstable nitroglycerin in mining and railroad construction projects. In 1875 Nobel invented the even safer blasting gelatin, or gelignite.

These inventions and holdings in the petroleum industry earned Nobel a huge fortune, which he left to the Nobel Foundation. Each year the foundation awards cash prizes in the fields of chemistry, physics, physiology or medicine, literature, economics, and peace.

ASTRONOMY & MATH

1866 English astronomer William Huggins (1824–1910) and English chemist William Miller (1817–70) discover the gaseous nature of some nebulas by studying their spectra.

1866 Italian astronomer Giovanni Schiaparelli (1835–1910) demonstrates that meteor showers are associated with the orbits of comets.

1866 French geologist Gabriel Daubrée (1814–96) suggests that the Earth's core is made of nickel–iron alloy.

1867 French astronomers Charles Wolf (1827–1918) and Georges Rayet (1839–1906) describe Wolf–Rayet stars. They are very hot stars that rapidly lose mass (as indicated by their irregular spectra).

1868 English astronomer William Huggins detects a Doppler shift (a shift to a longer wavelength) in the spectrum of the star Sirius and thereby demonstrates that the star is receding from Earth.

BIOLOGY & MEDICINE

1865 Austrian monk Gregor Mendel (1822–84) formulates Mendel's laws of inheritance.

1865 German botanist Julius von Sachs (1832–97) identifies chloroplasts, the structures in green leaves that contain chlorophyll.

1865 French physician Jean Villemin (1827–92) discovers the infectious nature of tuberculosis and states that it can be transmitted by contact between humans and animals, as well as from one animal to another.

1866 German anatomist Max Schultze (1825–74) distinguishes between rods and cones in the retina of the eye.

1867 English surgeon Joseph Lister (1827–1912) introduces phenol (carbolic acid) as a disinfectant in the operating room.

1867 German physiologist Julius Cohnheim (1839–84) explains the role of white blood cells in inflammation (in helping to form pus).

1868 In a rock shelter in southwestern France French paleontologist Louis Lartet (1840–99) excavates fossils of Cro-Magnon man, the earliest type of modern man, *Homo sapiens.*

PHYSICAL SCIENCES

1865 Belgian chemist Jean Servais Stas (1813–91) devises the first modern table of atomic weights using oxygen as a standard (set at 16).

1865 German physicist Rudolf Clausius (1822–88) coins the term *entropy* as a measure of the extent to which the energy of a system is unavailable (increasing the entropy decreases the energy).

1865 German chemist Joseph Loschmidt (1821–95) introduces Loschmidt's number, which is the number of particles (atoms or molecules) of gas per unit volume of the gas.

1866 German physicist August Kundt (1839–94) develops a method for determining the speed of sound in gases.

1866 Russian chemist Aleksandr Butlerov (1828–86) synthesizes isobutane, a gaseous hydrocarbon that later plays an important role in refrigeration.

1868 French astronomer Pierre Janssen (1824–1907) detects a bright yellow line in the sun's spectrum during an eclipse; English astronomer Joseph Lockyer (1836–1920) names this element helium.

1867 American surgeon John Bobbs (1809–70) introduces a surgical procedure called cholecystotomy to remove gallstones.

1866 The metric system is introduced in the United States but is largely ignored.

It is hard now to realize the dread and apprehension with which formerly even minor surgical operations were regarded. The change in our ideas is due partly to the discovery of anesthetics and perhaps even more to Lister's work.

KING GEORGE V OF THE UNITED KINGDOM (1927)

1865 In China French missionary and naturalist Armand David (1826–1900) discovers a new species of deer, Père David's deer (*Elaphus davidianus*).

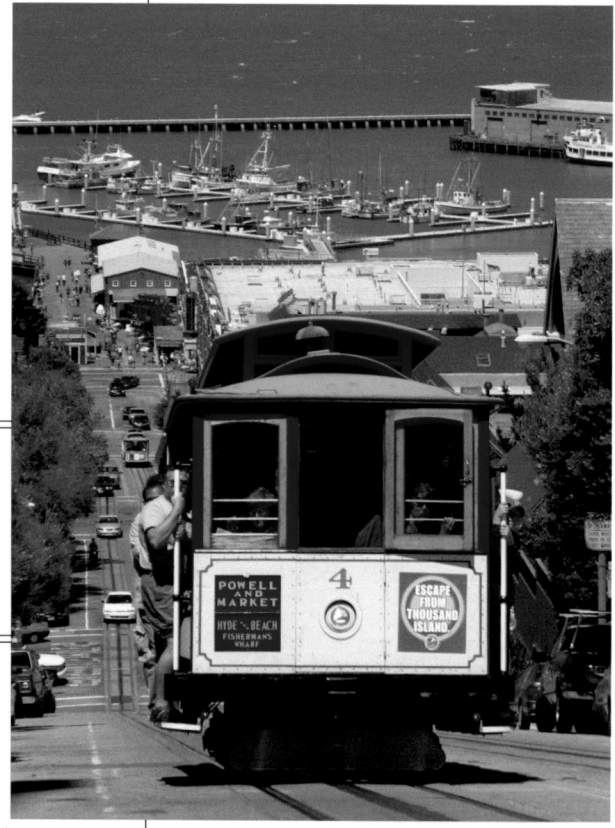

A cable car on a street in San Francisco, California

ENGINEERING & INVENTION	WORLD EVENTS

1865 German-born English metallurgist William Siemens (1823–83) and French engineer Pierre Martin (1824–1915) patent the open-hearth process for making steel.

1866 The Royal Aeronautical Society is founded in England.

1866 English engineer Robert Whitehead (1823–1905) builds a self-propelled torpedo, powered by compressed air.

1867 Swedish chemist Alfred Nobel (1833–96) patents dynamite in Britain. (U.S. patent 1868.)

1867 In Germany the first modern cantilever bridge, designed by German engineer Heinrich Gerber (1832–1912), is completed over the Main River.

1868 English inventor John Stringfellow (1799–1883) constructs a steam-powered model triplane.

Sticks of Alfred Nobel's explosive, dynamite

1865 Russian author Leo Tolstoy (1828–1910) publishes the first part of his great novel *War and Peace*, which he completes in 1869.

1867 Austria becomes Austria-Hungary with the establishment of the Dual Monarchy; already emperor of Austria, Francis Joseph I (r. 1848–1916) is now crowned king of Hungary at Budapest.

1867 The Italian revolutionary Giuseppe Garibaldi (1807–82) launches his third attempt to capture Rome for the nation of Italy but is defeated by the papal army and its French allies.

1867 German political philosopher Karl Marx (1818–83) publishes the first volume of his treatise on capitalist economics, entitled *Das Capital* (Capital).

1865 American locksmith Linus Yale (1821–68) perfects the cylinder lock and receives a second patent for it.

1865 American printer William Bullock (1813–67) invents the web-fed rotary printing press, which has the paper supplied to the press on a large roll.

1867 English-born American engineer Andrew Hallidie (1836–1900) invents the cable car, a type of streetcar that is hauled by a cable beneath the road surface.

1868 American engineer Eli Janney (1831–1912) invents the knuckle, or buckeye, coupler for railroad vehicles.

1868 American engineer George Westinghouse (1846–1914) designs the air brake for steam locomotives. It is soon adopted by railroads worldwide.

1865 Confederate forces under Robert E. Lee (1807–70) formally surrender at Appotomax Court House; the American Civil War (1861–65) comes to an end soon after.

1865 United States President Abraham Lincoln (1809–65) is assassinated by John Wilkes-Booth (1838–65).

1867 Russia sells Alaska to the United States for $7.2 million, about 2 cents an acre.

1867 The transportation of convicts from Britain to penal settlements in Australia comes to an end.

THE SUBMARINE

The first recorded attempt to build a submarine dates from about 1620, when Dutchman Cornelis Drebbel (1572–1633) covered a rowing boat with greased leather. It had waterproofed holes covered by leather flaps for the oars. In 1776 American student David Bushnell (ca 1742–1824) built a barrel-shaped, one-person submarine called the *Turtle*. It had a rudder, two hand-operated propellers (one for up-and-down movement and one for forward movement), and a hand ballast pump to allow the craft to surface.

A more successful submarine was built in France in 1801 by U.S. engineer Robert Fulton (1765–1815). The *Nautilus* was a slow, hand-cranked craft. At 21 feet (6.4 m) long, it could hold four people and enough air for three hours underwater. During the U.S. Civil War (1861–65), a replica of the submarine sank the Union ship *Housatonic* in Charleston Harbor, only to sink itself because its ram remained stuck in the ship's hull.

The first practical submarine, the U.S.S. *Holland*, was built in 1898. Designed by Irish-American John Holland (1840–1914), the craft used gas engines for surface propulsion and electric motors when submerged—a standard means of power for submarines until the launch of the nuclear-powered U.S.S. *Nautilus* in 1955.

Submarines have twin hulls: the gap between the hulls holds water that acts as ballast to make the vessel rise or sink in the water.

ASTRONOMY & MATH

BIOLOGY & MEDICINE

PHYSICAL SCIENCES

EUROPE

1870 English mathematician James Sylvester (1814–97) analyzes poetry mathematically in *The Laws of Verse*.

1872 German mathematician Richard Dedekind (1831–1916) publishes his theory of irrational numbers.

1872 The link between meteors and comets is reinforced when Hungarian astronomer E. Weiss predicts a meteor shower associated with a comet that had disappeared six years before. The shower occurs as predicted.

1872 Italian mathematician Luigi Cremona (1830–1903) introduces graphical statics, the use of graphical techniques to study forces in equilibrium.

1869 Swiss pathologist Johann Miescher (1844–95) isolates deoxyribonucleic acid (DNA), which he calls *nuclein*.

1869 English scientist Francis Galton (1822–1911) publishes his book *Hereditary Genius*. It becomes the basis of eugenics—the now disproven belief that genetics can be utilized to improve the physical and mental makeup of the human species.

1869 Norwegian physician Armauer Hansen (1841–1912) identifies the bacterium that causes leprosy, which is also known as Hansen's disease.

1869 German pharmacologist Matthias Liebreich (1839–1908) introduces the use of chloral hydrate as a sedative drug.

1869 French surgeon Gustav Simon (1824–76) pioneers nephrectomy, an operation to remove a kidney that is diseased.

1872 English-born chemist Robert Chesebrough (1837–1933) patents the process of making petroleum jelly. It is sold as a soothing ointment under the name of Vaseline.

1869 Russian chemist Dmitri Mendeleev (1834–1907) compiles the first Periodic Table of chemical elements.

1869 Northern Irish chemist and physicist Thomas Andrews (1813–85) publishes the results of his experiments on the liquefaction of gases, including the critical temperature for carbon dioxide.

1870 German physicist Ernst Abbe (1840–1905) introduces the use of his condenser to provide strong, even illumination for microscopes.

1870 German chemist Rudolf Fittig (1835–1910) makes aromatic hydrocarbons by combining two molecules of a halogen compound in the presence of sodium metal. It is known as the Wurtz–Fittig reaction.

1871 Irish physicist George Stoney (1826–1911) observes that three lines in the hydrogen spectrum have wavelengths in a simple ratio to each other. This finding is to be significant in interpreting atomic structure.

1872 German chemist Eugen Baumann (1846–96) prepares PVC (polyvinyl chloride). Much later, it becomes an important plastic.

THE AMERICAS

1869 American astronomer Charles Young (1834–1908) observes that during a solar eclipse the dark lines in the sun's spectrum brighten just before the eclipse is total.

1869 American meteorologist Cleveland Abbe (1836–1916) introduces the use of high-altitude balloons for studying the Earth's atmosphere.

1870 American astrophysicist Jonathan Lane (1819–80) publishes *On the Theoretical Temperature of the Sun*, in which he explains how gravitational contraction of gases in the sun caused it to heat up.

1872 American astronomer Henry Draper (1837–82) takes the first photograph of the spectrum of a star, Vega.

1869 American chemist John Hyatt (1837–1920) makes celluloid. His discovery is independent of the method used earlier by English chemist Alexander Parkes (1813–90) in 1855.

A young man poses on a "penny-farthing" bicycle, invented by James Starley in 1871. The penny-farthing was rendered obsolete by Starley's nephew's chain-driven "safety bicycle," designed several years later.

ASIA & OCEANIA

AFRICA & THE MIDDLE EAST

ENGINEERING & INVENTION	WORLD EVENTS
1869 French engineer Pierre Michaux (1813–83) constructs a steam-powered motorcycle.	**1870** The Franco–Prussian War (1870–71) breaks out; Prussian forces invade France, defeat the French army at Sedan, and lay siege to Paris. Emperor Napoléon III (r. 1852–70) is taken prisoner, bringing the Second Empire to an end.
1871 English engineer Francis Wenham (1824–1908) constructs a wind tunnel for testing airplane wings. It employs a steam-driven fan.	**1870** The annexation of the Papal States means that the unification of Italy is almost complete; only the Vatican Palace and its immediate environs remain outside the new nation.
1871 English inventor James Starley (1830–81) patents his "ordinary" bicycle with one large and one small wheel. It is nicknamed "penny-farthing" (a penny was a large coin and a farthing was a small coin).	**1871** Germany's Chancellor Otto von Bismarck (1815–98) declares Germany unified under William I, formerly king of Prussia but now emperor of the Second Reich (r. 1971–88).
1871 Belgian engineer Zénobe Gramme (1826–1901) markets a dynamo for heavy industrial use.	**1871** The Treaty of Frankfurt brings the Franco–Prussian War to an end. The French give up the disputed provinces of Alsace and Lorraine to Germany.
	1872 The secret ballot is introduced for elections in the United Kingdom.
1869 The Union Pacific transcontinental railroad is completed.	**1869** French settlers and French-speaking native peoples in what is now Manitoba rise up against the Canadian Confederation in the Red River Rebellion.
1869 American engineer Thomas Edison (1847–1931) makes an improved ticker-tape machine.	
1870 American engineer Lester Pelton (1829–1908) designs a new form of water turbine—the Pelton wheel impulse water turbine.	**1869** Susan B. Anthony (1820–1906) and Elizabeth Cady Stanton (1815–1902) found the National Women's Suffrage Association to campaign for women's suffrage (the right to vote) in the United States.
1871 American engineer Simon Ingersoll (1818–94) invents a pneumatic rock drill.	**1870** The 15th Amendment to the United States Constitution is passed, giving African Americans the right to vote.
1872 American gunsmith Benjamin Hotchkiss (1826–1885) invents a revolving-barrel machine gun.	**1871** The Great Chicago Fire destroys around 2,000 acres of the city of Chicago, leaving around 100,000 homeless.
	1869 The sailing clipper *Thermopylae* completes its maiden voyage from London to Sydney in 63 days. The voyage marks the beginning of a period of high-profile races between the fast cargo ships bringing tea from China to Europe.
1869 The Suez Canal is completed by French engineer Ferdinand de Lesseps (1805–94) from original plans by Austrian engineer Alois Negrelli von Moldelbe (1799–1858).	

THE BUILDING OF THE SUEZ CANAL

Located in Egypt and opened in 1869, the Suez Canal provided a waterway between Europe and Asia. Prior to the canal's construction ships traveling between Europe and Asia had to circumnavigate Africa or transport their cargoes over land.

A canal was dug in antiquity but fell into disuse by the eighth century. In 1858 Ferdinand de Lesseps, a French diplomat based in Cairo, was given the concession by the Viceroy of Egypt,

Sa'id Pasha (1822–63), to create the Suez Canal Company and construct a canal following the plans made by Austrian engineer Alois Negrelli. The excavation of the canal took 11 years, using the forced labor of up to 30,000 Egyptian workers.

The single-lane canal is around 100 miles (160 km) long. It incorporates several lakes and links the Mediterranean Sea at Port Said to the Gulf of Suez on the Red Sea. The canal has no locks since the terrain is flat.

The canal opened on November 17, 1869. Originally, its width was 200 feet (61 m) with a maximum depth of 24 feet (7.3m). (The canal has since been widened and deepened.) The passage of a ship takes up to 16 hours, traveling at about 8 knots (15 km) per hour. Today about 7.5 percent of the world's sea trade passes through the canal.

ASTRONOMY & MATH	BIOLOGY & MEDICINE	PHYSICAL SCIENCES

EUROPE

1873 French mathematician Charles Hermite (1822–1901) proves that *e* (the base of natural logarithms) is a transcendental number (an irrational number that cannot be represented by an equation in algebra).

1873 English mathematician William Shanks (1812–82) calculates π (pi) to 707 decimal places.

1873 English astronomer Richard Proctor (1837–88) proposes that craters on the moon were caused by the impact of meteorites, not by volcanoes as previously thought.

1874 French astronomer Jérôme Coggia (1849–1919) discovers Coggia's comet. It approaches to within 24,900 miles (40,000 km) of Earth, but will not return for more than 13,500 years.

1874 Russian-born German mathematician Georg Cantor (1845–1918) introduces the theory of transfinite numbers to mathematics.

1875 French astronomer Jules Violle (1841–1923) makes the first high-altitude measurement of the solar constant—the total amount of the sun's energy that reaches the top of the Earth's atmosphere.

1873 Italian physician Camillo Golgi (1844–1926) discovers the "black reaction," a new technique for staining nervous tissue with silver nitrate. Known as Golgi staining, it enables an entire nerve-cell body and its processes to be observed.

1873 Austrian physician Josef Breuer (1842–1925) discovers the sensory function of the semicircular canals in the ear, which help maintain balance.

1875 German physicians Wilhelm Erb (1840–1921) and Carl Westphal (1833–90) discover the knee-jerk reflex. This reflex gives a reaction to a stimulus without the involvement of the brain; it is sometimes used by physicians as a diagnostic aid.

1876 The gray squirrel (*Sciurus carolinensis*) is introduced into Britain from North America. It displaces the native red squirrels (*Sciurus vulgaris*).

1876 Polish-born German botanist Eduard Strasburger (1844–1912) describes mitosis, the process of cell division that results in two new identical cells. Belgian zoologist Edouard van Beneden (1846–1910) discovers centrosomes, the pair of structures that move apart as mitosis begins.

1873 Scottish physicist James Clerk Maxwell (1831–79) publishes *Electricity and Magnetism*, containing his electromagnetic theory of light—that light is a form of electromagnetic radiation (as also are radio waves and x-rays).

1873 Dutch physicist Johannes Van der Waals (1837–1923) derives Van der Waals' equation, which shows the relationship between the pressure and volume of a real gas (previous gas equations applied only to ideal, or perfect, gases).

1874 In his paper "On the Physical Units of Nature" Irish physicist George Stoney (1826–1911) coins the term *electrine* for the fundmental unit of electricity. He later (in 1891) changes it to *electron*.

1874 German chemist Othmar Zeidler synthesizes DDT (dichlorodiphenyl-trichloroethane), but does not realize its value as an insecticide.

1874 German chemist Ferdinand Tiemann (1848–99) synthesizes vanillin (the active taste ingredient in vanilla), the first artificial flavoring.

THE AMERICAS

1873 Canadian physician William Osler (1849–1919) discovers blood platelets (thrombocytes), small cells that are important in blood clotting.

1874 American physician Andrew Still (1828–1913) founds osteopathy, a system of medicine that mainly uses manipulation of bones and joints to treat disorders.

1876 American chemist and mathematical physicist J. Willard Gibbs (1839–1903) introduces the concept of chemical potential, which is important in determining whether a chemical reaction will take place.

ASIA & OCEANIA

Mr. Watson—Come here—I want to see you.

ALEXANDER GRAHAM BELL
FIRST WORDS SPOKEN ON A TELEPHONE, 1876

AFRICA & THE MIDDLE EAST

The European red squirrel has disappeared in many parts of Europe, replaced by the American gray squirrel.

ENGINEERING & INVENTION	WORLD EVENTS

1873 French engineer Amédée Bollée (1844–1917) constructs a steam-powered car.

1874 French engineer Jean-Maurice Baudot (1845–1903) patents a five-unit telegraph code, which later supplants Morse Code in continental Europe.

1875 A safe loading level for ships, known as the Plimsoll line, is introduced by an Act of the British Parliament. It becomes internationally recognized.

1876 German engineer Karl von Linde (1842–1934) develops the first practical refrigerator, which uses ammonia as a coolant.

1876 German engineer Nikolaus Otto (1832–91) builds a four-stroke internal combustion engine fueled by coal gas.

1876 Russian engineer Pavel Jablochkoff (1847–94) invents a self-adjusting arc lamp, known as an "electric candle."

1874 The first Impressionist exhibition is held in France. Claude Monet's (1840–1926) painting "Impression: Sunrise" gives the style its name, which was originally intended as a criticism.

1875 Rebellion breaks out in Bosnia against Ottoman rule. In Bulgaria the next year a similar uprising is brutally suppressed by the Ottoman army.

1875 A British polar expedition fails to reach the North Pole but succeeds in gathering scientific information and creating public interest in polar exploration, which will peak during the "Race for the Pole" at the end of the century.

1876 German composer Richard Wagner (1813–83) produces the complete *Ring Cycle* of operas for the first time.

1876 A new constitution restores the Spanish monarchy.

1874 The three-arch St. Louis Mississippi Bridge is built, designed by U.S. engineer James Eads (1820–87).

1875 Steam trains begin to run on an elevated railroad in New York City.

1876 Scottish-born American engineer Alexander Graham Bell (1847–1922) patents the telephone.

1876 American librarian Melvil Dewey (1851–1931) introduces the Dewey Decimal Classification system for cataloging library books.

1876 The Sioux army, led by Sitting Bull (ca 1831–90), defeat the U.S. forces led by General George Custer (1839–76) at the Battle of the Little Bighorn.

1876 The Molly Maguires, a violent workers' rights movement in the Pennsylvania coalfields, is broken up by the execution of ten of its leaders.

THE PERIODIC TABLE

By 1869, following discoveries using the new techniques of electrolysis and spectroscopy, there were 63 known chemical elements. They were the building blocks from which, in that year, Dmitri Mendeleev (1834–1907) constructed his famous periodic table.

Wishing to find some order in the apparent jumble of chemical elements, Mendeleev wrote the name of each on a card and then arranged the elements in order of increasing atomic weight (the average mass of each atom of the element). He found that if he started a new row of cards every eighth element, those with similar chemical properties fell one above the other in columns. Looking at the rows, he saw that properties tended to recur along each row—the properties possessed what he called "periodicity." He named his new grid the periodic table and even included additional "missing" elements that were still to be discovered. He predicted the chemical and physical properties of these elements, such as their atomic weights and melting points.

Mendeleev could not explain the reason for the periodicity of the elements. That explanation had to wait until scientists developed an understanding of the structure of atoms.

Today's periodic table contains about 50 more elements than in Mendeleev's time. They are arranged in order of their atomic numbers in seven horizontal "periods" of varying length. Two very long series of 14 elements each—the lanthanides following lanthanum (57) and the actinides following actinium (89)—are shown in separate lines at the foot of the table.

The Periodic Table (format: atomic number / symbol / atomic weight)

1	2	3	4	5	6	7	8	9	10	11	12	13	14	15	16	17	18
1 H 1.0079																	2 He 4.0026
3 Li 6.941	4 Be 9.0122											5 B 10.811	6 C 12.011	7 N 14.0067	8 O 15.9994	9 F 18.9984	10 Ne 20.1797
11 Na 22.9898	12 Mg 24.3050											13 Al 26.9815	14 Si 28.0855	15 P 30.9738	16 S 32.066	17 Cl 35.4527	18 Ar 39.948
19 K 39.0983	20 Ca 40.078	21 Sc 44.9559	22 Ti 47.88	23 V 50.9415	24 Cr 51.9961	25 Mn 54.9380	26 Fe 55.847	27 Co 58.9332	28 Ni 58.6934	29 Cu 63.546	30 Zn 65.39	31 Ga 69.723	32 Ge 72.61	33 As 74.9216	34 Se 78.96	35 Br 79.904	36 Kr 83.80
37 Rb 85.4678	38 Sr 87.62	39 Y 88.9058	40 Zr 91.224	41 Nb 92.9064	42 Mo 95.94	43 Tc 98.9072	44 Ru 101.07	45 Rh 102.9055	46 Pd 106.42	47 Ag 107.8682	48 Cd 112.411	49 In 114.82	50 Sn 118.710	51 Sb 121.76	52 Te 121.757	53 I 126.9045	54 Xe 131.29
55 Cs 132.9054	56 Ba 137.327	57 La 138.9055	72 Hf 178.49	73 Ta 180.9479	74 W 183.85	75 Re 186.207	76 Os 190.2	77 Ir 192.22	78 Pt 195.08	79 Au 196.9665	80 Hg 200.59	81 Tl 204.3833	82 Pb 207.2	83 Bi 208.9804	84 Po 208.9824	85 At 209.9871	86 Rn 222.0176
87 Fr 223.0197	88 Ra 226.0254	89 Ac 227.0278	104 Rf 261.11	105 Db 262.114	106 Sg 263.118	107 Bh 262.12	108 Hs (265)	109 Mt (266)	110 Uun (269)	111 Uuu (272)	112 Uub (277)	114 Uuq (285)		116 Uuh (289)		118 Uuo (293)	

58	59	60	61	62	63	64	65	66	67	68	69	70	71
Ce 140.115	Pr 140.9076	Nd 144.24	Pm 144.9127	Sm 150.36	Eu 151.965	Gd 157.25	Tb 158.9253	Dy 162.50	Ho 164.9303	Er 167.26	Tm 168.9342	Yb 173.04	Lu 174.967

90	91	92	93	94	95	96	97	98	99	100	101	102	103
Th 222.0381	Pa 223.0359	U 238.0289	Np 237.0482	Pu 244.0642	Am 243.0614	Cm 247.0703	Bk 247.0703	Cf 251.0796	Es 252.083	Fm 257.0951	Md 258.10	No 259.1009	Lr 262.11

ASTRONOMY & MATH

EUROPE

1877 Italian astronomer Giovanni Schiaparelli (1835–1910) reports the existence of "channels" on the surface of Mars, but his Italian word *canali* is mistranslated as "canal" and starts a long-standing argument.

1878 German astronomer Johann Schmidt (1825–84) publishes the last detailed map of the moon based on visual observation, hand-drawn by German astronomer Wilhelm Lohrmann (1796–1840).

1879 English astronomer George Darwin (1845–1912) suggests that the moon formed from crustal material flung off by the rapidly rotating Earth, with the moon moving gradually farther away as the Earth slowed down. The theory has been discredited only in the last 50 years. Currently the moon is thought to have formed after an Earth–asteroid collision.

1880 Scottish astronomer George Forbes (1849–1936) predicts the existence of "Planet X" orbiting beyond Uranus. The planet Pluto was found in 1930.

THE AMERICAS

1877 American astronomer Asaph Hall (1829–1907) discovers Phobos and Deimos, the two moons of Mars.

BIOLOGY & MEDICINE

EUROPE

1877 German bacteriologist Robert Koch (1843–1910) develops a method of staining bacteria (in order to study them through a microscope).

1877 German physiologist Wilhelm Kühne (1837–1900) suggests the name *enzyme* for a protein that acts as a catalyst in biochemical reactions.

1878 French physiologist Paul Bert (1833–86) demonstrates that nitrogen dissolved in the blood is the cause of "the bends" (decompression sickness), an illness suffered by divers and miners associated with significant drops in air pressure.

1879 Scottish surgeon William MacEwen (1848–1924) performs the first successful operation for the removal of a brain tumor.

1880 French parasitologist Alphonse Laveran (1845–1922) discovers the microorganism (a plasmodium) that causes malaria.

1880 French chemist Louis Pasteur (1822–95) identifies the *Streptococcus* bacterium.

1880 German bacteriologist Karl Eberth (1835–1926) discovers the bacterium that causes typhoid fever.

PHYSICAL SCIENCES

EUROPE

1877 French chemist Charles Friedel (1832–99) and U.S. colleague James Crafts (1839–1917) describe the Friedel–Crafts reaction, a method of introducing an alkyl group (such as methyl) into a benzene ring using an alkyl halide (such as methyl chloride) and a catalyst. The reaction becomes extremely important in organic chemistry synthesis.

1877 English physicist John Strutt, Lord Rayleigh (1842–1919), explains the nature of sound waves as alternate regions of high and low pressure in the air or another medium.

1878 German chemist Viktor Meyer (1848–97) identifies oximes, organic compounds characterized by the bivalent grouping C=NOH.

1879 Swedish chemist Per Cleve (1840–1905) discovers holmium and thulium. French chemist Paul Lecoq de Boisbaudran (1838–1912) discovers samarium.

1880 French physical chemist Pierre Curie (1859–1906) discovers the piezoelectric effect, which is the production of a voltage in a crystal that is under a mechanical stress.

THE AMERICAS

1879 American chemists Ira Remsen (1846–1927) and Constantine Fahlberg (1850–1910) discover saccharin, an artificial sweetener 2,000 times sweeter than sugar.

1879 American physicist Edwin Hall (1855–1938) observes the Hall effect, which is the production of a voltage across a conductor through which a current is flowing when it is placed in a magnetic field.

ASIA & OCEANIA

AFRICA & THE MIDDLE EAST

INSIDE STORY

Sound Waves

Sound waves are made by the vibration of an object or the air itself. When sound radiates out from a source, air does not move away from the source. Instead, the molecules in the air vibrate back and forth. Where the molecules are squeezed closer together, they are said to be compressed. Where they move apart, they are described as rarefied. The movement of the sound wave is the movement of this pattern of crowding and spreading out.

Compressed   Rarefied

Aviation pioneer Otto Lilienthal pilots one of his unpowered gliders. He steered by shifting his weight, as in a modern hang-glider.

ENGINEERING & INVENTION	WORLD EVENTS
1877 English physicist Joseph Swan (1828–1914) and American Thomas Alva Edison (1847–1931) develop the first electric light bulbs, demonstrated in 1878 (Swan) and 1879 (Edison).	**1877** An explosion caused by firedamp at a coal mine at Ballantyre, Scotland, kills more than 200 miners.
1877 Swedish engineer Carl de Laval (1845–1913) devises a centrifugal cream separator, the first practical application of the centrifuge.	**1877** Russia intervenes in the Balkans in support of local Slavs (Serbs and Montenegrins) rising against Ottoman rule. Britain and Austria ally to oppose Russian expansion in the region. A year later, a military standoff compels Russia to back down. The Berlin peace conference confirms the independence of Serbia, Romania, and Montenegro; Austria occupies Bosnia.
1877 German aeronautical pioneer Otto Lilienthal (1848–96) builds his first model glider.	

THOMAS EDISON

Thomas Alva Edison is America's most famous inventor. He was born in Milan, Ohio, in 1847. A childhood illness delayed his schooling and left him partially deaf. Edison's curiosity made him a poor student as a young man and later an easily distracted employee. After training as a telegraph operator, Edison patented a number of telegraph-related inventions, such as the quadruplex telegraph and an improved ticker-tape machine.

Many of Edison's initial inventions were successful, and he made a considerable amount of money from them. For example, the Automatic Telegraph Company paid him $40,000 for a machine that transmitted 500 words per minute. Using the

1879 English metallurgist Sidney Thomas (1850–85) and his cousin Percy Gilchrist (1851–1935) develop the basic (Gilchrist–Thomas) steelmaking process.

1879 English inventor Henry Lawson invents a chain driven bicycle, which he calls the bicyclette. It retains a number of features from the penny-farthing, such as the large front wheel, and is not a success.

Edison's phonograph used grooves etched into a wax cylinder to reproduce sound.

1877 American engineer Ephraim Shay (1839–1916) builds a geared steam locomotive, particularly suited to the steep grades on logging railroads.

1877 Thomas Alva Edison and Frenchman Charles Cros (1842–88) independently invent the phonograph.

1878 English-born American inventor David Hughes (1831–1900) devises the carbon microphone.

1879 American inventor James Ritty (1836–1918) patents the cash register.

1877 Large-scale labor unrest breaks out in the United States, with railroad strikes and riots.

1877 In the "Compromise of 1877" the disputed 1876 presidential election is resolved when the Democrats agree to concede defeat in exchange for the cessation of Reconstruction Republicans' attempts to reform and integrate the Southern states.

money gained from this and other inventions Edison moved to Menlo Park, 24 miles (39 km) from New York in 1876, where he built what he called an "inventions factory" that employed 50 technicians. Edison's Menlo Park laboratory was a commercial research facility in which scientists and engineers developed new technology.

At Menlo Park, Edison developed his most successful inventions. In 1877 he invented the phonograph as a dictating machine for business use. Edison went on to invent a megaphone, the kinetoscope (a type of movie projector), and a storage battery for a planned electric car. The light bulb, patented in 1879, proved his most enduring creation. The direct current electrical transmission method he developed to power his bulbs ultimately lost "the war of the currents" to alternating current systems developed by George Westinghouse (1846–1914) and Nikola Tesla (1856–1943).

1879 The first shipment of frozen meat is sent to England from Australia on board S.S. *Strathleven*. The trip lasts two months.

1879 The Zulu War breaks out in South Africa; British forces suffer a crushing defeat at Isandhlwana. The defeat of a modern British regiment by a Zulu force armed with spears and clubs shocks the colonial powers of the time.

GERMS AND DISEASE

DURING THE MIDDLE OF THE 19TH CENTURY scientists made the discovery that most diseases were caused by germs (microscopic bacteria or fungi) and not by "evil spirits" or "bad air," as previously assumed. With improved microscopes and new laboratory techniques, they set about tracking down these sometimes deadly microorganisms.

A view of bacterial cells multiplying. These cells have been stained with a special dye to make them easier to see.

As early as 1546 Italian physician Girolamo Fracastoro (ca 1478–1553), in his book *De Contagione et Contagiosis Morbis* (On Contagion and Contagious Diseases), suggested that germs are the cause of disease. Nobody took much notice, even after 1676, when Dutch scientist Antonie van Leeuwenhoek (1632–1723) first saw bacteria through a homemade microscope. (They were from his own mouth and were probably not disease-carrying.)

Then in 1840 German pathologist Jacob Henle (1809–85) put forward the idea that infection is caused by parasitic organisms, the so-called germ theory of disease, which was later proposed independently by French chemist Louis Pasteur (1822–95). In 1877 German bacteriologist Robert Koch (1843–1910) announced that bacteria could be stained to make them easier to study under a microscope. Seven years later Danish physician Hans Gram (1853–1938) extended this idea as a means of classifying bacteria, which since then have been dubbed either Gram-positive or Gram-negative, depending on their capacity to absorb a special stain. Bacteriologists also classify bacteria according to their shapes: coccus (round), bacillus (oval), spirochete (spiral), and so on.

Bacterial Discoveries

Once biologists knew what bacteria looked like, the hunt was on. The scientists who handled cultures of infectious diseases often put themselves at great risk, but results came quite quickly. In 1880 German bacteriologist Karl Eberth (1835–1926) found the bacillus that causes typhoid. In 1882 German bacteriologist Robert Koch found the bacterium that causes tuberculosis, and Germans Friedrich Löffler (1852–1915) and Wilhelm Schütz (1839–1920) identified the cause of the animal disease glanders. Later, in 1897 Danish veterinarian Bernhard Bang (1848–1932) discovered a bacillus that causes spontaneous abortion in cattle, and the Japanese bacteriologist Kiyoshi Shiga (1871–1957) found the cause of endemic dysentery.

Bacteria are not the only parasitic microorganisms to cause human diseases. Protozoans, for example, include the trypanosomes that cause sleeping sickness and Chagas' disease, the amoebas that result in amoebic dysentery, and the *Plasmodium* parasite responsible for malaria. Some microscopic fungi produce diseases that affect the skin or lungs. Most of these microorganisms were tracked down by 19th-century microbiologists.

In 1897 Dutch microbiologist Martinus Beijerinck (1851–1931) demonstrated that the microorganism that causes tobacco mosaic disease escapes through a filter that normally traps bacteria. He had discovered the

The various common shapes of bacteria are: monococcus (1), diplococcus (2), staphylococcus (3), vibrio (4), streptococcus (5), spirillum (6), spirochete (7), and bacillus (8).

first virus. A year later the virus that causes foot-and-mouth disease in cattle was discovered. Since then viruses have been found to be responsible for many diseases in humans, including yellow fever, influenza, polio, measles, and AIDS (acquired immune deficiency syndrome). Almost as fast as the bacteriologists found the bacteria that cause diseases, they managed to develop vaccines against them, so that people could be vaccinated and gain immunity. Vaccines for viral diseases proved more difficult but now exist for all the disorders named above except AIDS.

French physician Louis Pasteur holds the rabbits that he used for many of his early tests on vaccines. Pasteur confirmed the germ theory of disease and created the first vaccine for rabies.

KEY DATES

1546
Fracastoro suggests germs cause disease

1676
Van Leeuwenhoek discovers bacteria

1840
Henle's germ theory of disease

1884
Gram's stain to classify bacteria

1897
Beijerinck discovers viruses

ASTRONOMY & MATH	BIOLOGY & MEDICINE	PHYSICAL SCIENCES

EUROPE

1881 English mathematician John Venn (1834–1923) publishes *Symbolic Logic*, in which he introduces his ideas on logical relationships and develops Venn diagrams.

1884 German astronomer Max Wolf (1863–1932) discovers Wolf's comet, with an orbital period of only seven years.

1882 French anthropologist Alphonse Bertillon (1853–1914) develops the Bertillon system, which uses bodily measurements, physical descriptions, and photographs as a means of identifying criminals.

1882 German bacteriologist Robert Koch (1843–1910) discovers the bacterium that causes tuberculosis. A year later he discovers the bacterium that causes cholera.

1883 Swiss surgeon Emil Kocher (1841–1917) discovers the role of the thyroid gland in myxedema (goiter), and a year later German physiologist Moritz Schiff (1823–96) uses thyroid extract as a treatment for the disorder.

1884 German pathologist Edwin Klebs (1834–1913) and bacteriologist Friedrich Löffler (1852–1915) discover the microorganism that causes diphtheria (*Corynebacterium diphtheriae*).

1884 Danish physician Hans Gram (1853–1938) introduces a method of classifying bacteria by staining them.

1884 German bacteriologist Georg Gaffky (1850–1918) rediscovers the bacterium (*Salmonella typhi*) that causes typhoid fever.

1881 German scientist Hermann von Helmholtz (1821–94) demonstrates that hydrogen atoms have their electric charges in whole-number portions, implying that there is a unit of electrical charge (the charge has a finite minimum value).

1881 English physicist J. J. Thomson (1856–1940) uses Maxwell's equations of 1864 to predict that an object's mass changes when it becomes electrically charged (the concept of electromagnetic mass).

1882 German chemist Viktor Meyer (1848–97) discovers thiophene, an aromatic organic compound whose molecules consist of a ring of four carbon atoms and one sulfur atom. It later finds use as a solvent.

1883 Northern Irish engineer Osborne Reynolds (1842–1912) establishes the Reynolds number, which predicts how fluids will flow through pipes (e.g., whether or not the flow will be turbulent), enabling engineers to scale up models to design prototype machines.

1884 Swedish physical chemist Svante Arrhenius (1859–1927) begins to study the dissociation (splitting up) of electrolytes into ions in solution.

THE AMERICAS

1881 American astronomer Samuel Langley (1834–1906) makes a bolometer, a sensitive temperature-measuring device with which he measures the sun's radiation.

1881 American chemist and mathematical physicist J. Willard Gibbs (1839–1903) introduces a system of three-dimensional vectors.

1881 American astronomer Henry Draper (1837–82) and, a year later, Scottish astronomer David Gill (1843–1914) take the first photographs of comets.

1882 American physicist Albert Michelson (1852–1931) publishes his first calculation of the speed of light as 186,320 miles (299,853 km) per second. It is within 0.02 percent of the correct value and remained the most accurate measurement until Michelson improved on it in 1926.

ASIA & OCEANIA

German doctor Robert Koch (right), along with his contemporary French scientist Louis Pasteur, isolated the causes of many infectious diseases.

1883 Mount Krakatoa, an active volcano in Indonesia, erupts. The explosion is heard as far away as Perth, western Australia.

AFRICA & THE MIDDLE EAST

1883 The world's last quagga (an African animal resembling a zebra) dies in the Amsterdam Zoo.

ENGINEERING & INVENTION

1881 French engineer Charles Lartigue (1834–1907) constructs a steam-powered monorail railroad in Algeria. His design is also used for the monorail from Listowel to Ballybunion in Ireland, which opens in 1886.

1882 German engineer Werner von Siemens (1816–92) builds an electric trolleycar.

1883 Belgian engineer Étienne Lenoir (1822–1900) invents the spark plug (for internal combustion engines).

1884 American-born English inventor Hiram Maxim (1840–1916) makes the first fully automatic machine gun.

1884 English engineer Charles Parsons (1854–1931) develops a multistage steam turbine. It is used initially for powering boats.

Inventor Hiram Maxim demonstrates his machine gun.

1882 The first steam-powered electricity-generating plant in the United States, designed by American engineer Thomas Edison (1847–1931), opens on Pearl Street, New York City.

1884 American engineer Frank Sprague (1857–1934) forms the Sprague Electric Railway and Motor Company.

1884 German-born American inventor Ottmar Mergenthaler (1854–99) invents the linotype machine, which casts a whole line of type at once.

WORLD EVENTS

1881 Reforming Russian Tsar Alexander II (r. 1855–81) is assassinated by revolutionaries. He is succeeded by his reactionary and dictatorial son, Alexander III (1881–94).

1881 Romania becomes a kingdom, ruled by Carol I (r. 1881–1914).

1882 In the Phoenix Park Murders Britain's chief secretary for Ireland and his undersecretary are assassinated in Dublin by Irish nationalists (Fenians).

1883 Germany, Austro-Hungary, and Italy form the Triple Alliance.

1884 At the Berlin Conference European powers divide Africa into spheres of influence.

1881 James Garfield (1831–81) is assassinated by a disgruntled and probably insane campaign worker after less than a year as President of the United States.

1882 The Chinese exclusion act severely restricts Chinese immigration into the United States. Follow-up legislation will effectively end the immigration from eastern Asia.

1883 Chile emerges victorious from the War of the Pacific (1879–83), winning territory from Peru and all of Bolivia's coastal lands.

1882 The Indian Education Commission is established by Lord Ripon (1827–1909) to find ways of extending educational opportunities for Indian children.

1881 The First Boer War (1880–81) concludes with a British defeat at the battle of Majuba Hill. Britain concedes autonomy to Transvaal.

THE INTERNAL COMBUSTION ENGINE

In an internal combustion engine, fuel is burnt in a combustion chamber, causing the expansion of gases in the chamber that directly applies force to a movable part of the engine, such as a piston. This type of engine was devised by Belgian engineer Étienne Lenoir (1822–1900) in 1859 and improved by German engineer Nikolaus Otto (1832–91), who patented a coal-gas engine that worked in four stages, or strokes, in 1876.

In 1879, German engineer Karl Benz (1844–1929) made a two-stroke engine. It was lighter than a four-stoke engine, but less efficient. Benz and German engineer Gottlieb Daimler (1834–1900) independently made the first practical gasoline-burning internal combustion engines in 1885, heralding the age of the motor car.

Rudolf Diesel (1858–1913) designed the diesel engine in 1892, in which the compression cycle spontaneously ignites the fuel. Diesel engines are more efficient and cope better with moisture, making them ideal boat engines.

The stages of the four-stroke engine

$$S_{12}^{ik} \quad S_{kl}^{23} \quad S_{34}^{lm} \quad S^{4i} \quad \text{Wa}$$

$$S_{m}^{14} \quad S_{43}^{l}$$

Wechsel von Kovariant & Kontra

$$\mathcal{G} \quad S^{12}_{ik} \quad S_{2}^{23}_{k}{}_{l}$$

Dreier satz

$$S_{ik}^{11} \quad S^{2}_{kl} \quad S_{23}^{} \quad S^{31}_{mi} = 4$$

$$\int_i \quad S \cdot l \quad k \cdot l \cdot l \quad \pi \quad S_{23}^{}{}_{lm} \quad \gamma_m \gamma_i S_{mi} = 4$$

E VER SINCE AMERICAN FOUNDER AND SCIENTIST BENJAMIN FRANKLIN (1706–90) flew his kite in a thunderstorm in the 18th century, scientists had investigated the nature of electricity in order to better exploit this mysterious power. Eventually they established that static electricity is an accumulation of electric charges on an object, while current electricity is a flow of charges along a conductor such as a copper wire. Then in 1897 Cambridge University physicist J. J. Thomson (1871–1937) discovered the electron. The electron, a tiny negatively charged particle, is an essential part of all atoms and the elusive carrier of electric charge. Thomson's breakthrough was followed by the discovery by New Zealand-born Ernest Rutherford—who moved to Cambridge to work with Thomson—of the positively charged proton and predicting the existence of the uncharged neutron, which together nestle in the nuclei of nearly all atoms.

The discovery of the electron gave rise to a new branch of science, dubbed "electronics" in 1910. It began with the invention of radio, a method of transmitting radio waves—discovered by German physicist Heinrich Hertz (1857–94) in 1887—through the air. (The existing telegraph and the telephone were both restricted to places that were linked by wires.) In 1894 English physicist Oliver Hodge (1851–1940) used radio waves to transmit messages in Morse code; within less than a decade, Italian physicist Guglielmo Marconi (1874–1937) was transmitting Morse code messages from Cornwall in England, across the Atlantic Ocean, to Newfoundland in Canada. The first transmissions of music and human speech were made in 1906 by Canadian-born electrical engineer Reginald Fessenden (1866–1932) from a radio station in Massachusetts. Radios themselves meanwhile improved with the invention of electron tubes and the various circuits that employed them.

Another field that saw major advances was transportation. Great airships, the most famous being the Zeppelin—named for its designer Count Ferdinand von Zeppelin (1838–1917)—conquered the skies and established regular routes between continents. Their heyday did not last long. On a December day in 1093 U.S. brothers Wilbur (1867–1912) and Orville Wright (1871–1948) made the first heavier-than-air flight in North Carolina. Their biplane's longest flight that day lasted for just under a minute and covered 300 yards (280 m), but it opened up a new world of possibilities.

An illustrated French postcard from the early 1900s celebrates the achievement of French aristocrat Comte de Lambert, who in 1909 used a Wright brothers' biplane to circle 300 feet (90 m) above the Eiffel Tower, claiming an altitude record of 1,300 feet (396 m).

Financiers and city officials take the first train to run on New York City's subway, which opened on October 27, 1904. The subway used electric trains and served 28 stations.

On the railroads, meanwhile, steam-powered trains continued to rule, although the first electric trains were soon being developed. The first line to use electric trains was the City and South London Railway, a commuter subway that opened in 1890. The New York City subway followed in 1904.

Road transportation was also revolutionized when engineers began building motor cars. Earlier models used steam engines, but with the development of the internal combustion engine more powerful and efficient vehicles could be made. German engineers Karl Benz (1844–1929) and Gottlieb Daimler (1834–1900) and U.S. brothers Charles (1861–1938) and Frank Duryea (1869–1967) all produced gasoline-engined cars in the 1890s. But it was U.S. industrialist Henry Ford (1863–1947) who introduced mass-production techniques to car manufacturing at the start of the 20th century and made automobiles a part of everyday life. Sea travel improved, too, when in 1914 completion of the Panama Canal cut a total of 6,000 miles (9,650 km) off the voyage by sea between ports on the east and west coasts of America.

	1885	1889	1893	1897	1901
EUROPE	**1885** Austrian neurologist Sigmund Freud develops psychoanalysis. **1885** French scientist Louis Pasteur produces a rabies vaccine. **1886** German engineer Gottlieb Daimler makes a four-wheel car. **1887** German physicist Heinrich Hertz detects radio waves. **1887** Scottish inventor John Dunlop invents the pneumatic tire for bicycles.	**1889** The Eiffel Tower is completed in Paris. **1889** English inventor William Friese-Greene builds a motion-picture camera. **1891** German astronomer Max Wolf uses photography to discover an asteroid. **1891** Dutch anthropologist Eugène Dubois discovers fossils of human ancestor dubbed "Java man." **1891** English physicist John Poynting calculates the value of the gravitational constant. **1892** English scientist Francis Galton discovers that each human has unique fingerprints. **1892** Scottish physician James Dewar invents the vacuum bottle.	**1893** German inventor Rudolph Diesel builds the first compression–ignition (diesel) engine. **1893** French brothers Auguste and Louis Lumière make a motion-picture camera. **1895** German physicist Wilhelm Röntgen takes the first x-ray. **1896** French physicist Henri Becquerel discovers radioactivity. **1896** New Zealand-born English physicist Ernest Rutherford describes alpha and beta particles. **1896** Swedish physical chemist Svante Arrhenius proposes a link between the levels of carbon dioxide in the atmosphere and global temperatures.	**1897** Dutch botanist Martinus Beijirinck coins the term *virus*. **1897** German physicist Ferdinand Braun develops the cathode-ray tube. **1897** English physicist J. J. Thompson identifies the electron. **1898** English physician Ronald Ross discovers *Plasmodium*, the protozoal cause of malaria. **1900** German physicist Max Planck proposes quantum theory. **1900** The rigid airship *LZ-1*, designed by German engineer Graf Ferdinand von Zeppelin, makes its maiden flight. **1900** German chemist Friedrich Ernst Dorn discovers radon.	**1901** Italian physicist Guglielmo Marconi makes the first transatlantic radio broadcast. **1902** English physiologists Ernest Starling and William Bayliss coin the term *hormone* to describe secretin. **1903** Russian physiologist Ivan Pavlov describes the conditioned reflex. **1903** German surgeon Georg Perthes first uses x-rays to treat cancerous tumors. **1903** Russian rocket pioneer Konstantin Tsiolkovsky proposes the first practical theory of rocket propulsion. **1904** J. J. Thomson puts forward his model of the atom.
THE AMERICAS	**1885** American neurologist James Corning introduces spinal (epidural) anesthesia. **1885** American electrical engineer William Stanley develops the transformer. **1885** American architect William Jenney completes a steel-framed building in Chicago, the world's first skyscraper. **1886** American physician Reginald Fitz advocates appendectomy as a treatment for appendicitis.	**1889** American astronomer Edward Barnard takes the first pictures of the Milky Way. **1889** American undertaker Almon Strowger makes the first automated telephone exchange. **1892** New York City and Chicago are linked by a telephone line. **1892** American pathologists discover the bacterium that causes gas gangrene.	**1893** African-American surgeon Daniel Williams performs the first open-heart surgery. **1895** American astronomer James Keeler observes that Saturn's rings do not all rotate at the same speed. **1895** American inventor King Gillette designs the first disposable double-edged razor.	**1897** American physiologist Walter Cannon devises the barium meal to help diagnose digestive disorders. **1898** Irish-American John Holland builds the first modern submarine. **1900** Austrian-born American Karl Landsteiner discovers the ABO blood group system. **1897** A 40-inch (100-cm) refracting telescope is commissioned for the Yerkes Observatory in Williams Bay, Wisconsin.	**1901** Japanese-born American Jokichi Takamine isolates epinephrine (adrenaline). **1903** American brothers Wilbur and Orville Wright make the first sustained airplane flight. **1904** The first part of the New York City subway opens. **1904** American engineer Charles Kettering invents an electric cash register.
ASIA & OCEANIA		**1891** Australian inventor Lawrence Hargrave builds a successful model ornithopter—a flying machine propelled by flapping wings.	**1895** Australian-born David Bruce shows that the tsetse fly carries the parasite that causes sleeping sickness.	**1897** Japanese bacteriologist Kiyoshi Shiga identifies the bacterium that causes dysentery.	**1904** Japanese physicist Nagaoka Hantaro proposes the "Saturnian" theory of atomic structure.
AFRICA & THE MIDDLE EAST				**1899** Construction of a railroad between Istanbul and Baghdad begins.	**1901** The okapi is discovered by western explorers in central Africa. **1902** The first Aswan Dam is built in Egypt.

1905 | 1908 | 1911 | 1914 | 1917–1919

1905	1908	1911	1914	1917–1919
1905 German-born physicist Albert Einstein publishes his special theory of relativity.	**1908** German mathematician Ernst Zermelo introduces set theory.	**1911** Dutch physicist Heike Kamerlingh Onnes discovers superconductivity.	**1914** English physiologist Henry Dale and English chemist Arthur Ewins isolate acetylcholine.	**1917** Albert Einstein determines the cosmological constant.
1905 French cycling advocate Paul de Vivie invents the derailleur gear system for bicycles.	**1908** German chemist Fritz Haber discovers a way of making ammonia.	**1911** Scottish physicist C. T. R. Wilson invents the cloud chamber.	**1914** English military engineer Ernest Swinton proposes the concept of a tank.	**1917** English engineer Archibald Low invents an electronic control system for rockets.
1906 French mathematician Maurice Fréchet introduces functional calculus.	**1908** French anthropologist Marcellin Boule reconstructs a skeleton of a Neandertal.	**1911** German physicist Ferdinand Braun devises a scanning system for cathode-ray tubes.	**1914** English astronomer Arthur Eddington recognizes that nebulae are made up of millions of stars.	**1919** Austrian zoologist Karl von Frisch describes the "bee's dance."
1906 Austrian physician Clemens von Pirquet coins the term *allergy*.	**1909** Danish botanist Wilhelm Johannsen coins the term *gene*.	**1913** French physicist Charles Fabry discovers the ozone layer.	**1915** Scottish astronomer Robert Innes locates Proxima Centauri, the nearest star to the sun.	**1919** British aviators John Alcock and Arthur Brown make the first nonstop flight across the Atlantic Ocean.
1906 German chemist Paul Ehrlich establishes the structural formula of atoxyl.	**1909** Danish chemist Sören Sörensen introduces the concept of pH.	**1913** English geologist Arthur Holmes calculates Earth's age as 4.6 billion years.	**1916** Albert Einstein publishes his paper on the general theory of relativity.	**1919** Ernest Rutherford reports that he has artificially disintegrated nitrogen atoms by bombarding them with alpha particles.
1907 French engineer Louis Bréguet develops an early type of helicopter.	**1909** French aviator Louis Blériot flies across the English Channel.	**1913** English chemist Frederick Soddy discovers isotopes.	**1916** French physicist Paul Langevin experiments with ultrasound and produces a primitive form of sonar.	
	1910 Ernest Rutherford proves the existence of the nucleus of an atom.	**1913** Danish physicist Niels Bohr proposes his model of the atom.		
1905 American surgeon John Murphy pioneers arthroplasty.	**1908** The first Model T Ford comes off the assembly line.	**1911** American airman Calbraith Rogers makes the first flight (with stops) across the United States.	**1914** American biochemist Edward Kendall isolates thyroxine.	**1917** American nurse Margaret Sanger opens a birth control clinic in the United States.
1906 Canadian-born American engineer Reginald Fessenden makes AM (amplitude modulation) radio transmissions.	**1908** American physicist William Coolidge uses tungsten to make an incandescent filament lamp.	**1913** American geneticist Alfred Sturtevant introduces chromosome mapping.	**1915** American astronomer Walter Adams identifies Sirius B as the first white dwarf star.	**1917** Black & Decker make their first electric hand drill.
1907 Amercian zoologist Ross Harrison develops *in vitro* tissue culture.	**1908** American electrical engineer Edward Weston's cadmium cell (battery) is adopted as an international voltage standard.	**1913** American physicist Robert Millikan calculates the charge on an electron.	**1915** American surgeon Alexis Carrel performs open-heart surgery on a dog.	**1918** American physiologists William Howell and Luther Holt discover the anticoagulant heparin.
1907 Belgian-born American chemist Leo Baekeland invents bakelite plastic.		**1913** American physicist William Burton patents a thermal cracking method for processing crude oil.	**1916** American chemist Gilbert Lewis describes the nature of covalent chemical bonds.	**1919** American astronomer George Hale reveals that sunspots reverse their magnetic field every 22 to 23 years.
1905 Astronomer John Grigg observes a comet from his observatory in New Zealand.	**1908** The "Tunguska event" occurs in Siberia. It is thought to be the collision of a comet with Earth.	**1911** A public demonstration of an aircraft takes place in New Zealand.	**1915** Coal tar is shown to cause cancer by Japanese researchers.	**1917** A railroad crossing Australia from east to west is completed.
		1912 The Komodo dragon is found by Europeans in Indonesia.	**1916** Japanese physicist Kotaro Honda makes Alnico—an alloy of aluminum, nickel, and cobalt.	
		1912 Israeli chemist Chaim Weizmann uses bacteria to produce acetone.		

ASTRONOMY & MATH

EUROPE

1885 A supernova flares up in the Andromeda galaxy; no other supernova visible to the naked eye will appear until 1987.

1888 German astronomer Heinrich Kreutz (1854–1907) reveals the Kreutz sungrazer comets, which travel very close to the sun and orbit it in the opposite direction to most other comets.

1888 Danish astronomer Johan Dreyer (1852–1926) publishes the *New General Catalogue of Nebulae and Clusters of Stars* (NGC). Astronomers still use Dreyer's NGC numbers.

In the late 19th century the study of comets and their orbits was a very popular branch of astronomy, with many new comets being discovered and named.

THE AMERICAS

1886 American physicist Henry Rowland (1848–1901) maps 14,000 lines of the sun's spectrum, using his improved ultrafine diffraction grating.

BIOLOGY & MEDICINE

1885 Austrian neurologist Sigmund Freud (1856–1939) develops psychoanalysis as a diagnostic procedure.

1885 French chemist Louis Pasteur (1822–95) produces a vaccine against rabies.

1886 French neurologist Pierre Marie (1853–1940) describes the disfiguring disorder acromegaly (caused by the overproduction of growth hormone).

1886 Dutch botanist Hugo de Vries (1848–1935) observes that plants occasionally have offspring that differ markedly from their ancestors and later coins the term *mutations* to describe new forms or varieties of plants that arise randomly.

1887 German cell biologist Theodor Boveri (1862–1915) describes polar bodies (small cells that arise from the division of an unfertilized egg).

1888 German biologist Wilhelm von Waldeyer-Hartz (1836–1921) coins the term *chromosome*.

1885 American neurologist James Corning (1855–1923) introduces spinal (epidural) anesthesia.

1886 American physician Reginald Fitz (1843–1913) advocates appendectomy as a treatment for appendicitis. A year later physician Thomas Morton (1835–1903) performs the first successful operation in the United States.

PHYSICAL SCIENCES

1885 Austrian chemist Karl Auer von Welsbach (1858–1929) isolates the elements neodymium and praseodymium. They were previously thought to be a single element.

1885 Swiss physicist Johann Balmer (1825–98) deduces a mathematical formula for the lines in the atomic spectrum of hydrogen; it provides important information about atomic structure.

1886 German chemist Clemens Winkler (1838–1904) discovers germanium, whose existence was predicted in 1869 by Dmitri Mendeleev (1834–1907) from one of the gaps in his periodic table.

1887 German chemist Emil Fischer (1852–1919) synthesizes fructose, the sugar found in fruits.

1887 German physicist Heinrich Hertz (1857–94) detects radio waves.

1887 Austrian physicist Ernst Mach (1838–1916) observes that airflow becomes turbulent as it approaches the speed of sound.

1886 American chemist Charles Hall (1863–1914) and, independently, French chemist Paul Héroult (1863–1914) devise a method for the electrolytic extraction of aluminum from its ore. The Hall–Héroult process is the mainstay of the aluminum industry today.

1887 American physicist Albert Michelson (1852–1931) and American chemist Edward Morley (1838–1923) carry out an experiment that indirectly proves that the ether does not exist. (The ether was thought to be needed to "carry" light waves.)

ASIA & OCEANIA

AFRICA & THE MIDDLE EAST

HOW THINGS WORK

The Transformer

The transformer transfers electric energy from one AC (alternating current) circuit to another, either increasing (stepping up) or reducing (stepping down) the voltage. Transformers consist of two coils of wire wrapped around a magnetic core and work on the principle of magnetic induction. The current of the primary coil induces an alternating magnetic field in the core that induces a current in the secondary coil. In a step-down transformer the number of turns of wire on the primary coil is greater than the number of turns on the secondary coil, thus reducing the voltage. In a step-up transformer the secondary coil has more turns and therefore develops a higher voltage.

ENGINEERING & INVENTION

1885 German engineer Karl Benz (1844–1929) builds a three-wheeled car. A year later Gottlieb Daimler (1834–1900) makes a motorcycle. Both independently build internal combustion engines.

1885 German chemist Karl Auer von Welsbach (1858–1929) patents the gas mantle, which produces an incandescent white light in a coal-gas flame.

1886 German engineer Gottlieb Daimler produces a four-wheeled gasoline-engined car.

1887 Scottish inventor John Dunlop (1840–1921) develops the pneumatic tire for bicycles.

1887 German-born engineer Emile Berliner (1851–1929) devises the disk gramophone record. It soon supersedes the cylinder records of Thomas Edison's phonograph.

1885 American architect William Jenney (1832–1907) completes a steel-framed building in Chicago, the world's first skyscraper.

1885 American inventor Tolbert Lanston (1844–1913) patents a "monotype" machine for casting metal-type characters.

1885 American electrical engineer William Stanley (1858–1916) develops the transformer.

1886 American pharmacist John Pemberton (1831–88) invents Coca-Cola.

1886 The town of Montgomery, Alabama, becomes the first in the United States to have an electric trolley system.

Psychiatry is the art of teaching people how to stand on their own feet while reclining on couches.

SIGMUND FREUD

WORLD EVENTS

1885 The Prussian government, encouraged by Otto von Bismarck (1815–98), orders the expulsion of all ethnic Poles and Jews who do not hold German citizenship.

Gottlieb Daimler's 1886 automobile

1885 The Rock Springs Massacre, an outbreak of violence between white and Chinese miners, takes place in Rock Springs, Wyoming. Twenty-eight Chinese miners are killed, and hundreds more are injured or left homeless.

1886 The Statue of Liberty, a gift from the French people, is dedicated by President Grover Cleveland (1837–1908).

1885 The Panjdeh Incident, a military confrontation between Afghanistan and Russia, takes place. This increases tensions between Russia and the British Empire almost to the point of war.

Sigmund Freud's Jewish ancestry forced him to leave Nazi-controlled Vienna in 1938. He settled in London, England, and died the following year of oral cancer.

SIGMUND FREUD

Sigmund Freud (1856–1939) was an Austrian physician who founded the discipline of psychoanalysis. He was born in Freiburg, then part of the Austrian Empire, and studied neurology at Vienna University.

In 1885 Freud left Austria to study with the renowned French neurologist Jean-Martin Charcot (1825–1893). A year later Freud established his own clinic in Vienna and developed his revolutionary "talking cure," in which the patient was encouraged to try and explain his or her problems.

Freud's treatments centered on the concept of the unconscious—a set of desires, fears, and needs that direct people's actions without them being aware of their existence. He divided the human personality, or psyche, into three areas: the *ego*, the *superego*, and the *id*. The *ego* is the realistic, rational mind; the *superego* is the regulating conscience; and the *id* is the home of unconscious drives and desires. Freud believed that dreams were manifestations of these unconscious desires.

In his time Freud's ideas were highly controversial, especially his studies into human sexuality. Although many of his ideas about the nature of the psyche have now been disregarded, Freud's "talking cure" has become an essential part of modern psychoanalysis.

SOURCES OF ELECTRICITY

BEFORE 1800 SCIENTISTS KNEW ONLY ABOUT electricity that was stationary, or static. This static electricity consists of a positive or negative charge on an object, usually produced by friction. Then an Italian count produced an electric current—this was electricity on the move.

In 1791 Italian physician Luigi Galvani (1737–98) reported what he called "animal electricity." While dissecting a dead frog, he found that the animal's muscles twitched when he touched them with two different metals. Then in 1800 Alessandro Volta (1745–1827), an Italian count, replaced the animal tissue with a disk of cardboard soaked in salt solution. He put a piece of copper or silver on one side and a piece of zinc on the other side. Wires connected to the metal plates carried an electric current. Volta found he could obtain higher voltages by making a stack of such disks to form what became known as a voltaic pile, which was the first true battery.

Today scientists call such a battery a primary cell. The pieces of metal are called electrodes, and the solution between them is an electrolyte. In 1836 English chemist John Daniell (1790–1845) produced a more efficient type of primary cell. It consisted of a zinc rod electrode dipped in dilute sulfuric acid, contained in a porous earthenware pot. He immersed the pot in a copper container (which acted as the other electrode) containing copper sulfate solution. In the Daniell cell an electric current flows from the copper (the positive electrode, or anode) to the zinc (the negative electrode, or cathode). It gives a steadier current than Volta's cell and overcomes the problem of polarization—a build-up of hydrogen bubbles on the copper electrode that eventually stops the flow of electrons and causes the voltaic pile to stop working.

The Leclanché Cell

Invented in 1866 by French engineer Georges Leclanché (1839–82), the Leclanché cell also avoids polarization. It too has a zinc cathode, but it dips into an electrolyte of ammonium chloride solution. The anode is a carbon rod surrounded by powdered manganese dioxide. It produces about 1.5 volts. Today's common type of dry battery has the same system, using a zinc case containing a paste of ammonium chloride with a carbon rod surrounded by manganese dioxide down the center.

The German chemist Robert Bunsen (1811–99) also made a zinc–carbon primary cell; using acid electrolytes, it produces 1.9 volts. The cadmium cell,

A primary cell, such as the dry battery for a flashlight, can be used only until its chemicals run out, when it has to be thrown away (carefully). In this type of cell the electrolyte is a paste of ammonium chloride and gum. The zinc cathode forms the case of the battery, and manganese dioxide and carbon surround the central carbon anode.

DRY BATTERY

Zinc case

Carbon rod

Carbon and manganese dioxide

Ammonium chloride paste

ACCUMULATOR IN USE

Lead with lead oxide

Lead

Sulfuric acid

Sulfate ions

Hydrogen ions

ACCUMULATOR ON CHARGE

Sulfate ions

Hydrogen ions

A secondary cell, or accumulator, can be recharged when it runs down, and reused. It has lead and lead-oxide electrodes in a sulfuric acid electrolyte. When it is in use, sulfate ions react with the lead cathode to produce lead sulfate and release electrons. At the anode hydrogen ions from the acid and sulfate ions react with the lead oxide to produce lead sulfate and water. The reactions produce about two volts.

To recharge the accumulator, current from an outside source is passed through the battery in the opposite direction. This has the effect of reversing the reactions at the electrodes, reforming lead and lead oxide. The accumulator is then ready for use again (for example, car batteries).

Alessandro Volta took every opportunity to demonstrate his new battery. Here he shows it to Napoleon Bonaparte, emperor of France.

invented in 1893 by English-born American electrical engineer Edward Weston (1850–1936), produces 1.0186 volts, and in 1908 the scientific community accepted it as a standard of voltage. Known as the Weston standard cell, it has mercury (cathode) and a cadmium–mercury mixture (anode) as its electrodes, with cadmium sulfate solution as its electrolyte.

Accumulators

A primary cell stops working when it is fully discharged. A different type, called variously a secondary cell, a storage cell, or an accumulator, can be recharged. The lead–acid accumulator, devised in 1859 by a French chemist, Gaston Planté (1834–89), is the earliest and still the most commonly used kind. It has one electrode (or "plate") of lead and one of lead covered with lead oxide, which dip into a sulfuric acid electrolyte. This is the type of battery used in most cars. The alkaline nickel–iron accumulator, or Ni–Fe cell, is another type, devised in 1900 by American inventor Thomas Edison (1847–1931). When any accumulator becomes discharged, it can be connected to a supply of DC (direct current) and recharged. For example, while a car's motor is running the battery is continually recharged.

Primary and secondary cells convert chemical energy into electrical energy. To do so, they "consume" materials in the electrodes or electrolyte. A fuel cell, however, converts the chemical energy of a fuel directly into electrical energy. The first fuel cell that "consumed" hydrogen and oxygen gases was demonstrated in 1839 by Welsh physicist William Grove (1811–96).

KEY DATES

1800
Voltaic pile

1836
Daniell cell

1859
Lead-acid accumulator

1866
Leclanché cell

1893
Weston cadmium cell

1900
Nickel-iron accumulator

ASTRONOMY & MATH

1889 Italian astronomer Giovanni Schiaparelli (1835–1910) states, incorrectly, that the planet Mercury rotates on its axis so that it always presents the same face to the sun (as the moon always faces the Earth the same way).

1889 German astronomer Hermann Vogel (1842–1907) and American astronomer Edward Pickering (1846–1919) discover spectrographic binary stars, two-star systems that reveal they are double stars by the way their spectrum varies.

1890 English mathematical physicist Oliver Heaviside (1850–1925) introduces operational calculus for studying short-lived electrical phenomena.

1891 German astronomer Max Wolf (1863–1932) locates Brucia, the first asteroid discovered by photography.

BIOLOGY & MEDICINE

1889 French bacteriologists Émile Roux (1853–1933) and Alexandre Yersin (1863–1943) isolate the diphtheria toxin.

1890 German bacteriologist Emil von Behring (1854–1917) and coworkers develop antitoxins against diphtheria and tetanus.

1891 Dutch anthropologist Eugène Dubois (1858–1940) discovers fossils of the human ancestor "Java man," which he names *Pithecanthropus*. Today it is classified as *Homo erectus*.

1891 German physiologist Karl von Voit (1831–1908) demonstrates that the body converts excess sugars into glycogen as an energy reserve.

1892 English scientist Francis Galton (1822–1911) states in his book *Finger Prints* that no two people have the same fingerprints, and advocates the use of such prints in crime detection.

1892 German bacteriologist Robert Koch (1843–1910) introduces filtration of water to control a cholera epidemic in Hamburg, Germany.

PHYSICAL SCIENCES

1889 English chemist Frederick Abel (1827–1902) and Scottish physicist James Dewar (1842–1923) develop the propellant explosive cordite.

1889 Swedish physical chemist Svante Arrhenius (1859–1927) derives the Arrhenius equation, which provides a way of calculating the speed of a chemical reaction.

1890 Hungarian physicist Roland von Eötvös (1848–1919) demonstrates that gravitational mass and inertial mass are the same.

1891 Irish physicist George Stoney (1826–1911) coins the term *electron* for the fundamental unit of electricity (from his earlier *electrine* of 1874).

1891 English physicist John Poynting (1852–1914) calculates the value of the gravitational constant.

1889 American astronomer Edward Barnard (1857–1923) takes the first photographs of the Milky Way (our galaxy).

1892 Edward Barnard discovers Amalthea, one of Jupiter's moons.

1889 American microbiologist Theobald Smith (1859–1934) discovers the cause of Texas cattle fever, the protozoan parasite *Babesia*, and shows that it is transmitted by a cattle tick.

1892 American pathologists William Welch (1850–1934) and George Nuttall 1862–1937) discover *Clostridium welchii*, the microorganism that causes gas gangrene.

1891 American chemist Edward Acheson (1856–1931) makes carborundum (silicon carbide), an ultrahard compound used as an abrasive.

Each person's fingerprints have a unique pattern. Fingerprints are routinely used by the police to identify suspected criminals.

EUROPE

THE AMERICAS

ASIA & OCEANIA

AFRICA & THE MIDDLE EAST

INSIDE STORY

Fleming's Rules

In 1890 British scientist John Fleming formulated rules relating to electrical machines—the left-hand rule to motors and the right-hand rule to dynamos. When the first finger, second finger, and thumb are extended at right angles to one another, the first finger indicates the direction of the field, the second finger the direction of the current, and the thumb the direction of the force (motion).

ENGINEERING & INVENTION

1889 The Eiffel Tower is completed in Paris, France, designed by French engineer Gustave Eiffel (1832–1923).

1889 English inventor William Friese-Greene (1855–1921) builds a motion-picture camera.

1890 French engineer Clément Ader (1841–1926) builds a piloted steam-powered monoplane. However, it is unsuitable for sustained flight.

1891 German aeronautical pioneer Otto Lilienthal (1848–96) makes a steerable human-carrying glider.

1892 French engineer François Hennebique (1842–1921) develops prestressed concrete, in which the reinforcing rods are tensioned before the concrete is poured.

1892 Scottish physicist James Dewar (1842–1923) invents the vacuum bottle (sold as a flask under the trade name Thermos).

1889 American scientist Franklin King (1849–1911) devises the cylindrical tower silo for storing animal feed.

1889 American undertaker Almon Strowger (1839–1902) makes the first automatic telephone exchange (patented 1891).

1890 American inventor Herman Hollerith (1860–1929) creates a punch-card reader for recording the results of the 1890 United States census.

1891 American inventor George Blickensderfer (1850–1917) patents a portable typewriter.

1892 A telephone line linking New York City and Chicago goes into operation.

1891 English-born Australian inventor Lawrence Hargrave (1850–1915) builds a successful model ornithopter, propelled by flapping wings.

WORLD EVENTS

1889 An attempt to build a canal across the isthmus of Panama envisaged by French engineer Ferdinand de Lesseps (1805–94)—designer of the Suez Canal—fails.

1889 Charles Stuart Parnell (1846–91), leader of the Irish Nationalist cause in the British Parliament, is brought down by a scandal relating to an adulterous love affair.

1890 Kaiser Wilhelm II (r. 1888–1918) dismisses Germany's long-serving chancellor Otto von Bismarck (1815–98).

1889 Emperor Pedro II of Brazil (r. 1831–89) is overthrown in a military coup; the country becomes a republic.

1890 Sioux refugees are massacred at Wounded Knee, South Dakota, by U.S. cavalrymen.

1892 Pitched battles break out between striking workers and the owners of the Homestead Steelworks, Pittsburgh. The eventual outcome is a demoralizing defeat for organized labor in the United States.

Until the construction of the Chrysler Building in New York City in 1929, the Eiffel Tower in Paris was the tallest structure in the world.

1889 Japan's New Constitution establishes a diet or parliament but restricts its powers severely. The emperor will be Japan's true ruler.

1889 New Zealand holds its first democratic general election based on full male suffrage.

1889 British South Africa Company—run by Cecil Rhodes (1853–1902)—is granted a charter to exploit territories to the north of the British Cape Colony in what is now Zimbabwe.

THE EIFFEL TOWER

One of the most famous and instantly recognizable landmarks in the world, the Eiffel Tower (French: *Tour Eiffel*) is a masterpiece of iron construction. The building was designed by French civil engineer Gustave Eiffel and constructed between 1887 and 1889 in time to celebrate the centenary of the French Revolution. At the time of completion the tower—standing 984 feet (300 m) tall—was the tallest artificial structure in the world, nearly doubling the height of the previous record holder: the Washington Monument in Washington, D.C., which was completed in 1884.

The tower was constructed using 7,300 tons (6,600 tonnes) of iron. The structural girders and braces were made from a strong type of iron known as "puddle iron." About 2.5 million rivets were used to create the tower's lattice-work of girders, bars, and braces. At each of the tower's four corners, a lattice-girder pier tapers inward, with the four meeting to form a single vertical tower. The piers are connected at two levels by girders. These levels serve as viewing platforms for tourists and are accessible by stairways and elevators. A third level toward the summit is accessible only by elevator. The top of the tower can sway up to 3 inches (7.5 cm) in the wind. The tapering design of the tower enhances its resistance to wind. The tower can also lean up to 7 inches (18 cm) due to thermal expansion of the metal on the side facing the sun.

Although it is now an internationally recognized symbol of Paris, the tower was not well received at first by Parisians. A petition calling for its demolition was published in newspapers before it was even finished. In 1909 it was saved from demolition only because it had a useful role as a telecommunications tower.

THE INVENTION OF RADIO

At the beginning of the 20th century the Italian inventor Guglielmo Marconi was the first to develop radio into a reliable means of international communication.

RADIO IS A METHOD OF COMMUNICATION that uses electromagnetic radiation known as radio waves, which travel at the speed of light. It used to be called wireless to distinguish it from telegraphs and telephones, which both needed wires running between the sender and the receiver to transmit their signals.

Radio had its origins in the late 19th century. Scottish physicist James Clerk Maxwell (1831–79) predicted the existence of electromagnetic radiation in 1864 and concluded that light is just one part of the spectrum of electromagnetic radiation. German physicist Heinrich Hertz (1857–94) discovered a new type of radiation—radio waves—in 1887. He made electrical waves (then called Hertzian waves) by letting a high-voltage spark jump between two metal spheres.

In 1890 French physicist Édouard Branly (1844–1940) devised a way of detecting radio waves using a "coherer," a sealed glass tube containing iron filings and an electrode at each end. When radio waves are present, the filings cohere (stick together) and conduct electricity well enough to form part of a circuit. English physicist Oliver Lodge (1851–1940) improved the coherer in 1894 and used it together with a spark transmitter to send Morse code messages a distance of 490 feet (150 m).

Unaware of these developments, Italian physicist Guglielmo Marconi (1874–1937) also began experimenting with radio in 1894 and in the process invented a radio antenna and the use of a ground (earth) with the apparatus. He could soon transmit coded messages more than 1.8 miles (3 km). The invention, known as radiotelegraphy, developed rapidly, especially after Marconi moved to England in 1896. By 1901 he was able to transmit signals in Morse code across the Atlantic Ocean.

So far, radio was better than the telegraph only because it did not need wires. The telephone, which needs wires, can carry speech. Could radio be made to carry the human voice? This question led to the development of radiotelephony. The early work was done by Canadian-born American electrical engineer Reginald Fessenden (1866–1932), who invented modulation. Radiotelegraphy sends out pulses of short and long signals representing the dots and dashes of Morse code. In radiotelephony the transmitter sends out a continuous signal, called a carrier wave, whose amplitude (strength) is varied (modulated) in step with the variations in the sound signals from a microphone. Fessenden first demonstrated AM (amplitude modulation) in 1903, and in 1906 he transmitted speech and music from a radio station in Massachusetts.

Crystal Detectors

The new system needed a better detector. This came in the form of a crystal detector produced by American electrical engineer Greenleaf Pickard (1877–1956) in 1906. It used a crystal of carborundum, galena, or silicon and worked by rectifying the incoming radio signal, converting it from alternating current (AC) to direct current (DC). The detector connected to the radio circuit by an adjustable thin wire—a "cat's whisker."

English engineer John Fleming (1849–1945) had invented an even better rectifier and detector system in 1904. It was a two-electrode vacuum tube called a diode. Two years later American engineer Lee De Forest (1873–1961) added a third electrode to make the audion, a forerunner of the triode, which could be used as an amplifier to boost weak radio signals. With the aid of the new devices radio engineers could build better circuits for transmitters and receivers. In 1917 Marconi

This photograph shows the transmitter Marconi used in the first transatlantic radio broadcast from Cornwall, England, to Newfoundland, Canada, in 1901.

began making VHF (very high frequency) transmissions. By 1924 Marconi was sending speech signals from England to Australia using short-wave radio.

Radio receivers improved in 1912 when Fessenden devised the heterodyne circuit, which allowed more selective tuning. American engineer Edwin Armstrong (1890–1954) improved on this with the superheterodyne circuit in 1918, which can detect very weak signals. But Armstrong's major contribution came in 1933, when he invented FM (frequency modulation). In this technique the frequency (not amplitude) of the transmitted carrier wave is modulated by the broadcast signal, increasing the quality of the received sound.

Radiotelephony depends on a technique called modulation—the changing of one constant signal by another varying one. An audio-frequency signal from a microphone is amplified and made to vary ("modulate") an oscillator's radio-frequency signal, which is amplified again before being transmitted. At the receiver an antenna picks up the transmitted signal. It is amplified before being demodulated by a detector and amplified to reproduce the original audio signal in a loudspeaker.

In amplitude modulation used in AM radio the amplitude (strength) of a constant carrier wave is modulated by the audio signal. In FM radio (frequency modulation) the frequency of the carrier wave is modulated.

KEY DATES

1864
Radio waves predicted

1887
Discovery of radio waves

1890
Coherer for detecting radio waves

1894
Marconi's first radio transmissions

1903
Amplitude modulation (AM)

1904
Diode vacuum tube

1906
Triode vacuum tube

1933
Frequency modulation (FM)

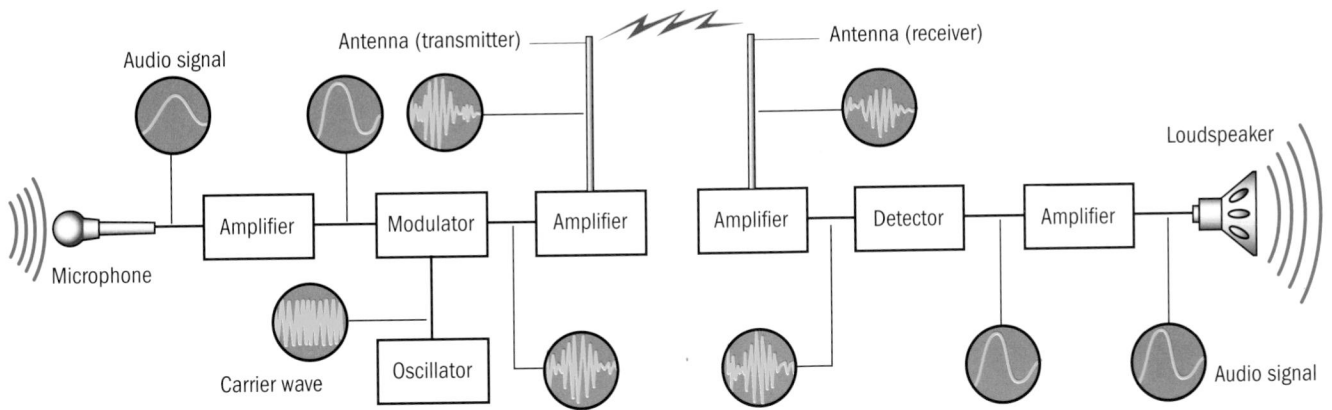

Audio signal

Antenna (transmitter)

Antenna (receiver)

Loudspeaker

Microphone

Amplifier

Modulator

Amplifier

Amplifier

Detector

Amplifier

Audio signal

Carrier wave

Oscillator

ASTRONOMY & MATH	BIOLOGY & MEDICINE	PHYSICAL SCIENCES

EUROPE

1893 British astronomer Walter Maunder (1851–1928) studies old records of sunspots and notices that very few were observed between 1615–1745. He deduces that the time (known as the Maunder minimum) corresponds to a "Little Ice Age."

1895 French mathematician Jules-Henri Poincaré (1854–1912) introduces topology as a branch of mathematics. It deals with the general geometrical properties of surfaces and space.

1896 Swedish physical chemist Svante Arrhenius (1859–1927) proposes a link between the levels of carbon dioxide (CO_2) in the atmosphere and global temperatures, a theory that has received much attention with the advent of global warming.

1893 Swiss physiologist Wilhelm His (1863–1934) describes the bundle of His, specialized muscle fibers in the heart that conduct nerve impulses that control the heartbeat.

1894 German chemist Emil Fischer (1852–1919) describes the "lock-and-key" system by which enzymes work.

1894 English physiologist Edward Sharpey-Schafer (1850–1935) demonstrates the existence of the pituitary hormone epinephrine (adrenaline).

1895 English botanist Frederick Blackman (1866–1947) discovers that gas exchange (oxygen and carbon dioxide) in plants takes place through pores in the leaves called stomata.

1896 English bacteriologist Almroth Wright (1861–1947) develops a vaccine against typhoid fever.

1896 German chemist Eduard Buchner (1860–1917) observes that fermentation of sugar (as in brewing and winemaking) is caused by enzymes in the yeast.

1894 Scottish physicist James Dewar (1842–1923) makes liquid oxygen, one of the first elemental gases to be liquefied.

1894 English physicist John Strutt, Lord Rayleigh (1842–1919), and Scottish chemist William Ramsay (1852–1916) discover the inert gas argon in air.

1895 Swedish chemist Per Cleve (1840–1905) and Scottish chemist William Ramsay (1852–1916) independently discover helium on Earth.

1895 German physicist Wilhelm Röntgen (1845–1923) takes the first x-ray.

1896 French physicist Henri Becquerel (1852–1908) discovers radioactivity.

1896 New Zealand-born British physicist Ernest Rutherford (1871–1937) describes and names alpha particles (which are helium nuclei) and beta particles (which are electrons).

1896 Dutch physicist Pieter Zeeman (1865–1943) observes the Zeeman effect, which is the splitting of atomic spectral lines in a strong magnetic field.

THE AMERICAS

1894 American astronomer Percival Lowell (1855–1916) sets up his private observatory at Flagstaff, Arizona, and begins the search for a ninth planet. The search ends with the discovery of Pluto by American astronomer Clyde Tombaugh (1906–97) in 1930.

1895 American astronomer James Keeler (1857–1900) observes that Saturn's rings do not all rotate at the same speed, contrary to the prediction in 1857 by Scottish physicist James Clerk Maxwell (1831–79).

1893 African-American surgeon Daniel Williams (1858–1931) performs the first open-heart surgery operation.

1895 Canadian physician Daniel Palmer (1845–1913) establishes the medical procedure of chiropractic.

An illustration from an early advertisement for the Gillette safety razor

ASIA & OCEANIA

1895 Australian-born physician and bacteriologist David Bruce (1855–1931) shows that the tsetse fly carries the parasite *Trypanosoma brucei* that causes sleeping sickness.

AFRICA & THE MIDDLE EAST

The Lowell Observatory in Flagstaff, Arizona—home of the discovery of Pluto

ENGINEERING & INVENTION

1893 German physicists Julius Elster (1854–1920) and Hans Geitel (1855–1923) make the first practical photoelectric cell.

1893 German inventor Rudolf Diesel (1858–1913) builds the first compression-ignition engine (diesel engine), patented in 1892.

1893 French brothers Auguste (1862–1954) and Louis (1864–1948) Lumière invent a motion-picture camera.

1893 The 3.9-mile- (6.3-km-) long Corinth Canal opens. It crosses the Greek mainland from northwest to southeast.

1895 Czech-born Austrian printer Karl Klic (1841–1926) founds the Rembrandt Intaglio Printing Company. It publishes reproductions of illustrations on paper by photogravure—a process invented by Klic in 1878, in which the printing plate consists of hundreds of minute ink-holding pits.

1893 American engineer Whitcomb Judson (d. 1905) patents the "clasp locker," a forerunner of the zipper.

1894 American physician John Kellogg (1852–1943) invents wheat flakes.

1895 American inventor King Gillette (1855–1932) has the idea for the disposable double-edged razor blade.

1896 American aeronautical pioneer Samuel Langley (1834–1906) builds a steam-powered airplane capable of sustained (but uncontrolled) flight.

1896 American engineer and patent lawyer Charles Curtis (1860–1953) invents an impulse steam turbine, later used in ships and electricity power plants.

1893 English-born Australian inventor Lawrence Hargrave (1850–1915) invents a human-carrying box kite.

WORLD EVENTS

1893 Scottish socialist Keir Hardie (1856–1915) founds Britain's independent Labour Party; as the Labour Party, it will replace the Liberal Party as one of the two main political parties (the other being the Conservative Party).

1893 Jewish French army officer Alfred Dreyfus (1859–1935) is wrongfully accused of treason in a case that will divide France for over a decade. Convicted by court-martial in 1894, his pardon was eventually won in 1906, after a long campaign by liberals such as writer Émile Zola (1840–1902) against the military establishment.

1894 Tsar Alexander III (r. 1881–94) dies. He is succeeded by his son, Nicholas II (r. 1894–1917).

1896 The first modern Olympic Games are staged in Athens, Greece.

1893 The failure of a number of major railroad companies causes panic on Wall Street and plunges the United States economy into a depression that will last another four years.

1894 The United States army imprisons leaders of the Hopi people on Alcatraz Island in San Francisco for sedition.

1895 The "Atlanta Compromise" speech by Booker T. Washington (1856–1915) proposes a cessation of African-American political activity in exchange for new educational opportunities.

1896 In the *Plessy v. Ferguson* case the United States Supreme Court rules that racial segregation is constitutional.

1893 The Durand Line is created, marking the border between British India and Afghanistan.

1894 Japan invades Korea, triggering the First Sino-Japanese War (1894–95).

1896 After its forces suffer a crushing defeat at the battle of Adowa, Italy is forced to recognize the independence of Ethiopia at the treaty of Addis Ababa.

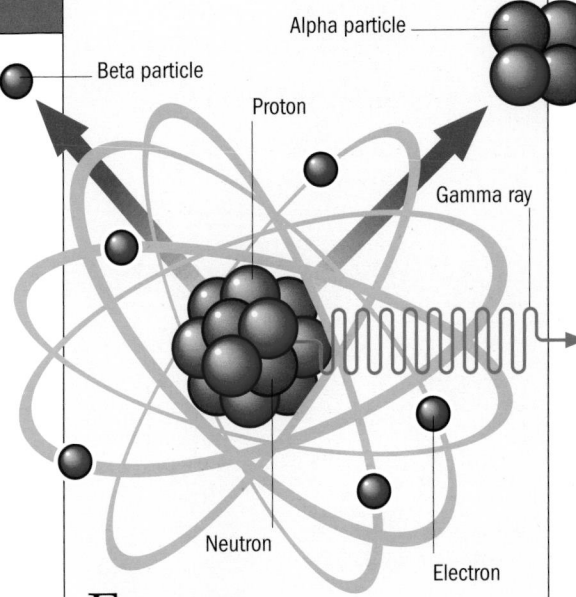

Alpha particle
Beta particle
Proton
Gamma ray
Neutron
Electron

ERNEST RUTHERFORD

Ernest Rutherford (1871–1937) was a New Zealand-born English physicist and one of the pioneers of nuclear physics. After studying in New Zealand, Rutherford won a scholarship to Cambridge University, England. There, he discovered that radioactive uranium gives off three kinds of rays: low-power alpha rays, penetrating beta rays, and highly ionizing gamma rays.

Two years later, during his tenure at McGill University, Montreal, Rutherford worked with English chemist Frederick Soddy (1877–1956) on the process of radioactive decay. They came up with the theory that radioactive decay takes place by a series of "transformations." This work eventually led to Soddy's discovery of the existence of isotopes.

Rutherford moved to Manchester University, England, in 1907. In 1910, he supervised Hans Geiger (1882–1945) and Ernest Marsden (1889–1971). In one experiment Geiger and Marsden fired positively charged alpha particles at a piece of gold foil. Most of the particles went through, but some bounced back. The scientists suggested that this was caused by a positive charge at the center of the gold atoms. This led Rutherford to create a model of the atom with a central, positively charged nucleus surrounded largely by empty space.

THE ELUSIVE ELECTRON

EVERY MODERN SCIENCE STUDENT KNOWS what an electron is and how important it is in understanding electricity and atomic physics. But things were different 100 years ago when an English physicist discovered what was the smallest particle of matter known at the time. Until the end of the 19th century various discoveries in physics had given rise to a host of unanswered questions such as: Objects can be made to hold a charge of static electricity, but what form does the charge take? In an electric current charges flow along a conductor, but what are these charges and are they different from the electrostatic ones? A high voltage across the plates of a vacuum tube produces cathode rays, but what are the rays made of? And if matter is made of atoms, what are atoms made of?

It turned out that the answers to these questions depended on an invention—the vacuum pump—that allowed scientists to remove nearly all the air from a piece of apparatus. One of the first experimenters to use it was the German glassblower and manufacturer of laboratory equipment Heinrich Geissler (1815–79). In about 1850 he sealed metal plates inside a glass vacuum tube containing only traces of a gas (such as neon or argon). He connected the plates to a source of high-voltage electricity and obtained pretty lighting effects as the gas glowed in the container.

The Geissler tubes became a popular novelty but were used for serious experiments by two German physicists: Julius Plücker (1801–68) in 1859 and Johann Hittorf (1824–1914) in 1869. The two scientists maintained that the light resulted from "rays" that left the negatively charged plate, or cathode, of the Geissler tube and traveled in straight lines to the anode. This fact was confirmed in 1879 by English physicist William Crookes (1832–1919), who also suggested that the "rays" may, in fact, be particles. Sixteen years later French physicist Jean Perrin (1870–1942) deflected these cathode rays using magnetic and electric fields, proving that they are made up of negative electric charges.

The Cavendish Laboratory

The scene was set for the pioneering experiments of an English physicist. Joseph John Thomson (1856–1940), always known as J. J. Thomson, was born near Manchester in the north of England. At the age of 14 he began to train as a railroad engineer. He then won a scholarship to Cambridge University, graduating in 1880. He went to work in the Cavendish Laboratory under John Strutt, Lord Rayleigh (1842–1919), and succeeded him to the professorship in 1884.

Thomson also deflected cathode rays with electric and magnetic fields, measured their speed (proving that they travel much more slowly than light waves),

J. J. Thomson carried out research at Cambridge University's Cavendish Laboratory for 39 years, the whole of his working life.

This diagram shows the flow of electricity in a metal wire. Electrons are basic components of all atoms, in which they normally orbit the nucleus. In most metals—such as the copper wire of an electric cable—many of the electrons wander away from their atoms to form a "sea" of free electrons (bottom section of diagram).

When a voltage is applied to the cable (middle section), the free electrons move and become the electric current flowing along the cable. Copper is an example of a metal that is said to have low resistance.

A metal with very high resistance, such as tungsten used for elements in electric heaters, has only a few free electrons (top section). As a result, a voltage causes only a small current to flow, and the metal becomes hot.

HIGH-RESISTANCE METAL—SMALL CURRENT FLOW

LOW-RESISTANCE METAL—CURRENT FLOW

LOW-RESISTANCE METAL—NO CURRENT FLOW

Atom of high-resistance metal

Electrons move

Free electron

Atom of low-resistance metal

Insulation

and more importantly, figured out the ratio of their charge (e) to their mass (m). This ratio, e/m, was 1,000 times smaller than that for a hydrogen ion (the smallest charged atom), and so Thomson deduced that cathode rays must consist of minute negatively charged particles. He announced the discovery of these first subatomic particles, which he called "corpuscles," in 1897. Two years later he found that they have a mass equal to about one two-thousandth of the mass of a hydrogen atom. Their existence had already been predicted in 1874 by the Irish physicist George Stoney (1826–1911), who in 1891 had named them "electrons." The electron turned out to be the long-sought-after unit of electricity responsible for electrostatic charges. Also, it became clear that a flow of electrons along a conductor con-

stitutes an electric current. And because electrons come from the metal of the cathode in a discharge tube, they must be a fundamental part of all atoms.

Thomson went on to study canal rays (positive rays emitted by the anode of a discharge tube). This work led in 1912 to a method of separating charged particles, which in turn was developed into the mass spectrograph in 1919 by English physicist Francis Aston (1877–1945). When Thomson retired in 1919, he was succeeded by his former assistant, New Zealand-born English physicist Ernest Rutherford (1871–1937). Rutherford eventually proposed a structure for the atom that included the atomic nucleus. Seven of Thomson's assistants later won Nobel prizes, an award that he received in 1906.

Many notable scientists, including J. J. Thomson, Ernest Rutherford, and Sir Lawrence Bragg, experimented in the Cavendish Laboratory at Cambridge University in England.

ASTRONOMY & MATH	BIOLOGY & MEDICINE	PHYSICAL SCIENCES

EUROPE

1897 Dutch astronomer Jacobus Kapteyn (1851–1922) discovers Kapteyn's star, which has the second-largest proper motion (meaning it is the second-fastest moving star).

1897 Irish-born English geologist Richard Oldham (1858–1936) distinguishes between the primary (P) and secondary (S) seismic waves produced by earthquakes.

1898 German astronomer Gustav Witt (1866–1946) discovers Eros, the first of the so-called near-Earth asteroids (in 1931 it passed within 14 million miles [23 million km] of Earth).

1898 German physicist Woldemar Voigt (1850–1919) introduces tensor mathematics, originally for handling vector transformations in physics problems.

1897 Danish veterinarian Bernhard Bang (1848–1932) discovers *Brucella abortus*, the cause of infectious abortion in cattle.

1897 German bacteriologist Friedrich Löffler (1852–1915) discovers the foot-and-mouth virus. Two years later he produces a vaccine.

1897 Dutch botanist Martinus Beijerinck (1851–1931) proves that tobacco mosaic disease is caused by something smaller than a bacterium. He calls the pathogen a "virus."

1897 Danish physician Niels Finsen (1860–1904) introduces the use of ultraviolet light to treat various skin disorders, such as cutaneous tuberculosis (lupus vulgaris).

1898 English physician Ronald Ross (1857–1932) finds *Plasmodium*, the microorganism that causes malaria, in the stomach of the *Anopheles* mosquito. He shows that the mosquito transfers the parasite from one human to another.

1900 Austrian neurologist Sigmund Freud (1856–1939) publishes his seminal book *The Interpretation of Dreams*.

1897 English physicist J. J. Thomson (1856–1940) identifies the electron, the first known subatomic particle.

1898 French physical chemists Marie (1867–1934) and Pierre (1859–1906) Curie discover the elements polonium and radium.

1898 German chemist Emil Fischer (1852–1919) synthesizes a type of purine. It is later found to be a key constituent of DNA (deoxyribonucleic acid) and RNA (ribonucleic acid).

1899 French chemist André Debierne (1874–1949) identifies actinium.

1899 German chemist Hans Henning prepares cyclonite for medical use. It is later used as the explosive RDX.

1900 German chemist Friedrich Ernst Dorn (1848–1916) discovers radon.

1900 German physicist Paul Drude (1863–1906) reveals that electrons carry electricity in an electric current.

1900 German physicist Max Planck (1858–1947) proposes quantum theory.

THE AMERICAS

1897 A 40-inch (100-cm) refracting telescope is commissioned for the Yerkes Observatory in Williams Bay, Wisconsin. It is still the world's largest refractor.

1899 American astronomer William Pickering (1858–1938) observes Phoebe, one of Saturn's moons.

1897 American physiologist Walter Cannon (1871–1945) pioneers the use of the barium meal to facilitate diagnostic x-rays of the stomach and the intestinal tract.

1900 Austrian-born American pathologist Karl Landsteiner (1868–1943) discovers A, B, and O blood groups and their intercompatability.

1900 Cuban-born American physiologist Aristides Aramonte y Simoni (1869–1931) discovers that yellow fever is transmitted through the bite of a mosquito.

1897 American physicist Robert Wood (1868–1955) observes electric field emission.

1900 Russian-born American chemist Moses Gomberg (1866–1947) prepares triphenylmethyl, the first chemical free radical—a highly active group of atoms with an unpaired electron (later to be important in reactions such as polymerization for making plastic polymers).

1900 American chemist Charles Palmer (1858–1939) invents the basic process for cracking crude oil, increasing the amount of gasoline obtained from a barrel of oil. It gains importance as automobiles become more widely used.

ASIA & OCEANIA

1897 Japanese bacteriologist Kiyoshi Shiga (1871–1957) identifies the cause of endemic dysentery, a bacillus known as *Shigella* for its discoverer.

1898 French scientist Paul-Louis Simond (1858–1947) identifies the plague bacillus in the tissues of dead rats in India.

AFRICA & THE MIDDLE EAST

Count Zeppelin's LZ-2, the successor of the first Zeppelin, LZ-1

Pierre and Marie Curie made many important discoveries in the field of radioactivity.

ENGINEERING & INVENTION

1897 German physicist Ferdinand Braun (1850–1918) develops the cathode-ray tube, later to be used in radar and television sets.

1897 English engineer Charles Parsons (1854–1931) builds a high-speed steam turbine boat, anticipating marine propulsion of the future.

1898 Work begins on the Paris Métro (subway). The first 6.25 miles (10 km) are opened in 1900.

1898 German engineer Wilhelm Schmidt (1858–1924) invents the superheater for steam locomotives, greatly improving their efficiency.

1898 German gunmaker Georg Luger (1849–1923) produces the Luger automatic pistol.

1899 The 165-mile (266-km) Dortmund-Ems Canal is completed across Germany, linking the industrial Ruhr district with the Ems River and the North Sea.

1900 The rigid airship *LZ-1*, designed by German engineer Graf Ferdinand von Zeppelin (1838–1917), makes its maiden flight.

1898 After three years, two months, and two days Canadian sailor Joshua Slocum (1844–1909) completes the first single-handed circumnavigation of the world in his sailboat *Spray*.

1898 Irish-American schoolmaster and engineer John Holland (1840–1914) builds the first modern submarine.

1899 American metallurgist Frederick Taylor (1856–1915) formulates "high-speed" steel (containing tungsten, chromium, and vanadium) for making machine tools.

1900 American engineer Thomas Edison (1847–1931) invents the nickel–iron accumulator (Ni–Fe cell).

WORLD EVENTS

1897 The First Zionist Congress meets in the town of Basle, Switzerland. Representatives from Jewish communities across Europe gather to discuss the creation of an internationally recognized Jewish state in Palestine.

1898 Russia's Marxist revolutionaries join together to form the Social Democratic Party.

1898 At the instigation of Russia's Tsar Nicholas II (r. 1894–1917) representatives of 26 countries gather for the first International Peace Conference at The Hague in the Netherlands.

ABO blood group antigens are present on the surface of red blood cells.

1897 The Klondike Gold Rush begins: thousands of hopeful prospectors head to the Klondike River region on the Canada–Alaska border.

1898 The U.S.S. *Maine*, an American battleship, explodes in the harbor at Havana, Cuba. The explosion was blamed, wrongly, on a mine and was one of the important triggers of the Spanish–American War.

1898 The Treaty of Paris ends the Spanish–American War. Spain cedes Puerto Rico, Guam, and the Philippines to the United States. Cuba gains independence.

1897 In China, German forces seize the port of Kiaochow Bay. A year later Russia leases the port of Lushun, renaming it Port Arthur.

1899 Construction begins of a railroad from Istanbul to Baghdad: Germany's involvement in the enterprise alarms rival European powers.

1899 The Second Boer War (1899–1902) breaks out between the British and the Boers in South Africa.

BLOOD GROUPS

Before the development of blood transfusions, surgical operations were very dangerous. Even if the patients avoided infection, there was a high risk of death from loss of blood during surgery. Bleeding was also a common cause of death during childbirth.

In the 19th century some physicians successfully performed blood transfusions. However, medical science could not explain why only about a half of the patients survived. Sometimes the transfusions worked perfectly, but on other occasions a patient's body was seen to attack and break down the infused blood, causing deadly toxic reactions.

In 1901 Austrian physician Karl Landsteiner (1868–1943) discovered that human blood belonged to four primary groups, depending on surface molecules, or antigens, on red blood cells. In addition, three of the blood types contained antibodies that rejected blood of other types. Landsteiner named these types A, B, AB, and O. The discovery transformed blood transfusions into a common and viable medical technique.

There were still problems with blood rejection, however, and Landsteiner continued his work. In 1937 Landsteiner and American physician Alexander Wiener (1907–76) conducted transfusion experiments with rhesus monkeys. They discovered an antigen that was sometimes present on the surface of red blood cells that they named the "rhesus factor." Wiener soon realised that the incompatibility of rhesus-positive and rhesus-negative blood was the cause of many transfusion complications and pregnancy-related blood disorders.

THE FIRST AUTOMOBILES

THE AUTOMOBILE WAS THE RESULT OF A LONG period of trial and error in the quest for a motorized road vehicle. The early machines used a steam engine, the only motive power available at the time. Credit for the first successful attempt goes to a French military engineer.

In 1770 Nicolas-Joseph Cugnot (1725–1804) built his second three-wheel gun carriage (he had built a smaller version in 1769). It was powered by a two-cylinder steam engine mounted on the single front wheel. It achieved a speed of 3 miles (5 km) per hour and was involved in the world's first motor accident when it demolished a wall. German engineer Charles Dietz built another three-wheel machine in 1835. It had a pair of rocking cylinders that worked cranks to move a chain drive to the rear wheels.

Experiments with steam vehicles continued, aimed at producing a tractor or a bus, rather than a smaller form of personal transportation. In England Scottish engineer

William Murdock (1754–1839) ran a model steam-powered road vehicle in 1784, and in 1789 American inventor Oliver Evans (1755–1819) fitted one of his high-pressure engines to a four-wheel land vehicle. English engineer Richard Trevithick (1771–1833) built a similar vehicle in 1801. It had large driving wheels with front wheels that were steered independently, and it could reach a speed of 10 miles (16 km) per hour. In 1829 English inventor Goldsworthy Gurney (1793–1875) began a regular steam coach service from London to Bath that ran at an average speed of 15 miles (24 km) per hour.

New Yorker Richard Dudgeon built a lightweight steam carriage in about 1865, and in 1873 French engineer Amédée Bollée (1844–1917) built a 12-seater carriage that he called L'Obéissante ("The Obedient One"). His La Mancelle ("The Young Lady from Le Mans") of 1878 had a front-mounted engine driving the rear wheels. It could travel at up to 25

KEY DATES

1769
Cugnot's first steam-powered gun carriage

1770
Cugnot's second steam-powered gun carriage

1829
Steam-powered road vehicle

1865
Lightweight steam carriage

1885
Benz three-wheeler

1886
Daimler four-wheel car

1893
Benz four-wheel car

1896
First U.S. automobile (Duryea) on sale

1908
Model T Ford

In 1908 Henry Ford produced the Model T, or "Tin Lizzy," as it was affectionately known by millions of Americans.

miles (40 km) per hour. Just as automobiles were becoming efficient, however, steam carriages fell into decline in the face of competition from the railroads.

Benz and Daimler

The next step in the development of the automobile came with the work of engineers Karl Benz (1844–1929) and Gottlieb Daimler (1834–1900) in Germany. They realized the potential of the new gasoline engine as a means of powering road vehicles. Benz's first car, a three-wheeler, dates from 1885. It had a 1-horsepower engine and a maximum speed of 8 miles (13 km) per hour. Daimler built his first car a year later, mounting his gasoline engine in a heavier four-wheel vehicle. At first he concentrated on producing engines for other makers' cars, and by 1889 he had a powerful, reliable 3.5-horsepower unit. By 1891 French engineers René Panhard (1841–1908) and Émile Levassor (d. 1897) were emulating Daimler and building cars with a chassis. The vehicles, known as *système Panhard* (Panhard system), had front-mounted Daimler engines to drive the rear wheels. They had modern Ackermann (double-pivoting) steering, a gear box, and a friction clutch. By 1893 Benz was making the more stable four-wheel cars with 3-horsepower engines. The same year saw the first gasoline-engined car built by U.S. inventor Charles Duryea (1861–1938) and his brother Frank (1869–1967). The first U.S.-made cars went on sale in 1896. One year later there was a brief reversion to steam power when the Stanley brothers of Massachusetts—Francis (1849–1918) and Freelan (1849–1940)—launched the Stanley Steamer.

Soon after the turn of the 20th century American industrialist Henry Ford (1863–1947) revolutionized car manufacture by introducing mass-production techniques. As a new chassis moved slowly along an assembly line, workers added the engine, transmission, wheels, and body. In 1908 the method produced the Model T. "You can have it in any color as long as it's black," declared Ford. The motor age was born.

By 1894 French motorists were organizing speed and endurance races for their Panhard and Levassor voitures sans chevaux (horseless carriages).

ASTRONOMY & MATH

BIOLOGY & MEDICINE

PHYSICAL SCIENCES

EUROPE

1902 English mathematician Bertrand Russell (1872–1970) introduces his paradox questioning contemporary set theory. Russell proposed a set that contains all sets that are not members of themselves. If this set is not a member of itself, then it must be included in itself, thus disqualifying it from being a member of itself.

1902 French meteorologist Léon Teisserenc de Bort (1855–1913) distinguishes the stratosphere and troposphere layers in the Earth's atmosphere.

1904 German astrophysicist Johannes Hartmann (1865–1936) reveals the presence of interstellar matter in space by studying stellar spectra.

1901 French physiologist Charles Richet (1850–1935) coins the term *anaphylaxis* to describe the life-threatening allergic reaction to an antigen to which an individual has become sensitized.

1901 Russian bacteriologist Élie Metchnikoff (1845–1916) determines the role of white blood cells in fighting infection.

1902 English physiologists Ernest Starling (1866–1927) and William Bayliss (1860–1924) isolate the digestive-juice stimulant secretin and later coin the term *hormone* to describe it.

1903 German surgeon Georg Perthes (1869–1927) first uses x-rays to treat cancerous tumors.

1903 German company A. G. Bayer markets Veronal (a barbiturate) as a sleeping pill.

1903 German chemist Eduard Buchner (1860–1917) isolates zymase—the first enzyme—in yeast.

1903 Russian physiologist Ivan Pavlov (1849–1936) develops the concept of the conditioned reflex (the way in which an action can be influenced by previous behavior).

1901 French chemist François Grignard (1871–1935) presents Grignard reagents (organometallic compounds containing magnesium and a halogen such as chlorine).

1902 English physicist Oliver Heaviside (1850–1925) and American engineer Arthur Kennelly (1861–1939) independently propose that a layer of ionized gases in the atmosphere "bounces" radio waves around the Earth.

1902 German chemist Emil Fischer (1852–1919) determines that proteins are polypeptides.

1903 Scottish chemist William Ramsay (1852–1916) obtains helium from the radioactive decay of radium. This confirms that alpha particles (produced by radium emission) consist of helium nuclei.

1903 Russian rocket pioneer Konstantin Tsiolkovsky (1857–1935) proposes the first practical theory of rocket propulsion.

1904 English physicist J. J. Thomson (1856–1940) puts forward his model of the atom—a spherical mass of positively charged matter with electrons inside it.

THE AMERICAS

1901 American astronomer Annie Cannon (1863–1941) adds spectral subclasses to complete the Harvard classification of stars, a system in which stars are assigned to seven different classes according to their surface temperature.

1904 American-born Argentine astronomer Charles Perrine (1867–1951) locates Himalia, the sixth moon of Jupiter. A year later he finds the seventh, Elara.

1901 The Rockefeller Institute for Medical Research opens in New York City.

1901 Japanese-born American chemist Jokichi Takamine (1854–1922) reports that he has successfully isolated epinephrine (adrenaline).

ASIA & OCEANIA

The okapi is a large mammal related to the giraffe, with zebralike stripes and an extremely long, flexible tongue.

1904 Japanese physicist Nagaoka Hantaro (1865–1950) puts forward the "Saturnian" theory of atomic structure, in which small electrons orbit a massive nucleus.

AFRICA & THE MIDDLE EAST

1901 The first okapi (*Okapia johnstoni*) to be seen by Western explorers is found in the rain forests of central Africa.

ENGINEERING & INVENTION	WORLD EVENTS

1901 German engineer August von Parseval (1861–1942) begins construction of a nonrigid airship (the *Parseval*).

1901 German engineer Eugen Langen (1833–95) builds a suspended monorail railroad in Wuppertal, Germany.

1901 Italian physicist and radio pioneer Guglielmo Marconi (1874–1937) makes the first transatlantic radio transmission.

1901 English engineer Hubert Booth (1871–1955) invents a vacuum cleaner powered by a gasoline engine.

1901 German physicist Ferdinand Braun (1850–1918) invents the crystal detector for tuning a radio. In 1906 it is improved by American engineer Greenleaf Pickard (1877–1956).

1903 Dutch physiologist Willem Einthoven (1860–1927) invents the electrocardiograph for recording the electrical activity of the heart.

1904 English engineer John Fleming (1849–1945) invents the diode valve (vacuum tube).

In 1901 a suspended monorail (Schwebebahn) began running in the German city Wuppertal.

1903 American brothers Wilbur (1867–1912) and Orville Wright (1871–1948) make the first sustained flight in a heavier-than-air airplane.

1904 The first section of the New York City subway opens, with electric trains serving 28 stations.

1904 American engineer Charles Kettering (1876–1958) invents an electric cash register.

1902 The first Aswan Dam is completed in Egypt, based on a design by English engineer William Willcocks (1852–1932).

Henri Giffard's airship of 1852 flew 17 miles (27 km) on its first flight.

1901 Britain's Queen Victoria (r. 1837–1901) dies and is succeeded by her son Edward VII (r. 1901–1910).

1903 Russia's Social Democratic Party splits between the minority Mensheviks and the majority (and more extreme) Bolsheviks.

1903 In Britain Emmeline Pankhurst (1858–1928) forms the Women's Social and Political Union to campaign for women's suffrage (the right to vote). Its supporters are known as suffragettes or suffragists.

1904 Britain and France become allies in the Entente Cordiale ("Friendly Understanding"), one of a series of defensive pacts formed in the decade before World War I (1914–18).

1901 President William McKinley (1843–1901) is assasinated by an anarchist. Vice President Theodore Roosevelt (1858–1919) succeeds him.

1902 Colombia's War of the Thousand Days (1899–1902) comes to an end, with 100,000 people killed.

1901 Various British colonies join to form the commonwealth of Australia.

1902 Japan allies with Britain to resist Russian expansion in eastern Asia.

1904 The Russo–Japanese War (1904–05) breaks out.

1901 Ashanti in northern Nigeria is annexed to Britain's Gold Coast colony (later Ghana).

AIRSHIPS

Only weeks after the first passengers flew in a Montgolfier hot-air balloon in 1783, a hydrogen gas-filled balloon soared over the rooftops of Paris. Early hydrogen-filled balloons could only travel with the wind and carry a small number of people. In 1852 French engineer Henri Giffard (1825–82) designed a craft that he called a *dirigible* (French for "steerable"). This consisted of a cylindrical gasbag with an open cabin, or gondola, suspended beneath to hold the pilot and engine. The design enabled sustained controlled flight for the first time. As lighter and more powerful engines were developed, airships became a more practical mode of transport.

The first rigid airship—with an internal metal framework that maintained an aerodynamic shape—was built by Austrian David Schwartz (1852–97) in 1897. But it was German engineer Graf Ferdinand von Zeppelin (1838–1917) who turned the concept into a commercially viable design. Zeppelin's first successful airship was the *LZ-3*, built in 1908.

Airships were used by both sides in World War I (1914–18) for both reconnaissance and bombing raids. In the 1920s and 1930s huge airships such as the *Graf Zeppelin* and the *Hindenburg* made frequent transatlantic flights. The disastrous wreck of the *Hindenburg* in 1937, coupled with tensions between the United States and Nazi Germany, ended the period. Soon after, advances in airplane design rendered airships obsolete.

ASTRONOMY & MATH	BIOLOGY & MEDICINE	PHYSICAL SCIENCES

EUROPE

1906 German astronomer August Kopff (1882–1960) discovers the short-period Kopff comet.

1906 Russian mathematician Andrey Markov (1856–1922) develops the theory of the Markov chain, a sequence of random events whose probabilities depend on previous events in the chain. This theory would later prove important in biology and physics.

1906 French mathematician Maurice Fréchet (1878–1973) introduces functional calculus to mathematics.

1906 Irish-born English geologist Richard Oldham (1858–1936) deduces that the Earth's core is molten.

1906 German astronomer Max Wolf (1863–1932) locates 558 Achilles, one of the so-called Trojan asteroids that orbit just in front of or behind Jupiter.

1905 French psychologists Alfred Binet (1857–1911) and Theodore Simon (1873–1961) devise a method of testing intelligence and ascribing an intelligence quotient (IQ) based on the results.

1906 French bacteriologists Albert Calmette (1863–1933) and Camille Guérin (1872–1961) begin work on developing the BCG vaccine (*Bacillus* Calmette–Guérin) against tuberculosis.

1906 German bacteriologist August von Wassermann (1866–1925) develops a blood-serum test for syphilis.

1906 Austrian physician Clemens von Pirquet (1874–1929) shows that hay fever is a reaction to pollen and coins the term *allergy*.

1906 German chemist Paul Ehrlich (1854–1915) establishes the structural formula of atoxyl. Four years later he produces Salvarsan 606, an early synthetic drug.

1906 English biochemist Frederick Gowland Hopkins (1861–1947) concludes that "accessory food factors," later called vitamins, are essential to health.

1905 German chemist Richard Willstätter (1872–1942) begins the work that will eventually reveal the molecular structure of chlorophyll.

1905 German-born physicist Albert Einstein (1879–1955) publishes his special theory of relativity. He also explains the photoelectric effect in terms of quanta ("packets") of light that strike a metal surface and liberate electrons from it.

1906 Russian botanist Mikhail Tsvett (1872–1919) separates plant pigments using paper chromatography.

1906 New Zealand-born English physicist Ernest Rutherford (1871–1937) measures the ratio of charge to mass for alpha particles and deduces that they are helium nuclei.

1906 German physical chemist Walther Nernst (1864–1941) announces the third law of thermodynamics: that at absolute zero the entropy (a measure of the ability to do work) of a perfect crystalline substance is zero.

THE AMERICAS

$$E = mc^2$$

ALBERT EINSTEIN, *ANNALEN DER PHYSIK*, 1905

1905 American surgeon John Murphy (1857–1916) pioneers arthroplasty, an operation to remodel a diseased joint.

1905 American embryologists Edmund Wilson (1856–1939) and Nettie Stevens (1861–1912) independently demonstrate the role of chromosomes in sex determination in insects.

1907 American zoologist Ross Harrison (1870–1959) introduces the technique of *in vitro* tissue culture (growing tissues in glass laboratory apparatus).

ASIA & OCEANIA

1905 Astronomer John Grigg (1838–1920) observes the third of the comets that bear his name from his observatory in Thames, New Zealand.

AFRICA & THE MIDDLE EAST

Workers pose for a photograph during the digging of the Simplon Tunnel, which links Italy to Switzerland. At the time of its completion, the 12-mile (20-km) tunnel was the longest in the world.

ENGINEERING & INVENTION

1905 French cycling advocate Paul de Vivie (1853–1930) invents the derailleur gear system for bicycles, allowing cyclists to climb hills with less effort and travel faster.

1906 Russian physicist Boris Golitsyn (1862–1916) creates an electromagnetic seismograph for detecting earthquakes.

1906 French physicist Jacques d'Arsonval (1851–1940) invents a freeze-drying technique used to preserve foods.

1906 The Simplon Tunnel under the Alps is completed, linking Italy to Switzerland.

1906 The British navy launches H.M.S. *Dreadnought*, the first modern battleship, armed with ten 12-inch (30.5-cm) guns and powered by steam turbines.

1907 A diesel-engined ship, the tanker *Djelo*, is launched at the Koloma Yard in Russia.

1907 French engineer Louis Bréguet (1880–1955) constructs a primitive kind of helicopter, the gyroplane.

1907 The German company Henkel markets the first synthetic household detergent (Persil).

1906 American engineer Lee De Forest (1873–1961) invents the audion tube.

1906 Canadian-born American electrical engineer Reginald Fessenden (1866–1932) makes AM (amplitude modulation) radio transmissions.

1907 Belgian-born American chemist Leo Baekeland (1863–1944) invents bakelite plastic.

1905 New Zealand inventor Richard Pearse (1877–1953) patents various innovations he used in his first flying machine in 1904. Due to his isolation from the centers of early aviation, however, his achievements pass largely unnoticed.

WORLD EVENTS

1905 In St. Petersburg the tsar's troops fire on demonstrating workers on Bloody Sunday, triggering a wider uprising. To quell the unrest, Nicholas II (r. 1894–1917) concedes limited reforms, including the establishment of an elected assembly, the duma.

1906 Russia's duma meets for the first time, only to be quickly dissolved by the tsar, who considers it too radical.

1906 A massive earthquake strikes San Francisco, destroying buildings and starting a fire that devastates the city.

With its heavy armor and huge mobile turret guns, H.M.S. Dreadnought *was the first modern battleship.*

1905 Japanese forces gain control of Manchuria and defeat the Russian Pacific fleet in the naval Battle of Tsushima.

1905 The Treaty of Portsmouth ends the Russo-Japanese War (1904–05). Japan gains northern Sakhalin and is given a free hand to establish a protectorate in Korea.

1906 Mahatma Ghandi (1869–1948) organizes a campaign of civil disobedience and nonviolent protest against discriminatory laws while working as a lawyer in South Africa.

ALBERT EINSTEIN

German-born theoretical physicist Albert Einstein is best known for his theory of relativity, one of the most important contributions in the history of science.

Einstein was born into a Jewish family and educated in Munich, Aarau, and Zurich. After graduating with a degree in physics in 1902, Einstein was unable to find work as a teacher. In 1905 he took a job as an examiner at the Swiss Patent Office while at the same time publishing his four papers on physics. The first dealt with Brownian motion, the random movement of particles suspended in a liquid or gas. In the second paper he explained the photoelectric effect (the production of electrons by a metal surface when struck by light) in terms of the new quantum theory of German physicist Max Planck (1858–1947). The third paper outlined his special theory of relativity, which deals with the relative motion of objects moving with uniform velocity. The fourth paper contained the equation $E = mc^2$, which states the equivalence of mass and energy, and employs c, the speed of light, as a universal constant. The concept was essential to the development of atomic weapons and modern physics. In 1916 Einstein published the general theory of relativity.

When the Nazis rose to power, Einstein left for the United States and began lecturing at Princeton in 1934. He became an American citizen in 1940 and spent his remaining years working toward a unified field theory.

THE AIRPLANE

E VEN BEFORE THE INVENTION OF LIGHTER-than-air flying machines, such as balloons and airships, people wanted to copy birds and fly. For this reason many early designs, such as those drawn by Leonardo da Vinci (1452–1519), had flapping wings. It was almost another 500 years before the ambition was realized.

A flapping-wing machine is called an ornithopter. No such machine was ever built except in model form; even if a full-size version had been built, it would not have worked because it depended on human muscle power for propulsion. (Human-powered aircraft have been built in recent times but aided by modern knowledge of aerodynamics, mechanisms, and materials.)

Kites and Gliders

The first heavier-than-air machines to fly were kites, invented by the Chinese in about 1000 B.C.E. In the late 19th century human-carrying kites were built, including one designed by English soldier Baden Baden-Powell (1860–1937) in 1894 and improved in 1901 by American showman "Colonel" Samuel Cody (1867–1913). Today's ski-kites and microlight aircraft continue the tradition. Real progress did not come, however, until people began to experiment with gliders. One of the first to do so was English inventor George Cayley (1773–1857). In 1808 he flew an unpiloted glider with a wing area of about 320 square feet (30 sq m). Then in 1853 he built a 300-pound (135-kg) person-carrying glider. The passenger was Cayley's footman—unaware that he was the first person ever to fly in a heavier-than-air machine. Three years later French naval officer Jean-Marie Le Bris

Leonardo da Vinci's sketches of a glider—from the early 16th century—was based on his study of bats' wings.

(1817–72) made a short gliding flight on a beach in northern France. In 1895 Scottish aviator Percy Pilcher (1866–99) made a part-controlled gliding flight in his hang glider, the *Bat*. A year later he built his fourth glider, the *Hawk*. It was steered by a tiller attached to a four-vaned rudder. In 1897 Pilcher broke the world record for flight when he flew 820 feet (250 m) in the *Hawk*. He died in 1899 from injuries sustained when the *Hawk* crashed.

German aeronautical pioneer Otto Lilienthal (1848–96) made a piloted flight in a steerable glider in 1891. His early machines copied birds' wings, but later he added a tail for stability and came up with the idea of two pairs of wings, one above the other. The pilot hung beneath the wings, as in a modern hang glider. The two-wing arrangement, later called a biplane, remained a feature of nearly all early flying machines. In 1893 Lilienthal tried birdlike jointed wings, but they failed, and in 1896 he became another glider pilot to crash to his death. In the United States Wilbur Wright (1867–1912) and his brother Orville (1871–1948) read about Lilienthal's pioneering work, which would influence their experiments. Also in the United States French-born American inventor Octave

Chanute (1832–1910) constructed an extremely stable biplane glider in 1896, which again was noted by the Wright brothers. By 1903 they had perfected human-carrying gliders of their own.

Steam Power

By the early 20th century engineers had developed what is now called an "airframe." Now all they needed was a suitable power source. At the time, the steam engine was the only possibility. As early as 1842 English-born American engineer William Henson (1812–1888) took out a patent for a monoplane aircraft with a steam engine, pusher propellers, and a cabin for several passengers. He was only ever to build a nonfunctional model. In 1848 English inventor John Stringfellow (1799–1883) also made a steam-powered model. It flew a short distance before crashing. In France in 1890 engineer Clément Ader (1841–1926) built a full-sized steam-powered monoplane, *Eole*. It flew—uncontrolled—for about 165 feet (50 m).

Another short-lived success was a huge machine built by American-born English inventor Hiram Maxim (1840–1916). His biplane of 1894 had two steam engines, each one driving its own propeller.

Launched along a set of rails, it managed to rise less than 3 feet (1 m) before falling to the ground. Two years later American Samuel Langley (1834–1906) built a large steam-powered model airplane. It flew for about 90 seconds and covered 875 yards (800 m).

In 1903 Langley built a full-sized airplane with a lighter gasoline engine. Two attempts to launch it from a barge in Washington, D.C., failed—each time the machine crashed into the Potomac River. The Wright brothers built their own gasoline engine out of lightweight aluminum and attached it to one of their gliders. The launch of this machine at Kitty Hawk, North Carolina, on December 17, 1903, heralded the start of sustained heavier-than-air flight. For the first time a human flew in a machine that took off and landed under full control. It was three years before Brazilian aviator Alberto Santos-Dumont (1873–1932) achieved the same feat in his own motorized glider.

The next advances mainly involved materials. Steel and other alloys replaced wood for airframes, and aluminum panels instead of varnished cloth were used to cover them. Jets superseded gasoline engines, and just 44 years after the Wright brothers' first flight, an airplane flew faster than the speed of sound.

The Wright brothers' biplane takes off from Kitty Hawk, North Carolina, on December 17, 1903.

KEY DATES

1808
Unpiloted glider

1848
Steam-powered model airplane

1853
Human-carrying glider

1890
Unpiloted steam-powered airplane

1891
Steerable human-carrying glider

1903
Sustained flight in gasoline-engined airplane

ASTRONOMY & MATH

EUROPE

1908 Following his publications of 1905 and 1907, Danish astronomer Ejnar Hertzsprung (1873–1967) introduces a method of classifying stars by plotting a graph of luminosity against temperature. It becomes the basis of the Hertzsprung–Russell diagram, published in 1913.

1908 German mathematician Ernst Zermelo (1871–1953) introduces set theory to mathematics.

1908 English-born Belgian astronomer Philibert Melotte (1880–1961) discovers Pasiphae, one of Jupiter's outer moons.

THE AMERICAS

1908 American physicist and astronomer Harold Babcock (1882–1968) detects the sun's weak magnetic field. In the same year American astronomer George Hale (1868–1938) observes the magnetic fields associated with sunspots.

BIOLOGY & MEDICINE

1908 English mathematician Godfrey Hardy (1877–1947) and German physician Wilhelm Weinberg (1862–1937) independently formulate an equation that describes the genetic equilibrium within a population. It is later known as the Hardy–Weinberg law.

1908 French anthropologist Marcellin Boule (1861–1942) reconstructs the first complete skeleton of an early Neandertal human found in France.

1909 English physiologist Henry Dale (1875–1968) discovers oxytocin, the hormone that causes the womb to contract during and after childbirth.

1909 Danish botanist Wilhelm Johannsen (1857–1927) coins the term *gene* for the factor that carries inheritable characteristics.

1910 French surgeon Alexis Carrel (1873–1944) develops the technique of making tissue cultures.

1910 German chemist Paul Ehrlich (1854–1915) prepares the synthetic drug Salvarsan 606, used in the treatment of syphilis.

In 1908 trees are knocked over and stripped of their leaves and branches in Siberia by the explosion known as the "Tunguska event."

1909 American pathologist Howard Ricketts (1871–1910) finds a new type of small bacteria (Rickettsia) that are often carried by ticks. In the same year he discovers the bacterium that causes typhus, which French bacteriologist Charles-Jules Nicolle (1866–1936) shows is carried from person to person by the body louse.

1910 Brazilian physician Carlos Chagas (1879–1934) first describes Chagas' disease, which is caused by a protozoan parasite (*Trypanosoma cruzi*).

PHYSICAL SCIENCES

1908 German chemist Fritz Haber (1868–1934) discovers the catalytic reaction for synthesizing ammonia from nitrogen and hydrogen. Later it is developed by German chemist Carl Bosch (1874–1940) and becomes the basis of industries that make fertilizers and explosives.

1908 French physicist Jean Perrin (1870–1942) calculates the value of Avogadro's number (the number of atoms or molecules in one mole of a substance.

1908 Dutch physicist Heike Kamerlingh Onnes (1853–1926) liquefies helium.

1908 German physicist Hans Geiger (1882–1945), working with New Zealand-born English physicist Ernest Rutherford (1871–1937), devises a method for detecting and measuring ionizing radiation.

1909 Danish chemist Sören Sörensen (1868–1939) introduces the concept of pH, a measure of acidity or alkalinity.

1910 Ernest Rutherford proves the existence of the nucleus of the atom after seeing an experiment by his assistant Ernest Marsden (1889–1970).

1908 American physicist William Coolidge (1873–1975) uses tungsten to make an incandescent filament lamp.

1908 English-born American electrical engineer Edward Weston (1850–1936) sees the Weston cadmium cell (battery) adopted as an international voltage standard.

1909 American Edward Davidson first uses carbon tetrachloride (tetrachloromethane) as a fire extinguisher.

Aviator Louis Blériot (right) stands in front of the Blériot IX aircraft in which he successfully crossed the English Channel from France and England.

ASIA & OCEANIA

AFRICA & THE MIDDLE EAST

I will build a motor car for the great multitude. It will be large enough for the family, but small enough for the individual to run and care for. It will be constructed of the best materials, by the best men to be hired, after the simplest designs that modern engineering can devise. But it will be so low in price that no man making a good salary will be unable to own one.

HENRY FORD, *MY LIFE AND WORK*

ENGINEERING & INVENTION

1909 French aviator Louis Blériot (1872–1936) flies across the English Channel. It is the first flight over an ocean in a heavier-than-air craft.

1909 Irish engineer Louis Brennan (1852–1932) builds and demonstrates a gyrostabilized monorail system.

1909 "SOS" is introduced as the international radio distress signal.

1910 French engineer Henri Fabre (1882–1984) builds the first seaplane.

1910 French chemist Georges Claude (1870–1960) invents neon discharge tubes for use in lighting and signs.

Workers at Henry Ford's Detroit factory add components to a partially assembled Model T.

1908 The first Model T Ford of American industrialist Henry Ford (1863–1947) comes off the assembly line at Detroit.

1908 The American Corning Flint Glassworks funds a research project to develop heat-resistant glass for railroad lanterns.

1908 American musician and physicist Dayton Miller (1866–1941) invents the *phonodeik* system of recording sound photographically.

1910 American airman Eugene Ely (1886–1911) makes the first airplane flight off a ship (the U.S.S. *Birmingham*).

WORLD EVENTS

1908 Taking advantage of an Ottoman Empire weakened by internal and external troubles, Bulgaria and Crete declare independence. Four years later the Balkan states of Serbia, Montenegro, and Albania join their independence struggle.

1910 A revolution takes place in Portugal: the monarchy is brought down and a republic proclaimed.

1910 George V (r. 1910–36) ascends the British throne at a time when the British Empire is at its peak, covering about a quarter of the globe.

1910 The National Association for the Advancement of Colored People (NAACP) is founded to campaign for the rights of African Americans.

THE HERTZSPRUNG– RUSSELL DIAGRAM

By the early 1900s it was possible to measure a star's apparent magnitude with accuracy. "Apparent magnitude" is the brightness with which a star glows in the sky. It depends on the star's actual luminosity and how far away it is. Danish astronomer Ejnar Hertzsprung (1873–1967) and American astronomer Henry Russell (1877–1957) used these measurements to relate a star's luminosity to its color. A star's color depends on its surface temperature and the range of electromagnetic radiation it gives off, known as its spectrum.

Hertzsprung found that bright blue–white stars seemed to follow the rule that brighter meant hotter, but that stars of the redder, cooler type could be divided into high- and low-luminosity groups. Since these stars have the same temperature, the differences in luminosity must be due to differences in size. Hertzsprung called the larger cool stars "giants." He published his ideas in 1905.

At Princeton, Russell developed similar ideas. By 1913 he had devised a diagram mapping luminosity against temperature. The Hertzsprung–Russell (HR) diagram acknowledged the contributions of both astronomers.

The Hertzsprung–Russell diagram plots stars' luminosity (vertical axis) against surface temperature (horizontal axis). The stars are not randomly scattered. Most of them lie on a line that runs from bright, hot blue stars at the top left to cool, faint red stars at the bottom right.

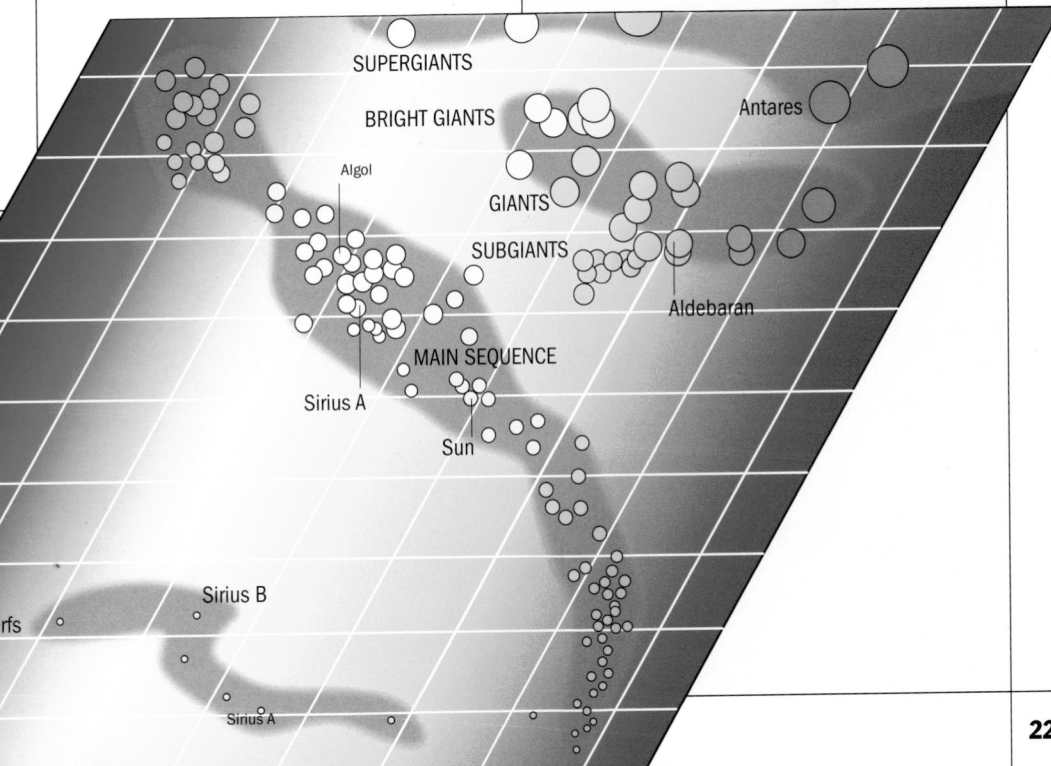

ASTRONOMY & MATH

EUROPE

1913 A photographic survey of the sky—206 photographs taken by English astronomer John Franklin-Adams (1843–1912) between 1903 and 1912—is published posthumously.

1913 French physicist Charles Fabry (1867–1945) reveals the existence of the ozone layer in the Earth's upper atmosphere.

1913 English geologist Arthur Holmes (1890–1965) uses rock radioactivity data to calculate the Earth's age as 4.6 billion years (in agreement with the modern value).

THE AMERICAS

1912 Austrian-born American physicist Victor Hess (1883–1964) observes cosmic rays, using a hot-air balloon.

1912 American astronomer Vesto Slipher (1875–1969) discovers reflection nebulas (near the Pleiades, an open cluster of stars in the constellation Taurus).

1912 American astronomer Henrietta Swan Leavitt (1868–1921) formulates the period-luminosity law, which is used to measure interstellar distances.

ASIA & OCEANIA

AFRICA & THE MIDDLE EAST

When it comes to atoms, language can be used only as in poetry. The poet, too, is not nearly so concerned with describing facts as with creating images and establishing mental connections.

NIELS BOHR, 1920

BIOLOGY & MEDICINE

1911 English physiologist Henry Dale (1875–1968) identifies histamine, a substance that is released into the bloodstream as part of the immune system response to injury or infection.

1912 German chemist Paul Ehrlich (1854–1915) introduces acriflavine for use as an antiseptic.

1912 German biochemist Heinrich Wieland (1877–1957) begins studying bile acids. He later discovers that they are steroids (complex molecules based on cholesterol).

1912 English geologist Charles Dawson (1864–1916) unearths fossils of prehistoric "Piltdown man" at a quarry in England. In 1953 they are revealed to be a hoax.

1913 American geneticist Alfred Sturtevant (1891–1970) introduces the technique of chromosome mapping to record the positions of genes along a chromosome.

1913 American biochemist Elmer McCollum (1879–1967) and his coworkers discover vitamin A (retinol).

1913 German-born American chemist Leonor Michaelis (1875–1949) and Canadian physician Maude Menten (1879–1960) develop a mathematical explanation of how enzymes act as catalysts.

1913 Hungarian-born American pediatrician Béla Schick (1877–1967) devises the Schick test for diphtheria. The same year German bacteriologist Emil von Behring (1854–1917) develops a vaccine against the disease.

1912 The world's largest extant lizard, the Komodo dragon (*Varanus komodoensis*), is recorded in Indonesia.

The Komodo dragon was discovered by Europeans in 1912.

PHYSICAL SCIENCES

1911 Dutch physicist Heike Kamerlingh Onnes (1853–1926) discovers superconductivity—the total loss of electrical resistance that some substances exhibit at very low temperatures.

1912 Austrian chemist Friedrich Paneth (1887–1958) and Hungarian-born chemist Georg von Hevesy (1885–1966) use radioactive substances as tracers to follow the paths of chemical reactions.

1912 German physicist Max von Laue (1879–1960) proves the diffraction of x-rays by crystals, which becomes the basis of x-ray crystallography.

1913 English chemist Frederick Soddy (1877–1956) concludes that some elements can exist in forms that differ only in atomic weight and calls them "isotopes."

1913 English physicist Henry Moseley (1887–1915) proposes that the frequencies of the lines in x-ray spectra of elements are related to their atomic numbers.

1913 Danish physicist Niels Bohr (1885–1962) proposes his model of the atom: a central, positively charged nucleus surrounded by orbiting electrons that are negatively charged.

1913 American physicist Robert Millikan (1868–1953) announces his famous oil-drop experiment, in which he balances the charge on an ionized drop of oil with the charge between two metal plates. From this he calculates the charge on an electron.

1913 American chemist William Burton (1865–1954) patents a high-temperature, high-pressure thermal cracking process for crude oil (breaking it down into simpler compounds using heat).

1912 Russian-born Israeli chemist and statesman Chaim Weizmann (1874–1952) devises a way of using bacteria to produce acetone by the fermentation of grain.

ENGINEERING & INVENTION

1911 Scottish physicist C. T. R. Wilson (1869–1959) invents the cloud chamber, used for studying subatomic particles.

1911 German physicist Ferdinand Braun (1850–1918) devises a scanning system for cathode-ray tubes, later used in radar and television.

1911 Prince Henry of Prussia (1862–1929) invents the windshield wiper for cars.

1912 The R.M.S. *Titanic* sinks on its maiden voyage, with the loss of 1,517 lives.

1913 German chemist Friedrich Bergius (1884–1949) conceives a method of converting coal to oil using high-pressure hydrogenation. The process is to be of great value to Germany during World War I (1914–18), when demand for oil increases dramatically.

1911 American airman Calbraith Rogers (1879–1912) makes the first flight (with stops) across the United States.

1912 American Elmer Sperry (1860–1930) invents an automatic pilot system for ships, which uses his gyrocompass.

1912 American Albert Berry makes the first parachute jump from an airplane.

1912 The largest railroad station in the world—Grand Central Station in New York City—is completed.

1911 The first public demonstration of a aircraft in New Zealand takes place near Aukland. By this time New Zealand's own aviation pioneer, Richard Pearse (1877–1953), had abandoned his experiments.

WORLD EVENTS

1911 Norwegian explorer Roald Amundsen (1872–1928) becomes the first person to reach the South Pole, beating the British expedition led by Robert Scott (1868–1912).

1912 The military alliance between the states of Germany, Austria–Hungary, and Italy is strengthened and renewed.

1913 The Home Rule Bill granting limited independence to Ireland is passed by Britain's House of Commons but rejected by the House of Lords.

Grand Central Station in New York City has 44 platforms, making it the largest railroad station in the world.

1911 Theodore Roosevelt (1858–1919) breaks with the Republicans to lead his own Progressive Party.

1912 U.S. forces invade Nicaragua. The country will remain under U.S. occupation for 20 years.

1912 Democrat Woodrow Wilson (1856–1924) becomes U.S. president.

1911 The purpose-built city of New Delhi becomes the capital city of India.

1911 Sun Yat-Sen (1866–1925) leads a nationalist revolution in China.

1912 Tibet and Mongolia both take advantage of the revolution in China to reclaim their independence, expelling Chinese officials.

1912 France imposes a protectorate on southern Morocco; the northern third of the country becomes a protectorate of Spain.

1913 The Native Land Act further reinforces the apartheid system of racial segregation in South Africa.

An artist's impression of the R.M.S. Titanic *sinking after striking an iceberg*

THE TITANIC

In 1909 construction began on the ship that would become the R.M.S. (Royal Mail Ship) *Titanic.* It was intended to be the biggest, safest, and most luxurious passenger ship ever built. Promotional materials proclaimed the ship to be "practically unsinkable" and described the opulent decor, extensive recreational facilities, and modern technology, including shipwide electric lighting and wireless radio communications equipment.

However, away from the bright lights of the first-class cabins many of the techniques and technologies used in the ship's construction were far from being the best available. Most importantly, the ship did not carry enough lifeboats, and its old-fashioned rudder was barely large enough for the ship to be considered seaworthy.

On its well-publicized first voyage in April 1911—from Southampton, England, to New York City—the *Titanic* struck an iceberg in the northern Atlantic. Although the iceberg was sighted by the ship's lookout, it was too late for the ship—with its poor maneuverability—to avoid. The iceberg gouged a tear in the side of the ship, inundating five of its bulkhead compartments with water.

The passengers and crew were not initially aware of the severity of the impact, and the first lifeboat was not lowered until almost an hour afterward. Distress signals were sent out, but the nearest ship was four hours' travel away. The ship sank in just under three hours. Of the 2,223 people on board, 1,517 died.

SYNTHETIC DRUGS

THE MID- TO LATE 19TH CENTURY SAW THE science of chemistry declare war on pain and physical suffering. Some of the new developments had their roots in traditional medicines, others were the result of years devoted to trial and error, and a few were simply pure luck.

Humans have used naturally occurring substances as medicines for thousands of years. Some of them, such as opiates, were used as analgesics (painkillers); but they were never very reliable, and they often had undesirable side effects.

A worker in a pharmaceutical company checks the production of aspirin pills.

The first wholly synthetic drugs were gases. In 1799 English chemist Humphry Davy (1778–1829) discovered the painkilling properties of nitrous oxide, also known as laughing gas. In 1815 similar properties were noted for ether vapor. Both proved to be popular social novelties due to their intoxicating side effects, but it was another 30 years before medical practitioners were to take advantage of their painkilling properties to perform surgery. In 1847 a stronger anesthetic gas, chloroform vapor, was developed by Scottish obstetrician James Simpson (1811–70) and used to help women during childbirth. None of the gases was free from side effects, notably that they made the patient unconscious, or at least insensible, and they were poisonous in large doses.

Salicylic Acid Synthesis

The use of certain plants to treat pain and fever has an extremely long history. Ancient Egyptians used myrtle, ancient Greeks and medieval Europeans used willow and meadowsweet, and Native Americans used birch. It turns out that all these plants contain the same active ingredient, named salicin for the scientific name for willow, *Salix*.

The medicinal use of willow was rediscovered by English clergyman Edward Stone (d. 1768). In 1763 Stone reported that he had successfully used willow bark to reduce fever in 50 of his patients. German pharmacist Johann Buchner (1783–1852) first isolated salicin from willow in 1828. Ten years later Italian chemist Raffaelle Pira extracted the active ingredient, salicylic acid, which took the form of colorless crystals. In 1853 French chemist Charles Gerhardt (1816–56) modified the structure of salicylic acid and created acetylsalicylic acid. But the crucial breakthrough came in 1859, when another German chemist, Hermann Kolbe (1818–84), figured out the chemical structure of salicylic acid and came up with a means of synthesizing it on a large scale—not from plants but from coal tar. Using the Kolbe reaction, the new drug went into mass production.

Salicylic acid was an effective painkiller, but it also caused severe stomach upsets, so there was an incentive to modify it. This was achieved by German chemist

Felix Hoffman (1868–1946) at the chemical company Bayer. Hoffman adapted Gerhardt's earlier formula to synthesize acetylsalicylic acid, and in 1899 the new drug was launched by Bayer as aspirin. At first, aspirin could be administered only by doctors, but in 1915 it became available without prescription.

Another painkilling drug with a bright future was developed at about the same time as aspirin. The analgesic and antifever effects of two very similar compounds, known as acetanilide and phenacetin, were recognized in 1886 and 1887 respectively. Phenacetin was launched as a drug for use in human patients in 1888. In more ways than one it was the direct forerunner of acetaminophen. Acetaminophen is a natural derivative of phenacetin, and the body converts one to the other very quickly. However, the significance of this was not realized immediately, and acetaminophen was not developed as a painkiller and antifever drug in its own right until the 1950s.

Salvarsan and Syphilis

A third important synthetic drug also being developed at the turn of the 20th century was a compound called arsphenamine. Sold under the proprietary name Salvarsan, this arsenic-based drug was used to treat the sexually transmitted disease syphilis. German chemist Paul Ehrlich (1854–1915) knew that some arsenic-containing compounds had antisyphilis

SALICYLIC ACID

○ Carbon

○ Hydrogen

○ Oxygen

ASPIRIN

Salicylic acid, extracted from the bark of the willow tree, was used in the past to relieve fevers and pain. The modern drug aspirin consists of an ethanoyl (acetyl) derivative of salicylic acid. The sodium salt of salicylic acid is also a mild painkiller and is used to treat rheumatism.

Paul Ehrlich used a systematic approach to drug development. His famous "compound 606" was marketed as Salvarsan, a treatment for syphilis, in 1910.

properties, so in 1906 he set about making and testing hundreds more. The 606th preparation turned out to be effective against the bacterium that causes syphilis (*Treponema pallidum*). The drug was improved a little in 1914 and became known as Neosalvarsan. However, the successful treatment of syphilis still needed a long and intensive series of injections.

The therapeutic advancements of the 20th century meant that the science of pharmaceutics had finally come of age. Synthesizing new compounds and tinkering with their structure to modify their effects is the basis of almost all modern drug development.

KEY DATES

1799
Laughing gas as painkiller

1815
Ether as painkiller

1828
Salicin isolated from willow

1847
Chloroform used in childbirth

1859
Salicylic acid in mass production

1899
Aspirin launched

1910
Salvarsan 606

ASTRONOMY & MATH	BIOLOGY & MEDICINE	PHYSICAL SCIENCES

EUROPE

1914 English astronomer Arthur Eddington (1882–1944) recognizes that many nebulae are, in fact, galaxies made up of millions of stars.

1915 Scottish astronomer Robert Innes (1861–1933) locates Proxima Centauri, the star nearest to the sun.

1914 English physiologist Henry Dale (1875–1968) and English chemist Arthur Ewins (1882–1957) isolate acetylcholine and later establish that it acts as a nerve transmitter, chemically passing on impulses from nerve to nerve.

1915 English bacteriologist Frederick Twort (1877–1950) and French-born Canadian bacteriologist Felix d'Hérelle (1873–1949) independently discover viruses that attack bacteria. Hérelle names them bacteriophages (meaning "bacteria-eaters").

1915 German physicist Arnold Sommerfeld (1868–1951) proposes that electrons orbit the atomic nucleus in ellipses, not circles.

1916 German-born physicist Albert Einstein (1879–1955) publishes his paper on the general theory of relativity, which mostly concerns gravity.

1916 French physicist Paul Langevin (1872–1946) experiments with ultrasound and produces a primitive form of sonar.

HOW THINGS WORK

Covalent and Ionic Bonds

A covalent chemical bond involves the sharing of electrons between two atoms. The top diagram shows the reaction between two atoms of hydrogen (H) and one of oxygen (O). (Only the outermost electron shells are shown.) As the atoms get close, they share a pair of electrons to form a molecule of water. The number of electrons in the outermost shell of the oxygen atom effectively becomes eight—a configuration that is particularly stable. Hydrogen has two electrons, which is also stable. The bottom diagram shows the reaction between a sodium (Na) atom and a chlorine (Cl) atom. As the atoms get close, an electron switches from the sodium to the chlorine, making a positive sodium ion and a negative chloride ion. The two ions form a molecule of sodium chloride. The component atoms are held together by an ionic bond, and the chlorine atom now has the stable number of eight electrons. The sodium ion is also stable.

COVALENT BOND

H   O   H   Two covalent bonds form H_2O Molecule of water

IONIC BOND

H   Cl   Electron switches atoms   Positive sodium ion and negative chloride ion form sodium chloride (NaCl)

THE AMERICAS

1915 American astronomer Walter Adams (1876–1956) identifies Sirius B as the first white dwarf star. It was first discovered in 1862 by American astronomer Alvan Clark (1832–97).

1916 American astronomer Edward Barnard (1857–1923) finds Barnard's Star, the second-closest star to the sun and the star with the greatest proper motion (the fastest-moving star).

1914 American biochemist Edward Kendall (1886–1972) isolates thyroxine, the principal hormone produced by the thyroid gland.

1915 American medical researcher Joseph Goldberger (1874–1929) reveals that the skin disorder pellagra is a deficiency disease, generally caused by a lack of vitamins, specifically niacin, in the diet.

1915 American surgeon Alexis Carrel (1873–1944) performs open-heart surgery on a dog.

1916 American physical chemist Gilbert Lewis (1875–1946) puts forward the idea that a covalent chemical bond involves a sharing of electrons (not a transfer of electrons as in an ionic bond).

1916 American physicist Robert Millikan (1868–1953) uses the photoelectric effect to confirm the value of Planck's constant.

ASIA & OCEANIA

1915 Japanese researchers Katsusaburo Yamagiwa (1863–1930) and Koichi Ichikawa show that coal tar is a carcinogen (a substance that causes cancer).

1916 Several scientists make special alloys, including Japanese physicist Kotaro Honda (1870–1954), who makes Alnico (a magnetic alloy of aluminum, nickel, and cobalt), and French engineer Pierre Chevenard (1888–1960), who makes Elinvar (a nickel–iron–chromium alloy used for watch springs).

AFRICA & THE MIDDLE EAST

ENGINEERING & INVENTION	WORLD EVENTS

1914 English military engineer Ernest Swinton (1868–1951) proposes the concept of a tank.

1914 The Canadian Grand Trunk Pacific Railway is completed.

1914 The world's largest ocean liner, S.S. *Bismarck*, is launched in Germany.

1914 German engineer Oskar Barnack (1879–1936) produces his prototype Leica camera.

1915 English inventor William Mills (1856–1932) invents the Mills bomb, a type of hand grenade used by British troops during World War I (1914–18).

1915 Dutch engineer Anthony Fokker (1890–1939) introduces an interrupter gear, which allows a machine gun to fire through the propeller of an airplane.

1915 The German company Junkers builds the first all-metal cantilever-wing airplane, the *Junkers J-1*.

1916 In Russia the Trans-Siberian Railroad is completed (begun in 1891).

1914 Archduke Franz Ferdinand (1863–1914), heir to the Austro–Hungarian throne, is shot dead by a Bosnian nationalist in Sarajevo.

1914 World War I begins, setting the Central Powers—Germany, Italy, and Austria–Hungary—against Britain, France, and Russia.

1916 The Easter Rising is suppressed by British troops in Ireland. Hundreds of Irish civilians and rebels are killed and thousands more wounded or arrested.

1916 The British and German naval fleets clash at the Battle of Jutland. Neither side emerges as a clear victor. It is the only major naval battle of the war.

1916 The Battle of the Somme takes place in northeastern France. The battle begins in July with a failed British attack on German lines in which about 20,000 British soldiers are killed in a single day. By the time the offensive ends in November, the combined number of dead and wounded from both sides has exceeded one million men.

1914 The 40-mile-long (64-km) Panama Canal, joining the Atlantic and Pacific oceans, is completed.

1914 American engineer John Hammer (1888–1965) invents a radio remote-control system.

1914 American inventor Garrett Morgan (1875–1963) produces a practical gas mask.

1915 American inventor Elmer Sperry (1860–1930) devises a high-intensity arc lamp (searchlight).

A pilot and gunner perform preflight checks in a World War I fighter plane. Airplane technology developed rapidly on both sides during the war.

Gas! Gas! Quick, boys!–An ecstasy of fumbling,

Fitting the clumsy helmets just in time;

But someone still was yelling out and stumbling

And flound'ring like a man in fire or lime…

Dim, through the misty panes and thick green light,

As under a green sea, I saw him drowning.

WILFRED OWEN, "DULCE ET DECORUM EST"

THE PANAMA CANAL

Soon after the Spanish conquered central America in the 16th century, they saw the advantages of a canal across the Isthmus of Panama. Engineers drew up various plans in the 1530s. However, it was not until after the opening of the Suez Canal in 1869 in Egypt that such a massive engineering project was considered feasible.

In 1878 an international company was granted a concession to dig the canal by the Colombian government, which controlled Panama. The company was led by French engineer Ferdinand de Lesseps (1805–94), designer of the Suez Canal. Poor planning and disease among the workers soon halted the construction.

With the permission of the new state of Panama, the United States took over construction of the canal in 1904. Presidents Theodore Roosevelt (1858–1919) and William Howard Taft (1857–1930) were enthusiastic supporters of the canal route devised by French engineer Adolphe de Brusly (1821–98). His design involved building an earth dam across the Chagres River to create Gatún Lake and linking this reservoir to the oceans through a series of locks.

Although many thousands died in the construction of the canal, efforts by the Surgeon General of the U.S. Army William Crawford Gorgas (1854–1920) to reduce the risk of disease—such as by exterminating mosquitoes—prevented many more deaths. With the help of heavy machinery, about 40,000 workers dug the 40-mile (64-km) canal. The project cost about $336 million in total, and the canal opened in 1920. In 1999 control and ownership was handed over to Panama.

William Crawford Gorgas

ASTRONOMY & MATH

EUROPE

1917 German-born theoretical physicist Albert Einstein (1879–1955) determines the cosmological constant, a term needed to "balance" his universe equation. Later he acknowledges the term is unnecessary and calls it his "biggest mistake."

1919 English theoretical physicist James Jeans (1877–1946) proposes a now discredited theory for the evolution of the solar system. He suggests that a near-collision between the sun and a passing star pulled off matter that later condensed into the planets.

THE AMERICAS

1919 American astronomer Edwin Hubble (1889–1953) begins his study of Cepheid variable stars in the Andromeda galaxy.

1919 American astronomer George Hale (1868–1938) reveals that sunspots reverse their magnetic field every 22 to 23 years.

BIOLOGY & MEDICINE

EUROPE

1917 Austrian neurologist Julius Wagner-Jauregg (1857–1940) successfully treats syphilis by deliberately giving the patient malaria.

1919 Austrian zoologist Karl von Frisch (1886–1982) describes the "bee's dance," the way in which honeybees communicate with one another.

> ### INSIDE STORY
>
> ## Bee's Dance
>
> When a worker bee finds a good source of pollen, she has to communicate the information to other bees in the hive. Austrian zoologist Karl von Frisch discovered in 1919 that she does this by a "dance" performed on the honeycomb, reenacting the trip she has taken. In the "waggle dance," the bee runs in two semicircles to form a flattened figure eight, waggling her abdomen as she runs along the straight middle section of the figure eight. The length of the straight and the frequency of waggle indicate the distance to the pollen. If the food lies within 80 feet (25 m) of the hive, she performs a "round dance," running several times in a circle with many changes of direction from clockwise to counterclockwise. Von Frisch's discovery significantly improved scientific understanding of the behavior of animals that live in swarms or large communal groups.

THE AMERICAS

1917 American nurse Margaret Sanger (1879–1966) opens the first birth control clinic in the United States. The following year in Britain Scottish paleobotanist Marie Stopes (1880–1958) publishes *Married Love*, a book about feminism and marriage.

1918 American physiologists William Howell (1860–1945) and Luther Holt (1855–1924) discover the natural anticoagulant heparin.

PHYSICAL SCIENCES

EUROPE

1917 German physicist Max Born (1882–1970) and chemist Fritz Haber (1868–1934) devise the Born–Haber cycle, which is a cycle of reactions that can be used to calculate the lattice energy of a crystalline solid.

1918 German physical Chemist Walther Nernst (1864–1941) puts forward his theory of chemical chain reactions. They are important in explaining light-triggered reactions.

1919 English physicist Francis Aston (1877–1945) develops the mass spectroscope for separating isotopes and discovers the two isotopes of neon, thus explaining why the atomic weight of the gas is not a whole number.

1919 German physicist Heinrich Barkhausen (1881–1956) establishes the Barkhausen effect: that the magnetization of iron takes place as a series of steps.

1919 New Zealand-born English physicist Ernest Rutherford (1871–1937) reports that he has artificially disintegrated nitrogen atoms by bombarding them with alpha particles.

THE AMERICAS

1918 American chemist Winford Lewis (1878–1943) develops the poison gas lewisite, an arsenic compound that causes blistering and respiratory irritation.

1919 American physical chemist Frederick Cottrell (1877–1948) devises a way of extracting helium from natural gas.

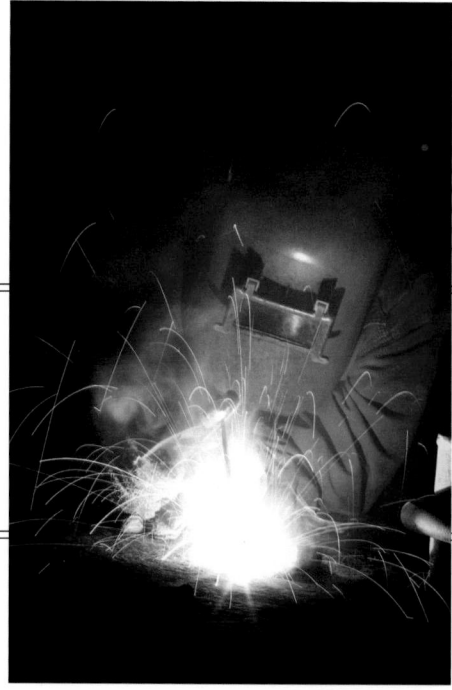

The arc welder for steel revolutionized the construction and ship-building industries.

It was quite the most incredible event that has ever happened to me in my life. It was almost as incredible as if you fired a 15-inch shell at a piece of tissue paper and it came back and hit you. On consideration, I realized that this scattering backward must be the result of a single collision, and when I made calculations I saw a system in which the greater part of the mass of the atom was concentrated in a minute nucleus.

ERNEST RUTHERFORD

EUROPE

THE AMERICAS

ASIA & OCEANIA

AFRICA & THE MIDDLE EAST

ENGINEERING & INVENTION	WORLD EVENTS

1917 English engineer Archibald Low (1888–1956) invents an electronic control system for rockets.

1918 The German company Junkers builds the world's first all-metal fighter airplane, the Junkers *J-10*.

1919 English aviator John Alcock (1892–1919) and Scottish aviator Arthur Brown (1886–1948) make the first nonstop transatlantic flight.

1919 Scottish physicist Robert Watson-Watt (1892–1973) patents a short-wave "radiolocator," the forerunner of radar.

1919 The British airship *R-34* is the first airship to cross the Atlantic Ocean. It flies from Edinburgh, Scotland, to Mineola, New York, in 108 hours 12 minutes.

1917 Following defeat on the battlefields of World War I (1914–18), Russia undergoes two separate revolutions. The first overthrows Tsar Nicholas II (r. 1894–1917) and establishes democratic government; the second, in November, brings the Bolsheviks, led by Vladimir Lenin (1870–1924), to power.

1918 British women aged 30 or more win the right to vote.

1918 World War I ends with the defeat of Germany and its allies. Both sides are left devastated by economic, political, and social repercussions of four years of war.

1919 The Treaty of Versailles imposes harsh peace terms on Germany, including the disbanding of most of the county's military, economic reparations, and the restoration of Alsace and Lorraine to France (captured during the Franco–Prussian War in 1871).

1919 Spartacists—German communists— stage an unsuccessful uprising in Berlin. In Hungary communists temporarily seize power under Béla Kun (1886–1938).

1917 The American Black & Decker company markets the first electric hand drill.

1917 The world's longest cantilever bridge, with a 1,800-foot (549-m) span, is completed over the St. Lawrence River in Quebec.

1918 American engineer Edwin Armstrong (1890–1954) invents the superheterodyne radio circuit. It is still in common use.

1918 A powerful 200-kilowatt radio transmitter begins sending signals from the naval station in New Brunswick, New Jersey.

1919 American airman Albert Read makes the first east–west crossing of the Atlantic Ocean—in stages—in a Curtiss flying boat.

1919 American engineer Elihu Thomson (1853–1937) invents the arc welder for steel.

1917 The United States declares war on Germany. In all, some two million American soldiers will travel to Europe to fight in World War I; 115,000 will be killed by the war's end in November 1918.

1919 A peace plan devised by President Woodrow Wilson (1856–1924) is adopted at the Versailles Conference, but the United States Congress rejects the treaty.

1919 The Volstead Act (coming into force in 1920) bans the manufacture or selling of alcohol.

1919 Mexican guerrilla leader Emiliano Zapata (1879–1919) is assassinated.

1917 The east–west trans-Australian railroad is completed.

1919 British forces open fire on demonstrators in Amritsar, India, killing 379 unarmed protesters.

1919 Ho Chi Minh (1890– 1969) founds the Indochinese Communist Party in the part of French Indochina that will eventually regain its independence as Vietnam.

1918 The Ottoman authorities negotiate a peace agreement at the end of World War I. Military defeat leads to the disintegration of the Ottoman Empire.

1919 Britain exiles Egyptian nationalist leaders, sparking an uprising that is put down by force.

The rapid-firing, compact Thompson submachine gun was patented in 1920.

THE MACHINE GUN

Machine guns are small-caliber weapons that keep firing as long as the trigger is pressed and ammunition is available. Some sort of mechanism automatically carries out the cycle of loading, firing, and extracting cartridge cases.

Although there had been some similar weapons in the past, the modern repeating gun had to await the invention of metal cartridges. American gunsmith Richard Gatling (1818–1903) patented the first gun of the type in 1862. It had a set of 10 barrels that were cranked around by hand. A drum on top of the weapon fed in cartridges under the force of gravity. It was used to devastating effect during the American Civil War (1861–65).

In 1883, American-born English inventor Hiram Maxim (1840–1916) patented his machine gun in England. It used energy produced by the weapon's recoil to extract the spent cartridge, recock the gun, and insert the next round into the breech. Early single-barrelled machine guns failed because the barrel soon overheated, causing it to bend. Maxim solved this by adding a water cooling system around the barrel.

During World War I light machine guns (LMG) were developed that could be carried and operated by just one soldier. Lighter still was the submachine gun (SMG). A well-known early example is the "Tommy gun," designed by and named for American army officer John Thompson (1860–1940) in 1920. It had a straight magazine or a higher-capacity drum magazine. Most SMGs have a rate of fire of between 500 and 800 rounds per minute.

CHAPTER 8

THE ATOMIC AGE

THE INVISIBLE WORLD OF THE ATOM DOMINATED SCIENTIFIC ADVANCE in the first half of the 20th century. The process of understanding atoms and learning how to harness their power produced many positive results, such as the invention of television and the development of radar. For many people, however, the idea of atomic energy became inextricably associated with destruction on an unprecedented scale when atomic bombs devastated the Japanese cities of Hiroshima and Nagasaki in August 1945. The distinctive mushroom cloud released by an atomic explosion—caused by superhot gases dragging dust and debris into the air—became a symbol of a new and frightening age, leaving even scientists concerned. On all sides of World War II (1939–45), academics and theoreticians found themselves questioning their consciences. Albert Einstein, whose work had done much to make the atomic bomb possible, ended up asking U.S. President Harry S. Truman not to use the weapon.

Warfare has always been a major motivation for advances in science. From bows that could fire farther to fortifications that could withstand cannonballs, the side that had the most advanced technology has usually had an advantage in conflict. In the 20th century, warfare became even more scientific. Research into radar, for example, received a boost because of the need to detect enemy aircraft and to aim naval guns

Since 1951 the United States has detonated more than 900 nuclear weapons, mostly underground, at the Nevada Test Site. This photograph from 1953 shows the U.S. nuclear test explosion known as Upshot-Knothole Grable. Currently, nine countries are known to have nuclear weapons.

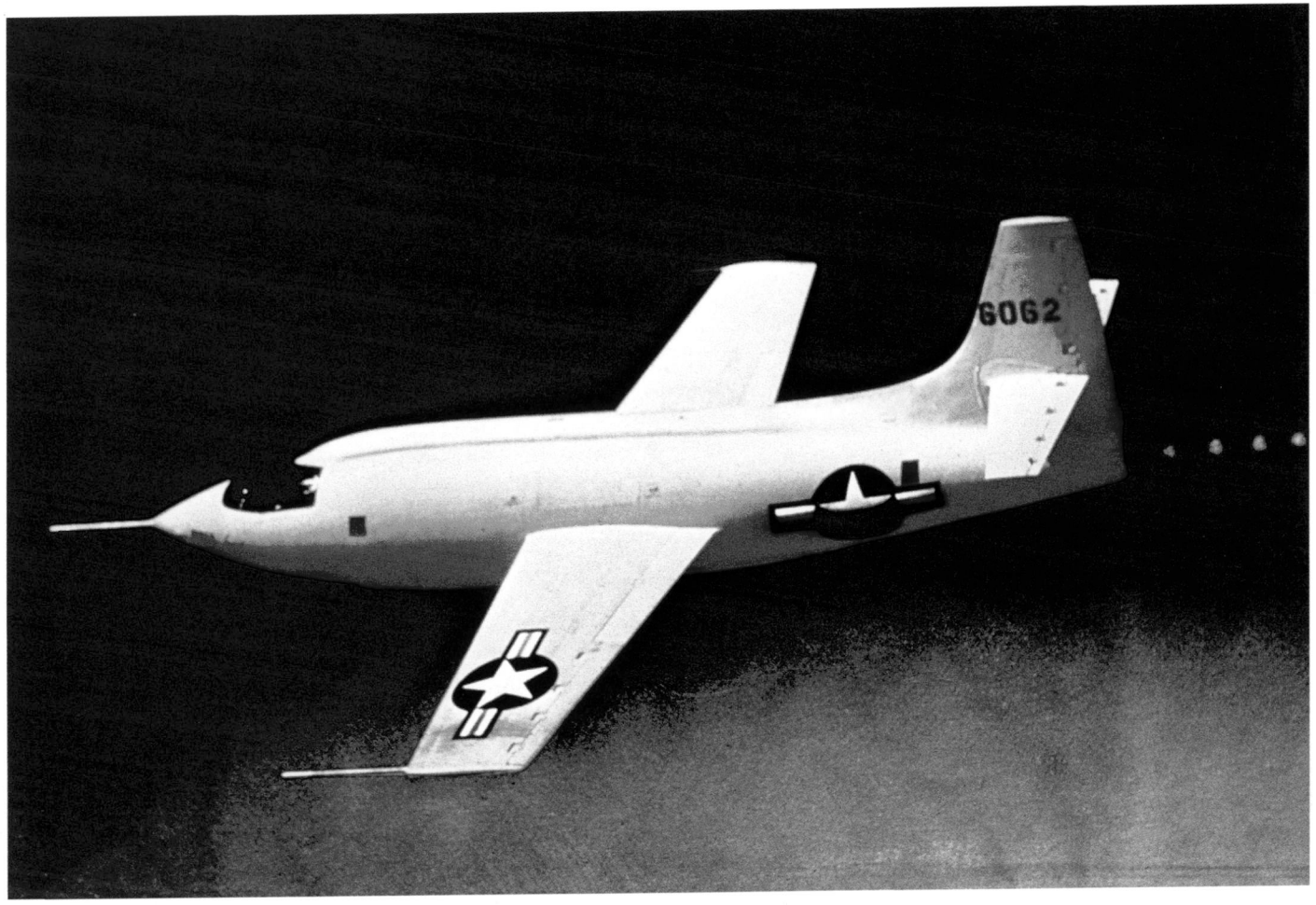

for long-range battles at sea. Rocket research made huge advances, particularly in Germany, where engineer Wernher von Braun (1912–77) pioneered long-range flying bombs; recruited by the U.S. National Aeronautics and Space Administration (NASA) after the war, von Braun played a key role in the space program.

Other wartime advances included improvements to conventional aircraft, such as the jet engine, and the development of the helicopter, pioneered by Russian-born American engineer Igor Sigorsky (1889–1972). In medicine, scientists came up with ways to mass produce the antibiotic penicillin, "accidentally" discovered in 1928, and needed in large quantities to treat the wounded.

The most significant scientific development of the war, however, was nuclear fission. It was just three years from the first demonstration of a controlled nuclear chain reaction in an atomic pile (an early type of nuclear reactor) in 1942 to the detonation of the atomic bombs in Japan. Within seven more years, U.S. scientists had developed and tested the much more powerful hydrogen bomb.

The year 1947 saw the invention of the transistor, the first solid-state device, which was to revolutionize the electronics industry. It appeared just in time for the first commercial computers, which could be made faster and more powerful now that they no longer depended on unreliable vacuum tubes. Portable transistor radios and electronic calculators soon became commonplace. Clothing and fabrics were revolutionized, too, by the manufacture of artificial fibers, such as nylon and polyester.

The Bell X-1 was the world's first supersonic aircraft. The plane made its first supersonic flight in 1947, piloted by U.S. Air Force Captain Charles "Chuck" Yeager. It was powered by a four-chamber rocket engine and could fly as fast as 1,471 miles (2,367 km) an hour—almost twice the speed of sound.

	1920	1923	1926	1929	1932
EUROPE	**1920** German astronomer Max Wolf observes dark clouds of matter in the Milky Way. **1920** Dutch airline KLM begins service between England and the Netherlands. **1921** Swiss psychiatrist Hermann Rorschach develops his inkblot test. **1922** New Zealand-born English physicist Ernest Rutherford predicts the existence of the neutron.	**1923** Austrian neurologist Sigmund Freud invents the concepts of the ego and the id. **1923** Germany company Benz makes the first diesel-engined trucks. **1923** Scottish inventor John Logie Baird makes a type of television. **1924** French physicist Louis de Broglie proposes the idea of wave-particle duality.	**1926** Austrian physicist Erwin Schrödinger formulates the wave equation for the hydrogen atom. **1926** Norwegian inventor Erik Rotheim invents the aerosol can. **1927** Belgian astronomer Georges Lemaître proposes the big bang theory for the origin of the universe. **1928** Scottish bacteriologist Alexander Fleming discovers the antibiotic penicillin.	**1929** German biochemist Adolf Butenandt isolates the hormone estrogen. **1929** German engineer Felix Wankel patents his rotary engine. **1930** Swedish biochemist Arne Tiselius invents electrophoresis. **1930** Austrian-born Swiss physicist Wolfgang Pauli predicts the existence of the neutrino. **1930** English engineer Frank Whittle invents the jet engine.	**1932** English physicist James Chadwick discovers the neutron. **1933** Swiss astrophysicist Fritz Zwicky proposes that space must contain invisible "dark matter." **1934** Danish biochemist Henrik Dam discovers a factor needed for blood clotting (vitamin K). **1934** The French company Citroën launches the first mass-produced front-wheel-drive car.
THE AMERICAS	**1920** American astronomer Vesto Slipher detects redshift in the light from galaxies. **1920** The Panama Canal opens. **1920** Regular radio broadcasts begin in the United States. **1921** German-born American physiologist Otto Loewi discovers the neurotransmitter acetylcholine. **1921** Canadian physiologist Frederick Banting isolates insulin. **1921** American physicist Albert Hull invents the high-frequency magnetron vacuum tube. **1922** American airman James Doolittle makes the first coast-to-coast flight across the United States.	**1923** Russian-born American electronics engineer Vladimir Zworykin invents the iconoscope TV camera tube. **1923** American pilots and their crews make the first flight around the world (with refueling stops). **1925** American physicist Robert Millikan observes cosmic rays in the upper atmosphere. **1925** American pathologist George Whipple finds iron in red blood cells. **1925** African-American biologist Ernest Just demonstrates that ultraviolet radiation can cause cancer.	**1926** American geneticist Hermann Müller uses x-rays to create genetic mutations in fruit flies. **1926** American inventor Robert Goddard launches a liquid-fuel rocket. **1926** American physical chemist Gilbert Lewis coins the word *photon* to describe a quantum of light. **1927** American physicist Clinton Davisson and coworkers confirm that electrons have wavelike properties. **1927** German-born American physicist Fritz London proposes a quantum theory of chemical bonding. **1927** American aviator Charles Lindbergh makes the first solo flight across the Atlantic Ocean.	**1929** German-born American physicist Albert Einstein first announces his unified field theory. **1930** American astronomer Clyde Tombaugh discovers the planet Pluto (now considered a dwarf planet). **1930** American electrical engineer Vannevar Bush builds an analog computer. **1930** American businessman Clarence Birdseye markets the first quick-frozen foods. **1930** The Chrysler Building is completed in New York City. **1931** The Empire State Building in New York City becomes the world's tallest building.	**1932** Synthetic rubber is marketed in the United States. **1932** American physicist Carl Anderson announces the existence of the positron. **1932** American physicist Ernest Lawrence operates one of the first particle accelerators. **1932** American electrical engineer William Kouwenhoven proposes the idea for a defibrillator. **1933** American biochemist George Wald discovers vitamin A in the retina of the eye. **1933** The first modern airliner, the Boeing 247, enters service. **1934** American scientist Royal Raymond Rife tests radio waves to treat cancer.
ASIA & OCEANIA			**1928** The Flying Doctor Service begins in Australia. **1928** Indian physicist Chandrasekhara Raman describes the effects of a beam of light in a transparent substance.	**1929** Japanese geophysicist Motonori Matuyama theorizes that the Earth's magnetic field has undergone reversals in its history.	**1932** The Sydney Harbor bridge is completed. **1933** The Tasmanian wolf, or thylacine, becomes extinct in the wild.
AFRICA & THE MIDDLE EAST		**1924** Australian-born South African anthropologist Raymond Dart discovers fossils of possible human ancestor *Australopithecus* in Africa.			

1935	1938	1941	1944	1947–1949
1935 Austrian zoologist Konrad Lorenz discovers imprinting in animals. **1935** Scottish physicist Robert Watson-Watt invents radar. **1936** German engineer Heinrich Focke builds a two-rotor helicopter. **1936** The Spitfire airplane makes its maiden flight. **1937** German-born English biochemist Hans Krebs explains the citric acid cycle.	**1938** German computer pioneer Konrad Zuse constructs a binary digital computer. **1938** German physicists Otto Hahn and Fritz Strassmann induce nuclear fission in uranium. **1939** Swiss chemist Paul Müller discovers the insect-killing properties of DDT. **1939** French physicists Irène and Frédéric Joliot-Curie show that uranium fission can lead to a chain reaction.	**1942** French underwater explorer Jacques Cousteau invents the aqualung, or scuba. **1942** German rocket engineer Wernher von Braun designs the V-1 flying bomb and the V-2 rocket bomb. **1942** English astronomer Harold Spencer Jones obtains an accurate value for the Earth–sun distance. **1943** Dutch-born American physician Willem Kolff constructs a kidney dialysis machine.	**1944** German forces begin launching V-1 flying bombs and V-2 rocket bombs against England. **1945** Soviet physicist Vladimir Veksler designs and builds a particle accelerator, the synchrocyclotron. **1945** Northern Irish engineer James Martin designs the ejector seat. **1946** Scientists obtain radar reflections from the moon.	**1947** English physicist Cecil Powell and Italian physicist Giuseppe Occhialini discover the pion (pi-meson). **1948** The World Health Organization (WHO) is founded. **1949** English computer engineer Maurice Wilkes and coworkers build EDSAC, the Electronic Delay Storage Automatic Calculator. **1949** The first jet airliner, the De Havilland Comet, flies in England.
1935 American seismologist Charles Richter devises the Richter scale to measure earthquake intensity. **1935** Canadian-born American physicist Arthur Dempster discovers the fissile isotope uranium-235 (later used in atom bombs). **1935** American amateur photographers Leopold Godowsky, Jr. and Leopold Mannes invent Kodachrome transparency film. **1936** American physicist Carl Anderson discovers the muon in cosmic rays. **1936** The Boulder Dam is completed. **1937** The world's first pressurized aircraft, the Lockheed XC-35, makes its maiden flight.	**1938** American physicists figure out the series of nuclear fusion reactions that "fuel" stars. **1938** Hungarian-born Argentine inventor Laszlo Biró makes a prototype of the ballpoint pen. **1939** The National Broadcasting Company (NBC) begins regular television transmissions. **1939** American physicist John Atanasoff makes a prototype electronic binary calculator. **1940** American zoologist Donald Griffin announces that bats "echolocate" using ultrasound. **1940** Austrian-born American pathologist Karl Landsteiner describes the Rhesus factor in human blood.	**1941** German-born American biochemist Fritz Lipmann shows the role of ATP (adenosine triphosphate) in the chemistry of cells. **1942** American radio astronomer Grote Reber compiles the first radio map of the universe. **1942** Belgian-born American biologist Albert Claude uses an electron microscope in biological studies. **1942** Italian-American physicist Enrico Fermi achieves the first controlled nuclear chain reaction. **1943** American scientists construct the world's first operational nuclear reactor.	**1944** Canadian-born American Oswald Avery and coworkers show that the cells of nearly all organisms have deoxyribonucleic acid (DNA) as their hereditary material. **1945** American biochemist Melvin Calvin begins his studies of photosynthesis using radioactive carbon-14 to follow the reactions. **1945** American scientists manufacture and test an atom bomb. **1946** American chemist Willard Libby develops radiocarbon dating. **1946** Swiss-born American physicist Felix Bloch and American physicist Edward Purcell develop nuclear magnetic resonance (NMR) spectroscopy.	**1947** American geneticist Joshua Lederberg reports that some bacteria can reproduce by conjugation. **1947** American airman Charles "Chuck" Yeager makes the first supersonic flight. **1947** American inventor Edwin Land demonstrates the Polaroid instant camera. **1948** American electrical engineer Peter Goldmark invents the long-playing phonograph record. **1949** American rocket engineers launch a two-stage rocket. **1949** The American company IBM makes a stored-program electromechanical computer Selective Sequence Electronic Calculator (SSEC).
1936 The last known Tasmanian wolf dies in captivity. **1936** A giant panda is captured alive in the wild.		**1943** Japanese theoretical physicist Sin-Itoro Tomonaga outlines the basic physical principles of quantum electrodynamics.	**1946** The Sony company is founded in Japan.	**1947** Armenian astronomer Viktor Ambartsumian describes stellar associations.
	1938 A thought-to-be-extinct fish, the coelacanth, is discovered off the eastern coast of South Africa.			**1948** English anthropologist Mary Leakey discovers fossils of possible ape ancestor *Proconsul africanus* in Africa.

1920–1922

CONCISE HISTORY OF SCIENCE AND INVENTION

ASTRONOMY & MATH	BIOLOGY & MEDICINE	PHYSICAL SCIENCES

EUROPE

1920 German astronomer Max Wolf (1863–1932) observes dark clouds of interstellar matter in Earth's galaxy, the Milky Way.

1920 English amateur astronomer and comet-hunter William Denning (1848–1931) discovers Nova Cygni, a star that experiences sudden outbursts of radiant energy.

1921 German mathematician Emmy Noether (1882–1935) begins to develop mathematical axioms ("rules") for algebra.

1921 English economist John Maynard Keynes (1883–1946) publishes his *Treatise on Probability*.

1921 Swiss psychiatrist Hermann Rorschach (1884–1922) introduces the Rorschach inkblot test for examining patients' personalities.

1921 English biochemist Frederick Gowland Hopkins (1861–1947) discovers glutathione, an important requirement for cell metabolism involving oxygen (respiration).

1921 Scottish bacteriologist Alexander Fleming (1881–1955) identifies the bacteria-killing enzyme lysozyme.

1922 English pharmacologist Edward Mellanby (1884–1955) establishes the use of cod-liver oil as a treatment for rickets in children.

1922 Scottish physiologist John Macleod (1876–1935) and coworkers first use insulin to treat patients with diabetes.

1920 Scottish chemist Arthur Lapworth (1872–1941) establishes the role played by electrons in organic chemical reactions.

1920 English physicist Francis Aston (1877–1945) formulates the so-called "whole number rule": that the mass of the oxygen isotope being defined, all the other isotopes have masses that are very nearly whole numbers.

1920 New Zealand-born English physicist Ernest Rutherford (1871–1937) predicts the existence of the neutron.

1922 German chemist Hermann Staudinger (1881–1965) coins the term *macromolecule* and recognizes that substances such as rubber are natural polymers.

THE AMERICAS

1920 American astronomer Vesto Slipher (1875–1969) detects a redshift in the light from galaxies, proving that they are receding (and providing evidence for an expanding universe).

1920 German-born American astronomer Walter Baade (1893–1960) discovers the asteroid Hidalgo, an object 18.6 miles (30 km) in diameter that follows a highly elliptical, cometlike orbit.

1922 Canadian astronomer John Plaskett (1865–1941) identifies the supergiant binary star known as Plaskett's star.

1921 German-born American physiologist Otto Loewi (1873–1961) discovers a chemical released by stimulated nerves, which English physiologist Henry Dale (1875–1968) later identifies as acetylcholine.

1921 Canadian physiologist Frederick Banting (1891–1941) isolates insulin, the hormone that controls the levels of the sugar glucose in the blood.

1922 American biochemist Elmer McCollum (1879–1967) discovers vitamin D (calciferol).

1922 American anatomist and embryologist Herbert Evans (1882–1971) discovers vitamin E (tocopherol).

1922 American psychologist G. Stanley Hall (1844–1924) publishes *Senescence*, one of the first books to discuss the social and psychological aspects of aging.

1920 Belgian-born American chemist Julius Nieuwland (1878–1936) polymerizes acetylene, producing divinyl acetylene.

1921 American chemist Thomas Midgley (1889–1944) discovers the "antiknock" properties of tetraethyl lead (it prevents preignition in gasoline engines).

1921 American physicist Arthur Compton (1892–1962) suggests that ferromagnetism is caused by spinning electrons.

In 1920 Max Wolf used photography to find dark clouds of matter in the Milky Way.

ASIA & OCEANIA

AFRICA & THE MIDDLE EAST

TURNING POINTS

Insulin

Produced in the pancreas by cells called the islets of Langerhans, insulin is a hormone that enables body cells to take up the blood sugar glucose. Glucose is used as an energy source by the body. If the body cannot make insulin, type I diabetes mellitus results. In 1921 Canadian physiologist Frederick Banting (1891–1941) isolated insulin from dogs and found that injecting it cured the symptoms of diabetes in a dog that had had its pancreas removed (and therefore could not produce its own insulin). Using a purer extract from calves, Banting and coworkers successfully treated terminally ill children with type I diabetes the following year. Purified animal insulin was soon available for sale. By the early 1980s insulin could be made by genetically modified bacteria containing the human insulin gene. Banting received the Nobel Prize for Physiology or Medicine in 1923 for his discovery.

ENGINEERING & INVENTION	WORLD EVENTS
1920 KLM, the Dutch National Airline, makes its first scheduled flight between Amsterdam in the Netherlands and London, England.	**1920** Admiral Nikolaus Horthy (1868–1957) leads a counterrevolution in Hungary.
1921 The first expressway in Germany (*Autobahn*) is completed.	**1921** The communist Red Army finally overcomes its White opponents in the civil war that has divided Russia since 1918.
1922 The British Broadcasting Company (later Corporation)—BBC—begins regular broadcasts in Britain.	**1921** Britain concedes autonomy to the Irish Free State, excluding six Ulster counties with a predominantly Protestant population; they remain part of the United Kingdom under the name of Northern Ireland.
1922 Swedish inventor Nils Dalen (1869–1937) patents the Aga solid-fuel stove.	**1922** The Union of Soviet Socialist Republics (USSR) is established; Soviet troops occupy Ukraine.
	1922 Facist leader Benito Mussolini (1883–1945) leads the March on Rome, taking power as Italy's prime minister.

VITAMINS

Vitamins are organic substances, essential in minute quantities, that regulate various chemical reactions in the body. While humans get most of their vitamins from their diet, vitamin D can be made by the body itself, and vitamin K is made by helpful microorganisms living in the intestine. Vitamins are distinct from other nutrients, such as sugars and proteins, that act as building blocks for cells and tissues or as sources of energy to fuel the chemical reactions in the body. Deficiencies of vitamins lead to various disorders.

In 1912 Polish biochemist Kazimierz Funk (1884–1967) isolated a substance from brown rice that he mistakenly believed to be vitamin B_1 (thiamin). Funk believed that the substance was essential for good health and because a chemical group called an amine was included in its structure, he named it "vital amine," later contracted to "vitamine." As more types of essential micronutrients were discovered, some were found not to contain an amine group and the name was further shortened to vitamin.

ENGINEERING & INVENTION	WORLD EVENTS
1920 The Panama Canal is officially opened by U.S. President Woodrow Wilson (1856–1924).	**1920** Mexican generals proclaim the Republic of Sonora, going on to defeat President Venustiano Carranza (1859–1920) and force the surrender of revolutionary leader Pancho Villa (1878–1923).
1920 American gunsmith John Thompson (1860–1940) patents the Thompson submachine gun (Tommy gun).	**1920** The Nineteenth Amendment gives U.S. women the vote.
1920 Station KDKA in Pittsburgh, Pennsylvania, begins the first regular radio broadcasts in the United States.	**1921** Republican Warren Harding (1865–1923) is sworn in as 29th president of the United States. One of his first significant steps is to raise custom barriers against European trade.
1921 American physicist Albert Hull (1880–1966) invents the high-frequency magnetron vacuum tube.	**1921** The Immigration Act (further tightened in 1924) limits the number of foreign nationals who can enter the United States.
1921 American airman John Macready (1887–1979) gives the first demonstration of crop spraying from an airplane.	
1922 American engineer Lee De Forest (1873–1961) creates a sound-on-film optical recording system for movies.	
1922 After five years of research Canadian-born American electrical engineer Reginald Fessenden (1866–1932) makes an improved echo sounder.	
1922 American airman James Doolittle (1896–1993) makes the first coast-to-coast flight across the United States, taking 21 hours 19 minutes.	

Almost all the vitamins we know today were discovered, isolated, and artificially synthesized in the first half of the 20th century. They include the fat-soluble vitamins A, D, E, and K, and the water-soluble vitamin C and B complex vitamins.

A drop from the nose of Fleming, who had a cold, fell onto an agar plate where large yellow colonies of a contaminant had grown, and lysozyme was discovered. ALEXANDER FLEMING	**1920** The map of Central Asia is redrawn as areas in the former empire of the Russian tsars are re-created as autonomous soviet socialist republics (ASSRs) of the Soviet Union. **1920** Britain grants Egypt independence under King Fuad I (r. 1917–36) but retains control over defense and foreign policy, the Suez Canal, and the administration of Sudan.

SUBATOMIC PARTICLES

Italian-American Physicist Enrico Fermi demonstrates the interaction between subatomic particles.

BY 1920 PHYSICISTS KNEW that every atom consists of a nucleus carrying a positive charge surrounded by a cloud of electrons carrying negative charge. This implied that the atom is not an "elementary particle"—an object that cannot be divided into smaller constituents. Before long, scientists were identifying a growing list of particles smaller than atoms.

The Proton and the Neutron

Ernest Rutherford (1871–1937), the New Zealand-born English physicist, found that when he bombarded nitrogen atoms with alpha particles, hydrogen nuclei were released. It followed that a nitrogen atomic nucleus must contain hydrogen nuclei. In 1920 Rutherford suggested the name *proton* for the hydrogen nucleus. The mass of a proton is 1,836 times that of an electron.

Since 1919 Rutherford had been professor of physics at Cambridge University and director of the Cavendish Laboratory. His research continued to center on smashing atomic nuclei by bombarding them with alpha particles (helium nuclei). In 1925 English physicist Patrick Blackett (1897–1974), working under Rutherford's direction, developed a device for recording the disintegration of atoms. But alpha particles were not powerful enough to smash large nuclei, which repelled them without disintegrating. It was not until 1932, when English physicist John Cockcroft (1897–1967) and Irish physicist Ernest Walton (1903–95) built the world's first particle accelerator at the Cavendish Laboratory that these larger atoms could be smashed. The device used powerful electromagnets to accelerate protons that were then directed at a target.

Using these advances, other physicists, such as Irène (1897–1956) and Frédéric (1900–58) Joliot-Curie discovered the existence of very high energy radiation quite unlike gamma radiation. English

physicist James Chadwick (1891–1974), working at the Cavendish Laboratory, suggested that this high-energy radiation consisted of particles with approximately the same mass as the proton, but carrying no electromagnetic charge. Chadwick conducted experiments bombarding the element boron to confirm his hypothesis. Because it carries no charge, the particle came to be called the "neutron." It is stable while it remains inside an atomic nucleus, but outside the nucleus a neutron decays into a proton, an electron, and an antineutrino.

The Neutrino and the Discovery of Antimatter

In 1930 Austrian Wolfgang Pauli (1900–1958) was studying beta radiation—a stream of electrons emitted by unstable atoms. The electrons seemed to lose energy, but no explanation could be found for the loss, which

KEY DATES

1920
Proton named

1925
Cloud chamber of 1911 developed further

1932
Positron identified; neutron identified

1934
Neutrino identified and named

1937
Muon discovered

In 1932 John Cockcroft and Ernest Walton created an atom splitter by charging a hollow metal chamber to 400,000 volts and injecting protons into it. The positively charged particles were driven away from the high positive voltage along a series of tubes kept at lower voltages and into a piece of lithium. Alpha particles that were formed in the collision caused flashes on an observation screen and were photographed.

appeared to contradict one of the most fundamental laws of physics: that energy cannot be created or lost. Pauli's solution to the riddle was to propose that beta radiation also contains a previously unknown particle with the unusual properties of possessing no charge and no mass when it is at rest. Italian-American physicist Enrico Fermi (1901–54) confirmed the existence of such a particle in 1934 and called it the "neutrino."

In 1928 English physicist Paul Dirac (1902–84), dissatisfied with the description of the electron, proposed an alternative. The equations describing Dirac's model predicted that it should be possible for an electron to possess a positive charge. American physicist Carl Anderson (1905–91) discovered this particle (later called the "positron") in 1932. It was the first antimatter particle to be identified.

In 1936, in collaboration with graduate student Seth Neddermeyer (1907–88), Anderson discovered the muon—a very unstable particle similar to an electron but 200 times more massive.

The European Organization for Nuclear Research (CERN), in Switzerland, is the world's largest particle physics lab. The image above shows a computer simulation of a lead-ion collision— a proposed experiment using the facility's Large Hadron Collider.

ASTRONOMY & MATH	BIOLOGY & MEDICINE	PHYSICAL SCIENCES
EUROPE		
1923 Austro-Hungarian rocket scientist Hermann Oberth (1894–1989) introduces the idea of escape velocity in his book *The Rocket into Interplanetary Space*. **1924** Danish astronomer Ejnar Hertzsprung (1873–1967) discovers DH Carinae, the first flare star (a red dwarf star that has brief bright episodes). **1924** English astronomer Arthur Eddington (1882–1944) figures out the mass–luminosity relation for stars. **1925** Swedish astronomer Bertil Lindblad (1895–1965) proposes that our galaxy (the Milky Way) is slowly rotating.	**1923** Austrian neurologist Sigmund Freud (1856–1939) introduces his concepts of the ego (the part of the mind in touch with reality) and the id (the instinctive unconscious mind). **1923** German biochemist Otto Warburg (1883–1970) demonstrates that cancerous cells absorb less oxygen than do normal cells. **1924** German psychiatrist Hans Berger (1873–1941) detects the electrical activity of the brain and later (1929) publishes his work on electroencephalography. **1925** Russian-born English biochemist David Keilin (1887–1963) names the important cellular protein cytochrome (which contains heme, a component of hemoglobin).	**1924** English physicist Edward Appleton (1892–1965) demonstrates the existence of the ionosphere, a layer of ionized gases in the upper atmosphere. **1924** French physicist Louis de Broglie (1892–1987) proposes the idea of wave-particle duality: that some entities (such as electrons) sometimes behave like waves and sometimes behave like particles. **1925** German chemist Walter Noddack (1893–1960) and his wife Ida Tacke (1896–1979) discover the element rhenium. **1925** German chemist Franz Fischer (1877–1947) and Czech chemist Hans Tropsch (1889–1935) devise a process for producing oil-type fuels from coal.
THE AMERICAS		
1925 American physicist Robert Millikan (1868–1953) observes cosmic rays in the upper atmosphere. **1925** American astronomer Edwin Hubble (1889–1953) introduces his classification scheme for galaxies.	**1923** American physicians George (1881–1967) and Gladys Dick (1881–1963) isolate the bacterium that causes scarlet fever. **1924** American pathologist George Whipple (1878–1976) and American physicians George Minot (1885–1950) and William Murphy (1892–1987) introduce the use of raw liver as a treatment for pernicious anemia. **1925** American pathologist George Whipple discovers iron in red blood cells. **1925** American psychologist John Watson (1878–1958) publishes *Behaviorism*, in which he sets out his ideas for improving society. **1925** African-American biologist Ernest Just (1883–1941) shows that UV radiation can cause cancer.	**1923** American physicist Arthur Compton (1892–1962) publishes his explanation of the Compton effect, which is the increase in the wavelength (loss in energy) of an x-ray or gamma ray when it collides with electrons. **1923** Dutch-born American physicist Peter Debye (1884–1966) and German physicist Erich Hückel (1896–1980) propose their theory of electrolytes. It states that electrolytes are fully ionized in dilute solution, and that oppositely charged ions are attracted to each other. **1923** American physical chemist Gilbert Lewis (1875–1946) defines an acid as a substance that accepts electrons.
ASIA & OCEANIA		
	Psychoanalysis is based on the ideas of the Austrian physician Sigmund Freud, who published his study of the human psyche, The Ego and the Id, *in 1923.*	
AFRICA & THE MIDDLE EAST		
	1924 Australian-born South African anthropologist Raymond Dart (1893–1988) discovers fossils of *Australopithecus* in Africa. They help establish Africa as the site of humankind's origins.	

ENGINEERING & INVENTION

1923 Spanish engineer Juan de la Cierva (1895–1936) successfully flies an autogyro, a helicopter-like airplane with a free-rotating horizontal propeller.

1923 German company Benz manufactures the first diesel-engined trucks.

1923 German company Ormig markets a spirit duplicator for making paper copies (using a dye-gelatin process).

1923 Scottish electrical engineer John Logie Baird (1888–1946) invents a television system that uses mechanical scanning.

1924 Swedish chemist Theodor Svedberg (1884–1971) develops the ultracentrifuge. It soon becomes standard equipment in biology and chemistry laboratories.

1923 Russian-born American electronics engineer Vladimir Zworykin (1889–1982) invents the iconoscope TV camera tube, while working at the Westinghouse laboratory.

1924 American pilots Erik Nelson, Lowell Smith, Leigh Wade, and their crews make the first around-the-world flight (with refueling stops) in three U.S. Navy biplanes.

1924 The American company Kimberly-Clark introduces Kleenex, the world's first disposable facial tissues.

1925 French-born American physicist Henri Chrétien (1879–1956) invents the anamorphic lens, which compresses images sideways. (Twenty-eight years later it is used for CinemaScope movies.)

WORLD EVENTS

1923 Hyperinflation devastates the German economy. French troops occupy the coal-rich Rühr region in response to the nation's failure to keep up with the war-reparation payments dictated by the Versailles peace treaty.

1923 Led by Prime Minister Ramsay MacDonald (1866–1937), the Labour Party comes to power in Britain for the first time.

1924 Vladimir Lenin (1870–1924) dies, unleashing a prolonged power struggle in the Soviet Union.

1925 Benito Mussolini (1883–1945) proclaims himself Il Duce ("The Leader") of a Fascist Italy.

1923 Republican Calvin Coolidge (1872–1933) succeeds as U.S. president following the sudden death of Warren Harding (1865–1923).

1924 The Coolidge administration is rocked by the Teapot Dome scandal, which forces the resignation of Secretary of the Interior Albert Fall (1861–1944).

1924 Native Americans are granted full U.S. citizenship.

Galaxies

Beginning in 1925, Edwin Hubble developed a classification scheme for galaxies based on their shapes. A galaxy is a huge disk of millions of stars. The so-called elliptical galaxies appear to be round, oval, or elongate depending on the angle from which we view them. Spiral galaxies reveal spiral arms as they rotate. Barred spiral galaxies have a bar or bridge of stars stretching across their center.

Images of elliptical (left), spiral (center), and barred spiral (right) galaxies taken by the Hubble Space Telescope

1923 Mustafa Kemal (1881–1938) establishes a republic in Turkey with its capital at Ankara.

WOLFGANG PAULI

Born in 1900 in Vienna, Austria, Wolfgang Pauli was a theoretical physicist who made important contributions to quantum mechanics—the behavior of matter and radiation at the atomic and subatomic level. Pauli was the son of a professor of physical chemistry, and he studied at Munich University, where he gained a doctorate in 1921. He worked with German physicist Max Born (1882–1970) at Göttingen University and with Danish physicist Niels Bohr (1885–1962) in Copenhagen before moving to Hamburg University in 1923. Five years later he moved to the Federal Institute of Technology in Zurich, where he remained until his death, although he spent World War II (1939–45) at Princeton.

In about 1924 Pauli added a fourth "spin" quantum number to the existing three to account for the anomalous Zeeman effect (the splitting of a spectral line into two or more components of slightly different frequency when the light source is placed in a magnetic field) and in 1925 revealed his exclusion principle (for which he was awarded the Nobel Prize for Physics in 1945). It states that no atom can have two electrons with the same four quantum numbers. In 1930 he postulated the existence of the neutrino, a neutral low-mass subatomic particle that must, he said, be produced during beta decay, the radioactive decay in which a neutron changes into a proton and a beta particle (electron).

Wolfgang Pauli (right) sits with two other physicists, Enrico Fermi (left) and Werner Heisenberg (center).

INVENTION OF TELEVISION

John Logie Baird examines his mostly mechanical television camera. The circle with holes cut through it is a Nipkow disk.

I
N OCTOBER 1925 SCOTTISH ELECTRICAL engineer John Logie Baird (1888–1946) transmitted the first television pictures in his London workshop. The systems designed to capture moving images for broadcast required a very different set of technologies from existing motion-picture cameras. The image had to be broken down into narrow strips, or "lines," which could then be encoded for transmission.

The First Television Pictures

All television cameras have some method of scanning an image. In the early 1920s Baird designed a system which used a rapidly spinning "Nipkow disk," patent-ed by Polish electrical engineer Paul Nipkow (1860–1940) in 1884. It is a disk—in Baird's case made of cardboard—pierced with a spiral of holes. As the disk rotates, an observer looking through it sees an object as a series of curved lines or scans, each line produced by a different hole in the disk. The first pictures, from 1925, depicted a ventriloquist's doll.

At first, Baird sent his television images along wires. In 1927 he transmitted pictures from London to Glasgow along a telephone line. A year later he sent pictures over the transatlantic telegraph cable to New York. In September 1929 the British Broadcasting Company (BBC; now Corporation) began experimental television broadcasts using Baird's mechanical system. The flickering images consisted of only 30 lines, although this was later increased. In 1932 Baird transmitted pictures by short-wave radio. The experimental broadcasts ended in 1935; and by the time national television broadcasting started in 1937, the BBC had adopted the 405-line electronic system developed by the British company Marconi–EMI. Television broadcasting was suspended during World War II (1939–45) to prevent the transmitters being used to guide enemy aircraft. Baird died before television broadcasting resumed, this time using an all-electronic system.

Electronic Systems

Scottish electrical engineer Alan Campbell-Swinton (1863–1930) figured out the principles of an electronic television system in 1908, although at that time the apparatus was not available to put his ideas into practice. He envisaged using a cathode-ray tube in both the television camera and the receiver. He proposed that a picture signal could be transmitted along wires or received anywhere using the newly invented radio.

In the United States Russian-born electronics engineer Vladimir Zworykin (1889–1982) abandoned Baird's spinning disks and went the electronic route from the beginning. He developed his iconoscope camera tube of 1923 from a cathode-ray tube, using a

ICONOSCOPE

Electron beam · Photosensitive plate · Horizontal deflection plates · Lenses · Vertical deflection plates · Image · Collector electrode · Electron gun

The iconoscope was the first successful television camera tube and was developed by Zworykin. A beam of electrons from an electron gun scans an image focused onto a photosensitive plate. Horizontal and vertical deflection plates force the electron beam to scan in a series of lines. Light striking the plate gives it a positive charge, and electrons not held by the charge bounce back to a collector electrode and form the video signal.

Electron gun · Vertical deflection plates · Screen · Electron beam · Focusing anode · Focusing coil · Horizontal deflection plates · Spot of light on screen

CATHODE-RAY TUBE

A cathode-ray tube, invented in 1897 by German physicist Ferdinand Braun (1850–1918), is the most common type of television receiver. It has an electron gun and deflection plates and a coil to focus the electron beam onto the screen at the front of the tube. Phosphor, which emits light when struck by electrons, coats the inside of the screen on which the scanned image builds up line by line.

beam of electrons for scanning. A lens focused light from a scene onto a so-called signal plate, which was coated with a mosaic of cesium–silver pellets. Each pellet released electrons in proportion to the amount of light falling on it, and the tube's electron beam replenished the electrons as it scanned across the signal plate. The electric current leaving the plate varied in accordance with the variations in light intensity—today we call such an output signal a video signal. American inventor Philo Farnsworth (1906–71) developed a similar camera in 1927 (patented 1930). Though Zworykin joined the Radio Corporation of America (RCA) and improved his system within a few years, from 1939 RCA was required to pay royalties to Farnsworth. In 1941 CBS made experimental color broadcasts from New York, although regular transmissions in color did not begin until 1951.

The Baird Televisor was the first fully operational television set. However, this mechanical device only had 30 lines of display and was soon superseded by higher-definition sets.

KEY DATES

1923
Zworykin invents iconoscope TV camera tube

1925
Baird's first television pictures

1929
BBC begins experimental TV broadcasts

1937
BBC begins national TV broadcasts

1938
Zworykin receives patent for iconoscope TV camera tube

1941
CBS begins experimental color TV broadcasts

ASTRONOMY & MATH

BIOLOGY & MEDICINE

PHYSICAL SCIENCES

EUROPE

1927 Belgian astronomer Georges Lemaître (1894–1966) first proposes what is known as the big bang theory of the origin of the universe.

1927 Dutch astronomer Jan Oort (1900–92) confirms the rotation of the Milky Way galaxy and locates its center (in the constellation Sagittarius).

1927 German astronomers Arnold Schwassmann (1870–1964) and Arno Wachmann (1902–90) discover (using photography) the comet Schwassmann–Wachmann 1, which has a circular orbit just beyond that of Jupiter.

1927 English zoologist Charles Elton (1900–91) publishes *Animal Ecology* and establishes the science of ecology.

1927 Portuguese neurologist António de Egas Moniz (1874–1955) detects brain tumors using cerebral angiography (in which a substance opaque to x-rays is injected into an artery serving the brain).

1928 Scottish microbiologist Alexander Fleming (1881–1955) "accidentally" discovers the antibiotic penicillin.

1926 English chemist Christopher Ingold (1893–1970) discovers mesomerism, a phenomenon in which the structure of a chemical compound "resonates" between two alternative forms.

1926 Austrian physicist Erwin Schrödinger (1887–1961) formulates the wave equation for the hydrogen atom. It is a mathematical expression that describes the behavior of an electron as it "orbits" the atom's nucleus.

1927 English chemist Nevil Sidgwick (1873–1952) introduces the modern theory of chemical valence, concerning the role of electrons in chemical bonds.

1927 German theoretical physicist Werner Heisenberg (1901–76) formulates his uncertainty principle.

Charles Lindbergh crossed the Atlantic in 1927 in his custom-built, single-engine plane, the Spirit of St. Louis.

THE AMERICAS

1927 German-born American physicist Fritz London (1900–54) proposes a quantum theory of chemical bonding.

1928 American astronomer Henry Russell (1877–1957) determines the abundance of elements in the solar atmosphere and finds that hydrogen is the principal element in the sun's atmosphere.

1928 Austrian-born American mathematician Richard von Mises (1883–1953) publishes *Probability, Statistics, and Truth*, a philosophical approach to probability.

1928 Hungarian-born American mathematician John von Neumann (1903–57) publishes a paper outlining his minimax theorem, the basic foundation of game theory.

1926 American geneticist Hermann Müller (1890–1967) uses x-rays to create genetic mutations in fruit flies (*Drosophila*).

1926 American biochemist James Sumner (1887–1955) is the first to crystallize an enzyme—urease.

1926 American biochemist John Abel (1857–1938) and coworkers crystallize insulin and show that it is a protein.

1927 Canadian anthropologist Davidson Black (1884–1934) identifies a new human fossil—Peking man (*Homo erectus*)—by a single tooth.

1928 Greek-born American physician George Papanicolaou (1883–1962) devises the Pap smear test for cancer of the cervix.

1928 American engineers Philip Drinker (1894–1972) and Louis Shaw (1886–1940) first use the iron lung, a respirator for patients with paralyzed chest muscles.

1926 American physical chemist Gilbert Lewis (1875–1946) coins the word *photon* to describe a quantum, or "particle," of light.

1927 American physicist Clinton Davisson (1881–1958) and coworkers demonstrate the diffraction of electrons, an experiment that confirms their wavelike properties.

ASIA & OCEANIA

One sometimes finds what one is not looking for.

ALEXANDER FLEMING

1928 The Flying Doctor Service is introduced in Australia.

1928 Indian physicist Chandrasekhara Raman (1888–1970) describes the Raman effect: When a transparent substance is illuminated by a beam of light of a single wavelength, some of the light is scattered and has frequencies higher and lower than that of the incoming light.

AFRICA & THE MIDDLE EAST

ENGINEERING & INVENTION	WORLD EVENTS
1926 English aviator Alan Cobham (1894–1973) flies around the world, leaving England June 30 and returning October 1.	**1926** Benito Mussolini (1883–1945) takes full control of Italy and bans opposition.
1926 Norwegian inventor Erik Rotheim (1898–1938) invents the aerosol can.	**1926** A. A. Milne (1882–1956) publishes *Winnie-the-Pooh*.
1926 Norwegian explorer Roald Amundsen (1872–1928) and American explorer Lincoln Ellsworth (1880–1951) fly over the North Pole in the airship *Norge*, designed and piloted by Italian engineer Umberto Nobile (1885–1978).	**1927** Joseph Stalin (1878–1953) emerges as the dominant figure in the collective leadership now ruling the Soviet Union. **1927** *In Search of Lost Time* by Marcel Proust (1871–1922) is published posthumously.
1928 German aviators Hermann Köhl (1881–1938) and Guenther von Hünefeld (1892–1929) and Irish army officer James Fitzmaurice (1898–1965) become the first to fly across the Atlantic from east to west.	

1926 American inventor Robert Goddard (1882–1945) successfully launches a liquid-fuel rocket.	**1927** *The Jazz Singer*, starring Al Jolson (1886–1950), inaugurates the era of "talking pictures" in the cinema.
1926 Designed by Polish-born American engineer Ralph Modjeski (1861–1940), the Delaware River Bridge (the world's longest suspension span) opens in Philadelphia. It is renamed the Benjamin Franklin Bridge in 1956.	**1927** Canada is voted into the League of Nations Council. **1928** Brazil's economy collapses as a result of the overproduction of coffee.
1927 American inventor Philo Farnsworth (1906–71) makes a television camera tube (patented 1930).	
1927 American aviator Charles Lindbergh (1902–74) makes the first solo flight across the Atlantic Ocean.	
1928 American inventor Jacob Schick (1878–1937) patents the electric shaver.	

Norge, a 350-feet (106-m) airship, flew over the North Pole in 1926.

1926 Japan's Emperor Yoshihito (r. 1912–26) dies. He is succeeded by his son Hirohito (r. 1926–89).

1928 Latin script replaces Arabic for writing the Turkish language.

ROCKETS

The Chinese first used rockets in the 1100s, both for ornamental fireworks and as weapons of war. Knowledge of rockets spread, and in 1288 the Moors used them in their attack on Valencia in Spain. Multistage rockets (with one rocket mounted on top of another) came next, and by 1715 the Russians had their own rocket factory near St. Petersburg.

Early rockets were solid-fuel rockets that burned gunpowder. In 1806 English engineer William Congreve (1772–1828) started making rockets with an explosive warhead. They could reach targets 1.5 miles (2.5 km) away.

Congreve rockets had a long wooden tail, or stick, like modern fireworks. To improve accuracy and stability in flight, English inventor William Hale (1797–1870) added three angled fins to the rocket exhaust, which made the missile spin in flight. Rockets no longer needed a long wooden tail. Hale rockets were used by the U.S. Army in the Mexican–American War (1846–48) and by both sides in the American Civil War (1861–65).

American inventor Robert Goddard (1882–1945) launched the first liquid-fuel rocket in 1926 and ushered in a new age. The rocket used gasoline and liquid oxygen. By 1935 Goddard's rockets could climb over 7,820 feet (2,400 m) at a speed of 620 miles (1,000 km) per hour.

In Germany, Hermann Oberth (1894–1989) led a research team that developed a gasoline/liquid oxygen rocket by 1931. Wernher von Braun (1912–77) joined the team in 1930 and directed the research that produced the V-1 and the V-2. The V-1 (also known as the Doodlebug) was a pulsejet-powered flying bomb. The V-2, with its 1.1-ton (1-tonne) warhead, was the first rocket-powered guided missile.

After the war von Braun and other German scientists continued their work in the United States. Progress continued rapidly there and in the Soviet Union, resulting in intercontinental ballistic missiles and the space launchers that dominated the space race for 30 years.

ASTRONOMY & MATH	BIOLOGY & MEDICINE	PHYSICAL SCIENCES

EUROPE

1930 Dutch mathematician Bartel van der Waerden (1903–96) publishes what becomes the standard work on abstract algebra, *Modern Algebra*.

1929 German biochemist Adolf Butenandt (1903–95) isolates the female sex hormone estrogen. Two years later he isolates the male hormone androsterone.

1929 German biochemist Hans Fischer (1881–1945) determines the structure of heme (a key part of hemoglobin, the red pigment in blood) and synthesizes it.

1930 Swedish biochemist Arne Tiselius (1902–71) introduces the technique of electrophoresis for separating proteins (later to become a key process in genetic fingerprinting).

1930 Swiss chemist Paul Karrer (1889–1971) determines the structure of carotene, the precursor of vitamin A, and goes on to synthesize both.

1929 Irish crystallographer Kathleen Lonsdale (1903–71) uses x-ray crystallography to prove the hexagonal structure of benzene.

1929 German physicists Walther Bothe (1891–1957) and Werner Kolhorster (1887–1946) use a pair of Geiger counters to detect the direction from which cosmic rays come, and establish that cosmic rays are charged particles.

1930 French physicist Louis Néel (1904–2000) determines the Néel temperature, the temperature above which an antiferromagnetic substance (which is not magnetic) becomes paramagnetic (slightly magnetic).

1930 Austrian-born Swiss physicist Wolfgang Pauli (1900–58) predicts the existence of the neutrino.

THE AMERICAS

1929 American astronomer Edwin Hubble (1889–1953) formulates Hubble's law, which relates the distance of a star to its velocity of recession from Earth.

1930 American astronomer Clyde Tombaugh (1906–97) discovers the planet Pluto (now considered a dwarf planet).

1930 American electrical engineer Vannevar Bush (1890–1974) builds an analog computer.

1931 Indian-born American astrophysicist Subrahmanyan Chandrasekhar (1910–95) calculates the possible Chandrasekhar limit, the maximum mass for a white dwarf star (equal to about 1.4 times the mass of the sun).

1931 Austrian-born American mathematician Kurt Gödel (1906–78) proves that any mathematical system that includes the laws of arithmetic must be inconsistent or incomplete.

1931 Italian-born American physicist Bruno Rossi (1905–93) finds that cosmic rays can travel through lead 3.2-feet (1-m) thick.

1929 Canadian-born American physical chemist William Giauque (1895–1982) determines that natural oxygen consists of three isotopes of masses 16, 17, and 18.

1929 German-born American physicist Albert Einstein (1879–1955) first announces his unified field theory, which attempts to bring all the fundamental forces into a single theory.

1930 Italian-born American physicist Bruno Rossi (1905–93) discovers the composition of cosmic rays—the primary rays being positively charged and the secondary rays being elementary particles and gamma rays.

1930 American chemist Thomas Midgley (1889–1944) demonstrates the properties of Freon, the first CFC (chlorofluorocarbon), invented by his team for use as a refrigerant.

1930 American chemist Wallace Carothers (1896–1937) discovers neoprene (patented 1937). His work leads to the first commercial production of synthetic rubber and nylon.

1931 American chemist Linus Pauling (1901–94) explains that benzene is stable because its molecule has two structures that resonate ("flip" back and forth).

ASIA & OCEANIA

1929 Japanese geophysicist Motonori Matuyama (1884–1958) postulates that the Earth's magnetic field has undergone reversals several times in its history.

Art deco in style, New York's Chrysler Building was the tallest building in the world on its completion in 1930. That record, however, was broken 11 months later with the completion of the Empire State Building, a few blocks away.

AFRICA & THE MIDDLE EAST

ENGINEERING & INVENTION	WORLD EVENTS
1929 German engineer Hugo Eckener (1868–1954) commands a Zeppelin airship that makes a 21-day around-the-world flight.	**1929** The Kingdom of Serbs, Croats, and Slovenes is renamed Yugoslavia.
1929 German engineer Felix Wankel (1902–88) patents his rotary engine.	**1929** Joseph Stalin (1878–1953) confirms his position as ruler of the Soviet Union by forcing his chief rival, Leon Trotsky (1879–1940), into exile. He launches the first five-year plan, aimed at modernizing the Soviet economy.
1929 English engineer Robert Davis (1870–1965) invents a decompression chamber for deep-sea divers and in the same year designs an escape apparatus for submarines.	
1930 English engineer Frank Whittle (1907–96) invents the gas turbine (jet) engine.	**1930** The Nazis (National Socialists) led by Adolf Hitler (1889–1945) run second in elections to the Reichstag (Germany's parliament), winning 107 seats.
1930 English engineer Barnes Wallis (1887–1979) starts using the geodesic construction technique for aircraft, which uses light, straight structural elements.	**1931** King Alfonso XIII (r. 1886–1931) leaves Spain as his country declares itself a republic.

1930 American businessman Clarence Birdseye (1886–1956) markets the first flash-frozen foods.	**1929** Republican Herbert Hoover (1874–1964) becomes U.S. president.
1930 American chemist Waldo Semon (1898–1999) invents a plastic called PVC (polyvinyl chloride).	**1929** The Wall Street Crash: American shares lose more than $40 billion in value in a single month. The crash contributes to the beginning of the Great Depression of the 1930s.
1930 American naturalist William Beebe (1877–1962) and American engineer Otis Barton build a bathysphere submersible for deep-sea studies.	**1930** Revolution in Brazil brings dictatorial powers to Getúlio Vargas (1882–1954).
1930 The 1,048-foot- (319.4-m-) tall Chrysler Building is completed in New York City, designed by American architect William van Alen (1883–1954).	
1931 American physicist Robert Van de Graaff (1901–67) invents the Van de Graaff high-voltage generator, which is later used as an atom smasher.	
1931 The Empire State Building in New York City becomes the world's tallest building.	

Frank Whittle (right) explains the workings of his jet engine to a journalist.

1929 Tajikistan—previously treated as part of Uzbekistan—becomes a separate Soviet republic.

1931 Japanese troops occupy Manchuria in northern China.

1929 The Riotous Assemblies Act is passed by the South African parliament to suppress protests by the country's black majority.

WANKEL ENGINE

Invented by German engineer Felix Wankel, the Wankel engine is the most widely used type of rotary engine. A Wankel engine works on a four-stroke cycle, and it is lighter and has fewer moving parts than the usual piston engine of similar power output. Instead of pistons it has a revolving rotor, so there is no need for a crankshaft to convert the up-and-down motion into rotary motion. Wankel first conceived his idea for a rotary engine in 1924 and received his first patent in 1929. However, it was not until 1957 that he built his first fully functional engine. The Wankel engine is still widely used in cars, notably by Mazda, and also in some go-carts, motorcycles, boats, and airplanes.

Gasoline/air mixture enters

Chamber containing fuel/air mixture

Inlet port | Rotor   Rotor

Induction

A gasoline/air mixture enters one of the chambers as the tip of the rotor goes past the inlet port.

Compression

The chamber containing the mixture decreases in size as the rotor turns, compressing the mixture.

Exhaust port

Spark plugs | Burned gases escape

Power

A pair of spark plugs ignites the mixture, which explodes and expands, "pushing" the rotor around.

Exhaust

Burned gases escape out of the exhaust port as the leading lobe of the rotor goes past.

PENICILLIN AND ANTIBIOTICS

I N THE EARLY PART OF THE 20TH CENTURY millions of people died every year from bacterial infections such as diphtheria, pneumonia, and septicemia. But the discovery of a mold that could kill germs would change all that.

From the late 19th century, thanks to the work of French chemist Louis Pasteur (1822–95) and others, scientists and medical practitioners recognized a new type of enemy—bacteria, or "germs." Many bacteria had been identified, and the conditions they caused were better understood. For example, staphylococci gave rise to boils and other skin infections, food poisoning, septicemia, and pneumonia; streptococci caused throat infections and various feverish conditions; and several bacilli produced tetanus, anthrax, diphtheria, and food poisoning.

The same kinds of organisms caused untold suffering when they infected wounds. Wound infection was the specialized area of Scottish bacteriologist Alexander Fleming (1881–1955). Unlike other medical researchers of the time, Fleming believed that the way to tackle infection was not to douse it with chemicals but to harness natural processes to do the job instead.

KEY DATES

1877
Pasteur observes anthrax-killing bacteria

1921
Fleming discovers lysozyme in living cells

1928
Fleming identifies penicillin

1940
Mice and humans treated with penicillin

c.1943
Penicillin in mass production

While the German chemist Paul Ehrlich (1854–1915) devoted himself to isolating chemical therapies, Fleming was in search of biological cures. By the mid-1920s he had already made a name for himself by discovering the enzyme lysozyme (1921), produced by living cells to break down other organic material. He thought that this kind of naturally occurring substance could hold the key to fighting bacterial infection.

Strange Mold

In 1928, after returning from vacation to his laboratory at St. Mary's Hospital in London, Fleming noticed something unusual about a culture of *Staphylococcus* that he had left developing in a petri dish. In his absence, a mold had grown in the dish, and it appeared to be killing the *Staphylococcus*. Fleming identified the strange mold as a species of *Penicillium* and discovered that the liquid it produced (penicillin) was equally effective at destroying a large number of different bacteria. More exciting still, it appeared to have no effect on healthy living tissue, so Fleming thought it could be safe to use on humans. But there were drawbacks. For a start, there were several disease-causing bacteria—notably those responsible for plague and cholera—on which it had no effect at all. (In fact, penicillin only works on gram-positive bacteria, in which the cell walls contain a thick layer of peptidoglycan—a substance that gives the bacteria shape and strength. Penicillin inhibits the formation of the peptidoglycan layer and thereby weakens the cell wall.) Even more disheartening was the fact that penicillin turned out to be very difficult to produce. For every milliliter of fluid secreted from the *Penicillium* mold, only about 0.000002 ml was active penicillin, and what tiny amounts could be extracted deteriorated easily.

The problems seemed insurmountable, but in 1939 a group of scientists at Oxford University in England led by Australian pathologist Howard Florey (1898–1968) and German biochemist Ernst Chain (1906–79) began following up Fleming's discovery. By 1940 they extracted penicillin and began

The image left shows a fruiting body of the mold Penicillium chrysogenum, *which is used to make penicillin antibiotics. Other species of* Penicillium *are used to make blue cheeses. Magnification x 500.*

testing it on mice. The results were startling. A dose of penicillin enabled mice to fight off infections that otherwise would have killed them. Florey then began treating a human patient who was dangerously ill with staphylococcal septicemia (blood poisoning). The patient improved a little; but the doses required were too large, and Florey's laboratory was unable to produce enough to keep up the treatment. The patient died, but the results were impressive enough to convince several pharmaceutical companies of penicillin's importance. Thanks to refinements in the production technique developed by English biochemist Norman Heatley (1911–2004), the "miracle drug" was being mass-produced in the United States and Britain by about 1943.

The development could not have come at a more crucial time. World War II was raging, and wounded Allied servicemen were the first to benefit. Thousands of lives were saved. After the war the benefits of penicillin were spread more widely. Deaths from diseases such as anthrax, pneumonia, and tetanus and from blood infections were cut dramatically. Fleming, Florey, and Chain received the 1945 Nobel Prize for Medicine. Heatley remained an unsung hero until 1990, when his contribution was recognized by an honorary degree from Oxford University.

Fleming's accidental discovery of penicillin marked the beginning of modern antibiotics. He also found that some bacteria could build up resistance to penicillin if exposed to repeated low doses.

ASTRONOMY & MATH	BIOLOGY & MEDICINE	PHYSICAL SCIENCES

EUROPE

1932 German astronomer Karl Reinmuth (1892–1979) observes the first Earth-crossing Apollo asteroid. It is lost soon after and not rediscovered until the 1970s.

1933 Swiss astrophysicist Fritz Zwicky (1898–1974) proposes that space must contain invisible "dark matter" (to account for the total mass in the universe).

1934 Swiss astrophysicist Fritz Zwicky and German-born American astronomer Walter Baade (1893–1960) predict the existence of neutron stars from their analysis of supernovas.

1932 German bacteriologist Gerhard Domagk (1895–1964) discovers the first sulfa drug, sulfanilamide. It is first used in 1935 against a streptococcal infection.

1933 Austrian-German chemist Richard Kuhn (1900–67) and coworkers isolate vitamin B_2 (riboflavin). The same year American chemist Roger Williams (1893–1988) discovers another B complex vitamin, pantothenic acid.

1934 German biochemist Adolf Butenandt (1903–95) identifies the female sex hormone progesterone.

1934 Danish biochemist Henrik Dam (1895–1976) discovers a factor needed for blood clotting, which a year later he calls vitamin K. American chemist Robert Williams (1886–1965) isolates vitamin B_1.

1932 English physicist James Chadwick (1891–1974) discovers the neutron.

1932 English physicist John Cockcroft (1897–1967) and Irish physicist Ernest Walton (1903–95) carry out the first nuclear fission by bombarding lithium with protons, using a linear accelerator they have invented.

1933 English chemist Charles Coulson (1910–74) and German physicist Erich Hückel (1896–1980) independently propose the molecular orbital theory to describe the behavior of bonding electrons in compounds.

1933 Polish chemist Tadeus Reichstein (1897–1996) and, working together, English chemists Norman Haworth (1883–1950) and Edmund Hirst (1898–1975) synthesize vitamin C (ascorbic acid).

THE AMERICAS

1932 American physiologist Walter Cannon (1871–1945) introduces the concept of homeostasis, in which the body's systems act together to maintain a condition of balance.

1932 American physician Armand Quick (1894–1978) develops the Quick test for blood clotting.

1932 Hungarian-born American biochemist Albert Szent-Györgyi (1893–1986) and American biochemist Charles King (1896–1986) independently prove that hexonuric acid is vitamin C; it is isolated and renamed ascorbic acid.

1933 American biochemist George Wald (1906–97) discovers vitamin A in the retina of the eye, later shown to be a precursor of rhodopsin (a red photosensitive pigment).

1934 American scientist Royal Raymond Rife (1888–1971) tests a cancer-curing treatment using radio waves on human patients.

1932 American chemist Harold Urey (1893–1981) and coworkers isolate deuterium (heavy hydrogen, the hydrogen isotope of mass 2). Two years later Australian physicist Mark Oliphant (1901–2000) discovers tritium (the hydrogen isotope of mass 3).

1932 Synthetic rubber is first marketed in the United States (by the DuPont Company) under the name Duprene, later renamed Neoprene.

1932 American physicist Carl Anderson (1905–91) announces the existence of the positron (positive electron). It is the first example of a particle of antimatter.

INSIDE STORY

Neutron Stars

A tiny neutron star lies at the very center of the Crab nebula, the remnant of a supernova explosion that was observed by Chinese astronomers in 1054. Fritz Zwicky and Walter Baade predicted the existence of such stars in 1934. They are the densest and smallest stars, consisting of tightly packed neutrons (so-called degeneracy matter). They have a mass similar to that of the sun but are only about 12 miles (20 km) across. Rapidly spinning neutron stars become pulsars, emitting high-energy pulses of radio waves.

ASIA & OCEANIA

1932 Anthropologist George Lewis discovers fossils of the hominoid *Ramapithecus* in northern India.

1933 The Tasmanian wolf (or thylacine) becomes extinct in the wild.

The cat's eye, a road safety device invented in 1934, consists of reflective glass spheres set in rubber and surrounded by cast iron.

AFRICA & THE MIDDLE EAST

ENGINEERING & INVENTION	WORLD EVENTS

1932 Dutch physicist Frits Zernike (1888–1966) invents the phase-contrast microscope.

1933 English engineer Alan Blumlein (1903–42) patents a system of stereophonic sound recording.

1934 The French company Citroën launches the first mass-produced front-wheel-drive car.

1934 The *Queen Mary*, the world's largest ocean liner, is launched in Glasgow, Scotland. The liner's maiden voyage takes place in 1936.

1934 English inventor Percy Shaw (1890–1976) patents "cat's eyes" (reflecting road markers).

1932 Famine in Ukraine follows the attempt of Soviet ruler Joseph Stalin (1878–1953) to impose the collectivization of agriculture.

1932 António Salazar (1889–1970) comes to power in Portugal. His Estado Novo ("New State") dictatorship will rule the nation for the next 36 years.

1933 Adolf Hitler (1889–1945) becomes chancellor of Germany; he assumes dictatorial powers and outlaws all political parties except the Nazi Party.

1934 Stalin eliminates political enemies in the Soviet Union; many are found guilty of invented crimes in "show trials" and shot, while millions more are deported to labor camps (gulags).

1932 American physicist Ernest Lawrence (1901–58) successfully operates the first cyclotron, one of the first particle accelerators, or atom smashers.

1932 American electrical engineer William Kouwenhoven (1886–1975) has the idea for a defibrillator to restart the heart of a patient with a heart attack.

1933 The first modern airliner, the Boeing 247, enters service.

1934 American engineer Laurens Hammond (1895–1973) designs the electronic organ that bears his name.

1934 American firearms engineer John Garand (1888–1974) designs the semiautomatic Garand M1 rifle, soon to become standard issue in the U.S. Army.

1934 American psychologist B. F. Skinner (1904–90) invents the Skinner box for studying the behavior of animals.

1932 The Chaco War (1932–35) between Bolivia and Paraguay begins. It is fought for possession of the disputed Northern Chaco region. Paraguay emerges victorious three years later.

1932 In the United States the Great Depression is at its worst, with more than 15 million workers unemployed.

1933 Prohibition (of alcohol) ends in the United States.

1934 After a drought in the Midwest, many U.S. farmers leave the "Dust Bowl."

1934 Lázaro Cárdenas (1895–1970) becomes president of Mexico, introducing a program of social reform.

1932 The Sydney Harbor Bridge, designed by English engineer Ralph Freeman (1880–1950), is completed. At the time it has the longest single span of any bridge in the world.

Skinner boxes are used to study animal behavior and learning. This box has a lever inside, which the rat learns to press to get a reward of food.

ARTIFICIAL FIBERS

The first attempts at creating an artificial fiber tried to copy silk, the most expensive of natural fibers. Natural silk contains cellulose, which is also found in plants. Methods of copying it involve dissolving cellulose (in the form of wood pulp or cotton) to make a solution that is forced through a tiny hole to make a strand. Chemicals harden the strand to form a fiber. The first patent for such a process—in the early 1800s—went to a Swiss chemist named Georges Audemars. In 1883, while searching for a material to make the filaments for his newly invented electric lamp, English physicist Joseph Swan (1828–1914) patented a process for making cellulose fibers by dissolving nitrocellulose (guncotton) in acetic acid (ethanoic acid) and forcing it through small holes.

In 1884 French chemist Hilaire de Chardonnet (1839–1924) made cotton waste into cellulose acetate (ethanoate) and dissolved it in a solvent. He forced the sticky solution through a mesh of small holes to make Chardonnet silk, later called acetate rayon. Cellulose was also used to make *Glanzstoff* in Germany and viscose rayon in Britain.

The first totally artificial fiber was produced in 1935 by American chemist Wallace Carothers (1896–1937). It was a polymer named nylon 66. His company, DuPont, released the top-secret product in 1938. Since then DuPont and other companies have produced several other kinds of nylon. In 1941 a different type of polymer, a polyester with the trade names Dacron and Terylene, was created. It is often blended with a natural fiber such as wool.

In 1964 both American and British researchers independently reinvented carbon fibers (originally invented by Joseph Swan). Manufacturers mix them with plastics to make materials of great strength and versatility. These composites are made into leisure products such as golf clubs, tennis rackets, and sailboat masts, as well as industrial items such as helicopter rotors and turbine blades.

ASTRONOMY & MATH	BIOLOGY & MEDICINE	PHYSICAL SCIENCES

EUROPE

1936 English mathematician and logician Alan Turing (1912–54) "invents" the hypothetical Turing machine, which determines whether or not a problem can be solved using a computer. A year later he devises a mathematical theory of computing and publishes his paper "On Computable Numbers."

1937 Russian mathematician Ivan Vinogradov (1891–1983) proves that every large even number can be expressed as the sum of four prime numbers.

1935 Austrian zoologist Konrad Lorenz (1903–89) discovers imprinting in animals.

1935 Portuguese neurologist António de Egas Moniz (1874–1955) introduces prefrontal lobotomy to treat personality disorders.

1937 German-born English biochemist Hans Krebs (1900–81) explains the citric acid cycle, also called the Krebs cycle. It is a series of reactions fundamental to the metabolism in aerobic (oxygen-consuming) organisms.

1937 Swiss-born Italian pharmacologist Daniel Bovet (1907–92) identifies the first antihistamine effective in treating allergies.

1937 Italian physician Ugo Cerletti (1877–1963) introduces electroconvulsive, or "shock," therapy (ECT) to treat schizophrenia.

1935 Swiss chemist Paul Karrer (1889–1971) determines the structure of vitamin B_2 (riboflavin) and synthesizes it.

1935 British chemists at ICI (Imperial Chemical Industries) develop a reproducible high-pressure synthesis of polyethene (also known as polyethylene or polythene).

1936 Danish physicist Niels Bohr (1885–1962) proposes a liquid-drop model of the nucleus.

1936 Danish seismologist Inge Lehmann (1888–1993) proposes that the Earth's inner core is solid and surrounded by liquid metal.

THE AMERICAS

1935 American radio engineer John Dellinger (1886–1962) confirms that sunspot activity causes interference with radio signals on Earth.

1935 American oceanographer William Ewing (1906–74) starts a seismic (earthquake) study of the seabed.

1935 American seismologist Charles Richter (1900–85) devises the Richter scale to measure earthquake intensity.

1935 German-born American astronomer Rupert Wildt (1905–76) detects that the large planets have ammonia and methane in their atmospheres.

1936 American mathematician Alonzo Church (1903–95) demonstrates that there is no single way in which a mathematical statement can be verified or proven.

1937 American electrical engineer George Stibitz (1904–95) of Bell Laboratories makes a binary adding machine (the Model K).

1935 American biochemist Wendell Stanley (1904–71) crystallizes tobacco mosaic virus.

1935 German-born American biochemist Rudolf Schoenheimer (1898–1941) uses deuterium (heavy hydrogen) as a tracer to follow biochemical reactions.

1937 American chemist Michael Sveda (1912–99) accidentally discovers the artificial-sweetening properties of cyclamates.

The giant panda is part of the bear family. This rare animal is found wild only in China.

1935 German-born American physicists Fritz (1900–54) and Heinz (1907–70) London announce the so-called London equations concerning superconductors.

1935 Canadian-born American physicist Arthur Dempster (1886–1950) discovers the fissile isotope uranium-235. It is used later in atom bombs.

1935 American biochemist William Rose (1887–1985) discovers threonine, the last of the so-called essential amino acids.

1936 American chemist Robert Williams (1886–1965) announces the structure of vitamin B_1 (thiamin) and its synthesis.

1936 American physicists Russian-born George Gamow (1904–68) and Hungarian-born Edward Teller (1908–2003) put forward a theory to account for beta decay by a radioactive isotope.

1936 American physicist Carl Anderson (1905–91) discovers the muon (mu-meson) in cosmic rays. The muon is a negatively charged particle some 200 times as massive as the electron.

ASIA & OCEANIA

1936 The last-known Tasmanian wolf, or thylacine (*Thylacinus cyanocephalus*), dies at Hobart Zoo in Tasmania, Australia.

1936 The first giant panda (*Ailuropoda melanoleuca*) is captured alive in the wild by clothing designer Ruth Harkness, widow of adventurer William Harkness.

AFRICA & THE MIDDLE EAST

The Boulder (Hoover) Dam was built on the Colorado River between 1931 and 1935. The hydroelectric power it produces is distributed among three states: Nevada, Arizona, and California.

ENGINEERING & INVENTION

1935 German engineer Willy Messerschmitt (1898–1978) designs the Bf-109 single-seat fighter airplane.

1935 Scottish physicist Robert Watson-Watt (1892–1973) invents radar, which is also being developed in Germany.

1936 German engineer Heinrich Focke (1890–1979) builds and successfully demonstrates a two-rotor helicopter.

1936 The Supermarine Spitfire fighter airplane, designed by English engineer Reginald Mitchell (1895–1937), makes its maiden flight.

1937 The Swiss company Nestlé begins marketing instant coffee (Nescafé).

1935 The coin-operated parking meter, invented by American editor Carlton Magee (1873–1946), is introduced in the United States.

1935 American musicians and amateur photographers Leopold Godowsky, Jr. (1900–83) and Leopold Mannes (1899–1964) invent Kodachrome transparency film.

1936 The Boulder Dam is completed on the Colorado River.

1937 The world's first pressurized aircraft, the Lockheed XC-35, makes its maiden flight.

1937 San Francisco's Golden Gate Bridge, designed by American engineer Joseph Strauss (1870–1938), is completed.

1937 American physicist Chester Carlson (1906–68) invents xerography, a dry photocopying process (patented 1940).

WORLD EVENTS

1936 The Spanish Civil War (1936–39) breaks out between right-wing forces led by General Francisco Franco (1892–1975) and the leftist Popular Front government. It will end in victory for Franco.

1938 Pablo Picasso (1881–1973) paints "Guernica" to protest the bombing of the Basque town of that name in the Spanish Civil War.

1936 African-American athlete Jesse Owens (1913–80) wins four golds at the Berlin Olympics.

1937 *Gone with the Wind* by Margaret Mitchell (1900–49) is published.

1937 American aviator Amelia Earhart (1897–1937) disappears on a flight across the Pacific.

HOW THINGS WORK

Early Photocopiers

The earliest types of photocopiers used the xerography process. The item to be copied is moved across the light source (instead of the light moving to scan the item as in most modern machines). A lens focuses an image of the item onto a drum (1), where it produces an electrostatic copy as a pattern of electric charges. Particles of charged toner powder stick to the pattern (2) and transfer to a sheet of blank paper as the drum rotates (3). A heater partly melts the toner to "fix" the image onto the paper (4).

Image
Light
Toner sticks to pattern of electrically charged particles
Lens
Image on drum
Image printed onto paper
1
2
Image "fixed" by heated rollers
3
4

HELICOPTERS

As early as 1480 Italian artist Leonardo da Vinci (1452–1519) sketched a design for an aircraft that carried a large, vertically mounted screw. He reasoned that if the screw rotated fast enough, the craft would rise into the air. However, he did not know about the phenomenon of torque, which would actually make the craft rotate while the screw remained still.

Four centuries later, Italian Carlo Forlanini (1847–1918) and Frenchman Gustave de Ponton d'Amécourt (1825–88) made models of steam-powered helicopters. Forlanini's model had a pair of rotors turning in opposite directions on the same shaft. Driven by a small steam engine, they lifted the craft to a height of 49 feet (15 m), where it hovered for nearly a minute.

By the beginning of the 20th century gasoline engines powered machines that could hover a short distance off the ground for a short time. These early helicopters were not directionally stable, which is crucial for sustained flight. Many engineers tried to solve this problem, including Russian-born American Igor Sikorsky (1889–1972) and German Heinrich Focke (1890–1979). Focke's Fa-61 twin-rotor machine could fly backward as well as forward at a speed of 75 miles (120 km) per hour and a height of more than 7,800 feet (2,400 m). It set an endurance record of 1 hour 20 minutes in the 1930s.

Finally, in 1939 Sikorsky flew the first practical single-rotor machine. It could take off vertically and reached a forward speed of 43 miles (70 km) per hour. It had an enclosed cabin and a latticework tail carrying a small vertical propeller. The second propeller overcame the long-standing problem of torque in a single-rotor machine, since it kept the whole machine from rotating. The U.S. and British forces used improved versions of the Sikorsky VS-300 helicopter. The military helicopter came into its own during the Korean War (1950–53), transporting troops and casualties, and in the Vietnam War (1954–75), as aerial artillery.

ASTRONOMY & MATH	BIOLOGY & MEDICINE	PHYSICAL SCIENCES

EUROPE

1938 The asteroid Hermes—first located in 1937 by German astronomer Karl Reinmuth (1892–1979)—approaches within 485,000 miles (780,000 km) of Earth, closer than any other observed asteroid at the time.

1938 German computer pioneer Konrad Zuse (1910–95) constructs a binary digital computer (the Z1).

1939 Under the pseudonym Nicolas Bourbaki, a group of French mathematicians publishes *Elements of Mathematics*, the first of many books on contemporary mathematics.

1939 Danish astrophysicist Bengt Strömgren (1908–87) identifies Strömgren spheres, regions of ionized gas (mainly hydrogen) surrounding a hot star.

1938 May & Baker pharmaceutical company produces sulfapyridine, the sulfa drug used to treat pneumonia.

1939 Swiss chemist Paul Müller (1899–1965) determines the insect-killing properties of DDT.

1940 German-born British biochemist Ernst Chain (1906–1979) and Australian pathologist Howard Florey (1898–1968) extract and purify penicillin and perform the first clinical trials of the drug.

1940 Swiss psychologist Carl Jung (1875–1961) publishes *The Integration of Personality*.

1938 German physicists Otto Hahn (1879–1968) and Fritz Strassmann (1902–80) induce nuclear fission in uranium.

1939 German chemist Richard Kuhn (1900–67) and coworkers isolate vitamin B_6 (pyridoxine) in yeast and synthesize it within a few months.

1939 French chemist Marguerite Perey (1909–75) discovers the radioactive element francium. (She calls it actinium K and changes its name to francium in 1945.)

1939 French physicists Irène (1897–1956) and Frédéric Joliot-Curie (1900–58) show that uranium fission can lead to a chain reaction.

THE AMERICAS

1938 American astronomer Seth Nicholson (1891–1963) discovers Lysithea, a small moon of Jupiter.

1938 Russian-born American astrophysicist Otto Struve (1897–1963) establishes the presence of hydrogen ions in space.

1938 German-born American physicist Hans Bethe (1906–2005) and colleagues determine the series of nuclear fusion reactions that "fuel" stars.

1939 American physicist John Atanasoff (1903–95) makes a prototype electronic binary calculator (the Atanasoff-Berry Computer, or ABC).

1939 German-born American geophysicist Walter Elsasser (1904–91) postulates the existence of eddy currents in the Earth's semiliquid outer core to account for the Earth's magnetism.

1938 American physician Florence Seibert (1897–1991) isolates and purifies tuberculin used in the skin test for tuberculosis.

1939 French-born American bacteriologist René Dubos (1901–82) isolates tyrothricin. Tyrothricin (Gramacidin) is the first commercial antibiotic to be marketed.

1939 American zoologist Victor Shelford (1877–1968) introduces the concept of biomes (major geographical areas, such as tundra or desert, that support their own range of organisms).

1940 American zoologist Donald Griffin (1915–2003) announces that bats "echolocate" using ultrasound.

1940 Austrian-born American pathologist Karl Landsteiner (1868–1943) describes the Rhesus (Rh) factor in human blood.

1938 American chemist Roy Plunkett (1910–94) synthesizes the "nonstick" plastic PTFE (polytetrafluorethylene, or Teflon).

1939 German-born American physicist Albert Einstein (1879–1955) advises President Franklin Roosevelt (1882–1945) that the discovery of nuclear chain reactions would lead to the atomic bomb.

1940 Canadian-born American chemist Martin Kamen (1913–2002) discovers the isotope carbon-14.

1940 Three heavy radioactive elements are identified this year: astatine by Italian-born American physicist Emilio Segrè (1905–89) and coworkers, neptunium by American physicist Edwin McMillan (1907–91) and coworkers, and plutonium by American physical chemist Glenn Seaborg (1912–99) and coworkers.

1940 American physical chemist Philip Abelson (1913–2004) introduces the diffusion method for separating the isotopes of uranium, an early enrichment process.

1940 Austrian-born American physicist Maurice Goldhaber (1911–) introduces the use of beryllium as a moderator (neutron-absorber) in a nuclear reactor.

ASIA & OCEANIA

American shipyards built about 2,750 Liberty ships during World War II.

AFRICA & THE MIDDLE EAST

1938 American professor J. L. B. Smith (1897–1968) identifies a coelacanth (*Latimeria chalumnae*)— a fish previously thought to be extinct—off South Africa.

The farther an experiment is from theory, the closer it is to the Nobel Prize.

FRÉDÉRIC JOLIOT-CURIE,

ENGINEERING & INVENTION

1938 The British steam locomotive *Mallard* gains the title of the world's fastest steam engine, with a speed of 126 miles (203 km) per hour. The record still stands.

1938 Italian Achille Gaggia (1895–1961) files a patent for an espresso coffee machine (not manufactured until 1946).

1938 German engineer Ferdinand Porsche (1875–1951) designs the Volkswagen "Beetle" car.

1939 English radio engineers John Randall (1905–84) and Henry Boot (1917–83) invent the cavity magnetron UHF radar tube.

1940 German engineer Paul Schmidt invents the pulsejet engine. It is later used to power V-1 flying bombs.

1938 German-born American engineer Anton Flettner (1885–1961) constructs his Fl-265 "synchropter," a small helicopter with counter-rotating rotors; it first flies in 1939.

1938 American radio engineers Russell (1898–1959) and Sigurd Varian (1901–61) invent the klystron UHF radar transmitter tube.

1938 American physicist Katherine Blodgett (1898–1979) creates nonreflective glass.

1938 Hungarian-born Argentine inventor Laszlo Biró (1899–1985) makes a prototype of the first ballpoint pen.

1939 The National Broadcasting Company (NBC) begins regular television transmissions in the United States.

1940 Hundreds of Liberty ships, designed by American engineer William Gibbs (1886–1967), are built to replace ships lost to German submarines.

1940 The Tacoma Narrows suspension bridge in Washington State collapses owing to oscillation (resonant vibration). The phenomenon is explained by Hungarian-born American engineer Theodore Kármán (1881–1963).

WORLD EVENTS

1938 German troops take over Austria and the Sudetenland region of Czechoslovakia.

1939 The first Nazi concentration camp is established at Dachau in Germany.

1939 The Axis powers—Italy and German—sign a formal treaty of cooperation, the "Pact of Steel."

1939 Adolf Hitler (1889–1945) and Joseph Stalin (1879–1953) sign the German–Soviet Nonaggression Pact.

1939 Germany invades Poland; Britain and France declare war on Germany, beginning World War II (1939–45).

1940 Germany occupies Denmark, Norway, the Netherlands, and France.

1938 The 40-hour working week is established in the United States.

1939 The U.S. economy begins to rebound after the recession of 1938. It is mainly due to European demand for weapons and war materials.

1940 Leon Trotsky (1876–1940) is assassinated in Mexico on Stalin's orders.

Ferdinand Porsche's design for the German "people's car" (Volkswagen Type 1) dates from 1938.

1938 Oil reserves are discovered in Saudi Arabia.

1940 An Italian attempt to invade Egypt from Libya is driven back by British and Australian forces.

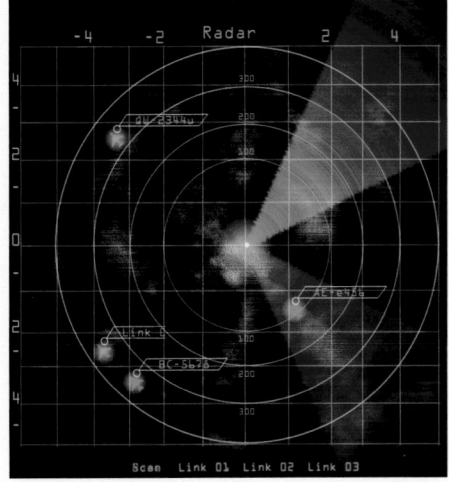

RADAR

During the 1920s and 1930s radio engineers in the United States and Europe reported that passing aircraft distorted their broadcasts. Part of the radio signal had "bounced" off the airplane. Researchers realized that this type of radio reflection could provide a way of detecting planes and other objects such as ships and icebergs.

Radar stands for "**ra**dio **d**etecting **a**nd **r**anging." To detect a plane, a radar set transmits a pulse of very-high-frequency radio waves. A receiving antenna picks up any radio echoes that return. The direction of the returning signal reveals the direction of the target and its range can be calculated from the time it takes for the signal to travel out and back.

In 1904 German engineer Christian Hülsmeyer (1881–1957) took out the first patent for a radar set. Research continued in various countries. By World War II (1939–45) Britain had built a chain of radar antennas along the eastern and southern coastline of England to detect incoming German planes. In Germany engineers adapted radars to aim guns, particularly antiaircraft guns.

Radar has since had many peacetime applications. Astronomers have picked up radar signals reflected back from several planets. The National Aeronautics and Space Administration (NASA) used radar signals from orbiting space probes to map the bottom of Earth's oceans. In addition, weather forecasters make extensive use of satellite radar images.

ASTRONOMY & MATH	BIOLOGY & MEDICINE	PHYSICAL SCIENCES

EUROPE

1941 Russian astronomer Dmitri Maksutov (1896–1964) builds a new type of reflecting telescope with a wide angle of view.

1942 English astronomer Harold Spencer Jones (1890–1960) obtains an accurate value for the Earth–sun distance—equal to 1 astronomical unit, or 93,000,626 miles (149,670,000 km).

1942 English physicist Stanley Hey (1909–2000) discovers that sunspots are a source of ultrashort radio waves.

1943 English engineer Thomas Flowers (1905–98) and English logician and mathematician Alan Turing (1912–54) build Colossus, an all-electronic stored-program computer, for breaking German military codes.

1943 Physicians at the University of Stockholm, Sweden, introduce the use of xylocaine as a local anesthetic.

1943 Swiss chemist Albert Hofmann (1906–2008) accidentally discovers the hallucinogenic properties of the drug LSD (lysergic acid diethylamide).

1943 Dutch (later American) physician Willem Kolff (1911–) constructs the first kidney dialysis machine (secretly in German-occupied Netherlands).

1941 The German company I.G. Farbenindustrie begins to manufacture polyurethane plastics.

1941 Soviet nuclear physicist Georgii Flerov (1913–90) observes spontaneous nuclear fission in uranium.

1942 Swedish physicist Hannes Alfvén (1908–95) suggests that plasmas such as ionized gases and liquid metals passing through magnetic fields in space create electromagnetic waves.

THE AMERICAS

1941 American mathematician Abraham Albert (1905–72) begins formulating his theories on nonassociative algebra, which he publishes in 1942.

1942 American radio astronomer Grote Reber (1911–2002) compiles the first radio map of the universe.

1942 American physicist John Atanasoff (1903–95) and coworkers complete the development of the ABC, a vacuum-tube electronic calculator with a memory. However, work is interrupted by World War II.

1943 American astronomer Carl Seyfert (1911–60) discovers Seyfert galaxies, which have active nuclei and spectra that indicate a high degree of ionization.

1941 German-born American biochemist Fritz Lipmann (1899–1986) shows the role of ATP (adenosine triphosphate) as the carrier of chemical energy in cells.

1941 American biochemists George Beadle (1903–89) and Edward Tatum (1909–75) observe cell reactions that are controlled by genes.

1941 Canadian-born American surgeon Charles Huggins (1901–97) uses female sex hormones to treat prostate cancer in men.

1942 Belgian-born American biologist Albert Claude (1898–1983) first uses an electron microscope in biological studies.

1942 Italian-born American microbiologist Salvador Luria (1912–91) obtains the first high-quality electron micrographs of a bacteriophage (a virus that attacks bacteria).

1943 American biochemist Britton Chance (1913–) establishes the existence of enzyme-substrate complexes in explaining how enzymes work.

1942 American chemist Louis Fieser (1899–1977) develops napalm for use as an incendiary weapon dropped from the air.

1942 Italian–American physicist Enrico Fermi (1901–54) achieves the first controlled nuclear chain reaction, at the University of Chicago.

1942 American biochemist Vincent du Vigneaud (1901–78) establishes the structure of biotin, one of the B complex vitamins.

1943 The American company Dow Corning is established and begins manufacturing silicone plastics.

1943 American scientists complete the world's first operational nuclear reactor at Oak Ridge, Tennessee.

ASIA & OCEANIA

1943 Japanese theoretical physicist Sin-Itiro Tomonaga (1906–79) publishes a paper on the basic physical principles of quantum electrodynamics.

AFRICA & THE MIDDLE EAST

At Oak Ridge, Tennessee, Enrico Fermi and his colleagues developed a nuclear reactor to make plutonium. The plutonium was used in the atomic bomb dropped on Nagasaki, Japan, in 1945.

ENGINEERING & INVENTION	WORLD EVENTS
1941 German rocket engineer Walter Dornberger (1895–1980) designs the A-4 liquid-fuel rocket.	**1941** Germany invades the Soviet Union; the Germans advance to Moscow by December but are forced back by the cold weather.
1941 English chemists John Whinfield (1901–66) and James Dickson produce the plastic Dacron (Terylene).	**1942** The Nazis adopt the "final solution," a genocide campaign aimed at the total extermination of the Jews; mass deportations to the death camps follow.
1942 French underwater explorer Jacques Cousteau (1910–97) invents the aqualung, or scuba (self-contained underwater breathing apparatus).	**1942** Defeat at Stalingrad, Russia, ends further German expansion in the east.
1942 German rocket engineer Wernher von Braun (1912–77) designs the V-1 flying bomb and the V-2 rocket bomb.	**1943** The Nazis suppress a Jewish uprising in the Warsaw ghetto in Poland.
1942 The German air force flies the Me-262, the first operational jet airplane, designed by engineer Willy Messerschmitt (1898–1978).	**1943** Allied forces land in Italy.

1943 The Battle of Kursk, the biggest tank battle in history, ends in a narrow victory for the Soviet army against the Germans. |
| **1941** French-born American electrical engineer Henri-Gaston Busignies (1905–81) invents a high-frequency direction finder for plotting the positions of aircraft.

1942 The Manhattan Project, to make an atom bomb, begins in the United States. | **1941** At a secret meeting off the coast of Newfoundland President Franklin Roosevelt (1882–1945) and British leader Winston Churchill (1874–1965) set out the terms of the Atlantic Charter for the future of postwar Europe.

1941 The Japanese bomb the American naval base at Pearl Harbor in Hawaii. |
| | **1942** Japanese troops advancing through Burma (Myanmar) reach the border with India.

1943 Famine spreads through Bengal in India. |

The 47-foot (14-m) V-2 rocket bomb had a launch speed of 2,500 feet (760 m) per second to carry it high into the upper atmosphere. It came down silently 200 miles (320 km) away at more than three times the speed of sound.

WERNHER VON BRAUN

Wernher von Braun was an engineer and pioneer rocket scientist. He was born in 1912 into a prosperous German family and attended universities in Berlin and Zurich, where he studied engineering. From 1930 he made experimental rockets. The ballistics and munitions branch of the German army, under rocket engineer Walter Dornberger (1895–1980), noticed his work. With the backing of Adolf Hitler (1889–1945), von Braun went to the newly established rocket research center at Peenemünde on the Baltic Sea coast, where in 1936 he became director. There he worked on the "vengeance weapon" 2 (V-2). This huge rocket used liquid oxygen and alcohol, weighed more than 11 tons (10 tonnes), and delivered a warhead containing 1.1 tons (1 tonne) of explosives. Many of the 4,300 V-2s launched from 1944 fell in Belgium and England.

At the end of the war von Braun surrendered to the U.S. Army and went to work in the United States. There he adapted a V-2 to carry a nuclear warhead. He was recruited by the National Aeronautics and Space Administration (NASA) and in 1958 oversaw the successful launch of *Explorer I*, the United States's first artificial satellite. He also headed the team that built the Mercury capsules for the piloted spaceflight program, culminating in the orbital flight of John Glenn (1921–) in 1962. In 1960 von Braun became director of the Marshall Space Flight Center, developing the three-stage Saturn V rocket for NASA's Apollo missions. The climax of this work came in 1969 when astronauts landed on the moon.

ASTRONOMY & MATH	BIOLOGY & MEDICINE	PHYSICAL SCIENCES

EUROPE

1944 Dutch physicist and radio astronomer Hendrik van de Hulst (1918–2000) predicts that interstellar space emits microwave radio waves at a wavelength of 21.1 cm.

1944 German physicist and astrophysicist Carl von Weizsäcker (1912–2007) proposes a theory for the origin of the solar system, a version of the nebular hypothesis first proposed by French astronomer Pierre-Simon de Laplace (1749–1827) in 1796.

1946 English physicist Edward Appleton (1892–1965) detects radio emissions from sunspots.

1946 Hungarian physicist Zoltán Bay (1900–92) and investigators at the U.S. Army Signal Corps Laboratory independently obtain radar reflections from the moon.

1946 Swedish pharmacologist Ulf von Euler (1905–83) identifies the hormone norepinephrine (noradrenaline).

1946 British surgeon Thomas Cecil Gray introduces (1913–2008) the use of curare (a Native American arrow poison) in general anesthesia.

1944 English biochemists Archer Martin (1910–2002) and Richard Synge (1914–94) complete the development of their paper chromatography technique.

1944 German biochemist Hans Fischer (1881–1945) determines the structure of the bile pigment bilirubin and synthesizes it.

1945 English crystallographer Dorothy Hodgkin (1910–94) uses x-ray crystallography to determine the structure of penicillin.

1945 Soviet physicist Vladimir Veksler (1907–66) designs and builds a particle accelerator called the synchrocyclotron.

1946 English chemist Robert Robinson (1886–1975) figures out the structure of the alkaloid drug strychnine.

THE AMERICAS

1944 German-born American astronomer Walter Baade (1893–1960) classifies stars into two types: Population I (younger stars in galaxy arms) and Population II (older stars in galaxy nuclei).

1944 American mathematician Howard Aiken (1900–73) and coworkers from IBM complete the Harvard Mark I, an automatic sequence-controlled calculator.

1944 Hungarian-born American mathematician John von Neumann (1903–57) and German-born American mathematician Oskar Morgenstern (1902–76) establish that game theory has a mathematical basis.

1944 American pioneer computer engineers John Eckert (1919–95) and John Mauchly (1907–80) devise the mercury delay line store (a computer memory device). Two years later they complete ENIAC (Electronic Numerical Integrator And Computer), a fully electronic computer.

1944 Canadian-born American bacteriologist Oswald Avery (1877–1955) and coworkers demonstrate that nearly all organisms have DNA (deoxyribonucleic acid) as their hereditary material.

1944 Ukrainian-born American biochemist Selman Waksman (1888–1973) discovers the bacteria-killing drug streptomycin.

1944 American pediatrician Helen Taussig (1898–1986) and American surgeon Alfred Blalock (1899–1964) introduce a pulmonary bypass operation to treat the heart defect in "blue babies."

1945 American biochemist Melvin Calvin (1911–97) begins his studies of photosynthesis using radioactive carbon-14 as a tracer to follow the reactions.

1946 In the United States, German-born biologist Max Delbrück (1906–81) and biologist Alfred Hershey (1908–97) independently find that genetic material from two different viruses can combine to form a new virus.

1944 American physical chemist Glenn Seaborg (1912–99) and coworkers isolate the radioactive elements americium and curium.

1944 American chemist Robert Woodward (1917–79) and coworkers synthesize the antimalarial drug quinine.

1946 American chemist Willard Libby (1908–80) begins work on radiocarbon dating—perfected a year later—which estimates the age of old organic material from the amount of radioactive carbon-14 isotope it still contains.

1946 American experimental physicist Luis Alvarez (1911–88) designs a proton linear accelerator.

1946 Swiss-born American physicist Felix Bloch (1905–83) and American physicist Edward Purcell (1912–97) develop the technique of nuclear magnetic resonance (NMR) spectroscopy, which becomes a powerful tool in chemical analysis.

ASIA & OCEANIA

1946 The Japanese company Sony is founded (originally as Tokyo Tsushin Kogyo) by Japanese engineer Akio Morita (1921–99).

AFRICA & THE MIDDLE EAST

Aeronautical inventor Igor Sikorsky stands beneath the helicopter he designed.

ENGINEERING & INVENTION	WORLD EVENTS
1944 The German air force employs the unsuccessful Messerschmitt Me-163B Komet rocket-powered airplanes as interceptors.	**1944** On D-Day (6 June) Allied troops commanded by General Dwight D. Eisenhower (1890–1969) land in Normandy, France, at the start of the campaign to liberate Europe.
1944 German forces begin launching V-1 flying bombs and V-2 rocket bombs against southeastern England.	**1945** Adolf Hitler (1889–1945) commits suicide as the Soviet Red Army reaches Berlin.
1945 Engineers working for the British Rolls-Royce company develop the afterburner for jet engines.	**1945** Germany surrenders on May 7, ending the war in Europe; the next day, May 8, is celebrated as VE (Victory in Europe) Day.
1945 Northern Irish engineer James Martin (1893–1981) designs the ejector seat for aircraft, which will save the lives of thousands of pilots.	**1946** Italy becomes a republic after a referendum decides in favor of abolishing the monarchy.

NUCLEAR MAGNETIC RESONANCE

Nuclear magnetic resonance (NMR) is a phenomenon based on the magnetic properties of an atom's nucleus; NMR also refers to the technique used to study the magnetic resonance of molecules.

NMR was first discovered and measured in molecular beams by Galacian-born American physicist Isidor Rabi (1898–1988) in 1938. In 1946 Americans Felix Bloch and Edward Purcell used Rabi's technique on liquids and solids. The technique involves exposing a chemical in solution simultaneously to high-frequency radio radiation in a surrounding coil and a very strong magnetic field provided by powerful magnets. A second coil detects the radio frequencies that are absorbed by the chemical. They are analyzed in a signal detector and plotted as a spectrum. In the example below the NMR spectrum distinguishes between the hydrogen atoms (H) in two different chemical groupings within the chemical bromoethane (CH_3-CH_2-Br). The peaks on the chart correspond to the CH_3 and CH_2 groups.

One application of NMR, magnetic resonance imaging (MRI), is used for diagnosing medical conditions.

1944 The Delaware Aqueduct, part of New York City's water-supply system, is completed. It includes an 85-mile (137-km) tunnel, later extended to 105 miles (169 km)—at the time the world's longest tunnel.	**1945** President Franklin Roosevelt (1882–1945) dies in office less than six months after becoming the only U.S. president in history to be reelected to a fourth term.
1944 Russian-born American engineer Igor Sikorsky (1889–1972) sets the design of the modern helicopter with the VS-36A, which has an adjustable-pitch main rotor and a single vertical tail rotor for stability.	**1945** Argentine Juan Perón (1895–1974) is released from jail and made president of Argentina.
1944 American physicist Robert Dicke (1916–97) makes a radiometer for detecting microwave radiation.	
1945 American government scientists make and test an atom bomb.	
1945 Austrian-born American electrical engineer Rudolf Kompfner (1909–77) invents the traveling-wave amplifier for microwave signals, such as those used in radar.	
1946 American engineer Percy Spencer (1894–1970) invents the microwave oven while working for the Raytheon Company.	

Dorothy Hodgkin's research using x-ray crystallography determined the structure of various natural molecules, including penicillin (1945), vitamin B_{12} (1954), and insulin (1969).

1945 One month after atomic bombs are dropped on Hiroshima and Nagasaki, Japan surrenders to the Allies.

1945 The Arab league is founded with seven initial members; it aims to speak for all Arab nations.

1946 Syria and Transjordan win independence from, respectively, France and Britain.

Signal detector

Powerful magnet

Sample solution

Radio frequency signal in

Chart recorder

CH_2

CH_3

NMR spectrum of CH_3-CH_2-Br

NUCLEAR FISSION

Ernest Walton, photographed in 1932, sits in a protective cage away from the particle accelerator that he and John Cockcroft designed at the Cavendish Laboratory, Cambridge.

IN THE EARLY 20TH CENTURY PHYSICISTS WERE learning what happens when atoms are bombarded with subatomic particles. Their experiments led them to realize that under certain circumstances such bombardment could release huge amounts of energy through nuclear fission in nuclear reactors, which could be used to generate electricity. In January 2005 there were 439 operational reactors worldwide, producing 16 percent of all electricity.

In 1932 Irish physicist Ernest Walton (1903–95) and English physicist John Cockcroft (1897–1967) began experimenting with high-energy protons in the particle accelerator they had built in Cambridge, England. In Paris in 1934 French physicists Irène (1897–1956) and Frédéric (1900–58) Joliot-Curie found that proton bombardment sometimes produced radioactive isotopes of the target atoms. Two years later Italian-American physicist Enrico Fermi (1901–54), working in Rome, found that neutrons—discovered in 1932 by English physicist James Chadwick (1891–1974)—were more effective than protons at smashing atoms.

Uranium Bombardment

Neutron bombardment usually produced heavier atoms through neutron absorption; but when Fermi bombarded atoms of certain heavy elements, especially uranium, he found that much lighter nuclei were produced. In 1939 German physicists Otto Hahn (1879–1968) and Fritz Strassmann (1902–80) identified the products of uranium bombardment as elements with about half the mass of uranium. Hahn and Strassmann had demonstrated that the uranium nuclei had broken apart. Fission had occurred.

The same year Lise Meitner (1878–1968), an Austrian-born physicist working in Stockholm, and her Austrian nephew Otto Frisch (1904–79), working in Copenhagen with Danish physicist Niels Bohr (1885–1962), explained this result. The uranium nucleus absorbed a neutron, causing it to vibrate violently and then divide into two parts with the release of about 200 million electron volts of energy (= 3.204×10^{-11} joules). Hahn and Strassmann then found that, in addition to a large amount of energy, uranium fission released neutrons that could trigger fission in other uranium nuclei, raising the possibility of a chain reaction that would release a prodigious amount of energy. The Joliot-Curies and Leo Szilard (1898–1964) confirmed this experimentally. Szilard was a Hungarian-born American physicist working with Fermi, then at Columbia University, New York.

Three isotopes of uranium occur naturally, always in the same proportions: Uranium-238 (U-238)

American physicist J. Robert Oppenheimer, sometimes referred to as "The Father of the Atomic Bomb," was the scientific director of the Manhattan Project, which created the world's first nuclear weapons.

accounts for 99.28 percent, U-235 for 0.71 percent, and U-234 for 0.006 percent. Bohr calculated that fission would occur more readily in U-235 than in either of the other isotopes. This meant that a way had to be found to separate the isotopes—a technique now known as "enrichment." Bohr also figured out that fission would be more effective if the neutrons were slowed down. Szilard and Fermi suggested surrounding the uranium with a "moderator"—a substance such as graphite or heavy water that slows neutrons.

Just before the outbreak of war in 1939 Bohr and American physicist John Wheeler (1911–2008) published a paper describing the complete fission process. Also in 1939 French physicist Francis Perrin (1901–92) showed that a certain "critical mass" of uranium is needed to sustain a chain reaction by ensuring that enough of the neutrons released strike other uranium nuclei. Perrin also introduced the idea of adding a substance that absorbs (rather than slows) neutrons as a way to control the rate of the fission reaction. Rudolf Peierls (1907–95), a German-born physicist working in England, extended these ideas. Designed by Fermi and called "an atomic pile," the first working reactor began operating on December 2, 1942, at the University of Chicago. In 1951 the Experimental Breeder Reactor, built at Idaho National Engineering Laboratory near Idaho Falls, Idaho, became the first reactor to generate electricity.

The Manhattan Project

It became apparent that a sustained fission reaction could be used to create a bomb of immense power. Work to develop an atom bomb began in Britain and the United States. The two programs merged in August 1942 to form the Manhattan Project, with American physicist J. Robert Oppenheimer (1904–67) as scientific director. The first successful test took place in New Mexico on July 16, 1945.

Research in the Soviet Union had been proceeding independently, and by 1940 Soviet scientists also understood the principles of fission. But it was 1942 before Stalin became convinced that a bomb could be developed, and a program led by nuclear physicist Igor Kurchatov (1903–60) began. The first Soviet reactor entered operation in 1948, and the first Soviet bomb was detonated in August 1949.

KEY DATES

1932
Cockcroft and Walton particle accelerator

1934
Joliot-Curies produce radioactive isotopes

1936
Fermi uses neutrons to smash atoms

1939
Hahn and Strassman identify products of uranium fission

1942
First nuclear reactor

1945
First atom bomb tested

1951
Nuclear reactor built to generate electricity

URANIUM FISSION

Fission occurs when a slow-moving neutron strikes a U-235 atom. The atom's nucleus absorbs the neutron and divides into two lighter nuclei with the release of neutrons. If the neutrons strike other U-235 nuclei the latter also undergo fission, setting up a chain reaction. The fission of 2.2 pounds (1 kg) of U-235 nuclei releases 20,000 megawatt-hours of energy.

ASTRONOMY & MATH	BIOLOGY & MEDICINE	PHYSICAL SCIENCES

EUROPE

1948 English astronomer Fred Hoyle (1915–2001) and Austrian-born English astronomers Hermann Bondi (1919–2005) and Thomas Gold (1920–2004) propose the steady-state theory of the universe (i.e., that it is not expanding—it maintains a constant average density).

1949 English computer engineer Maurice Wilkes (1913–) and coworkers build EDSAC, an Electronic Delay-Storage Automatic Calculator.

1947 Italian biologist Rita Levi-Montalcini (1909–) finds nerve growth factor (NGF) in chick embryos.

1948 The World Health Organization (WHO) is founded.

1947 English physicist Cecil Powell (1903–69) and Italian physicist Giuseppe Occhialini (1907–93) discover the pion (pi-meson), a heavy subatomic particle, in cosmic rays.

1948 Scottish biochemist Alexander Todd (1907–97) synthesizes ADP and ATP (adenosine diphosphate and adenosine triphosphate).

1949 English chemists George Porter (1920–2002) and Ronald Norrish (1897–1978) study ultrafast chemical reactions, using pulses of light in the technique known as flash photolysis.

1948 Hungarian-born English electrical engineer Dennis Gabor (1900–79) puts forward the principles of holography.

THE AMERICAS

1948 Dutch-born American astronomer Gerard Kuiper (1905–73) locates Miranda, a small inner moon of Uranus. A year later he finds Nereid, Neptune's moon.

1948 American mathematician Norbert Wiener (1894–1964) coins the term *cybernetics*.

1948 American astronomers Harold (1882–1968) and Horace (1912–2003) Babcock detect the sun's magnetic field.

1949 German-born American astronomer Walter Baade (1893–1960) discovers the asteroid Icarus, which passes very close to the sun (and the Earth).

1949 American pioneer computer engineers John Eckert (1919–95) and John Mauchly (1907–80) construct BINAC, a BINary Automatic Computer.

1949 The American company IBM makes a stored-program electromechanical computer Selective Sequence Electronic Calculator (SSEC).

1949 American astronomer Fred Whipple (1906–2004) proposes the "dirty snowball" theory of comets, suggesting that they consist mainly of ice with accumulated rocky debris.

1947 German-born American biochemist Fritz Lipmann (1899–1986) isolates coenzyme A (CoA), a substance needed to ensure the effectiveness of certain enzymes.

1947 Microbiologist Mildred Rebstock discovers the antibiotic chloramphenicol (Chloromycetin) in a sample of soil from Venezuela.

1947 American geneticist Joshua Lederberg (1925–2008) reports that some bacteria can reproduce by conjugation (joining together as in sexual reproduction).

1948 American biochemists Philip Hench (1896–1965) and Edward Kendall (1886–1972) introduce the use of cortisone to treat patients with rheumatoid arthritis.

1948 American organic chemist Karl Folkers (1906–97) and coworkers isolate vitamin B_{12} (cyanocobalamin), the factor that prevents pernicious anemia.

1949 American microbiologists John Enders (1897–1985) and Frederick Robbins (1916–2003) culture the virus that causes poliomyelitis.

1947 American physicist Willis Lamb (1913–2008) observes the Lamb shift, a small difference in energy between two levels in the atomic spectrum of hydrogen.

1948 Karl Folkers determines the structure of the bacteria-killing drug streptomycin.

1948 American theoretical physicist Richard Feynman (1918–88) and coworkers and, independently, American physicist Julian Schwinger (1918–94) formulate new versions of quantum electrodynamics.

1949 American physical chemist Glenn Seaborg (1912–99) and team produce the radioactive element berkelium by bombarding americium with alpha particles (helium nuclei).

1949 German-born American physicist Maria Goeppert-Mayer (1906–72) proposes the "shell" theory of the atomic nucleus (which pictures its component protons and neutrons moving in shells analogous to those occupied by electrons).

ASIA & OCEANIA

1947 Armenian astronomer Viktor Ambartsumian (1908–96) describes stellar associations, groups of stars in the galaxy's spiral arms (but not as closely linked as a star cluster).

Mary Leakey and her husband Richard Leakey examine fossil finds from Olduvai Gorge in the Serengeti plains of northern Tanzania, Africa.

AFRICA & THE MIDDLE EAST

1948 English anthropologist Mary Leakey (1913–96) discovers fossils of the hominoid *Proconsul africanus* in Africa.

ENGINEERING & INVENTION

1947 The first nuclear reactor in Europe is built at Harwell, England.

1947 Soviet gunsmith Mikhail Kalashnikov (1919–) produces the AK-47 assault rifle (used by Soviet forces from 1949).

1948 Swiss-born Belgian physicist August Piccard (1884–1962) designs the bathyscaphe submersible craft.

1948 The first turboprop airliner, the Vickers Viscount, makes its maiden flight in England.

1949 The first jet airliner, the de Havilland Comet, flies in England.

1947 American airman Charles "Chuck" Yeager (1923–) makes the first supersonic flight, in a Bell X-1 rocket-propelled airplane.

1947 American inventor Edwin Land (1909–91) demonstrates the Polaroid instant camera.

1947 American architect Richard Buckminster Fuller (1895–1983) devises the geodesic dome construction for large buildings.

1947 American physicists John Bardeen (1908–91) and Walter Brattain (1902–87) and English-born American William Shockley (1910–89) build the point-contact transistor. A year later Shockley conceives the junction transistor.

1948 American electrical engineer Peter Goldmark (1906–77) invents the long-playing phonograph record.

1948 American instrument maker Leo Fender (1909–91) and coworkers market the first solid-body electric guitar.

1949 American rocket engineers launch a two-stage rocket (a German V-2 with a small rocket mounted on its nose) in New Mexico.

WORLD EVENTS

1947 Britain's Labour Government introduces a free, tax-financed National Health Service.

1949 Two separate states are formed in Germany: the democratic Federal Republic of Germany (West Germany) and the communist People's Republic of Germany (East Germany).

1949 The Greek Civil War (1946–49) between communists and monarchists ends in victory for the monarchists.

1949 The North Atlantic Treaty Organization (NATO) is set up to defend Europe and North America from the threat of Soviet aggression.

1947 President Harry S. Truman (1884–1972) commits the United States to support free peoples in the struggle against communist totalitarianism (the "Truman Doctrine"); immediate aid is given to Greece and Turkey.

1947 Secretary of State George Marshall (1880–1959) announces a plan to help Europe rebuild its war-shattered economies (the Marshall Plan).

1947 Congress's investigations into communist influence in the movie industry lead to the imprisonment of 10 Hollywood screenwriters and directors who have refused to cooperate with the House Un-American Activities Committee.

1948 The Organization of American States is formed to promote regional peace and security.

1947 India and Pakistan separate; violence mars the partition, with about 500,000 deaths.

1948 The Jewish state of Israel declares itself an independent nation.

1949 The South African National Party introduces apartheid, separating white from black South Africans.

WORLD HEALTH ORGANIZATION

Established on April 7, 1948 (the first World Health Day), the World Health Organization (WHO) is one of the original agencies of the United Nations (UN). Headquartered in Geneva, Switzerland, WHO was set up to improve international cooperation for better health conditions across the world. It took over from the Health Organization of the League of Nations (created in 1923) and the International Public Office of Health at Paris (set up in 1909). Those two organizations had focused on the control of epidemics, quarantine measures, and the standardization of drugs.

An African boy is vaccinated against smallpox and measles. By 1980 WHO had eradicated smallpox—the first disease to be eliminated by humans.

WHO's mission is to help all people attain "the highest possible level of health." WHO defines health not merely as the absence of disease or infirmity but as "a state of complete physical, mental, and social well-being."

WHO collects and distributes health information. It monitors many diseases and helps control many infectious diseases through education or by promoting mass vaccination programs. It helps improve sanitation to prevent disease. This work has helped reduce the incidence of many diseases, including malaria, sexually transmitted infections, and cholera. The organization also helps governments set up long-term national health plans.

Comets

Fred Whipple likened the nucleus of a comet to a dirty snowball and suggested that it consists of a collection of ice and small solid particles, together extending a few miles across. A bright coma develops around the nucleus as it evaporates on approaching the sun. There may be one or two tails pointing away from the sun, one made of dust or gas and one consisting of ions.

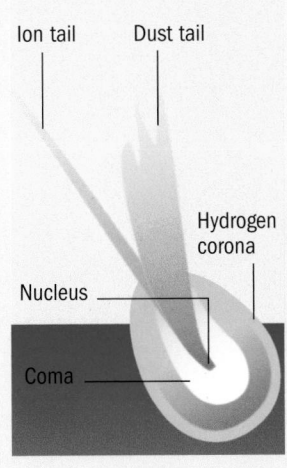

Ion tail
Dust tail
Hydrogen corona
Nucleus
Coma

THE FIRST COMPUTERS

A COMPUTER IS AN ELECTRONIC MACHINE that can perform various tasks involving the processing of information or data under instructions from a program. Today the term most often applies to a digital computer, which handles its data in the form of digits or numbers expressed in binary notation.

Binary is a number system that uses only two digits, 1 and 0, represented in the computer's activities and memory as on and off pulses of electric current. According to the definition above, the first computers were used by the U. S. Army and Navy toward the end of World War II (1939–45). They were massive vacuum-tube machines developed from electronic calculating machines of the late 1930s, which in turn derived from earlier mechanical calculating machines. The first calculator was the abacus, a frame with beads invented around 3,000 B.C.E. and still used in parts of China and Japan. The task of multiplication is simplified by logarithms, invented in 1614 by Scottish mathematician John Napier (1550–1617) and "mechanized" in the slide rule designed in 1622 by English mathematician William Oughtred (1574–1660).

French scientist Blaise Pascal (1623–62) probably invented the first mechanical adding machine in 1642. It had a system of intermeshed cogs, a method also adopted by English mathematician Charles Babbage (1792–1871) in his "Analytical Engine" of 1833. Babbage's machine could be programmed for a particular calculation and was therefore technically a computer (although not electronic). Calculating machines with keyboards—called comptometers—were developed from the 1880s by inventors such as the American William Burroughs (1855–98).

Most early methods of feeding data into programmable machines used punched tape or punched cards. In about 1805 French inventor Joseph Jacquard (1752–1834) designed a loom that could weave various patterns in carpets by following instructions on an endless belt of punched cards. American inventor Herman Hollerith (1860–1929) employed similar cards to record and analyze the results of the 1890 U. S. census. The company that Hollerith formed later became part of International Business Machines (IBM).

Electronic Computers

Electromechanical calculators appeared in the 1930s, invented by American scientists such as Vannevar Bush (1890–1974) and John Atanasoff (1903–95). By 1942 Atanasoff had constructed an electronic calculator (the ABC), using vacuum tubes, that could also be programmed for processing data. Two years later at Harvard, American mathematician Howard Aiken (1900–73) had a manually operated digital machine controlled by punched paper tape, and in 1946 the all-electronic ENIAC (Electronic Numerical Integrator And Calculator) computer was in service, although it too still employed vacuum tubes.

A machine built at Princeton in 1946 by John von Neumann (1903–57), a Hungarian-born American mathematician, was the first with a stored program that used binary numbers. The idea was incorporated into UNIVAC I, designed by American computer engineers John Eckert (1919–95) and John Mauchly (1907–80) and in 1951 the first computer to be manufactured in bulk in the United States. They modified

KEY DATES

1833
Babbage's "Analytical Engine"

1890
Hollerith punched cards

1942
Electronic calculator

1946
ENIAC and Neumann's stored-program computer

1951
First mass-produced computer (UNIVAC I)

The stored-program computer built at Manchester University in 1949 occupied an entire laboratory. Despite its size, it had far less computing power than a modern laptop.

The women above hold circuit boards from a range of early electronic computers. As technology improved circuit boards became smaller.

it to use magnetic tape storage a year later. In 1949 a team at Manchester University, England, also built a stored-program machine under the guidance of English mathematician Alan Turing (1912–54), who had worked at Princeton. The Manchester machine was so successful that the British government commissioned the Ferranti company to manufacture it.

After the invention of the transistor in the late 1940s, computers became faster and smaller. By the mid-1960s silicon chips had arrived, so that circuits designed in 1970 incorporated a complete computer microprocessor on a single chip. Today microchips are used not only in personal computers but also in embedded systems in domestic appliances, automobiles, and industrial robots.

Early computers used punched cards as a means of inputting data and computer programs.

AFTER 1950 TWO OF THE MAJOR TECHNOLOGICAL DEVELOPMENTS OF WORLD War II (1939–45)—radar and rockets—were put to a wide range of uses. Radar employs very-high-frequency radio waves, and in the 1940s it was radar engineers who first began detecting radio waves from space. After the war their converted radar sets became radio telescopes, and the new science of radio astronomy began. Soon invisible objects were detected emitting radio waves from the remotest regions of the universe. These objects are now identified as quasars—first identified by American astronomer Allan Sandage (1926–) in 1960—and pulsars, observed by Northern Irish astronomer Jocelyn Bell Burnell (1943–) and English astronomer Anthony Hewish (1924–) in 1967.

Rockets left over from the German war effort were adapted to explore the upper atmosphere and space. In 1957 the Soviets launched the world's first artificial satellite, Sputnik 1, and a "space race" soon developed between the Soviet Union and the United States as a technological manifestation of the ideological stand-off known as the Cold War. In 1961, the Soviets claimed the distinction of putting the first human into space: cosmonaut Yuri Gagarin (1934–68). In responses, a major U.S. effort culminated in the National Aeronautics and Space Administration's (NASA) Apollo Program.

Deoxyribonucleic acid (DNA) was first isolated in 1869 by Swiss physician Friedrich Miescher. However, it was not until 1952 that scientists proved that DNA was the hereditary material of most life-forms. Its molecular structure—an elegant double helix—was elucidated in 1953 by Francis Crick, Maurice Wilkins, and James Watson.

In 1969 astronaut Neil Armstrong (1930–) was the first human to walk on the moon, closely followed by Buzz Aldrin (1930–). By the end of 1972 another ten American astronauts had walked on the surface of the moon.

In life sciences attention was focused on the microscopic level with the development of molecular biology. The new branch of science studies the structures and functions of large molecules found in living organisms, such as proteins and nucleic acids. American chemist Linus Pauling (1901–94) made many advances in this new scientific field, but the breakthrough came in 1953 when English biophysicist Francis Crick (1916–2004), New Zealand-born biophysicist Maurice Wilkins (1916–2004), American biophysicist James Watson (1928–), and British physical chemist Rosalind Franklin (1920–58) discovered the structure of the deoxyribonucleic acid (DNA) molecule: the famous double helix. It is a major component of chromosomes in the cell nucleus, the genetic material that determines an organism's hereditary characteristics.

Another major scientific development during this period was the invention of the laser. In 1960 American physicist Theodore Maiman (1927–2007) created the first laser, using an artificial crystal of aluminium oxide (ruby) to emit light. Lasers are now widely used to read compact discs (CDs) and digital versatile discs (DVDs), to measure distances, to cut tissue in delicate surgery, and even to saw through metal.

THE WORLD AT A GLANCE

CONCISE HISTORY OF SCIENCE AND INVENTION

	1950	1953	1956	1959	1962	
EUROPE	**1950** English physicians Richard Doll and Bradford Hill establish a link between smoking and lung cancer. **1950** English ophthalmologist Harold Ridley implants an artificial lens in an eye to treat cataract. **1952** English physiologists Alan Hodgkin and Andrew Huxley discover the ionic mechanisms of nerve-cell activity.	**1953** English engineer Christopher Cockerell begins work on the hovercraft. **1953** English biophysicist Francis Crick, American biophysicist James Watson, New Zealand-born biophysicist Maurice Wilkins, and English physical chemist Rosalind Franklin determine the structure of deoxyribonucleic acid (DNA).	**1956** Romanian cell biologist George Palade identifies ribosomes. **1957** Soviet scientists launch the first artificial satellites to orbit Earth, Sputnik 1 and Sputnik 2. **1957** The rotary Wankel engine is put into production in West Germany. **1958** Scottish surgeon Ian Donald introduces the use of an ultrasound scan to examine unborn babies.	**1959** French physician Jérôme Lejeune establishes that Down syndrome is caused by the presence of an extra chromosome. **1959** The German company Voigtlander produces a zoom lens for its cameras. **1959** The British Austin Motor Company launches the Mini car. **1961** Soviet cosmonaut Yuri Gagarin becomes the first man in space.	**1962** Scottish biochemist James Black prepares beta-blockers. **1963** Soviet cosmonaut Valentina Tereshkova becomes the first woman in space. **1964** Scottish physicist Peter Higgs predicts the existence of the Higgs boson. **1964** Kidney dialysis in the home is introduced in Britain and the United States.	
THE AMERICAS	**1950** American surgeon John Gibbon, Jr. develops the heart–lung machine. **1951** German-born American physicist Erwin Müller invents a microscope that can produce images of single atoms. **1951** German-born American physicist Polykarp Kusch builds a cesium atomic clock. **1951** Austrian-born American physician Carl Djerassi synthesizes norethindrone, the basis of the oral contraceptive pill for women. **1952** American geneticist Joshua Lederberg identifies plasmids in bacteria. **1952** U.S. government scientists explode the first hydrogen bomb.	**1953** American surgeon John Gibbon, Jr. performs the first successful open-heart surgery on a human patient using his heart–lung machine. **1953** U.S. military engineers develop a surface-to-air missile (SAM). **1954** American engineer Richard Buckminster Fuller patents the geodesic dome for roofing large buildings. **1955** The first computer using transistors instead of vacuum tubes is built in the United States by Bell Laboratories. **1955** Italian-born American physicist Emilio Segrè and American Owen Chamberlain discover the antiproton.	**1956** American physicists Clyde Cowan and Frederick Reines discover the neutrino. **1956** The company Ampex markets a videotape recorder. **1956** American computer programmers devise the FORTRAN language. **1958** American scientists launch Explorer 1, the first American Earth satellite. **1958** The National Aeronautics and Space Administration (NASA) is founded. **1958** American physician Clarence Lillehei invents a heart pacemaker, which has to be worn outside the patient's body. **1958** American electronic engineers invent integrated circuits.	**1960** Hungarian-born American biophysicist Georg von Békésy shows how sound waves stimulate the cochlea in the inner ear. **1960** American astronomer Allan Sandage makes the first optical identification of a quasar. **1960** American physicist Theodore H. Maiman invents the ruby laser. **1961** American astronaut Alan Shepard makes a suborbital flight in the spacecraft Freedom 7. **1961** The American company Texas Instruments produces the first silicon chips. **1962** American physicist Leon Lederman discovers the muon neutrino.	**1962** American communications satellite Telstar 1 relays live TV transmissions. **1962** American physicist Leon Lederman discovers the muon neutrino. **1962** American electronic engineer Nick Holonyak invents the light-emitting diode (LED). **1962** American electronic engineer Paul Weimer invents thin-film transistors. **1964** NASA's space probe Mariner 4 makes a successful flyby of Mars. **1964** American theoretical physicist Murray Gell-Mann predicts the existence of the quark. **1964** American computer programmers invent the BASIC language.	
ASIA & OCEANIA	**1952** Australian astronomer Colin Gum locates the nearby Gum nebula, the remains of a supernova explosion.	**1955** Indian scientist Narinder Kapany develops optical fibers for carrying light over long distances.	**1957** Japanese physicist Leo Esaki describes how electrons can penetrate a "barrier" in a semiconductor. **1958** Australian engineer David Warren invents the "black box" flight data recorder.	**1960** Felt-tip pens are first made by the Japan Stationery Company (later called Pentel).	**1962** French-born Australian immunologist Jacques Miller works out the role of the thymus in the immune system of infants. **1964** Bullet trains begin service in Japan.	
AFRICA & THE MIDDLE EAST				**1959** The Kariba Dam is completed in Africa. **1960** Kenyan anthropologist Jonathan Leakey discovers remains of *Homo habilis* in Tanzania.		

1965	1968	1971	1974	1977–1979
1965 Soviet cosmonaut Aleksei Leonov is the first person to walk in space.	**1968** Swiss biophysicist Werner Arber isolates restrictive enzymes, which cut DNA.	**1971** The Swiss company Hoffmann-LaRoche presents a liquid-crystal display.	**1975** Argentine-born British molecular biologist César Milstein, English-born Danish immunologist Niels Jerne, and German immunologist Georges Köhler develop monoclonal antibodies.	**1977** English biochemist Frederick Sanger and coworkers elucidate the first full genome (of a virus).
1966 The Soviet Luna 9 spacecraft soft-lands on the moon.	**1969** The British-French supersonic airliner Concorde makes its maiden flight in France.	**1972** Soviet space probe Venera 8 soft-lands on Venus and returns data from the surface.	**1976** The British-French supersonic airliner Concorde enters service.	**1978** The first "test-tube" baby is born in England.
1966 An electronic fuel-injection system for automobile engines is developed in Britain.	**1970** Swiss computer programmer Niklaus Wirth invents PASCAL programming language.	**1972** Swiss biochemist Jean-François Borel develops the immunosuppressive drug cyclosporin-A, which prevents rejection following organ transplants.	**1976** Engineers complete the pilot bore for the new road tunnel through the St. Gotthard Pass in the Swiss Alps.	**1979** German physicists announce the discovery of the gluon.
1967 Northern Irish astronomer Jocelyn Bell Burnell and English astronomer Antony Hewish detect the first pulsar.	**1970** Soviet space probe Luna 16 returns lunar soil samples to Earth.			**1979** The Swedish company Ericsson markets the first cellular telephones.
1965 American geneticist Charles Yanofsky and coworkers establish that the sequence of codons in a gene determines the sequence of amino acids in a protein.	**1968** Italian-born American inventor Candido Jacuzzi invents the whirlpool bath named for him.	**1971** American electronic engineer Ted Hoff and coworkers make a single-chip microprocessor (Intel 4004).	**1974** NASA space probe Mariner 10 reaches Mercury.	**1977** American astronomers observe the rings of Uranus.
1966 NASA's space probe Surveyor 1 soft-lands on the moon.	**1968** American computer engineer Douglas Engelbart invents the computer mouse.	**1971** American electronic companies produce pocket calculators.	**1975** American engineer Edward Roberts markets the first commercial personal computer in kit or assembled form, the Altair 8800.	**1977** Molecular biologists discover that some genes contain sequences of "nonsense" DNA that appear to have no genetic function. They are named introns.
1966 American geneticist Richard Lewontin develops gel electrophoresis (now routinely used in genetic fingerprinting).	**1969** Canadian electronic engineer Willard Boyle and American electronic engineer George Smith invent the charge-coupled device (CCD).	**1971** The American company Centron markets a dot matrix printer.	**1975** The American company IBM markets a laser printer for computers.	**1977** American government scientists develop a neutron bomb.
1966 American inventor Stephanie Kwolek invents Kevlar.	**1969** The U.S. Boeing Company flies its 747 jet for the first time.	**1973** American and English physicists begin to develop nuclear magnetic resonance imaging (MRI) scanning.	**1976** American virologists identify oncogenes, which can convert normal cells into cancer cells.	**1977** American physicist Leon Lederman identifies the short-lived upsilon particle.
1967 Domestic microwave ovens are marketed in the United States.	**1969** NASA's Apollo 11 makes the first piloted moon landing. Astronaut Neil Armstrong becomes the first man to walk on the moon's surface. Buzz Aldrin joins him.	**1973** NASA space probe Pioneer 10 flies by Jupiter.	**1976** American physicist Martin Perl discovers the tau subatomic particle.	**1978** Chlorofluorocarbons (CFCs) are banned as aerosol-can propellants by the U.S. government.
1967 American biochemist Arthur Kornberg uses DNA polymerase to make "synthetic" DNA.		**1973** Physicists at Bell Laboratories produce a continuous-wave laser that can be tuned to different wavelengths.	**1976** American computer designers Steven Jobs and Stephen Wozniak found the computer company Apple.	**1979** The earliest recognized cases of acquired immunodeficiency syndrome (AIDS) occur in California and Florida.
1965 Japanese astronomers discover the bright sun-grazing comet Ikeya-Seki.	**1970** China and Japan launch artificial Earth satellites.	**1972** In Australia astronomer B. J. Harris provides evidence that most unidentified radio sources in space are compact.	**1974** Japanese chemist Hideki Shirakawa produces a flexible film that has metallic properties.	**1977** Soviet scientists unearth a baby mammoth that has been frozen in the permafrost of Siberia.
1966 Chinese electronics engineer Charles Kao helps invent the fiber-optic cable.	**1970** The Japanese company Canon Business Machines markets a pocket calculator with a printout.		**1976** The Japanese company Matsushita introduces the VHS format for video cassettes.	**1979** Matsushita introduces a liquid-crystal flat-screen television receiver.
1967 South African surgeon Christiaan Barnard performs the first successful heart transplant.	**1968** The power plant at the Aswan High Dam in Egypt goes into operation.	**1972** Kenyan anthropologist Richard Leakey finds an intact skull of *Homo habilis* in Africa.	**1976** The Ebola virus is first identified after outbreaks in Africa.	**1978** The world's longest floating bridge is completed on the Demerara River in Guyana.

	ASTRONOMY & MATH	BIOLOGY & MEDICINE	PHYSICAL SCIENCES

EUROPE

1950 Dutch astronomer Jan Oort (1900–92) postulates the existence of the Oort cloud, a spherical region centered on the sun that contains all the long-period comets; it extends into space a third of the way to the next nearest star.

Jonas Salk, in his laboratory, examines virus samples that were used to develop the polio vaccine.

1950 English physicians Richard Doll (1912–2005) and Bradford Hill (1897–1991) establish a link between tobacco smoking and lung cancer.

1951 Danish biochemist Kaj Linderstrøm-Lang (1896–1959) classifies proteins into three structural levels: chains; helices and pleated sheets; and folded sheets.

1952 English physiologists Alan Hodgkin (1914–98) and Andrew Huxley (1917–) discover the ionic mechanisms of nerve cell activity.

1950 German-born French physicist Alfred Kastler (1902–84) develops optical pumping, which excites atoms to emit radiation—a key step toward making a laser.

1951 German chemist Ernst Fischer (1918–) investigates ferrocene and later shows it to be a "sandwich" compound with an iron atom between two five-sided carbon organic rings.

1952 Soviet physicists Aleksandr Prokhorov (1916–2002) and Nikolai Basov (1922–2001) work out the principle of the maser and the laser.

THE AMERICAS

1951 German-born American astronomer Walter Baade (1893–1960) detects visible objects that coincide with radio sources in space.

1951 American astronomer William Morgan (1906–94) provides evidence that Earth's galaxy (the Milky Way) is a typical spiral galaxy.

1950 American surgeon John Gibbon, Jr. (1903–73), develops the heart–lung machine, later used in the open-heart surgery.

1950 American biochemists George Hitchings (1905–98) and Gertrude Elion (1918–99) develop the antimalarial drug pyrimethamine (Daraprim). A year later they synthesize 6-mercaptopurine (6MP), used for treating leukemia.

1951 Austrian-born American physician Carl Djerassi (1923–) synthesizes the compound norethindrone, the basis of the oral contraceptive pill for women.

1952 American geneticist Joshua Lederberg (1925–) identifies plasmids, circular pieces of DNA in bacteria.

1952 American physician Jonas Salk (1914–95) develops a vaccine against polio.

1952 American surgeon Charles Hufnagel invents an artificial heart valve.

1950 American physicist James Rainwater (1917–86) and colleagues propose a new model of the atomic nucleus, whose shape is not perfectly spherical but distorted.

1951 American chemist Linus Pauling (1901–94) discovers the spiral structure of some proteins, soon to be important in understanding the DNA (deoxyribonucleic acid) molecule.

1951 Canadian-born American physicist Walter Zinn (1906–2000) designs the first experimental breeder reactor near Idaho Falls, Indiana. A breeder reactor creates more fissionable material than it consumes.

1951 American researchers Fred Joyner and Harry Coover (1919–) at the Eastman Kodak Company rediscover cyanoacrylate (first found in 1942 in a search for materials to make clear plastic gunsights during World War II). It is marketed in 1958 and becomes known as "superglue."

1952 American government scientists explode the first hydrogen bomb. A year later Soviet scientists successfully test their own hydrogen bomb.

ASIA & OCEANIA

1952 Australian astronomer Colin Gum (1924–60) locates the Gum Nebula, the largest and nearest nebula, the remains of a supernova explosion of 11,000 years ago.

AFRICA & THE MIDDLE EAST

This image taken by the Hubble Space Telescope shows Messier 81, a spiral galaxy about 12 million light-years away from Earth.

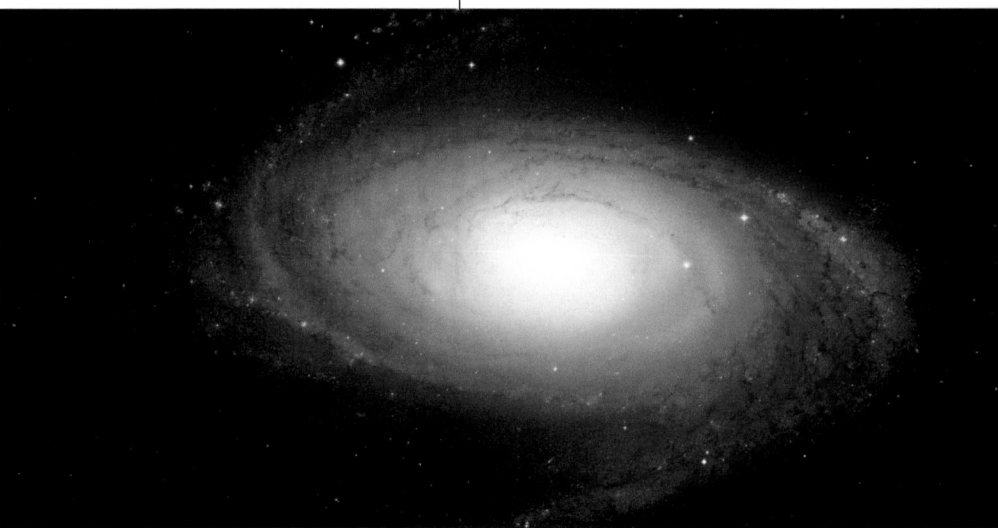

ENGINEERING & INVENTION	WORLD EVENTS
1950 Britain's first electricity-generating nuclear reactor becomes operational at Windscale (later renamed Sellafield) in northwestern England.	**1950** France, West Germany, Italy, the Netherlands, Belgium, and Luxembourg form the European Coal and Steel Community, an important precursor of the European Union.
1950 English mathematician and logician Alan Turing (1912–54) proposes the Turing test to determine whether or not a computer has real intelligence (whether it can "think").	
1950 English ophthalmologist Harold Ridley (1906–2001) implants an artificial lens in a patient's eye to treat blindness caused by a cataract.	
1952 A De Havilland Comet makes the first scheduled flight by a jet airliner (from London to Johannesburg).	
1950 The United States Air Force establishes the Semi-Automatic Ground Environment (SAGE) system to collect radar and other data and process it in real time, using the Whirlwind computer at the Massachusetts Institute of Technology.	**1950** Senator Joseph McCarthy (1908–1957) publishes claims of communist infiltration in the U.S. State Department. This begins a period of anticommunist purges in many areas of American public life.
1950 The first jet fighter aerial combats take place between U.S. F-86s and Soviet MIG-15s in the Korean War.	**1952** The United Nations building is completed in New York City.
1950 English-born American physicist William Shockley (1910–89) and coworkers build the first working junction transistor.	
1951 German-born American physicist Erwin Müller (1911–77) invents the field ion microscope, which can produce images of single atoms.	
1951 German-born American physicist Polykarp Kusch (1911–93) constructs a cesium atomic clock—the most accurate device for measuring time.	
1952 American engineer Fred Waller (1886–1954) presents the Cinerama widescreen system for movies, using three projectors. It is largely superseded a year later by the CinemaScope system, which uses a single projector with a special lens.	
1952 Prolific Japanese inventor and computer engineer Yoshiro Nakamatsu (1928–) patents many important features of the floppy disk drive.	**1950** Chinese troops invade Tibet.
	1950 The Korean War begins between the communist North, aided by Chinese forces, and the south, backed by a U.S.-led United Nations force.
	1952 Japan regains its independence as the postwar U.S. occupation ends.
	1952 A group of army officers in Egypt overthrow the monarchy and establish a republic.
	1952 With UN approval Ethiopia takes over the neighboring state of Eritrea.

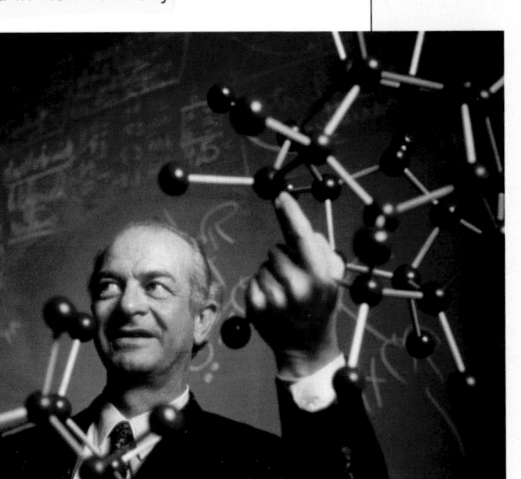

Linus Pauling demonstrates the chemical bonds that hold molecules together.

LINUS PAULING

Linus Pauling was an American chemist whose main work concerned the bonding of atoms in molecules. Born in Portland, Oregon, he studied chemical engineering at Oregon State Agricultural College and received his doctorate from the California Institute of Technology (Caltech). After studying in Europe, he became associate professor of chemistry at Caltech in 1927, rising to full professor four years later. He remained there until 1963.

From 1928 Pauling researched crystal structure and developed the idea of ionic radius to describe the space occupied by ions in crystals. He investigated the structure of molecules in general and proposed the valence bond theory. In 1931 he wrote his most important paper, "The Nature of the Chemical Bond." In it he accounted for the shapes of molecules by introducing the idea of hybrid orbitals, in which the atomic orbitals (the space around an atom in which electrons orbit) of combining atoms "blend" to form a new orbital encompassing the atoms and representing the chemical bond between them. In organic chemistry he studied hemoglobin and other proteins. In 1951 he showed that some proteins have a helical (spiral) structure. After World War II (during which he was consultant to the explosives division of the National Defense Research Commission) Pauling campaigned against nuclear weapons. His campaigning was influential in the discontinuation of aboveground nuclear tests, which led to the signing of the Partial Test Ban Treaty by the United States, the Soviet Union, and the United Kingdom in 1963.

Pauling was the first person to receive two unshared Nobel prizes—Chemistry (1954) and Peace (1962).

ASTRONOMY & MATH	BIOLOGY & MEDICINE	PHYSICAL SCIENCES

EUROPE

1954 Soviet engineers begin development of multistage ICBMs (intercontinental ballistic missiles), culminating three years later with the 100-foot (30.5-m) R-7 missile. Known to NATO as the SS-6, code name "Sapwood," it has a range of 5,000 miles (8,000 km). It is utilized in space exploration and is used to launch Sputnik 1 in 1957 and cosmonaut Yuri Gagarin into space in 1961. This rocket gives the Soviets their early lead in the space race.

1955 English astronomer Martin Ryle (1918–84) builds a large radio interferometer for detecting radio sources in outer space. (His first, two-instrument interferometer, with which he detected the radio source Cassiopeia A, was made in 1948.)

1953 English biophysicist Francis Crick (1916–2004), New Zealand-born British biophysicist Maurice Wilkins (1916–2004), and American biophysicist James Watson (1928–) determine the structure of the deoxyribonucleic acid (DNA) molecule. Their findings owe much to the work of English physical chemist Rosalind Franklin (1920–58), who produced images of the double helix using x-ray crystallography.

1953 Austrian-born British biochemist Max Perutz (1914–2002) modifies hemoglobin with mercury atoms in order to make x-ray diffraction studies of its structure.

1953 German chemist Karl Ziegler (1898–1973) develops the Ziegler process for making polyethene.

1955 English biochemist Frederick Sanger (1918–) sets out the sequence of amino acids in the hormone insulin (a protein).

1955 English crystallographer Dorothy Hodgkin (1910–94) works out the structure of cyanocobalamin (vitamin B_{12}) using a computer.

THE AMERICAS

1953 U.S. military engineers develop a 35-foot (10.7-m) surface-to-air missile (SAM), with a range of 25 miles (40 km)—later named Nike Ajax. The same year, personnel from the Redstone Arsenal first launch the U.S. Army's Redstone Rocket. The rocket is later adapted for use in early U.S. space missions.

1954 Alongside the development of ICBMs to compete with Soviet military hardware, American rocketeers plan a series of satellite launchers. The program eventually leads to the Scout of 1960—length 73 feet (22 m), range 1,000 miles (1,610 km)—preceded by the four-stage Jupiter and two-stage Vanguard of 1958. The 1961 Atlas satellite launcher is also designed for use as an ICBM—length 73 feet (22 m), range 11,000 miles (17,700 km).

1955 American radioastronomer Kenneth Franklin (1923–) detects radio emission from Jupiter.

1953 American surgeon John Gibbon, Jr. (1903–73), performs the first successful open-heart surgery on a human patient, using his heart–lung machine to supply oxygen.

1953 American biochemist Vincent du Vigneaud (1901–78) synthesizes oxytocin, the pituitary-gland hormone that causes contractions of the womb in childbirth; it is the first artificially made human hormone.

1954 A mass field trial of the polio vaccine, developed by Jonas Salk (1914–95), is conducted in the United States. It is injected by needle and found to be safe and effective in reducing the incidence of polio.

1955 Spanish-born American geneticist Severo Ochoa (1905–93) discovers an enzyme in bacteria that enables him to synthesize ribonucleic acid (RNA). (It is later found to be a catalyst for breaking down RNA, not synthesizing it.)

1953 American chemist Stanley Miller (1930–) produces simple amino acids and other "life chemicals" by exposing a mixture of gases similar to those in Earth's early atmosphere to ultraviolet light and electric sparks (to simulate lightning).

1955 American chemist Albert Ghiorso (1915–) and coworkers isolate the new radioactive element mendelevium by bombarding einsteinium-253 with alpha particles. Three years later they discover nobelium by bombarding curium with carbon ions.

1955 Italian-born American physicist Emilio Segrè (1905–89) and American Owen Chamberlain (1920–2006) discover the antiproton (a particle with the same mass as a proton but with a negative charge).

1955 Scientists at American company General Electric produce small synthetic diamonds from graphite, following experimentation by American physicist Percy Bridgman (1882–1961).

ASIA & OCEANIA

AFRICA & THE MIDDLE EAST

A De Havilland Comet, flown by the British Overseas Airways Corporation, was the world's first jet airliner.

ENGINEERING & INVENTION	WORLD EVENTS
1953 English engineer Christopher Cockerell (1910–99) begins work on the hovercraft (air-cushion vehicle), patented two years later. **1953** Radial ply tires for production-line cars are introduced by the Pirelli company in Italy and the Michelin company in France. **1954** The first Soviet experimental nuclear power plant opens at Obinsk. **1954** French inventor Marc Grégoire invents the nonstick cooking pan. **1955** The British company Rolls-Royce continues development of an experimental VTOL (vertical take-off and landing) aircraft, nicknamed the "Flying Bedstead."	**1953** On the death of Joseph Stalin (1878–1953), Nikita Khrushchev (1894–1971) becomes leader of the Soviet Union. He quickly begins dismantling Stalin's cult of personality. **1953** The Allies end their postwar occupation of West Germany and Austria; West Germany joins NATO (North Atlantic Treaty Organization). **1953** The Soviet controlled countries of Eastern Europe form the Warsaw Pact in response to NATO.
1953 Chinese-born American computer engineer An Wang (1920–90) constructs a computer with a magnetic-core memory. **1953** American physicists Gerald Pearson (1905–87), Calvin Fuller (1902–94), and coworkers at Bell Laboratories develop the silicon solar cell for electricity production. **1953** The American F-100A Super Sabre becomes the U.S. Air Force's first supersonic fighter airplane. **1954** American truck operator Malcolm MacLean (1914–2001) introduces standard containers for transporting goods by truck, train, or ship. **1954** American engineer Richard Buckminster Fuller (1895–1983) patents the geodesic dome for roofing large buildings. **1954** The nuclear-powered submarine USS *Nautilus* is commissioned in the United States. **1955** The first computer using transistors instead of vacuum tubes is built in the United States by Bell Laboratories.	**1953** Dwight D. Eisenhower (1890–1969) is inaugurated as U.S. president in succession to Harry S. Truman (1884–1972). **1953** A military coup in Argentina deposes Juan Perón (1895–1974). **1955** In Montgomery, Alabama, Rosa Parks (1913–2005) is arrested for violating race laws after refusing to give up her bus seat to a white passenger. *The nonstick pan was first designed by French inventor Marc Grégoire.*
1955 Indian scientist Narinder Kapany (1927–) develops optical fibers for carrying light over long distances with little loss in intensity.	**1953** A CIA-backed coup in Iran deposes Mohammed Mossadegh (1882–1967) and his nationalist government and reinstates Reza Pahlavi (1919–1980) as shah. **1953** The Korean War (1950–53) ends; North and South Korea remain divided along the cease-fire line. The two sides have never signed a formal peace treaty ending the war.
	1954 Rebels organized by the *Front de Libération Nationale* (National Liberation Front) launch a war of independence against French rule in Algeria.

HOVERCRAFT

The hovercraft, or air-cushion vehicle (ACV), is a craft capable of traveling swiftly over water, land, or other treacherous surfaces such as marshes and ice sheets. The vehicle works by floating on a cushion of air, which is produced by large fans that force air through vents around the outer edge of the craft. A flexible rubber skirt traps the air in place, while the fans act like propellers to move the craft along. The vehicle is steered by rudders resembling those used on airplanes. Small ACVs have gasoline engines, while most commercial and military ACVs have powerful gas turbine engines. Large ACVs can carry a 70-ton (64-tonne) load at speeds of up to 45 miles (72 km) per hour.

The first experimental hovercrafts were constructed during World War I (1914–18), and several other prototypes were built and tested in Europe during the first half of the 20th century. These early craft were not practical, nor were they reliable or easy to control. The first ACVs to demonstrate that the craft had practical uses were designed by British inventor Christopher Cockerell and built by British aviation firm Saunders–Roe, which had previously specialized in manufacturing flying boats. Innovations such as the flexible side-skirts were added, and the first full-size prototype was built in 1959. This ACV was capable of carrying four passengers, a pilot, and a copilot.

Within ten years, massive hovercraft capable of carrying hundreds of people, and also vehicles, were making scheduled trips across the English Channel between England and France. However, the use of ACVs as high-speed passenger ferries has now largely stopped.

Military hovercraft are still widely used because they can travel equally well on land and water. Since ACVs hover above the surface, they are also used for safely crossing areas rendered impassable to conventional vehicles by land mines. The largest military hovercraft is the Russian Zubr class LCAC, first built in 1988. It can hold three tanks or up to 500 troops.

DNA—THE DOUBLE HELIX

PRIOR TO THE 1950S SCIENTISTS ALREADY understood that genes carried on chromosomes were the units of inheritance. They also knew that chromosomes were made up of a mixture of proteins and a complex compound known as deoxyribonucleic acid, or DNA.

In 1951 American chemist Linus Pauling (1901–94) developed a technique for resolving the structures of large biological molecules. He described a class of proteins whose molecules took the form of a helix—a three-dimensional spiral. Well aware that genes were "the next big thing" in scientific research, Pauling soon turned his attention to identifying the structure of DNA.

For biology graduate Francis Crick (1916–2004) at Cambridge University, England, the structure of DNA was something of an obsession. Crick was supposed to be researching hemoglobin, the iron-containing, oxygen-carrying molecule found in red blood cells. But his enthusiasm for DNA outweighed his interest in his formal studies, and he found a willing accomplice in James Watson (1928–), an American biophysicist who arrived at Cambridge in 1951. Together Watson and Crick began informally working on the problem. Their work had to be low key because at the time competition between the great research institutes was frowned on by the scientific community, and deciphering the structure of DNA

KEY DATES

1951
Helical proteins

1952
Pauling model

1953
Watson and Crick papers describing the double helix structure of DNA

When not undergoing replication, DNA is tightly coiled and packed into structures called chromosomes.

Bases on free nucleotides pair with exposed bases on an unzipped chain and link to form a new strand. Base pairings are always consistent.

Replication in action: DNA strands are "unzipped" by enzymes, and each strand acts as a template for a new double helix.

The structure of DNA resembles the shape of a twisted ladder—the famous "double helix." The sides of the ladder are made up of sugar (deoxyribose) molecules linked by phosphate groups. The "rungs" of the ladder are made of pairs of bases. To replicate itself, DNA molecules "unzip" lengthwise. Spare nucleotides (units of DNA structure made up of a base, a sugar, and a phosphate group) are drawn to the two unzipped strands and link up to form new DNA strands.

was the stated aim of another group, at Kings College, London. There New Zealand-born biophysicist Maurice Wilkins (1916–2004) and British physical chemist Rosalind Franklin (1920–58) were involved in a series of complex experiments using x-ray diffraction to determine the structure of DNA. Franklin had all but dismissed the idea that DNA might be a helix, but Watson and Crick thought otherwise. In 1951 they produced a model of DNA as a triple helix. Franklin was among the first to disagree—the structure did not conform to her x-ray diffraction data. Watson and Crick admitted their mistake and went back to the drawing board. In 1952 Linus Pauling presented his own model of DNA. His model too showed the molecule as a helix with three intertwined strands. However, Pauling too had got it wrong—as other scientists were quick to point out.

Breakthrough

DNA contains four different chemical compounds—adenine, thiamine, guanine, and cytosine—known as bases. The realization that these molecules naturally pair off in a predictable way set Watson and Crick on the right track. On learning from the work of a scientist at Columbia University, Austrian-born chemist Erwin Chargaff (1905–2002), that the base adenine always paired with thiamine, and that guanine paired

with cytosine, Watson and Crick made their breakthrough in understanding not only the structure of DNA—a double helix—but also the way in which the molecule is able to replicate. They published their results in the journal *Nature* in April 1953 and accepted the Nobel Prize for Physiology or Medicine in 1962, together with Maurice Wilkins (Franklin had died from cancer in 1958).

Rosalind Franklin's x-ray crystallography of DNA was crucial to Watson and Crick's discovery of its structure.

ASTRONOMY & MATH	BIOLOGY & MEDICINE	PHYSICAL SCIENCES

EUROPE

1957 The Jodrell Bank radio telescope, with a steerable dish 250 feet (76.2 m) across, is completed in the north of England.

1957 Soviet scientists launch the first artificial satellites to orbit Earth, Sputnik 1 and Sputnik 2 (meaning "fellow traveler"). Sputnik 1 weighs 184 pounds (83.6 kg) and orbits in 96 minutes. Sputnik 2 carries the dog Laika, the first living creature in space.

1958 Soviet scientists launch Sputnik 3, carrying scientific instruments, into Earth orbit. There were ten Sputniks in all: Sputniks 4, 5, and 6 tested reentry procedures, 7 and 8 were failed flights to the planet Venus, and 9 and 10 were test flights for the piloted Vostock program.

1956 Romanian cell biologist George Palade (1912–2008) identifies ribosomes, the small cellular structures that are responsible for assembling the proteins in cells.

1958 Scottish surgeon Ian Donald (1910–87) uses an ultrasound scan to examine an unborn baby in its mother's womb.

1957 Commercial production of polypropene (polypropylene) plastic begins in Italy, using a process developed by Italian chemist Giulio Natta (1903–79) and German chemist Karl Ziegler (1898–1973). It is quickly utilized in a variety of applications from automobile parts to household packaging.

1957 German physicist Rudolf Mössbauer (1929–) discovers the Mössbauer effect, which is a nuclear process concerning the recoil-free emission of gamma rays by atomic nuclei in a crystal lattice.

THE AMERICAS

1956 American astrophysicist Herbert Friedman (1916–2000) discovers that solar flares produce x-rays.

1957 American physicist Eugene Parker (1927–) discovers the solar wind, streams of particles ejected from the sun.

1958 American scientists launch Explorer 1, the first American Earth satellite, using a four-stage Jupiter rocket. It is the first of more than 70 Explorers launched up to the end of the year 2000.

1958 The National Aeronautics and Space Administration (NASA) is founded.

1958 American physicist James Van Allen (1914–2006) confirms the presence of the Van Allen radiation belts, using data from a Geiger counter on board NASA's Explorer 1. The two belts are made up of energetic charged particles trapped by Earth's magnetic field. Later that year Explorer 4 maps the trapped radiation.

1956 American chemist Robert Woodward (1917–79) synthesizes reserpine, a drug used to treat high blood pressure and psychotic behaviors.

1956 Chinese-born American biochemist Choh Hao Li (1913–87) and coworkers determine the order of the 39 amino acids in molecules of adrenocorticotropic hormone (ACTH).

1958 American physician Clarence Lillehei (1918–99) invents a heart pacemaker, which has to be worn outside the patient's body. An internal pacemaker, implanted into the patient's body, is invented a year later by Swedish surgeon Åke Senning (1915–2000).

The massive radio telescope at Jodrell Bank, in northwestern England

1956 American physicists Clyde Cowan (1919–74) and Frederick Reines (1918–98) discover the neutrino, a subatomic particle with no charge and zero mass at rest.

1956 American physicist Leon Cooper (1930–) identifies Cooper pairs, which are pairs of electrons in a superconductor (accounting for its lack of electrical resistance).

1957 Japanese physicist Leo Esaki (1925–) describes the tunnel effect, by means of which electrons can penetrate a "barrier" in a semiconductor. Three years later he produces a tunnel diode that makes use of the effect.

ASIA & OCEANIA

HOW THINGS WORK

Solar Wind

The solar wind, discovered by Eugene Parker in 1957, consists of an endless current of high-energy charged particles that stream out from the sun's corona into interplanetary space. By the time they reach Earth, the particles are traveling at between 125 and 160 miles (200 and 260 km) per second. They distort Earth's magnetosphere (the area of space around Earth controlled by the planet's magnetic field) into a teardrop shape leading away from the sun. It is the solar wind that causes the tails of comets to always face away from the sun, regardless of the direction of travel. The interaction between the solar wind and the magnetosphere is the cause of the auroras seen in the skies near the North Pole (northern lights) and South Pole (southern lights).

AFRICA & THE MIDDLE EAST

ENGINEERING & INVENTION	WORLD EVENTS
1956 The world's first commercial nuclear power plant is commissioned at Calder Hall in Britain. **1957** The rotary Wankel engine, invented by Felix Wankel (1902–88), is put into production in West Germany. **1957** A fire at Windscale (later Sellafield) nuclear power plant in Britain causes a radiation leak. **1957** English engineer Lionel Pilkington (1920–95) develops the float glass process for making large sheets of plate glass. **1958** English engineer Alex Moulton (1920–) develops a folding bicycle, designed to fit in the trunk of a car.	**1956** The Soviet Union sends armored units into Hungary to suppress an attempted anticommunist uprising. **1957** The European Economic Community (EEC), later the European Union (EU), is created by the Treaty of Rome. **1958** Summoned back to power from retirement, General Charles de Gaulle (1890–1970) founds France's Fifth Republic, modernizing the constitution and establishing the stable political system still in use today.

An ultrasound image of a fetus in the womb. Unlike x-ray imaging, ultrasound scans pose no potential threat to a developing fetus.

1956 The company Ampex markets a videotape recorder, designed by Russian-born American electronics engineer Alexander Poniatoff (1892–1980). **1956** American computer programmer John Backus (1924–2007) and coworkers at IBM Corporation devise the FORTRAN (Formula Translator) computer language. It becomes commercially available the following year. **1957** American physicist Clarence Zener (1905–93) invents the Zener diode, a type of semiconductor used in voltage-limiting circuits. **1957** Russian-born American physicist Vladimir Zworykin (1889–1982) creates a color television device that uses ultraviolet light to observe living cells. **1957** The American company Smith Corona markets a portable electric typewriter. **1958** American electronic engineers Jack Kilby (1923–2005) and Robert Noyce (1927–90) independently invent integrated circuits, which greatly reduce the size and increase the reliability of circuits for computers and other electronic devices.	**1956** Cuban revolutionary Fidel Castro (1926–) launches a guerrilla campaign to overthrow the dictatorship of Fulgencio Batista (1901–73). **1956** "In God We Trust" is adopted as the national motto of the United States. **1957** The governor of Arkansas, Orval Faubus (1910–94), calls out the National Guard to prevent black students from enrolling at a high school in Little Rock.
1958 Australian engineer David Warren (1925–) invents the "black box" flight data recorder (it is, in fact, orange to make it easy to find at a crash site).	**1956** Pakistan becomes the world's first Islamic Republic. **1958** In China Mao Zedong (1893–1976) initiates the Great Leap Forward—a three year plan for accelerated economic development that ends in disaster and famine following failed harvests.
	1956 Egypt's leader, Gamal Abdel Nasser (1918–70), nationalizes the Suez Canal; in the ensuing Suez Crisis Britain and France send troops to Egypt, but international pressure forces them to withdraw. **1957** Ghana becomes the first British colony in Africa to gain independence.

NEW CHEMICAL ELEMENTS

Until 1937 there were only four gaps in the periodic table up to element number 92 (uranium). The gaps were at elements 43, 61, 85, and 87. That changed when scientists began to use particle accelerators such as the cyclotron, invented in 1932 by U.S. physicist Ernest Lawrence (1901–58).

At first scientists used particle accelerators as "atom smashers" to split elements into smaller components. Atoms of elements such as molybdenum, bismuth, or neodymium were bombarded with nuclei of deuterium (heavy hydrogen) or helium. Experiments using these techniques led to the discovery of technetium (atomic number 43) in 1937, astatine (85) in 1940, and promethium (61) in 1945. (Francium—atomic number 87—was discovered from the radioactive decay of another element in 1939.)

Experiments using particle accelerators to force atoms and particles together led to the discovery of yet more elements. In 1940 U.S. physical chemists Edwin McMillan (1907–91) and Philip Abelson (1913–2004) bombarded uranium-238 with slow neutrons to make neptunium (93). Also in 1940 McMillan, U.S. scientist Glenn Seaborg (1912–99), and coworkers bombarded uranium-238 with deuterium nuclei and created plutonium (94). Other elements followed in rapid succession: curium (96) and americium (95) in 1944, berkelium (97) in 1949, and californium (98) in 1950. Decades later more elements were isolated using these techniques, including seaborgium (106) in 1974, meitnerium (109), isolated in 1982 and named in 1997, and hassium (108) in 1984.

There are now about 116 chemical elements, but there—for the time being—the list ends. Scientists have created only a few atoms of the heaviest elements, which last for no more than a few seconds. Even heavier atoms are theoretically possible, but anything after element 120 would be so unstable that it could have only a fleeting existence.

ASTRONOMY & MATH	BIOLOGY & MEDICINE	PHYSICAL SCIENCES

EUROPE

1959 Soviet scientists launch three Lunik space probes to the moon; Lunik 1 flies past the moon, Lunik 2 crashes on the moon's surface, and Lunik 3 orbits the moon and sends back photographs of the far side. They are the first of 24 such probes.

1960 The Soviet Union launches two dogs, Belka and Strelka, on a 24-hour flight into space in Sputnik 5; they return safely to Earth.

1961 Soviet cosmonaut Yuri Gagarin (1934–68) becomes the first man in space on an 108-minute flight in his spacecraft Vostok (meaning "east"); the spacecraft parachutes back safely to Earth.

1961 Soviet Venera 1 space probe flies by Venus and records scientific data.

1959 Austrian-born British biochemist Max Perutz (1914–2002) determines the structure of the hemoglobin molecule.

1959 Northern Irish surgeon Denis Burkitt (1911–93) describes Burkitt's lymphoma, a disfiguring cancerous condition that most commonly affects children in Africa.

1959 French physician Jérôme Lejeune (1926–94) establishes that Down syndrome is caused the presence of an extra chromosome.

1960 French biologists François Jacob (1920–) and Jacques Monod (1910–76) coin the term *messenger ribonucleic acid* (mRNA) to describe the molecule that carries genetic code from DNA to sites in the cell where proteins are assembled.

1960 English biochemist John Kendrew (1917–97) deciphers the structure of the myoglobin molecule.

1960 English physicist Charles Oatley (1904–96) and coworkers develop the scanning electron microscope.

THE AMERICAS

1959 Researchers at the Stanford Research Institute in California make radar contact with the sun.

1960 American astronomer Allan Sandage (1926–) makes the first optical identification of a quasar (quasistellar object), an active celestial object more luminous than dozens of galaxies. In 1963 Dutch-born American astronomer Maarten Schmidt (1929–) measures its enormous redshift and proves it is billions of light-years away.

1960 The National Aeronautics and Space Administration (NASA) launches Pioneer 5 space probe to investigate the solar wind.

1960 NASA launches TIROS 1, the first weather satellite, into Earth orbit.

1961 American radio astronomer Frank Drake (1930–) formulates the Drake equation, which estimates the number of planets in our galaxy (the Milky Way) that may have technologically advanced civilizations.

1961 American astronaut Alan Shepard (1923–98) makes a suborbital flight in his spacecraft Freedom 7.

1960 American biochemist Lyman Craig (1906–74) isolates and purifies parathormone, the hormone produced by the parathyroid glands in the neck that controls calcium levels in the blood.

1960 American biologist James Bonner (1910–96) ascertains that RNA is synthesized on chromosomes.

1960 American cardiologist Paul Zoll (1911–99) develops the implant pacemaker to enable a damaged heart to beat normally.

1960 American zoologists John Prescott (1935–98) and Kenneth Norris (1924–98) discover that bottlenose dolphins produce ultrasonic pulses in a form of echolocation to detect objects under water.

1960 Hungarian-born American biophysicist Georg von Békésy (1899–1972) shows how sound waves stimulate the cochlea in the inner ear.

1961 American surgeon Judah Folkman (1933–2008) proposes (correctly) the existence of a substance called angiogenesis factor that cancerous tumors secrete to stimulate the growth of blood vessels and thereby the blood supply to a growing tumor.

1960 American chemist Robert Woodward (1917–79) synthesizes the green plant pigment, chlorophyll.

1961 American chemist Albert Ghiorso (1915–) and coworkers isolate the new radioactive element lawrencium.

Bathyscaphes, such as the Trieste *above, are designed to withstand the enormous pressures that exist at the depths of the ocean. The two-person crew sits in the steel sphere beneath the main hull.*

ASIA & OCEANIA

Russian cosmonaut Yuri Gagarin reclines strapped into the capsule of his Vostok spacecraft prior to making his historic first orbit of Earth.

AFRICA & THE MIDDLE EAST

1960 Kenyan anthropologist Jonathan Leakey (1940–) discovers remains of the oldest-known human, *Homo habilis* ("handy man"). Found at Olduvai Gorge, Tanzania, the fossils are about 2 million years old.

I can see the clouds, and their shadow over the Earth. It is beautiful.

YURI GAGARIN, SPEAKING FROM *VOSTOK 1*

ENGINEERING & INVENTION	WORLD EVENTS
1959 The German company Voigtlander produces a zoom lens for its cameras, providing a range of focal lengths with a single lens.	**1961** High-profile Russian ballet star Rudolf Nureyev (1938–93) requests asylum in France while touring with the Kirov Ballet.
1959 The United Kingdom Atomic Energy Authority commissions a fast-breeder nuclear reactor.	**1961** The Non-Aligned Movement comes into being at a conference in Belgrade, Yugoslavia, hosted by President Tito (1892–1980). It is comprised of nations, mostly from the developing world, that refuse to align themselves with either the United States or the Soviet Union.
1959 The British Austin Motor Company launches the Mini, an automobile designed by Greek-born British engineer Alec Issigonis (1906–88).	
1961 A 200,000-volt cable under the English Channel joins the electricity systems of England and France to enable them to "share" power during off-peak periods.	
1959 The nuclear-powered cargo vessel *Savannah* is named by First Lady Mamie Eisenhower in the U.S.; the completed ship is launched in 1962.	**1959** Fidel Castro (1926–) overthrows the dictatorship of Fulgencio Batista (1901–73) and turns Cuba into a socialist state.
1960 U.S. Navy bathyscaphe *Trieste*, guided by Swiss explorer Jacques Piccard (1922–2008) and U.S. Navy officer Don Walsh (1931–), descends the 35,810-ft (10,916-m) Marianas Trench in the Pacific Ocean.	**1961** John F. Kennedy (1917–63) is inaugurated as the 35th president of the United States.
1960 American nuclear-powered submarine U.S.S. *Triton* makes a submerged circumnavigation of the world.	**1961** The U.S.-backed invasion of Cuba at the Bay of Pigs ends in failure. The majority of the Cuban exiles who took part in the invasion are imprisoned or executed by Fidel Castro's government, and attempts to conceal the extent of U.S. involvement fail.
1960 American Digital Equipment Corporation markets the PDP-1, the precursor of the mini computer. It has a keyboard and TV-type monitor.	
1960 American physicist Theodore H. Maiman (1927–2007) invents the ruby laser—the first operable laser.	**1961** Freedom Riders challenging segregation laws on interstate transportation are attacked by angry mobs in Alabama and Mississippi.
1961 U.S. Navy *Strato-Lab V* balloon rises to 113,740 feet (34,667 m), piloted by Malcolm Ross (1919–85) and Victor Prather (1923–61), and achieves a world-record altitude for an air balloon.	
1961 The American company Texas Instruments produces the first silicon chips.	
1960 The Japan Stationery Company (later known as Pentel) markets the first felt-tip pens.	**1959** Fleeing Chinese communist rule, the 14th Dalai Lama (r. 1950–), the spiritual and political leader of Tibet, seeks asylum in India, where he establishes a government in exile.
	1961 Kuwait gains independence from the United Kingdom.
1959 The 420-foot- (128-m-) high Kariba Dam is completed on the Zambia/Zimbabwe border.	**1960** South African police fire on antiapartheid demonstrators in the black township of Sharpeville, killing 69 people.
	1961 Wars of independence begin in the Portuguese colonies of Angola and Mozambique.

NASA

The "Space Race" began when the Soviet Union launched Sputnik 1, which became the first human-made object in space. This turned a previously secret arms race with the United States into a public technological rivalry, with both sides seeking to score space "firsts" as symbols of technical superiority.

Explorer 1, the first satellite launched by the United States, reached orbit in February 1958, four months after Sputnik. Concerned that the United States had fallen behind technologically, Congress passed the National Aeronautics and Space Act, establishing the National Aeronautics and Space Administration (NASA) and allocating a large budget for the development of space technology.

The new government agency, headquartered in Washington, D.C., assumed control of all space research being conducted by the military. Along with these projects, NASA gained a group of the German rocket experts who had moved to the United States after World War II, including Wernher von Braun (1912–77).

In 1961 Alan Shepard (1923–98) became the first American in space. By 1969 NASA's Apollo program had put Neil Armstrong (1930–) and Buzz Aldrin (1930–) on the moon. NASA has also sent out many unpiloted probes to explore the solar system. Several of these have landed on and explored other planets. In the 1970s NASA launched the space station Skylab. In the 1980s and 1990s the Space Shuttle was NASA's main focus. Future projects include building a Shuttle replacement, completion of the International Space Station, and putting a human on Mars by 2037.

ASTRONOMY & MATH	BIOLOGY & MEDICINE	PHYSICAL SCIENCES

EUROPE

1962 Italian-born American physicists Riccardo Giacconi (1931–), Bruno Rossi (1905–94), and coworkers discover the first nonsolar x-ray source (the star Scorpius X-1). Two years later American astrophysicist Herbert Friedman (1916–2000) discovers another x-ray source in the Crab Nebula.

1963 Soviet cosmonaut Valentina Tereshkova (1937–) becomes the first woman in space on a 48-orbit flight in her spacecraft Vostok 6.

1964 American radio astronomers Arno Penzias (1933–) and Robert Wilson (1936–) accidentally detect cosmic background microwave radiation. Their discovery convinces most astronomers that the big bang theory is correct.

1962 Scottish biochemist James Black (1924–) prepares beta-blockers, drugs used in the treatment of patients with angina and hypertension (high blood pressure).

1964 Kidney dialysis in the home is introduced in Britain and the United States.

1962 Welsh physicist Brian Josephson (1940–) identifies the Josephson effect, in which an electric current flows through two superconductors separated by a very thin layer of insulator.

1964 Scottish theoretical physicist Peter Higgs (1929–) and coworkers predict the existence of the Higgs boson, a zero-spin subatomic particle with nonzero mass.

1964 Northern Irish physicist John Bell (1928–91) proposes Bell's theorem, which resolves apparent disagreements between relativity and quantum theory.

THE AMERICAS

1962 American astronaut John Glenn (1921–) is the first American to orbit the Earth on a three-orbit flight in Friendship 7 (part of the Mercury space program).

1962 The National Aeronautics and Space Administration's (NASA) space probe Mariner 2 flies by Venus.

1962 American communications satellite Telstar 1 (Bell Telephones/NASA) relays live TV transmissions between the United States and Europe.

1964 NASA's lunar space probe Ranger 7 takes 4,000 high-quality video pictures of the moon's surface before crash-landing on the moon.

1964 NASA's space probe Mariner 4 makes the first successful flyby of Mars, sending back photographs of the planet's surface.

1964 NASA starts the Gemini space program, which will launch 12 spacecraft (ten with two-person crews) on Titan II rockets.

1962 In her book *Silent Spring* American naturalist Rachel Carson (1907–64) awakens public awareness of the effects of chemical pesticides on the environment.

1962 American microbiologist Thomas Weller (1915–2008) develops a vaccine against rubella (German measles).

1962 British-born American chemist Neil Bartlett (1932–2008) makes the first compound of a rare gas (xenon).

1962 American physicist Leon Lederman (1922–) discovers the muon neutrino, a subatomic particle with zero charge and zero mass.

1962 American chemist Charles Pedersen (1904–89) synthesizes crown ethers, molecules that selectively bind specific metal ions in solution.

1963 American chemist Howard Rogers (1915–95) and researchers at the Polaroid Corporation led by Elkan Blout (1919–2006) develop the chemistry for producing "instant" color photographs.

1964 American theoretical physicist Murray Gell-Mann (1929–) predicts the existence of the quark, a fundamental subatomic particle with a fractional (i.e., nonintegral) charge.

ASIA & OCEANIA

The more clearly we can focus our attention on the wonders and realities of the universe about us, the less taste we shall have for destruction.

RACHEL CARSON, *SILENT SPRING* (1962)

1962 French-born Australian immunologist Jacques Miller (1931–) determines the role of the thymus in the immune system of infants.

Robert Moog poses with an early Moog synthesizer. Although large, expensive, and difficult to operate, the instrument soon attracted many high-profile musicians.

AFRICA & THE MIDDLE EAST

ENGINEERING & INVENTION

1962 The Bendorf Bridge—a concrete double cantilever with a central span of 673 feet (202 m)—is completed over the Rhine River in Germany. Its designer is German engineer Ulrich Finsterwalder (1897–1988).

1963 British company Courtaulds develops a method of manufacturing carbon fibers.

1963 The Dutch company Philips introduces audio cassette tapes.

1964 The German company NSU markets the Spider, the first mass-produced Wankel-engined car.

1962 American electronic engineer Nick Holonyak, Jr. (1928–) of the General Electric Company invents the light-emitting diode (LED).

1962 The seven-bit 128-character American Standard Code for Information Interchange (ASCII) is introduced in the States.

1962 American electronic engineer Paul Weimer (1914–2005) of the RCA Corporation invents thin-film transistors, an important contribution to solid-state circuits.

1963 South African-born American engineer Allan Cormack (1924–98) invents the CAT (computerized axial tomography) scanner.

1964 American computer programmers John Kemeny (1926–92) and Thomas Kurtz (1928–) invent the computer language BASIC (Beginner's All-purpose Symbolic Instruction Code).

1964 American engineer Robert Moog (1934–2005) invents a music synthesizer.

1964 The Verrazano-Narrows Bridge, linking Brooklyn with Staten Island, opens. At the time it is the world's longest suspension bridge, with a span of 4,260 feet (1,298 m).

1964 In Japan the Tokaido Shinkansen train line opens. It links Tokyo and Osaka and deploys the new 100-mile- (160-km-) per-hour bullet trains.

WORLD EVENTS

1963 During a visit to Berlin U.S. President John F. Kennedy (1917–63) emphasizes his support for the people of West Berlin, stating, "*Ich bin ein Berliner*" ("I am a citizen of Berlin").

1964 Premier Nikita Khrushchev (1894–1971) is ousted from power in the Soviet Union.

1963 Martin Luther King, Jr. (1929–68) delivers his "I have a dream" speech at the Lincoln Memorial during a civil rights march on Washington, D.C.

1963 President John F. Kennedy is assassinated in Dallas, Texas, and is succeeded by Vice President Lyndon B. Johnson (1908–73).

1964 The Civil Rights Act opposing racial discrimination becomes law in the United States.

The Verrazano-Narrows Bridge in New York links Staten Island with Brooklyn.

1962 Chinese troops occupy the Aksai Chin region of Kashmir, provoking hostilities with India.

1964 An alleged torpedo attack on two U.S. destroyers in the Gulf of Tonkin leads to U.S. entry into the Vietnam War (1959–75).

1962 Algeria gains independence from France, with Ahmed Ben Bella (1918–) as its first prime minister (later president).

1964 Nelson Mandela (1918–) is sentenced to life imprisonment in South Africa for sabotage and treason.

ECHOLOCATION

In 1938 two young researchers at Harvard University, Donald Griffin (1915–2003), and Robert Galambos (1914–), were trying to find out how bats could see and hunt in the dark. Using special recording equipment that shifted the pitch of the bats' calls down into the range of human hearing, they were able to hear the rapid clicks that the bats made as they flew. They correctly identified these sounds as evidence of the bats' ability to detect the size and location of objects by the sound of their own reflected calls, a process called "echolocation."

In 1960 another pair of researchers, zoologists John Prescott (1935–98) and Kenneth Norris (1924–98), discovered that dolphins and many other types of whales navigate and hunt using the same method. The clicks, along with other ambient sounds, generate sound waves that reflect off solid objects. The click is generated by a complex system of reverberating chambers and airways around the animals' blowholes. It can be focused in a particular direction in order to give a more accurate idea of the location of an object. The vibrations of the reflected sound are transferred through the jawbone to the ear. There are features in the jaws of some dolphins that are not symmetrical. They may allow dolphins to judge the direction from which reflected sound has come.

The process of interpreting the information received from the clicks is believed to take place at a subconscious level, in much the same way as the sensory information from eyes and ears. Some research has suggested that dolphins are able to "see," or build up three-dimensional visualizations of the objects that they detect through echolocation.

Echolocation has since been discovered in other animals, including some shrews and tenrecs and two types of bird.

ASTRONOMY & MATH	BIOLOGY & MEDICINE	PHYSICAL SCIENCES

EUROPE

1965 Soviet cosmonaut Aleksei Leonov (1934–) is the first person to walk (tethered) in space; he leaves space capsule Voskhod 2 for 12 minutes.

1966 The Soviet Luna 9 becomes the first spacecraft to make a soft landing on the moon. Later that year Luna 10 becomes the first to go into orbit around the moon.

1966 French astronomer Audouin Dollfus (1924–) locates Janus, one of Saturn's moons. Its existence is later confirmed in 1980 by Voyager 1 photographs.

1967 Northern Irish astronomer Jocelyn Bell Burnell (née Bell, 1943–) and English astronomer Antony Hewish (1924–) detect the first pulsar.

1965 English biophysicist Francis Crick (1916–2004) and South African-born British microbiologist Sydney Brenner (1927–) identify the codons that signal "stop" messages in deoxyribonucleic acid (DNA). These termination codons complete the protein-building process.

1967 German physicist Bernd Matthias (1918–80) and coworkers produce a superconducting alloy that functions at 20 K, the highest temperature so far achieved for a superconductor.

TURNING POINTS

Microwave Ovens

Self-taught American engineer Percy Spencer (1894–1970), who worked for the company Raytheon, had the idea for a microwave oven after noticing that a candy bar had melted while he was making a radar set in the 1940s. Raytheon patented his idea in 1947. A few cumbersome models were made, but it was not until 1967 that the first domestic microwave was marketed. Microwave ovens use microwave radiation to heat water and other polarized molecules in food. They cook quickly, efficiently, and safely. Since the late 1960s, the ovens have become smaller, more powerful, and easier to use. More than 90 percent of U.S. households now have a microwave oven.

THE AMERICAS

1965 The National Aeronautics and Space Administration (NASA) achieves several high-profile sucesses: Ranger 8 returns over 8,000 photographs before crashing on the moon; Pioneer 6 orbits and monitors the sun; two Gemini spacecraft rendezvous in Earth orbit.

1965 NASA launches the world's first commercial communications satellite *Early Bird* (later Intelsat 1).

1966 NASA's space probe Surveyor 1 soft-lands on the moon and sends back more than 11,000 photographs. Lunar Orbiter 1 and Lunar Orbiter 2 send back photographs of the far side of the moon.

1967 NASA's space probe Mariner 5 makes a close flyby of Venus. In the same year a fire kills three Apollo astronauts during a ground test.

1965 American geneticist Charles Yanofsky (1925–) and coworkers establish that the sequence of codons in a gene determines the sequence of amino acids in a protein.

1967 American biochemist Arthur Kornberg (1918–2007) uses DNA polymerase, the enzyme that assembles nucleotides, to make biologically active "synthetic" DNA.

1967 In the United States, Argentine-born surgeon René Favaloro (1923–2000) conducts a successful coronary bypass operation.

1967 Greek-born American physician George Cotzias (1918–77) introduces the use of the drug L-dopa as a treatment for Parkinsonism.

1965 American physicists Moo-Young Han (1934–) and Yoichiro Nambu (1921–) introduce the idea of "color" as a way of classifying one aspect of the new subatomic articles known as quarks.

1966 American geneticist Richard Lewontin (1929–) develops the technique of gel electrophoresis for separating proteins (a method now routinely used in genetic fingerprinting).

1966 Construction of the powerful linear accelerator at the Stanford Linear Accelerator Center (SLAC) is completed.

1966 The American Atomic Energy Commission announces that Weston, Illinois, is the site chosen for the new National Accelerator Laboratory, housing a 200 GeV particle accelerator.

1967 American physicist Steven Weinberg (1933–) and Pakistani physicist Abdus Salam (1926–96) independently state versions of the electroweak theory, which unifies the electromagnetic and weak nuclear forces.

1967 The National Accelerator Laboratory is commissioned in Batavia (formerly Weston), Illinois.

ASIA & OCEANIA

1965 Japanese astronomers Ikeya Kaoru (1926–) and, independently, Seki Tsutomu (1930–) discover the bright sun-grazing comet Ikeya-Seki. It splits in three as it passes the sun.

South African surgeon Christiaan Barnard performed the first human-to-human heart transplant.

AFRICA & THE MIDDLE EAST

1967 South African surgeon Christiaan Barnard (1922–2001) performs the first successful heart transplant. The patient lives for 18 days with his new heart.

ENGINEERING & INVENTION	WORLD EVENTS
1965 The Soviet Antonov An-22 jet airliner, the world's largest military and freight-carrying aircraft, makes its maiden flight.	**1966** Concerned that membership is impairing French sovereignty, France withdraws from the North Atlantic Treaty Organization (NATO).
1965 The Mont Blanc road tunnel between France and Italy is opened.	
1966 An electronic fuel-injection system for automobile engines is developed in Britain.	
1967 The first production model of the British Hawker Harrier GR Mark I V/STOL (Vertical/Short Take-Off and Landing) combat airplane makes its maiden flight.	
1967 The ocean liner *Queen Elizabeth 2* is launched in Britain.	

1965 American Digital Equipment Corporation introduces the first mini computer.	**1965** Militant black leader Malcolm X (1925–65) is assassinated in New York City.
1966 American inventor Stephanie Kwolek (1923–) invents the ultrastrong synthetic fiber Kevlar. Five times stronger than steel, it is used in a wide variety of industrial products today, including fiber-optic cables, aircraft parts, canoes, and bullet-proof vests.	**1967** Guerrilla leader Che Guevara (1928–67) is killed in Bolivia.
	1967 During a visit to Montreal, Canada, French President Charles De Gaulle (1890–1970) declares his support for the independence of Quebec.
1966 American electronic engineer Ray Dolby (1933–) devises the Dolby noise-reduction system (type A) for sound recordings.	
1967 Scientists at Bell Laboratories develop the bubble memory for computers.	
1967 American engineer Joseph Engelberger (1925–) at General Motors perfects a reprogrammable computer-controlled industrial robot.	
1967 The American company Raytheon markets the first domestic microwave oven.	

Modern body armor contains the ultra-strong fiber Kevlar, which can stop bullets.

1966 Chinese electronics engineer Charles Kao (1933–) and George Hockham of British company Standard Telecommunications Laboratories invent fiber-optic cable.	**1965** India and Pakistan go to war for a second time over the province of Kashmir.
1967 Chinese scientists explode a hydrogen bomb over Lop Nor in western China.	**1965** American bombing of targets in North Vietnam begins.
	1965 Civil war divides Nigeria as the eastern province of Biafra attempts to break away. The conflict continues until 1970.

RADIO TELESCOPES

American radio engineer Karl Jansky (1905–50) first detected radio waves from outer space in 1931. He used an improvised antenna of wood and wire. Six years later American engineer Grote Reber (1911–2002) built a radio telescope in his backyard and became the world's first radio astronomer. The telescope had a dish-shaped antenna 31 feet (9.4 m) across and received signals at a wavelength of 1.9 meters. Because radio wavelengths are so much longer than those of light, radio telescopes have to be considerably larger than the mirrors of reflecting telescopes to get similar resolution. By 1942 Reber, using the shorter wavelength of 60 centimeters, had built up a radio map of the universe.

The first big single radio telescope was constructed in 1957 for Manchester University at Jodrell Bank, in England, under the supervision of English radio astronomer Bernard Lovell (1913–). The 250-foot (76.2-m) dish achieved fame almost immediately when it tracked Earth's first artificial satellite, the Soviet Sputnik 1. Cornell University completed the largest single radio telescope over a natural depression in the ground at Arecibo in Puerto Rico. It consists of an aluminum metal mesh 1,000 feet (305 m) across with a radio receiver suspended on wires at its focus.

The resolving power of even such huge dishes is limited, and to obtain greater detail astronomers used the principle of the interferometer (using two widely separated telescopes). Scientists mount two or more radio telescopes on railroad tracks to easily vary the distances between them. Communications cables carry the signals from the telescopes to a computer, which analyzes the signals. Radio astronomers employ a few widely separated telescopes in the technique known as a very large array (VLA). In 1980 the National Radio Astronomy Observatory completed a VLA near Socorro, New Mexico. This array has 27 antennas on a Y-shaped track extending for a total of 19 miles (32 km). It is the equivalent of a single dish 22 miles (36 km) across.

ASTRONOMY & MATH	BIOLOGY & MEDICINE	PHYSICAL SCIENCES

EUROPE

1969 English astrophysicist Donald Lynden-Bell (1935–) proposes that there are supermassive black holes at the centers of galaxies.

1970 Soviet space probe Luna 16 returns lunar soil samples to Earth. Luna 17 lands a roving vehicle, Lunokhod 1, on the moon's surface. Soviet Venera 7 lands on Venus and is the first spacecraft to transmit data from the surface of another planet.

1968 Swiss biophysicist Werner Arber (1929–) isolates enzymes that cut the deoxyribonucleic acid (DNA) of viruses that infect bacteria. They become known as restrictive enzymes and are important later in genetic engineering experiments.

1969 English physiologist Robert Edwards (1925–) and English obstetrician Patrick Steptoe (1913–88) fertilize the first human eggs *in vitro*.

1969 English chemist Dorothy Hodgkin (1910–94) uses x-ray crystallography and computers to determine the molecular structure of insulin.

HOW THINGS WORK

In Vitro Fertilization

When a woman who wants to have a baby has difficulty becoming pregnant, doctors may recommend *in vitro* fertilization (IVF). *In vitro*, Latin for "in glass," describes any procedure that is carried out in the laboratory, for example in a test tube, rather than within a patient's body. For this reason, babies born using the technique have become known as "test-tube" babies. The physician first gives the woman a hormone injection to stimulate the production of eggs and then recovers the eggs from her ovary using a suction device. Next the eggs are fertilized by a sample of the father's sperm. The fertilized eggs continue to grow in a nutrient solution until they have divided repeatedly to form a ball of cells called a blastocyst. This early embryo is then implanted in the mother's womb, where it develops in the usual way into a baby. Although eggs were first successfully fertilized *in vitro* in 1969, the first baby produced using the technique was not born until 1978.

THE AMERICAS

1968 The National Aeronautics and Space Administration (NASA) launches a UV observatory satellite, OAO-2, into Earth orbit.

1968 NASA's Apollo 7 spacecraft (the first piloted Apollo mission) makes 163 Earth orbits, and Apollo 8 orbits the moon.

1969 NASA's Apollo 9 spacecraft makes 151 Earth orbits, testing docking and undocking of modules. Apollo 10 orbits the moon, and Apollo 11 makes the first piloted moon landing. Astronaut Neil Armstrong (1930–) becomes the first man to walk on the moon's surface. Buzz Aldrin (1930–) joins him, while Michael Collins (1930–) remains orbiting the moon in the command module. Later that year Apollo 12 also lands on the moon.

1970 NASA's Apollo 13 mission is aborted without a moon landing because of an onboard explosion, but the crew returns safely.

1970 Large reflecting telescopes are installed at observatories at Mauna Kea, Hawaii (88 inches/2.24 m), and Kitt Peak, Arizona (158 inches/4 m).

1968 American physician Norman Shumway (1923–2006) performs the first heart transplant in the United States.

1969 American geneticist Jonathan Beckwith (1935–) and coworkers isolate a single gene, lacZ.

1969 In the United States a report suggesting a link between cyclamates and cancer leads to a ban on their use as artificial sweeteners a year later.

1970 American paleontologist Edwin Colbert (1905–2001) discovers in Antarctica fossils of *Lystrosaurus* (a prehistoric reptile also found in India and Africa), providing evidence for the theory of continental drift (because these landmasses must once have been joined).

1970 American molecular biologists Howard Temin (1934–94) and David Baltimore (1938–) identify reverse transcriptase, an enzyme that transcribes RNA (ribonucleic acid) into DNA and later becomes important in genetic engineering.

1969 American chemist Robert Woodward (1917–79) and Polish-born American chemist Roald Hoffmann (1937–) propose the Woodward–Hoffmann rules concerning the formation of products in organic reactions.

1969 American biochemist Gerald Edelman (1929–) works out the sequence of amino acids in the immunoglobulin molecule.

ASIA & OCEANIA

1970 Artificial Earth satellites are launched by China and Japan.

American astronaut Edwin "Buzz" Aldrin stands on the surface of the moon in a photograph taken by fellow astronaut Neil Armstrong.

AFRICA & THE MIDDLE EAST

1968 South African surgeon Christiaan Barnard (1922–2001) carries out his second heart transplant operation. This time the patient, Philip Blaiberg (1909–69), lives for 19 months after the successful operation.

ENGINEERING & INVENTION	WORLD EVENTS
1968 The Soviet Tu-144 supersonic airliner, conceived by Russian designer Andrei Tupolev (1888–1972), makes its maiden flight.	**1968** Student unrest spreads across Europe, protesting the Vietnam War (1959–75) and local grievances; students' and workers' strikes almost topple the French government.
1969 The British-French supersonic airliner Concorde makes its maiden flight in France.	**1968** The Czech government, led by Alexander Dubchek (1921–92), institutes the Prague Spring of liberal reforms, quickly crushed by Warsaw Pact troops.
1969 A nuclear-powered cargo vessel, the 29,000-ton (26,000-tonne) *Otto Hahn*, is launched in West Germany. (It is named for the German chemist whose work led to the discovery of nuclear fission.)	**1968** In Northern Ireland violence between the majority Protestant community and demonstrators demanding enhanced civil rights for the Catholic minority sparks a 30-year period of violence known as the "Troubles."
1970 Swiss computer programmer Niklaus Wirth (1934–) invents PASCAL programming language, named in honor of French scientist Blaise Pascal (1623–62).	

1968 The Lockheed C-5 Galaxy makes its maiden flight in the United States and becomes the world's largest airplane.	**1968** U.S. civil rights leader Martin Luther King Jr. (1929–68) is assassinated in Memphis, Tennessee.
1968 Italian-born American inventor Candido Jacuzzi (1903–86) invents the whirlpool bath named for him.	**1968** Democratic presidential hopeful, Robert Kennedy (1925–68), brother of assassinated President John F. Kennedy (1917–63), is shot dead after a campaign rally in Los Angeles.
1968 American computer engineer Douglas Engelbart (1925–) devises the computer mouse.	**1970** As opposition to the Vietnam War gains momentum in the United States, four student protesters are shot dead by the National Guard on the campus of Kent State University, Ohio.
1969 Canadian electronic engineer Willard Boyle (1924–) and American electronic engineer George Smith (1930–) invent the charge-coupled device (CCD). It soon replaces photographic film in many applications.	
1969 In the United States the Boeing Company flies its 747 (Jumbo) jet for the first time.	
1970 American Gary Gabelich (1940–84) sets a world land speed record of 622.287 miles (1,001 km) per hour in the rocket-powered car *Blue Flame* at Bonneville Salt Flats, Utah.	
1970 The 400-seater Boeing 747 Jumbo jet goes into service on the transatlantic run. Two years later an air cargo version goes into service, carrying freight between New York and Frankfurt, West Germany.	

1970 The Japanese company Canon Business Machines markets a pocket calculator with a printout.	**1968** Vietcong insurgents launch the Tet offensive against South Vietnam, almost capturing the capital, Saigon, before retreating.
	1970 Civil war breaks out in Jordan when King Hussein (r. 1952–1999) expels the Palestine Liberation Organization.

1968 In Egypt the power plant at the new Aswan High Dam goes into operation.	**1969** Colonel Muammar al-Gadhafi (1942–) overthrows the monarchy and proclaims himself Libya's leader.
	1970 Biafra surrenders to Nigerian forces, giving up its three-year struggle.

PULSARS

In 1967 two British astronomers, Jocelyn Bell Burnell (1943–) and Anthony Hewish (1924–), were using a radio telescope to study quasars—the centers of galaxies. Bell noticed a source of radiation that was pulsing on and off about once a second. Unable to explain the source of this mysteriously regular radio signal, the astronomers named it LGM–1, a reference to the "little green men"—a light-hearted nickname for extraterrestrial intelligent life.

In 1968, other astronomers proposed that LGM–1 was a rotating neutron star. Such stars are very dense and small—about 12.4 miles (20 km) across—and spin rapidly. They emit a beam of electromagnetic radiation. If the beam points toward Earth while the star spins, it can be detected by radio telescopes as pulses of radio waves. The name *pulsar*—a contraction of "pulsating star"—was coined to describe this type of star. Other pulsars were soon discovered, with pulse rates varying from a few milliseconds to several seconds.

Most pulsars are thought to have been formed after the explosions of stars (supernovas) and are sometimes found in remnants of supernovas (the clouds of gas and plasma thrown out by exploding stars).

At the heart of the Crab Nebula is the Crab Pulsar, a neutron star that spins 30.2 times each second.

ASTRONOMY & MATH	BIOLOGY & MEDICINE	PHYSICAL SCIENCES

EUROPE

1971 Soviet space probe Mars 2 goes into orbit around Mars (two weeks after Mariner 9), and Mars 3 lands on the surface but its TV camera fails. Soviet spacecraft Soyuz 10 docks with Salyut 1, the first space station in Earth orbit. Later that year three Soviet cosmonauts die as they reenter Earth's atmosphere onboard Soyuz 11.

1972 Soviet space probe Venera 8 soft-lands on Venus and returns data from the surface for 50 minutes.

1973 Czech astronomer Lubos Kohoutek (1935–) discovers (photographically) the nonperiodic comet Kohoutek.

1972 Scottish biochemist James Black (1924–) develops the drug cimetidine, which blocks the secretion of stomach acids and is used to treat ulcers.

1972 Swiss biochemist Jean-François Borel (1933–) develops the immunosuppressive drug cyclosporin-A, used to prevent rejection of organs following transplant operations.

1972 French mathematician René Thom (1923–2002) introduces catastrophe theory, which soon has applications in physics and other sciences.

This design was etched onto a plaque on the Pioneer 10 space probe. It contains a picture of a man and woman with an image of the probe in the background. It also gives the location of Earth relative to the sun, and of the sun relative to nearby pulsars in a way which scientists believe could be decoded by other intelligent life.

THE AMERICAS

1971 American astronomer Irwin Shapiro (1929–) identifies so-called superluminal sources—quasar components that seem to move apart faster than the speed of light.

1971 The National Aeronautics and Space Administration's (NASA) Apollo 14 makes the third piloted lunar landing and returns with rock samples. Apollo 15 lands the Lunar Rover Vehicle. Mariner 9 goes into orbit around Mars, eventually sending back more than 7,000 detailed pictures.

1972 NASA launches Landsat 1, the first Earth resources satellite. It also launches space probe Pioneer 10. Apollo 16 and Apollo 17 make the final landings on the moon.

1973 NASA space probe Pioneer 10 flies by Jupiter. NASA launches Pioneer 11 and four Skylab space station missions.

1973 Using data from the Vela Earth satellite, American astronomers detect bursts of gamma rays originating in outer space. One of the sources is later nicknamed "Geminga" (in Milanese dialect meaning "it's not there").

1972 American authorities restrict the use of DDT insecticide because of its effects on the environment and its inhabitants.

1972 American molecular biologist Paul Berg (1926–) produces hybrid deoxyribonucleic acid (DNA).

1972 American psychiatrist David Janowsky and coworkers propose that bipolar disorder ("manic depression") is caused by an imbalance between two kinds of chemical neurotransmitters in the brain.

1973 American and English physicists begin to develop nuclear magnetic resonance imaging (MRI scanning), later used in medical diagnosis.

1973 American biologists Stanley Cohen (1935–) and Herbert Boyer (1936–) invent a way of cloning genetically engineered molecules in foreign cells.

1971 Chinese-born American biochemist Choh Hao Li (1913–87) synthesizes the human growth hormone.

1972 The National Accelerator Laboratory in Weston (now eastern Batavia), Illinois, commissions its 200 GeV accelerator, later upgrading it to 400 GeV. In 1974 the laboratory is renamed Fermilab.

1972 American theoretical physicist Murray Gell-Mann (1929–) begins formulating a new branch of physics, quantum chromodynamics (QCD). It describes nuclear interaction in terms of quarks.

1973 Physicists at Bell Laboratories produce a continuous-wave laser that can be tuned to different wavelengths. A year later they have lasers that can produce light pulses of less than a trillionth of a second.

ASIA & OCEANIA

1972 In Australia astronomer B. J. Harris (1925–75) provides evidence that most unidentified radio sources in space are compact, when he discovers that 60 percent of them scintillate (as in the "twinkling" of stars).

The development of the continuous-wave laser and the rapidly pulsing laser at Bell Laboratories in 1973 was important in the development of lasers for surgical purposes, such as eye surgery, pictured here.

AFRICA & THE MIDDLE EAST

1972 Kenyan anthropologist Richard Leakey (1944–) finds an intact skull of 1.9 million-year-old human ancestor *Homo habilis* in Africa.

1971 The Swiss company Hoffmann–LaRoche presents a liquid-crystal display.

1971 Experimental electric power plants employing magnetohydrodynamic (MHD) generators go into service in West Germany and the Soviet Union.

1972 The A300B Airbus large-bodied jet airliner, built by a European consortium, makes its maiden flight at Toulouse, France.

1973 A Soviet Tu-144 supersonic airliner crashes at the Paris Air Show. Tu-144s begin carrying mail and cargo two years later, but the aircraft is retired in 1979.

1971 American electronic engineer Ted Hoff (1937–) and coworkers introduce a single-chip microprocessor (Intel 4004).

1971 American electronic engineers Jack Kilby (1923–2005) at Texas Instruments and Robert Noyce (1927–90) at Intel Corporation produce pocket calculators.

1971 The American company Centron markets a dot matrix printer.

1972 American computer engineer Nolan Bushnell (1943–) founds the computer company Atari, Inc., and creates the popular video game Pong, which employs a liquid crystal screen.

1973 The 1,368-foot (417-m) World Trade Center—a complex of buildings including the famous Twin Towers—officially opens in New York City, designed by American architect Minoru Yamasaki (1912–86).

1973 Construction work begins on the CN Tower in Toronto, Canada. When completed three years later, this radio and TV mast becomes the world's tallest structure at 1,815 feet (553 m) tall.

1971 Women win the right to vote in Switzerland, the last European country to introduce universal suffrage.

1972 At the Munich Olympics in Germany Palestinian terrorists from the Black September group kill two Israeli athletes and take nine others hostage; a bungled police rescue attempt results in their deaths.

1972 Intruders, all either indirectly or directly employed by the re-election campaign team for Republican President Richard Nixon (1913–94), are caught breaking into the offices of the Democratic National Committee in the Watergate Hotel, Washington, D.C. They are carrying cameras and electronic surveillance equipment.

1973 With the help of the CIA, right-wing military forces under General Augusto Pinochet (1915–2006) overthrow the elected socialist government in Chile; its leader Salvador Allende (1908–73) commits suicide. Many prominent supporters of Allende are gathered up and executed before the end of the year.

1973 The former dictator to Argentina, Juan Perón (1895–1974), returns to Argentina after 18 years in exile. Aged 77, he resumed the presidency as head of the Justicialita Party but dies the following year; his second wife, Isabel (1931–), succeeds him in power.

Concorde's nose cone dipped to improve visibility for its pilots when the airplane took off and landed.

CONCORDE

In the spring of 1969 a new kind of airliner capable of traveling at supersonic speeds took to the skies over Toulouse, southern France. The new Aérospatiale–BAC (British Air Corporation) Concorde was designed to fly at an altitude of 60,000 feet (18.3 km) and reach speeds of up to 1,320 miles (2,090 km) per hour—more than twice the speed of sound. Concorde's first flight was the culmination of about 20 years of research and development in France and Britain.

In 1962 Aérospatiale in France and BAC in Britain—using funding and technical assistance supplied by their respective governments—began to cooperate on a new concept. This new supersonic airliner design would incorporate features from previous supersonic projects. The resulting design had an elegant delta wing layout and engines that could maintain supersonic speeds with relative fuel efficiency.

Two other rival planes were developed in the 1960s. The first, the Soviet Tupolev Tu-144, resembled Concorde in many respects but could fly neither as fast nor as high and was marred by technical faults. The other, the Boeing 2707, never advanced beyond the planning stage.

Concorde was not the success its designers had initially hoped for, however. The rising price of oil, combined with political issues and the aircraft's deafening engine noise, discouraged many prospective operators from buying the airplanes. Despite its initial promise, it was only ever sold with government subsidies to the national airlines of Britain and France, beginning service in 1976. In 2000 a tire exploded on an Air France Concorde during takeoff, damaging one of the engines. The plane crashed, killing all passengers and crew. The fleet was grounded while the crash was investigated. Although a limited commercial service briefly resumed, Concorde was retired in Britain and France in 2003.

LASERS

LASER BEAMS CAN CUT METAL MUCH MORE precisely than saws and are also used in delicate eye surgery. Surveyors use lasers to measure distances, and lasers mounted on aircraft produce the detail needed to make highly accurate maps of the ground surface. Some computer printers use lasers, and without them there would be no CDs, DVDs, or Blu-ray Discs.

Theodore H. Maiman disassembles the world's first laser, which he made in 1960. The key component is inside the glass vessel—the ruby crystal that emits the laser beam.

In 1917 German-born physicist Albert Einstein (1879–1955) recognized that it should be possible to stimulate atoms and molecules so that they emit light. That is the principle behind the laser, but it was not until the 1950s that physicists suggested a device that could generate a laser beam. In 1952 American physicist Charles H. Townes (1915–) described a way to stimulate molecules of ammonia to emit microwave radiation using the principle of the maser—**m**icrowave **a**mplification by **s**timulated **e**mission of **r**adiation. Townes built the first maser in 1953. Masers are used in atomic clocks and radio telescopes and to amplify weak signals from satellites.

Microwave radiation is invisible, but in 1958 Townes and Arthur Schawlow (1921–99), another American physicist, published a paper showing that it was theoretically possible to make a device that would emit visible light. It would produce **l**ight **a**mplification by **s**timulated **e**mission of **r**adiation—the laser. Townes and Schawlow did not make any such device, however. It was American physicist Theodore H. Maiman (1927–2007) who made the first laser in 1960.

KEY DATES

1917
Einstein proposes stimulated emission

1952
Maser conceived

1958
Laser proposed in theory

1960
Maiman's ruby laser invented

When a substance absorbs energy such as heat, its atoms or molecules jump from a low-energy level to a high-energy level. As they drop back to the low-energy level, they emit surplus energy in the form of light. Ordinarily, each of the atoms or molecules emits light independently of the others and at different wavelengths. But if the substance is exposed to very intense light of a particular wavelength during the brief instant it is at its high-energy level, it will emit light at the same wavelength as the light shining on it. That is how the substance is stimulated, and stimulation further intensifies the light. The next step is to amplify the light by the use of mirrors. A mirror at one end of the device reflects light back through the substance being stimulated. A half-silvered mirror at the opposite end reflects some of the light but allows the remainder to escape as a laser beam. A laser emits a narrow beam of coherent light, that is, light of a single wavelength and therefore color, in which all the waves are in step.

Mirror

Atoms excited by intense flash release energy in the form of light.

Spiral flash tube

Jacket

Ruby crystal

Partially silvered mirror

As atoms release more energy, the energy is reflected backward and forward between the mirrors until it is powerful enough to break through the partially silvered mirror in the form of a concentrated beam.

In the ruby laser, both ends of a cylindrical rod of ruby crystal are polished flat and coated with silver to make a mirror at one end and a partial mirror at the other. The ruby is enclosed in a jacket to keep it cool. A spiral tube surrounding the ruby emits flashes of light. Atoms in the ruby absorb energy from the tube and emit light. The beam emerges from the partially silvered end.

Many substances can be stimulated to emit coherent light. In his laser Maiman used a ruby crystal—an artificial crystal of aluminum oxide. Neodymium has also been used in lasers, as have liquids and gases such as carbon monoxide and a mixture of helium and neon.

The light beam from a flashlight diverges, so it illuminates a large area. A laser beam is more focused. By passing the beam through the wrong end of a telescope, the divergence is reduced further. Lasers of this type are used to guide machines that lay pipelines and drill tunnels. A ruby laser can drill through a diamond.

When a laser beam strikes a surface, the surface absorbs some of its energy and its temperature rises. Lasers produce such strong heat over such a small area that they can be used to trim excess material from electronic components and even to perform surgery.

Narrow laser beams can also be used to measure distances. When a pulse strikes a surface, some of it is reflected. Since the speed of light is always the same, distance is calculated from the time that elapses between the emission of the pulse and the arrival of its reflection. This is called lidar (light radar).

Watched by the theater nurse, a surgeon uses a laser during an operation. The laser beam allows the surgeon to make a much smaller and more precise incision than would be possible with a scalpel or knife, thereby reducing the trauma suffered by the patient.

ASTRONOMY & MATH	BIOLOGY & MEDICINE	PHYSICAL SCIENCES

EUROPE

1974 Soviet probe Mars 4 flies by Mars. Mars 5 enters orbit. Mars 6 ejects a lander that crashes onto the planet. The lander from Mars 7 misses the planet.

1975 Soviet Venera 9 and Venera 10 space probes land on Venus and send back pictures of the surface.

1975 The European Space Agency (ESA) is formed. In its first year it launches Cos-B, a gamma-ray observatory satellite, into Earth orbit; during its seven-year lifetime the satellite detects 25 gamma-ray sources.

1975 Argentine-born British molecular biologist César Milstein (1927–2002), English-born Danish immunologist Niels Jerne (1911–94), and German immunologist Georges Köhler (1946–95) develop monoclonal antibodies, used to produce antibodies with predetermined specificities.

1975 German-born Scottish pharmacologist Hans Kosterlitz (1903–96) and British pharmacologist John Hughes (1942–) discover enkephalins, chemicals produced in the brain that control pain and other sensations.

1976 An accident at a pesticide plant at Seveso, Italy, releases a cloud of poisonous dioxin gas that kills hundreds of farm animals.

THE AMERICAS

1974 American astrophysicists Joseph Taylor (1941–) and Russell Hulse (1950–) observe the first binary pulsar while working at the Arecibo radio telescope in Puerto Rico.

1974 American astronomer Charles Kowal (1940–) discovers Leda, the 13th moon of Jupiter to be found.

1974 The National Aeronautics and Space Administration (NASA) space probe Mariner 10 (launched in 1973) reaches Mercury.

1975 American astronomer Vera Rubin (1928–) measures the proper motion of our galaxy (the Milky Way) as 310 miles (500 km) per second.

1975 In a mission known as Apollo–Soyuz Test Project NASA's Apollo 18 and the Soviet Soyuz 19 space capsules link up in Earth orbit.

1976 NASA's Viking 1 and Viking 2 space probes soft-land on Mars and send back data and pictures. The landscape is seen to consist mostly of rocks and boulders.

1974 American biochemist Gertrude Elion (1918–99) and coworkers produce the antiherpes drug acyclovir, the first successful antiviral medicine, but do not announce the fact until 1978.

1974 American paleoanthropologist Donald Johanson (1943–) unearths fossils of the hominid *Australopithecus afarensis* (a female, nicknamed "Lucy") in Ethiopia. She is known to have walked upright.

1976 French-born American physiologist Roger Guillemin (1924–) reports the existence of endorphins, morphinelike chemicals released in the brain that relieve pain after injury to the body.

1976 The first known outbreak of Legionnaire's disease occurs in the United States. Two years later the bacteria that cause it (*Legionella*) are isolated.

1976 American virologists J. Michael Bishop (1936–) and Harold Varmus (1939–) and coworkers identify oncogenes, which can convert normal cells into cancer cells.

1976 Indian-born American chemist Har Khorana (1922–) and coworkers insert an artificial gene into a living cell (*Escherichia coli*) and observe that it functions fully.

1974 Mexican-born American scientist Mario Molina (1943–) and American scientist F. Sherwood Rowland (1927–) issue warnings about the damaging effect CFCs (chlorofluorocarbons) are having on the Earth's ozone layer.

1974 American physicists Samuel Ting (1936–) and Burton Richter (1931–) discover independently the J/psi particle, a type of long-lived meson.

1975 Chemists at the American company DuPont perfect the production of polyethylene terephthalate (PET) plastic for making beverage bottles.

1976 American physicist Martin Perl (1927–) discovers a subatomic particle that he names the tau particle (or tauon). It is a massive lepton with a negative charge.

ASIA & OCEANIA

A view of the surface of Mars taken by the Viking 2 robotic lander.

1974 Japanese chemist Hideki Shirakawa (1936–) produces a flexible film that has metallic properties by (accidentally) adding a concentrated catalyst solution while synthesizing polymers.

AFRICA & THE MIDDLE EAST

1976 The Ebola virus (Filoviridae family) is first identified after outbreaks in western Sudan and Zaire (now the Democratic Republic of the Congo).

ENGINEERING & INVENTION	WORLD EVENTS
1974 Architects propose making buildings with windows of electrochromic glass that darkens when a low-voltage electric current is applied, thereby reducing a building's energy loss.	**1974** A bloodless military coup in Portugal, led by General Antonio de Spinola (1910–96), brings more than 40 years of dictatorship to an end.
1976 The British–French supersonic airliner Concorde enters service in January. The first flights begin to operate between Paris and Rio de Janeiro and between London and Bahrain. Flights to Washington, D.C., begin later the same year.	**1975** General Francisco Franco (1892–1975), dictator of Spain since 1939, dies. The monarchy is restored under his chosen successor, Juan Carlos (r. 1975–), grandson of Spain's last king, who immediately sets about reintroducing democratic politics.
1976 Construction engineers complete the 10.2-mile (16.4-km) pilot bore for the new road tunnel through the St. Gotthard Pass in the Swiss Alps. It opens four years later, becoming the longest road tunnel in the world.	
1974 The 1,450-foot (442-m) Sears Tower, at the time the world's tallest building, is completed in Chicago.	**1974** U.S. President Richard Nixon (1913–94) resigns under threat of impeachment for authorizing illegal bugging of his political opponents at the Watergate complex in Washington, D.C.
1974 The American company General Motors introduces catalytic converters for cars.	
1974 American chemical engineer Arthur Fry (1931–) invents the semiadhesive Post-it Note.	**1976** Democratic candidate Jimmy Carter (1924–) is elected 39th president of the United States.
1975 The American company IBM markets a laser printer for computers. A year later it introduces an inkjet printer.	
1975 American engineer Edward Roberts (1941–) markets the first commercial personal computer (PC) in kit or assembled form, the Altair 8800.	
1975 American computer programmers Bill Gates (1955–) and Paul Allen (1953–) found the Microsoft Corporation.	
1975 NASA's Jet Propulsion Laboratory begins to employ charge-coupled devices (CCDs) instead of photographic film to record images in astronomical telescopes.	
1976 American computer designers Steven Jobs (1955–) and Stephen Wozniak (1950–) found the computer company Apple.	

Apple 1 computers, made in 1976, were sold as a complete circuit board; the owner had to purchase a case, keyboard, and monitor separately.

1974 India announces that it has successfully tested its first atomic bomb, becoming the sixth nation to develop nuclear weapons.	**1974** Floods and a devastating famine grip the new country of Bangladesh.
1976 The Japanese company Matsushita introduces the VHS (video home system) format for video cassettes.	**1975** North Vietnamese troops enter the South Vietnamese capital, Saigon, reuniting the country under communist rule.
	1976 Mao Zedong (1893–1976), China's leader since 1949, dies.
	1974 Ethiopia's long-term emperor Haile Selassie I (r. 1930–74) is deposed in a communist-led military coup.
	1974 Protests against the apartheid regime in South Africa break out in the black township of Soweto, near Johannesburg; police kill 176 demonstrators.

SEMICONDUCTORS

A semiconductor is a substance that sometimes has the properties of an insulator (which conducts electricity poorly) but under some conditions allows an electric current to flow through. The best-known semiconductor is silicon. It is used to make microchips inside computers and domestic appliances.

The first semiconductor applied in a device was a crystal of galena. It was used to make a rectifier (a device that allows current to flow in just one direction) in early radio sets.

In 1958, American electronic engineer Jack Kilby (1923–2005) realized that rather than making transistors one at a time several could be made together and placed on the same semiconductor by overlaying different impurities (which were found to improve a semiconductor's properties). Other components, such as diodes, capacitors, and resistors, could then be added. Kilby had invented the integrated circuit. A year later planar technology was developed. This process spreads different layers onto a wafer of silicon to make a flat transistor, and then evaporates metal strips onto the surface to make the necessary connections.

Much smaller than postage stamps, the chips in computers, digital cameras, and all other modern electronic devices are plastic cases enclosing layers of transistors and related components, together with the wiring linking them, on the surface of a sliver of silicon.

ASTRONOMY & MATH

BIOLOGY & MEDICINE

PHYSICAL SCIENCES

EUROPE

1979 The European Space Agency (ESA) launches its first space rocket, Ariane 1, from the Guiana Space Center, French Guiana.

In the 1970s, scientists realized that chlorofluorocarbons (CFCs), which were used in aerosol cans, were damaging the ozone layer.

1977 English biochemist Frederick Sanger (1918–) and coworkers elucidate the first full sequence of deoxyribonucleic acid (DNA) bases (of a virus).

1978 The first "test-tube" baby is born in England.

1979 English biologist James Lovelock (1919–) publishes *Gaia: A New Look at Life on Earth*, in which he hypothesizes that Earth can be regarded as a self-regulating superorganism.

1977 Research chemists in the Soviet Union discover a way of making graphite-free synthetic diamonds directly from methane gas.

1978 German physicist Wolfgang Paul (1913–93) and coworkers trap neutrons in a magnetic storage ring and measure the lifetime of a neutron, which is found to be about 15 minutes.

1979 A group of German physicists announce the discovery of the gluon, a particle postulated to carry the strong nuclear force.

THE AMERICAS

1977 American astronomers on the Kuiper Airborne Observatory observe the rings of Uranus.

1977 American astronomer Charles Kowal (1940–) discovers Chiron, an outer solar system body. At first thought to be an asteroid, then a comet, it is now classified as a centaur object.

1977 The National Aeronautics and Space Administration (NASA) launches Voyager 1 and Voyager 2 space probes toward Jupiter and the outer planets.

1978 American astronomers James Christy (1938–) and Robert Harrington (1942–93) locate Pluto's moon Charon.

1978 NASA's Pioneer Venus space probes reach Venus; the Orbiter goes into orbit around the planet, and the multiprobe drops four probes into the atmosphere.

1977 American molecular biologist Phillip Sharp (1944–) and, independently, English-born molecular biologist Richard Roberts (1943–) discover that some genes contain sequences of "nonsense" DNA that appear to have no genetic function. They are named introns. They separate sequences of exons, which do code for part or all of the gene product or for one of its control functions.

1979 The earliest recognized cases of the disease that later becomes known as AIDS occur in California and Florida. In the 1990s examination of medical reports and blood samples suggests that the actual first AIDS case in the United States probably occurred in 1969.

1977 American physicist G. Samuel Hurst (1927–) and coworkers report the use of a laser-based technique to detect a single cesium atom among 1019 argon atoms.

1977 New Zealand-born American chemist Alan MacDiarmid (1927–2007), American chemist Alan Heeger (1936–), and Japanese chemist Hideki Shirakawa (1936–) produce electrically conducting polyethyne (polyacetylene) by incorporating iodine into the plastic's structure.

1977 American physicist Leon Lederman (1922–) identifies the short-lived upsilon particle (a type of meson with a mass about ten times that of the proton).

1978 The U.S. government plans banning lead antiknock additives to gasoline.

1978 The U.S. government bans the use of chlorofluorocarbons (CFCs) as propellants in aerosol cans because they damage the Earth's ozone layer.

INSIDE STORY

AIDS

Acquired immune deficiency syndrome (AIDS) occurs when the immune system is damaged by the human immunodeficiency virus (HIV) and cannot fight infections and cancers. The earliest known cases of HIV and AIDS came from central Africa. Scientists believe that the disease originally was transferred to humans through contact with infected blood from chimpanzees (killed as "bush meat"). AIDS is believed to have reached the United States in the late 1960s via African migrant workers living in the Caribbean island of Haiti. The disease was not identified and named until 1982, although it first came to the attention of U.S. physicians in the late 1970s when groups of gay men began dying of opportunistic infections, pneumonia, and the cancer Kaposi's sarcoma.

ASIA & OCEANIA

1977 Soviet scientists unearth a baby mammoth that has been frozen in the permafrost of Siberia for 40,000 years.

Geological change usually takes thousands of years to happen, but we are seeing the climate changing not just in our lifetimes but also year by year.

JAMES LOVELOCK

AFRICA & THE MIDDLE EAST

ENGINEERING & INVENTION	WORLD EVENTS
1978 The first optical fiber telephone link in Europe goes online between two towns in East Anglia, England.	**1977** Czech dissidents found the prodemocracy Charter 77 reform movement, one of the first organizations to openly challenge government authority in a Warsaw Pact nation.
1979 The British company Post Office Telecommunications introduces the world's first viewdata service, Prestel.	**1979** Margaret Thatcher (1925–) leads the Conservative Party to electoral victory, becoming Britain's first woman prime minister.
1979 The Swedish company Ericsson markets the first cellular telephones (mobile phones); cellphone networks are tested in Tokyo and Chicago.	
1979 Dutch engineer Joop Sinjou of the Philips company and Japanese engineer Toshi Tada Do of Sony independently develop digital compact discs (CDs). Used at first for music and images, they are soon adopted by the computer industry as storage devices.	

1977 American inventor Paul MacCready (1925–2007) wins $95,000 for building a pedal-powered airplane, *Gossamer Condor*. Piloted by American cyclist Bryan Allen (1952–), it makes a 1.15-mile (1.9-km) controlled flight. Allen makes the first human-powered flight across the English Channel in *Gossamer Albatross* two years later.	**1978** In Jonestown, Guyana, 914 members of a religious cult run by the reverend Jim Jones (1938–78), including 260 children, commit suicide by taking poison.
1977 American Interactive Systems Corporation makes the UNIX computer operating system commercially available. (It was first developed in 1969 by American company Bell Laboratories.)	**1979** Nicaraguan dictator Anastasio Somoza Debayle (1925–80) is overthrown after a sustained guerrilla campaign by left-wing Sandinista rebels.
1977 American government scientists develop a neutron bomb. Rather than a powerful explosion, neutron bombs release a massive blast of deadly ionizing radiation.	
1978 The American helium balloon *Double Eagle II*, with three pilots aboard, flies across the Atlantic Ocean.	
1979 An accident at the nuclear plant at Three Mile Island, Pennsylvania, results in a radiation leak.	

The famous "Blue Marble" photograph taken of Earth on the return voyage of Apollo 17, the last piloted moon mission.

1979 The Japanese company Matsushita introduces a liquid-crystal flat-screen television receiver.	**1979** Amid growing civil unrest and economic instability Shah Mohammad Reza Pahlavi (r. 1941–79), who has ruled Iran with the backing of western intelligence agencies since 1941, is forced to step down; the Muslim religious leader Ayatollah Ruhollah Khomeini (1902–89) returns from exile to establish an Islamic state.

1978 The world's longest floating bridge, spanning 6,074 feet (1,851 m), is completed across the Demerara River in Guyana.	**1978** War breaks out between Ethiopia and Somalia over the disputed Ogaden region.

THE APOLLO PROGRAM

In May 1961 American president John F. Kennedy (1917–63) pledged that the United States would land a man on the moon within the next ten years. In July 1969 two American astronauts fulfilled that promise and stepped onto the lunar surface. The spacecraft that took them there—Apollo 11—represented the culmination of an eight-year project, a technological endeavor on a scale never before seen.

The purpose of earlier Apollo missions had been to test the various launch procedures, rockets, and modules before making the final landing. In January 1967 the first planned Apollo flight ended in disaster. Three astronauts died in a fire during a launch-pad test. In early 1968 the National Aeronautics and Space Administration (NASA) made three unpiloted launches. In October 1968 Apollo 7 took three astronauts on a 163-orbit flight around Earth. Two months later Apollo 8 carried three astronauts to the moon, where they made ten orbits. March 1969 saw the testing of the lunar module in Earth orbit by Apollo 9, and later that year in a low orbit around the moon.

Then came Apollo 11. Launched in July 1969 and crewed by Neil Armstrong (1930–), Edwin "Buzz" Aldrin (1930–), and Michael Collins (1930–), it reached the moon without a hitch. Armstrong and Aldrin descended to the surface in the lunar module on July 20 and spent two hours taking photographs and collecting samples. Collins remained in orbit around the moon in the command module.

The Apollo program continued for another six years after Apollo 11 and returned to the moon a further six times before being cancelled in 1975.

CHAPTER 10

THE MODERN WORLD

A maglev, or magnetic levitation, train streaks through Shanghai, in China. Maglev transportation uses powerful magnets to lift and propel trains along the tracks. The vehicles are faster and smoother than conventional trains and can reach speeds of up to 310 miles (500 km) per hour.

SCIENCE AND TECHNOLOGY CONTINUE TO BUILD ON THE KNOWLEDGE accumulated over many centuries, as described in the previous chapters of this book. Astronomy continues to advance with the aid of the Hubble Space Telescope and other instruments placed in Earth orbit by reusable space shuttles. Space travel has become so "routine" that some missions carry fee-paying space "tourists." In physics, scientists carry on searching for superconductors that will function at ever higher temperatures, investigating molecule-sized machines in nanotechnology, and refining solid-state devices to make computers smaller but more powerful.

Physicists at the European Organization for Nuclear Research, known as CERN, are attempting to re-create the conditions just after the big bang at the beginning of the universe with the largest particle accelerator ever built, known as the Large Hadron Collider. Chemists continue to study the effects of greenhouse gases on the atmosphere and to investigate possible links with global warming, while governments around the world pledge to reduce their countries' carbon emissions.

The space shuttle Columbia *touches down at Edwards Air Force Base, in California, after its first orbital mission in 1981. The story of the space shuttle is one of triumph and tragedy. It was involved in some of the National Aeronautics and Space Administration's (NASA) greatest achievements, such as placing the Hubble Space Telescope in Earth orbit, as well as in its two worst disasters, in 1986 and 2003, when all crew members perished.*

A highway of cables links routers and servers in an Internet exchange point and data center in Los Angeles. Such facilities are necessary to cope with today's levels of Internet traffic.

In biology, research remains concentrated on cloning animals with a view to finding a source of stem cells for treating various human disorders. The techniques of genetic fingerprinting have been perfected and, thanks to the Human Genome Project, the complete human genome has been published. Biologists have studied sequences of DNA from the remains of extinct animals, such as the dodo, solitaire, woolly mammoth, and even from Neandertals. Gene therapy—the insertion of a functional gene into body cells to replace a faulty version of the gene—is still in its infancy and is seen as controversial by its opponents, but it may hold the promise of treating and curing certain genetic disorders, such as cystic fibrosis. Unfinished business includes the production of vaccines against disorders such as human variant Creutzfeldt–Jakob disease (CJD) and acquired immune deficiency syndrome (AIDS), and the elusive cure for cancer.

Many current developments in technology involve the Internet and the World Wide Web. Personal computers (PCs) have become more and more versatile, enabling people to contact each other and have access to information anywhere in the world almost instantly. Most people now carry cell phones, many of which can be used to send text messages, surf the Internet, play music, and take digital photographs, in addition to verbal communication. And with a modern satellite navigation system, we can pin down a person's location to within a couple of yards. But despite all this, science has so far proved unable to come up with adequate defenses against natural disasters such as tsunamis, tornadoes, and hurricanes.

	1980	1984	1988	1992	1996	
EUROPE	**1980** A treatment for kidney stones that uses ultrasound waves to break them up is introduced in Germany. **1980** English engineer Clive Sinclair designs the ZX80 computer. **1981** The high-speed TGV (*Train à Grande Vitesse*) is introduced in France. **1983** French virologist Luc Montagnier and American physician Robert Gallo discover the human immunodeficiency virus (HIV).	**1984** Danish reproductive physiologist Steen Willadsen clones the first mammal, a sheep. **1985** Danish-born computer programmer Bjarne Stroustrup invents the programming language C++. **1986** The Soviet Union launches space station Mir into Earth orbit. **1987** British surgeons in England carry out the first heart/lung/liver triple transplant operation.	**1988** Greek cyclist Kanellos Kanellopoulos pilots a human-powered aircraft across the Aegean Sea. **1991** Researchers in England briefly achieve controlled nuclear fusion. **1990** The two opposite halves of the Channel Tunnel meet under the English Channel. **1990** English computer scientist Tim Berners-Lee begins to devise the World Wide Web.	**1992** Scientists at the University of Pisa, Italy, make the most accurate determination so far of the acceleration of free fall (acceleration due to gravity). **1992** Experimental digital FM radio broadcasts begin in France. **1994** English mathematician Andrew Wiles offers a proof of Fermat's last theorem. **1994** The Channel Tunnel rail link opens between England and France.	**1996** Medical researchers establish a link between bovine spongiform encephalopathy (BSE) and Creutzfeldt–Jakob Disease (CJD). **1996** Scottish biologist Ian Wilmut at the Roslin Institute, Edinburgh, Scotland, clones a sheep named Dolly. **1996** Physicists at the European Organization for Nuclear Research (CERN) in Switzerland produce the first example of antimatter.	
THE AMERICAS	**1980** The Very Large Array (VLA) system of radio telescopes begins operation in New Mexico. **1981** The National Aeronautics and Space Administration's (NASA) first space shuttle, *Columbia*, makes its maiden flight. **1981** IBM Corporation introduces the first personal computer (PC), using MS-DOS (Microsoft disk-operating system). **1982** Eli Lilly & Company produces genetically engineered insulin. **1983** NASA's space probe Pioneer 10 passes Pluto. **1983** American biochemist Kary Mullis invents the polymerase chain reaction (PCR) to multiply small samples of deoxyribonucleic acid (DNA).	**1984** American Microsoft Corporation launches the Windows computer applications program. **1984** American company Apple markets the Macintosh computer, which uses screen icons. **1987** Engineers from American company AT&T install the first fiber-optic telecommunications cable under the Atlantic Ocean. **1985** American researchers isolate the first gene that (when faulty) is responsible for a cancer (retinoblastoma, which affects the eye). **1985** Chemists in the United States produce a new allotrope of carbon called buckminsterfullerene.	**1988** American climatologist James Hansen predicts that increased levels of "greenhouse gases" will lead to global warming. **1989** NASA's Voyager 2 space probe reveals that Neptune has rings. **1989** Boeing company's High Technology Center produces a photocell that converts more than a third of incident solar radiation into electricity. **1990** NASA's space shuttle *Discovery* places the Hubble Space Telescope into orbit around the Earth. **1990** The Human Genome Project gets under way, directed by American biophysicist James Watson.	**1992** Anticancer drug taxol gets official approval in North America. **1993** American physicians introduce gene therapy for cystic fibrosis. **1993** American company Intel markets the Pentium microprocessor chip. **1994** Fragments of comet Shoemaker–Levy 9 are observed colliding with Jupiter. **1994** A genetically modified tomato called Flavr Savr is marketed in the United States. **1994** American scientists announce the discovery of the subatomic particle called the top quark. **1995** American computer programmer James Gosling introduces Java as a programming language.	**1996** NASA's space shuttle *Atlantis*, docks in space with Russian space station Mir. **1996** American astronomer David McKay and coworkers find traces of what might be primitive microscopic life in a meteorite that originated from Mars. **1996** American researchers Theodore Poehler and Peter Searson develop an all-plastic battery. **1997** The Hubble Space Telescope locates the brightest known star in the universe. **1997** American geneticist Huntington Willard assembles an artificial human chromosome.	
ASIA & OCEANIA	**1980** Japanese company Sony Corporation markets the compact disc (CD). **1982** Australian bacteriologist Barry Marshall isolates *Helicobacter pylori*, a cause of stomach ulcer.	**1985** The 33.5-mile (53.9-km) Seikan Tunnel is completed in Japan. **1985** Japanese company Seiko-Epson markets a television set that uses a liquid crystal display for its screen.	**1990** Japanese scientists launch a space probe to the moon. **1991** Japanese researcher Sumio Iijima makes carbon nanotubes.	**1992** Japanese chemists use palladium atoms to make stable polymers of buckyballs. **1994** Japanese rocket engineers launch their new heavy-lifting rocket, H-2.	**1996** Japanese research chemists synthesize cellulose. **1997** Paleontologists in China discover fossils of *Protarchaeopteryx*, a reptilian creature with birdlike characteristics.	
AFRICA & THE MIDDLE EAST	**1983** English-born Kenyan anthropologist Meave Leakey finds fossils of 16-million-old hominoid *Silvapithecus*.	**1984** Kenyan anthropologist Richard Leakey and coworkers find a 1.6-million-old skeleton of *Homo erectus*. **1984** Israeli physicists produce quasicrystals.	**1988** Israel makes its first successful space launch. **1988** Anthropologists discover a 92,000-year-old fossil of *Homo sapiens* in Israel.	**1993** Anthropologists from Berkeley discover remains of the oldest known hominoid, *Ardipithecus ramidus*. **1994** A new Ebola virus is identified in Africa.		

1998	2000	2002	2004	2006–PRESENT
1998 A team of international scientists determines the entire genetic code, or genome, for a nematode. **1998** Swiss scientists produce a titanium dioxide solar cell that is twice as efficient as standard solar cells. **1999** Swiss balloonist Bertrand Piccard and English balloonist Brian Jones circumnavigate the world in their hot-air balloon, *Breitling Orbiter 3*.	**2000** Russia launches a service module that together with two other modules already in orbit form the new International Space Station (ISS). **2000** The world's longest road tunnel (15.2 miles/24.5 km) is completed in Norway. **2000** The Pyrenean ibex becomes extinct. **2001** Gray wolves are found living wild in Germany (they have not been seen in the wild for 150 years).	**2002** English inventor David Baker patents the Land Shark, a high-speed amphibious car. **2003** Austrian sportsman Felix Baumgartner jumps from an airplane and skyglides across the English Channel. **2003** 350,000-year-old footprints of an upright-walking human are discovered in Italy. **2003** Chemist Leonid Khryashtchev makes an organic compound that contains krypton.	**2005** Scientists extract and decode DNA from two cave bears that died 40,000 years ago. **2005** After a seven-year trip, the Cassini–Huygens space probe—a joint venture between the European Space Agency and NASA—reaches Saturn. **2005** European consortium Airbus Industrie's Airbus 380 makes its maiden flight from Toulouse, France.	**2007** A 405-year-old clam is discovered by Welsh researchers off the coast of Ireland. **2008** Researchers in England create human–cow embryos, which survive for three days. **2008** The Large Hadron Collider at CERN begins its experiments.
1998 Zoologists discover five new species of small salamanders in Mexico. **1998** American researchers at Johns Hopkins University successfully grow human stem cells in the laboratory. **1998** Astronomers in Hawaii discover a near-Earth asteroid that passes within the Earth's orbit. **1998** American dentists first use lasers for "drilling" teeth. **1999** Computer virus Melissa spreads rapidly by e-mail to infect more than 100,000 computers around the world. **1999** The Hubble Space Telescope is serviced by astronauts in the space shuttle *Discovery*.	**2000** Scientists working on the Human Genome Project produce a rough draft of the sequence of the human genome. **2000** American paleontologist Dale Russell discovers a fossilized dinosaur heart. **2000** Geneticists figure out the complete genome of the fruit fly *Drosophila*. **2000** American surgeon Robert Jarvik begins work on the Jarvik–2000 artificial heart. **2001** The uncrewed *Southern Cross II* (Global Hawk spy plane) crosses the Pacific Ocean. **2001** American researchers clone a human embryo.	**2002** NASA's space probe Mars Odyssey begins mapping the surface of Mars. **2002** Researchers at Texas A&M University unveil their clone of a domestic cat. **2002** American researchers at the University of New York at Stony Brook make a synthetic virus. **2002** American chemists Lester Andrews and Bruce Bersten make a compound of uranium and the rare gas neon. **2003** NASA's Wilkinson Microwave Anisotropy Probe satellite analyzes microwave background radiation to reveal that the universe is 13.7 billion years old.	**2004** The first commercial spaceflight occurs when SpaceShipOne takes to the air. **2004** Physicists from Penn State University announce a helium-based "supersolid" that flows through another material without friction. **2005** American geophysicist Joseph Dwyer and coworkers discover that flashes of lighting also produce x-rays. **2005** Astronomer Michael Brown announces the discovery of a large remote object (Eris) in the solar system. **2005** American scientists make the smallest measurement of mass ever made when they weigh a cluster of xenon atoms.	**2006** The dwarf planet Eris is found to be larger than Pluto. **2006** NASA's spacecraft New Horizons is launched on its journey to Pluto. **2006** Analysis of a fossil found in Canada shows it to be a "missing link" between fish and four-legged vertebrates. **2007** A chlorophyll-producing bacterium is discovered in hot springs at Yellowstone National Park. **2007** U.S scientists create flexible batteries by weaving carbon nanotubes into paper.
1998 The world's largest passenger airport opens in Hong Kong, China. **1998** Two Japanese satellites in Earth orbit carry out the first automatic docking.	**2000** Japanese chemist Katsuyoshi Hoshino and coworkers announce a new way of "fixing" nitrogen in air to produce ammonium perchlorate.	**2003** Yang Liwei becomes the first Chinese astronaut to orbit the Earth. **2003** An outbreak of the severe acute respiratory syndrome (SARS) virus in Asia spreads worldwide.	**2004** Scientists in South Korea clone human embryos for stem cells. **2004** An 18,000-year-old skeleton of a 3-foot (1-m) tall humanoid is found in Indonesia. It is named *Homo floresiensis*.	**2007** The Baiji, or Chinese river dolphin, is now thought to be extinct. **2008** The Indian Space Research Organization launches Chandrayaan-1, an unpiloted lunar spacecraft.
1998 A whole skeleton of a 36-foot (11-m) fish-eating dinosaur is found in Niger, Africa.		**2003** A new group of insects, named Mantophasmatodea, is discovered in Africa.	**2005** Two new species of mouse lemurs are found in Madagascar.	

ASTRONOMY & MATH	BIOLOGY & MEDICINE	PHYSICAL SCIENCES

EUROPE

1980 French astronomers Pierre Laques (1934–), Raymond Despiau, and Jean Lecacheux (1944–) discover Helene, a small moon of Saturn that takes only 2.7 days to orbit the planet.

1980 Russian cosmonauts from the Soyuz 35 spacecraft set an endurance record by spending 185 days aboard the orbiting Salyut 6 space station.

1980 German company Dornier Medical Systems announces a treatment for kidney stones that uses ultrasound waves to break them up painlessly inside the patient. The technique, called ultrasonic lithotripsy, replaces the need for intrusive surgery.

1980 German physicist Klaus von Klitzing (1943–) discovers the quantum Hall effect, in which the production of a voltage in material carrying a current in a magnetic field at very low temperatures takes place in "steps" rather than continuously.

THE AMERICAS

1980 Data from the National Aeronautics and Space Administration's (NASA) Voyager 1 space probe enable American astronomers to identify Saturn's moons Pandora, Prometheus, Telesto, Atlas, and Calypso.

1980 Polish-born American mathematician Benoit Mandelbrot (1924–) continues his research into fractals, which are mathematical curves generated by successive subdivision.

1980 The Very Large Array (VLA), a system of 27 radio telescopes at Socorro, New Mexico, begins operation.

1981 American astronomer Joseph Cassinelli and coworkers identify the star R136a, which is 2,500 times more massive than the sun.

1981 American astronomer Harold Reitsema and coworkers identify Neptune's inner moon Larissa.

1981 NASA's first space shuttle, *Columbia*, makes its maiden flight, proving that a reusable spacecraft is feasible.

1981 NASA's space probe Voyager 2 flies by Saturn and sends back pictures of the planet and its moons.

1980 American experimental physicist Luis Alvarez (1911–88) and his son Walter (1940–), a geologist, put forward the theory that a meteorite collision with Earth gave rise to the K-T event, which probably led to the extinction of the dinosaurs.

1980 American researchers at Harvard synthesize interferon, a substance that shows promise as a treatment for viral diseases and some forms of cancer.

1980 The U.S. Supreme Court rules that genetically engineered life-forms can be patented.

1981 Researchers at the Merck Institute for Therapeutic Research, Pennsylvania, produce a vaccine against the hepatitis-B virus.

1981 The American Center for Disease Control and Prevention (CDC) first acknowledges acquired immune deficiency syndrome (AIDS) as a communicable disease.

1980 A device called an undulator is installed in the SPEAR storage ring of Stanford Radiation Laboratory's synchrotron to increase its power.

1981 Romanian-born American physicist Adam Heller (1933–) and American Ferdinand Thiel (1933–) construct a liquid-junction solar cell.

ASIA & OCEANIA

AFRICA & THE MIDDLE EAST

The Very Large Array in New Mexico combines 27 radio telescopes in a Y-shaped configuration.

ENGINEERING & INVENTION	WORLD EVENTS
1980 The 10-mile (16-km) St. Gotthard Tunnel in Switzerland is opened, making it the world's longest road tunnel.	**1980** President Tito of Yugoslavia (1892–1980) dies.
1980 English engineer Clive Sinclair (1940–) designs an inexpensive computer, the ZX80.	**1980** Polish workers led by Lech Walesa (1943–) establish the independent Solidarity trade union; the organization will play a pioneering role in the downfall of communism in Eastern Europe.
1981 French railway company SNCF introduces its new high-speed train, the TGV (*Train à Grande Vitesse*).	
1981 *Solar Challenger*, a solar-powered aircraft, crosses the English Channel.	**1980** The Summer Olympics in Moscow are boycotted by 50 nations, including the United States, in protest at the Soviet invasion of Afghanistan.
1981 The 4,626-foot- (1,410-m-) long suspension bridge across the Humber River in northeastern England becomes the world's longest single-span bridge.	**1981** Pope John Paul II (1920–2005) is seriously injured by a gunman in St. Peter's Square, Rome.

BENOIT MANDELBROT

ENGINEERING & INVENTION	WORLD EVENTS
1980 Microsoft Corporation, founded by Bill Gates (1955–) and Paul Allen (1953–), develops MS–DOS (Microsoft disk-operating system), a computer operating system, and licenses it to IBM Corporation.	**1980** Former Hollywood actor Ronald Reagan (1911–2004) defeats Jimmy Carter (1924–) in the race for the White House; Carter's reelection chances are seriously damaged by the disastrous failure of a mission to rescue U.S. hostages held in Iran.
1980 American company Hughes Aircraft makes a machine that uses a laser for cutting cloth, reducing costs for the mass production of garments.	**1980** Bolivia is taken over by a military junta backed by cocaine barons.
1981 American company Hewlett-Packard launches a 32-bit silicon chip for its computers.	**1980** More than 120,000 Cubans are allowed to immigrate to the United States.
1981 IBM Corporation introduces the first personal computer (PC), using Microsoft's MS-DOS operating system. Within a year Compaq and Columbia Data Products produce "clones," machines that will run the same programs as the IBM.	**1980** Ex-Beatle John Lennon (1940–80) is shot and killed by an obsessed fan in New York.
	1980 MTV begins transmission on U.S. television.

Benoit Mandelbrot (1924–) is a Polish-born American mathematician who is best known for developing fractals. He was born in Warsaw, the son of a Lithuanian Jewish merchant, but moved with his family to Paris in 1936 to escape persecution by the Nazis. Forced to move again in 1939, they lived in Tulle in southern France during World War II. Despite a very patchy education, after the war Mandelbrot attended the École Polytechnique in Paris, and in 1952 obtained his doctorate from the University of Paris.

After several brief appointments in the United States, Switzerland, and France, Mandelbrot went in 1958 to the IBM Research Center, at Yorktown Heights, New York. He remained there until 1987, when he became professor of mathematics at Yale. He developed the idea of fractals while considering how to measure the length of a coastline. Every inlet has smaller inlets, which also have tiny inlets of their own. He pointed out that tree bark is not smooth, and mountains are not perfect cones, so how do you measure them? He outlined his ideas (first developed in 1980) in his 1982 book *The Fractal Geometry of Nature*. Fractals have applications in various areas of science (such as the growth of crystals), in chaos theory, in cartography, and in computer graphics.

ENGINEERING & INVENTION	WORLD EVENTS
1980 A wind-assisted commercial vessel, the *Shin-Aitoku-Maru*, is launched in Japan. It has computer-controlled vertical sails.	**1980** Japan becomes the world leader in manufacturing, surpassing the United States as the leading automaker. It also has eight out of the ten largest banks in the world.
1980 The Japanese Sony Corporation and Dutch company Philips market the audio compact disc (CD) for commercial use. Later (1985) it is adapted as the CD-ROM.	**1981** Sikhs begin fighting for independence in the Punjab.
	1980 The Iran–Iraq War (1980–88) breaks out.
	1980 Zimbabwe gains independence under Robert Mugabe (1924–).
	1981 President of Egypt Anwar el-Sadat (1918–1981) is assassinated.

CONCISE HISTORY OF SCIENCE AND INVENTION

ASTRONOMY & MATH	BIOLOGY & MEDICINE	PHYSICAL SCIENCES

EUROPE

1982 Soviet Venera 13 and Venera 14 space probes reach Venus and release landers that collect data as they descend through the corrosive atmosphere.

1982 Soviet cosmonaut Svetlana Savitskaya (1948–), in a Soyuz spacecraft, becomes the second woman in space, 19 years after Valentina Tereshkova (1937–) orbited the Earth.

1983 The Soviet Venera 15 space probe reaches Venus and orbits the planet, using a radar scanner to map the surface.

1982 Biologist Karl Stetter (1941–) discovers bacteria living in hot seawater near black smokers on the seabed.

1982 Biochemists Louis Chedid and Michael Sela (1924–) prepare the first totally synthetic vaccine (against diphtheria).

1983 French virologist Luc Montagnier (1932–) and American physician Robert Gallo (1937–) discover the human immunodeficiency virus (HIV) that causes AIDS.

1983 Swiss biologist Walter Gehring (1939–) and coworkers discover the homeobox gene —a sequence of about 180 base pairs common to most eukaryote organisms— that controls their development.

1982 German physicist Peter Armbruster (1931–) and coworkers at the Institute for Heavy Ion Research in Darmstadt, Germany, make a few atoms of element 109 (later named meitnerium) by bombarding bismuth-209 with nuclei of iron-58.

1983 The meter is redefined in terms of the distance light travels in a vacuum in a particular time (1/299,792,458 of a second).

1983 Italian physicist Carlo Rubbia (1934–) and coworkers discover W and Z particles (belonging to the group known as intermediate vector bosons and carriers of the weak force).

THE AMERICAS

1982 American astronomer Eleanor Helin discovers the slow-moving, near-Earth asteroid Nereus (asteroid 4660).

1982 The National Aeronautics and Space Administration's (NASA) space shuttle *Columbia* is first used for commercial purposes on its fifth mission, when it places two communications satellites into Earth orbit.

1983 Data from the Infrared Astronomical Satellite (IRAS) reveals a new asteroid (no. 3200) that passes close to the sun. It is named Phaethon and is the first asteroid to be discovered by instruments in space.

1983 American mathematicians Leonard Adleman (1945–) and Robert Rumely announce a new way of finding prime numbers (numbers that can be divided only by 1 and themselves).

1983 NASA's space probe Pioneer 10 passes Pluto and becomes the first human-made object to leave the solar system.

1983 U.S. astronaut Sally Ride (1951–) becomes the first American woman in space.

1983 NASA launches its second space shuttle, *Challenger*.

1982 Eli Lilly & Company begins producing genetically engineered insulin (used in the treatment of diabetes).

1982 American biochemist Stanley Prusiner (1942–) introduces the term *prions* to describe the infective agents responsible for scrapie and other spongiform encephalopathy diseases such as Creutzfeldt–Jakob Disease.

1982 American physician William DeVries (1943–) and coworkers in Salt Lake City, Utah, implant the first Jarvik-7 artificial heart (made of aluminum and plastic); the patient lives for 112 days. The use of the Jarvik heart is discontinued in 1990.

1983 American biochemist Kary Mullis (1944–) invents the polymerase chain reaction (PCR), a method of multiplying small samples of DNA (deoxyribonucleic acid) that will become important in genetic fingerprinting.

1983 The immunosuppressive drug cyclosporine is approved for use in the United States, making transplant operations much safer. Three years later Japanese researchers discover an alternative immunosuppressive—FK506—produced by a fungus.

Sally Ride, the first American woman in space, was one of the five crew of the space shuttle Challenger's *second flight.*

ASIA & OCEANIA

1982 Australian bacteriologist Barry Marshall (1951–) isolates and cultures *Helicobacter pylori*, a bacterium that causes peptic ulcers.

It's easy to sleep floating around—it's very comfortable. But you have to be careful that you don't float into somebody or something!

SALLY RIDE

AFRICA & THE MIDDLE EAST

1983 English-born Kenyan anthropologist Meave Leakey (1942–) finds fossils of the hominoid *Sivapithecus*, dated at about 16 million years old.

ENGINEERING & INVENTION	WORLD EVENTS
1982 The Thames Barrier is completed downstream of London, England. Normally lowered to allow the passage of shipping, it can be raised if exceptionally high tides threaten to cause flooding in the city. It is raised for the first time the following year. **1983** English driver Richard Noble (1946–) takes the land speed record at 633.468 miles (1,019.44 km) per hour in his jet car *Thrust 2* at Black Rock Desert, Nevada.	**1983** Buoyed by success in the Falklands War (1982), Britain's Prime Minister Margaret Thatcher (1925–) wins a landslide general election victory. **1983** The United States deploys Cruise missiles in Britain and Pershing missiles in West Germany.

CELL PHONES

The development of cellular telephones and their associated technology has been rapid since the 1980s. The cellular telephone network divides a geographical area into cells. Because cell phones and base stations use low-power transmitters, the same frequencies (indicated by matching colors in the diagram below) can be reused in nonadjacent cells. At first, all transmissions were analog (meaning that signals were sent as a continuous stream or wave). From about 1990 service providers began to use digital technology, which breaks up the wave and sends it in short bursts that are better suited to carry data quickly and without distortion.

Early cell phones were heavy and bulky. The first truly portable commercial cell phone was produced by Motorola in 1983 and weighed 16 ounces (450 g). The latest phones now weigh as little as 3 ounces (85 g). Most modern cell phones have other uses than just as a means of verbal communication. These include text messaging (texting), taking photographs and videos (and sending and receiving them), sending and receiving emails, playing music, and accessing the Internet.

1982 Engineers in California complete Solar One, the world's largest solar power plant, which can produce 10 megawatts of electric power. **1982** American computer programmer Mitchell Kapor (1950–) founds the American Lotus Corporation and produces the Lotus 1-2-3 software. **1983** In the United States the first mobile telephones, or cellphones, are introduced in Chicago, Illinois. **1983** American IBM Corporation launches the PC-XT, a personal computer with a built-in 10-megabyte hard disk drive. **1983** American company Apple markets a consumer computer that uses a mouse and pull-down menus. **1983** The 4,150-foot- (1,265-m-) long dam across the American River in California becomes the world's largest thin-arch dam.	**1982** Argentina and Britain go to war over sovereignty of the Falkland Islands (Malvinas) and South Georgia; the British forces prevail. **1983** U.S. Marines are sent to Grenada to reverse a leftist military coup.

The Thames Barrier, completed in 1982, can be raised to prevent high tides from the North Sea from flooding London, England.

1983 Japanese physicist Akio Sasaki invents an optical transistor.

	1982 Israel occupies Lebanon. **1983** Drought in Ethiopia results in millions of deaths through starvation.

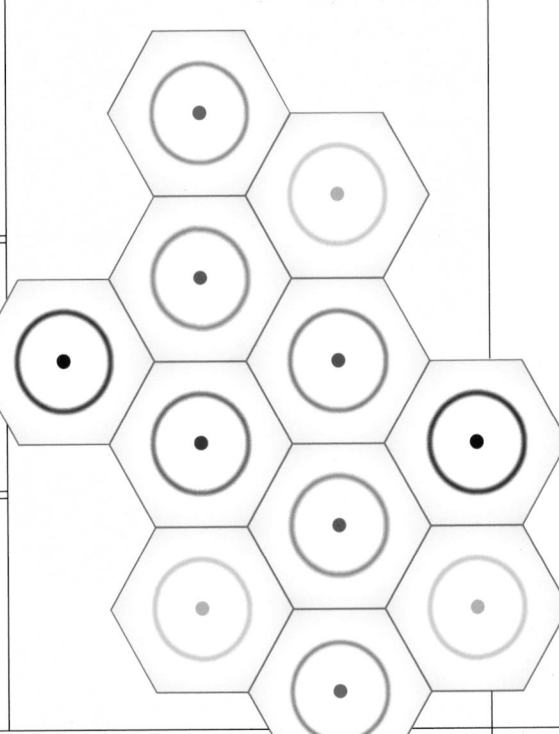

PERSONAL COMPUTERS

THE PERSONAL COMPUTER (PC) IS A FAMILIAR item in many homes all over the world. People use PCs to play games, write letters, and manage domestic and business accounts. E-mail takes only seconds to deliver messages and pictures to the other side of the globe. PCs are used to shop, make travel arrangements, book hotels, and buy theater and concert tickets. It is hard to imagine a world without PCs.

Yet PCs are relatively new. The first fully electronic computer was built in 1946 at the University of Pennsylvania. Called ENIAC (Electronic Numerical Integrator and Calculator), it contained 18,000 vacuum tubes and used 100 kilowatts of power.

All the early computers used vacuum tubes, or valves. Those machines were so huge that they filled a large room, and so unreliable (because of tube failures) that teams of engineers had to remain constantly on hand to keep them working. The invention of the transistor in 1947 offered a smaller, more dependable replacement for the vacuum tube, and the invention of the integrated circuit in 1958 opened up the possibility of miniaturization. Computers began to shrink in size.

IBM launched its first personal computer in 1981. The IBM PC 5150 was fitted with an Intel 8088 microprocessor. The machine used magnetic tape to load data and had an optional floppy disk drive and printer.

Even so, it was not until 1975 that a computer appeared that was both affordable and small enough to use at home. Micro Instrumentation and Telemetry Systems (MITS) of Albuquerque, New Mexico, sold the Altair 8800 for $495 assembled, and in kit form for just $395. The Altair 8800 measured 17 x 18 x 7 inches (43 x 46 x 18 cm) and was based on a 2-MHz Intel 8080 processor. It had no monitor, keyboard, or printer and only 256 bytes of memory. The user programmed it by means of switches along the front of the box, and read the output from a pattern of flashing lights on a front panel. In 1976 MITS equipped their computers with an 8-inch (20-cm) floppy-disk drive for storing data.

Operating Systems

Computer software—the programs that run useful applications such as word processing or games—will work only if the computer is able to communicate with a storage device such as a disk drive. This process requires special software in the form of an operating system. In 1972 American computer scientist Gary Kildall (1942–94) devised PL/M (Programming Language/Microprocessor). It allowed engineers to write programs that were burned into the ROM (read-only memory) of the Intel 4004 processor. These processors were used to control devices such as traffic lights and domestic appliances such as washing machines. The following year Kildall wrote software that allowed the user to read data files stored on a disk and write files onto the disk. He called it CP/M (Control Program/Microcomputer), and it was the first operating system for small computers. CP/M was instantly successful, but when International Business Machines Corporation (IBM) needed an operating system for its small computers, the company offered both CP/M and DOS (Disk Operating System). DOS was a rival system developed by American computer programmer Bill Gates (1955–) of Microsoft in 1980. As MS-DOS, the Microsoft operating system eventually came to dominate the market, although some computer enthusiasts still use CP/M. WordStar, launched in 1979, was the first popular word-processing program. At first, it ran on CP/M, although later versions ran on MS-DOS.

Affordable Computers

Computers remained expensive, however, until 1980, when English engineer Clive Sinclair (1940–) designed the ZX80. In the United States it cost $199.95 ready made. The ZX80 measured about 8 x 8 inches (20 x 20 cm), had 1 kilobyte of RAM (random-access memory), and a membrane keyboard. It connected to a TV receiver. Sinclair followed the ZX80 a year later with the ZX81. It used audio cassette tapes for storage.

IBM introduced its first small computer in 1981, calling it a "personal computer" (PC). Within a year

In a modern computer, backup memory is stored on hard disks inside the disk drive. A large memory store consists of a stack of hard disks, mounted on the same spindle and accessed simultaneously.

Disks can rotate at speeds of 100 miles (160 km) per hour or more. Data is stored as magnetic fields in areas of the disk as small as 40 millionths of an inch (1 micrometer) across.

A read/write head is mounted on the end of a carriage. It swings in and out across each disk as required. The head "flies" a few millionths of an inch above the disk surface.

or two, rival manufacturers were marketing cheaper imitations, known as "IBM clones." All of them resembled the IBM PC and used MS-DOS. Modern PCs are the direct descendants of those "clones."

Computers respond to instructions in machine code written in binary, and a computer program comprises page after page of zeros and ones. Machine code is difficult to write and check for errors. Computer programmers needed a simpler code. The first of them became available in 1957. It had been devised by American programmer John Backus (1924–2007) at IBM and was called FORTRAN (FORmula TRANslator). It was the first high-level programming language, but it was designed for scientists. Teachers still needed a language that students could master easily, and in 1964 American computer programmers John Kemeny (1926–92) and Thomas Kurtz (1928–) at Dartmouth College, New Hampshire, announced their solution to the problem: the Beginner's All-Purpose Symbolic Instruction Code, or BASIC.

The power of a PC depends on the speed of its processor and the amount of memory it has. Both have increased rapidly, and are still doing so, allowing modern computers to perform tasks far beyond the capacity of their predecessors. The first multimedia PC appeared in 1991, and English computer scientist Tim Berners-Lee (1955–) created the World Wide Web in 1990. Broadband Web access now allows users to download music and movies.

The Altair 8800 of 1975 was the forerunner of today's personal computers. Advertised to enthusiasts through Popular Electronics *magazine, its designers envisaged sales of a few hundred. However, it proved so popular that they sold more than ten times that number within one month.*

Carriage

Hard disks

Carriage drive

Read/write head

Drive motor

KEY DATES

1946
ENIAC

1947
Transistor

1956
Integrated circuit

1964
BASIC programming language

1972
CP/M operating system for small computers

1975
Altair 8800

1980
MS-DOS

1980
ZX80

1981
IBM's first PC

1990
World Wide Web

ASTRONOMY & MATH	BIOLOGY & MEDICINE	PHYSICAL SCIENCES

EUROPE

1984 Soviet cosmonaut Svetlana Savitskaya (1948–) becomes the first woman to walk in space, on a Soyuz mission.

1985 The Soviet Union launches its first two-stage Zenit rocket. By 2001 this type of rocket launches a total of 28 satellites into orbit around Earth.

1984 The 2,000-year-old body of Celtic "Lindow Man" is found preserved in a peat bog in northern England.

1984 Danish reproductive physiologist Steen Willadsen (1944–) clones the first mammal, a sheep, using the nucleus of an embryonic sheep cell.

1984 English geneticist Alec Jeffreys (1950–) perfects the technique of genetic fingerprinting, which involves identifying sequences of deoxyribonucleic acid (DNA).

1985 The first case of the disease bovine spongiform encephalopathy (BSE) is diagnosed in cattle in Britain.

1984 German physicist Peter Armbruster (1931–) and coworkers at the Institute for Heavy Ion Research in Darmstadt, Germany, using a linear accelerator, produce atoms of element 108 (hassium) by bombarding lead-208 with nuclei of iron-58. Russian scientists at Dubna, Moscow, also produce hassium by the same method.

THE AMERICAS

1984 Astronomers at the European Southern Observatory in Chile discover that Neptune has a partial ring system.

1984 American astronaut Bruce McCandless (1937–) makes the first untethered space walk, from the space shuttle *Challenger*.

1985 Astronomers at Cornell University report eight infrared galaxies revealed by the Infrared Astronomical Satellite (IRAS).

1985 Images from the National Aeronautical and Space Administration's (NASA) Voyager 2 reveal Puck, the largest of the inner moons of Uranus. It is named for a mischievous sprite of folklore.

1985 NASA's space probe International Cometary Explorer (ICE) flies through the tail of comet Giacobini–Zinner. A year later it flies by Halley's comet.

1985 NASA launches its fourth space shuttle, *Atlantis*.

1984 American anthropologist Andrew Hill finds a fossil jawbone of the hominid *Australopithecus afarensis* in Kenya.

1984 American biologist Robert Sinsheimer proposes the Human Genome Project.

1985 American researchers isolate the first gene that (when it malfunctions) is responsible for a type of cancer called retinoblastoma (a malignant tumor affecting the eye).

This Cray 2 supercomputer installed at NASA's Ames Research Center, Moffett Field, California, had a memory capacity of 2 billion bytes and contained about 240,000 computer chips.

1985 Several chemists, including Robert Curl (1933–) and Richard Smalley (1943–2005) in the United States, produce a new allotrope of carbon called buckminsterfullerene (also known as "buckyballs").

HOW THINGS WORK

Genetic Fingerprinting

Genetic fingerprinting is the name commonly given to the technique of identifying sequences of nucleotides along a molecule of deoxyribonucleic acid (DNA). This pattern is unique to each individual because no two people have identical DNA (aside from identical twins). As a result, the technique can be used as a method of identification, for example, in forensic examinations. Scientists obtain the DNA from small samples of body tissue, such as blood, saliva, hair, sperm, or cells scraped from the inside of the mouth.

ASIA & OCEANIA

1984 Indian astronomer J. Bhattacharyya (1950–) and team observe two new rings of Saturn when they occlude (block the light from) a distant star.

1984 An accidental escape of toxic methyl isocyanate from the Union Carbide pesticide plant in Bhopal, India, kills thousands of people.

AFRICA & THE MIDDLE EAST

1984 Kenyan anthropologist Richard Leakey (1944–) and coworkers, working near Lake Turkana in northern Kenya, discover the 1.6-million-year old skeleton of *Homo erectus* (nicknamed "Turkana boy").

1984 Israeli physicist Dany Shechtman (1941–) and coworkers produce quasicrystals, which are solids with some long-range internal order but lacking the symmetry of true crystals.

ENGINEERING & INVENTION

1985 A Concorde supersonic airliner flies from London, England, to Sydney, Australia, in the record time of 17 hours, 3 minutes.

1985 German physicist Gerd Binnig (1947–) and coworkers develop the atomic force microscope.

1985 Danish-born computer programmer Bjarne Stroustrup (1950–) at Bell Laboratories invents C++, a high-level computer programming language.

1985 British company Inmos introduces the T414 transputer (for use in parallel computers).

1984 American physicist Dennis Matthews invents an x-ray wavelength laser.

1984 American Microsoft Corporation launches the Windows computer applications program for the IBM PC and compatible computers.

1984 American company Apple markets the Macintosh computer, which uses screen icons, a mouse, and a graphical user interface.

1985 American undersea explorer Robert Ballard (1942–) uses the remote-controlled robot Argo to film the wreck of S.S. *Titanic*, the British liner that sank on its maiden voyage in 1912 after hitting an iceberg in the North Atlantic Ocean.

1985 American company Adobe Systems introduces PostScript, a page-description computer language.

1985 American company Cray Research markets the Cray-2 supercomputer, followed three years later by the twice-as-fast Cray Y-MP.

1985 The world's longest railroad tunnel, the 33.5-mile (53.9-km) Seikan Tunnel, is completed between the islands of Honshu and Hokkaido in Japan.

1985 Japanese company Seiko-Epson markets a small television set that uses a liquid crystal display for its screen.

WORLD EVENTS

1984 More than a million marchers force the French government to abandon its challenge to the independence of religious schools.

1985 Mikhail Gorbachev (1931–) comes to power in the Soviet Union following the death of Konstantin Chernenko; Gorbachev adopts a reformist agenda based on *glasnost* (openness) and *perestroika* (reconstruction).

Underwater explorer Robert Ballard located the wreck of the Titanic *in 1985. The ship lay at a depth of 12,000 feet (3,660 m) off the coast of Newfoundland.*

1984 A group of top popular music artists come together as U.S.A. for Africa to record the song "We Are The World," written by Michael Jackson (1958–) and Lionel Richie (1949–). The record is sold to raise funds for drought and famine victims in Ethiopia.

1984 Indian troops storm the Golden Temple, a Sikh holy site at Amritsar, where armed militants seeking an independent Punjab ("Khalistan") have taken refuge; more than 700 rebels are killed.

1984 India's premier Indira Gandhi (1917–84) is assassinated by members of her bodyguard.

1984 A famine strikes Ethiopia and Sudan in East Africa, claiming about 100,000 lives. In 1985 Live Aid rock concerts in Philadelphia, London, Moscow, and Sydney raise $60 million for famine victims.

OZONE LAYER AND CFCS

Ozone (O_3) is a molecule that consists of three oxygen atoms. (Such molecules are called triatomic.) It is less stable than diatomic oxygen (O_2), which is the most common form of the gas in the air at ground level. Ground-level ozone is a pollutant, and high levels can damage the respiratory system of animals. In the upper atmosphere—between 6 and 31 miles (10–50 km) above Earth's surface—a layer of ozone blocks harmful ultraviolet (UV) radiation produced by the sun.

The ozone layer was discovered in 1913 by French physicists Charles Fabry (1867–1945) and Henri Buisson (1873–1944). British meteorologist G. M. B. Dobson (1889–1976) began to monitor ozone levels in the late 1920s.

In 1985, British scientists working in Antarctica reported a 40-percent depletion of ozone in the layer over the continent. Monitoring of the depletion has led to a worldwide phase-out of chemicals called chlorofluorocarbons (CFCs). These chemicals, invented by American chemist Thomas Midgley (1889–1944) in 1928, are mainly used as refrigerants. Once released into the atmosphere, CFCs slowly diffuse up to the ozone layer. There, UV rays from the sun cause them to react with ozone, breaking it down. This leads to a higher amount of UV reaching ground level, increasing the risk of skin cancer.

The purple area shows the ozone hole above the South Pole, in Antarctica.

ASTRONOMY & MATH	BIOLOGY & MEDICINE	PHYSICAL SCIENCES

EUROPE

1986 The Soviet Union launches space station Mir into Earth orbit. It becomes the first permanently crewed space station.

1986 European Space Agency's (ESA) probe Giotto passes within 375 miles (600 km) of Halley's comet. The same year a Japanese probe passes within 93,210 miles (150,000 km) of the comet and Soviet probes pass within about 5,280 miles (8,500 km).

1987 Soviet cosmonaut Yuri Romanenko (1944–) returns to Earth after a record 326 days in space station Mir.

1987 The British-Dutch William Herschel Telescope is completed at Roque de los Muchachos Observatory in the Canary Islands. The 13.8-foot (4.2-m) reflecting telescope is fitted with spectroscopes and cameras.

1987 British surgeons John Wallwork and Roy Calne (1930–) at Papworth Hospital, Cambridge, England, carry out the first heart/lung/liver triple transplant operation. The patient survives for ten years.

1987 German zoologist Hans Fricke uses a submersible to observe coelacanths (*Latimeria chalumnae*)—for a long time thought to be extinct—swimming in their natural habitat deep in the Indian Ocean.

1986 German physicist Georg Bednorz (1950–) and Swiss physicist Alex Müller (1927–) make "high-temperature" superconductors that function at 35 K (−460.67°F; −238.15° C). In 1987 Chinese physicist Ching-Wu Chu (1941–) and coworkers make one that superconducts at 98 K (−347.27°F; −175.15°C).

1986 An explosion at the Chernobyl nuclear reactor in the Ukraine releases radioactivity that produces widespread poisonous fallout in Europe and the Soviet Union.

1987 German chemist Herbert Naarmann and coworkers make an electrically conducting plastic by "doping" polyethyne (polyacetylene) with iodine.

THE AMERICAS

1986 More data from the National Aeronautical and Space Administration's (NASA) Voyager 2 reveal a new set of inner moons of Uranus, named Belinda, Cordelia, Cressida, Desdemona, Juliet, Ophelia, and Portia (after Shakespearian characters).

1986 NASA's space shuttle *Challenger* explodes soon after launch, killing all seven crew members.

1986 NASA's space probe Voyager 2 flies by Uranus.

1987 Canadian astronomer Ian Shelton (1958–) discovers the supernova SN1987A in the Large Magellanic Cloud galaxy, the brightest since 1604.

1987 Astronomer R. Brent Tully announces his discovery of the Pisces–Cetus supercluster of galaxies, the largest feature so far found in the Universe.

1986 American pharmacologist Louis Ignarro (1941–) identifies the substance EDRF (endothelium-derived relaxing factor)—named in 1980 by American pharmacologist Robert Furchgott (1916–)—as nitric oxide.

1986 American geneticist Louis Kunkel (1949–) identifies a gene for Duchenne muscular dystrophy.

1986 American biotechnology company Agracetus carries out field trials of genetically engineered tobacco.

1986 Physician Fred Turck introduces the use of diazepine tranquilizers, soon to become some of the most prescribed drugs in Western society.

1987 The last wild Californian condor (*Gymnogyps californianus*) is captured and placed in a breeding program.

1987 Paleontologist Kevin Aulenback finds a "nest" of fossilized dinosaur eggs in Alberta, Canada. In the same year American paleontologist Wade Miller discovers a 150-million-year-old dinosaur egg containing a fossilized embryo (detected by x-rays).

1986 Physicists at Lawrence Livermore National Laboratory in the United States bring about laser-induced nuclear fusion.

1987 American physicists discover the longest-lived radioisotope found so far, selenium-32, with a half-life of 1.1×10^{20} years.

In 1986 the world's fishing nations introduced a world ban on killing whales (with a few exceptions for traditional societies).

ASIA & OCEANIA

AFRICA & THE MIDDLE EAST

The first disposable or single-use cameras were marketed in 1987.

ENGINEERING & INVENTION	WORLD EVENTS
1986 European consortium Airbus Industrie announces the Airbus A320, the first commercial aircraft to use "fly-by-wire" (computer-controlled) technology. **1986** English businessman Richard Branson (1950–) makes a record-breaking trip across the Atlantic Ocean in his speedboat *Virgin Atlantic Challenger II*. **1987** Richard Branson and Swedish aeronautical engineer Per Lindstrand (1948–) make the first crossing of the Atlantic Ocean in a hot-air balloon, *Virgin Atlantic Flyer*. **1987** French company Agrotechnic devises a process for making a synthetic milk substitute from soybeans.	**1986** Spain and Portugal join the European Community, bringing the membership to 12 countries (Greece having joined in 1981). **1987** British Prime Minister Margaret Thatcher (1925–) leads the Conservative Party to a third successive victory, the first such achievement in 20th-century British politics. **1987** On a visit to Berlin, U.S. President Ronald Reagan (1911–2004) calls on Soviet leader Mikhail Gorbachev (1931–) to "tear down" the Berlin Wall.
1986 A bicycle ridden by Fred Markham establishes a human-powered land speed record of 65.48 miles (105.38 km) per hour. **1986** American pilots Dick Rutan (1938–) and Jeana Yeager (1952–) complete a nine-day nonstop flight around the world in their airplane *Voyager*. **1986** The 1,525-foot (465-m) Alex Fraser Bridge in Canada becomes the world's longest cable-stayed bridge. **1987** Engineers from American company AT&T install the first fiber-optic telecommunications cable (TAT-8) under the Atlantic Ocean. **1987** American company Kodak and Japanese company Fuji market 35mm disposable cameras. **1987** American researchers James Van House and Arthur Rich (1937–90) develop the positron microscope, which works in a similar way to an electron microscope but instead of electrons makes use of positrons ("positive electrons") produced by a radioactive isotope.	**1986** On Black Monday (October 19) stock markets in New York and then around the world experience a major crash, wiping billions of dollars off the value of shares. **1987** At a New York auction, "Irises" by Vincent van Gogh (1853–90) becomes the most expensive piece of art in history, selling for US$40 million. **1987** The United States and the Soviet Union sign the first ever nuclear arms reduction treaty, covering the two countries' medium- and short-range arsenals. **1987** Condom commercials run on U.S. television to combat the spread of AIDS.
1986 Japanese manufacturers demonstrate a digital audio tape (DAT) system. **1987** Japanese Airlines introduces telephones on their airplanes that employ communications satellites to link calls to land lines.	**1986** President Ferdinand Marcos (1917–89) of the Philippines is deposed by a "people power" movement led by Corazon Aquino (1933–), widow of Benigno Aquino (1932–83). **1986** Martial law, first imposed in 1949, is finally lifted in Taiwan.
	1986 Tripoli is attacked by U.S. warplanes flying from British bases in retaliation for the support of international terrorism by Libyan leader Colonel Muammar al-Gaddafi (1942–).

THE SPACE SHUTTLE

Plans for the space shuttle date back to 1972. The National Aeronautics and Space Administration (NASA) wanted a cargo-carrying rocket that could go into space, carry out its mission, return to base, and be used again and again.

At launch, the shuttle consists of three parts: an airplanelike orbiter, a large external tank that holds extra fuel, and two solid rocket boosters. The flight deck has seats for seven crew, and the mid-deck serves as a wardroom, kitchen, and gym, and has a bathroom. The payload bay can carry up to 27.6 tons (25 tonnes). The bay also has a robot arm called the Remote Manipulator System. It deploys and retrieves payloads and acts as a "ladder" for space-walking astronauts.

After launch, the boosters fall off; the external tank is jettisoned once the shuttle is in Earth orbit. At the end of a mission, the crew retrofire the maneuvering rockets to slow it down. As it reenters the Earth's atmosphere, thermal tiles on the wings and fuselage glow red hot with the heat generated by friction with the air.

NASA has built six space shuttles and made more than 120 trips. Two disasters, in 1986 and 2003, resulted in the deaths of both crews. The shuttle program was due to finish in 2010, when it would be replaced by a new kind of spacecraft.

ASTRONOMY & MATH	BIOLOGY & MEDICINE	PHYSICAL SCIENCES

EUROPE

1988 English theoretical physicist and mathematician Stephen Hawking (1942–) publishes a popular account of cosmology, *A Brief History of Time*, which becomes an international best-seller.

1988 The first Soviet space shuttle, *Buran*, makes an uncrewed test flight.

1989 The European Space Administration (ESA) launches astrometry satellite Hipparcos (High Precision Parallax Collecting Satellite) for measuring precisely the locations of stars. By 1993 it locates 120,000 selected stars.

1988 Dutch company CCA Biochem introduces polylactide biodegradable polymer for making surgical sutures (stitches) and artificial skin to treat burns.

A genetically modified mouse, or OncoMouse, was patented in the United States in 1988.

1988 At Imperial College, London, physicists Paul French and Roy Taylor produce a short-pulse x-ray laser.

1988 English physicist Richard Friend makes a diode entirely of plastic using polyethyne (polyacetylene).

THE AMERICAS

1988 The National Aeronautical and Space Administration's (NASA) space shuttle program restarts with a successful launch of *Discovery*.

1989 NASA's Voyager 2 space probe reveals that Neptune has a system of rings and discovers five inner moons—Despina, Galatea, Proteus, Thalassa, and Naiad—and rediscovers Larissa (first seen 1981).

1989 NASA launches space probes Galileo (to Jupiter) and Magellan (to Venus). The following year Magellan makes a radar map of the surface of Venus.

1988 The U.S. Patent Office grants a patent for a genetically engineered mouse (the first issued for a vertebrate animal).

1988 American climatologist James Hansen (1941–) predicts that increased levels of "greenhouse gases," such as carbon dioxide, in the Earth's atmosphere will lead to global warming.

1988 American physicians at the Presbyterian Hospital in Pittsburgh, Pennsylvania, begin performing double-lung transplant operations.

1989 Virologist Qui-Lim-Choo and coworkers confirm their earlier (1987) discovery of the virus that causes the liver disorder hepatitis-C.

1989 Scientists find the Chicxulub meteor crater on the floor of the Gulf of Mexico. It is thought to be the impact site of a meteorite that gave rise to the K-T event, which may have led to the extinction of the dinosaurs.

1989 Physicians in the United States use fetal brain tissue to treat Parkinson's disease.

1988 American physicist Frank Filisko (1942–2008) prepares a fluid whose viscosity (stickiness) can be varied by applying an electric field to it.

This false-color image of the surface of Venus was created from data collected by the Magellan space probe. The probe used radar-imaging to map the cloudy planet's surface.

ASIA & OCEANIA

1988 Japanese mathematician Yoichi Miyaoka offers a proof of Fermat's last theorem (that the equation $x^n + y^n = z^n$ has no solutions in positive integers x, y, and z if n is an integer greater than 2). Later it is found to be insufficiently rigorous. A valid proof finally comes in 1994.

1988 The Human Genome Organization (HUGO), with headquarters in Singapore, is established to promote international collaboration in the field of human genetics.

AFRICA & THE MIDDLE EAST

1988 Israel makes its first successful space launch from its site at Palmachim.

1988 Anthropologists from France and Israel discover in an Israeli cave fossils of a 92,000-year-old *Homo sapiens*, the oldest anatomically modern human to be found.

ENGINEERING & INVENTION

1988 Greek cyclist Kanellos Kanellopoulos (1957–) pilots the human-powered aircraft *Daedalus* across the Aegean Sea from Crete to Santorini. The 74.6-mile (120-km) crossing takes him 3 hours, 54 minutes.

1988 An explosion on Piper Alpha, an oil-drilling platform in the North Sea, results in a fire in which 167 people are killed.

1988 The F-117A Nighthawk Stealth fighter, which is "invisible" to radar, is revealed to the public, five years after being procured by the U.S. Air Force.

1988 A wind-powered 3-megawatt electricity generator with a single propeller blade 320 feet (97.5 m) across is installed in Hawaii.

1988 American IBM Corporation researchers use a scanning tunneling microscope to produce an image of a benzene molecule.

1988 The U.S. National Oceanic and Atmospheric Administration begins operations in Aquarius, an underwater habitat in the Caribbean, inside which a crew of six can work for nine hours a day.

1989 The Bell/Boeing V-22 Osprey tilt-rotor airplane with vertical take-off and landing makes its maiden flight.

1989 Boeing company's High Technology Center produces a photocell that converts more than a third of incident solar radiation into electricity.

1989 American computer engineer Seymour Cray (1925–96) establishes a company to build the Cray 3 supercomputer; it goes out of business in 1995.

1988 Integrated services digital network (ISDN) is launched in Japan as a world standard for digital data communications.

WORLD EVENTS

1988 A U.S. airliner is destroyed by a terrorist bomb over the Scottish town of Lockerbie, killing 270 people; a Libyan agent will eventually be convicted of the atrocity.

1989 Across Europe the communist regimes of Soviet satellite countries (Czechoslovakia, East Germany, and Poland) collapse as their citizens demand democratic reform.

1989 In Romania communist dictator Nicolae Ceaucescu (1918–1989) is deposed and executed.

1988 Vice President George H. W. Bush (1924–) is elected 41st president of the United States.

1988 The United States and Canada sign a comprehensive free-trade agreement, becoming effective on January 1, 1989.

1988 Use of crack—a derivative of cocaine—becomes increasingly popular.

1989 U.S. troops invade Panama and arrest military dictator Manuel Noriega (1934–) on drug-trafficking, racketeering, and money laundering charges.

1989 General Colin Powell (1937–) becomes the first African-American chairman of the U.S. Joint Chiefs of Staff.

1989 Oil tanker *Exxon Valdez* runs aground on reefs in Prince William Sound, Alaska, spilling an estimated 10 million gallons (40 million l) of crude oil.

STEPHEN HAWKING

Stephen Hawking is an English theoretical physicist and mathematician best known for his popular account of cosmology, *A Brief History of Time*. He was born in Oxford, England, and graduated from the university there, although he received his doctorate from Cambridge University in 1966. He became professor of gravitational physics at Cambridge in 1977 and two years later was appointed Lucasian Professor of Mathematics. At this time his main interest was relativity and its implications for the big bang (at the start of the universe) and black holes (in which enormous gravitational fields result from the collapse of stars).

Hawking showed mathematically that only angular momentum, electric charge, and mass are conserved when a black hole forms, although in 1974 he proposed that black holes could also evaporate and release heat radiation. Mass is lost by what is called the Hawking process. His "no-boundary proposal" of 1983 states that both space and time are infinite and have no physical boundaries.

In 1963 Hawking developed the incurable degenerative neuromuscular disease amyotrophic lateral sclerosis and since then has spent his life in a wheelchair. He communicates through a computer speech synthesizer.

Stephen Hawking floats free in a zero-gravity flight in April 2007.

ASTRONOMY & MATH	BIOLOGY & MEDICINE	PHYSICAL SCIENCES

EUROPE

1991 Britain's first astronaut, chemist Helen Sharman (1963–), goes into Earth orbit on board a Soviet spacecraft.

1990 British geneticists Peter Goodfellow (1951–) and Robin Lovell-Badge (1953–) discover the male sex-determining gene on the human Y chromosome.

An engineer checks one of the boring machines used to make the Channel Tunnel, which provides a rail link between England and France.

1990 British company ICI introduces a biodegradable plastic, called Biopol. It also invents Klea 134a, a harmless hydrocarbon substitute for chlorofluorocarbons (CFCs).

1990 French molecular biologist Jean-Marie Lehn (1939–) prepares synthetic compounds called nucleohelicates, which mimic natural deoxyribonucleic acid (DNA).

1990 The nuclear physics research facility at the European Organization for Nuclear Research (CERN) in Switzerland commissions the new Large Electron–Positron Collider (LEP) for carrying out particle experiments.

1991 Researchers at the Joint European Torus (JET) project in England briefly achieve controlled nuclear fusion.

THE AMERICAS

1990 Using nine-year-old data from the National Aeronautical and Space Administration's (NASA) Voyager 2 space probe, American astronomer Mark Showalter (1957–) locates Saturn's tiny innermost moon Pan—just 12 miles (20 km) across.

1990 NASA's Voyager 1 space probe returns photographs from deep space showing the whole of the solar system.

1990 NASA's space shuttle *Discovery* places the Hubble Space Telescope into orbit around the Earth. Over the next 15 years the telescope will provide astronomers with detailed images of the solar system, the galaxy, and distant objects in the universe.

1991 NASA uses the space shuttle *Atlantis* to place the Compton Gamma Ray Observatory (CGRO) satellite into Earth orbit; it operates until 2000.

1991 NASA sends its Upper Atmosphere Research Satellite into orbit around Earth. It studies the effects of chlorofluorocarbons (CFCs) on the ozone layer.

1990 The Human Genome Project gets under way, directed by American biophysicist James Watson (1928–).

1991 Canadian scientists discover fossils of the oldest known multicellular animal (a sponge). It is 600 million years old.

1991 American electronics engineer Kenneth Matsumura invents a small portable electrocardiograph machine that gives its wearer advanced warning of heart problems. In the same year American physicists William and Jean Bennett (father and daughter) develop an electrocardiograph triggered by heartbeat sounds (the dynamic spectral phonocardiograph, or DSP).

1990 American researchers make the lightest known solid, a silicon dioxide aerogel with a density of only 5 ounces per cubic foot—a cubic yard would weigh only 8 pounds (5 kg per cu m).

ASIA & OCEANIA

1990 Japanese scientists launch a space probe to the moon, where it releases a small satellite into lunar orbit.

1991 Japanese researcher Sumio Iijima (1939–) makes carbon nanotubes (microscopically small tubes of carbon).

AFRICA & THE MIDDLE EAST

English computer scientist Tim Berners-Lee devised the World Wide Web in 1990.

ENGINEERING & INVENTION

1990 British and French workers greet each other when the two opposite halves of the new Channel Tunnel meet in the rock under the English Channel.

1990 A Concorde supersonic airliner flies from London, England, to New York, United States, in the record time of 2 hours, 53 minutes.

1990 From this year all new cars sold in Europe have to be capable of running on nonleaded gasoline.

1990 English computer scientist Tim Berners-Lee (1955–) begins to devise the World Wide Web.

1991 With a central span of 1,739 feet (530 m), the Skarnsundet Bridge in Norway is the world's longest cable-stayed bridge.

1990 American Northrop/McDonnell Douglas consortium reveals the prototype of its new YF-23 Advanced Tactical Fighter (ATF) aircraft. Two months later Lockheed/General Dynamics/Boeing unveil their competing YF-22 design.

1990 American Microsoft Corporation releases the Windows 3 computer operating system.

1990 American company Kodak announces the invention of a Photo CD disc.

1990 Nanotechnology researchers at American IBM Corporation use an atomic force microscope to manipulate 35 xenon atoms on a nickel plate to draw the letters "IBM."

1990 The amount of electricity generated in the United States by nuclear power plants rises to 20 percent of total output (it is nearly 75 percent in France).

1991 American engineer Alvon Elrod (1928–) invents a car engine that has a camshaft with variable cams, to minimize fuel consumption at any engine speed.

1990 A new section of the trans-Siberian railroad opens in Russia between Baikal and Amur, with four large tunnels and 3,000 bridges.

1990 The world's largest church, the Basilica of Our Lady of Peace, is completed in Yamoussoukro, Côte d'Ivoire (Ivory Coast), West Africa.

WORLD EVENTS

1990 Boris Yeltsin (1931–2007) becomes the first freely elected president of Russia.

1990 East and West Germany are reunited.

1990 Margaret Thatcher (1925–) quits as British prime minister after 11 years.

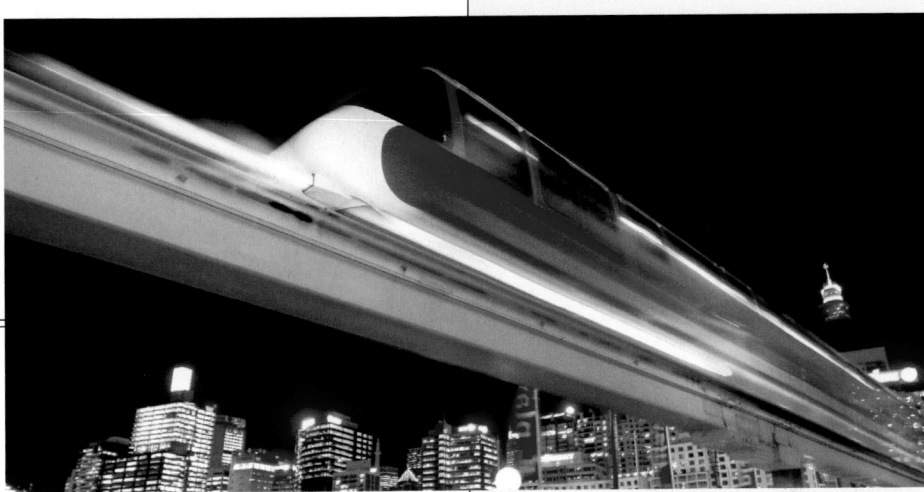

The Japanese maglev (magnetically levitated) train uses powerful superconducting magnets to reach speeds of up to 310 miles (500 km) per hour.

1990 General Pinochet (1915–2006) steps down as military ruler of Chile, restoring civilian rule after 17 years.

1990 Nicaragua's communist Sandinista government is voted out of power with the election of Violetta Chamarro (1929–).

1990 Benazir Bhutto (1953–2007) is relieved of her post as prime minister of Pakistan after being accused of corruption.

1990 Democracy campaigner Aung San Suu Kyi (1945–) wins Myanmar's general election; the ruling military junta declares the result void and places her under house arrest.

1990 After 27 years in jail veteran South African antiapartheid leader Nelson Mandela (1918–) is freed from detention.

1991 A U.S.-led coalition of forces under a UN mandate undertakes to liberate Kuwait, which was invaded by Iraq in 1990; Iraqi forces crumble in the ensuing Gulf War (1990–91).

SUPERCONDUCTORS

A superconductor is a substance that offers no resistance to the flow of electricity. Superconductors were first discovered in 1911, and for many years scientists thought that superconductivity occurs only at temperatures that are very close to absolute zero (0 K = –459.67°F, or –273.15°C). The temperature below which superconductivity occurs is known as the transition temperature (Tc). Until 1985 the highest Tc known at ordinary atmospheric pressure was 23.2 K (–481.91°F, or –249.95°C) for an alloy of niobium.

Breakthroughs in the 1980s and 1990s came with the discovery of a "high-temperature" ceramic superconductor with a Tc of about 35 K (–460.67°F; –238.15°C). Although 35 K is still an extremely low temperature, the discovery raised the possibility of much higher Tcs, and it stimulated more research. In 1993, a Tc of 153 K (–248.27°F; –120.15°C) was found in a mercury-based ceramic subjected to high pressure.

Wires made from superconducting material are used to make superconducting magnets. They have several uses in magnetic separation and medical imaging and also in magnetically levitated (maglev) trains. Magnets make the train float, eliminating friction between train and track. In 2003 a test vehicle reached a speed of 361 miles (581 km) per hour on the Yamanashi Maglev Test Line in Japan.

ASTRONOMY & MATH

EUROPE

1992 The Roman Catholic Church reverses the verdict of the 1633 trial of Italian scientist Galileo Galilei (1564–1642) at which he was convicted of heresy.

1992 The European Space Administration's (ESA) space probe Giotto passes within 124 miles (200 km) of comet Grigg–Skjellerup.

1992 The space probe Ulysses, a joint venture between the National Aeronautics and Space Administration (NASA) and ESA, passes within 236,000 miles (380,000 km) of Jupiter, inside the orbit of its moon Io, on its way to the sun.

THE AMERICAS

1992 Astronomers discover an object that crosses the orbits of Saturn, Uranus, and Neptune. An estimated 93 miles (150 km) across, it is probably an asteroid (assigned no. 5145) but may be a comet. They name it Pholus.

1992 NASA's space shuttle *Endeavour* makes its first flight. In 1993 it carries out repairs to the Hubble Space Telescope in Earth orbit.

1992 NASA launches its Extreme Ultraviolet Explorer (EUVE) satellite into Earth orbit to study the heavens at very short ultraviolet wavelengths (between 1 and 100 nanometers).

1992 NASA's space probe Pioneer Venus 1 burns up on entering the atmosphere of Venus.

1993 Radio astronomers make the first observations with the complete Very Long Baseline Array (VLBA) series of ten radiotelescopes, located across the United States and its overseas territories.

1993 American astronomers Carolyn Shoemaker (1929–) and David Levy (1948–) discover a new comet, which is named Shoemaker–Levy 9.

ASIA & OCEANIA

1992 The space probe *Geotail* (developed by Japanese scientists and managed by NASA) is launched to examine the Earth's magnetosphere (the pear-shaped magnetic field that surrounds the Earth and extends into space).

AFRICA & THE MIDDLE EAST

BIOLOGY & MEDICINE

1992 Anticancer drug taxol, extracted from the bark of yew trees, gets official approval in North America by the U.S. Food and Drug Administration. It is used mainly for treating ovarian cancer.

1992 Surgeons at the University of Pittsburgh Medical Center perform a transgenic transplant of a baboon's liver into a human patient.

1993 American physicians introduce gene therapy for the congenital disorder cystic fibrosis.

1993 American physicians develop a way of detecting acquired immume deficiency syndrome (AIDS) in newborns and young infants.

1993 American physician Susan Perrine and coworkers carry out trials using the fatty acid derivative butyrate as a new treatment for sickle-cell anemia.

1992 The world population reaches 5.4 billion people, with about 1.2 billion in China alone.

1993 American anthropologist Tim White (1950–) and coworkers from Berkeley discover in Africa remains of *Ardipithecus ramidus*, the oldest hominoid australopithecine fossil found so far.

PHYSICAL SCIENCES

EUROPE

1992 Scientists at the University of Pisa, Italy, make the most accurate determination so far of the acceleration of free fall (acceleration due to gravity), not far from where Italian scientist Galileo Galilei is said to have first measured it in about 1602.

Princeton University's Tokamak Fusion Test Reactor is used to research nuclear fusion. Many scientists see nuclear fusion as a possible power source of the future.

THE AMERICAS

1992 Research scientists at the American company General Electric report making extrahard diamonds using the isotope carbon-13 (natural diamonds are made of carbon-12).

1993 Soviet-born American physicist Alexei Abrikosov (1928–) explains the workings of type-II superconductors (which, unlike type-I, remain superconducting even in a strong magnetic field). They depend on an arrangement of atoms known as an Abrikosov vortex lattice.

1993 The Tokamak fusion reactor at the Princeton Plasma Physics Laboratory produces 5.6 megawatts of power (in a one-second burst) but requires more than this amount of energy to operate it.

1993 American research chemists discover a way of making liquid methanol (methyl alcohol) from the gas methane (natural gas) using a low-temperature mercury vapor catalyst. It could provide a way of making a liquid fuel from a gaseous one.

ASIA & OCEANIA

1992 Japanese chemists use palladium atoms to make stable polymers of buckyballs (the C_{60} allotrope with a spherical arrangement of carbon molecules).

ENGINEERING & INVENTION

1992 The 223-foot (68-m) *Destriero* establishes a new powerboat record for crossing the Atlantic Ocean in 2 days and 10 hours.

1992 Dutch company Philips markets the CD-i interactive computer disk.

1992 Experimental digital FM radio broadcasts begin in France.

A photograph from the Hubble Space Telescope reveals a spiral galaxy deep within the universe.

1992 The U.S. Air Force and U.S. Navy finance construction in Alaska of the High Frequency Active Auroral Research Program (HAARP) to try to reduce the effects of the aurora borealis (northern lights) on satellite communications.

1992 In Davis, California, the Advanced Photovoltaic Systems company assembles a huge array of thin-film photovoltaic cells that produce 400 kilowatts of electrical power.

1993 American engineers produce two cost-effective "free-swimming" submersible robots: the *Odyssey* (designed by James Bellingham), deployed in Antarctica, and the Autonomous Benthic Explorer (ABE), developed originally by Albert Bradley and deployed off Bermuda.

1993 The state of Iowa interlinks all of its 99 counties with a fiber-optic cable network.

1993 Researchers at the University of Colorado construct the first all-optical programmable computer.

1993 American company Intel markets the Pentium microprocessor for computers.

1992 Japanese Sony Corporation introduces transistors made from ceramic semiconductors. The same year it markets the first digital audio MiniDisc.

1993 Japanese company Mazda announces plans to construct a fuel-efficient car using a Miller-cycle internal combustion engine.

1993 The Third River irrigation canal is completed in Iraq, linking the Tigris and Euphrates Rivers near Baghdad.

WORLD EVENTS

1993 Czechoslovakia separates into two states, the Czech Republic and Slovakia, after a peaceful plebiscite approves this "Velvet Revolution."

1993 Nations of the European Community (now renamed the European Union) sign the Maastricht Treaty, committing them to a program of ever closer union.

1992 Bill Clinton (1946–) becomes the 42nd President of the United States.

1993 A terrorist bomb explodes in the World Trade Center in New York.

1993 Toni Morrison (1931–) becomes the first African-American woman awarded the Nobel Prize in Literature.

1992 Hindu militants destroy a 16th-century mosque on an ancient Hindu holy site at Ayodhya in India; more than 1,000 die in the ensuing Hindu–Muslim rioting.

1992 A UN peacekeeping mission to Somalia ends in conflict between U.S. forces and troops loyal to warlord General Mohamed Farrah Aidid (1934–96). The conflict continues until 1995.

HUBBLE SPACE TELESCOPE

The Hubble Space Telescope (HST) is named for American astronomer Edwin Hubble (1889–1953). It was completed by the National Aeronautics and Space Administration (NASA) in 1985 and placed in orbit by the space shuttle *Discovery* in 1990. It follows an orbit 377 miles (607 km) above Earth and is designed to be serviced and updated from time to time by the space shuttle.

The HST is an aluminum cylinder 43 feet (13 m) long and 14 feet (4.3 m) across. Electric power comes from two 40-foot (12-m) solar panels. Two high-gain antennas transmit signals to ground control at the Goddard Space Flight Center. The cylinder houses a reflecting telescope with a prime mirror 94.5 inches (2.4 m) across. There are also five detectors of various types.

HST can photograph objects 50 times fainter than anything visible from the ground. In 1994 HST photographed fragments of the comet Shoemaker–Levy 9 crashing into Jupiter. By the end of 1995 it took photographs of some of the most distant objects in the universe, recording faint galaxies 12 billion light-years away. In 1998 the HST directly imaged an extrasolar planet orbiting a star in the constellation Taurus. A more powerful telescope is currently being developed to replace HST.

High-gain antenna

Secondary mirror

Primary mirror

Solar panel

Instruments

ASTRONOMY & MATH	BIOLOGY & MEDICINE	PHYSICAL SCIENCES

EUROPE

1994 English mathematician Andrew Wiles (1953–) offers a proof of Fermat's last theorem.

1995 The European Space Agency (ESA) launches the French Infrared Space Observatory (ISO) into a highly elliptical Earth orbit.

1995 Russian cosmonaut Valeri Polyakov (1942–) clocks the longest space mission to date, returning after 438 days aboard the space station Mir.

1995 Swiss astronomers Michael Mayor (1942–) and Didier Queloz (1966–) discover an extrasolar planet (orbiting the star 51 Pegasi).

INSIDE STORY

Genetically Modified Plants

Plants can be genetically engineered to modify their properties, for example, to make them grow faster, tolerate cold and drought better, or simply taste nicer. Genetically engineered crops can have their own inbuilt insecticides or be made resistant to high doses of sprayed-on pesticides. Similar crops engineered to grow in arid or salty soils can boost farming productivity in developing countries. The first genetically engineered food to be granted a licence for human consumption was the Flavr Savr tomato, which was first sold in 1994. The fruit ripens on the vine without going soft (and so does not get damaged during shipping to the supermarket) because of the presence of a gene that blocks the action of the enzyme polygalacturonase, which causes fruit to soften naturally.

THE AMERICAS

1994 The National Aeronautics and Space Administration's (NASA) and U.S. Strategic Defense Initiative Organization's space probe Clementine goes into orbit around the moon and maps the surface. Its intended later trip to the near-Earth asteroid Geographos is abandoned after a rocket malfunctions.

1994 The Hubble Space Telescope confirms the existence of the Kuiper belt, a spherical region at the edge of the solar system where comets originate.

1994 Fragments of comet Shoemaker–Levy 9, first seen in 1993, collide with Jupiter.

1995 NASA's space probe Galileo sends its own probe into Jupiter's atmosphere. It radios back data for an hour before being crushed by the pressure.

1995 American Norman Thagard (1943–) becomes the first U.S. astronaut aboard a Russian spacecraft when he joins the crew of a Soyuz craft to reach the Mir space station. He returns 105 days later on the space shuttle *Atlantis*.

1994 A genetically modified tomato called Flavr Savr is marketed by the company Calgene in the United States.

1995 American company Thermo Cardiosystems introduce the LVAD (left ventricular assist device), an implanted pump for heart patients.

1994 American scientists at Fermilab announce the discovery of the evasive subatomic particle called the top quark.

1995 American geophysicists Xiaodong Song and Paul Richards detect the rotation of the Earth's solid inner core through computer analysis of seismic waves.

1995 American physicist Eric Cornell (1961–) and coworkers produce a Bose–Einstein condensate, a fourth state of matter.

ASIA & OCEANIA

1994 Japanese rocket engineers launch their new heavy-lifting rocket, H-2.

1994 Paleontologists from Pakistan and the United States discover fossils of a whale that had hind limbs.

1994 Scientists record the first giant muntjac (a type of deer) in northern Vietnam. It is given the scientific name *Muntiacus vuquangensis*.

AFRICA & THE MIDDLE EAST

1994 A new Ebola virus (Ebola hemorrhagic fever) is identified in Côte d'Ivoire (Ivory Coast) and Gabon in Africa; other outbreaks occur in 1995 in Zaire (now the Democratic Republic of the Congo).

ENGINEERING & INVENTION	WORLD EVENTS
1994 The Channel Tunnel rail link opens between England and France for freight, cars and trucks (carried in railroad wagons), and passengers. It is the longest tunnel under the sea at that time.	**1994** Cheychnya's attempt to break away from the Russian government is thwarted by the Russian army.
1994 The 16,800-ton (15,000-tonne) ferry *Estonia* sinks in the Baltic Sea off Finland with the loss of almost 900 lives.	**1995** The Dayton Peace Accord brings the bloody civil war in Bosnia to an end; the state is divided between a Muslim–Croat federation and a Bosnian Serb republic.
1994 Scottish inventor Jonathan Copus invents the biogun, a device that uses a stream of negatively charged ions to kill bacterial and fungal infections.	
1995 The 2,808-foot (856-m) Pont de Normandie in Le Havre, France, is completed and is for a few years the world's longest cable-stayed bridge.	

FERMAT'S LAST THEOREM

Pierre de Fermat (1601–65) was a French mathematician who made many important contributions to number theory, geometry, and the development of calculus and probability theory. Fermat posed the theorem that the equation $x^n + y^n = z^n$ has no solutions in positive integers x, y, and z if n is an integer greater than 2. If $n = 3$, for example, the theorem states that there are no positive integers x, y, and z such that $x^3 + y^3 = z^3$. No mathematicians could prove or disprove the theorem (although proofs for specific values of n were devised), which became known as Fermat's last theorem. Fermat himself claimed to have found a proof, which he never published. After seven years of work, English mathematician Andrew Wiles proposed his proof in 1993. After finding an error, Wiles with help from Richard Taylor (1962–) revised the proof. He published his now watertight proof in 1995.

Andrew Wiles outlines his first attempt to prove Fermat's last theory to fellow mathematicians in Cambridge, England, in 1993.

1994 American businessman Jon Zeeff launches the world's first Internet shopping mall with Grant's Flowers and Greenhouses.	**1994** The North American Free Trade Agreement (NAFTA) links the United States, Canada, and Mexico in an enlarged free-trade zone.
1995 American company Lockheed introduces the Athena rocket launcher vehicle, originally called the Lockheed Martin Launch Vehicle (LMLV), for placing satellites into low Earth orbit.	**1995** A truck bomb planted by right-wing extremists destroys a federal building in Oklahoma City, killing 168 people.
1995 For the first time the number of trucks and cars in the United States exceeds 200 million—more than one for every adult member of the population.	
1995 American computer programmer James Gosling (1955–) of Sun Microsystems company introduces the Java computer-programming language.	

	1995 Despite international protests, France resumes nuclear weapons testing at Muroroa Atoll in French Polynesia.
	1995 The Japanese port of Kobé suffers extensive damage in a major earthquake; 6,000 people die.

Eurostar trains carry passengers between England and France or via the Channel Tunnel. The trains can reach speeds of 186 miles (300 km) per hour.	**1994** Interethnic violence in Rwanda claims more than one million lives.
	1994 Nelson Mandela (1918–) is elected president of South Africa.
	1995 Israeli Prime Minister Yitzhak Rabin (1922–95) is assassinated by an extreme nationalist opposed to his policies.

CONCISE HISTORY OF SCIENCE AND INVENTION

ASTRONOMY & MATH	BIOLOGY & MEDICINE	PHYSICAL SCIENCES

EUROPE

1996 Ariane 5, the new uncrewed space rocket of the European Space Administration (ESA), explodes on its first launch.

1996 Medical researchers establish a link between bovine spongiform encephalopathy (BSE) and Creutzfeldt–Jakob Disease (CJD), a human brain disorder that generally affects middle-aged and elderly people. A year later the diseases are shown to have the same cause by Moira Bruce working in Edinburgh, Scotland, and, independently, John Collinge and coworkers in London, England.

1996 Scottish biologist Ian Wilmut (1944–) at the Roslin Institute, Edinburgh, Scotland, clones a sheep named Dolly. Two years later Dolly gives birth to a lamb in the normal way.

1996 Physicists at the laboratories at the European Organization for Nuclear Research (CERN) in Switzerland produce antihydrogen (consisting of hydrogen atoms with positrons instead of electrons and antiprotons instead of protons as their nuclei). It is the first example of antimatter.

THE AMERICAS

1996 The National Aerospace and Space Administration's (NASA) space shuttle *Atlantis*, carrying American astronaut Shannon Lucid (1943–), docks in space with Russian space station Mir. Lucid returns to Earth on Atlantis six months later—the most time spent in space by a woman.

1996 American scientists launch the astronomical satellite Polar into Earth orbit. It carries 11 instruments for studying (among other things) the Earth's magnetosphere, the solar winds, and the aurora.

1997 The Hubble Space Telescope locates the brightest star in the universe; it is ten million times as bright as the sun.

1997 Canadian astronomer Brett Gladman (1966–) and coworkers at the Palomar Observatory, California, discover a small outer moon of Uranus, which they name Caliban. In the same year Philip Nicholson (1951–) discovers another small outer moon, Sycorax.

1997 NASA's space probe Mars Pathfinder soft-lands on Mars and releases a small six-wheel rover vehicle called Sojourner. About 16,500 images are sent back to Earth.

1996 American astronomer David McKay (1936–) and coworkers at the Johnson Space Center, Houston, find traces of what might be primitive microscopic life in a meteorite that originated from Mars.

1997 American geneticist Huntington Willard (1952–) assembles an artificial human chromosome that successfully replicates.

1997 Following their work of 1995 on Bose–Einstein condensates, American physicist Eric Cornell (1961–) and coworkers produce an atomic laser.

NASA's rover Sojourner hitched a ride on the space probe Mars Pathfinder. The rover was used to study the geology of the surface of Mars.

ASIA & OCEANIA

1996 Japanese amateur astronomer Yuji Hyakutake (1950–2002) discovers a new long-period (14,000 years) comet, named Comet Hyakutake. It passes within 9 million miles (14.9 million km) of Earth.

1997 The avian influenza ("bird flu") virus is isolated from a human patient in Hong Kong. After six patients die, the entire chicken population of Hong Kong is slaughtered.

1997 Paleontologists in China discover fossils of *Protarchaeopteryx*, a reptilian creature with birdlike characteristics.

1996 Japanese research chemists synthesize cellulose.

AFRICA & THE MIDDLE EAST

ENGINEERING & INVENTION

1996 The company DaimlerChrysler produces its second experimental vehicle powered by fuel cells, a car (the first, in 1994, was a panel truck).

1997 British fighter pilot Andy Green (1962–) sets the supersonic land speed record when he reaches 763.035 miles (1,227.99 km) per hour in the twin-jet car *Thrust SSC*.

1997 British author and inventor Ian Harrison files a patent for a dual-hinged refrigerator door that can be opened from either the left- or right-hand side.

1996 American researchers Theodore Poehler and Peter Searson develop an all-plastic battery.

1997 Edible food packaging is introduced in the United States.

1997 NASA's solar-powered airplane *Pathfinder* reaches a record altitude of 71,490 feet (21,790 m) during a flight over Hawaii.

Completed in 1996 the 241-foot (73.5-m) Petronas Towers in Kuala Lumpur, Malaysia, become the world's tallest buildings.

WORLD EVENTS

1996 Boris Yeltsin (1931–2007) becomes president of Russia.

1997 Conservative rule in Britain ends after 18 years when the Labour Party under its young leader Tony Blair (1953–) wins a landslide general election victory.

1997 Diana, Princess of Wales (1961–97), is killed in a car accident in Paris. About two billion people across the world watch her funeral on television.

1996 The United States increases its efforts to restrict illegal immigration from Mexico by hiring more U.S. Border Patrols and erecting 40 miles (65 km) of 14-foot (4.25-m) fence along its border with Mexico.

1996 Bill Clinton (1946–) is reelected, the first Democrat president to win a second term since 1936.

1997 American Tiger Woods (1975–) becomes the youngest golfer to win the U.S. Masters tournament in Augusta, Georgia.

1997 U.S. tobacco companies pay out $368.5 billion in claims made against them by former smokers.

1997 Bill Clinton apologizes to almost 400 African-American men in Alabama who were left untreated for the sexually transmitted infection syphilis as part of a government experiment between 1932 and 1972.

1996 The Tabilan overrun the Afghan capital Kabul.

1997 Hong Kong reverts to Chinese rule after 155 years of British sovereignty.

1997 Reformist Mohammed Khatami (1943–) is elected president of Iran.

CLONING ANIMALS

Early animal cloning experiments involved splitting sea urchin and salamander embryos so that two identical twins, or clones, developed. By the late 1950s scientists could create frog clones by transferring a nucleus from an

Ian Wilmut and Dolly the sheep.

adult cell into an egg cell from which the original nucleus had been removed, creating an exact replica of the animal from which the nucleus was taken. Using the nucleus of fully mature cells proved that adult cells keep a full set of genetic material, despite only expressing part of that material. The nucleus of a cell from a frog's intestine still "knew" how to make all the other cell types in a whole frog.

Making clones of mammals is much trickier because mammalian cells are much smaller than amphibian cells. But in 1996 Scottish scientist Ian Wilmut (1944–) created "Dolly the sheep." He fused an enucleated sheep's egg cell with an udder cell from an adult ewe. The resulting cell became an embryo, which was implanted into the uterus of a mature ewe. The ewe subsequently gave birth to a lamb that became an animal celebrity. Dolly went on to bear six lambs of her own in the normal way, but her health was poor. In 2001 she developed premature arthritis, and in 2003 she was diagnosed with lung disease and had to be put down. There was speculation as to whether Dolly's ill health was the result of her unusual origin.

Since Dolly, many more mammals have been cloned. In 1997 Wilmut and his team created Polly, a sheep cloned from fetal cells genetically altered to include a human gene. Other cloned animals include pigs, cattle, mice, and, in 2005, a racehorse.

ASTRONOMY & MATH	BIOLOGY & MEDICINE	PHYSICAL SCIENCES

EUROPE

1998 Dutch astronomers detect a large galaxy 20 million light-years away in a region previously thought to be nearly empty.

1998 The Astronomical Technology Centre (ATC) is established at the Royal Observatory, Edinburgh, for the design and production of astronomical instruments and associated technology for terrestrial observatories and space missions.

1999 The European Space Agency (ESA) launches XMM-Newton, the X-Ray Multi-Mirror Observatory, into Earth orbit. It consists of three aligned telescopes for making observations at x-ray wavelengths.

1999 Russia abandons its Mir space station, after 13 years of occupation.

1998 After 15 years' work a team of international scientists, including English biologist John Sulston (1942–), determines the genome for a whole animal, *Caenorhabditis elegans*, a tiny nematode worm.

1999 The British government bans the advertising of tobacco products on television and on roadside billboards.

1999 French paleontologists unearth fossils of 30 million-year-old *Baluchitherium* (also known as *Paraceratherium*). The largest ever land mammal, the rhinoceroslike beast stood 18 feet (5.5 m) tall.

1999 According to the World Health Organization (WHO), AIDS becomes the primary cause of death in Africa.

1999 Russian researchers at the Joint Institute for Nuclear Research in Dubna, Moscow, create element 114 by bombarding plutonium-244 with calcium-48 nuclei.

In 1999 the hot-air balloon Breitling Orbiter 3 *circumnavigated the world in 19 days, 21 hours, and 55 minutes.*

THE AMERICAS

1998 The National Aeronautics and Space Administration (NASA) launches its space probe Deep Space 1, the first of the New Millennium Program missions, using new technology such as ion propulsion rockets.

1998 Astronomers at the University of Hawaii discover a 130-foot (40-m) near-Earth asteroid that passes within Earth's orbit.

1999 The Hubble Space Telescope has its second service since being placed in orbit in 1990. The mission is carried out by astronauts in the space shuttle *Discovery*.

1999 Canadian astronomers Matthew Holman (1967–), J. J. Kavelaars, and Brett Gladman (1966–) find three outer moons of Uranus.

1999 American astronaut Eileen Collins (1956–) is the first woman to command a space shuttle when *Columbia* is launched to place the Chandra X-ray Observatory (CXO) into an elliptical Earth orbit.

1999 NASA launches its Stardust space probe to rendezvous with comet Wild-2 in 2004. It returns to Earth with samples of dust from the comet in 2006.

1998 Zoologists discover five new species of small salamanders in tropical Mexico. They are assigned to the genus *Thorius*.

1998 American researchers at Johns Hopkins University successfully grow human stem cells in the laboratory (stem cells may one day be used to treat various cellular disorders).

1998 Researchers in Hawaii clone 50 mice from adult cells, and Japanese scientists clone eight calves.

1998 American dentists first use lasers for "drilling" teeth.

1999 American scientists create element 118 by fusing lead-208 with krypton-86, but it decays to form element 116.

ASIA & OCEANIA

1998 Two Japanese satellites in Earth orbit carry out the first automatic docking, using laser sensors. The Japanese Institute of Space and Astronautical Sciences also launches its Planet-B space probe to Mars.

1999 Chinese archaeologists uncover 4,000-year-old human remains with evidence of a healed craniotomy (also known as trepanning, a surgical operation to make a hole in the skull).

AFRICA & THE MIDDLE EAST

1998 Paleontologists find a whole skeleton of a 36-foot (11-m) fish-eating dinosaur in a desert in Niger, Africa.

INSIDE STORY

Caenorhabditis elegans

The first multicellular animal to have its genome—its hereditary information encoded in deoxyribonucleic acid (DNA)—sequenced was the nematode roundworm *Caenorhabditis elegans* in 1998 by a team of international scientists. The worm's genome is about 100 million base pairs long, with about 20,000 genes. Research into this free-living, transparent worm, which grows to about 0.04 inches (1 mm) in length, was first begun by South African biologist Sydney Brenner (1927–) in 1974, and it soon proved to be a very useful biological model. Adult *C. elegans* worms have about 1,000 body cells and scientists learned what each cell does. About 300 of the cells are neurons, and scientists have studied the neurons involved in many of the worm's behaviors, including mating and chemotaxis—movement toward chemicals in the worm's environment. Scientists have also found it relatively easy to block specific genes to elucidate their function in the worm.

ENGINEERING & INVENTION	WORLD EVENTS

1998 Swiss scientists produce a titanium dioxide solar cell. It is twice as efficient as standard solar cells.

1998 The Paris subway opens a new route, Meteor (Métro Est-Ouest Rapide), with fully automated driverless trains.

1999 Swiss psychiatrist and balloonist Bertrand Piccard (1958–) and English balloonist Brian Jones (1947–) circumnavigate the world in their hot-air balloon, *Breitling Orbiter 3*.

1998 Voters in Northern Ireland and the Irish Republic endorse the Good Friday Agreement, bringing the prospect of peace after 30 years of paramilitary violence.

1998 Serbian paramilitaries ravage the Yugoslav province of Kosovo, conducting ethnic cleansing against the Albanian populace, but withdraw after the North Atlantic Treaty Organization (NATO) orders airstrikes against Serbia. The conflict continues into 1999.

1998 Germany establishes a pension fund to compensate Jewish Holocaust survivors in Central and Eastern Europe.

1999 Poland, Hungary, and the Czech Republic join NATO.

1999 Computer virus Melissa spreads rapidly by e-mail to infect more than 100,000 computers wordwide. Other viruses of the year that wreak havoc are called Chernobyl and ExploreZip.

1998 The weather phenomenon El Niño causes high temperatures, drought, and tornadoes in the United States.

1999 U.S President Bill Clinton (1946–) and Mexican President Ernesto Zedillo (1951–) work together to combat drug trafficking.

1999 A Senate trial acquits President Bill Clinton of perjury and obstruction of justice.

1999 The founder of Amazon.com, Jeff Bezos (1964) is named *Time* magazine's Man of the Year for his significant input into launching the online shopping revolution.

Eileen Collins, the first woman to command a space shuttle, poses in her orange Launch and Entry Suit.

1998 The world's largest passenger terminal opens at the new Chek Lap Kok Airport in Hong Kong, China.

1998 The government of Pakistan is overthrown in a military coup; General Pervez Musharraf (1943–) becomes head of state.

1999 East Timor votes for independence from Indonesia; after much violence it will achieve its goal in 2002.

1998 The terror group al-Qaeda bombs U.S. embassies in Kenya and Tanzania, killing more than 200 people.

1999 A major earthquake in northern Turkey claims 17,000 lives.

MILLENNIUM BUG

Toward the end of the 1990s computer experts predicted that a phenomenon known as the "millennium bug," or the Y2K problem, would automatically take effect at midnight on December 31, 1999. They had realized that the Basic Input Output System (BIOS) programs in most computers contained a fundamental error. It meant that the computer would not recognize the date 2000 and would set the time back to an incorrect date, usually January 1, 1900. It was said that, unless corrected by expensive software, the "bug" would erase memories or make computers crash, with terrible consequences for homes and businesses worldwide. Air-traffic control and transportation systems would malfunction; machines in hospitals would suddenly stop; and domestic appliances containing microchips would fail. Many organizations took precautions to prevent or lessen the effects, often at considerable cost. But on January 1 nothing happened: The millennium bug did not exist.

At about the same time computer viruses that were started deliberately became a problem. They generally spread as attachments to e-mails, hence the advice from experts not to open any attachments from unknown senders.

People in Hong Kong, worried about the millennium bug, withdraw money from their bank accounts on December 30, 1999.

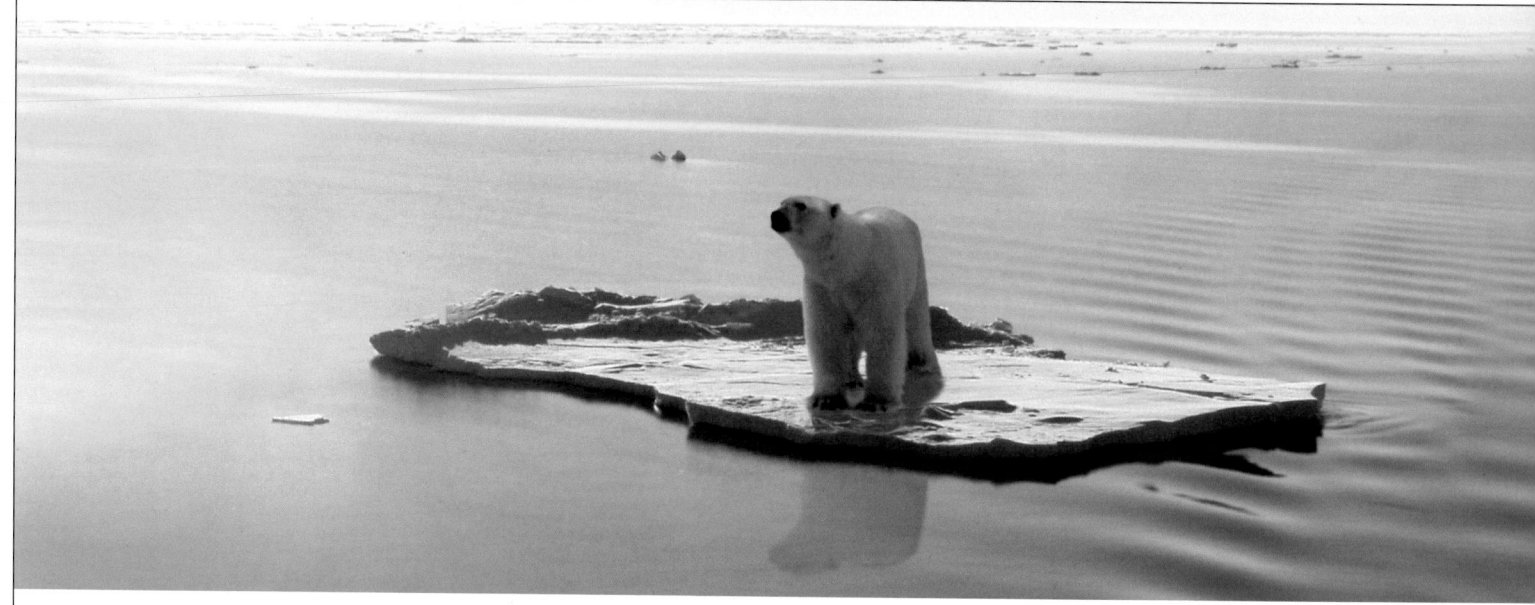

THE GREENHOUSE EFFECT AND GLOBAL WARMING

I N THE MINDS OF MOST PEOPLE THE GREENHOUSE effect is inextricably linked with the phenomenon of global warming, but it is also one of the fortuitous natural phenomena that make the planet habitable. The Earth has benefited from it for billions of years. The overall effect is an insulating one—the natural greenhouse effect keeps the Earth's average temperature about 60°F (32°C) higher than it would otherwise be. The principles of the phenomenon and the term *greenhouse effect* were first described by French mathematician Jean Fourier (1768–1830) in 1827. Experimental evidence supporting Fourier's ideas was provided by Irish physicist John Tyndall (1820–93) in 1859. Tyndall demonstrated that gases including water vapor and carbon dioxide (CO$_2$) could trap heat.

During the early 20th century scientists were aware that the Earth's climate had previously undergone dramatic changes and that it was currently enjoying a period of relative warmth, called an interglacial period. Aware of the greenhouse role of CO$_2$, Swedish physical chemist Svante Arrhenius (1859–1927) suspected that ice ages might have been caused by reduced levels of atmospheric CO$_2$. Then he thought of something else. He calculated the amount of CO$_2$ being released into the atmosphere by human activities and realized that such output could eventually begin to have the reverse effect. In 1896 he was the first to suggest that, instead of facing global cooling, the world may experience global warming as a result of industrial emissions. But the prospect was a distant one, and even Arrhenius was not concerned by it.

Rising Levels of Carbon Dioxide

The idea was revived four decades later in 1939 by English hobby meteorologist Guy Stewart Callendar (1989–1964). After reviewing historical records, he suggested that increases in temperatures and CO$_2$ levels were linked. The suggestion was rejected by many climatologists, who thought that natural checks and balances, such as the absorption of excess CO$_2$ by oceans, would render such changes impossible.

But Callender's suggestion had sown a seed of doubt, and the idea refused to go away. The evidence, however, remained thin and open to question. Climatologists desperately needed better models and more data. Over the latter part of the 20th century, they gradually became available.

Global warming has reduced the sea-ice habitat of polar bears. With a shrinking range to find sufficient food, the species is now under serious threat.

Most scientists now agree that curbing the emissions of greenhouse gases, such as those that result from burning fossil fuels, is vital in combating climate change.

In the 1960s it became possible to measure accurately atmospheric carbon dioxide levels, and over the ensuing years it became apparent that they were indeed rising rapidly. Throughout the late 20th century scientists were uncovering layers of complexity relating to the way the Earth's climate systems work, making it almost impossible to give firm predictions.

During the 1980s records from around the world showed an increase in temperatures, but an enhanced greenhouse effect remained only one of many proposed causes. Climate models began to take account of variables such as ocean absorption and clouds. The year 1988 marked something of a turning point. Globally, it was the hottest year on record (there have been many hotter ones since), and it was the year that public awareness of the possibility of global warming took off. American climatologist James Hansen reiterated that increased levels of CO_2 in the atmosphere would lead to global warming.

Between 1890 and 1990 the amount of CO_2 in the atmosphere rose by a quarter, from 280 to 345 parts per million by volume. By the early 1990s human civilization was churning out 6.6 billion tons (6 billion tonnes) of CO_2 gas a year—5.5 billion tons (5 billion tonnes) from the burning of fossil fuels and 1.1 billion tons (1 billion tonnes) from burning down rain forests. At the same time, other greenhouse gases were increasing at an even greater rate: methane at 1 percent a year and chlorofluorocarbons (CFCs) at 6 percent each year. Both gases are markedly more efficient at trapping solar radiation than CO_2.

By the end of the 20th century, scientists reached a general consensus that the world is undergoing a significant warming and that the trend is the result of human activities contributing to an enhanced greenhouse effect. Climate models were providing alarming predictions about what these changes would mean: rising sea levels, violent storms, floods, and droughts

in quick succession. Some governments had already begun taking steps to limit their national output of greenhouse gases and, in 1997, 84 nations made a firm commitment to curb emissions by signing up to the Kyoto Protocol, which came into effect in 2005.

In natural conditions most carbon dioxide is absorbed by phytoplankton in the sea and by forest trees. As humans create more and more carbon dioxide, excess amounts accumulate in the atmosphere. This absorbs the solar energy that is radiated back from the surface of the Earth, trapping the heat so that global temperatures begin to rise. This creates the so-called "greenhouse effect."

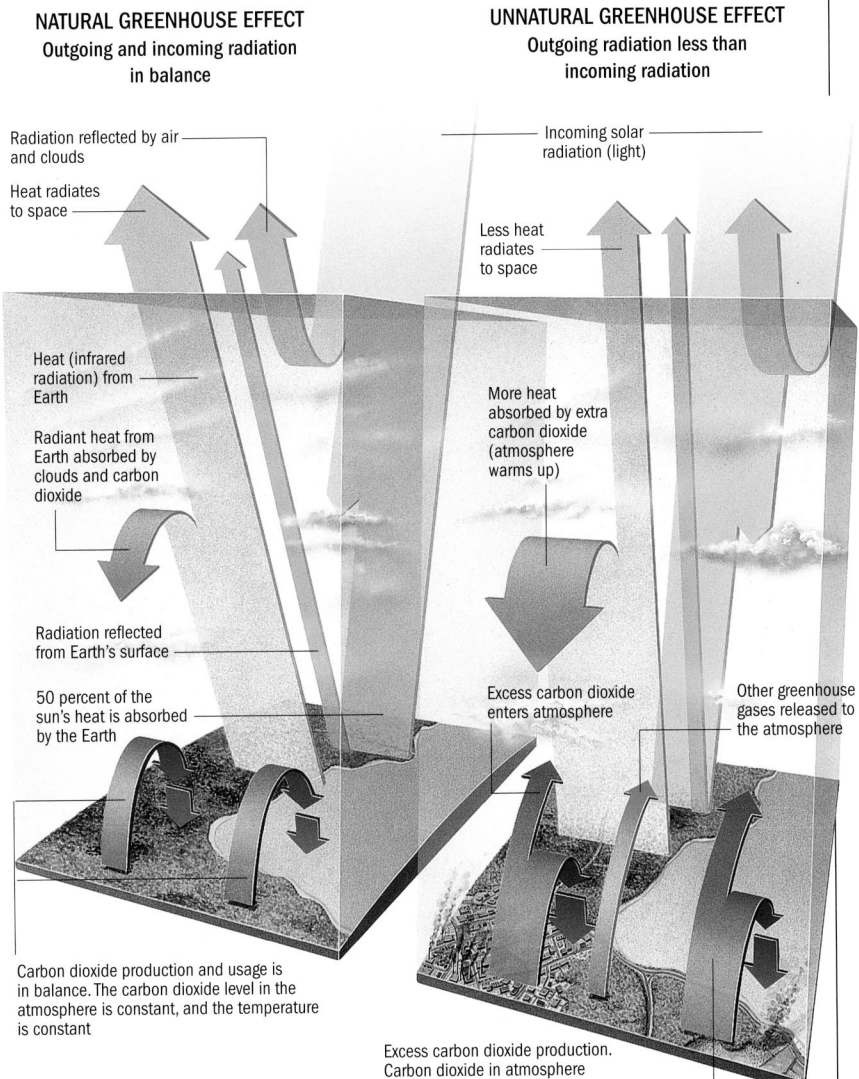

NATURAL GREENHOUSE EFFECT
Outgoing and incoming radiation in balance

Radiation reflected by air and clouds

Heat radiates to space

Heat (infrared radiation) from Earth

Radiant heat from Earth absorbed by clouds and carbon dioxide

Radiation reflected from Earth's surface

50 percent of the sun's heat is absorbed by the Earth

Carbon dioxide production and usage is in balance. The carbon dioxide level in the atmosphere is constant, and the temperature is constant

UNNATURAL GREENHOUSE EFFECT
Outgoing radiation less than incoming radiation

Incoming solar radiation (light)

Less heat radiates to space

More heat absorbed by extra carbon dioxide (atmosphere warms up)

Excess carbon dioxide enters atmosphere

Other greenhouse gases released to the atmosphere

Excess carbon dioxide production. Carbon dioxide in atmosphere increases, and temperature rises

ASTRONOMY & MATH	BIOLOGY & MEDICINE	PHYSICAL SCIENCES

EUROPE

2000 The European Space Administration (ESA) launches four Cluster satellites to explore the Earth's magnetosphere.

2000 Russia launches the Zvezda service module that (together with Zarya and Unity, which are already in orbit) forms the basis of the new International Space Station. Later that year an American astronaut and two Russian cosmonauts travel in a Russian Soyuz spacecraft to become the first crew of the new space station.

2001 Russia's abandoned space station Mir reenters the Earth's atmosphere and largely burns up.

2000 The Pyrenean ibex (*Capra pyrenaica*) goes extinct when the last individual dies in Ordesa National Park, Spain.

2001 Gray wolves (*Canis lupus*) are found living wild in Germany (they have not been seen in the wild for 150 years).

2001 An epidemic of foot-and-mouth disease leads to the slaughter of thousands of cattle in Britain.

We are here to celebrate the completion of the first survey of the entire human genome. Without a doubt, this is the most important, most wondrous map ever produced by humankind.

PRESIDENT BILL CLINTON

THE AMERICAS

2000 The National Aeronautics and Space Administration's (NASA) space probe Galileo passes close to Jupiter's moon Io.

2000 A carbonaceous chondrite meteorite crashes near Tagish Lake in the Yukon. Its composition is thought to be similar to the materials from which the sun and solar system evolved.

2000 A camera on NASA's Cassini space probe reveals a new asteroid (no. 2685), which is named Masursky for American planetary scientist Harold Masursky (1922–90), who worked on most of NASA's missions from the 1960s to the 1980s.

2001 NASA's orbiter Mars Odyssey enters orbit around Mars.

2001 NASA launches its Genesis probe to collect samples of the solar wind.

2001 NASA's space probe NEAR (Near Earth Asteroid Rendezvous), later renamed NEAR Shoemaker, lands on and photographs the surface of the asteroid Eros.

2001 The fourth of the 323-inch (8.2-m) reflecting telescopes is added to complete the Very Large Telescope (VLT) at Paranal Observatory in the Atacama desert, Chile.

2000 Scientists on the Human Genome Project produce a rough draft of the sequence of the human genome (using more than 3 billion characters).

2000 American paleontologist Dale Russell discovers a fossilized dinosaur heart.

2001 American researchers clone a human embryo but do not allow it to develop further.

2001 Surgeons in New York City use computers and "telepresence" to operate on a woman in France.

2000 Geneticists figure out the complete genome sequence of the fruit fly *Drosophila*, the most widely used experimental animal in the study of genetics.

2001 NASA's Trans-Iron Galactic Element Recorder (TIGER) makes its first ascent on the helium-filled Ultra Long Duration Balloon (ULDB) on a 30-day flight over Antarctica. Its mission is to detect heavy elements from iron to zirconium in cosmic rays originating in outer space.

ASIA & OCEANIA

2000 Japanese chemist Katsuyoshi Hoshino and coworkers announce a new way of "fixing" nitrogen in air using bright light and composite plastics to produce ammonium perchlorate (meaning that the nitrogen is converted to ammonium).

AFRICA & THE MIDDLE EAST

On September 11, 2001, Islamic terrorists flew airliners into the World Trade Center in New York City and the Pentagon in Washington, D.C.; a fourth plane crashed in Pennsylvania.

ENGINEERING & INVENTION

2000 In Norway the 15.2-mile (24.5-km) Lærdal Tunnel is completed, making it the world's longest road tunnel.

2000 British inventor Matthew Allwork (1963–2003) perfects a gyrostabilized camera that runs along tracks to televise athletics events. It is first used at the Olympic Games in Sydney, Australia.

2001 British inventor Ron Northedge patents a valve for controlling fluid flow that uses a rare-earth magnet, with no springs or continuous electricity supply.

2000 Divers in South Carolina raise the wreck of the Confederate submarine *H. L. Hunley*, which sank in 1864 during the American Civil War.

2000 American surgeon Robert Jarvik (1946–) begins work on the Jarvik–2000 artificial heart.

2001 The uncrewed *Southern Cross II* (Global Hawk spy plane) crosses the Pacific Ocean.

2001 International Launch Services, a joint U.S.–Russian venture, introduces the two-stage Proton M rocket, which can place a payload of 3.2 tons (2.9 tonnes) directly into a geostationary orbit around Earth.

2001 The twin towers of the World Trade Center in New York City, the world's second largest building, are destroyed by terrorist attacks.

WORLD EVENTS

2000 Serbia's president Slobodan Milosevic (1941–2006) is ousted in a popular uprising; he will later be indicted for war crimes and put on trial by an international court.

2000 Vladimir Putin (1952–) is elected president of Russia.

2000 Republican George W. Bush (1946–) emerges the winner in a disputed U.S. presidential election. He is reelected in 2004.

2000 Hilary Clinton (1947–) becomes the first First Lady elected to public office, winning a U.S. Senate seat in New York.

2000 Vicente Fox (1942–) becomes president of Mexico.

2001 The United States leads an invasion of Afghanistan, whose government is accused of harboring terrorists.

2000 The first-ever meeting takes place between the leaders of North and South Korea.

2001 Pakistan is a major ally in the U.S. invasion of Afghanistan.

2000 Israel ends its occupation of Southern Lebanon.

2000 The United States endorses the creation of a Palestinian state.

INSIDE STORY

"Love Bug"

Early in 2000 a computer virus known as the "Love Bug" forced computer systems across Europe to close down. It spread to the United States within a few hours. Possibly the reason why it spread so fast was because it originated in an attachment to an e-mail entitled "I love you... ." As soon as the attachment was opened, copies of the same e-mail were sent automatically to each name listed in the user's address book. Not only did the "bug" overload e-mail servers, it also infected certain files on the victim's machine. Within a few months at least 13 variants of the original virus had been identified. Since then a range of new antivirus products have been introduced to prevent future infections.

THE HUMAN GENOME PROJECT

A genome is a compete set of genes or genetic instructions that make up an organism. Because all organisms inherit their genes from the previous generation, the genome also provides important information about that organism's ancestry. In humans, as in other organisms, faults or mutations in the genetic code often lead to medical conditions known as genetic disorders.

Genes are instructions carried on chromosomes. Chromosomes are made of deoxyribonucleic acid (DNA). The human genome is a code spelled out in four letters: A, T, C, and G. The letters represent the chemical bases adenine, thiamine, cytosine, and guanine, which link up to form the "rungs" of DNA's twisting ladderlike structure.

This computer screen display shows a sequence of human DNA as a series of colored bands. Each color represents a specific base.

The Human Genome Project was launched in 1990, with research institutes in several countries collaborating. Its aims were to sequence the letters of the human genetic code and identify all the genes. The project took 13 years to complete, with most of the sequencing done in laboratories in the United States. Advances in sequencing techniques pioneered by entrepreneurial scientist J. Craig Venter (1946–) helped speed up the project. In February 2001 the first draft of the genome, a list of about three billion bases, was published. The full sequence—containing about 25,000 different genes—was published in 2003.

ASTRONOMY & MATH	BIOLOGY & MEDICINE	PHYSICAL SCIENCES

EUROPE

2003 The Netherlands reports an epidemic of avian influenza ("bird flu").

2003 Footprints of an upright-walking human that lived 350,000 years ago are reported to have been discovered in Italy.

"Copycat" or "CC" was the first successfully cloned cat.

2002 German chemist Hans Gerd-Boyen at the University of Ulm discovers a new isotope of gold that resists powerful oxidizing agents and holds out promise for use as a catalyst.

2003 Chemist Leonid Khryashtchev at Helsinki University, Finland, makes an organic compound of a rare gas by reacting ethyne (acetylene) with krypton.

THE AMERICAS

2002 The National Aeronautic and Space Administration's (NASA) space probe Mars Odyssey begins mapping the surface of Mars, using thermal emission imaging.

2002 Astronomers at the observatory at Mauna Kea in Hawaii locate 11 new moons of Jupiter (bringing the total number to 39).

2002 The crew of NASA's space shuttle *Columbia* upgrades the Hubble Space Telescope in orbit around the Earth.

2003 NASA's space shuttle *Columbia* is destroyed when it breaks up 16 minutes before it is due to land on Earth, killing all of the crew. Shuttle flights are suspended until 2005.

2003 NASA's Wilkinson Microwave Anisotropy Probe satellite makes a detailed cosmic microwave background radiation map of the universe. The map reveals the universe to be 13.7 billion years old.

2002 Researchers at Texas A&M University reveal their clone of a domestic cat, which they name "Copycat."

2002 American researchers at the University of New York at Stony Brook produce a synthetic virus.

2002 The U.S. Food and Drug Administration approves clozapine as the first drug to reduce the risk of suicidal behavior.

2002 American chemists Lester Andrews and Bruce Bersten synthesize a compound of uranium and the rare gas neon.

The crew of the space shuttle Columbia *died in 2003 when the shuttle disintegrated during reentry into Earth's atmosphere. The incident was a result of damage to the shuttle's thermal protection system during its launch.*

ASIA & OCEANIA

2002 Astronomers in China and Japan observe the reappearance of Comet Ikeya-Zhang, which has not been seen for 341 years.

2003 Astronaut ("taikonaut" in China) Yang Liwei becomes the first Chinese astronaut to orbit the Earth in a 21-hour flight in China's first crewed spacecraft, Shen Zhou 5.

2003 An outbreak of the severe acute respiratory syndrome (SARS) virus in Asia spreads worldwide.

AFRICA & THE MIDDLE EAST

2003 A new group of insects called Mantophasmatodea is discovered in southern Africa.

ENGINEERING & INVENTION

2002 English inventor David Baker patents the Land Shark, a high-speed amphibious car.

2003 Austrian "extreme" sportsman Felix Baumgartner jumps from an airplane and skyglides across the English Channel. He makes the 22-mile (35-km) crossing in 14 minutes.

2003 Concorde makes its last flight.

2003 The last old-style Volkswagen Beetle is made in Puebla, Mexico.

Austrian Felix Baumgartner tests his carbon glider before his successful attempt to cross the English Channel in 2003.

WORLD EVENTS

2002 The Euro—the new currency of the European Union—begins circulating.

2002 Queen Elizabeth (1900–2002), the Queen Mother, of Britain dies aged 101.

2003 Energy company Enron declares bankruptcy, the largest bankruptcy case in U.S. history.

2003 The United States launches an attack on Iraq.

INSIDE STORY

Synthetic Virus

In 2002 a team of of scientists from the State University of New York at Stony Brook made a synthetic poliovirus. The researchers downloaded the genome sequence of the virus from the Internet, ordered it in fragments from a mail-order supplier, and then assembled it into the complete genome. The scientists injected their virus into mice, which became paralyzed and died. Synthetic viruses could be an important tool for gene therapy, in which viruses are used to carry genes into the cells of people with genetic disorders to replace or correct faulty genes. The creation of a synthetic virus also led to fears that bioterrorists would be able to make and spread lethal viruses such as smallpox.

2002 Islamic terrorists bomb nightclubs in Bali, Indonesia, killing about 200 people.

2002 The dispute between India and Pakistan over the Kashmir region threatens to turn into a nuclear war.

2003 Unrest breaks out in the Darfur region of Sudan, where government troops and their allies kill some 180,000 people and displace two million.

2003 An earthquake in Iran kills more than 40,000 people.

SARS

Severe acute respiratory syndrome, or SARS, was the first serious new contagious disorder of the 21st century. SARS is caused by a virus and affects the respiratory tract. Symptoms include high fever, chills, headache, cough, and diarrhea. Most infected people also develop pneumonia and breathing difficulties. In the SARS outbreak of 2002–03, which affected about 8,000 people, almost 800—about 1 in 10 sufferers—died. The disease originated in China and soon spread outside the country. The virus is passed on via the coughs and sneezes of those infected or by touching a contaminated object, such as a door handle, that had been touched by an infected person. The virus may also be able to travel in the air.

As with many other viral infections—including common cold, influenza, and HIV infection—medical scientists have not found a cure for SARS. Treatment aims at relieving symptoms, such as fever and breathing difficulties. With effective isolation of affected people, an outbreak of the disease can be contained. Chinese scientists produced a vaccine against SARS virus in 2004.

Schoolchildren in Hong Kong wear masks to protect themselves against SARS infection.

	ASTRONOMY & MATH	BIOLOGY & MEDICINE	PHYSICAL SCIENCES

EUROPE

2004 The Russian Soyuz TMA-4 spacecraft with a three-man crew docks with the International Space Station (ISS).

2004 The European Space Agency's (ESA) Beagle II lander, carried aboard the National Aeronautical and Space Administration's (NASA) Mars Express space probe, vanishes during its landing attempt on Mars.

2005 After a seven-year trip, the Cassini–Huygens space probe reaches Saturn. NASA's Cassini orbits the planet, while ESA's Huygens probe parachutes onto the surface of Saturn's massive moon Titan. It sends back data and pictures of what looks like an ice-strewn landscape.

2005 Scientists extract and decode the deoxyribonucleic acid (DNA) of two cave bears that died 40,000 years ago in the Austrian Alps.

An artist's impression shows the moment when a projectile from NASA's Deep Impact space probe collided with Comet Tempel 1.

THE AMERICAS

2004 NASA scientists obtain images of a "planetoid," named Sedna, orbiting beyond Neptune at the edge of the solar system.

2004 The first commercial spaceflight takes place when SpaceShipOne, funded by American computer programmer and entrepreneur Paul Allen (1953–), takes to the air and reaches a height of 337,600 feet, or 63.9 miles (103 km).

2005 Astronomer Michael Brown (1965–) announces the discovery of a remote object larger than Pluto. It becomes a candidate to be the tenth planet in the solar system.

2005 A projectile dispatched from NASA's Deep Impact space probe successfully collides with Comet Tempel 1, throwing out a huge plume of icy debris. Deep Impact is unharmed and redirected toward another comet.

2005 Astronomers discover 12 new moons orbiting Saturn.

2005 NASA space shuttle *Discovery* restarts the shuttle program with a successful flight to the International Space Station (ISS). It returns 14 days later after delays due to problems with heat-shield tiles. NASA grounds the shuttle fleet indefinitely.

2005 American researchers at Knoxville, Tennessee, grow human eggs in the laboratory by culturing ovarian stem cells in a hormone-rich solution.

2005 The Genographic Project is announced —a project spanning five continents that aims to map the history of human migration using DNA.

2005 Brazilian government figures indicate that the Amazon rain forest is being destroyed at record levels.

2004 Physicists from Penn State University announce a helium-based "supersolid" that flows through another material without friction.

2005 American geophysicist Joseph Dwyer and coworkers discover that lightning flashes also produce bursts of x-rays.

ASIA & OCEANIA

2005 The National Space Development Agency (NASDA) of Japan launches a weather satellite into Earth orbit, providing Japan with an independent weather forecasting facility.

2004 Medical researchers in South Korea clone human embryos to obtain stem cells for therapeutic purposes.

2004 Paleontologists announce the discovery of an 18,000-year-old skeleton of a 3-foot (1-m) tall humanoid on Flores Island, Indonesia. They name it *Homo floresiensis*.

AFRICA & THE MIDDLE EAST

2005 German zoologists on the Indian Ocean island of Madagascar identify two new tiny species of mouse lemurs (*Microcebus*).

ENGINEERING & INVENTION	WORLD EVENTS

2005 European consortium Airbus Industrie's Airbus 380 makes its maiden flight from Toulouse, France. At 240 feet (73 m) long, with a wingspan of 239 feet (72.8 m) and able to carry an average of 550 passengers, it is the world's largest passenger plane. It can fly nonstop between any of the world's major airports.

2005 The International Thermonuclear Experimental Reactor project is announced to build a nuclear fusion reactor in France; the project is expected to run for 35 years.

2004 Terrorist attacks on trains in Madrid kill 190 people.

2004 Ten more countries join the European Union: Poland, Lithuania, Latvia, Estonia, the Czech Republic, Slovakia, Slovenia, Hungary, Malta, and Cyprus.

2004 The Russian army ends a terrorist siege at a school in Beslan, North Ossetia-Alania. More than 330 people are killed and at least 700 more are injured.

2005 Pope John Paul II (1920–2005) dies.

2005 Four explosions on public transport in London kill 56 people and injure more than 700 others.

2005 American company Boeing launches the Boeing 777-200LR airliner, designed to carry 300 passengers across the world nonstop in 18 hours.

2005 American adventurer Steve Fossett (1944–) lands at Salina, Kansas, after a 67-hour solo nonstop flight around the world in a jet-powered plane.

2005 American scientists use highly sensitive scales to measure the mass of a cluster of xenon atoms at just a few billionths of a trillionth of a gram—the smallest measurement of mass ever made.

2005 American researchers produce the world's smallest brushes, with bristles more than a thousand times finer than a human hair.

2004 George W. Bush (1946–) begins a second term as the U.S. President.

2005 Hurricane Katrina hits the Gulf Coast of the United States, resulting in one of the worst natural disasters in U.S. history.

2005 American cyclist Lance Armstrong (1971–) wins the Tour de France for an unprecedented seventh consecutive time.

Archaeologist Tony Djubiantono holds the skull of Homo floresiensis.

2004 An undersea earthquake triggers a tsunami that devastates Indonesia and other parts of southern Asia, killing about 300,000 people.

The Airbus A380 test crew wave from a platform in front of the world's biggest airliner after its four-hour maiden flight from Toulouse Blagnac airport in France.

2004 The first municipal elections in 40 years are held in Saudi Arabia. Woman are not allowed to vote or run for office.

2004 The first free elections in 50 years are held in Iraq.

THE HOBBIT

In 2003, a team of Australian and Indonesian paleontologists found skeletal remains, including a skull, of a previously unknown hominoid species in the Liang Bua cave in Flores, an island in Indonesia. The team named the species *Homo floresiensis*, for the island of Flores. *H. floresiensis* lived until about 18,000 years ago and is thought to be a descendant of *H. erectus*, which lived in Africa, Asia, and Europe and also gave rise to modern humans, *H. sapiens*.

H. floresiensis grew to about 40 inches (100 cm) tall, had long arms, and a small skull—similar to the size of a chimpanzee's skull but with more humanlike features. The team published their findings in 2004, and the press soon nicknamed the species "hobbits," for the race of short humanlike creatures featured in the novels of J. R. R. Tolkien.

Some scientists disputed whether *H. floresiensis* was a species in its own right. They believe that the skull that was found belonged to a modern human with a disease, such as the genetic disorder microcephaly, which results in a small brain and skull. Others believe *H. floresiensis* was a population of slender (gracile) modern humans. However, the skeletal remains seem unlikely to provide any deoxyribonucleic acid (DNA) that would help resolve the relationship of *H. floresiensis* to modern humans.

THE WORLD WIDE WEB

ABOVE: *More than 70 percent of people in the United States use the Internet.*

THE WORLD WIDE WEB ALLOWS USERS ACROSS the world access to a vast amount of data and enables rapid communication with other users at the click of a mouse. It uses telephone lines or radio to link computers into a network that extends across the world. It allows computer users to gain access to billions of Web pages as well as video, movies, and music. English computer scientist Tim Berners-Lee (1955–) devised the Web in 1990.

Computer links had existed since the 1970s. They were developed originally for the use of scientists working for the Advanced Research Projects Agency (ARPA) of the U.S. Department of Defense as a network known as ARPANET. Stanford University set up a commercial version of ARPANET in 1974.

In 1981 the City University of New York launched BITNET. It could be used by university scientists throughout the eastern United States, provided they used IBM mainframe computers. European versions soon followed: EUNET in 1982 and the European Academic and Research Network (EARN) in 1984.

These networks were limited by the difficulty of generating information on one computer in a form that could be read by other computers. The problem was solved within each network, but there were so many systems that computers belonging to one network were unable to communicate with computers from another.

As early as 1974, however, computer scientists at ARPA and Stanford University had devised a system called a transmission control protocol/internet protocol (TCP/IP) to allow computers to send data between networks. ARPA adopted TCP/IP in 1982. Networks could finally be linked: The Internet had been born and, with it, e-mail. Messages between

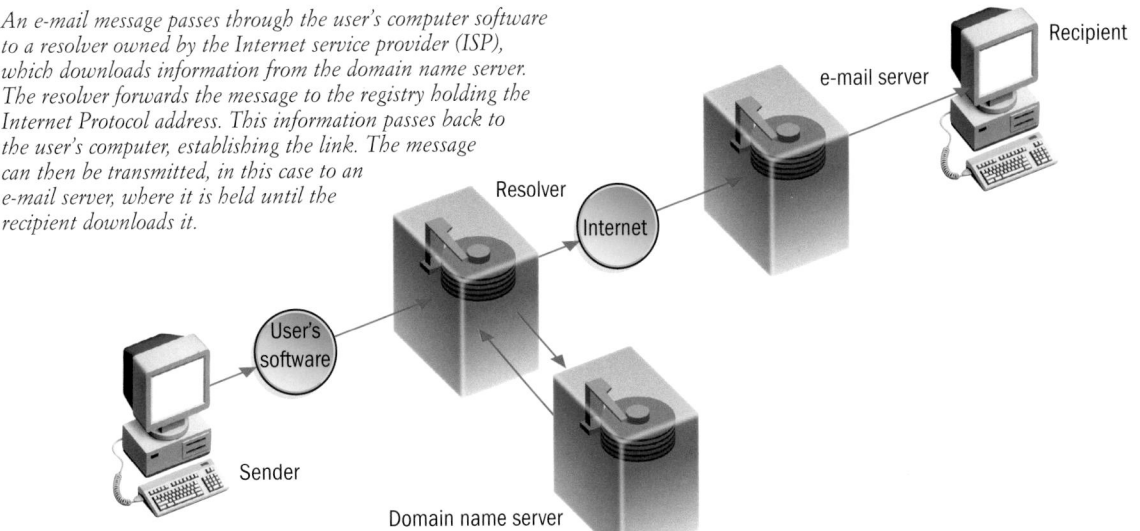

An e-mail message passes through the user's computer software to a resolver owned by the Internet service provider (ISP), which downloads information from the domain name server. The resolver forwards the message to the registry holding the Internet Protocol address. This information passes back to the user's computer, establishing the link. The message can then be transmitted, in this case to an e-mail server, where it is held until the recipient downloads it.

KEY DATES

1980
Tim Berners-Lee releases Enquire

1981
BITNET launched

1982
EUNET launched; Internet born

1984
EARN launched; domain names introduced; JANET launched

1985
NSFNET launched

1990
Tim Berners-Lee names the World Wide Web

1991
NSFNET opened to the public; the Web released to the public

1992
"Information superhighway project"

1993
Mosaic X, the first Web browser, introduced

1993
World Wide Web certified by CERN as being in the public domain

computers had to be routed. This meant that each host (any computer linked to a network) had to be allotted a unique address. At first, it was sufficient to allocate a name to each host, but in 1984 the system became more sophisticated with the introduction of domain name servers. A domain name server is a computer that stores lists of domain names and can route requests accordingly. Domain names include http:// (hypertext transfer protocol), www (World Wide Web), ac (academic), edu (education), com (commercial), and gov (government), as well as national identifiers, such as uk (United Kingdom) and nl (Netherlands).

The Internet received a further boost when, also in 1984, British government backed the Joint Academic Network (JANET) to serve British universities. In 1985 the U.S. National Science Foundation set up NSFNET to extend Internet use to all authorized persons on every American campus. NSFNET concluded agreements with the owners of other networks and made TCP/IP mandatory for all participants. In 1991 NSFNET allowed access to private computers.

Tim Berners-Lee

Since 1980 Tim Berners-Lee had been searching for a way to allow physicists to communicate with one another using different computer systems. His first program, devised in 1980, was called "Enquire-Within-Upon-Everything." It allowed certain types of computers to exchange data using hypertext transfer protocol, which links documents on different computers, allowing the user to move swiftly from one to another. It was not until 1990, however, that Berners-Lee developed Enquire into the World Wide Web.

In 1991 the program was published on the Internet, free for anyone to use. The World Wide Web was born. It grew slowly. By the end of 1993 there were no more than about 150 sites connected to it. But 1993 was the year American Mark Andreessen (1971–) of the National Center for Supercomputing Applications in Illinois released the first browser, Mosaic X (later renamed Netscape). A browser hides the links between documents. Instead of typing in the address of a required document, the user simply clicks on a hypertext link indicated by words in a different color. Where the Internet linked computers, the World Wide Web linked documents. Today there are more than 20 million Web sites and more than 20 billion Web pages.

An employee wanders through Amazon.com's depot in Seattle. Founded in 1994, Amazon.com is the biggest online retailer in the United States.

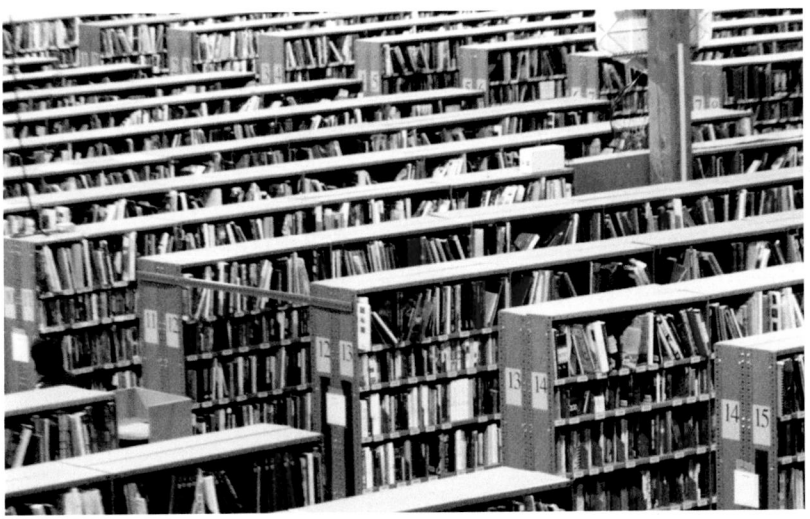

	ASTRONOMY & MATH	BIOLOGY & MEDICINE	PHYSICAL SCIENCES

EUROPE

2006 A space mission led by the French Space Agency launches COROT (COnvection ROtation and planetary Transits), a telescope with spectroscopic detectors, to look for extrasolar planets. It finds its first planet, COROT-Exo-1b, in 2007.

2008 Jules Verne, an unpiloted European cargo spacecraft, is launched to resupply the International Space Station.

2007 A team at Roslin Institute in Scotland develop genetically modified chickens that lay eggs containing proteins that can fight cancer.

2007 Researchers from Wales discover a 405-year-old clam off the coast of Ireland.

2008 Researchers at Newcastle University in England create human–cow embryos, which survive for three days. The hybrid embryos—which would provide stem cells to develop therapies for neurological disorders such as Alzheimer's—were made by injecting human deoxyribonucleic acid (DNA) into enucleated cow egg cells.

2008 The Large Hadron Collider at the European Organization for Nuclear Research (CERN) begins its experiments, with about one billion people watching the switch-on live worldwide. Nine days later the collider develops a fault and is shut down for repairs.

THE AMERICAS

2006 The dwarf planet Eris (discovered the previous year by astronomers at the Palomar Observatory in California) is found to be larger than Pluto.

2006 The National Aeronautics and Space Administration's (NASA) spacecraft New Horizons is launched on its nine-year journey to Pluto.

2006 Genesis I, an experimental space habitat designed and built by American firm Bigelow Aerospace, is launched into Earth orbit.

2007 American astronomer Travis Barman at the Lowell Observatory in Arizona detects water vapor on extrasolar planet HD 209458 using spectroscopy.

2008 NASA's Messenger spacecraft makes two flybys of Mercury, with a third and final flyby in late 2009.

2006 Analysis of a 375-million-year-old fossil found in the Canadian territory of Nunavut shows it to be a "missing link" between fish and tetrapods (four-legged vertebrates). The animal is given the name *Tiktaalik roseae* and nicknamed the "fishapod."

2007 Geneticist J. Craig Venter (1946–) publishes his entire genetic sequence—the first genome published of a single person.

2007 Scientists sequence protein fragments found in soft tissue recovered from the fossil bones of a 68 million-year-old *Tyrannosaurus rex* and a half-million-year-old mastodon.

2007 A chlorophyll-producing bacterium—which transforms light into chemical energy like plants—is discovered in several of the hot springs at Yellowstone National Park.

2008 A previously unknown species of uakari monkey is discovered in the Amazon and named *Cacajao ayresii.*

2007 A team of researchers from Massachusetts Institute of Technology light a 60-watt bulb by transferring energy through the air from a power source not physically connected to the bulb. The team refers to the transfer of energy as "WiTricity" (wireless electricity).

2008 Former NASA scientist John C. Mankins uses radio waves to transmit solar power between two Hawaiian islands.

2008 Scientists from Princeton University propose that a series of volcanic eruptions in India may have killed the dinosaurs, rather than a meteor impact in the Gulf of Mexico.

ASIA & OCEANIA

2008 The Indian Space Research Organization launches Chandrayaan-1, an unpiloted lunar spacecraft.

2007 Clouded leopards on Borneo and Sumatra are declared a separate species from the clouded leopards on mainland Asia after DNA studies.

2007 Last seen in 2004 the Baiji, or Chinese river dolphin (*Lipotes vexillifer*), is now believed to be extinct.

AFRICA & THE MIDDLE EAST

Scientists think that Tiktaalik roseae *lived in shallow water and used its fins to prop itself up.*

ENGINEERING & INVENTION

2007 The Airbus A380 makes its first commercial flight, from Singapore to Sydney.

2009 British engineer Richard Jenkins breaks the world land-speed record when his wind-powered *Greenbird* car reaches 126.1 miles (202.9 km) per hour in Nevada.

2006 The Boeing 747 Large Cargo Freighter (LCF), known as the *Dreamlifter*, makes its maiden flight.

2007 Apple markets its iPhone, a multimedia smartphone with a touch screen.

2007 U.S scientists create printable, flexible batteries by weaving black carbon nanotubes into paper.

2008 Wind power—a growing source of energy—now accounts for just over 1 percent of total electricity in the United States.

WORLD EVENTS

2007 Bulgaria and Romania join the European Union.

2007 Gordon Brown (1951–) replaces Tony Blair (1953–) as prime minister of Britain.

2008 Dmitry Medvedev (1965–) becomes president of Russia, replacing Vladimir Putin (1952–).

A scientist tests the magnets that bend and focus the beams of particles in the Large Hadron Collider.

2008 Barack Obama (1961–) becomes the first African-American president of the United States.

2008 More than 133,000 people are killed in Myanmar by Cyclone Nargis.

2008 Robert Mugabe (1924–) is reelected as president of Zimbabwe after a controversial election.

INSIDE STORY

The Baiji

Also called the Chinese river dolphin, the baiji is now thought to be extinct (or with too few alive to maintain the species). Historically, this freshwater dolphin was found in a 1,000-mile (1,700-km) stretch of the Yangtze (Chang Jiang) River, from Yichang in the west to the mouth of the river, near Shanghai. Many factors have led to its demise in recent decades, including pollution, habitat loss due to dam building, entanglement in fishing nets, collisions with boats, illegal electric fishing, and low stocks of its fish prey. A six-week survey in 2006 failed to find any baijis, and the last unattested sighting was in 2004. Its extinction makes it the first aquatic mammal to disappear since the Japanese sea lion and Caribbean monk seal in the 1950s.

THE LARGE HADRON COLLIDER

The Large Hadron Collider (LHC) is the world's largest particle accelerator. Built by the European Organization for Nuclear Research (CERN), LHC is located in an underground circular tunnel with a circumference of 17 miles (27 km) near Geneva, Switzerland.

Protons were circulated in the collider for the first time on September 19, 2008. Nine days later an electrical fault in the collider led to problems, and it was shut down for several months.

More than 10,000 scientists and engineers from all over the world are involved in LHC's setup and experiments. Planned experiments will help solve many unanswered questions in high-energy physics. For example: Does the Higgs boson exist? What are dark matter and dark energy? Are there extra dimensions?

The circular tunnel of the collider contains two beam pipes that run parallel but intersect at four different points. In the experiments, each pipe contains a beam of particles; in one pipe the particles travel clockwise, in the other counterclockwise. In most of the experiments protons from opposing beams, traveling at 99.99 percent of the speed of light, will collide at the intersection points. Other planned experiments will collide heavy ions, such as lead ions.

The collisions release concentrated energy and simulate the conditions immediately after the big bang at the beginning of the universe, when there are thought to have been various types of short-lived particles and quark-gluon plasma. Particle detectors—located at LHC's intersection points—will look for new types of particles, the origins of mass, extra dimensions, quark-gluon plasma, and antimatter.

ILLUSTRATIONS CREDITS

General Reference

Allaby, Michael, and Derek Gjersten, eds. *Makers of Science*. New York: Oxford University Press, 2002.

Asimov, Isaac. *Asimov's Biographical Encyclopedia of Science and Technology*. Garden City, New York: Doubleday, 1972.

Boorstin, Daniel J. *The Discoverers*. New York: Random House, 1983.

Boyle, David. *The Tyranny of Numbers*. London: HarperCollins, 2000.

Bryson, Bill. *A Short History of Nearly Everything*. New York: Broadway Books, 2003.

Bunch, Bryan H., and Alexander Hellemans. *The History of Science and Technology*. Boston: Houghton Mifflin, 2004.

Carey, John, ed. *The Faber Book of Science*. Boston: Faber and Faber, 1995.

Carruth, Gorton. *The Encyclopedia of American Facts and Dates*. New York: HarperCollins, 1997.

Crystal, David, ed. *The Cambridge Biographical Dictionary*. New York: Cambridge University Press, 1996.

Daintith, John, ed. *A Dictionary of Chemistry*. New York: Oxford University Press, 2000.

Daintith, John, ed. *A Dictionary of Scientists*. New York: Oxford University Press, 1999.

Daintith, John, and R. Rennie, eds. *The Facts on File Dictionary of Mathematics*. New York: Facts on File, 2005.

Darton, Mike, and John Clark. *The Macmillan Dictionary of Measurement*. New York: Macmillan, 1994.

Day, Lance, and Ian McNeil, eds. *Biographical Dictionary of the History of Technology*. New York: Routledge, 1996.

Diamond, Jared. *Guns, Germs and Steel*. New York: W. W. Norton and Co., 1997.

Dyson, James, and Robert Uhlig, ed. *A History of Great Inventions*. New York: Carroll and Graf Publishers, 2001.

le Fanu, James. *The Rise and Fall of Modern Medicine*. New York: Carroll and Graf Publishers, 2000.

Giscard d'Estaing, Valerie, A. *The Book of Inventions and Discoveries*. London: Queen Anne Press, 1990.

Glover, Linda K., *et al. National Geographic Encyclopedia of Space*. Washington, D.C.: National Geographic Society, 2005.

Gribbin, John. *Science, A History, 1543–2001*. New York: Allen Lane, 2002.

Harrison, Ian. *The Book of Inventions*. Washington, D.C.: National Geographic Society, 2004.

Hoskin, Michael, ed. *The Cambridge Concise History of Astronomy*. New York: Cambridge University Press, 1999.

The Hutchinson Dictionary of Scientific Biography. Abingdon, England: Helicon, 2007.

Inventions that Changed the World. Pleasantville, New York: Reader's Digest Association, 1999.

Kagan, Nick, ed. *National Geographic Concise History of the World: An Illustrated Time Line*. Washington, D.C.: National Geographic Society, 2006.

Luck, Steve, ed. *Philip's Science and Technology Encyclopedia*. London: George Philip Limited, 1998.

McLeish, John. *Number*. New York: Fawcett Columbine, 1992.

Margotta, Roberto. *The History of Medicine*. Feltham: Hamlyn, 1968.

Meadows, Jack. *The Great Scientists*. New York: Oxford University Press, 1997.

Messadié, Gerald. *Great Inventions through History*. New York: Chambers, 1991.

Messadié, Gerald. *Great Scientific Discoveries*. New York: Chambers, 1991.

Millar, David, *et al. The Cambridge Dictionary of Scientists*. New York: Cambridge University Press, 1996.

Muir, Hazel, ed. *Larousse Dictionary of Scientists*. New York: Larousse, 1996.

Philip's Astronomy Encyclopedia. London: George Philip Limited, 2002.

Philip's Science and Technology People, Dates and Events. London: George Philip Limited, 1999.

Porter, Roy. *The Greatest Benefit to Mankind*. New York: W. W. Norton and Co., 1998.

Rockwood, Camilla, ed. *Chambers Biographical Dictionary*. Edinburgh: Chambers, 2007.

Silver, B. L. *The Ascent of Science*. New York: Oxford University Press, 1998.

Smith, Jacqueline. *The Facts on File Dictionary of Earth Science*. New York: Facts on File, 2006.

Tallack, Peter, ed. *The Science Book*. London: Weidenfeld and Nicolson, 2003.

Trefil, James. *Cassell's Laws of Nature*. London: Cassell, 2002.

Waites, Gillian. *The Cassell Dictionary of Biology*. London: Cassell, 1999.

Waller, John. *Fabulous Science*. New York: Oxford University Press, 2004.

Webster's New Biographical Dictionary. Springfield, Massachusetts: Merriam-Webster, 1983.

Whitfield, Peter. *Landmarks in Western Science*. London: The British Library, 2004.

Williams, E. T., and C. S. Nicholls, eds. *The Dictionary of National Biography*. New York: Oxford University Press, 1981.

Williams, Trevor I., ed. *A Biographical Dictionary of Scientists*. New York: Wiley, 1974.

Williams, Trevor I. *A History of Invention*. New York: Checkmark Books, 2000.

Chapter 1: Origins of Science Prehistory-850 B.C.E.

Burrell, Roy E. C. *First Ancient History*. Oxford: Oxford University Press, 1994.

Duncan, David E. *Calendar: Humanity's Epic Struggle to Determine a True and Accurate Year*. New York: Bard, 1998.

Haywood, J. *World Atlas of the Past*. New York: Oxford University Press, 1999.

James, Peter, and Nick Thorpe. *Ancient Inventions*. New York: Ballantine Books, 1994. (Also used for Chapters 2 and 3.)

Landels, J. G. *Engineering in the Ancient World*. Berkeley: University of California Press, 2000. (Also used for Chapters 2 and 3.)

Romer, John. *The Great Pyramid: Ancient Egypt Revisited*. New York: Cambridge University Press, 2007.

Wells, Spencer. *The Journey of Man: A Genetic Odyssey*. Princeton, New Jersey: Princeton University Press, 2002.

What Life Was Like on the Banks of the Nile: Egypt, 3050–30 B.C. Alexandria, Virginia: Time-Life Books, 1996.

Zimmer, Carl. *Smithsonian Intimate Guide to Human Origins*. New York: Collins, 2005.

Chapter 2: Classical and Early Medieval Science 849 B.C.E.-999 C.E.

Brockman, John, ed. *The Greatest Inventions of the Past 2,000 Years*. New York: Simon and Schuster, 2000. (Also used for Chapters 3, 4, 5, 6, 7, 8, and 9.)

Coes, Michael D. *The Maya*. New York: Thames and Hudson, 2005.

Fagan, Brian M., ed. *The Seventy Great Inventions of the Ancient World*. London: Thames and Hudson, 2004.

Hill, Donald R. *A History of Engineering in Classical and Medieval Times*. New York: Routledge, 1996. (Also used for Chapter 3.)

Kaplan, Robert. *The Nothing that Is: A Natural History of Zero*. New York: Oxford University Press, 2000.

Martin, Sean. *Alchemy and Alchemists*. Harpenden, Hertfordshire: Pocket Essentials, 2006. (Also used for Chapters 3 and 4.)

Pearson, Anne. *Ancient Greece*. New York: DK Publishing, 2007.

What Life Was Like When Longships Sailed. Alexandria, Virginia: Time-Life Books, 1998.

Wilkinson, Philip. *What the Romans Did for Us*. London: Boxtree, 2000. (Also used for Chapter 3.)

Woodman, Richard. *The History of the Ship*. New York: Lyons Press, 1997. (Also used for Chapters 4, 5, 6, 7, 8, and 9.)

Chapter 3: Late Medieval and Renaissance Science 1000-1624

Clegg, Brian. *The First Scientist: A Life of Roger Bacon*. New York: Carroll and Graf Publishers, 2003.

Gately, Iain. *Tobacco: The Story of How Tobacco Seduced the World*. New York: Grove Press, 2001.

Gravett, Christopher. *Castles and Fortifications from around the World*. Ludlow, England: Thalamus Publishing, 2006.

Kelly, Jack. *Gunpowder*. New York: Basic Books, 2004.

Kelly, John. *The Great Mortality: An Intimate History of the Black Death, the Most Devastating Plague of All Time*. New York: HarperCollins Publishers, 2005.

Ochoa, George, and Carter Smith. *Atlas of Hispanic-American History*. New York: Facts On File, Inc., 2008.

Peterson, Harold L. *The Book of the Gun*. London: Paul Hamlyn, 1962. (Also used for Chapters 4 and 5.)

Thompson, Logan. *Guns in Colour*. London: Octopus, 1981. (Also used for Chapters 4, 7, and 8.)

White, Michael. *Leonardo: The First Scientist*. New York: St. Martin's Press, 2000.

Zuckerman, Larry. *The Potato: How the Humble Spud Rescued the Western World*. New York: North Point Press, 1999.

Chapter 4: The Scientific Revolution 1625-1774

Blunt, Wilfrid. *The Compleat Naturalist: A Life of Linnaeus*. New York: Viking Press, 1971.

Clark, David H., and Stephen P. H. Clark. *Newton's Tyranny*. New York: W. H. Freeman and Company, 2001.

Cleempoel, Koenradd van. *Astrolabes at Greenwich: A Catalogue of the Astrolabes in the National Maritime Museum, Greenwich*. New York: Oxford University Press, 2005.

Emsley, John. *The Shocking History of Phosphorus*. London: Macmillan, 2000. (Also used for Chapter 5.)

Gleick, James. *Isaac Newton*. New York: Pantheon Books, 2003.

Holmes, Richard. *The Age of Wonder: How the Romantic Generation Discovered the Beauty and Terror of Science*. New York: Pantheon Books, 2009.

Inwood, Stephen. *The Man Who Knew Too Much: The Strange and Inventive Life of Robert Hooke, 1635–1703*. London: Macmillan, 2002.

Lane, Nick. *Oxygen: The Molecule that Made the World*. New York: Oxford University Press, 2002.

Sobel, Dava. *Galileo's Daughter*. New York: Walker and Co., 1999.

Sobel, Dava. *Longitude: The True Story of a Lone Genius Who Solved the Greatest Scientific Problem of His Time*. New York: Walker and Co., 1995.

Chapter 5: The Industrial Revolution 1775-1839

Benton, Michael J. *When Life Nearly Died*. New York: Thames and Hudson, 2003. (Also used for Chapter 6.)

Burton, Anthony. *Thomas Telford*. London: Aurum Press, 1999.

Cadbury, Deborah. *The Dinosaur Hunters*. London: Fourth Estate, 2000.

Chambers, Paul. *Bones of Contention*. London: John Murray, 2002. (Also used for Chapter 6.)

Faraday, Michael. *The Philosopher's Tree: A Selection of Michael Faraday's Writings*. Philadelphia: Institute of Physics Publishing, 1999.

Morus, Iwan. R *Michael Faraday and the Electrical Century*. London: Icon Books Ltd, 2004. (Also used for Chapter 6.)

Osborne, Roger. *The Floating Egg*. London: Random House, 1999. (Also used for Chapter 6.)

Vaughan, Adrian. *Isambard Kingdom Brunel*. London: John Murray, 1993. (Also used for Chapter 6.)

Wall, John. *First in the World: The Stockton & Darlington Railway*. Stroud, England: Sutton Publishing, 2001.

Chapter 6: The Age of Steam 1840-1884

Auerbach, Jeffrey A. *The Great Exhibition of 1851: A Nation on Display*. New Haven, Connecticut: Yale University Press, 1999.

Emsley, John. *Nature's Building Blocks*. New York: Oxford University Press, 2001. (Also used for Chapters 7, 8, and 9.)

Fant, Kenne. *Alfred Nobel: A Biography*. New York: Arcade, 1993.

Friedel, Robert, and Paul Israel. *Edison's Electric Light*. New Brunswick, New Jersey: Rutgers University Press, 1986.

Henig, Robin M. *A Monk and Two Peas*. London: Weidenfeld and Nicholson, 2000.

Parrish, Thomas D. *The Submarine: A History*. New York: Viking, 2004.

Shrenk, Friedemann, and Stephanie Müller. *The Neanderthals*. New York: Routledge, 2008.

Stewart, Gail B. *The Suez Canal*. San Diego, California: Lucent Books, 2001.

Strathern, Paul. *Mendeleyev's Dream*. New York: Hamish Hamilton, 2000.

Uglow, Jenny. *The Lunar Men*. New York: Farrar, Straus, and Giroux, 2002.

Chapter 7: The Age of Electricity 1885-1919

Ballard, Robert. *Titanic: The Last Great Images*. Philadelphia, Pennsylvania: Running Press, 2008.

Brian, Denis. *Einstein*. New York: John Wiley and Sons, 1996.

Garfield, Simon. *Mauve*. London: Faber and Faber, 2000.

Grant, R. G. *Flight: 100 Years of Aviation*. New York: DK Publishing, 2002.

Kramer, Peter D. *Freud: Inventor of the Modern Mind*. New York: HarperCollins, 2006.

Messadié, Gerald. *Great Modern Inventions*. New York: Chambers, 1991. (Also used for Chapters 8 and 9.)

Parker, Matthew. *Panama Fever: The Epic Story of One of the Greatest Human Achievements of All Time—the Building of the Panama Canal*. New York: Doubleday, 2007.

Weightman, Gavin. *Signor Marconi's Magic Box*. London: HarperCollins, 2003.

Weinberg, Steven. *The Discovery of Subatomic Particles*. New York: Cambridge University Press, 2003.

Who's Who in the Twentieth Century. New York: Oxford University Press, 1999. (Also used for Chapters 8 and 9.)

Chapter 8: The Atomic Age 1920-1949

Bird, Kai, and Martin J. Sherwin. *American Prometheus: The Triumph and Tragedy of J. Robert Oppenheimer*. New York: A. A. Knopf, 2005.

Buderi, Robert. *The Invention that Changed the World*. New York: Simon and Schuster, 1996.

Close, Frank. E. *Particle Physics: A Very Short Introduction*. New York: Oxford University Press, 2004.

Fisher, David E., and Marshall. J. Fisher. *Tube: The Invention of Television*. Washington, D.C.: Counterpoint, 1996.

Hege, John. B. *The Wankel Rotary Engine: A History*. Jefferson, North Carolina: McFarland and Co., 2001.

Jackson, R., ed. *Helicopters: Military, Civilian, and Rescue Rotorcraft (The Aviation Factfile)*. San Diego, California: Thunder Bay Press, 2005.

Lee, Kelley. *World Health Organization (WHO)*. New York: Routledge, 2008.

Macfarlane, Gwyn. *Alexander Fleming: The Man and the Myth*. Cambridge, Massachusetts: Harvard University Press, 1984.

Ward, Bob. *Dr. Space: The Life of Wernher von Braun*. Annapolis, Maryland: Naval Institute Press, 2005.

Chapter 9: The Space Age 1950-1979

Beniada, Frédéric, and Michel Fraile. *Concorde*. St. Paul, Minnesota: Zenith Press, 2006.

Gribbin, John. *In Search of the Double Helix*. New York: McGraw-Hill, 1985.

Lagerkvist, Ulf. *DNA Pioneers and Their Legacy*. New Haven, Connecticut: Yale University Press, 1998. (Also used for Chapter 10.)

Pauling, Linus. *Scientist and Peacemaker*. Corvallis: Oregon State University Press, 2001.

Reynolds, D. W. *Apollo: The Epic Journey to the Moon*. New York: Harcourt, 2002.

Thomas, Jeanette, A., Cynthia F. Moss, and Marianne Vater, eds. *Echolocation in Bats and Dolphins*. Chicago: The University of Chicago Press, 2004.

Watson, James, D. *The Double Helix: A Personal Account of the Discovery of the Structure of DNA*. New York: Atheneum, 1968.

Chapter 10: The Modern World 1980-Present

Campbell-Kelly, Martin, and William Aspray. *Computer: A History of the Information Machine*. Boulder, Colorado: Westview Press, 2004.

Cossons, Neil, ed. *Making of the Modern World*. London: John Murray, 1997.

DeVorkin, David, H., and Robert W. Smith. *Hubble: Imaging Space and Time*. Washington, D.C.: National Geographic Society, 2008.

Global Warming. New York: Time Home Entertainment, 2007.

Hawking, Stephen W. *A Brief History of Time: From the Big Bang to Black Holes*. New York: Bantam Books, 1988.

Lincoln, D. *The Quantum Frontier: The Large Hadron Collider*. Baltimore: Johns Hopkins University Press, 2009.

Mandelbrot, Benoit B. *The Fractal Geometry of Nature*. San Francisco: W. H. Freeman, 1982.

Morwood, Mike J., and Penny van Oosterzee. *The Discovery of the Hobbit: The Scientific Breakthrough that Changed the Face of Human History*. Milsons Point, New South Wales: Random House Australia, 2007.

Riordan, Michael, and Lillian Hoddesdon. *Crystal Fire: The Birth of the Information Age*. New York: W. W. Norton and Co., 1997.

Singh, Simon. *Fermat's Enigma: The Epic Quest to Solve the World's Greatest Mathematical Problem*. New York: Walker, 1997.

INDEX

CONCISE HISTORY OF SCIENCE AND INVENTION

PUBLISHED BY THE NATIONAL GEOGRAPHIC SOCIETY

John M. Fahey	*President and Chief Executive Officer*
Jr. Gilbert M. Grosvenor	*Chairman of the Board*
Tim T. Kelly	*President, Global Media Group*
John Q. Griffin	*Executive Vice President;*
	President, Publishing
Nina D. Hoffman	*Executive Vice President;*
	President, Book Publishing Group

PREPARED BY THE BOOK DIVISION

Barbara Brownell Grogan	*Vice President and Editor in Chief*
Marianne R. Koszorus	*Director of Design*
Carl Mehler	*Director of Maps*
R. Gary Colbert	*Production Director*
Jennifer A. Thornton	*Managing Editor*
Meredith C. Wilcox	*Administrative Director, Illustrations*

STAFF FOR THIS BOOK

Susan Straight	*Editor*
Elizabeth Thompson	*Editorial Assistant*
Caitlin Mertzlufft	*Intern*

Erin Dolan	*Consultants*
Leon Gray	
Jolyon Goddard	*Text Editor*
David Poole	*Design Manager*
Dave Allen	*Designers*
Joan Curtis	
Steve McCurdy	
Ben Hollingum	*Assistant Editor*
Sophie Mortimer	*Picture Manager*
Andrew Webb	*Picture Researcher*
Lindsey Lowe	*Editorial Director*
Alastair Gourlay	*Production Director*
Richard Berry	*DTP Design*
Heather Dunleavy	
Indexing Specialists	*Indexer*
(UK) Ltd	
Tim Cooke	*Managing Editor*

MANUFACTURING AND QUALITY MANAGEMENT

Christopher A. Liedel	*Chief Financial Officer*
Phillip L. Schlosser	*Vice President*
Chris Brown	*Technical Director*
Nicole Elliott	*Manager*
Rachel Faulise	*Manager*

The National Geographic Society is one of the world's largest nonprofit scientific and educational organizations. Founded in 1888 to "increase and diffuse geographic knowledge," the Society works to inspire people to care about the planet. It reaches more than 325 million people worldwide each month through its official journal, *National Geographic*, and other magazines; National Geographic Channel; television documentaries; music; radio; films; books; DVDs; maps; exhibitions; school publishing programs; interactive media; and merchandise. National Geographic has funded more than 9,000 scientific research, conservation and exploration projects and supports an education program combating geographic illiteracy. For more information, visit nationalgeographic.com.

For more information, please call 1-800-NGS LINE (647-5463) or write to the following address:

National Geographic Society
1145 17th Street N.W.
Washington, D.C. 20036-4688 U.S.A.

Visit us online at www.nationalgeographic.com

For information about special discounts for bulk purchases, please contact National Geographic Books Special Sales: ngspecsales@ngs.org

For rights or permissions inquiries, please contact National Geographic Books Subsidiary Rights: ngbookrights@ngs.org

ISBN: 978-1-4262-1677-0 (special sale edition)

LIBRARY OF CONGRESS CATALOGING-IN-PUBLICATION DATA

Concise history of science & invention : an illustrated time line / edited by Jolyon Goddard.
    p. cm.
  Includes index.
  ISBN 978-1-4262-0544-6 (trade)
  1. Science--History--Chronology. 2. Inventions--History--Chronology. I. Goddard, Jolyon. II. Title: Concise history of science and invention.
  Q125.C576 2009
  509--dc22
  2009018460

Printed in China

15/WIN/1

Using Access™ for Windows™, Special Edition

ROGER JENNINGS
RON PERSON

Using Access™ for Windows™, Special Edition

Copyright © 1993 by Que® Corporation.

All rights reserved. Printed in the United States of America. No part of this book may be used or reproduced in any form or by any means, or stored in a database or retrieval system, without prior written permission of the publisher except in the case of brief quotations embodied in critical articles and reviews. Making copies of any part of this book for any purpose other than your own personal use is a violation of United States copyright laws. For information, address Que Corporation, 11711 N. College Ave., Carmel, IN 46032.

Library of Congress Catalog No.: 92-70889

ISBN: 0-88022-966-7

This book is sold *as is*, without warranty of any kind, either express or implied, respecting the contents of this book, including but not limited to implied warranties for the book's quality, performance, merchantability, or fitness for any particular purpose. Neither Que Corporation nor its dealers or distributors shall be liable to the purchaser or any other person or entity with respect to any liability, loss, or damage caused or alleged to be caused directly or indirectly by this book.

96   95   94   93   5   4   3   2   1

Interpretation of the printing code: the rightmost double-digit number is the year of the book's printing; the rightmost single-digit number, the number of the book's printing. For example, a printing code of 93-1 shows that the first printing of the book occurred in 1993.

Screen reproductions in this book were created using Collage Plus from Inner Media, Inc., Hollis, NH.

Using Access for Windows, Special Edition is based on Version 1.0 of Microsoft Access and Microsoft Windows 3.1.

Publisher: Lloyd J. Short

Associate Publisher: Rick Ranucci

Operations Manager: Sheila Cunningham

Plan Manager: Tom Bennett

Acquisitions Editor: Sarah Browning

Book Designer: Scott Cook

Production Team: Jeff Baker, Claudia Bell, Katy Bodenmiller, Julie Brown, Jodie Cantwell, Paula Carroll, Laurie Cssey, Brad Chinn, Jeanne Clark, Michelle Cleary, Lisa Daugherty, Brook Farling, Joy Dean Lee, Cindy L. Phipps, Angela Pozdol, Caroline Roop, Linda Seifert, Michelle Self, Greg Simsic, Phil Worthington

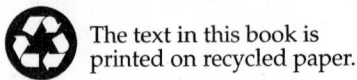

This book is dedicated to my wife, Alexandra.

CREDITS

Title Manager
Walter R. Bruce, III

Product Director
Steven M. Schafer

Production Editor
Fran Blauw

Editors
Jo Anna Arnott
William A. Barton
Elsa M. Bell
Lori Cates
Barb Colter
Kelly Currie
Robin Drake
Donald R. Eamon
Jeannine Freudenberger
Cindy Morrow
J. Christopher Nelson
Heather Northrup
Joy M. Preacher
Colleen Totz
Becky Whitney

Technical Editors
Michael Gilbert
Alan Handler

Formatter
Jill L. Stanley

Editorial Assistant
Elizabeth D. Brown

Composed in *Cheltenham* and *MCPdigital* by Que Corporation.

Roger Jennings is a consultant specializing in Windows database, word processing, and multimedia applications. He was a member of the Microsoft beta-test team for Microsoft Access, Word for Windows 2.0, Windows 3.1, Windows for Workgroups, Video for Windows, Visual Basic for DOS, Visual Basic 2.0, and the Microsoft Professional Toolkit for Visual Basic. He is the author of *Discovering Windows 3.1 Multimedia* and *Using Visual Basic*; a contributing author to *Killer Windows Utilities*; and was a technical editor for *Using Word for Windows 2,* Special Edition and *Using Windows 3.1,* Special Edition, each published by Que Corporation.

Roger Jennings has more than 25 years of computer-related experience and has presented technical papers on computer hardware and software to the Academy of Sciences of the USSR, the Society of Automotive Engineers, the American Chemical Society, and a wide range of other scientific and technical organizations. He is a principal of OakLeaf Systems, a Northern California software development and consulting firm; you may contact him via CompuServe (ID 70233,2161) or the Internet (70233.2161@compuserve.com).

Ron Person, the author of Part IV of this book, has written more than a dozen books for Que Corporation, including *Using Windows 3.1*, Special Edition; *Using Excel 4 for Windows*, Special Edition; *Using Word for Windows 2*, Special Edition; and *Windows 3.1 QuickStart*. Ron is the principal consultant for Ron Person & Co., a San Francisco based consulting firm that operates nationwide. He is a Microsoft consulting partner for Microsoft Excel and Microsoft Word for Windows. Ron's firm helps corporations develop in-house programming skills and support expertise for the embedded macro languages of Microsoft Access, Excel, and Word for Windows. You may contact Ron at

Ron Person & Co.   (415) 989-7508 Voice
P.O. Box 5647   (707) 539-1525 Voice
3 Quixote Court   (707) 538-1485 FAX
Santa Rosa, CA 95409

Thanks to Monte Slichter, Joe Howard, and Kim Hightower of Microsoft Corporation, members of the Microsoft Access support team during the beta test cycle for Access. Their prompt replies to questions concerning the pre-release versions of Access is especially appreciated.

Steve Schafer, product director, provided valuable insight and suggestions for the development of this book's content and organization. Sarah Browning, acquisitions editor, made sure that I did not fall too far behind the manuscript submission schedule. Fran Blauw, production editor, put in long hours to add last-minute changes incorporated in the release candidates of Access and still meet a tight publication schedule. Technical editing was done by Michael Gilbert and Alan Handler, each of whom are experts in specific areas of database technology. Their contributions to this book are gratefully acknowledged. The responsibility for any errors or omissions, however, rests solely on my shoulders.

Trademarks

TABLE OF CONTENTS

I Learning Access Fundamentals

II Using Queries, Forms, and Reports

III Integrating Access with Other Applications

V Using Advanced Access Techniques

VI Programming with Access Basic

Appendixes

Introduction

Microsoft Access is a new and powerful relational database management system designed specifically for the Windows environment. Access duplicates most of the capabilities of client-server database systems that are leading the way in transferring database applications from mini-computers and mainframes to networked PCs— a process called *downsizing*. Despite Access's power, the system is easy for nonprogrammers to use. Access has an intuitive user interface, similar to that of Excel and Word for Windows 2.0. Toolbar buttons offer shortcuts for menu commands; and Wizards handle most of the chores of creating new forms, graphs, and reports. A new approach to context-sensitive Help systems, called *Cue Cards*, helps you learn the basic operations of Access.

Access introduces a new approach to writing macros that automate repetitive database operations. Access incorporates a full-featured programming language, *Access Basic*, modeled on Visual Basic. The syntax is easy to learn, yet Access Basic provides a vocabulary rich enough to satisfy veteran xBase and Paradox application developers. Access is designed for multiuser applications where database files are shared on networks, and Access incorporates a sophisticated security system to prevent unauthorized persons from viewing or modifying the databases you create.

Access has a unique database structure that combines all related data tables and their indexes, forms, reports, macros, and Access Basic code within a single file. Access has the capability to import data from the more popular PC database and spreadsheet files. Access also can attach dBASE, FoxBase, Paradox, and Btrieve files to databases and use the files in their native formats. You also can use Access on work-stations that act as clients of networked file servers in client-server database systems. Access, therefore, fulfills all the requirements of a professional relational database management system, as well as a front-end development tool for use with client-server databases.

The contributors to this book are seasoned users of database management systems and Windows. The author, Roger Jennings, has more than 10 years of experience in developing database systems for personal computers. Ron Person, who wrote Part IV of this book, "Powering Access with Macros," has written more than a dozen books for Que Corporation, including *Using Excel 4 for Windows,* Special Edition. This book, therefore, isn't just a recompilation of the manuals that are shrink-wrapped with the installation disks. *Using Access for Windows,* Special Edition, makes comparisons between Access and other popular database management applications when such comparisons are appropriate. This feature makes the book a useful tool in determining whether Access is the appropriate database manager for you or the organization for which you work.

This book provides extensive coverage on using your existing database files in their native formats—alone, or with those in Access's own file structure. Many readers have used the dBASE dot prompt and programming, Paradox macros and PAL, or both. References to both *xBase* (the name applied to applications that use dialects of the dBASE programming language) and the Paradox Application Language (PAL) are made throughout this book. If you aren't an xBase or Paradox user, just skip these references. You don't need experience in using a relational database management program, however, in order to create useful, even complex, database applications with what you learn in this book.

Several chapters of this book are devoted to using Access with other Windows applications, such as Microsoft Excel and Word for Windows, and the *applets* supplied with these applications: Microsoft Graph, Draw, and WordArt. Applets are small but useful applications supplied as components of major applications; Paintbrush, for example, is a Windows applet. Using the new multimedia features found in Windows 3.1 with Access also is covered.

Who Should Read This Book?

Using Access for Windows, Special Edition, takes an approach that is different from most books about database management applications. This book doesn't begin with the creation of a database for Widgets, Inc.; nor does it require you to type a list of fictional customers for their new Widget II product line in order to learn the basics of Access. Instead, this book makes the following basic assumptions about your interest in Microsoft's new relational database management system:

- You have one or more PCs operating in a business, professional, institutional, or government agency setting.

- You are using or have decided to use Microsoft Windows 3.x, Windows for Workgroups, or Windows NT as the operating environment for at least some, if not all, of your PCs.

- You are able to navigate Microsoft Windows 3.x using the mouse and keyboard. Books about DOS database managers no longer attempt to teach you DOS, nor will *Using Access for Windows* try to teach you Windows fundamentals. If you are new to Windows, some helpful books about Windows 3.x are listed in the bibliography later in this Introduction.

- You aren't starting from "ground zero." You now have or will have access via your PC to data that you want to process with a Windows database manager. You already may have acquired Access and want to learn to use it more quickly and effectively. Or, you may be considering using Access as the database manager for yourself, your department or division, or your entire organization.

- Your existing data is in the form of one or more database-, spreadsheet, or even plain text files that you want to manipulate with a relational database management system. Access can process the most common varieties of all three types of files.

- If your data is on a mini- or mainframe computer, you are connected to that computer by a local area network or through terminal emulation software and an adapter card. Otherwise, you are able to obtain the data on PC-compatible disks; some people call this method *SneakerNet* or *FootWare*.

If some or all of your data is in the form of ASCII or ANSI text files, or files from a spreadsheet application, you need to know how to create an Access database from the beginning and import the data into Access's own .MDB file structure. If your data is in the form of dBASE-compatible, Paradox, or Btrieve files, you can attach the files as tables and continue to use them in the format native to your prior database manager. This capability is an important advantage to have during conversion from one database management system to another. Each of these subjects receives thorough coverage in this book.

Using Access for Windows, Special Edition, is designed to accommodate readers who are new to database management, occasional or frequent users of dBASE or Paradox for DOS or Windows, or seasoned database application developers.

How This Book Is Organized

Using Access for Windows is divided into six parts that are arranged in increasing levels of detail and complexity. Each division after Part I draws on the knowledge and experience you have gained in the prior parts, so use of the book in a linear, front-to-back manner is recommended during the initial learning process. After you have absorbed the basics, *Using Access for Windows* becomes a valuable reference tool for the advanced topics.

Quick starts introduce the subject matter of the first four parts to give you a "feel" for Access and to provide a brief introduction to the subject matter of the chapters that follow. Quick starts use the Northwind Traders (NWIND.MDB) sample database provided with Access that contains data which is similar to data created by standard accounting software for the PC. The Northwind Traders sample database is used to minimize the amount of data entry required for you to experiment with the examples presented in this book.

The six parts of *Using Access for Windows* and the topics they cover are described in the following sections.

Part I

Part I, "Learning Access Fundamentals," introduces you to Access and many of the unique features that make Access the easiest to use of all database managers. The chapters in Part I deal almost exclusively with tables, the basic elements of Access databases.

Chapter 1, "Placing Access in Perspective," provides a brief history of the development of Access, describes how it fits into the gamut of database managers now in use, and compares Access's features with those of other database managers.

In Chapter 2, "Up and Running with Access Tables: A Quick Start," you learn how to open an Access database, view a table, use a typical query, add a few new data items, view the results of your work, and finally print a formatted report.

Chapter 3, "Navigating within Access," shows you how to navigate Access by explaining its toolbar and menu choices and how they relate to the structure of Access.

Chapter 4, "Working with Access Databases and Tables," delves into the details of Access tables, how to create tables, and how to choose the optimum data types from the many new types Access offers.

Chapter 5, "Attaching, Importing, and Exporting Tables," explains how you import and export files of other database managers, spreadsheet applications, and even ASCII files you may download from information utilities such as Dow Jones News Service or government-sponsored databases.

Part II

Part II, "Using Queries, Forms, and Reports," explains how to create Access queries to select the way you view data in tables, design forms for data entry and editing, and print formatted reports from data contained in tables.

Chapter 6, "Using Query by Example: A Quick Start," shows you how to choose data from tables and organize the selected data into query tables. You also learn how to choose and then display the portion of the Northwind Traders data in which you are interested.

Chapter 7, "Understanding Operators and Expressions in Access," introduces you to the operators and expressions that you need to create queries that provide a meaningful result. You use the Immediate window of the Access Basic code editor to evaluate the expressions you write.

In Chapter 8, "Creating Queries and Joining Tables," you create relations between tables, called *joins*, and learn how to develop action queries that add data to tables.

Chapter 9, "Creating and Using Forms," and Chapter 10, "Designing Custom Forms," show you how to design custom forms for viewing and entering your own data with Access's advanced forms design tools.

Chapter 11, "Printing Formatted Reports," describes how to design and print fully formatted reports with Access.

Part III

Part III, "Integrating Access with Other Applications," shows you how to use the new object linking and embedding features of Windows 3.1 with Access.

Chapter 12, "Introducing OLE: A Quick Start," departs from the conventional quick start format and explains how Object Linking and Embedding (OLE), formally introduced in Windows 3.1, works and how you use OLE with Access.

Chapter 13, "Using the OLE Field Data Type for Graphics," introduces the new OLE field type for tables and explains how you use OLE fields to incorporate images, sounds, and even music, within your tables.

Chapter 14, "Adding Graphics and Color to Forms and Reports," shows you how to add graphic images to your forms and reports with OLE.

Chapter 15, "Using Access with Microsoft Excel," gives you detailed examples of exchanging data between Access and Excel worksheets by using OLE and the two dynamic data exchange functions that you can use with Access forms and reports.

Part IV

Part IV, "Powering Access with Macros," written by contributing author Ron Person, is your introduction to the use of the first level of programming provided by Access.

Chapter 16, "Automating Applications with Macros: A Quick Start," shows you how to write macros that run queries and open other forms when you click a command button control you place on a form.

Chapter 17, "Understanding Access Macros," explains how you create the macros that automate your applications, and gives you examples of combining Access's standard macro actions into macro objects that take the place of programming code required by other relational database managers.

Chapter 18, "Creating Macros for Forms, Reports, and Custom Menus," gives you specific examples of useful macros that you can use for tasks such as opening a form, changing a form's size, adding and deleting records, and printing a form.

Part V

Part V, "Using Advanced Access Techniques," covers the theoretical and practical aspects of relational database design and Structured Query Language (SQL), and then goes on to describe how to set up and use Access on a local area network.

Chapter 19, "Exploring Relational Database Design and Implementation," describes the process you use to create relational database tables from real-world data—a technique called *normalizing the database structure*. This chapter explains how to use the Analyzer library included with Access to create a dictionary that fully identifies each object in your database.

Chapter 20, "Working with Structured Query Language," explains how Access uses SQL to create its own queries and how you write your own SQL statements.

Chapter 21, "Using Access in a Network Environment," begins by describing typical network environments in which you may use Access. It then explains how to set up Access to share database files on a network and how to use the security features of Access to prevent unauthorized viewing of or tampering with your database files.

Part VI

Part VI, "Programming with Access Basic," assumes that you have no programming experience in any language. Part VI explains the principles of writing programming code in Access Basic and applies the principles to using Dynamic Data Exchange (DDE) to exchange data with an Excel worksheet.

Chapter 22, "Writing Access Basic Code," describes how to use Access Basic to create user-defined functions and write simple procedures that you activate with macros.

Chapter 23, "Exchanging Data with Access Basic DDE," gives you a complete, working application that uses Access Basic DDE commands to create a relational table from data in a worksheet.

Chapter 24, "Adding On-Line Help for Users," outlines the techniques you use to create applications for others to use, including how to write Help files to answer users' questions about how the application works.

Chapter 25, "Looking at Future Versions of Access and Windows," concludes with predictions about the future of both Access and Windows.

Appendixes

Appendix A, the glossary, presents a glossary of the terms, abbreviations, and acronyms used in this book that may not be familiar to you and cannot be found in commonly used dictionaries.

Appendix B, "Naming Conventions for Access Objects," incorporates a proposed set of standardized naming conventions for Access objects and Access Basic variables.

Appendix C, "Binary and Hexadecimal Arithmetic," explains binary and hexadecimal arithmetic for nonprogrammers.

Appendix D, "Values for the STK_21.XLS Worksheet," provides data values for the stock price worksheet that you use with the example applications in Chapters 15 and 23.

Appendix E, "Data Dictionary for the Personnel Actions Table," shows you how to implement the Personnel Actions table that is used for many of the examples in this book.

Appendix F, "Installing Access," supplies detailed information on installing Access on your computer, including how you select files to install when using the Custom Setup Installation option.

How This Book Is Designed

The following special features are included in this book to assist readers:

Picture Object
Refers to the toolbar or toolbox icon shown in the margin.

- Readers who have never used a database management application are provided with quick start examples to gain confidence and experience while using Access with the Northwind Traders demonstration data set. Like Access, this book uses the *tabula rasa* approach: each major topic begins with the assumption that the reader has no experience with the subject. When buttons from the toolbar or control object toolbox are used, an icon with the title of the tool is displayed in the last margin. Warnings are provided when actions or code is explained that may lead to unexpected results or potential problems.

xBase

Symbol that indicates similarity to xBase usage or structure.

- Users of the two major DOS database managers will find margin icons that identify important points of similarity with or departures from xBase and Paradox methodologies. These icons are accompanied by brief explanations and, where necessary and possible, short workarounds (methods of implementing the equivalent of xBase and Paradox commands not available in Access). Many of these icons also will apply to other DBMs that have related macro or programming languages.

PDOX

Symbol indicating difference from Paradox usage or structure.

Tips, cautions, and warnings are indicated by special icons in the margin that are derived from the icons that appear in Windows' message boxes:

- Tips, identified by the lowercase "i" (standing for *information*) offer advice and shortcuts that aid you in using Access, and explain the few anomalies you find in Version 1.0 of Access. In a few cases in this book, tips explain similarities or differences between Access and other database management applications. These tips are based on the experience the authors gained during more than one year of testing successive alpha and beta versions of Access.

- Cautions are indicated by an exclamation point where an action can lead to an unexpected or unpredictable result; the text provides an explanation of how you can avoid such a result.

- Warnings, identified by Windows' critical stop icon, indicate that pursuing a particular course of action can lead to serious problems, including loss of data or irreparable damage to your Access database file.

Most software manuals require you to wade through all the details relating to a particular function of an application in a single chapter or part, before you progress to the next topic. In contrast, *Using Access for Windows* first takes you through the most frequently used steps to manipulate database tables, and then concentrates on using your existing files with Access. Advanced features and nuances of Access are covered in later chapters. This type of structure requires cross-referencing so that you can easily locate more detailed or advanced coverage of the topic. Icons showing the image of a book, like the sample shown here, point you to the page on which the related content begins.

For Related Information:

▶▶ "Importing and Attaching Existing Files," p. 28.

FROM HERE...

Typographic Conventions Used in This Book

This book uses various typesetting styles to distinguish between explanatory and instructional text, text you enter in dialog boxes, and text you enter in code-editing windows.

Typefaces and Fonts

Terms employed by the graphics profession are used in this book to designate typefaces and fonts used in forms and reports. The terms *typeface* and *face* are substituted interchangeably for the term *font* when referring to multiple sizes of the same typeface. *Font* is used to indicate type in a single size, such as Courier New 12, indicating the Courier New (TrueType) family, 12 point size, Roman (regular) style. A typeface *family* includes all available styles of a face: black, bold, normal, light, condensed, expanded, italic, oblique, and so on.

The term *font* is used by printers to mean a collection of characters of a single typeface, style, and size. In the days of metal type, these characters were stored in trays with compartments of varying sizes proportional to the frequency of use of the character. When Hewlett-Packard introduced its first LaserJet series of laser printers, the term *font* was properly applied to the choices offered, because each was a bit map of a specific family, style, and size, like Courier 10 Italic. Printers using the Adobe PostScript page description language, which introduced scalable typefaces, used *font* instead of *typeface* or *face* to describe the outline used to create typefaces. This transgression was perpetuated by the Microsoft/Apple TrueType products designed to compete with PostScript.

Key Combinations and Menu Choices

Key combinations that you use to perform Windows operations are indicated by joining the keys with a plus sign: Alt+F4, for example. This indicates that you press and hold the Alt key while pressing the function key F4. In the rare cases in which you must press and release a Control key, and *then* enter another key, the keys are separated by a comma without an intervening space: Alt,F4, for example. Key combinations that perform menu operations which would require more than one keystroke are called *shortcut keys*. An example of such a shortcut is the new Windows 3.1 key combination, Ctrl+C, which substitutes for the **C**opy choice of the **E**dit menu.

To select a menu option with the keyboard instead of the mouse, you press the letter that appears in bold type in the menu option. Sequences of individual menu items are separated by a space: **E**dit **C**ut, for example. The Alt key required to activate a choice from the main menu is assumed and not shown.

Successive entries in dialog boxes follow the tab order of the dialog box. *Tab order* is the sequence in which the caret moves when you press the Tab key to move from one entry or control option to another, a process known as *changing the focus*. The entry or control option that has the focus is the one that receives keystrokes or mouse clicks. Command buttons, option buttons, and check box choices are treated similarly to menu choices, but their access key letters aren't set in boldface type. Textbox entries to choose a file sometimes are shown with the menu choices that precede them, as in the example **File O**pen DATABASE.MDB.

When, for example, you must substitute a name of your own making for a textbox entry, lowercase italics are used for the substitutable portion, as in the example **File** Save **As** *filename* .MDB. Here, you substitute the name of your file for *filename*, but the .MDB extension is required, because it is in a Roman (standard) face. File and path names are capitalized in the text and headings of this book but conform to standards established by Windows 3.1 common dialog boxes—all lowercase—in code examples.

SQL Statements and Keywords in Other Languages

Keywords of SQL statements, such as SELECT, are set in all uppercase, as are the keywords of foreign database programming languages when they are used in comparative examples, such as DO WHILE...ENDDO. Ellipses indicate intervening programming code that isn't shown in the text or examples.

Square brackets that appear within Access Basic SQL statements don't indicate optional items as they do in syntax descriptions. In this case, the square brackets are used in lieu of quotation marks to frame a literal string or to allow use of a table and field names, such as [Personnel Actions], that include embedded spaces or special punctuation, or field names that are identical to reserved words in Access and Access Basic.

Typographic Conventions Used for Access Basic

This book uses a special set of typographic conventions for references to Access Basic keywords in the presentation of Access Basic examples:

■ Monospace type is used for all examples of Access Basic code, as in the following statement:

```
Dim NewArray ( ) As Long
ReDim New Array (9, 9, 9)
```

■ **Boldface monospace** type is used for all Access Basic keywords and type-declaration symbols, as shown in the preceding example. Standard function names in Access Basic also are set in boldface type so that keywords, standard function names and reserved symbols stand out from variable and function names and values you assign to variables.

■ *Italic monospace* type indicates a replaceable item. For example,

```
Dim DataItem As String.
```

■ ***Bold italic monospace*** type indicates a replaceable keyword, such as a data type, as in

```
Dim
DataItem As DataType
```

DataType is replaced by a keyword corresponding to the desired Access Basic data type.

■ Ellipsis (...) substitutes for code not shown in syntax and code examples, as in `If...Then...Else...End If`.

System Requirements for Access

Access must be installed on an 80286-, 80386- or 80486-based IBM-compatible PC with a fixed disk drive capable of running Windows 3.0 or higher in standard or enhanced mode. You will find execution of Access on computers using the 80286 CPU to be quite slow, and operation may be glacial when used with large tables. Although the documentation accompanying Access says that you can use Access on a computer with only 2M of RAM, a bare minimum of 4M is recommended. If you plan to use Access for extensive handling of graphic images or run it often with other applications using object linking and embedding (OLE), 8M of RAM should be installed. Using OLE to manipulate complex objects, such as large bit maps, requires substantial amounts of memory.

Installing Access requires a total of about 10M of free disk space, and you should reserve at least 50 percent more disk space to store the databases you create. Access, Windows 3.1, and Windows for

Workgroups have been tested under Stac Electronics' Stacker 2.x fixed disk file compression application during the course of writing this book. Each of these programs has been found to operate satisfactorily with Stacker.

A mouse or trackball isn't a requirement for using the Access applications you create, but you need one of these two pointing devices to select and size the objects that you add to forms and reports using Access's toolbox. Because a pointing device is required to create Access applications, this book dispenses with the traditional "Here's how you do it with the mouse..." and "If you want to use the keyboard..." duplicate methodology in step-by-step examples. Designing your Access applications with shortcut keys to eliminate mouse operations, however, speeds keyboard-oriented data entry by enabling the operator to keep his or her fingers on the keyboard during the entire process.

Chapters 15 and 23 use data from a large worksheet of stock prices created by Ideas Unlimited that is available for downloading from CompuServe Information Services. You need a modem and communication software—and a CompuServe account—to obtain the data. If you are one of the few PC users who doesn't have a modem, now is the time to install one. An external modem is recommended for users who are new to PC telecommunications, because the light-emitting diodes let you know what is happening (or not happening), and external modems don't occupy a valuable adapter card slot.

Although upgrading to Windows 3.1 isn't necessary to use Access, the investment in Windows 3.1 upgrade software and the time to install it (not long) are worthwhile. The principal advantages of Windows 3.1 are the incorporation of TrueType scalable typefaces, improved networking operation, and a more robust operating environment. Windows 3.1 has subtle changes that will speed the operation of most of your Windows applications.

Other Sources of Information for Access

SQL and relational database design, which are discussed in Chapters 19 and 20, are the subject of myriad guides and texts covering one or both of these topics. You will find that using the Windows and Multimedia APIs with Access is much easier if you have the reference information at hand.

Bibliography

Introduction to Databases, by James J. Townsend, gives a thorough explanation of personal computer databases and their design. This book is especially recommended if the subject of PC databases is new to you.

Using SQL, by Dr. George T. Chou, provides a detailed description of SQL, concentrating on the dialects used by dBASE IV and Oracle databases, and explains the essentials of the design of relational database systems.

American National Standards Institute (ANSI) supplies copies of its standards and those originating from the International Standards Organization (ISO), headquartered at the United Nations facility in Geneva. You can get copies of ANSI Standard X3.135.1-1989 by writing to the following address:

> American National Standards Institute
> 11 West 42nd Street
> New York, NY 10036
> (212) 642-4900 (Sales Department)

You can get a copy of a draft of the proposed revisions to ANSI X3.135.1-1989 currently under consideration by the X3 committee by contacting the following:

> Global Engineering Documents
> 2805 McGaw Avenue
> Irvine, CA 92713
> (800) 854-7179

SQL Access Group (SAG) is a consortium of users and vendors of SQL database management systems. SAG publishes a number of standards that supplement ANSI X3.135. The Open DataBase Connectivity (ODBC) API proposed by Microsoft Corporation is derived from SAG's Call-Level Interface (CLI) standard.

> SQL Access Group
> 1010 El Camino Real, Suite 380
> Menlo Park, CA 94025
> (415) 323-7992 x221

Microsoft Windows 3.1 Software Development Kit (SDK) documentation supplies valuable guidance on Windows programming and provides the syntax for the 600 or so functions that make up the Windows 3.1 Application Programming Interface (API). You need the SDK, or its equivalent, if you want to use Windows functions with your Access Basic code. The SDK documentation is available as a set from the publisher and at most technical bookstores (Redmond, WA: Microsoft Press, 1992).

On-Line Sources

Your modem-equipped PC enables you to tap the resources of on-line commercial and government databases, as well as special-interest electronic Bulletin Board Systems (BBSs) run by individuals and organizations.

CompuServe

Microsoft supports many of its software products in the Microsoft Applications forum (GO MSAPP) on CompuServe Information Services. At the time this book was published, a section hadn't been created for Access, because Access hadn't been released formally. Although Access is a new product, you can expect activity in the new Access forum to be brisk, with sample files for downloading, messages regarding technical questions, and assistance from Microsoft and independent experts. For information on joining CompuServe, which costs about $13.00 per hour to use at 2,400 baud, call (800) 848-8199.

The Microsoft Knowledge Base (GO MSKB) contains text files of technical tips, workarounds for bugs, and other useful information about Microsoft applications. Use "Access" as the search term, but remember to turn on your communication software's capture-to-file feature because the information is in the form of messages that scroll down your screen, not in the form files.

Windows for Workgroups, also an unreleased Microsoft product when this book was written, will be supported by Microsoft on CompuServe. Check the Advanced Windows forum (GO WINADV) to see when and where you can access the Windows for Workgroups section.

Data Based Advisor magazine operates a forum on CompuServe (GO DBA) that covers a wide range of database topics, including client-server systems. *DBMS* magazine also has its own forum (GO DBMS) on CompuServe. You can expect both of these forums to cover Access development topics.

Other On-Line Sources of Information

Private electronic bulletin boards (BBSs) are a rich source of information on database topics in general. As use of Access becomes widespread, you can expect several BBSs across the country to specialize in Access application development, or at least devote a conference or a files section to Access. The telephone numbers and the subjects in which BBSs specialize are listed in local computer-based periodicals and magazines devoted to on-line telecommunication.

Learning
Access
Fundamentals

PART

I

OUTLINE

Placing Access in Perspective

This book was written during a unique period in the history of database management systems for personal computers. The two major PC database products, Borland International's dBASE and Paradox—which together claim 70 percent of the market—had yet to emerge from a long development cycle as Windows applications. Microsoft Corporation was readying its contender, Access, for the forthcoming Windows database bout. Product reviews in industry periodicals speculated about the outcome based on pirated alpha and beta copies of the software, combined with guesswork and innuendo. Dire predictions were made for some products, and accolades were bestowed on others—sometimes, it seemed, at random.

In the spring of 1992, before Access entered the formal beta-testing stage, Microsoft purchased Fox Holdings, Ltd., the publisher of database managers for DOS-based PCs and Apple Macintosh computers. Both FoxBASE and FoxPro are based on the original dBASE programming language and use the dBASE "industry standard" file structure. At the time this book was written, FoxPro developers were awaiting the long-promised FoxPro for Windows that began limited beta testing in July 1992.

Computer Associates, Inc., the second-largest independent software publisher in the world, purchased Nantucket Corporation, FoxPro's principal competitor in the DOS-based database market. CA, as Computer Associates is known, is a major supplier of database applications for mainframe computers and publishes CA-dbFast, a dBASE clone for Windows. Independent developers use Nantucket's Clipper, now CA-Clipper, to create fast PC database applications. Like FoxPro, Clipper is based on an extended version of the dBASE language and uses the dBASE file structure. Clipper developers were looking forward to Aspen, the code name for the next generation of what is now CA-Clipper; they hoped that CA would deliver quickly the promised Windows version of Aspen.

This chapter is written in *backgrounder* form. The chapter provides a perspective view of Access, how it relates to the present and future spectrum of PC databases, what you can accomplish with Access, and how it compares with other DOS and Windows database managers. This chapter defines some of the Access terminology that may be unfamiliar if you aren't conversant with the concept of object-oriented programming. Microsoft's implementation of some Access features provides insight into changes you can expect in future Windows applications. This backgrounder information, therefore, includes some speculation about the future of macros and programming languages in Windows applications.

Understanding Desktop Database Management

Three types of application software are preeminent on the millions of desktop computers in use today—word processors, spreadsheet applications, and database managers. At least 95 percent of all PCs probably have at least one of these types of applications installed. Word processors such as WordPerfect and Word for Windows are always members of the top ten software lists. Spreadsheet applications such as 1-2-3, Excel, and Quattro Pro also appear regularly in these lists. Desktop database managers, however, dominated by dBASE IV and Paradox, seldom made the ranks of the top sellers.

An estimated 60 percent of all business-oriented programs created since the introduction of the personal computer have been devoted to database applications. If this estimate is even close to correct, why don't PC database managers lead word processors and spreadsheet applications in sales? The primary reason is that relational database management applications haven't been easy to use effectively.

The term *relational* means that data is stored in multiple files or separate tables linked together (*related*) by data elements that the files or tables have in common. Designing an efficient file structure with the correct relations between the files or tables isn't a simple process. Most relational database managers require programming ability in order to create useful applications and readable reports. This requirement for database application programming has created a mini-industry of independent consultants who write custom programs in the Paradox Application Language (PAL) or in xBase, the term used to describe the dBASE III+ programming language and its derivatives, such as Clipper and FoxPro.

Microsoft's intention with Access is to move the creation of database applications closer to the user environment and blur the distinction between end users and application developers. This intention follows Microsoft's approach in creating Visual Basic, the first language product that made Windows programming—formerly the sole province of an elite corps of C language coders—truly accessible to people who have no programming background. The most important Access characteristic is that you don't have to write programs unless you want to perform complex or specialized operations.

Looking at Access's History

Early versions of Windows and OS/2 Presentation Manager, which IBM and Microsoft developed jointly, provided the foundation for a new category of PC software whose watchwords were ease of use and consistency across different types of applications. Both products adhered to a standard, called Common User Access (CUA), for how computers communicate with users. CUA, established as part of IBM's System Application Architecture (SAA), was destined for use across IBM's entire line of computer products. Despite the obvious advantages of CUA, however, early versions of Windows and OS/2 made no significant impact on America's desktops.

The two mainstream applications, Word for Windows and Excel, that ran under Windows 2.0 and Windows/386 were no match in the sales race for the DOS versions of WordPerfect and Lotus 1-2-3. Word for Windows and Excel, however, gained a following of devoted users. One reason for these programs' acceptance was their availability for both PCs and Macintosh computers. Specialty applications, such as PageMaker (a desktop publishing program designed originally for the Macintosh) and Micrografx Designer and CorelDRAW! (graphic arts packages), achieved their initial success under Windows/386.

Then Microsoft introduced Windows 3.0 on May 22, 1990. The program was an instant hit and achieved the all-time sales record for a computer application; more than 7 million copies were licensed in its first 18 months. Industry publications estimate that from 12 to 15 million people will have used Windows 3.0 and 3.1 by the end of 1992. Windows 3.x implements the CUA in a *graphical user interface* (GUI), pronounced *gooey* that is both intuitive and attractive—two key reasons for its success. The acceptance of Windows 3.0 carried Word for Windows and Excel into prominence as major league players in their categories, and forced Lotus Corporation to introduce 1-2-3 for Windows and WordPerfect Corporation to create WordPerfect for Windows.

Prepare yourself for a multitude of three-letter acronyms and abbreviations, such as CUA, GUI, DDE, and OLE when you read about Windows database managers—commonly used pronunciations for acronyms are given when applicable. This book uses DBM as the abbreviation for *database manager*, but in many publications you see DBMS, short for *database management system* or RDBMS (for *relational database management system*). A complete glossary of Windows and database terms is in Appendix A. You may want to refer to the glossary if the terms in this introduction to Access are new to you, or just skip over them now; they are explained at appropriate locations in the text.

Word for Windows was in Version 2.0b, and Excel 4.0a had just been released when this book was written, a little more than two years after the introduction of Windows 3.0, and yet no major database management application for Windows had emerged. Specialty products, such as Software Publishing's Superbase 4 and Computer Associates' CA-dBFast, were in software stores, but did not achieve mainstream application status. Despite premature product announcements, rumors in trade publications, and all the other hype associated with vaporware, the long-awaited dBASE for Windows and Paradox for Windows weren't yet on the shelves. Lotus Corporation, an industry leader with a major stake in Windows applications, hadn't even announced a Windows DBM candidate. Why not?

Creating a database management system that nonprogrammers can use and that still satisfies the requirements of professional database application developers isn't an easy task. Writing code that simply creates a Windows version of dBASE or Paradox isn't the hurdle; CA-dBFast, for instance, enables you to write Windows database applications using the dBASE language made popular by Ashton-Tate. Using CA-dBFast, however, *requires* programming ability, and a majority of Windows users aren't programmers. The trick is in designing a Windows DBM that isn't just a rehash of a DOS product, but one that takes full advantage of the Windows GUI. A useful DBM must eliminate the need to know or learn programming techniques to display the data you want and print it in the style you want. The DBM also must have a full-featured programming language so that independent application developers will use the product—without them, you cannot have a mainstream database management product. For DBM application publishers, including Borland and Microsoft, this process was much more difficult than they had imagined.

Despite difficulties and one false start, Microsoft finally created a Windows database manager for everyone when it released Access 1.0 on November 16, 1992. An Access display of three tables from the sample Northwind Traders database is shown in figure 1.1.

FIG. 1.1

Three tables from the sample Access database.

Looking at the Basics of Access

Access is a relational database management system and an application generator designed for the Windows graphical user interface. It had a long gestation period and was redesigned many times during its development. Bill Gates, founder and chief executive officer of Microsoft, announced the impending arrival of Access at a Chicago meeting of the Corporate Association for Microcomputer Professionals (CAMP) in September 1991. Access, with its code name Cirrus, had been the subject of industry rumors since early 1991, about two years after Microsoft had abandoned work on a predecessor Windows 2.x database product named Omega.

Microsoft adopted the best features of DOS dBASE and Paradox, both relational DBMs, for Access. To complete the package, the company added the form and report design methodology and much of the programming methodology from its highly acclaimed Visual Basic language application. A toolbar, similar to the one in Word for Windows 2.0 and Excel 4.0, provides shortcuts for menu operations. The toolbox you use to create forms and reports was borrowed from Visual Basic. Wizards, introduced with Excel 4.0, create forms and reports at the click of a button. You can automate multistep procedures with *macros*. You create macros by choosing a sequence of actions to be performed from lists provided by Access. You can call on Cue Cards to provide advice at every step in learning Access. Detailed on-line help, using the advanced help functions of Windows 3.1, requires just a few mouse clicks to explain how a feature works or to provide the syntax of an Access Basic programming instruction.

Access's Advantages

A major advantage of not having a widely accepted PC DBM is that you do not have to carry the baggage of backward compatibility. When Microsoft created Access, it could start with a clean slate. Some of the advantages Access therefore has over widely used DOS DBMs are shown in the following list:

- *File structures optimized for database integrity:* Access users don't have to be concerned about the myriad individual files that comprise conventional PC databases. One file holds all—tables, indexes, forms, report definitions, macros, and Access Basic programs related to the database. Other Windows DBMs are obligated to use their DOS predecessor's database structure.

- *Internal table management:* The DBM, not DOS, handles the separate elements that comprise the database. Access therefore is free from many constraints imposed by DOS and minimizes differences when it is adapted for use under other operating systems, such as Windows NT and the Macintosh System 7.

- *Long table names:* The use of a single database file frees Access from the DOS limit of eight-character file names for table names. You can include spaces in Access table names and use descriptive titles such as Customer Names and Addresses.

- *Long field names that can include spaces:* This capability enables Access to use the field names, rather than field name aliases, as display titles and report headers. Field names can be as long as 64 characters and can include punctuation symbols. dBASE, for instance, has a 10-character field name limit, permits no spaces, and allows only a few punctuation symbols in field names.

■ *Standardized, consistent keywords and syntax:* A Windows version of dBASE, for example, must be backward-compatible with programming code written for DOS versions. Both end users and developers expect to be able to use the xBase syntax they have memorized and much of the programming code they have written with the Windows version. New keywords added for programming in the Windows environment, therefore, must not conflict with keywords in earlier versions. Creating new, unique keywords often leads to awkward and sometimes incomprehensible command verbs. Microsoft created Access Basic, a derivative of Visual Basic, specifically for database programming in the Windows environment. Visual Basic's syntax already was optimized for object-method, event-driven programming in the Windows environment. Microsoft just embellished Visual Basic with new command keywords and data types specific to database operations to create the Access Basic dialect. Visual Basic 2.0 has adopted many of the Access Basic keywords to make Visual Basic more compatible with database applications.

Although the following sections describe briefly the benefits of these Access features, the advantages of Access over DOS-based and other Windows database managers become ever more evident as you progress through this book.

Query by Example

Database managers require a method of describing the characteristics of the data in which you are interested so that it can be distinguished from the remainder of the information that doesn't pertain to your immediate needs. This method is called a *query*. Modern relational DBMs implement queries with a specialized computer *application language* designed specifically for database applications. This language, *Structured Query Language*, is abbreviated SQL and pronounced either "seekel" or "sequel." The section "Attaching Client-Server Files with the ODBC API" discusses SQL briefly. Application languages, such as SQL, are similar to *programming* or *system languages*, such as COBOL, BASIC, and C; application languages, however, are designed for a specific purpose and usually have a more limited, specialized vocabulary.

Like any other language, SQL requires study and practice before you can use it effectively. dBASE and its dialects, in addition to Paradox PAL, combine application and system programming functions in a single language. Access does this also, but in a different way, which is described in the section "Macros" later in this chapter.

One of Microsoft's objectives in designing Access was to eliminate the requirement for either application or system programming to update, view, and print selected data. Both application and system programming capabilities would be provided as options for advanced users and application developers. Microsoft accomplished this objective by using a graphical *query by example* (QBE) methodology. IBM developed query by example as a means for nonprogrammers to create SQL queries by filling in blanks on an 80-column video display unit. Paradox introduced character-based graphical QBE to the PC, and QBE was largely responsible for Paradox's success. FoxPro and dBASE IV also use character-based graphical QBE to display selected data. An example of a QBE form created in dBASE IV Version 1.5 appears in figure 1.2.

FIG. 1.2

A QBE query edit form in Borland dBASE IV Version 1.5.

Windows is the ideal environment for implementing QBE in truly graphical form. Scalable, proportionally spaced typefaces free you from the bondage of DOS's 24 rows of 80 characters. Windows enables you to view more information on your display and print more attractive and readable reports. Windows' built-in graphics engine lets you display and manipulate bit-mapped (.BMP and .DIB files) and vector-based (WMF) images, and add them to forms and reports. You can pick tables and fields from standard list boxes with a mouse click. Access draws lines between field names to show relationships between tables. Imagine attempting to duplicate the typical Access graphical query shown in figure 1.3 using the dBASE DOS character mode displayed in figure 1.2.

FIG. 1.3

A typical multitable query created with Access for Windows Query tool.

For Related Information:

▶▶ "Creating Your First Query," p. 238.

▶▶ "Joining Tables To Create Multitable Queries," p. 306.

▶▶ "What Is Structured Query Language?," p. 830.

FROM HERE...

Database Files and Tables

Access has its own database file structure, similar to that used by client-server DBMs, and uses the .MDB extension. It differs from traditional PC databases in that a single file contains all the related tables, indexes, forms, and report definitions. Even the programming code you write in Access Basic is included in the .MDB file. You don't have to be concerned about the intricacies of the .MDB file structure because Access handles all the file-management details for you.

All the field data types familiar to xBase and Paradox users are available in Access, and some new and useful ones (such as Currency for monetary transactions) have been added. dBASE users will have to adapt to using the term *table* for file, and *database* to indicate a group of related tables or files. *Records* commonly are called *rows*, and *fields* are *columns*. Paradox, Excel, and 1-2-3 users will find Access terminology to be familiar. Paradox users will appreciate dealing with only one .MDB file rather than the myriad files that make up a multitable Paradox database.

FROM HERE...

For Related Information:

▶▶ "Using Database Tables," p. 71.

Importing and Attaching Existing Files

Rest assured that you don't have to rekey the data in your existing PC database or spreadsheet files to be able to use Access. Importing files with industry standard formats into Access databases is quick and easy. Exporting them back to their original format is just as simple.

In addition to the capability to manipulate data in tables built into Access's own .MDB file structure, Access can use the PC database files in the following list in their own native file format; this process is called *attaching* tables. You don't have to import tables into a .MDB database to manipulate them with Access's arsenal of database tools. This capability is important when you change to Access from another database manager that you continue to use until your Access application is complete and tested. Access has drivers that enable it to import or attach files created by the following DBMs:

- *xBase:* .DBF and .DBT files created with dBASE III or IV, and other applications that create or maintain them, such as CA-Clipper, FoxBASE+, and FoxPro (however, you cannot attach .DBF files created by FoxPro 2.0). The use of existing index files is limited to dBASE III NDX and dBASE IV .MDX structures; CA-Clipper NTX and FoxPro .IDX and CDX indexes aren't supported. Access is capable of maintaining NDX and MDX index files and even creating them, if necessary.

- *Paradox:* .DB table files and .PX primary index files. Paradox's .X# and .Y# secondary index files, and .F, .R, .SET, .VAL, and .SC files are among the other Paradox varieties not supported.

- *Btrieve files:* Access reads the .DDF data dictionary file you choose and then provides a dialog box that enables you to select which table or tables to import or attach.

Access attaches xBase, Paradox, and Btrieve files. You use these three popular file types in a *native* process: You don't need another application to work with them. You can attach files created by other database managers through the Open Database Connectivity application programming interface described in the following section, "Attaching Client-Server Files with the ODBC API."

In addition, Access can import (but not attach) files from the following applications that are not database managers:

- *Excel* .XLS spreadsheet files. Columns correspond to fields and rows are treated as records. If the first row of the spreadsheet file contains the column name, Access uses the names for the fields.

- *1-2-3* .WKS, .WK1, and .WK3 spreadsheet files.

- *ASCII or ANSI text* files using comma- or tab-delimited formats, often called mail-merge files. These files are used most often as an intermediary format for importing data from database file types not supported directly by Access.

- *Text files* with columns defined by fixed numbers of characters, divided into rows by newline pairs (carriage return and line feed). Text files are commonly obtained from information utilities, such as Dow Jones News Service or CompuServe. Access provides a dialog box to set the starting character position and the number of characters for each field (see fig. 1.4).

FIG. 1.4

The Import/Export Setup dialog box for importing delimited and fixed-width text files.

Access can export files in any format it can import. If you export an Access table containing a Memo field to a dBASE III or dBASE IV file structure, a dBASE .DBF and a .DBT memo file are created with the file name you choose. To export a Btrieve file, you must have an Xtrieve data dictionary file (.DDF) for the destination database because Access cannot create a .DDF for you.

Attaching Client-Server Files with the ODBC API

Client-server databases are stored on a computer (the *server*) dedicated to supplying data to other (client) computers by way of a local area network (LAN). Special adapter cards and software are required to connect your PC to client-server databases running on micro-, mini-, and mainframe computers. Client-server databases play the predominant role in downsizing database applications from mini- and mainframe computers to PCs. When you move a database system that runs on a larger-scale computer to a smaller, less costly one, you *downsize* it. The introduction of Intel 80486-based PCs and PC-compatible disk drives with gigabyte capacities (1 gigabyte = 1 billion bytes) has made downsizing mini- and mainframe database systems to lower-cost, PC-based client-server applications practical.

Access uses the Microsoft Open Database Connectivity (ODBC) application programming interface (API) to provide access to any database system for which ODBC drivers are available. An *application programming interface* is a standardized method by which an application communicates with elements of the computer's operating system or environment. Applications use the Windows API in GDI.EXE, a Windows dynamic link library (DLL), for example, to perform all display operations. The use of the ODBC API enables a standard set of SQL statements in any application to be translated to commands recognized by the database. The *driver* is responsible for translating the standard SQL statements into language the attached database understands. Windows uses drivers to adapt its standard API to specific combinations of hardware, such as displays, keyboards, and printers. Similarly, the ODBC API uses drivers to translate standard SQL commands to commands that are compatible with various DBMs. An ODBC driver is required for each different type of database you use with Access, except for the three types listed in the preceding section. Access includes an ODBC Administrator application, one of whose windows is shown in figure 1.5, to assist you in attaching tables in client-server databases.

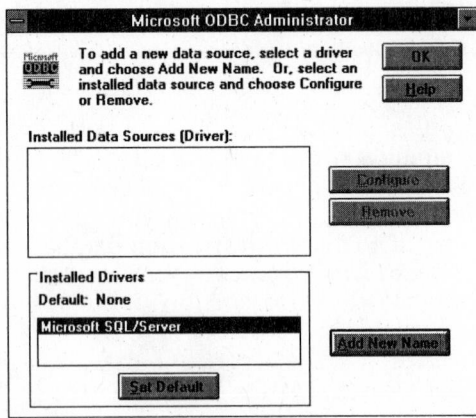

FIG. 1.5

The ODBC Administrator tool supplied with Access.

The ODBC API is based on a standard called the X/Open SQL Call Level Interface (CLI) developed by the SQL Access Group, an organization composed of hardware manufacturers, software suppliers, and SQL database users. Microsoft has announced that access to client-server and a variety of other PC databases will be added to a future version of Excel through the use of an ODBC driver set. Because Microsoft has published the standards for creating ODBC drivers, any DBM supplier can make its database product compatible with Access by writing the appropriate driver. Access 1.0 supports the following client-server databases:

- *Microsoft SQL Server* databases on LAN Manager or Novell networks and *Sybase SQL Server* databases on UNIX servers

- *Oracle* databases on UNIX, OS/2, and other server platforms

- *Rdb* databases on DEC computers

- *IBM DB2* (level 1 and level 2) databases

When Access was released, only SQL Server was supported by an ODBC driver. Microsoft plans to supply the remaining three drivers, as each one is certified, with interim releases of Access 1.0.

You can expect the publishers of major client-server database management systems to provide ODBC drivers for their products as Microsoft's ODBC API becomes more widely used. To attach another client-server database, you install its driver. The new database then appears in the Installed Data Sources list box (refer to fig. 1.5). If the client-server DBM you are using isn't one of the four included in the preceding list, check with the supplier to determine whether an ODBC-compliant driver is available for the DBM.

The ODBC API is the first element of Microsoft's Windows Open Services Architecture (WOSA) that has been added to commercial Windows applications. WOSA ultimately will include a group of APIs that enable Windows applications to manipulate data residing in any format on any type of computer located anywhere in the world. Enterprise-wide sharing of data through local- and wide-area networks, using LAN cabling, dial-up and dedicated telephone lines, and microwave or satellite transmission, primarily employs large mainframe computers as centralized database servers.

One of the trends in enterprise-wide computing is the use of distributed database systems. *Distributed* database systems enable elements of a large database to be stored on servers in different locations that act as though they were a single large server. As advanced Windows operating systems such as Windows NT are developed and WOSA becomes a reality, PCs will capture a larger share of the server market. Access is designed to play an important role in enterprise-wide, distributed database systems—creating the applications users need to view and update data.

For Related Information:

► "Using ODBC Drivers with Client-Server Database Systems," p. 875.

► "Extension of the ODBC APIs," p. 1082.

Application Development

The majority of time spent with database managers involves a fixed sequence of repetitive activities. Data-entry procedures, such as adding new sales orders or creating invoices are—or should be—routine operations. If you are creating a monthly sales report or evaluating patient response to a medical protocol, the basic queries, views, and report formats undoubtedly remain the same for successive periods— only the dates that define the period change. Whether you are using Access for your own purposes or are responsible for its use by others, you undoubtedly will use Access to create *database applications*. A database application consists of the following elements:

■ *Databases* that contain all the individual tables necessary for the application.

■ *Tables* that contain the individual pieces of data or to which new data elements are added.

■ *Queries* that establish the relationships between data in the tables and select the data of specific interest and then display the selected data in tabular form.

■ *Forms* used to view or update existing data as well as to add new data.

■ *Reports* that summarize data and format it for display on your screen or for printing.

■ *Macros* that automate repetitive operations without the necessity for using a structured programming language. You don't have to create macros for every application, but you probably will.

■ *Modules* that contain Access Basic programming code necessary to perform operations beyond the capabilities of macros. Macros suffice for all but the most sophisticated database applications.

Access provides buttons, shown in the margin, that enable you to change quickly between the elements that comprise your database application. Databases, tables, queries, forms, and reports are created by manipulating symbols with a mouse to create objects, such as a frame in which to display a bit-mapped image, and then by defining the properties of these objects with selections from lists or simple keyboard entries. The concept of objects in Access is explained later in this chapter in the section "Objects, Methods, and Events."

Technically, you can create a database application with only database, table, and query objects. If you want only to view selected data in tabular form or export data to another application, these three objects are sufficient. If you create an application for others to use, however, you probably will want to add one or more form objects for data-entry and editing operations. Forms enable your application to control the way data is entered, including validation of new or edited data for conformance to rules you establish. You probably will want to add a macro or two to make access to the forms automatic. The next step is to create reports that summarize the data entered on the forms. Macros can be added to display or print forms automatically. At this point, you have completed a full-scale database application.

Operating Modes

Access has three operating modes you select by clicking the Database Window's command buttons:

- *Run mode*, the default or start-up condition, in which you select and use the objects you or others have created. The command button's caption is Open for tables, queries, and forms, and Run for macros and modules (but it is disabled when you select modules).

  Run

- *New mode* for creating new database objects. When you click the button for an object and click New, you enter Design mode.

  New

- *Design mode* for editing the objects that comprise your application. You add control objects to a form or report in Design mode.

  Design

All application development is conducted in New and Design modes. You then test your newly created or edited objects in Run mode. A fourth mode, Start-up, occurs when no database has been opened or when you close your database. You can perform a number of utility functions on database files, such as compaction, encryption, and decryption. Access also can repair damaged database files in Start-up mode.

System and Application Programming Languages

Much controversy exists between programmers about which language is "the best," and the question probably will never be settled. C programmers staunchly defend C's flexibility, and those who prefer Pascal contend that, unlike C, Pascal produces code that is readable by people other than the author. BASIC programmers defend its ease of use and universality. Arguments erupt between database application developers about the relative merits of Paradox PAL and xBase dialects such as FoxBASE and Clipper. An example of this contention is a series of messages that appeared in mid-1991 on CompuServe's Data Based Advisor xBase forum (GO DBA) that, fortunately, were collected and preserved in a file (PDXFOX.ZIP). Much of the following is based on Dale W. Harrison's essay, contained in PDXFOX.ZIP, on programming language classification in reply to the forum's combatants.

Programming languages are divided into two major categories: procedural and nonprocedural. A graphical classification of the more common programming languages is shown in figure 1.6. Structural linguists and formal language theorists might argue with the classification methods, but the methods should suffice for the limited purposes here.

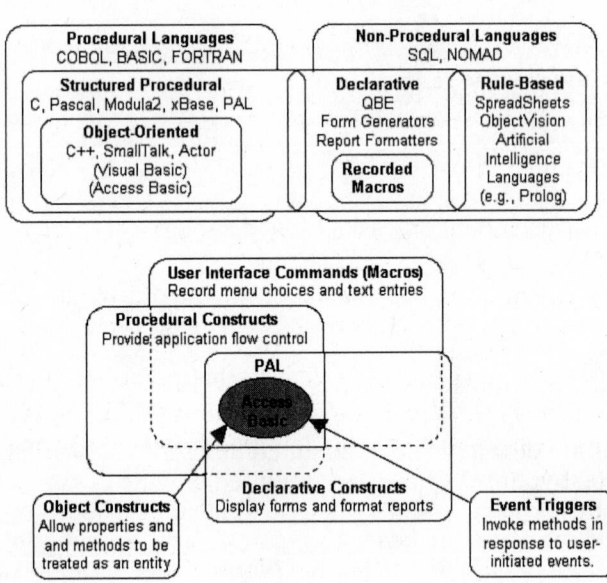

FIG. 1.6

A graphical classification of computer language types.

The following list briefly describes each of the language classes shown in figure 1.6:

- A language is classified as *procedural* if it includes conditional (IF ... THEN ... ELSE, CASE ... CASE ELSE, SWITCH) and looped (DO WHILE, DO UNTIL, FOR ... NEXT) execution constructs for program flow control and provides the capability to break applications into separate procedures that may be executed (DO, CALL) by name. The language may include unconditional (GOTO) or conditional (ON ... GOTO) branches as long as they may specify a label name, not a line number. FORTRAN, COBOL, QuickBASIC, and QBasic are commonly used examples of procedural languages.

- A language is *structured* procedural if it doesn't include GOTO instructions or, if it does, GOTOs don't have to be used to execute any other member of the instruction set. Pascal has a GOTO instruction, but you don't have to (and generally shouldn't) use it. QuickBASIC, QBasic, Visual Basic, and Access Basic require the ON ERROR GOTO instruction for error handling and provide no substitute or work-around. Because these BASIC dialects technically aren't structured, the parentheses in figure 1.6 are necessary. Access Basic is considered structured in this book, and GoTo instructions are used only where they are absolutely necessary.
  C, xBase, ADA, and Modula2 are other commonly used structured procedural languages.

- Structured procedural languages that enable data (properties) and code (methods) to be combined and treated as a single entity are *object-oriented*. Some languages, such as SmallTalk and C++, are more object-capable than others, but all of them offer the capability to create reusable blocks of code that you can treat as opaque containers. The container's contents don't concern the user of an object; what you put in the container and what you can get out of it are what counts. Both Visual Basic and Access Basic are object-oriented, although neither language has all the object accoutrements of C++, such as multiple inheritance. Object-method, a new classification of computer programming languages, has been assigned in this book to both Visual Basic and Access Basic.

- Languages are *event-driven* if they execute blocks of code (methods) in response to user- or hardware-initiated events. Events may be a mouse click on a menu command or a keystroke. After executing the code to process methods appropriate to the event and the properties of the object or objects involved, the application returns to an idle state and awaits another one. Any language category listed here may be event-driven, but most event-driven languages are object-oriented. Applications written for Windows are event-driven—a capability necessary for supporting Windows' multitasking capabilities. Like all object-method languages, therefore, Access Basic is event-driven.

■ *Nonprocedural* languages lack the flow-control instructions of procedural languages and don't have to have a formal syntactical structure. The dBASE dot-prompt commands and SQL are the most widely used nonprocedural languages. Both dBASE and SQL have a formalized syntax.

■ *Declarative* nonprocedural languages lack a formal syntax and rely on a set of predetermined user actions, such as using a menu or toolbar to create the elements of a data entry form or filling in blanks with keyboard entries. QBE is a widely used declarative nonprocedural language in which the entries you type in the columns are converted into a language such as SQL. The form and report generators in most database applications for DOS use declarative constructs to display a form or print a report.

■ *User-interface*. User-interface (macro) languages are a subclass of the nonprocedural declarative type. Most macro languages record user-initiated events, such as menu commands and text box entries, and then play them back on command. The events might be recorded as keywords of a procedural language or, as in Word for Windows and Paradox, they might have their own distinct keywords that are (or can be) embedded in a procedural language. Recorded macros often are called scripts; *script*, however, traditionally refers to a procedural language with a nonstandard syntax, such as those used in data communication languages such as ProComm and CrossTalk. Many application setup or installation programs, especially programs for installing Windows applications, use scripts. Access macros differ from traditional recorded macros and are the subject of a later section, "Macros."

■ In some nonprocedural languages, the user creates a set of rules and enters values that are processed in accordance with the rules. Most artificial intelligence (AI) languages (Prolog, for example), use this *rule-based* technique. Rule-based nonprocedural languages include those used in spreadsheet applications and Borland's ObjectVision, which establishes rules through a graphic technique called "decision trees."

Many languages combine both structured procedural and nonprocedural declarative elements; these two boxes, therefore, overlap in figure 1.6. The BROWSE and LIST constructs are examples of declarative keywords in xBase. xBase has many nonprocedural (dot-prompt) statements included in its procedural language. Excel, 1-2-3, and

Quattro Pro macros include conditional execution capability. Transact-SQL, the SQL dialect of Microsoft SQL Server, adds BEGIN and END to identify procedures, in a manner similar to Pascal's. Transact-SQL has IF ... THEN and WHILE constructs also to execute statements conditionally or repetitively. Transact-SQL, therefore, is nonprocedural with a little structured-procedural flavoring. Programming languages get placed in categories determined by the majority of their commands.

For Related Information:

▶▶ "What Is Structured Query Language?," p. 830.

▶▶ "Introducing Access Basic," p. 922.

▶▶ "Controlling Program Flow," p. 937.

FROM HERE...

Objects, Methods, and Events

Every element of the data contained in most databases is a full or partial representation of a tangible, real-world object. All the invoices, customers, suppliers, food products, and employees represented in the tables of the Northwind Traders demonstration database are real-world objects. Access treats as objects the representations of real-world objects in its tables. In fact, Access treats *everything* you create with it as an object. Databases, tables, queries, forms, reports, macros, and modules all are just classes of objects to Access.

Objects can contain other objects. A database object contains all the other object classes that comprise it: tables, queries, forms, reports, macros and modules. Text boxes that display data and frames which show images contained in the tables of your database are classified as control objects and are contained within your form and report objects. After you create any object, such as a form, in Access, you assign it a unique name. You then can disregard the way you created the object and use it for its intended purpose.

Objects possess characteristics, such as size and color, and behavior that comprises the actions they perform. In object-oriented terminology, an object's characteristics are called its *properties*, and its behavior is represented by *methods*. Properties and methods are *encapsulated* within the object. In conventional programming practice, properties (data values) and methods (programming code) have been treated as two distinct elements. Encapsulation of properties and methods within objects is the principal feature that distinguishes object-oriented or object-method implementations from conventional programming techniques.

Each class of object has a collection of methods that apply to all members of the class and determine the behavior of the class as a whole. Access determines the methods applicable to the object class, except for modules, for which you determine the methods to be used. You choose the methods to be implemented by including Access Basic method keywords in the programming code you write. If you create a macro, you select the methods you want to use from a list of macro action methods provided by Access. Both macros and modules use the object-method approach but differ in their implementation.

When you create a QBE query, you create an *instance* of the query class object. An instance of an object is a representation of the object, such as a window on your display or a printed report, with a new set of properties. The set of methods used for each instance is identical. The three overlapping Access tables in figure 1.1, at the beginning of the chapter, are three instances of the table object, each with different table name and field name properties.

Events occur when you open a menu, click a command button, or press a key. These examples are just a few of the stimuli that Windows interprets as events. Nothing happens in Windows or your application until an event occurs. When you click a menu command, for instance, Windows sends a message to Access that indicates the choice you made. If the active window contains an instance of a query object and you choose a query window menu item, Access executes the query class method appropriate to the choice you made. After the method has finished its task, Windows and your application return to an idle state and wait for the next event to trigger execution of another method.

Macros

Virtually everyone who has used one of the major word processing or spreadsheet applications is somewhat familiar with macros and how they are used to automate repetitive processes. If you are like most users of these applications, the majority of your macros consist of recorded menu commands and keystrokes. You may have used a macro editor to embellish your macros or simply to edit erroneous keystrokes. Rather than record keystrokes, power users and application developers usually write macros in whatever macro editor the application offers.

Access prepares you for the new world of macros for Windows applications. Access macros are composed of sequences of special methods, called *actions*, that you choose from the choices in a drop-down list box. The term *action* is used to distinguish macro methods from the methods that are keywords in Access Basic. You create a sequence of actions in a macro editor window rather than by the traditional method of recording your menu commands and keyboard entries. If the methods require properties, called *action arguments*, you enter them from multiple-choice lists or type names in a text box. Access has no provision for recording macros; instead, you use the drag-and-drop method. Click the icon for the Sales by Month report, drag it to an empty Action cell, and drop it there. The OpenReport action for the Sales by Month is created for you automatically. Then select what you want to happen when the report is opened by making a choice from the View drop-down list box—in this case, print the report.

When you choose a macro and click the Run button, the equivalent of a "macro start" event triggers the first macro action. The macro action sends messages to the Window in which your form or report is stored. Successive macro actions send their messages to the Window and don't wait for the preceding macro action to be completed. This process continues until the last instruction in the macro has been sent and acted upon. Then Windows and your application return to the idle state and wait for user input from the mouse or keyboard. If you are accustomed to macros that operate sequentially and wait for completion of one action before proceeding to the next (as in WordPerfect, for example), writing your first Access macros should be an interesting experience.

Another reason for implementing a new approach to the creation of macros in Access is standardization of macros between Windows applications. The next generation of Microsoft's mainstream applications are expected to share a common set of action keywords, such as Open and Close (a Window) or DoMenuItem to perform a particular menu command. Future Windows applications are expected to execute the common action keyword set. In addition, each application will have action keywords specific to its class, such as OpenTable, that are applicable to database applications.

Access's new approach to macros has the most significance to people who program in the WordBASIC macro and programming language of Word for Windows. WordBASIC was the first BASIC-dialect macro language incorporated in a Windows application. When you record a Word for Windows macro, menu commands are translated to special WordBASIC keywords, such as EditCut and FileOpen, that are expected to be part of the repertoire of standard macro action keywords. These macro action keywords have no counterparts as instructions in any other BASIC dialect.

The purpose of standardizing macro action keywords is to enable you ultimately to write a single macro whose actions are executed by several applications in a chosen sequence. A single macro in the future might perform the following tasks:

1. Launch Access and open a database

2. Run a query on the current data in the database's tables

3. Copy the query table data to the Clipboard and close Access

4. Launch Excel and open a spreadsheet

5. Paste the query table content to the spreadsheet

6. Perform a statistical analysis on the data

7. Copy the result of the analysis to the Clipboard

8. Save the spreadsheet file and close Excel

9. Launch Word for Windows and open a document

10. Paste the result from Excel at the location of a document bookmark

11. Print the revised Word for Windows document

12. Save the revised document file and close Word for Windows

The sequence of actions in the future is initiated by clicking an icon in the appropriate Program Manager group that represents the macro. Using cross-application macros, you don't have to create macros in the individual applications or write a single line of programming code. Implementing a cross-application macro requires that all the participating applications share a similar macro syntax. Microsoft calls this standard syntax Command Architecture.

Macro Manager, a new Windows accessory that Microsoft says is destined for a "future version of Windows" supplements or replaces Windows' present Recorder applet. Macro Manager can execute macros within any Windows application that supports Command Architecture. You can expect the following Macro Manager capabilities:

■ Each application registers its special keywords, perhaps in the registration database file (REG.DAT), so that Macro Manager knows that the special action keyword is valid for the application.

■ You choose an application from Macro Manager's list of applications that register themselves as Command Architecture-compliant.

■ You choose from a list of macro action keywords supported by the application. The application also registers valid values for each action argument, when this is possible.

■ You can add If conditions that determine whether a particular action should be taken.

■ You can create a cross-application macro by recording mouse clicks and keystrokes or by dragging and dropping icons.

What Macro Manager portends for Word for Windows and Excel, as well as for other Windows word-processor and spreadsheet applications, is the division of macro instructions and programming code into two separate objects, as in Access. Macros you record in future versions of Word for Windows and Excel most likely will be translated into standardized macro action keywords saved in a template or macro sheet. Although this separation is a major change for Excel and Word for Windows users, Microsoft likely will provide macro-translation applets that do all—or at least most—of the work for you.

For Related Information:

▶▶ "Creating a New Macro," p. 685.

▶▶ "Windows 3.2 and Macro Manager," p. 1079.

FROM HERE...

The Access Basic Programming Language

Several years ago, Bill Gates said that all Microsoft applications that used macros would share a common macro language built on BASIC. His choice of BASIC isn't surprising when you consider that the Microsoft behemoth was built on the foundation of Gates' BASIC interpreter. It ran in 8K on the early predecessors of the PC. Gates reiterated his desire for a common macro language in an article that appeared in *One-to-One with Microsoft* in late 1991.

Before the release of Access, Gates' edict had been observed in only one Microsoft product, Word for Windows. If you have created Word for Windows macros or made just minor changes to ones you have recorded, you should be pleased to know that Access uses a similar programming language (see fig. 1.7). As indicated in the preceding section, however, Access Basic isn't a macro language. You create your own macro actions with Access Basic functions and procedures. You can execute any macro action keyword from Access Basic by preceding it with a new DoCmd and a space. Many macro action keywords seem to be the same as Access Basic keywords. Except for MsgBox and SendKeys, action keywords and Access Basic keywords that are identical in name have a different syntax and perform different—but usually related—functions.

FIG. 1.7

The Access Basic
code editing
window for
modules.

```
Microsoft Access - [Module: Introduction To Programming]
 File   Edit   View   Run   Window   Help

Procedure: FillExcel

Sub FillExcel (TableOrQuery)
' Accepts: the name of a Table or Query
' Performs: Opens the table or query results and dumps the data to
'           Excel (starting Excel if necessary). Memo and OLE fields
'           are ignored.
' Returns: nothing
' From: Chapter 9, "Dynamic Data Exchange"

' TableOrQuery is the name of a Table or Query
Dim dbCurrent As Database, dsResult As Dynaset, ssFields As Snapshot
Dim Chan As Integer, Topiclist As String, Sheetname As String
Dim Rownum As Integer, Row As Variant, Cell As Variant
    Chan = StartApp("Excel", "System")     'See code given earlier
    If Chan < 0 Then
        MsgBox Error(Abs(Chan))
        Exit Sub

Ready                                                          NUM
```

Access Basic and Visual Basic are two members of a family of languages known as Object Basic. Soon you will be able to use Object Basic dialects with Word for Windows and Excel, as well as with many of Microsoft's other mainstream applications. If you have used Visual Basic, writing Access Basic code is a snap (refer to fig. 1.7). Version 2 of Visual Basic, the language on which Access Basic is modeled, includes many of the new keywords added by Access. Microsoft has announced that a "future version" of Visual Basic will be used to "compile" macros created by Macro Manager.

Your first use of Access Basic probably will be the creation of functions to make complex calculations. Creating an Access Basic function to substitute for calculations that have many sets of parentheses is a relatively simple process and a good introduction to writing Access Basic code. When you write expressions as Access Basic functions, you can add comments to the code that execute the function to make their purpose and construction clear to others. Comments help your memory, too, when you revise an application after it has been in use for a few months.

Your next step is to create Access Basic procedures you can call from macros using the RunCode action. You use procedures to perform operations that cannot be accomplished by macro actions. RunCode executes only an Access Basic function but ignores the function's return value. You can write the procedure as a function or write a short function that calls a procedure.

For Related Information:

▶▶ "The Object Basic Root Language," p. 923.

▶▶ "Windows 3.2 and Macro Manager," p. 1079.

FROM HERE...

Language Standardization Considerations

Language standardization is one of the principal factors you should consider, especially if you are choosing a PC-based DBM for use by your organization. The financial investment in training employees to use new macro and programming languages can exceed the purchase cost of the application by 10 to 100 percent. Standardized macro action keywords and similar macro syntax across all of your most frequently used applications to bring users to the intermediate and advanced skill levels reduces training costs.

dBASE (which was derived from BASIC) is unquestionably the current root PC database system language. All xBase languages are derived from dBASE, and each xBase dialect adds its own particular set of keywords to enhance the root language's usefulness. Standardized Visual Basic dialects, Microsoft's root language for Windows, will be used with Microsoft's future word processing, spreadsheet, database, project management, and even multimedia authoring applications. Access is a wise choice for a company-wide DBM if you use other Microsoft applications or are planning to convert to them. The time spent learning Access Basic pays dividends when you or your firm's staff turn to programming in other Microsoft languages. Not surprisingly, other software publishers may use the xBase approach to create their own xBasic dialects.

When Microsoft designed Access, it made the Access Basic language a module of Access. Executives in charge of Microsoft's database development program said in a 1992 interview in *DBMS* magazine that Access was designed for "language independence." *Language independence* means that you can replace or supplement the use of Access Basic with other programming languages such as xBase or C++ to create Access applications. Microsoft's Tod Nielsen, says that the capability to use the FoxBase dialect of xBase with Access may occur in 1994 or 1995.

SQL is, and will continue to be, the preeminent data-handling language for client-server DBMs. Most PC-based DBMs now support SQL, either as a primary language or as an alternative to the DBM's native language. You can absorb most of SQL by studying the SQL syntax of the QBE queries you create in Access's SQL window. If you are serious about learning to use SQL or you already know the language, you can edit your current QBE queries or start new ones from scratch in the SQL window.

Libraries

Programmers who use system and application programming languages such as C, Pascal, and Basic use libraries of functions and other program elements they can combine as a group into their programs. When you link a library into a program written in one of these languages, all the functions it contains are accessible to the program you write. Visual Basic has a similar capability, called *custom controls*, that enables you to add new types of control elements to forms from the Visual Basic toolbox. Libraries are useful because you can treat them as objects. You must know only what they contain, and you can disregard the details of their contents and how the individual functions were created.

Access provides the capability to link libraries to your databases. Libraries can contain any or all elements of an Access application, including their own databases. Wizards that create standard types of forms, reports, and graphs for you are contained in the WIZARD.MDA Access library. ANALYZER.MDA creates data dictionaries that contain detailed information about the objects in your Access database. Access uses UTILITY.MDA to perform several of its built-in functions.

Access libraries can be shared by any Access application. You can create libraries that contain standard functions in the form of Access Basic code that all your applications can use, and not have to add the module with the functions to each application. Libraries let you incorporate Access Basic code for special macros in libraries and then use application macros to call the library function. You even can create your own Wizards to help users learn how to use an application. If you are familiar with Windows dynamic link libraries, you will see that Access libraries share many of their characteristics. Access libraries, however, are easier to use than are Windows DLLs. You can expect to see a wide range of Access libraries, published by third-party developers, that perform specialized functions such as statistical analysis. Many of these products will be similar to the special-purpose libraries intended to complement Clipper and FoxBase.

Understanding How Access Differs from Traditional DBMs

Superficially, Access isn't much different from traditional database managers designed to operate under DOS, combined with a database front end for Windows. A database *front end* differs from a DBM in that it doesn't have its own file structure, but provides access to databases, usually to a number of different varieties of the client-server type. Like the front ends, Access uses graphics forms to view, enter, and edit data. Access creates formatted reports on any printer supported by Windows, as do all other Windows DBMs and front ends.

The important differences between Access and other Windows DBMs and front ends aren't what each one does. All DBMs and database front ends enable you to create QBE or SQL queries, forms with graphics, and fully formatted reports. Most offer some type of macro capability, and several have programming languages of their own. The important differences are how the products differ in their approach to creating database applications and the ease with which you learn the approach each product offers.

OLE: A New Type of Data

Microsoft has introduced a new method of incorporating text and graphics in a database with the OLE field data type. Object linking and embedding (OLE) was formally introduced with Windows 3.1. OLE had been incorporated within PowerPoint from its inception, however, and was added to Excel in Version 3.0 and to Word for Windows in Version 2.0. Windows 3.1 now implements OLE through two Windows dynamic link libraries: OLECLI.DLL and OLESVR.DLL. The advantage of a Windows dynamic link library (DLL) is that one copy of the DLL provides its services to all the applications that need it. Word for Windows 2.0 was the first application to use OLECLI.DLL and OLESVR.DLL to add OLE compliance. You don't have to upgrade to Windows 3.1 to use Access, however, because these two OLE DLLs are included with Access, as they were with Word for Windows 2.0.

Access's use of OLE was introduced earlier in this chapter. That part of the chapter concentrated on using OLE for bit-mapped graphics because it is OLE's most frequent use for the majority of Access users. Figure 1.8 shows a form displaying a vector drawing (a Windows meta file stored in .WMF file format) of a city street map stored in an OLE field. The significance of the OLE field extends much farther than its use as a substitute for the graphic or BLOB field data type of other DBMs.

FIG. 1.8

A street map stored as a Windows meta file in an OLE field.

OLE fields enable any type of data that can be created or edited by an OLE server to be stored (embedded) within a table. You can embed waveform audio files, bit-mapped images, vector-based drawings, Excel spreadsheets, and even Word for Windows documents in a single OLE field or several different OLE fields in the same table. Some of the advantages of the OLE Object field data type compared with graphic or BLOB fields follow:

- Images may be stored as vector drawings in OLE fields. Vector drawings usually have much smaller file sizes than bit-mapped images of equivalent size.

- You can create OLE links to files so that keeping duplicate copies of the data in your database table and in the original file isn't necessary. This process conserves disk space, especially with bit-mapped images and waveform audio files that have a tendency to be very large.

- Files linked to, rather than embedded in, OLE fields have the advantage of providing your application with the most current version of the data. If you are sharing files on a network, you can link to files on the server. Any editing done to the linked file since the last time you used it in Access is displayed or heard.

- You can use Windows 3.1's Object Packager to embed or link objects for which you don't have an OLE server. For example, you can embed or link MIDI files in an OLE field by creating a packaged object consisting of Media Player and an .MID file.

The storage of different types of data in a single field violates a basic tenet of relational database design: A single field in a database may represent only a single type of data. For example, the Invoice Number field of all records of an Invoice table may contain invoice numbers and nothing else. You probably would want to create individual OLE-type fields, therefore, for each type of OLE data you plan to incorporate in a table.

For Related Information:

▶▶ "The Importance of OLE," p. 510.

▶▶ "Embedding and Linking Graphics Files in Tables," p. 546.

FROM HERE...

The Form Designer

All Windows DBMs incorporate a method for creating the forms used for entering, editing, and viewing data contained in tables. Some Windows DBMs continue to use the traditional xBase @ X, Y SAY and @ X, Y GET instructions for form design. More graphics-oriented DBMs provide buttons to add labels, the equivalent of the xBase SAY command, text boxes that substitute for GETs, and other objects such as picture boxes to display bit-mapped images to a form. You click the button and then manipulate, in a window that represents your form, the object the button creates for you.

The Access form design system was taken directly from Microsoft's Visual Basic, with minor modifications. If you have used Visual Basic, you can see in figure 1.9 the similarities between the Access and Visual Basic toolboxes. If you aren't familiar with Visual Basic, the toolbox is the window with the north-by-northwest arrow at the top. Microsoft had a good reason for choosing the Visual Basic approach to form design: Visual Basic has received rave reviews in virtually every PC-oriented computer publication for its technical excellence and intuitive design interface. Visual Basic has been successful also in the application language marketplace. The variety of third-party add-on products available for Visual Basic attest to its success.

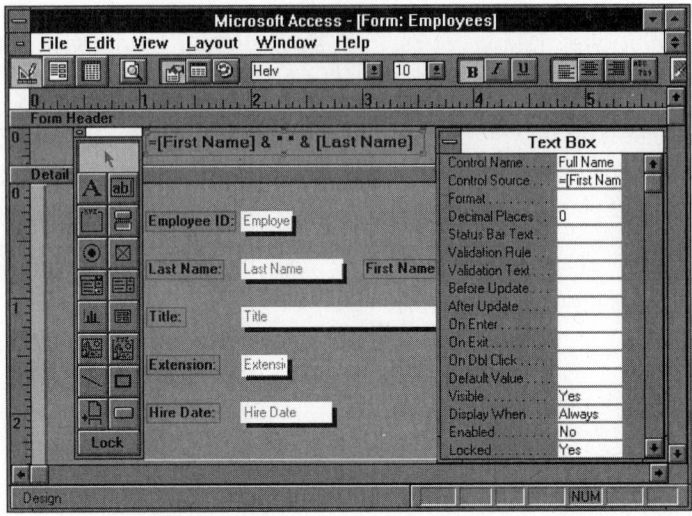

FIG. 1.9

Editing or creating a form in Access.

Access makes quick work of creating a simple form to display and edit data. Someone new to Access spent less than five minutes creating the Street Map form in figure 1.8. You click the toolbox button for the type of object you want to place on the form and then place the mouse cursor at the upper left corner of the location at which you want to place the object. Then you drag the cross-hair mouse pointer to the right and down until the object is the size you want. You set other properties for the object by making selections from the Properties window, shown for the text box that holds the heading for Northwind's Employees form.

FROM HERE...

For Related Information:

▶▶ "Using the Form Design Window," p. 386.

▶▶ "Using the Toolbox To Add Controls," p. 423.

Cue Cards and Wizards

One problem in creating a database management system is that no accepted format exists for the application's opening screen. Word processors present a screen that represents a blank piece of paper. When you start typing, characters appear, more or less where you would expect them. Similarly, spreadsheet applications open with the familiar columnar pad. The cell invites you to enter numbers, and moving between cells with the arrow keys is intuitive for most people. Database managers open either with a blank screen (like Access), a set of mysterious icons, or an array of menu commands that are indecipherable to the first-time user. The first question that comes to mind is, "How do I get this thing going?"

One way to learn how to use an application is to read the accompanying manuals. The average database manager's collection of manuals is a multivolume set that weighs several pounds and measures half a foot wide. The manuals can be more intimidating than the opening screen. The natural thing to do is to choose **Help Contents**, but which of the 20 or more choices do you make? Microsoft came up with the answer when it created Access's Cue Cards. Just click the Cue Cards button to display the first Cue Card. Work with Data is a logical topic to start a database application. When you click this option, the Cue Card that is displayed tells you that you don't have a database open and politely suggests that you open one. The next Cue Card in the sequence tells you how to open a database file. A typical series of three Cue Cards is shown superimposed in figure 1.10.

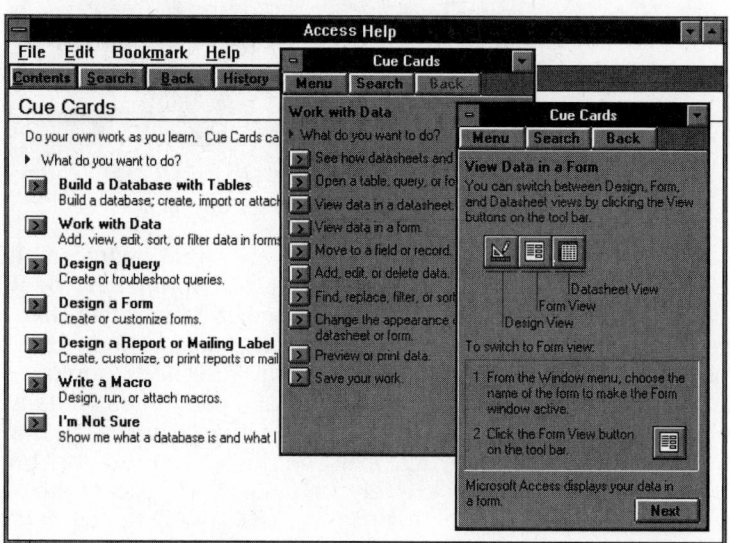

FIG. 1.10

Cue Cards for the Work with Data topic.

Cue Cards, which are dealt from the deck in the sequence you select with the arrow keys, are available for all the basic functions Access can perform. As with the suggestion that you open a database file, Cue Cards make suggestions based on the status of Access at the time you invoke them.

Some operations in Access are complex and require many steps to complete successfully. A good example is the creation of graphs from data contained in a query object. Wizards are even better than Cue Cards—they do most of the work for you. The first two dialog boxes of the GraphWizard are shown in figure 1.11. You receive the option to use a Wizard or "go it alone" and hope for the best when you elect to create a new form or report, or add a graph or chart to a form or report.

FIG. 1.11

Two of the Wizard windows for creating Access graphs and charts.

Access's GraphWizard is particularly adept at extracting information in the appropriate way to create a useful chart or graph. When the Wizard produced the chart in figure 1.12, for instance, it determined that the source of the data, Employee Sales per Month, was a report. The Wizard then ran the report to obtain the total sales for each employee in the list for each month. Because one of the selected fields contained numbers and the other consisted of text, the Wizard surmised that the numbers belonged on the vertical axis and the text on the horizontal axis. No manual operations were required in order to create the chart in figure 1.12, other than selecting the source of the data, the fields to be charted, and a few minor adjustments to the size of the type used for the title and legends in the charts.

Wizards are available to assist you in creating new forms, reports, and graphs. The three Access Wizards were written by Microsoft in Access Basic. Wizard windows are Access forms, and the forms and the code that creates them are contained in a special read-only Access library database called WIZARD.MDA. You can expect third-party developers to create new and unique genies, oracles, or sybils for many other purposes.

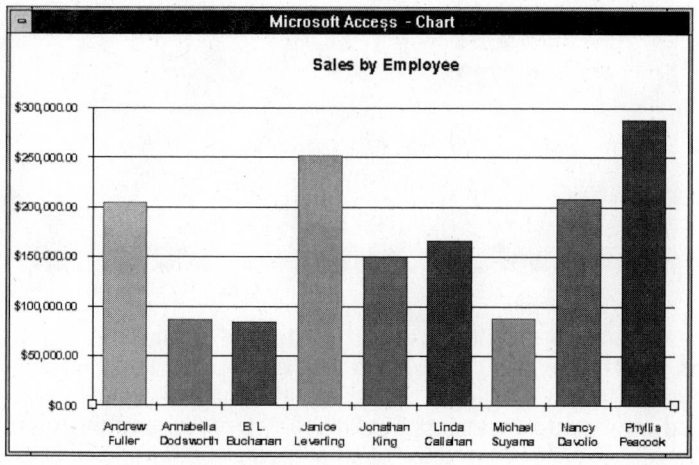

FIG. 1.12

A bar chart created by Access's GraphWizard.

Cue Cards and Wizards give first-time users the extra help needed to overcome the hurdle of learning how to use an application as complex as a database manager. You don't need the Cue Cards after a few hours with Access. After you have become adept at creating forms and reports, you probably will abandon the Form Wizard and Report Wizard in favor of starting with blanks. No matter how expert you become with Access, however, you are unlikely to give up the services of the Graph Wizard.

Designing Reports

All DBMs incorporate a method of creating reports from a database, but they vary widely in the techniques they use to design the reports. Designing the reports you will use for printing the data contained in Access tables and queries follows the same methodology as that used for forms. Reports are designed primarily for printing, but you can view reports on your display and even incorporate reports within other reports. You cannot, however, combine reports into forms. The reports design window is shown in figure 1.13.

FIG. 1.13

Editing or creating a report in Access.

Reports consist of headers used to group and summarize detailed information. You might want to prepare, for example, a report of the sales made each month by each employee in the marketing department. The detailed information consists of all the invoices issued during the month. A header is created for each salesperson, and then the invoices resulting from the individual's orders are listed as a group under the header, followed by total sales for each person. A grand total of all invoices appears at the bottom of the report, in a region called the *report footer*. A report from the Northwind Traders sample database is shown in figure 1.14.

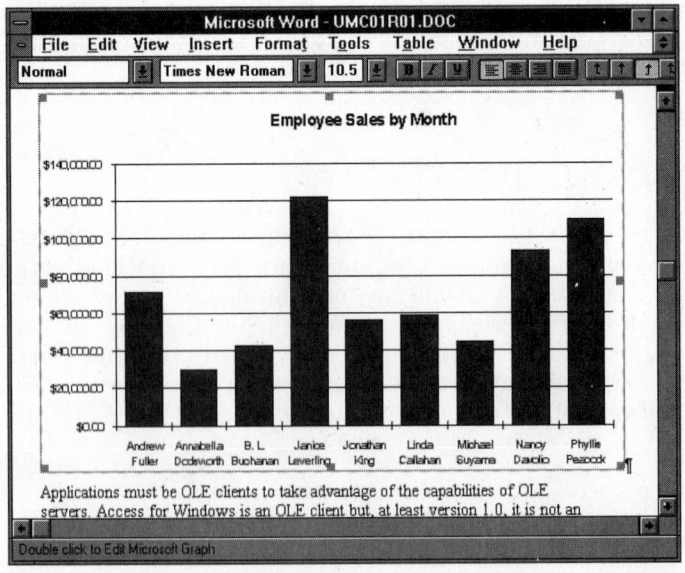

FIG. 1.14

The Employee Sales by Month report printed by a laser printer.

For Related Information:

▶▶ "Types of Access Reports," p. 457.

FROM HERE...

The Code Editor

Windows DBMs, as a whole, and database front ends are oriented toward creating applications that don't require the use of a programming language. Many front ends offer macros but not a built-in programming language. Other front ends provide a programming language but no equivalent to Access macros. The DBMs and front ends that provide true programming capability often use nonstandard languages and obscure syntax. Some DBMs and front ends require that you use a C-language compiler if you want to perform more complex operations than those offered as built-in functions. Access gives you the option of using macros, Access Basic programming modules, and combinations of macros and modules to create your database applications.

The interactive programming code editor provided by Access is modeled on Visual Basic's editor. The code editor consists of a window in which you enter or edit Access Basic code that is stored in a Module object of the active database, much like the stored procedures of SQL Server and other client-server databases (see fig. 1.15). If you are an xBase or Paradox programmer, you must get used to combining all your code and data in a single database file.

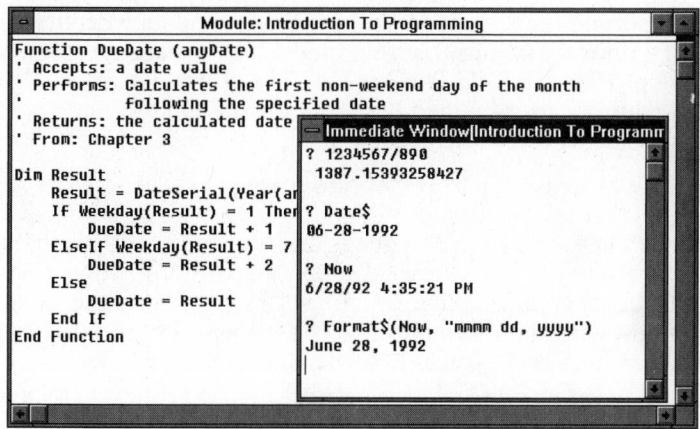

FIG. 1.15

The Code Editor and Immediate windows in the Access Basic editor.

Access Basic is a line-oriented, interpreted language; every time you enter a line of Access Basic instructions, its interpreter checks the line's syntax to make sure it conforms to the rules of the language. If the code editor finds an error it can correct, such as a missing quotation mark or the use of ENDIF rather than End If, it fixes the problem for you. xBase programmers should appreciate the latter correction. The editor changes the case of keywords to their upper- and lowercase convention where necessary and adds any spaces it believes are appropriate. If the interpreter cannot fix an entry error, you receive a message box that describes your transgression. When all errors have been eradicated, the interpreter converts the line to tokenized or p-code (pseudocode) and stores it in the module. Access Basic calls this process *compiling*, but the result isn't the object or machine code created by C and Pascal compilers that you must link with libraries to obtain an executable file. Pseudocode modules, such as dBASE IV's *.DBO files, execute much more rapidly than they would if syntax checking were required every time your application executed the code in the module.

An advantage of using an interpreted language is the ability to step through instructions or procedures one at a time to find problems with your code or determine the value of a questionable variable. More sophisticated compilers, such as CA-Clipper for xBase, have this capability but require a separate application to do it. The Access Basic code editor provides this capability through its Immediate Window (refer to fig. 1.15). When you call up the Immediate Window, you can view the values of variables by typing a question mark and the name of the variable, or run individual procedures and functions to exterminate bugs.

Access Basic differs from xBase and its dialects by referring to PROCEDUREs as Subs and executing them with the Call instruction rather than with the DO command. The Procedure keyword in Access Basic is reserved for the execution of SQL statements written in ANSI SQL, with minor variations. User-defined functions are created much like those of xBase or PAL. The Access code editor accommodates only one procedure or user-defined function at a time in its window, even if it consists only of three lines.

Although Cue Cards aren't provided to teach you how to write Access Basic code, the help system provided for Access Basic includes an entry for every keyword in the language and example code for the majority of keywords. A help window for a new keyword for Access Basic, AppendChunk, is shown in figure 1.16, with a portion of the example code window that shows you how to use AppendChunk with large nondatabase files or data in OLE fields.

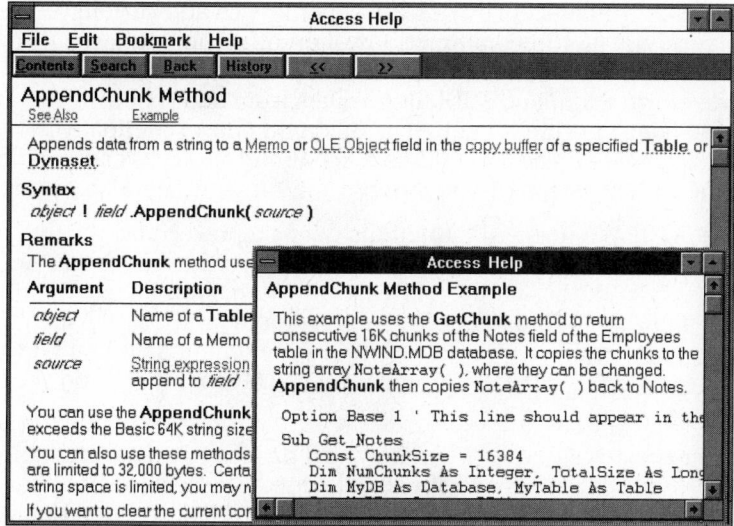

FIG. 1.16

Help windows
for Access Basic
with example
code.

Access Basic includes Visual Basic's capability to operate on data contained in files external to the database. You can read and write text and binary files using the familiar Open, Close, Print #, and other file-manipulation instructions familiar to BASIC programmers.

Extending Access with Windows DLLs

Access can use any of the functions contained in the Windows application programming interface (API) through Access Basic modules. You use the Declare Function or Declare Sub keywords in the declarations section of a module to make any function of Windows DLLs accessible to your program. This process, called *registering function prototypes*, essentially is identical to external DLL function prototype declarations in WordBASIC and Visual Basic applications. After you have declared the function's prototype, you can use the function to return values or to perform its operations as though it were native to Access Basic.

An example of a Windows API function you are likely to want to use is WinHelp(). It lets you add context-sensitive help files to your applications using the WinHelp engine. Many Access Basic objects enable you to set their HelpFile and HelpContextID properties so that the user of your application can press F1 to obtain help on a subject, determined by the value of HelpContextID. To create help files for your database users, you must have the Microsoft Windows Help Compiler and a word-processing application capable of creating rich text format (RTF) files, such as Word for Windows.

The Windows API even provides the capability to add to your forms and reports the multimedia functions offered by the Windows 3.1 media control interface (MCI) commands. Using MCISendString( ), you can play waveform audio and MIDI files, tracks from audio CDs, and even almost-full-motion video together with sound in conjunction with forms. (You also can add multimedia capability to Access applications using the OLE Object field data type.)

The use of the Windows API functions opens a powerful capability and, like powerful functions in any language, requires that you be an Access power user to take advantage of them fully. You should have the documentation for the Microsoft Software Development Kit (SDK) for Windows 3.1 or its equivalent if you intend to use functions in the Windows API and the Multimedia Development Kit (MDK) to understand the MCI commands.

You can expect Microsoft and many third parties to create extensions in the form of DLLs designed specifically for Access as the need for them becomes evident. If you need special mathematical functions for scientific or engineering applications, you can add them in the form of third-party DLL functions that you declare and call in the same manner as you do for the Windows API. Access 1.0 doesn't support the Visual Basic custom controls that enable you to add new control objects to the design toolbox. It wouldn't be surprising to see custom control capability added to a future version of Access. In the meantime, you can simulate custom control capabilities by creating special-purpose forms with standard control objects that run procedures written in Access Basic.

FROM HERE...

For Related Information:

▶▶ "Adding Multimedia Objects to Your Tables," p. 579.

Access and Workgroups

Database files are more likely than any other type of files to require that they be shared by multiple users. Information stored in a database is valuable only if it is current and accessible to everyone who needs it. Maintaining currency means that only one version of the database exists—the latest one. Accessibility implies that any authorized user can view the file while others are viewing its contents or updating it. Accessibility is achieved by file sharing, one of the reasons Access requires that DOS' SHARE.EXE be loaded in a multiuser environment. Almost all PC DBMs now provide for basic file-sharing operations for networked use with the requisite file- and record-locking procedures. Access doesn't differ greatly from other present-day PC DBMS in this respect.

Access is designed, however, specifically for sharing Access databases with members of *workgroups*. A workgroup can consist of any number of people who are allowed permission to open one or more Access databases, usually by means of a local area network (LAN). File sharing by workgroups is a standard feature of client-server databases operating under server-based LANs. Access, however, is the first self-contained PC database management application designed specifically for use in the Windows 3.x environment that complies fully with the database administration and security standards necessary to create a truly secure database system. A *secure* database system within a workgroup environment has the following requirements:

- The information stored in database files must be encrypted so that a text-listing or file-editing utility application cannot be used to read the contents of the file.

- A password must be entered to launch the database management application on any computer that is physically capable of opening secure database files (all computers connected to a LAN in which any other connected computer is capable of sharing secure database files resident on its hard disk).

- Each user must be included within a group consisting of all users of the DBM that will have access to any secure files.

- Each user must be assigned a unique user name and a personal identification number (PIN) to be able to open a particular secure database file.

- Users must be identified specifically as administrators of the database system, creators or owners of individual secure databases, or other users of these databases.

- Users must be granted permission to view and modify objects or data on a selective basis under control of database administrators and the creators of particular databases.

- Permissions must be granted to users based on the workgroups to which they belong. Such permissions are called *implicit* relations because they are implied by the workgroup to which the user belongs and are granted to all its members.

- Members of the administrative group and the database creator must have the capability to override implicit workgroup permissions and create *explicit* permissions for specific database objects.

Access complies with these requirements; the Access security system was modeled on the system used by Microsoft SQL Server. If you properly administer Access and the database applications you create, you can safely share your Access databases with others. You can be assured that your databases are secure from unauthorized access or modification, except perhaps by the most ingenious hacker or a new, undetectable virus.

Microsoft added extensive workgroup security features to Access in anticipation of the release of Windows for Workgroups, the version of Windows 3.1 that enables users to share files and printers without installing and managing a "full-fledged" network. Windows for Workgroups is available in a stand-alone version or as an upgrade to Windows 3.1. Windows for Workgroups is a *peer-to-peer* networking application; it enables any computer on which it is installed to share files on hard disks or CD-ROM drives with other computers running Windows for Workgroups. Peer-to-peer networks don't require that computers be dedicated to acting as file or printer servers. All the computers are equal as far as the network is concerned.

All peer-to-peer networks, such as Artisoft's LANtastic and Novell's NetWare Lite, include file and printer sharing. Windows for Workgroups, however, has a number of features devoted exclusively to Windows-related operations, such as DDE operations between different computers, a network version of the Windows Clipboard, and OLE operations across the network. You must have a network card compatible with Windows for Workgroups and wiring between networked computers, but you don't need a network administrator or a three-foot shelf of documentation to install and run your workgroup network. 10BaseT network cards let you use standard twisted-pair telephone wire or even hardware-store telephone extension cables between computers. Network administration is a cooperative activity between members of the workgroup. Even if you are connected to a Microsoft LAN Manager or Novell NetWare network, you can run your own mini-network with Windows for Workgroups to take advantage of its additional Windows benefits.

Run-Time Access

A principal reason for the early success of Nantucket Corporation's (now Computer Associates') Clipper compiler was that developers could write applications in the dBASE III language and then compile their programs to a self-contained executable file. Users of Clipper-compiled applications don't have to have a copy of dBASE or the run-time version of dBASE to run the .EXE files Clipper creates. Other xBase products offer similar capabilities.

Microsoft has announced that a run-time version of Access will be available in early 1993. The run-time version enables applications to be executed, but not designed or modified, and has a distribution license for an unlimited number of copies of the run-time library.

Converting from Other DBMs, DBARS, and Front Ends

Individuals and organizations that have made a substantial investment in learning to use applications for database management, database application and reporting, and client-server front ends are loathe to change to a new DBM. People or companies who have a greater investment in thousands of lines of source code in xBase or PAL are understandably even more reluctant to make the change.

dBASE and xBase DBMs

dBASE and its xBase relatives are structured-procedural system programming languages, derived from BASIC, with an application language for database file-handling functions embedded within them. Most languages add declarative constructs such as BROWSE and LIST. Some languages incorporate a menu-based implementation of a portion of the available command set, but CA-Clipper and CA-dBFast, for example, are designed solely for programmers. The first release of Borland's dBASE for Windows is expected to be in the programmer-only category too. If you are a dBASE or xBase programmer, you will want to know how compatible Access Basic is with the language in which you are fluent.

Access Basic is a self-contained system programming language, but Access for Window's macro capability is sophisticated enough to enable most applications to be created without writing a single line of Access Basic code. If you are an independent database consultant or you create xBase applications for use by your employer on a full- or part-time basis, using Access macros instead of writing *.PRGs improves your productivity, often as much as fivefold. Macros can accelerate the creation of usability-evaluation prototypes for more complex applications.

Experienced dBASE, FoxPro, or Clipper programmers will see that the structure of the event-oriented programs written in Access Basic is considerably different from the traditional, top-down code of the procedural xBase languages. Access Basic, an object-oriented language, shares many of the attributes of C++, such as encapsulation of code and data within objects (related to Clipper's code blocks), inheritance of the properties and methods of other objects, late binding of procedures, and polymorphism. Chapter 12 defines these terms. Although you can argue that Access Basic isn't yet a fully qualified object-oriented language, it is treated that way in this book.

Menu-driven xBase applications traditionally are written in the form of nested DO WHILE .T. ... ENDDO loops with internal DO CASE ... ENDCASE structures to call individual procedures that perform the function selected by the user. When you are writing Windows applications, the Windows message loop replaces the DO WHILE structures. Your application waits for a message indicating an event, such as a mouse click on a menu command in one of its windows. When this type of message is received, an event handler (your procedure) processes user input. Then your application "goes to sleep" and waits for the next user action.

After you get a "feel" for event-oriented program structures, rewriting your xBase code in Access Basic will not be especially difficult. Again, Access macros help you by enabling you to write individual procedures you call with RunCode. The creation of a new Access application with Access Basic requires less than half the time required to write the equivalent DOS application in Clipper. The same ratio should hold true for FoxPro 2.0.

Access Basic cannot call assembly language procedures or functions written in C with the LOAD and CALL commands or the CALL() function, because it doesn't support external *.BIN or *.OBJ files. To use routines you have written in assembly or C, you must recompile them as one or more Windows dynamic link libraries. DLLs are created most commonly with a combination of Microsoft C and the Windows 3.1 Software Development Kit (SDK), or with compilers that include SDK functions, such as Microsoft Quick C for Windows, Borland's C++ 3.x, Turbo C++ 3.x for Windows, or Turbo Pascal for Windows.

Borland dBASE IV for Windows, which can compile dBASE code in a Windows DLL, will provide developers with an interesting alternative to using C compilers and the SDK to make their investment in writing user-defined functions (UDFs) and other specialized routines for manipulating xBase files pay Access dividends. You just compile the UDFs or complete procedures in a DLL with dBASE for Windows, declare the prototypes, and call the functions or procedures from your Access Basic code. You can create simple Access Basic functions that return values or call your UDFs from RunCode actions in macros. Make sure that your DLL doesn't attempt to write to the display with SAYs or expect keyboard entries from GETs.

Access applications don't execute with the blazing speed of compiled Clipper applications. The slowdown is imposed by Windows' extensive use of graphics and, in many cases, the hardware on which Windows is run; the speed reduction is common to all Windows applications. If you avoid the temptation to decorate your applications with bit-mapped images, and provide workstations running speed-sensitive applications with display accelerator adapter cards, most users probably will not notice the difference. If they do, blame Windows.

Paradox and PAL

Access and Paradox share many common characteristics: table terminology, query by example, and extensive use of macros, for example. Many techniques for creating Windows applications are shared by Paradox for Windows and Access. Unlike Paradox, however, Access isn't saddled with a requirement for backward compatibility with the language and file structure of an earlier DOS product. Because Access files and indexes are optimized for the Windows environment, well-designed Access applications usually execute faster than do their Paradox for Windows equivalents.

Paradox uses the term *script* to include those macros you record as well as those you write in PAL, and it stores both in files with the extension .SC. Although Access treats macros and modules as two different objects, you can run macros from Access Basic and call Access Basic functions from macros. The outcome, therefore, is the same as having both in the same .SC file. PAL is a single-application dialect of xBase; like Sanskrit, it may ultimately be of interest only to database historians. To paraphrase John Maynard Keynes, "In the long run, single-application languages are all dead."

The same comments and caveats regarding xBase conversions apply to your existing PAL scripts. Because PAL has spawned few of its own equivalents of the xBase clones, you aren't faced with the complexities of a multitude of third-party extensions. PAL departs further from BASIC in its command and function keywords than does xBase. Line-for-line translation of PAL to Access Basic, therefore, is difficult but not impossible.

On the other hand, the orientation of Paradox to predesigned displays and recorded scripts provides an alternative approach. If you import or attach your Paradox table files to Access and then duplicate your Paradox screen images with Access's form designer, you can mimic most Paradox menu commands by the appropriate sequence of macro instructions. If two computers fit on your desk, one that runs Paradox for

DOS and the other used to create your Access clone, you can accelerate the process substantially. This duplication creates the basic structure of your Access application. After you have cloned the basic
Paradox forms and their menu functions, you can add Access Basic
functions and procedures, called by the RunCode macro instruction, to
perform those Paradox operations that lack standard macro instructions in Access Basic.

The version of PAL provided with DOS-based Paradox 4.0 and
Paradox for Windows 1.0 incorporates a multitude of changes to
accommodate the "object orientation" of these two new products.
You must rewrite your PAL code if you use Paradox for Windows.
You will have to relearn many programming practices and tricks
you used with PAL in its new object-oriented version. When you
are deciding whether to convert from Paradox 3.5 to Paradox for
Windows or to Access, being able to reuse existing source code
shouldn't be a major consideration.

Other Windows Database Managers

The prolonged absence of a Windows database management application from Ashton-Tate/Borland, Microsoft, or Lotus Corporation provided an opening for smaller firms to create products to meet the
unfulfilled demand. Software Publishing's Superbase and Computer
Associates' CA-dBFast Windows are just a few of the xBase or related
products to emerge during this period. Many of these products, in all
probability, eventually will succumb to the combined competitive on-
slaught from Microsoft and Borland. The few survivors will serve niche
markets with specialized features not provided by the mainstream
DBMs.

Several Windows DBMs have added client-server connectivity to their
products in an attempt to stake a claim in the already crowded front-
end territory described in the following section. Such enhancements
are tactical, not strategic, and are not likely to play a major role in determining market share. The most likely "keepers" in the Windows database manager market are Access and the Windows versions of Paradox,
FoxPro, dBASE IV, and CA-Aspen.

Database Access and Reporting Applications

Database applications are classified as access and reporting (DBAR) systems if they are limited to or designed primarily for displaying data within existing databases or transferring it to and from other Windows applications by dynamic data exchange. These products usually support a variety of common DOS database formats, together with 1-2-3 and Excel spreadsheet formats, and use a subset of SQL to create queries. They seldom are used for production-volume data entry, and many don't provide the capability to update or add database records.

Pioneer Software's Q+E is an example of a DBAR application whose primary function is transferring database information to other Windows applications by way of DDE. A special version of Q+E has been included with Excel since Version 3.0, in addition to a set of macros to help in using Q+E. Q+E relies on the DDE client application to format and print the data it returns. Because Q+E uses ANSI SQL to create queries, conversion from Q+E to Access is only a matter of writing down your SQL statements, attaching the required database file or files to an Access database, and then typing the statements back into Access's SQL Window, with some minor modifications, to create an identical query. The DDE instructions you use in Excel or Word for Windows to connect with Q+E as a DDE server are similar to those that use Access for the same purpose.

Access combines the analysis and reporting capabilities of DBARs with the database-creation and data-entry functions of a DBM. You can choose from 81 different graph and chart types with the Microsoft Graph OLE server applet provided. Access can display and edit images or even let you listen to waveform audio and MIDI files; most DBARs, at least in their 1992 versions, cannot do the same. In most cases, because Access macros can duplicate whatever procedures can be created with a DBAR, programming isn't required.

Client-Server Front Ends

The trend toward moving database applications from mainframes and minicomputers to PC local area networks is well established. This trend has caused a rapid increase in the market for client-server DBMs, such as Oracle and Microsoft SQL Server. Client-server DBMs were designed for use with networked PCs, and networking capability was "tacked on" to traditional PC products such as dBASE and Paradox. The major advantages of client-server DBMs over the traditional PC database products are shown in the following list:

- Use of a standardized database access language, SQL
- Increased security against unauthorized access to sensitive data
- Internal safeguards for data integrity
- Improved network performance in most cases
- Better database administration utilities
- Inclusion of mainframe DBM access systems

These characteristics made downsizing to PC-based systems more palatable to data-processing management because client-server DBMs resemble those used on mainframe computers and offer many of the same features.

As client-server DBMs gained a foothold in the market, front ends that access client-server databases such as PowerBuilder and Gupta SQL Windows (the "back ends") proliferated. At the time this book was written, Microsoft had reported that more than 125 "shipping front ends" existed just for SQL Server. The majority of these front ends are designed for use with Windows. Windows apparently will be the dominant environment for client-server front ends, unless IBM's OS/2 Version 2.0 is accepted overwhelmingly.

Most front-end applications combine a query methodology—usually graphical QBE—with a forms generator and report writer. All the applications use SQL to process queries, and the majority provide a method of creating macros or writing programs to create applications. In the aggregate, they have built a database tower of Babel by creating script or programming languages of their own that, like Basque, have obscure linguistic roots. Becoming proficient in some of these languages involves the same magnitude of study as learning ancient Aramaic or Sanskrit, and is likely to return similar economic rewards.

Front ends designed to generate efficient source code in the C language that you then may incorporate in C applications you write are exceptions, not the rule. These products are more closely related to computer-aided software engineering (CASE) tools than to database front ends. The QuickCASE:W abbreviation for Caseworks' CASE:W included with Microsoft QuickC for Windows is an example of a CASE tool for C; it writes source code that you then modify and add to as necessary. Combining CASE tools with the Open Database Connectivity APIs enables C programmers to create fast front ends without having to write a great deal of code. This capability, of course, benefits only the C programming community.

Again, Access has the edge over existing products because of its use of Access Basic and Bill Gates' edict regarding the use of dialects of Object Basic by all mainstream Microsoft applications. C programmers will continue to use C and C++, but many of them now use Visual Basic to prototype applications that will be written in C. It is just a matter of time until most other Windows programmers use an Object Basic dialect or a flavor of xBase for Windows.

Chapter Summary

Both database users and developers have been waiting since at least May 1990 for an industrial-strength Windows DBM that has the following components:

- An interface consistent with other mainstream Windows applications

- The capability to import or manipulate a variety of popular database file formats

This chapter has demonstrated that Access satisfies these requirements.

The remaining chapters in Part I discuss Access tables, in the MDB format native to the application and in the form of xBase and Paradox files attached to Access. The emphasis in this book is on learning how to import and attach data from existing data sources rather than how to create databases from scratch. The book takes this approach because most Access users or prospective users have at least some data in a format compatible with Access that can be attached or imported and made into a useful Access database.

Quick start chapters at the beginning of Parts I and II of this book describe how to create and use tables, queries, forms, and reports. The first quick start, in Chapter 2, briefly introduces Access and its tables. Chapter 3 provides in-depth coverage of the Access user interface, including multiple menu structures and the toolbar buttons that appear when you perform various tasks. Starting with Chapter 4, the remainder of the book provides detailed, step-by-step methods for learning how to get the most out of Access.

Up and Running with Access Tables: A Quick Start

The quick start chapters in this book are designed to give you a concise overview of functions covered in more detail in succeeding chapters. Quick start examples, like most of the other examples in this book, use the Northwind Traders sample database that is supplied with Access. *Northwind Traders* is a fictitious wholesaler of specialty food products whose accounting system is an Access database application created by Microsoft. The sample database includes tables, forms, and reports that a small firm may use to automate its invoicing, inventory control, ordering, and personnel operations.

This quick start introduces you to Access tables and shows you how to perform the following tasks:

- Launching Access and opening the Northwind Traders database

- Opening a table and viewing its contents

- Selecting records and editing the data they contain

■ Using Design mode to view the properties of the table and its fields

■ Printing the contents of a table

The remainder of Part I (Chapters 3 through 5) expands on these subjects and describes in detail the creation and use of Access tables.

This quick start assumes that you have installed Access. If you haven't installed Access, you can refer to Appendix F for instructions on setting up Access on your fixed disk.

Starting Access

To start Access and open the Northwind Traders database, NWIND.MDB, perform the following steps:

Access

1. Double-click the Access icon in the Access application group.

   As Access is loading, a copyright notice appears with the name and organization that was entered during the installation process. Then Access's sparse opening window appears, as shown in figure 2.1.

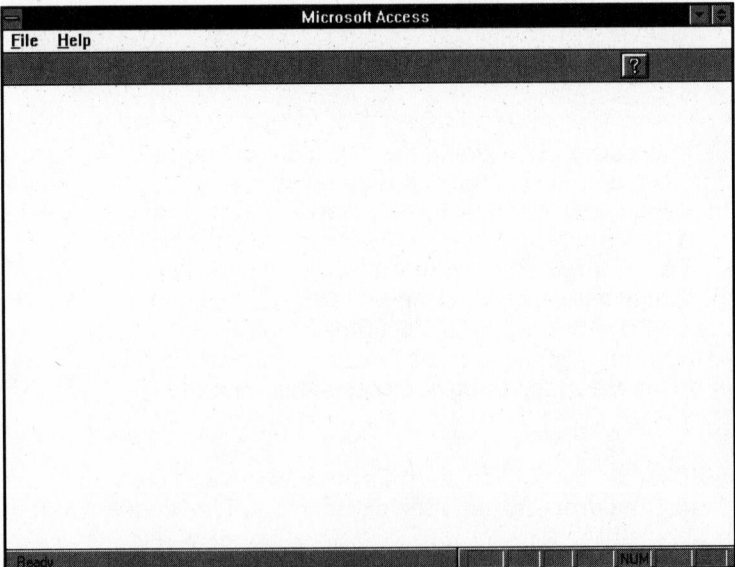

FIG. 2.1

The Access blank opening window.

2. Choose **F**ile from the main menu. The **F**ile menu appears, as shown in figure 2.2.

> If you have run Access previously, the file names of up to four Access database files you have opened may appear above the E**x**it command in the **F**ile menu.

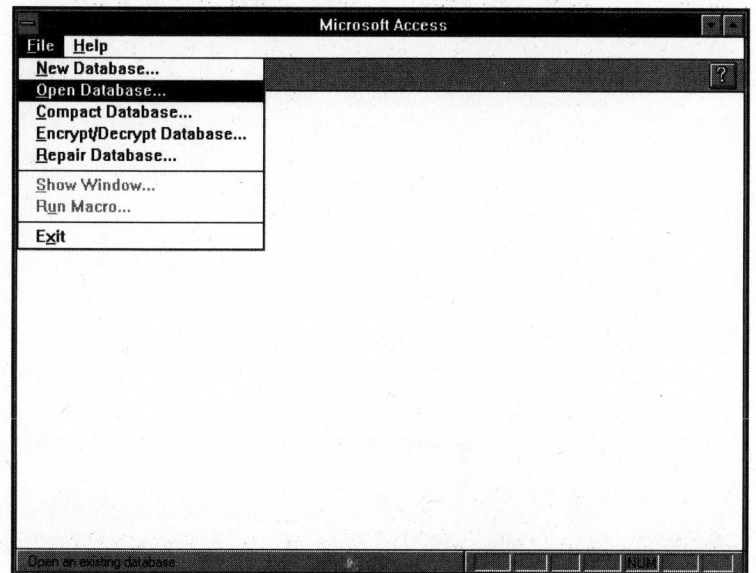

FIG. 2.2

The Access **F**ile menu.

The screen shown in figure 2.2 and the other screens throughout this chapter have sizeable borders. When you launch Access, its display is *maximized*—it fills your entire display. Figure 2.2 shows Access operating in a normal, sizeable window. To change to a sizeable window, click the Application Control menu symbol at the upper left corner of the display, and then choose **R**estore. Click and drag the sides of Access's window to make it the size you want.

3. Choose the **O**pen Database command from the **F**ile menu. The Open Database dialog box appears, as shown in figure 2.3.

> If this is the first time you have used an application designed for Windows 3.1, you see that the Open Database dialog box has a new appearance. This dialog box is one of the common dialog boxes created by Windows, rather than by your application. Instead of choosing the active disk drive as an option

in the Directories list box, you select the drive from the choices offered in a drop-down list box. Access uses drop-down list boxes extensively.

4. Double-click nwind.mdb in the File Name combo box to open the Northwind Traders sample database.

The Database window for the Northwind Traders database appears, as shown in figure 2.4.

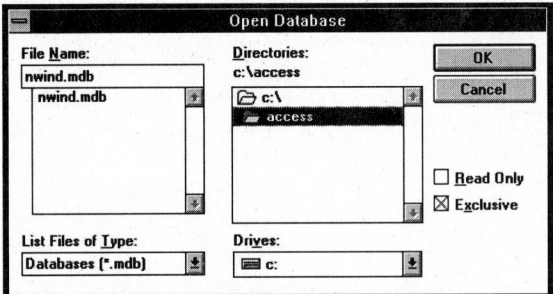

FIG. 2.3

The Open
Database dialog
box.

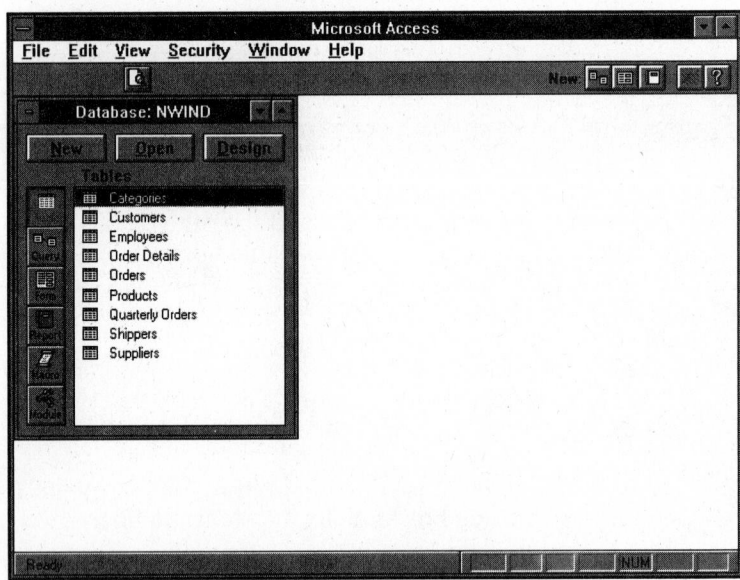

FIG. 2.4

The Database
window for the
Northwind
Traders sample
database.

You can use several other methods to open a file in the common Open Database dialog box. You can click nwind.mdb to place it in the text box and then choose OK. Or, you can type **nwind** in the text portion of the combo box and choose OK. A *combo box* consists of a text box above a list from which you can choose an entry. Access adds the default .MDB extension for you. Double-clicking is the fastest and most mistake-proof method of opening a file.

The Database window is your "home base" for all operations with the sample database or databases you create. Almost every operation you perform with Access begins with a choice you make from the Database window.

After you open a database file, a number of new buttons appear on the toolbar under the main menu bar. *Toolbar buttons*, a common feature of new Windows applications, are shortcuts for menu choices. Any operation you can perform by clicking a toolbar button can be performed by making two or more menu choices. Using the toolbar buttons is much quicker and, once you learn what the symbols mean, more intuitive than using Windows' standard menu structure.

Using Database Tables

This quick start is devoted to exploring tables, which are the basic elements of all databases and the portion of the Access database file where data is stored.

Viewing Data in Tables

To display the contents of the Categories table, which describes the types of products in which Northwind trades, double-click Categories in the Database window's list of tables. The Categories table appears, as shown in figure 2.5.

> You also can display the Categories table by clicking Categories and then clicking the Open button or pressing Enter. The double-clicking method is quicker, however.

The normal method of displaying the information contained in relational database tables is the familiar row-column technique used by spreadsheet applications. Every widely used PC database manager uses row-column presentation for data contained in tables. The rows of a table are known as *records*, and the columns are referred to as *fields*. A record contains information on a single object, such as one class of product or a particular invoice. A field contains the same type of information, such as a product code, for all records in a table. In this book, the intersection between a row and a column—a single field of a single record—is called a *data cell*. A data cell contains a single piece of information. The terms *data item* and *data entity* often are used as synonyms for *data cell*.

Figure 2.5 shows the data in the Categories table in what Access calls *Datasheet view*—the default method of displaying a table. You select the Datasheet view, if another type of view is active, by clicking the Datasheet button, which resembles a spreadsheet, on the toolbar. Or, you can choose **D**atasheet from the View menu. Datasheet view also is the default for viewing the results of queries; you can see a Datasheet view of the table or query when you are creating an Access form.

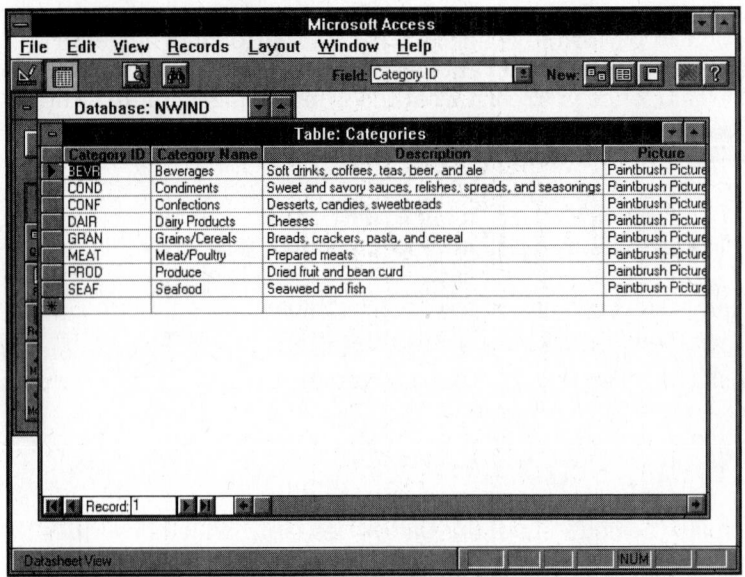

FIG. 2.5

The datasheet display of the records in the Categories table.

Selecting and Editing Data Records

To change the data contained in any cell of the table (other than in OLE Object fields that are used to display pictures), select the cell by clicking it with the mouse or by using the arrow keys. Selected content is indicated by the white on black (reverse) appearance of the cell. The default selected cell is the first field of the first record of the table. All contents of that cell are selected when you first display the table.

If you type a character into a cell when its entire content is selected, the character you type replaces what was in that cell.

You can recover from an accidental replacement by pressing Esc; this action restores the original content, but *only* if you have not yet selected a different cell. When you make a change in a data cell and then move to a new data cell, the change is made to the content of the table. Click the selected data cell to deselect the entire contents of the cell.

You can select any cell to edit by positioning the mouse pointer at the point within a cell where you want to make the change, and then clicking your mouse. The mouse pointer resembles an I-beam when it is located within the contents of data cells. The editing cursor, a thin vertical line called the *caret* by Windows and this book, but often referred to as the *insertion point* in other texts, appears.

The conventional text-editing functions of Windows applications apply to Access. At this point, you shouldn't change the data, called *values*, of the data cells. Changes to values may affect the appearance of examples in later chapters. If you do make a change, a pencil symbol appears in the gray box at the left of the window corresponding to the record whose value you have changed. You can return to the original value by pressing Esc. If you click an OLE field, indicated in figure 2.5 by a cell containing the words Paintbrush Picture, the cell is given a thicker, gray border and the caret does not appear. You cannot edit the text of an OLE field.

You use the empty record at the bottom of the table, indicated by the asterisk (*) in the selection button column for the record, to add a new record to the table. If you enter any data into a cell of this record, a new record containing the data you entered is added to the table. If you accidentally add data in this "tentative append" record, click the Record selection button to select the record, and then press Del. A dialog box appears requesting confirmation of your deletion. Choose OK.

If you use the arrow keys to select a data cell, all contents of the cell are selected. You cannot click the corner of a cell and drag the mouse pointer to a cell the opposite corner of an imaginary rectangle to select a group of cells, as you would with Excel. You can, however, select an entire record by clicking the selection button for that record, or you can select a group of records by dragging the mouse down the selection button column. Records and groups of records most often are selected in order to copy the records to the Windows Clipboard. Notice that when you select a cell with the keyboard or the mouse, the triangular arrow moves to the selected record. The button with the triangular arrow is called the *current record pointer*.

You use the left set of buttons in the bar at the bottom of the datasheet window to position the current record pointer within the bounds of the table. Click the left arrow button to position the current record pointer at the first record in the table, and click the right arrow button to move to the last or bottom record of the table. The left and right arrow buttons move the pointer one record at a time in the direction indicated. You can enter a record number in the Record text box or use the vertical scroll bar to position the active record pointer. The vertical scroll bar appears only if more records are present than will fit in the vertical dimension of the datasheet window.

The horizontal scroll bar enables you to view fields that lie to the right of the far right visible field. Use the left and right arrows for small movements, or use the scroll box to make large moves to the left or right. You also can traverse several fields by clicking the region of the scroll bar between the scroll box and the arrow.

To select all data cells in a field, click the button containing the field name at the top of the datasheet. When the mouse pointer is over a field name, the pointer changes to a down arrow. You can search for cells within the field you select that contain a particular group of characters by clicking the toolbar's Find button—a pair of binoculars. The Find in Field dialog box appears, as shown in figure 2.6.

FIG. 2.6

The Find in Field dialog box.

Enter the characters you want to find in the Find What text box. Then open the Where drop-down list box by clicking the down arrow, and choose Any Part of Field. You can search up or down from the position of the current record by selecting the Up or Down Direction option buttons. Click the Find First button to search for the first occurrence of a match, and then click the Find Next button to locate other matches. After you find all matching records or no matching records, a dialog box appears stating that you have reached the end of the table. Click the Close button to return to the Table window.

Viewing and Editing Graphics

Chapter 1 discussed the significance of the new OLE field data type; one of the reasons for choosing the Categories table for this quick start is that it includes bit-mapped graphic images stored in an OLE field. If you double-click one of the Paintbrush Picture data cells, Windows 3.1's Paintbrush window appears with the bit-mapped image displayed, as shown in figure 2.7. You can use Paintbrush to display the image or to edit. Because Windows 3.1's Paintbrush is an OLE server, all of Paintbrush's bit-mapped image display and editing capabilities are available to you while you are using Access.

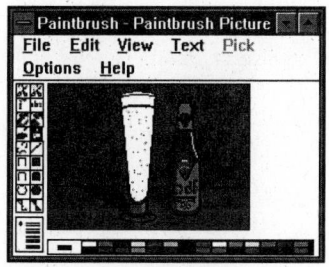

FIG. 2.7

A bit-mapped image displayed using Windows Paintbrush.

When you're finished viewing an image, double-click the Application Control menu symbol in the upper left corner of Paintbrush's window to close the image. You also can exit an OLE server by choosing Exit & Return from the server's File menu. If you have made any changes to the image, a dialog box appears asking whether you want to update the Access table. In this case, click No to retain the original image.

Using Design Mode

Design mode for tables displays the characteristics of each field in the table in a grid format similar to a spreadsheet. To view the design of the Categories table, click the Design Mode button, which appears as an architect's triangle and pencil, at the left end of the toolbar. Your Design mode view appears as shown in figure 2.8. Alternatively, you can choose Table **D**esign from the **V**iew menu.

You can view and edit the properties that apply to the table object as a whole in the Table Properties window shown in figure 2.9. Click the Properties button on the toolbar (a hand pointing to a window) or choose Table Properties from the View menu to display the Table Properties window. The Table Properties window enables you to enter a text description of the table and assign the *primary key field*, which is the field with the symbol of the key in its selection button column. The primary key field is the field or combination of fields that is used to uniquely identify each record in the table. Most tables are indexed on a single primary key field and do not permit duplicate keys. *Indexes* are internal tables that speed the creation of query result tables by simulating the sorting of the table on the value of the key field. Key fields establish the relations by which multiple tables of a database are linked when you create a query. The term *relational database* indicates database management applications (DBMs) that are capable of linking tables by key fields.

FIG. 2.8

The Design mode view of a table.

FIG. 2.9

The Table Properties window.

Each field in a table requires a unique name and must be assigned a field data type. Field names, data types, and an optional text description of the field are entered in the design grid. Click the Properties Table button, or double-click the Application Control button on the Properties Table to close it so that the entire design grid is visible. Text is the most common type of data in tables; therefore, Text is the default data type. A number of other field data types are available in Access; you already have been introduced to the OLE field data type. Click one of the Data Type cells, and then click the down arrow to open the Data Type drop-down list box to display the Data Type choices offered by Access. Click the arrow again to close the list box. Field data types in Access include various numeric formats, date and time, and other types that you learn about in later chapters of this book.

Printing the Contents of a Table

Access enables you to print the contents of your table without creating a fully formatted report. You may want to print raw table data to proofread the new records you have created or the old ones you have edited. The Print Preview window is much like the one offered by Word for Windows and Excel. The Print Preview window enables you to see how certain material would appear if printed.

To see how the Categories table would appear if printed, click the toolbar's Preview button for example, (the magnifying glass). The Print Preview window, shown in figure 2.10, appears after much disk activity and a short wait. The title of the Print Preview window reflects what you're preparing to print. In this example, the title is Table:Categories. You also can choose the Print Preview option from the File menu to display the Print Preview window.

To see a magnified view of how the printed version of your table will appear, click the surface of the simulated sheet of paper in the Print Preview window. When the mouse pointer is on the paper, the pointer turns into the shape of a magnifying glass, as shown in figure 2.10. Place the magnifying glass over the image; otherwise, when the window is magnified, the view will be of a blank page and you will wonder where the table went. Figure 2.11 shows the magnified (zoomed) view of the Categories table. Click again to restore the original, unreadable version of the report. The Zoom button has an effect similar to clicking the mouse.

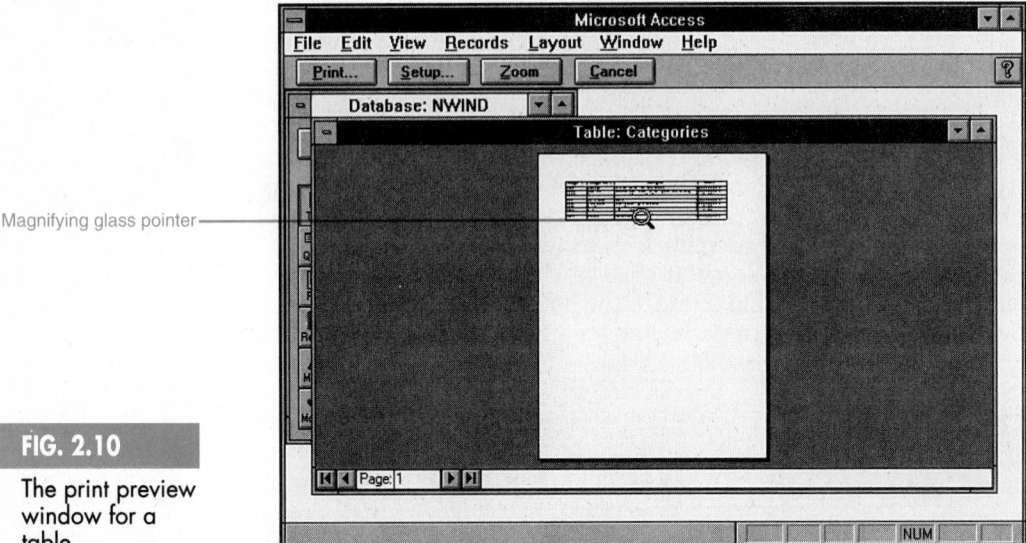

Magnifying glass pointer

FIG. 2.10

The print preview
window for a
table.

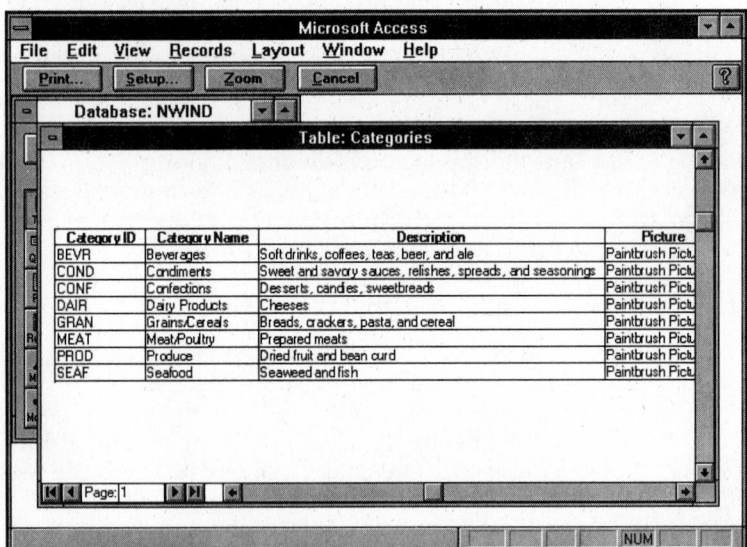

FIG. 2.11

A magnified view
of the Categories
table.

When you are ready to print, click the Print button on the toolbar. The
Print dialog box appears, as shown in figure 2.12.

To print in Landscape mode with your laser printer or to otherwise change your printer's settings, click the Setup button and make the appropriate changes in the Print Setup dialog box shown in figure 2.13. You can reset the printing margins by entering different values in the Margins text boxes. Choose OK to reopen the Print dialog box and choose OK to print the table.

FIG. 2.12

The Print dialog box.

FIG. 2.13

The Print Setup dialog box.

Now that you have run the gamut of the basic operations available for Access tables, double-click the Document Control button to close the Print Preview window and return to the Database window. Now, you may open one or more of the other tables that comprise the Northwind Traders database to learn a bit more about their contents. The Employees table includes scanned images of photographs of the fictional staff of Northwind Traders. The Suppliers table lists an eclectic group of food-processing firms from many points on the globe. You can see most of the international characters, such as umlauts and tildes, in Windows' ANSI character set in the supplier name and address fields. Both Access and Windows 3.1 are available in a wide range of languages besides English.

Chapter Summary

This quick start gave you a feel for the methods you can use to view and manipulate the data contained in tables. The basic operations you learned in this chapter are applicable, in general, to all other functions of Access, as should be the case with any well-designed application.

Your next step is to learn more about the overall plan that Microsoft drew up for the user interface of Access. The plan was implemented by changing toolbar buttons and menu choices depending on whether you are viewing or creating tables, queries, forms, reports, macros, or modules. Chapter 3 describes how Access is organized, as well as how you manage multiple document windows, keyboard commands, and Access's Help system.

The remainder of Part 1, Chapters 4 and 5, is devoted to Access tables: using tables provided in the sample database, creating new tables, and importing and attaching files created by other database management systems.

Navigating within Access

This chapter describes how Access is structured and organized to expedite the design and use of the database objects it offers. A substantial portion of this chapter consists of tables that list the functions of window control icons, toolbar buttons, and a vast array of function and key combinations. Many function and key assignments are derived from other Microsoft applications, such as Excel (F2 for editing) and Word for Windows (Shift+F4 to find the next occurrence of a match). These assignments don't duplicate those key assignments to which you may have become accustomed when using dBASE, xBase, or Paradox.

This chapter is a reference to which you can return when you conclude that a keystroke combination may be a better choice for an action than a mouse click, but you cannot remember the required combination. An explanation of the structure and content of the Help system for Access also is included in this chapter.

Understanding Access's Functions and Modes

Access, unlike word processing and spreadsheet applications, is a truly multifunctional program. Although word processing applications, for example, have many sophisticated capabilities, their basic purpose is to support text entry, page layout, and formatted printing. All of a word processing application's primary functions and supporting features are directed to these ends. All word processing operations are performed using views representing a sheet of paper—usually 8 1/2 inches by 11 inches. Most spreadsheet applications use the row-column metaphor for all their functions—even for writing highly sophisticated programs in their macro languages.

Defining Access Functions

To qualify as a full-fledged relational database management system, an application must perform the following four basic but distinct functions, each with its own presentation (called a *view*) to the user:

1. *Data organization:* Involves the creation and manipulation of tables that contain data in conventional tabular (row-column or spreadsheet) format, called *Datasheet view* by Access.

2. *Table linking and data extraction:* Links multiple tables by data relationships to create temporary tables stored in your computer's memory or temporary disk files that contain the data you choose. Access uses *queries* to link tables and to choose the data to be stored in a temporary table called a *dynaset*. A dynaset consists of the data that results from running the query, and it is stored in your computer's memory. The capability to link tables by relations distinguishes relational database systems from simple list-processing applications, called *flat-file managers.* Data extraction limits the presentation of dynasets to specific groups of data that meet criteria you establish. *Expressions* are used to calculate values from data, such as an extended amount by multiplying unit price and quantity, and to display the calculated values as if they were a field in one of the tables.

3. *Data entry and editing:* Requires design and implementation of data viewing, entry, and editing forms as an alternative to tabular presentation. A form enables *you*, rather than the *application*, to control how the data is presented. Forms are much easier than dynasets or tables in tabular format for most persons to use for data entry, especially when many fields are involved. The capability to print forms, such as sales orders and invoices, is a definite benefit to the user.

4. *Data presentation:* Requires creation of reports that are capable of summarizing the information in tables or dynasets that you can view and print (this is the last step in the process). The capability to provide meaningful reports is the ultimate purpose of any database management application. Also, the management of an enterprise usually lends more credence to reports that are attractively formatted and contain charts or graphs that summarize the data for those officials who take the "broad brush" approach.

The four basic functions of Access that are implemented as views are organized into an application structure represented graphically in figure 3.1. If you are creating a new database, you use the basic functions of Access in the top-down sequence shown in the illustration. You choose the function to be performed by clicking a button in the Datasheet window, except for security and printing operations, which are menu choices. In most views, you can use the Print Preview window that leads to printing operations by clicking a toolbar button.

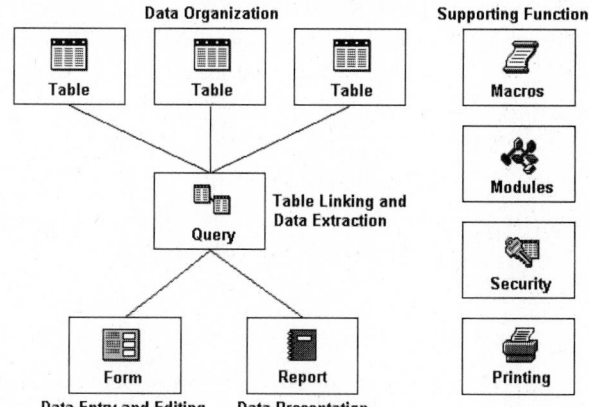

FIG. 3.1

The basic and supporting functions of Access.

Four supporting functions apply to all the basic functions of Access:

1. *Macros:* A sequence of actions that automate repetitive database operations. You create a macro by choosing actions from a list of available actions in Access, in the order in which you want them to appear. You can use a macro, for example, to open a report, print the report, and then close the report. The terms *open* and *close,* as they are used in Access, are explained in the next section.

2. *Modules:* Functions and procedures written in the Action Basic programming language. You use Action Basic functions to make calculations that are more complex than those that can be expressed easily by a series of conventional mathematical symbols, or to make calculations that require decisions to be made. Action Basic procedures are written to perform operations that exceed the capabilities of standard macro actions. You run Action Basic procedures by invoking them with the macro action RunCode.

3. *Security:* Functions available as menu choices only. Security functions enable you to give permission for other people to use your database in a multiuser environment. You may grant access to user groups and individuals, and you may restrict their ability to view or modify all or a portion of the tables in the database.

4. *Printing:* Enables you to print virtually anything you can view in Access's Run mode. You can print your Access Basic code, but not the macros you write.

The terms *open* and *close* have the same basic usage in Access as in other Windows applications, but usually involve more than one basic function:

■ Opening a database makes its content available to the application through the Database window described in Chapter 2. You may open only one database at a time during ordinary use of Access. Writing Action Basic code enables you to operate with tables from more than one database. You can achieve the equivalent of multiple open Access databases by attaching tables from other databases.

■ Opening a table provides a Datasheet view of its contents.

■ Opening a query opens the tables involved but does not display them. Access then runs the query on these tables to create a tabular dynaset. Changes made to data in the dynaset cause corresponding changes to be made to the data in the tables associated with the query.

■ Opening a form or report automatically opens the table or query with which it is associated. Both forms and reports usually are associated with queries, but a query also can employ a single table.

■ Closing a query closes the associated tables.

■ Closing a form or report closes the associated query and its tables.

Defining Access Operating Modes

Access has three basic operating modes:

Access

- *Start-up:* Enables you to compress, encrypt, decrypt, and repair a database by commands from the File menu prior to opening a database. These commands, discussed at the end of the chapter, aren't available after you have opened a database.

- *Design:* Enables you to create and modify the structure of tables and queries, develop forms to display and edit your data, and format reports for printing.

- *Run:* Displays your table, form, and report designs in individual document windows (Run is the default mode). You execute macros by choosing one and then selecting Run mode. Run mode is not applicable to Action Basic modules, because functions are executed when encountered as elements of queries, forms, and reports. Procedures in modules are run by macro commands.

You can select Design or Run mode by choosing command buttons in the Datasheet window, buttons on the toolbar, or commands from the View menu.

You can change the default conditions under which Access displays and prints your tables, queries, forms, and reports by choosing the View Options menu command. Commands that are applicable to Access as a whole, and those that apply only to tables, are described near the end of this chapter.

Understanding Access's Table Display

You probably are familiar with the basic terms for many of the components that comprise the basic window in which all conventional Windows applications run. The presentation of Access windows differs with each of the basic functions Access performs. Because Part I of this book deals almost exclusively with tables, Table view is used in the examples that follow. Figure 3.2 shows Access for Windows' basic display for operations with tables. The individual components of the window are described in table 3.1.

FIG. 3.2

The Access
display for tables.

Table 3.1. Components of the Access Display for Tables

Term	Description
Active window	The window to which all mouse and keyboard actions are directed. When an application or document is active, its title bar appears in color (dark blue, unless you have changed your Windows color scheme). If both the application title bar and a document title bar are active, the document title bar will receive the mouse and keyboard actions.
Application control icon	The icon or symbol for the Application Control menu that controls the presentation of the Application window. You display the Application control menu by clicking the icon or pressing Alt+Space bar.
Application title bar	A bar at the top of the application's window that displays its name. You can move the entire application, if it isn't maximized, by clicking the application title bar and dragging it to a new position.

Term	Description
Application window	The window within which Access is displayed. Each application you launch runs within its own application window.
Caret	A vertical flashing line that indicates the insertion point for keyboard entry in areas of a window that accept text.
Current Record button	Indicates a single selected record in the table. When you are editing the current record, the button icon becomes a pencil, rather than a triangular arrow. The Current Record button also is called the *record pointer*.
Current Record selection buttons and window	Buttons that position the record pointer to the first, next, preceding, and last record number in the table. If a key field has been specified, the current record number is not the record number corresponding to the sequence of its addition to the database (as is the case with xBase and Paradox) but the sequence of the record in the sorting order of the primary key.
Database window	The window that controls the operating mode of Access and selects the current function of the active document window. You choose the component of the database to display in the document window, such as a particular table, from those displayed in the Database window.
Document Control icon	The icon or symbol for the Document Control menu that controls the presentation of a document window. You access the Document Control menu by clicking the icon or pressing Alt+- (hyphen).
Document title bar	A bar at the top of each document's window that displays the document's name. You can move the document, if it isn't maximized, by clicking the application title bar and dragging the document to a new position.
Document window	The window in which a component of an Access database is displayed. Tables, queries, forms, reports, macros, and modules are referred to as *documents* in Windows terminology. You can have multiple Access documents of any type open simultaneously. These windows are called *multiple document interface (MDI) child windows*, because the Access application window is their *parent*.

continues

Table 3.1. Continued

Term	Description
Field scroll bar	Enables you to view fields of tables that are outside the bounds of the document window. Record scroll bars provide access to records located outside the document window.
Function icons	Six buttons that choose whether the active document window displays tables, queries, forms, reports, macros, or modules.
Inactive window	A window in the background, usually with a white or grayed title bar. Clicking the surface of an inactive window makes it the active window and brings it to the front. If an inactive window is not visible because other windows obscure it, you can make the window active by choosing the window's name from the **W**indow menu.
Maximize icon	Clicking the *application's* Maximize icon causes Access to occupy your entire display. Clicking the *document's* Maximize icon causes the document to take over the entire display. Figure 3.3 shows a maximized table document.
Menu bar	A horizontal bar containing main menu choices. These choices remain constant, but the choices in the drop-down menus corresponding to the main menu selections change, depending on the status of Access.
Minimize icon	Collapses the application or document window to an icon at the bottom of your display.
Mode buttons	Three buttons that determine the operating mode of Access. *Open* places Access in Run mode. *New* or *Design* puts Access in Design mode, where you can create or edit tables.
New Record	A button with an asterisk that indicates the location of the next record to be added to a table. Entering data in the new record appends the record to the table and creates another new record.
Restore icon	A double set of triangular arrows that, when clicked, returns the window from full display to its normal size, with moveable borders. When displayed, the Restore icon takes the place of the Maximize icon in the upper right corner of the window.

Term	Description
Status bar	A bar located at the bottom of the application window that displays prompts and indicators, such as the status of the Num Lock key.
Toolbar	A bar containing command buttons that duplicate the more commonly used menu choices. The number and type of toolbar buttons change depending on which basic function of Access you are using.

Maximized Document Windows

Access uses a windowing technique that you should know about before you accidentally minimize or close Access when you intended to minimize or close a maximized document. After you click the Maximize icon of a document window, the document window takes the place of the application window and occupies the entire display, except for the menu bar and toolbar (see fig. 3.3). Most other Windows applications that display multiple documents, such as Word for Windows and Excel, have a similar capability to expand a document to occupy the entire window.

FIG. 3.3

An Access table in a maximized document window.

The Document Control and Document Restore icons move to the extreme left and right, respectively, of the menu bar. The title of the document takes the place of the application title in the title bar at the top of the display. To return the document window to its original size, established when the application window was first active, click the Document Restore icon or click the Document Control icon. Then, choose **R**estore from the Document Control menu. You can close the document window by double-clicking the Document Control icon. If you accidentally double-click the Application Control icon just above the Document Control icon, however, you close Access for Windows. You receive no warning that you are about to exit Access unless you have changed the design of an object.

Document Windows Minimized to Icons

Working with several overlapping windows limits each window to a size that enables you to select another by clicking its surface with the mouse. This overlapping may overly restrict your view of the data the windows contain. You can minimize Access document windows and the Database window to icons that remain within the application window, as shown in figure 3.4. If you minimize a document window to an icon, rather than closing it, you quickly can return the window to its original size by double-clicking the icon. If you single-click the icon, you can choose how the window reappears by using the Document Control menu, as shown for the Database window in figure 3.4.

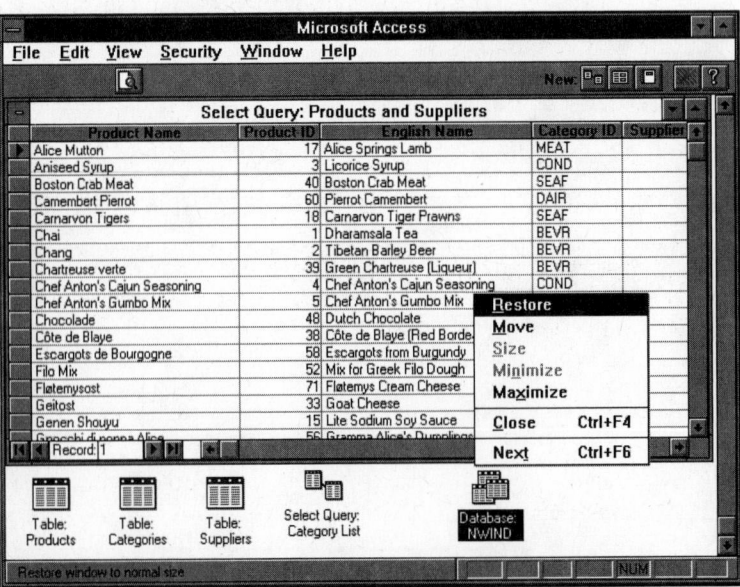

FIG. 3.4

Tables, queries, and a form minimized to icons within the application window.

If you choose to display your document window in maximized form by choosing Maximize from the Document Control menu that appears when you click the icon, the document hides the icons at the bottom of the application window. In this case, use the Window menu and choose the document you want. If you size your document windows like the window in figure 3.4 by dragging their borders, you can avoid the substantial mouse movement and two-step menu-selection process to choose the active document.

The Toolbar in Table View

The buttons that appear in Access's toolbar change according to the function that Access is performing at the time. When you are working with tables, the toolbar appears as in figure 3.5. The toolbar buttons are described in table 3.2.

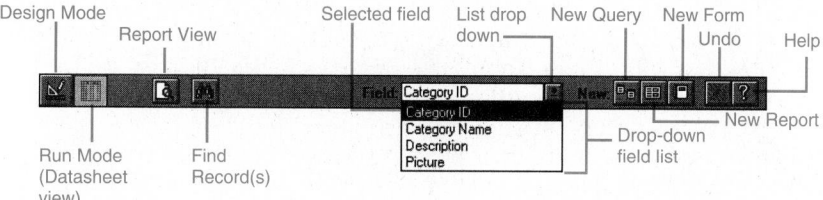

FIG. 3.5

The Access toolbar in Table Datasheet view.

Toolbar buttons represent shortcuts to traditional selection methods, such as choosing menu commands or choosing command or option buttons in a particular sequence. The Alternate Method column of table 3.2 lists how you can achieve the same effect as clicking a toolbar button by using the menus or the command buttons in the Database window.

Table 3.2. Appearance and Functions of Buttons and Other Elements of the Table Toolbar

Icon	Button	Alternate Method	Function
	Table Design Mode	View Table Design	Changes table display to Design mode. In Design mode, you specify the properties of each field of the table.
	Table Datasheet View	View Datasheet	Returns table display to Run mode (Datasheet view) from Design mode.

continues

Table 3.2. Continued

Icon	Button	Alternate Method	Function
	Report View	**File Print Preview**	Displays the contents of a table in report format and enables you to print the contents of the table.
	Find Record(s)	**Edit Find**	Displays the Find in Field dialog box that locates records with specific characters in a single field or all fields.
	Selected Field	Click field name button with mouse	Displays the field selected for editing or searching. You cannot edit the entry in the selected field text box.
	List Drop-Down	Click field name button with mouse	Opens the drop-down list of all fields in the table.
	Drop-Down Field List	Click field name bar with mouse	Displays all fields in the table. If more fields exist than will fit in the vertical dimension of the list, a vertical scroll bar is provided. You can click once to select the field and close the list.
	New Query	Database window, Query New	Changes to Design mode and creates a New Query window displaying the field list box for the first table on the table list or the table you have opened in Datasheet view.
	New Report	Database window, Report New	Changes to Design mode and displays a dialog box that enables you to select whether to use the Report Wizard or a blank report to create a new report for summarizing data or printing.

Icon	Button	Alternate Method	Function
	New Form	Database window, Form New	Changes to Design mode and displays a dialog box that enables you to choose between using the Form Wizard or a blank form to create a new form for data display or editing. Click the Run Mode button to return to Table Datasheet view.
	Help	F1 key or **Help Contents Tables**	Displays the Help menu for tables. When you request help by clicking the Help button, the context (in this case, tables) is used by the WinHelp Engine to display the appropriate menu. The F1 key serves the same purpose.
	Undo	**Edit Undo**	Returns you to the status immediately preceding the last action you took. The Undo button is inactive (the eraser is gray) if there is no action to undo. Access provides a single-level Undo feature; it will repeal only one action.

Access's toolbar has a fixed width, anchored at its left edge. If you reduce the width of Access's application window by dragging either vertical border inward, you first lose the Help button, then the Undo button, and finally the New buttons from right to left. Operating Access in a maximized window usually is best, because all the toolbar buttons are easily accessible.

Using Keyboard Operations

Although Access is oriented to using a mouse to make selections, keyboard equivalents are provided for most of the actions that the majority of seasoned Windows users perform with mouse clicks. Many data-entry operators, however, aren't accustomed to using a mouse, trackball, or other pointing device. Constant shifting of a hand from the keyboard to the mouse and back can reduce data-entry rates by more than half. Operators may expect your application to behave identically to that of the DOS data-entry screen of xBase or Paradox applications to which they have become accustomed. Keyboard operations, therefore, are as important in a data-entry environment as in word processing applications. Consequently, the rather dry exposition of key combinations appears here rather than being relegated to fine print in an appendix.

If you would like to experiment with the various keyboard operations that are described in the following sections, you would be wise to work with a copy of the database. When you're using a copy, you don't need to worry about making changes that affect the sample database. Experimenting also gives you the opportunity to try the database-compacting operation in Access.

To compact NWIND.MDB to a new copy of NWIND.MDB, follow these steps:

1. Close all open document windows. You may leave the Database window open.

2. Choose **C**lose Database from the **F**ile menu. Access reverts to its blank opening window.

3. Choose **C**ompact Database from the **F**ile menu to open the Compact From dialog box. File compaction is described near the end of this chapter. In this case, the file is compacted to make a copy of the NWIND.MDB file.

4. Double-click NWIND.MDB in the Database to Compact From dialog box. The Compact To dialog box appears. You can double-click the default file name, DB1.MDB, in the Filename text box. Or, you can enter a more creative name, such as **ILLWIND.MDB**, and choose OK. Compacting a database file with a new name creates a new, compacted database that you can use for testing.

5. Choose **O**pen Database from the **F**ile menu and double-click DB1.MDB or the name of your file.

6. Open the Customers table by double-clicking its entry in the Database window.

In the tables that follow, the term *field* is used in place of the more specific description, *data cell* or *cell*, to maintain consistency with Access's documentation and the Help windows. A *field*, in conventional database terminology, indicates the collection of data consisting of the contents of the field in each record of the table.

Data Entry and Editing Keys

Arrow keys and combinations are, for the most part, identical to those used in other Windows applications. Little resemblance exists between these combinations and the key combinations used by DOS database managers. The F2 key, used for editing cell contents in Excel, has a different function in Access—it toggles between Editing and Select mode. *Toggle* means to alternate between two states. In the Editing state, the caret indicates the insertion point in the field, and the key combinations shown in table 3.3 are active. If the field is selected (indicated by a black background with white type), the editing keys behave as indicated in table 3.4. The term *grid* in the tables that follow indicates a display in tabular form that doesn't represent fields and records. The list of fields and their descriptions in Table Design mode is an example of a grid.

Table 3.3. Keys for Editing Fields, Grids, and Text Boxes

Key	Function
F2	Toggles between displaying the caret for editing and selecting the entire field. The field must be deselected (black type on a white background) and the caret must be visible in order for the following examples to operate as shown.
→	Moves the caret right one character until you reach the last character in the line.
Ctrl+→	Moves the caret right one word until you reach the last word in the line.
End	Moves the caret to the end of the line.
Ctrl+End	Moves the caret to the end of a multiple-line field.
←	Moves the caret one character to the left until you reach the first character in the line.
Ctrl+←	Moves the caret one word to the left until you reach the first word in the line.
Home	Moves the caret to the beginning of the line.
Ctrl+Home	Moves the caret to the beginning of the field in multiple-line fields.
Backspace	Deletes the entire selection or the character to the left of the caret.
Delete	Deletes the entire selection or the character to the right of the caret.

continues

Table 3.3. Continued

Key	Function
Ctrl+Z or or Alt+Backspace	Undoes typing, a Replace operation, or any other change to the record since the last time it was saved. An edited record is saved to the database when you move to a new record or close the editing window.
Esc	Undoes changes to the current field. Press Esc twice to undo changes to the current field and to the entire current record, if other fields were edited.

Operations that select the entire field or a portion of the field, as listed in table 3.4, generally are used with the Windows Clipboard operations described in table 3.5. Selecting an entire field, and then pressing the Del key or typing a character is a quick way of ridding the field of its original contents.

Table 3.4. Keys for Selecting Text in Fields, Grids, and Text Boxes

Selection	Key	Function
Text within a field	F2	Toggles between displaying the caret for editing and selecting the entire field. The field must be selected (white type on a black background) in order for the following examples to operate as shown.
	Shift+→	Selects or deselects one character to the right.
	Ctrl+Shift+→	Selects or deselects one word to the right.
	Shift+←	Selects or deselects one character to the left.
	Ctrl+Shift+←	Selects or deselects one word to the left.
Next field	Tab or Enter	Selects the next field. "Setting Default Options," later in this chapter, tells you how to change the effect of the Enter key.

Selection	Key	Function
Record	Shift+Space bar	Selects or deselects the entire current record.
	↑	Selects the preceding record when a record is selected.
	↓	Selects the next record when a record is selected.
Column	Ctrl+Space bar	Toggles selection of the current column.
	→	Selects the column to the right (if a column is selected and there is a column to the right).
	←	Selects the column to the left (if a column is selected and there is a column to the left).
Fields and records in Extend mode	F8	Turns on Extend mode. You will see EXT in the status bar In Extend mode, pressing F8 extends the selection to the word, field, record, and all records.
	Shift+F8	Reverses the last F8 selection.
	Esc	Cancels Extend mode.

Table 3.5. Keys for Windows Clipboard Operations

Key	Function
Ctrl+C or Ctrl+Ins	Copies the selection to the Windows Clipboard.
Ctrl+V or Shift+Ins	Pastes the contents of the Clipboard at the location of the caret.
Ctrl+X or Shift+Del	Copies the selection to the Clipboard, and then deletes it. This operation also is called a *cut*.
Ctrl+Z or Alt+Backspace	Undoes your last Cut, Delete, or Paste operation.

Function Key Assignments

All 12 function keys of the 101-key extended keyboard are assigned to specific purposes by Access. Some keys, such as Shift+F4 (which you press to find the next occurrence of a match with the Find dialog box), are derived from other Microsoft applications—in this case, Word for Windows. You use function keys with the Shift, Alt, and Ctrl keys to enable users to perform up to 96 functions by using the 12 keys.

Global Function Keys

Global function key assignments, except for F11 and Alt+F1, are used by Windows, rather than by Access, to perform functions that are identical in all Windows applications. Table 3.6 lists the global function key assignments.

Table 3.6. Global Function Key Assignments

Key	Function
F1	Displays context-sensitive help related to the present basic function and status of Access.
Shift+F1	Adds a question mark to the mouse pointer. Place the mouse pointer with the question mark over an object on-screen for which you want help, and click the mouse.
Ctrl+F4	Closes the active window.
Alt+F4	Exits Access or closes a dialog box if one is open.
Ctrl+F6	Selects each open window in sequence as the active window.
F11 or Alt+F1	Selects the Database window as the active window.
F12 or Alt+F2	Opens the File Save As dialog box.
Shift+F12 or Alt+Shift+F2	Saves your open database; the equivalent of the **File Save** menu choice.

Function Key Assignments for Fields, Grids, and Text Boxes

Access assigns function key combinations that aren't reserved for global operations to actions that are specific to the basic function you are performing at the moment. Table 3.7 lists the function key combinations that are applicable to fields, grids, and text boxes. You may see some repetition of information from the previous tables; this repetition is unavoidable if the tables are to be complete.

Table 3.7. Function Keys for Fields, Grids, and Text Boxes

Key	Function
F2	Toggles between displaying the caret for editing and selecting the entire field.
Shift+F2	Opens the Zoom box for entering expressions and other text.
F4	Opens a drop-down combo box or list box.
Shift+F4	Finds the next occurrence of a match of the text entered in the Find or Replace dialog box, if the dialog box is closed.
F5	Moves the caret to the record number box. Enter the number of the record you want to display and press Enter.
Ctrl+F5	Adds a new record to the table.
Shift+F5	Saves a record to the database.
F6	In Design view, cycles between upper and lower parts of the window. In Datasheet view and Form view, cycles through the header, body (detail section), and footer.
Shift+F6	In Datasheet view and Form view, cycles through the footer, body (detail section), and header.
F7	Opens the Find dialog box.
Shift+F7	Opens the Replace dialog box.
F8	Turns on Extend mode. Press F8 again to extend the selection to a word, the entire field, the whole record, and then all records.
Shift+F8	Reverses the F8 selection process.
Esc	Cancels Extend mode.

The Module window is designed for writing Access Basic code, the subject of Part VI of this book. Table 3.8 lists the purposes of the function keys. The Module window shows many of the characteristics of Windows' Notepad applet, including the F3 key, which you use for searching.

Table 3.8. Function Keys in the Module Window

Key	Function
F2	Views procedure
Shift+F2	Goes to procedure selected in Module window
F3	Finds next occurrence of text specified in the Find or Replace dialog box
Shift+F3	Finds preceding occurrence of text specified in the Find or Replace dialog box
F5	Continues execution of code after a break condition
F6	Cycles between upper and lower panes (if you have split the window)
F7	Opens the Find dialog box
Shift+F7	Opens the Replace dialog box
F8	Single step
Shift+F8	Procedure step
F9	Toggles a breakpoint at the selected line

Shortcut Keys for Fields and Text Boxes

You use shortcut keys to minimize the number of keystrokes required to accomplish common tasks. Most shortcut key combinations use the Ctrl key with other keys. Ctrl+C, Ctrl+V, and Ctrl+X for Clipboard operations are examples of global shortcut keys in Windows 3.1. Shortcut keys applicable to field and text box entries are listed in table 3.9.

Table 3.9. Shortcut Keys for Fields in Tables and Text Boxes

Key	Function
Ctrl+; (semicolon)	Inserts the current date
Ctrl+: (colon)	Inserts the current time
Ctrl+Alt+Space bar	Selects all records of the table—the equivalent of choosing Select All Records from the Edit menu
Ctrl+' (apostrophe) or Ctrl+" (quote)	Inserts the value from the same field in the preceding record
Ctrl+Enter	Inserts a newline character (carriage return plus line feed) in a text box
Ctrl++ (plus)	Adds a new record to the table
Ctrl+– (minus)	Deletes the current record from the table
Shift+Enter	Saves all changes to the current record

Setting Default Options

You may set about 100 options that establish the default settings for the system as a whole, and also those for the six functions defined by the buttons in the Database window. You aren't likely to change default options until you are more familiar with Access, but this book is both a tutorial guide and a reference, and options are a basic element of Access's overall structure.

You set defaults by choosing View from the main menu and then choosing Options. The Options dialog box appears, as shown in figure 3.6. General, Keyboard, and Printing category options apply to the system as a whole. Datasheet options apply to both forms and queries. The remainder of the option categories are specific to other basic functions.

You choose a category by clicking it with the mouse or by using the up- and down-arrow keys. As you change a category, the options for that category appear in the Items list box. Most of the items require Yes/No or multiple-choice entries that you select from drop-down list boxes which you open by clicking the drop-down button to the right of the entry fields. In some cases, you must enter a specific value from the keyboard. After you complete your changes, choose OK to close the dialog box. If you decide not to implement your changes, choose Cancel to exit the Options dialog box.

FIG. 3.6

The Options
dialog box.

System Defaults

Access uses a special Access database, SYSTEM.MDA, to store all
default properties for displaying and printing the contents of tables,
queries, forms, reports, and modules. Access stores these properties in
tables, along with other tables that determine the behavior of Access,
in SYSTEM.MDA.

SYSTEM.MDA is vital to the proper operation of Access. You
should keep a backup copy of SYSTEM.MDA on a disk. If you make
changes to any options or implement the security features of
Access, you should create an updated backup when your changes
or additions are complete.

General Options

General options, as described in table 3.10, consist of choices that
apply to Access as a whole. Default values established by Access are
shown in bold type in the table. You probably will not need to change
any of these options, with the possible exception of the default database directory. When you create your own databases, you should store
them in a directory dedicated to databases in order to simplify backup
operations. A dedicated database directory is a good place to keep a
backup copy of SYSTEM.MDA.

Table 3.10. General Options for the Access System

Option	Value	Function
Show Status Bar	**Yes**/No	Displays (**Yes**) or hides (No) the status bar at the bottom of the window.
Show System	Yes/**No**	Displays (Yes) or hides (**No**) system objects in the Database window.
OLE/DDE Timeout	0-300 (**30**) seconds	Determines the time after which Access stops retrying failed OLE or DDE operations.
Show Tool Bar	**Yes**/No	Displays (**Yes**) or hides (No) the toolbar.
Confirm Document Deletions	**Yes**/No	Displays (**Yes**) or doesn't display (No) a confirmation message box before deleting an object from the database.
Confirm Action Queries	**Yes**/No	Displays (**Yes**) or doesn't display (No) a confirmation message box before Access runs an action query.
New Database Sort Order	**General** and other languages	Sets the alphabetical sort order used for new databases. You can change the sort order for an existing database by selecting a different sort order setting and then compacting the database by choosing File Compact.
Ignore DDE Requests	Yes/**No**	Ignores (Yes) or doesn't ignore (**No**) DDE requests from other applications.
Default Find/Replace Behavior	**Fast** Search or General Search	Use **Fast** Search or General Search as the default for **E**dit **F**ind and **E**dit Replace operations. **Fast** tests the current field and requires a match of the entire field. General tests all fields and matches any part of the field. Changes you make don't take effect until your next Access session.

continues

Table 3.10. Continued		
Option	**Value**	**Function**
Default Database Directory	A valid (**working**) directory	Changes the default directory for the File Open Database dialog box. The default is the Access working directory, indicated by a period.
Confirm Record Changes	**Yes**/No	Displays (**Yes**) or doesn't display (No) a confirmation message box before deleting or pasting records, or before changes are made with the Edit Replace command.

Keyboard Options

Keyboard Behavior

Keyboard options, as listed in table 3.11, are especially important if you are accustomed to a particular type of arrow-key behavior. Bold type indicates the default value established by Access. You probably will want to change keyboard options more than any of the other categories, except perhaps printing. You can make the arrow keys behave as if you are editing xBase fields, rather than using their default behavior, which duplicates that of Excel, for example.

Printing Options

You use printing options to set default margins for printing datasheets, the code in modules, or new forms and reports. Table 3.12 lists the available options, with their default values in bold type. Changes you make to the printing options don't affect existing forms and reports. You must modify the printing properties of each existing form and report in Design view in order to change the printing margin.

Margins usually are expressed in inches. If you are using an international version of Access, margin settings are in centimeters. You also can specify margin settings in *twips*, the default measurement of Windows. A twip is 1/20 of a printer's point. A point is 1/72 inch, so a twip is 1/1440 inch.

Table 3.11. Keyboard Options for the Access System

Option	Value	Function
Arrow Key Behavior	**Next Field**/Next Character	The right or left arrow key selects the next or preceding field (**Next Field**) or moves the insertion point to the next or preceding character (Next Character). Choose Next Character if you want to duplicate the behavior of xBase.
Move After Enter	No/**Next Field**/Next Record	Enter does not move the insertion point (No), it moves the insertion point to the next field (**Next Field**), or it moves the insertion point to the next record (Next Record).
Cursor Stops at First/Last Field	Yes/**No**	Pressing the right- or left-arrow keys, Enter, or Tab cycles (Yes) or does not cycle (**No**) the insertion point from the first to the last or the last to the first field in a row.
Key Assignment Macro	A valid macro name	Establishes the name of the key assignment macro. Use this name when you assign a macro to a key combination. The default name of the key assignment macro is *AutoKeys*.

Table 3.12. Printing Options for All Access Functions

Option	Value	Function
Left Margin	0-page width (**1"**)	Establishes the default left margin.
Top Margin	0-page height (**1"**)	Establishes the default top margin.
Right Margin	0-page width (**1"**)	Establishes the default right margin.
Bottom Margin	0-page height (**1"**)	Establishes the default bottom margin.

The one-inch default margins are arbitrary; you may want to reset them to your preference before creating any forms or reports of your own. If you are using a laser printer, refer to its manual to determine the maximum printable area. The printable area determines the minimum margins you can use.

Defaults for Datasheet View

You use Datasheet View options to customize the display of all query datasheets, and new table and form datasheets (see table 3.13). As with printing options, to change the display format of existing table and form datasheets, you must edit the appropriate properties of the table or form in Design view. The options you set here don't apply to forms and reports created with Wizards. Each Wizard has its own set of default values. In table 3.13, default values appear in bold type.

Table 3.13. Options for Datasheet Views

Option	Value	Function
Default Gridlines Behavior	**On**/Off	Shows (**On**) or hides (Off) gridlines in datasheets, duplicating the **Layout Gridlines** menu choice.
Default Column Width	0 to 22 in. (**1 in.**)	Sets the width of columns in datasheets. You adjust the column width of datasheets by dragging the dividing lines between column names with the mouse.
Default Font Name	Name of a typeface on your system	Sets the typeface of field names and data in datasheets, duplicating the **Layout Font** menu choice. The default is MS Sans Serif.
Default Font Size	Varies with typeface	Sets the size of field names and data in datasheets, duplicating the **Layout Font** menu choice. The default is **8**- point type.

Option	Value	Function
Default Font Weight	All common weights	Sets the weight of field names and data in datasheets. Choices are Thin, Extra Light, Light, Normal, Medium, Semibold, Bold, Extra Bold, or Black. Few typefaces, however, offer all these weights. The default is **Normal**.
Default Font Italic	Yes/**No**	Displays field names and data in italic style.
Default Font Underline	Yes/**No**	Underlines field names and data.

Using Cue Cards

Cue Cards are a unique feature of Access, and you can expect to see them in future versions of many Microsoft applications. Cue Cards are designed to interactively guide you through the basic operations of Access. You choose a topic by clicking a button. Then a new series of buttons displays dialog boxes with text and graphic images that explain elements of the topic you chose.

To examine some of the Cue Cards that are provided with Access, perform the following steps:

1. Close all document windows, but leave the Database window open.

2. Click the Help (?) button on the toolbar or choose **C**ontents from the **H**elp menu. The Help Table of Contents window appears, as shown in figure 3.7.

3. Click the Cue Cards button. The Cue Cards main menu appears, as shown in figure 3.8. You can choose **C**ue Cards from the **H**elp menu as a shortcut to this point. To learn more about Cue Cards, click the *hot spot*, About Cue Cards, at the bottom of the Help window.

When you click *hot spot* text, usually shown in green, you receive an explanation of the hot spot topic. Hot spot topics in regular text open small pop-up windows that ordinarily define the hot spot term. Hot spots in bold text are links to windows in the Help file related to the topic of the hot spot.

FIG. 3.7

The Help Table
of Contents
window for
Access.

FIG. 3.8

The Cue Cards
main menu.

4. Because this is your introduction to Access, and possibly to the
   subject of databases as a whole, click the I'm Not Sure button on
   the Cue Cards main menu to display Cue Cards that describe databases and their component parts. The first Cue Card for the Database topic, the Show Me menu, appears as shown in figure 3.9.

5. Click the See What a **Database** Is button. The first real Cue Card, shown in figure 3.10, defines the term *database* in its generic usage.

6. Click the Next button to display the next card in the deck, shown in figure 3.11, which describes Access databases in more specific terms.

FIG. 3.9

The initial Show Me menu for the Database topic.

FIG. 3.10

The Cue Card that defines databases in general.

FIG. 3.11

A Cue Card
describing
Access
databases.

7. As you continue to click the Next button, the information contained in the successive Cue Cards becomes increasingly specific until you run out of cards and are returned to the preceding Cue Card menu. You can return to the preceding card or menu by clicking the Back button, or you can go to the top of the deck by clicking the Menu button. Close the Cue Card window or menu by double-clicking the Control Menu symbol in the upper left corner of the card. You also can click the Control Menu symbol once, and then select Close from the menu to close the Cue Card window.

Using Access Help

The Access Help system is extensive and easy to use. All the new Help functions incorporated in Windows 3.1's WinHelp Engine are used by Access's Help system.

This section discusses methods of getting help with specific functions and objects of Access. Chapter 24, "Adding On-Line Help for Users," describes how you can aid users of your applications by writing Help files of your own to accompany your Access applications.

Context-Sensitive Help

Context-sensitive help tries to anticipate your need for information by displaying Help windows related to the operating mode, function, and operation in which you are involved or attempting to perform. You can get context-sensitive help in two ways: by pressing the F1 key, or by using the Help mouse pointer that appears after you press Shift+F1.

If, for example, a dialog box is open when you press F1, you receive information on the purpose of the dialog box and the effects of your entries and choices. Figure 3.12 shows the Help window for the Find dialog box, which also is applicable to the **Edit Find** command.

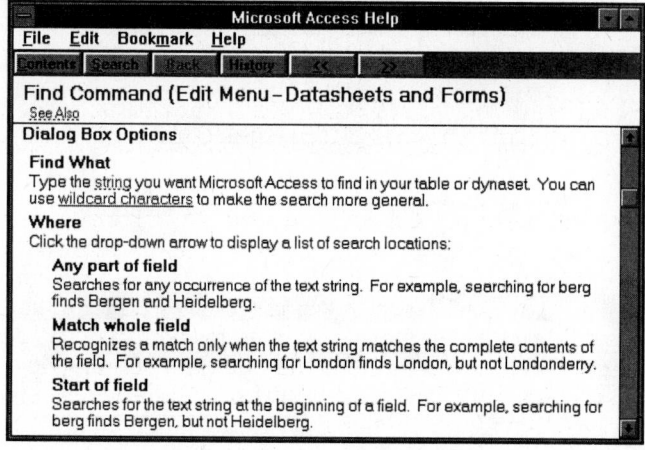

FIG. 3.12

The Help window for the Find command and dialog box.

You can reposition and resize the Help window by dragging its borders with your mouse. Click and drag the Help title bar to reposition the Help window. If more information is in the Help file on the topic you selected than will fit in the window, a vertical scroll bar appears at the right of the window. Drag the scroll box down to display additional text.

Most of Access's Help windows include hot spots that provide additional information about a topic. Hot spots with dotted underlines, such as See Also in figure 3.12, display definition windows that generally are used to define terms used in the window, but they also can be used to create *jumps* to other related topics. If you click the See Also hot spot, the definition window of figure 3.13 appears. You can click any of the hot spots in that window to *jump* to the topic shown with the solid underline in the figure.

If you click the string hot spot in figure 3.12, the definition of the term *string* appears in the definition window, as shown in figure 3.14.

Clicking the wildcard characters hot spot in figure 3.12, which has a solid underline, results in a jump to the Help window for the Wildcard topic, displayed in figure 3.15.

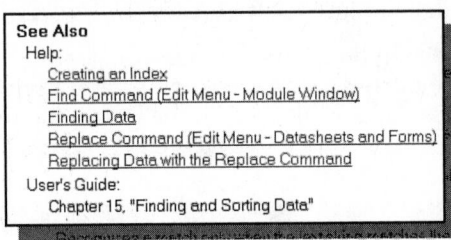

FIG. 3.13

The definition window displayed by the See Also hot spot.

FIG. 3.14

The definition window for the word *string*.

FIG. 3.15

A related Help window displayed by clicking a topic hot spot.

After you read the Help window for the topic to which you jumped, click the Back button to return to the preceding Help window. Each of the Help buttons is explained later in this chapter.

The second method of getting context-sensitive help is to press Shift+F1 and then place the mouse pointer with the question mark on the item with which you need help. Click the mouse button; the topic related to the object appears. Figure 3.16 shows an example that explains the toolbar when a database is open but no database object is present in a document window.

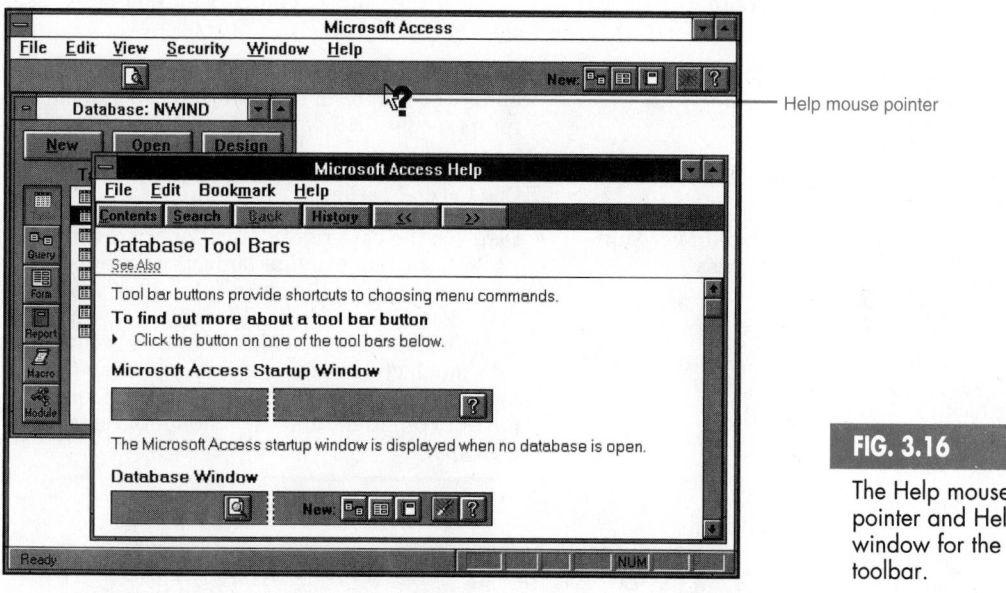

Help mouse pointer

FIG. 3.16

The Help mouse pointer and Help window for the toolbar.

The Help window in figure 3.16 shows a different method of creating hot spots. Bit-mapped icons can be used in Help files as a substitute for the green underlined text for topic jumps. Here, you click the image of the toolbar button to get help on how to use the button.

Help Menu

An alternative to the use of context-sensitive help is provided by Access's Help menu. Table 3.14 lists the options presented by the Help menu.

You can get a more general form of help by choosing Content from the Help menu. In this case, you always start from square one—the table of contents of the entire Help system shown in figure 3.17. You click the hot spot or icon that represents the subject about which you want to learn. This action causes a jump to the first Help window for the subject, which often provides several additional choices for more detailed help on a specific topic.

Table 3.14. Access's Help Menu Options

Option	Function
Contents	Displays the table of contents of the Access Help system (see fig. 3.17).
Search	Displays a Search dialog box that enables you to enter a search term to find topics that include the term (see fig. 3.18).
Cue Cards	Displays the first Cue Card in the deck (see "Using Cue Cards," earlier in this chapter).
About Microsoft Access	Displays the copyright notice for Microsoft Access, the name and organization you entered during setup, and the serial number of your copy of Access. Effective with Windows 3.1, you also are told the mode in which Windows is running, how much conventional memory you have installed, whether you have a math coprocessor in your computer, and the amount of remaining disk space.

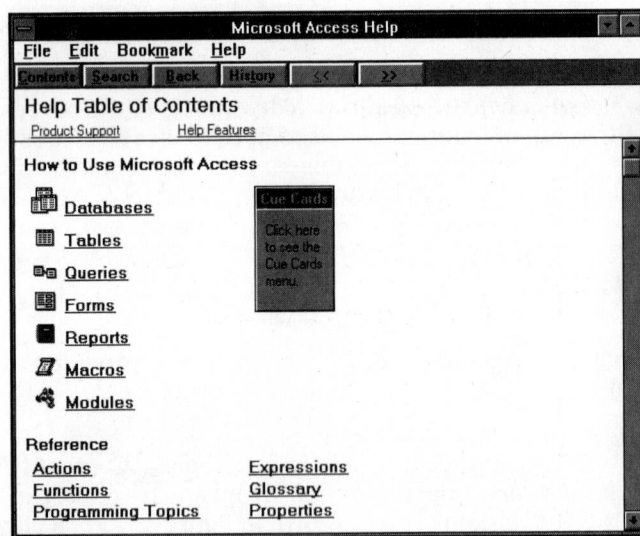

FIG. 3.17

Access's Help Table of Contents window.

  You can return to the table of contents window at any time by clicking the Contents button.

Search

The Windows 3.1 WinHelp Engine has a useful function that enables you to search the contents of the Help system based on a word or fragment of a word you enter in a text box. Click the Search button to display the Search dialog box shown in figure 3.18.

In the text box, enter a word for which you want to search, and press Enter or choose OK. If Access finds matches among the Help topics, it displays the matches in the list portion of the Search Topic combo box. Subjects shown in lowercase letters are index entries for groups of topics that appear in the Select a Topic list box. Double-click the topic you want to display, or click the topic and then click the Go To button. The example in figure 3.18 is the result of entering **find** and clicking finding data in the Search list box. After you double-click Find Command, the Help window in figure 3.12 appears.

Back

The WinHelp Engine keeps a history of each Help window you have viewed, as illustrated in figure 3.19. You can locate any of the subjects that you have reviewed previously in your present Access session by dragging the scroll box, if your list of selections exceeds the depth of the window. When you find the prior topic that you want to review, double-click the entry. Or, you can use the multistep approach by clicking the Back button. If this is your first Help screen in a sequence, the Back button is inactive.

You can use the two remaining buttons in the Help window, backward (<<) and forward (>>), to scroll through topics related to the topic you selected. Topics are assigned context numbers, and the << and >> buttons display windows in the sequence of their Help context numbers assigned by Microsoft's authors.

Search

Type a **word**, or select one from the list. Then choose Show Topics.

[Close]

[finding data]

[Show Topics]

```
finding data
finding Help information
finding records (Access Basic)
finding records (macros)
finding records (navigating)
FindLast
```

Select a **topic**, then choose Go To.

[Go To]

```
Find Command (Edit Menu - Datasheets and Forms)
Find Command (Edit Menu - Module Window)
Find, Replace, or Sort Data (Cue Cards)
Finding Data
Options Command - General options
Replacing Data
Using Wildcard Characters
```

FIG. 3.18

The Search dialog box.

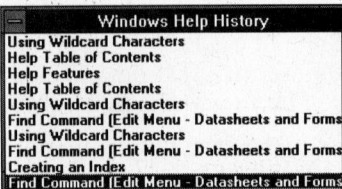

Help Window Menu Choices

In addition to the buttons, the Help window includes a menu with the choices shown in table 3.15.

Table 3.15. Options for Datasheet Views

Option	Function
File Open	Enables you to select a different Help file. The default extension of Help files is .HLP.
Print Topic	Prints the currently visible Help topic on your printer.
P**r**int Setup	Displays the Printer Setup dialog box to change printer settings.
E**x**it	Closes the Help window.
Edit **C**opy	Opens a text box in which you can select all or a portion of the Help text and copy it to the Windows Clipboard.
Annotate	Enables you to add your own comments to the current Help topic.
Bookmark Define	Displays a dialog box in which you can enter an alias for the current Help topic for quick access.
Bookmark Names	Choices representing the bookmarks you have created.
Help **How to Use Help**	Help windows containing instructions on how to use the WinHelp Engine (also called **H**elp on Help in some applications). Select this topic to get additional information on **H**elp menu choices.
Always on **T**op	Enables you to choose the current window as the first window that appears when you choose Help.

Option	Function
About Help	Displays the copyright notice for the current version of Windows installed, the version of the WinHelp Engine in use, the licensing boilerplate, the mode in which you are operating Windows, the amount of free memory (including virtual memory), and the percentage of both RAM and virtual memory presently consumed by Windows and running applications.

Using Database Functions in Start-Up Mode

Three functions exist that you can perform only when you are in Access Start-up mode with no database open. You access the database functions from the File menu. If you have a large database, these operations will take a considerable amount of time. Each of the operations described in the following paragraphs involve two dialog boxes. In the first dialog box, you choose the database in which the operation is to be performed; in the second dialog box, you enter the name of the file that is to be created by the operation. Default file names for new files are DB#.MDB, where # is a sequential number assigned by Access, beginning with 1.

Compacting Databases

After you have made numerous additions and changes to objects within a database file, especially additions and deletions of data in tables, the database file can become disorganized. Like xBase files, when you delete a record, you don't automatically regain the space in the file that the deleted data occupied. You must compact the database, the equivalent of xBase's PACK command, to optimize both its file size and the organization of data within the tables that the file contains.

xBase

PACK

To compact a database, perform the following steps:

1. From the File menu, choose Compact Database. The Database to Compact From dialog box appears, as shown in figure 3.20.

2. Double-click the name of the database file you want to compact. Or, click the name and then choose OK. The Database to Compact Into dialog box appears, as shown in figure 3.21.

3. Enter the name of the new file that is to result from the compaction process in the File Name text box. If you choose to replace the existing file with the compacted version, you see a message box requesting confirmation of your choice. Choose OK.

4. Access creates a compacted version of the file. The progress of the compaction is shown in a red bar in the status bar. If you decide to use the same file name, after compaction, the new file replaces the preceding file.

FIG. 3.20

The Database to Compact From dialog box.

FIG. 3.21

The Database to Compact Into dialog box.

Periodically compacting files generally is the duty of the database administrator in a multiuser environment, usually in relation to backup operations. It is a good practice to back up your existing file on disk or tape before creating a compacted version.

Encrypting and Decrypting Databases

If other persons have access to your database, either from a file server or within a work group using peer-to-peer networking systems, encrypting the file prevents unauthorized persons from reading its contents with a text editor or file-editing application. You use the same process as that for file compaction to create a new encrypted file or to replace the "clear" version with the encrypted file. If you select Encrypt/ Decrypt Database from the File menu and the database you open has been encrypted previously, you are given the opportunity to obtain a decrypted version. File security is the subject of Chapter 21, "Using Access in a Network Environment."

Repairing Databases

A database can become corrupted as the result of the following factors:

- Hardware problems in writing to your database file, either locally or on a network server

- An unrecoverable application error (UAE) in Access or another application running in Windows 3.0 when an Access database file is open and has been modified

- The equivalent of a UAE in Access with Windows 3.1

- A power failure that occurs after you have made modifications to an Access database file

Access includes a database repair facility that you can use to recover a usable database file from the majority of corrupted files resulting from the preceding list of events. The process is the same as that for creating compacted and encrypted versions of the file.

Occasionally, a file may become corrupted without Access detecting the problem. This lack of detection is more often the case with corrupted indexes. If Access or your application behaves strangely when you open an existing database and display its contents, try repairing the database. Choose Repair Database from the File menu, and then follow the same steps as described for compacting the database.

Chapter Summary

This chapter explained the structure of Access for Windows, the terminology and appearance of your display, keyboard combinations for editing fields and text boxes, and shortcut keys. Options for establishing the default methodology for Access as a whole and the table function were discussed. An explanation of the extensive, context-sensitive help authored by Access was included so that users not familiar with the new features of the Windows 3.1 WinHelp Engine can take full advantage of these features. You also learned how to use Access's Cue Cards to get additional help. If you design your own applications, you may want to have your users or clients review this chapter as an introduction to some of the changes they can expect when switching from a DOS-based database application.

In Chapter 4, you begin to apply what you learned in this chapter in order to work with Access tables. The majority of the examples in Chapter 4 continue to use the Northwind Traders database, but you will add your own tables to expand its capabilities. In Chapter 5, you start working with tables created from your existing database or spreadsheet applications by using the Import and Attach functions of Access.

Working with Access Databases and Tables

The traditional definition of a database is *a collection of related data items that are stored in an organized manner*. Access is unique among database management applications for the PC because of its all-encompassing database structure. Access databases include the following elements in a single database file:

■ *Tables* that store data items in a row-column format similar to that used by spreadsheet applications. You may include up to 32,768 tables in an Access database, and you may work on (open) up to 254 tables at one time. You can import tables from other database applications (such as xBase and Paradox), client-server databases (such as Microsoft SQL Server), and spreadsheet applications (such as Microsoft Excel and Lotus 1-2-3). In addition, you can attach other database tables to Access databases. Attaching, importing, and exporting tables is the subject of Chapter 5.

■ *Queries* that display selected data contained in up to 16 tables. Queries enable you to determine how data is presented by choosing the tables that comprise the query and up to 255 specific fields (columns) of these tables. You determine which records (rows) are displayed by deciding which criteria the data items in the query data must meet in order to be included in the display. Creating queries is explained in Chapters 6 and 8.

- *Forms* that display data contained in tables or queries and enable you to add new data and update or delete existing data. You can incorporate pictures and graphs in your forms, and, if you have a sound card, include narration and music in your form. You learn how to create forms in Chapters 9 and 10, and you learn how to add graphics to forms in Chapter 14.

- *Reports* that print data from tables or queries in virtually any format you want. Access enables you to add graphics to your reports so that you can print a complete, illustrated catalog of products from an Access database. Access's report capabilities are much more flexible than those of most other database management applications, including those designed for mini- and mainframe computers. Creating reports is covered in Chapter 11.

- *Macros* that automate Access operations. Access macros take the place of programming code required by other database applications, such as xBase, to perform specific actions in response to user-initiated events, such as clicking a command button. In most cases, you can create a fully functional database application without writing any programming code at all. Macros are the subject of Chapters 16 through 18.

- *Modules* that contain Access Basic code you write to perform operations that the standard collection of macros included in Access do not support. You learn how to write Access Basic code in Chapter 22.

A better definition of an Access database may be *a collection of related data items and the methods necessary to select, display, update, and report the data*. This is a very important distinction between Access and other database management applications. Even client-server database systems, such as Microsoft SQL Server, that include all related tables within a single database do not include the equivalent of forms and reports within the database. You must use another application, called a *front-end*, to display, edit, and report data stored in client-server databases. You can use Access to create front-ends for client-server databases by attaching tables from the client-server database to your Access database. Creating front-ends for client-server databases probably will be one of the major applications for Access in medium- to large-size firms.

This chapter introduces you to Access databases and tables—the fundamental elements of an Access application. You will see many references in this book to the term *Access application*. An Access application is an Access database that has the following characteristics:

■ It contains the tables, queries, forms, reports, and macros necessary to display the data in a meaningful way and update the data
as necessary. If you are creating a front-end application, all the
tables may be attached from the client-server database.

■ It does not require that users of the database know how to design
any of its elements. All elements of the database are fully predefined during the design stage of the application. In most cases,
you will want to restrict other users from intentionally or uninten-
tionally changing the design of the application.

■ It is automated by Access macros so that users make choices
from command buttons or custom-designed menus, rather than
from the pick-lists in the Database window you used in Chapter 2,
"Up and Running with Access Tables: A Quick Start."

As you progress through the chapters in this book, you create a model
of an Access application called *Personnel Actions*. Later in this chapter,
you create the Personnel Actions table. In the following chapters, you
add new features to the Personnel Actions application until, when you
reach Chapter 18, you have a complete, automated method of adding
and editing Personnel Actions data. When you are learning Access,
therefore, it is important that you read this book in a sequential manner, at least through Chapter 18. Make sure to perform the example
exercises for the Personnel Actions application each time you encounter them, because succeeding examples build on your prior work.

For Related Information:

▶▶ "Using ODBC Drivers with Client-Server Database Systems,"
p. 875.

FROM HERE...

Understanding Relational Databases

All database managers enable you to enter, edit, view, and print information contained in one or more tables that are divided into rows and
columns. At this point, the definition of a database manager (DBM)
doesn't differ from that of a spreadsheet application—most spreadsheets can emulate database functions. Three principal characteristics
distinguish most database managers from spreadsheet applications:

- All DBMs are designed to deal efficiently with very large amounts of data—much more than spreadsheets can handle conveniently.

- Relational DBMs easily link two or more tables so that they appear to the user as if they are one table. This process is difficult or impossible to accomplish with spreadsheets.

- Relational DBMs minimize information duplication by requiring repetition of only those data items, such as product or customer codes, by which multiple tables are linked.

DBMs that cannot link multiple tables are called *flat-file managers* and are used primarily to compile simple lists such as names, addresses, and telephone numbers. The Windows Cardfile applet is an example of a rudimentary, but useful, flat-file manager.

Because relational databases eliminate most duplicate information, they minimize data storage and application memory requirements. Figure 4.1 shows a typical relational database that a manufacturing or distributing firm may use. This database structure is similar to that of the Northwind Traders sample database provided with Access.

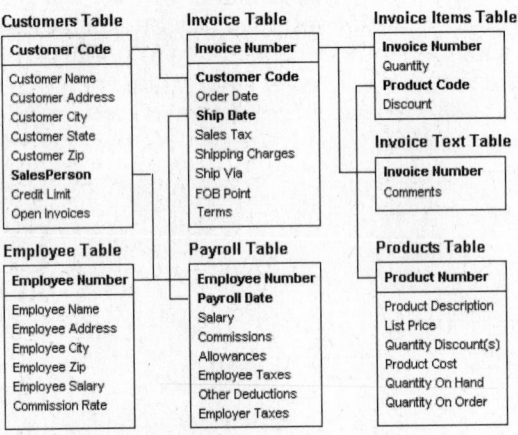

FIG. 4.1

A portion of a typical database for a manufacturing or distributing firm.

If your job is to create an invoice-entry database, you don't need to enter a customer's name and address more than once. Just assign each customer a unique number or code and add a record containing this information to the Customers table. Similarly, you don't need to enter the names and prices of the standard products for each invoice. You assign unique codes to products, and then add records for them to the Products table. When you want to create a new invoice for an existing customer, you enter the customer code and type the codes and quantities for the products ordered. This process adds one record (identified by an automatically assigned sequential numeric code) to the Invoices table and one record for each different item purchased to the Invoice Items table.

Each table is related to the other by the customer, invoice, and product codes and numbers, shown by the connecting lines between the tables in figure 4.1. The codes and numbers shown in boxes are unique; only one customer corresponds to a particular code and one invoice or product corresponds to a given number. When you display or print an invoice, the Invoice table is linked (called a *join*) with both the Customers and Invoice Items tables by their codes. In turn, the Invoice Items table is joined with the Products table by the product code. Your query (view) of the desired sales order(s) displays the appropriate customer, invoice, items, and product information from the linked records. (Queries are explained in the following section.) You can calculate quantity-price extensions, including discounts, by multiplying the appropriate values stored in the tables. You can add the extended items, sales taxes, and freight charges; you also can calculate the total invoice amount. These calculated values need not be included (and in a properly designed database never are included) in the database tables.

For Related Information:

▶▶ "Joining Tables To Create Multitable Queries," p. 306.

▶▶ "The Process of Database Design," p. 780.

FROM HERE...

Using Access Database Files and Tables

Access has its own database file structure, similar to that used by client-server DBMs, and uses the .MDB extension. As discussed in the introduction to this chapter, Access differs from traditional PC databases in that all the related tables, indexes, forms, and report definitions are contained in a single file. Even the programming code you write in Access Basic is included in the .MDB file. You don't need to be concerned with the intricacies of the .MDB file structure, because Access handles all the details of file management for you.

All the field data types familiar to xBase and Paradox users are available in Access, as well as some new and useful field data types, such as Currency for monetary transactions. dBASE users will need to learn to use the term *table* for file and *database* to indicate a group of related tables or files, the equivalent of dBASE's CATALOG. Records commonly are called *rows*, and *fields* often are called *columns*. Users with Paradox, Excel, or 1-2-3 experience will find the terminology of Access quite familiar. Paradox users will appreciate dealing with only one .MDB file, instead of the myriad files that make up a multitable Paradox database.

The Access System Database

In addition to database files with the .MDB extension, Access includes a master database file named SYSTEM.MDA. This file contains information about the following:

- Access .MDB sample databases

- Databases you create

- Options you establish by choosing **O**ptions from the **V**iew menu

- Permissions for others to use the database and each of its elements when you share your database files in a network environment

Sharing database files and granting permission for others to use the files is covered in Chapter 21, "Using Access in a Network Environment."

FROM HERE...

For Related Information:

◄◄ "Setting Default Options," p. 101.

Access Library Databases

Another category of Access database files is *Libraries*. Libraries are Access databases, often having an .MDA extension to distinguish them from user databases, that you can attach to Access through an entry in the MSACCESS.INI file in your \WINDOWS directory. When you attach an Access library, all the elements of the library database are available to you in a sample or user database. A *user* database is a database you create. The Access Wizards that you use to create forms, reports, and graphs (WIZARD.MDA)—as well as ANALYZER.MDB—are Access library database files. Analyzer is a library that you can use to create data dictionaries for user databases. A *data dictionary* is a detailed written description of each of the elements of a database. Library databases are an important and unique feature of Access. Microsoft and other third-party firms are expected to provide a wide range of Access libraries to add new features and capabilities to Access.

For Related Information:

▶▶ "Creating a Transaction Form with the FormWizard," p. 377.

▶▶ "Access's Integrated Data Dictionary System," p. 808.

FROM HERE...

Creating a New Database

If you have experience with relational database management systems, you may want to start building your own database as you progress through this book. In this case, you need to create a new database file at this point. If database management systems are new to you, it is better to explore the sample databases supplied with Access as you progress through the chapters of this book, and design your first database using the principles outlined in Chapter 19, "Exploring Relational Database Design and Implementation." Then come back to this point and create your new database file.

To create a new database, follow these steps:

1. Launch Access, if it is not running.

2. When Access is running and the Database window is visible, click its title bar to make the Database window the active window.

   Access

   This action is called giving the Database window the *focus*. When a window has the focus, the background of its title bar is usually blue; when a window does not have the focus, it is inactive and its title bar is usually white. If you have changed from the default Windows color scheme by using the Control Panel's Colors function, these colors will be different.

3. Choose New Database from the File menu.

   The Access application window must be empty, or the Database window must be active, in order for the New Database and other database file options to be present when you select the File menu. The New Database dialog box appears as shown in figure 4.2.

   Access supplies the default file name, DB1.MDB, for new databases. (If you have previously saved a database file as DB1.MDB, Access proposes DB2.MDB as the default.)

4. Enter a file name for the new database in the File Name text box, using conventional DOS file-naming rules (you cannot use spaces or punctuation in the name, other than the period used as the extension separator). You can use any extension you want for an Access database, but only files with the .MDB extension are associated with Access by File Manager.

5. Choose OK to create the new database.

   If a database was open when you created the new database, Access closes any windows associated with the database and the Database window. During the process of creating the database, the following message appears in the status bar:

   `Verifying System Objects`

   Whenever you open a new or existing database, Access checks to see whether all the elements of the database are intact. Access's main window and the Database window for the new database (named NEW.MDB for this example) appear as shown in figure 4.3.

You use the same procedure to add tables to a new database as to an existing database. Adding tables to a database is explained in the section, "Adding a Table to an Existing Database," later in this chapter.

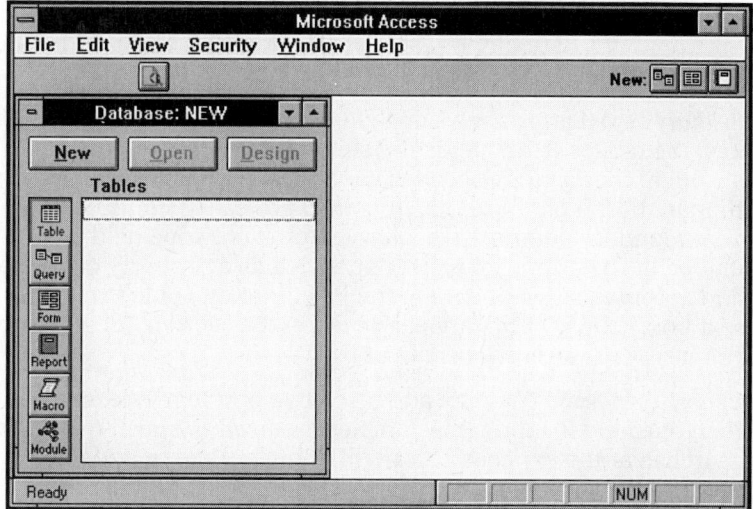

FIG. 4.3

Access's main window and the Database window for a newly created database.

Each new database occupies 64K of disk space when you create it. Most of the 64K is space reserved for adding the information necessary to specify the names and locations of other database elements that are contained in the database file. Because of the way data is stored in Access tables, what appears to be an excessive amount of reserved space quickly is compensated for by Access's more efficient data storage methods.

Understanding the Properties of Tables and Fields

Before you add a table to a new database you create or to one of the sample databases supplied with Access, you need know the terms and conventions used by Access to describe the structure of a table and the fields that contain the data items that comprise the information stored in the table. With Access, you specify properties of tables and fields.

Properties of Access tables apply to the table as a whole. In most cases, entering table properties is optional. You enter properties of tables in text boxes of the Table Properties window, shown in figure 4.4, that you display by clicking the Properties button on the toolbar in Table Design view. The three properties of Access tables follow:

■ *Description:* An optional explanation of the purpose of the table for use with a data dictionary. Data dictionaries are used to document databases and database applications.

■ *Primary key:* If more than one field is to be included in the primary key, the names of the fields are separated by semi-colons, as shown in the Table Properties window of figure 4.4. Primary keys that are based on more than one field are called multiple-field, compound, or composite primary keys. If only one field is included in the primary key, it is specified as a property of the field and automatically appears in the Primary Key Table Properties text box. Primary keys are explained in the section, "Selecting a Primary Key," later in this chapter.

■ *Index1 ... Index5:* You may add up to five optional indexes on more than one field for the table. Indexes are used to speed queries and searches at the expense of a slightly longer time to add new records. Access automatically creates an index on the primary key field(s); you do not need to add an index property for a composite primary key. As with primary keys, indexes on more than one field are called multiple-field, compound, or composite indexes. Indexes on single fields are specified as a field property, not as a table property. You cannot include fields with Yes/No, Memo or OLE Object data types in composite indexes.

Index1 ... Index5 is considered a single property in the list because it is a set of related properties that may range in number of members from 0 to 5.

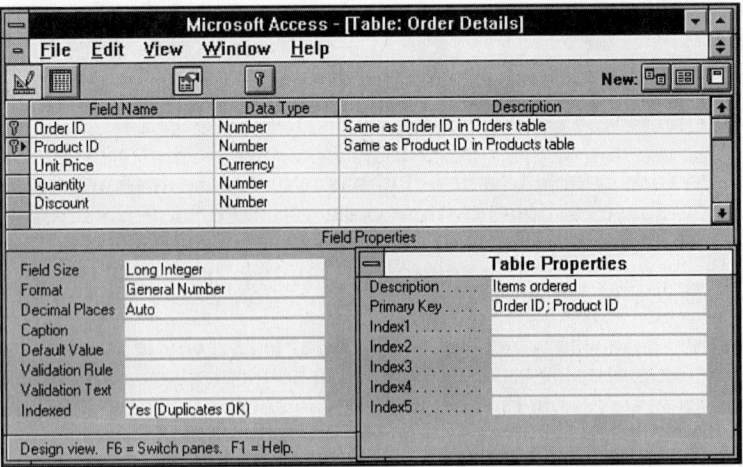

FIG. 4.4

The Table Design window for the Order Details table.

You assign each field of an Access table a set of properties from the following list. The first three field properties are assigned within the *Table Design grid*, the upper pane of the Table Design window shown in figure 4.4. The Primary Key property is assigned by selecting the field and clicking the Primary Key button on the toolbar. The remaining property values are selected from drop-down list or combo boxes, or typing values in text boxes, in the lower Field Properties pane of the Table Design window.

- *Field Name:* You enter the name of the field in the first column of the Table Design grid. Field names may contain up to 64 characters and may include embedded (but not leading) spaces and punctuation—except periods (.), exclamation marks (!), and square brackets ([]). Field names are mandatory, and you cannot assign the same field name to more than one field.

- *Data Type:* You select data types from a drop-down list box in the second column of the Table Design grid. Data types include Text, Number, Currency, Date/Time, Yes/No, Memo, and OLE Object. Choosing a data type is the subject of the next section of this chapter.

- *Description:* You can enter an optional description of the field in the text box in the third column of the Table Design grid. If you add a description, it appears in the status bar at the lower left of Access's window when you select the field for data entry or editing.

- *Primary Key:* To choose a field as the Primary Key field, select the field by clicking the field selection button to the left of the Field Name column, and then click the Primary Key button on the toolbar. (See "Selecting a Primary Key," later in this chapter, for instructions on how to create a composite primary key.)

- *Field Size:* You enter the field size for the Text data type in the Field Size text box. (See "Fixed-Length Text Fields," later in this chapter, to learn how to choose a text field size.) For Numeric data types, you choose the field size by making a selection from a drop-down list box. Field size is not applicable to the Counter, Currency, Memo, or OLE Object data type.

- *Format:* You can choose a standard format in which to display the values in the field from the drop-down combo box's list applicable to the data type you chose. Alternatively, you can enter a custom format in the text box (see "Custom Display Formats," later in this chapter). The Format property does not affect the data values; it affects only how these values are displayed.

■ *Decimal Places:* You can choose Auto or a specific number of decimal places from the drop-down combo box's list, or you can enter a number in the text box. The Decimal Places property applies only to Number and Currency fields. Like the Format property, the Decimal Places property affects only the display, not the data values, of the field.

■ *Caption:* If you want a name (other than the field name) to appear in the field name header button in Table Datasheet view, you can enter an alias for the field name in the Caption list box. The restrictions on punctuation symbols do not apply to the Caption property. (You can use periods, exclamation points, and square brackets.)

■ *Default Value:* You can specify a value that is automatically entered in the field when a new record is added to the table by entering the value in the Default Value text box. The current date is a common default value for a Date/Time field. (See "Setting Default Values of Fields," later in this chapter, for more information.) Default values are not applicable to fields with Counter or OLE Object field data types.

■ *Validation Rule:* Validation rules are used to test the value entered in a field against criteria you supply in the form of an Access expression. Expressions are explained in Chapter 7, "Understanding Operators and Expressions in Access." The Validation Rule property is not available for fields with Counter, Memo, or OLE Object field data types.

■ *Validation Text:* You enter the text that is to appear in the status bar if the value entered does not meet the Validation Rule criteria.

■ *Indexed:* You can choose between an index that allows duplicate values or one that requires each value of the field to be unique from the drop-down list box. You remove an existing index (except from a field that is a single Primary Key field) by choosing No. The Indexed property is not available for Memo or OLE Object fields. (See "Adding Indexes to Tables," later in this chapter, for more information on indexes.)

Adding your first table, Personnel Actions, to the Northwind Traders database, requires that you choose appropriate data types, sizes, and formats for the fields of your table.

For Related Information:

▶▶ "Working with Data Dictionaries," p. 806.

▶▶ "Using Access Indexes," p. 815.

FROM HERE...

Choosing Field Data Types, Sizes, and Formats

You must assign to each field of a table a field data type, unless you want to use the Text data type that Access assigns as the default. One of the principals of relational database design is that all the data in a single field consist of one type of data. Access provides a much wider variety of data types and formats from which to choose than most PC database managers. Besides the data type, you can set other field properties that determine the format, size, and other characteristics of the data that affect its appearance and the accuracy with which numerical values are stored. Table 4.1 lists the field data types you can choose for data contained in Access tables.

Table 4.1. Field Data Types Available in Access		
Information	**Data Type**	**Description of Data Type**
Characters	Text	Text fields are most common, so Access assigns Text as the default data type. A Text field can contain up to 255 characters, and you can designate a maximum length less than or equal to 255. Access assigns a default length of 50 characters. A fixed-length Text data type is the equivalent of xBase's Character field and Paradox's Alphanumeric field.

continues

Table 4.1. Continued

Information	Data Type	Description of Data Type
	Memo	Memo fields can contain up to 32,000 characters and are used for descriptive comments. Memo fields are similar to those of xBase, except that the data in the Memo field is included in the table, rather than in a separate file. The contents of Memo fields are displayed in Datasheet view. A Memo field cannot be a key field, and you cannot index a Memo field.
Numeric Values	Number	A variety of numeric data subtypes are available. You choose the appropriate data subtype by selecting one of the Field Size property settings listed in table 4.2. You determine how the number is displayed by setting its Format property to one of the formats listed in table 4.4.
	Counter	A *counter* is a numeric (Long Integer) value that is incremented by one for each new record you add to a table. A Counter field creates the equivalent of xBase's and Paradox's record number. The maximum number of records in a table that uses the Counter field is slightly more than 2 million.
	Yes/No (Logical fields)	Logical (Boolean) fields in Access use numeric (integer) values: -1 for Yes and 0 for No. You use the Format property to display Yes/No fields as Yes or No, True or False, On or Off, or -1 or 0. (True also can be represented by any nonzero number.) Logical fields cannot be key fields, and they cannot be indexed.

Information	Data Type	Description of Data Type
	Currency	Currency is a special fixed format with four decimal places designed to prevent rounding errors that would affect accounting operations where value must match to the penny (similar to the Paradox Currency data type).
Dates and Times	Date/Time	Dates and times are stored in a special fixed format. The date is represented by the whole number portion of the Date/Time value, and the time is represented by its decimal fraction. You control how dates are displayed by selecting one of the Date/Time Format properties listed in table 4.4.
Large Objects	OLE Object (BLOBs, binary large objects)	Includes bit-mapped graphics, vector-type drawings, waveform audio files, and other types of data that can be created by an OLE server application, some of which are listed in table 4.3. You cannot assign an OLE object as a key field, and you cannot include an OLE field in an index.

Regardless of the length that you set for Text fields in Access, they are stored in the database file in variable-length records. All trailing spaces are removed. This technique conserves the space that is wasted in xBase files, for example, where text is stored in fixed-length character fields. Fixed-length character fields in conventional PC DBMs waste the bytes used to pad short text entries in long fields.

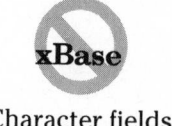

Character fields

Choosing Field Sizes for Numeric and Text Data

The Field Size property of a field makes the final determination of the data type that is used by Number fields or the number of characters for fixed-length text fields. Field Size properties are called *subtypes* to distinguish them from the *data types* listed in table 4.2. For numbers, you choose a Field Size property from list provided by the Field Size drop-down list box in the lower Field Properties pane of the Table Design window, as shown in figure 4.5.

Subtypes for Numeric Data

The Number data type of table 4.2 isn't a fully specified data type. You must choose one of the subtypes from those listed in table 4.3 for the Field Size property to properly define the numeric data type. To choose a data subtype for a Number field, follow these steps:

1. Choose the Data Type cell of the Number field for which you want to make the subtype selection.

2. Click the Field Size text box in the Field Properties window. You also can press F6 to switch windows, and then use the arrow keys to position the caret within the Field Size text box.

3. Click the drop-down arrow to open the list box of choices shown in figure 4.5. You can press the F4 key to open the list box, if you prefer.

4. Choose the data subtype. Data subtypes are described in table 4.3. Making a selection closes the list box.

After you select a Field Size property, you choose a format property from those listed in table 4.4 to determine how the data is displayed. The Currency data type is included in table 4.4, because it also can be considered a subtype of the Numeric data type.

Regardless of how you format your data for display, the number of decimal digits, range, and storage requirement remains that chosen by Field Size. With the exception of the Byte data type, these data types are available in most dialects of Basic, including Visual Basic 1.0. All the data types listed in table 4.2 are included in Access Basic and are reserved words of the language. You cannot use a reserved data type word for any purpose in Access Basic functions and procedures other than to specify a data type.

Table 4.2. Subtypes of the Number Data Type Determined by the Field Size Property

Field Size	Decimals	Range of Values	Bytes	xBase	Paradox
Double	15 places	-1.797 * 10^308 to +1.797 * 10^308	8	Numeric	Numeric
Single	7 places	-3.4 * 10^38 to +3.4 * 10^38	4	N/A	N/A
Long Integer	None	-2,147,483,648 to +2,147,483,647	4	N/A	N/A
Integer	None	-32,768 to 32,767	2	N/A	Short Number
Byte	None	0 to 255	1	N/A	N/A
Currency (a data type, not a subtype)	4 places	-922337203685477. 5808 to +922337203685477. 5808	4	N/A	N/A

The xBase and Paradox columns of table 4.2 indicate the Access data types that correspond to data types in common use with these two types of DOS DBMs.

Both xBase DBMs and Paradox store numbers with 15 significant-digit precision. Neither xBase nor Paradox, however, offers the full range of values of numbers having Access's Double Field Size property. All references to Paradox in this book apply to Version 3.5. Paradox 4.0 had just been released and Paradox for Windows was in the beta test stage when this book was written, and Version 1.0 of Access is compatible only with Paradox 3.5 (and earlier) tables.

As a rule, you choose the Field Size property that results in the smallest number of bytes that will encompass the range of values you expect and that will express the value in sufficient precision for your needs. Mathematical operations with Integer and Long Integer proceed much more quickly than those with Single and Double data types (called *floating-point* numbers) or the Currency and Date/Time data types (*fixed-point* numbers).

xBase

Numeric data type

PDOX

Numeric and Short Number data types

Fixed-Length Text Fields

xBase

Character fields

PDOX

Alphanumeric
fields

You can create a fixed-length Text field by making entries the Field Size property. Access creates a 50-character Text field by default. Enter the number, from 1 to 255, in the Field Size cell corresponding to the fixed length you want, as shown in figure 4.6. Entries longer than the field size selected are truncated, meaning that the far right characters beyond the limit you set are lost. You therefore should choose a field length that will accommodate the maximum number of characters you expect to enter in the field. Fixed-length Text fields behave identically to the Character and Alphanumeric field data types of xBase and Paradox applications.

If you delete the value of the Field Size property, a variable-length Text field is created. The advantages of fixed-length Text fields over their variable-length counterparts in Access will become evident when you reach the section of this chapter on custom formatting fields.

FIG. 4.6

Assigning a fixed
length to a Text
field in the Field
Size cell.

Field Properties	
Field Size	15
Format	
Caption	
Default Value	
Validation Rule	
Validation Text	
Indexed	No

The data type determines the kind of values that users can store in the field. Press F1 for help on data types.

Design view. F6 = Switch panes. F1 = Help.   NUM

Subtypes for the OLE Object Data Type

Fields that have data types other than characters and numbers must use the OLE (Object Linking and Embedding) Object data type. Object Linking and Embedding is described in Chapter 12, "Introducing OLE: A Quick Start," and the OLE field data type is explained in Chapter 13, "Using the OLE Field Data Type for Graphics." Because many subtypes of OLE data exist, this data type enables you to violate the rule of database design that says all data in a field must be of a single data type. Typical OLE Object subtypes are listed in table 4.3. To avoid breaking the rule, separate OLE Object fields should be created for different OLE data subtypes.

Table 4.3. Subtypes of the OLE Object Data Type and OLE Servers That Create Them

OLE SubType	File Format	Created by OLE Servers
Bit-mapped graphics	.BMP, .DIB, .TIF	Windows 3.1 Paintbrush, Micrografx Picture Publisher 3.1
Vector-based drawings	.WMF	Microsoft Draw, Windows DRAW! with OLE, CorelDRAW!, PowerPoint
Formatted text	.RTF	Windows 3.1 Write, Word for Windows 2.0, Lotus Ami Pro
Unformatted Text	.TXT	Object Packager (with Windows Notepad as the application)—Memo fields are a better choice
Spreadsheet	.XLS, .DIF	Microsoft Excel 3.0 and later
Waveform Audio	.WAV	Sound Recorder, Media Vision Pocket recorder
MIDI Music Files	.MID	Media Player 2, a Microsoft OLE server applet that can be used for MIDI files, was in the beta testing stage when this book was written

In the case of OLE Object fields, the data subtype is determined by the OLE server used to create the data, rather than by an entry in a text box or a selection from a list box. Windows 3.1's Object Packager OLE server enables you to embed files created by applications that aren't OLE servers. You can, for example, embed .TXT files and .MID files (for which no OLE servers were known to be commercially available at the time this book was written) with Object Packager.

Selecting a Display Format

You establish the Format property for the data types you choose so that Access will display them appropriately for your application. You choose a format by selecting the field, and then clicking the Format text box in the Field Properties window. Figure 4.7 shows the choices Access offers for formatting the Integer data type. You format number, Date/Time, and Yes/No data types by selecting a standard format or creating your own custom format. The two methods are described in sections that follow.

FIG. 4.7

Assigning a standard format to an Integer field from the Format list box.

Standard Formats for Number, Date/Time, and Yes/No Data Types

Access provides 17 standard formats that are applicable to the numeric values in fields of the Number, Date/Time, and Yes/No data types. The standard formats shown in table 4.4 probably will meet most of your needs.

Table 4.4. Standard Display Formats for Access Number, Date/Time and Yes/No Data Types

Data Type	Format	Appearance
Number	General Number	1234.5
	Currency	$1,234.50
	Fixed	12345
	Standard	1,234.50
	Percent	0.1234 = 12.34%
	Scientific	1.23E+03
Date/Time	General Date	10/1/92 4:00:00 PM
	Long Date	Thursday, October 1, 1992
	Medium Date	10-Oct-92
	Short Date	10/1/92
	Long Time	4:00:00 PM
	Medium Time	04:00 PM
	Short Time	16:00

Data Type	Format	Appearance
Yes/No	Yes/No	Yes or No
	True/False	True or False
	On/Off	On or Off
	None	-1 or 0

The Short Date format is similar to the Date data type in xBase and Paradox, except that leading zeros for months and days having a value less than 10 aren't displayed. The 4 date formats are included in the 11 date formats offered by Paradox; the other 7 Paradox formats can be created by using custom formats described in the next section. The Short Time format is equivalent to that which you would obtain from an xBase SUBSTR(TIME(),5) expression. A Double data type with Currency format appears identical to Paradox's Currency data type.

Date data type and TIME()

The Null Value in Access Tables

Fields in Access tables can have a special value, Null, which is a new term for most users of PC-based database management systems. The Null value indicates that the field contains no data at all. Null isn't the same as a numeric value of zero, nor is it equivalent to blank text that consists of one or more spaces. Null is similar, but not equivalent, to an empty string (a string of zero length, often called a *null string*). For now, the best synonym for *Null* is *no entry*.

Currency data type and date formats

The Null value is useful for determining whether an entry has been made in a field, especially numeric fields in which zero values are valid. Until the advent of Access, the capability to use Null values in database managers running on PCs was limited to fields in the tables of client-server database systems, such as Microsoft SQL Server. The Null value is used in the sections "Custom Display Formats" and "Setting Default Values of Fields," later in this chapter.

Custom Display Formats

To duplicate precisely the format of xBase's Date data type or one of the seven date formats offered by Paradox that is not a standard format in Access, you must create a custom format. You create a custom format by creating an image of the format using combinations of the special set of characters, called *placeholders*, listed in table 4.5. An example of a custom format for date and time is shown in figure 4.8.

FIG. 4.8

Creating a
custom date and
time format from
entries in the
Format text box.

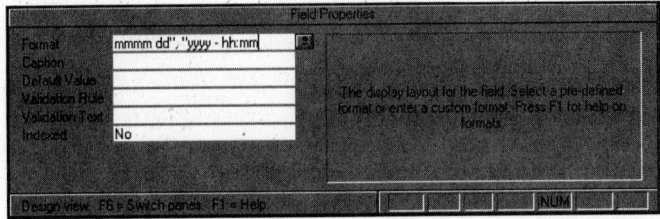

Except as noted, the example numeric value used in table 4.5 is 1234.5.
Bold type is used to distinguish the placeholders you type from the
surrounding text. The resulting display is shown in monospace type.

Table 4.5. Placeholders for Creating Custom Display Formats

Placeholder	Function
Null string	Displays the number with no formatting. Choose the Null string by deleting the value in the Format Text field of the Field Properties window.
0	Displays a digit, if one exists in the position, or a zero if not. You can use the 0 placeholder to display leading zeroes for whole numbers and trailing zeroes in decimal fractions. **00000.000** displays 01234.500.
#	Displays a digit, if one exists in the position; otherwise, displays zeroes. The # placeholder is equivalent to 0, except that leading and trailing zeroes aren't displayed. **#####.###** displays 1234.5.
$	Displays a dollar sign in the position. **$###,###.00** displays $1,234.50.
.	Displays a decimal point at the indicated position in a string of 0 and # placeholders. **##.##** displays 1234.5.
%	Multiplies the value by 100 and adds a percent sign in the position shown with 0 and # placeholders. **#0.00%** displays 0.12345 as 12.35% (12.345 is rounded to 12.35).
, (comma)	Adds commas as thousands separators in strings of 0 and # placeholders. **###,###,###.00** displays 1,234.50.
E- e-	Displays values in scientific format with sign of exponent for negative values only. **#.###E-00** displays 1.2345E03. **0.12345** displays 1.2345E-01.

Placeholder	Function
E+ e+	Displays values in scientific format with sign of exponent for positive and negative values. **#.###E-00** displays 1.2345E+03.
/	Separates the day, month, and year to format date values. **mm/dd/yy** displays 06/06/92. You can substitute hyphens to display 06-06-92.
m	Months placeholder for dates. **m** displays 1, **mm** displays 01, **mmm** displays Jan, and **mmmm** displays January.
d	Days placeholder for dates. **d** displays 1, **dd** displays 01, **ddd** displays Mon, and **dddd** displays Monday.
y	Years placeholder for dates. **yy** displays 92, and **yyyy** displays 1992.
: (colon)	Separates hours, minutes, and seconds in format time values. **hh:mm:ss** displays 02:02:02.
h	Hours placeholder for time. **h** displays 2, and **hh** displays 02. If an AM/PM placeholder is used, **h** or **hh** displays 4 PM for 1600 hours.
m	Minutes placeholder for time. **m** displays 1, and **mm** displays 01. **hhmm "hours"** displays 1600 hours. Access determines whether m is used to format a date or time by its context.
s	Seconds placeholder for time. **s** displays 1, and **ss** displays 01.
AM/PM	Displays time in 12-hour time with AM or PM appended. **h:mm AM/PM** displays 4:00 PM. Alternate formats include am/pm, A/P, and a/p.
@	Indicates that a character is required in the position in a Text or Memo field. You can use @ to format telephone numbers in a Text field, as in @@@-@@@-@@@@ or (@@@) @@@-@@@@.
&	Indicates that a character is optional in the position in a Text or Memo field.
>	Changes all text characters in the field to uppercase.
<	Changes all text characters in the field to lowercase.
*	Displays the character following the asterisk as a fill character for empty spaces in a field. **"ABCD"*x** in an eight-character field appears as ABCDxxxx.

The Format drop-down combo box is one of the few examples in Access where you can choose from a list of options or type your own entry. Format is a true drop-down combo box; boxes in which you can only make a choice from a list are called *drop-down list boxes*. You don't need to enter the quotation marks shown in figure 4.8 surrounding the comma and space in the Format text box (**mmmm dd", "yyyy - hh:mm**), because Access does this for you. The comma is a nonstandard formatting symbol for dates (but it is standard for number fields). Nonstandard formatting characters automatically are enclosed in double quotation marks when you create them in the Field Properties window.

When you change the format or any other property of a field, and then change to Datasheet view in Run mode to view the result of your work, you are asked to confirm the change with the dialog box shown in figure 4.9.

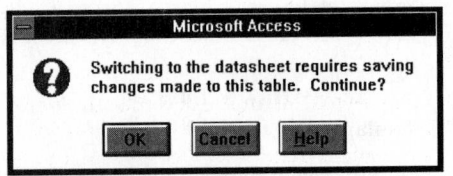

If you apply the custom format string **mmmm dd", "yyyy - hh:mm** (shown in fig. 4.8) to the Birth Date field of the Employees table, the Birth Date field entries appear as shown in figure 4.10. For example, Nancy Davolio's birth date appears as December 08, 1948 - 00:00. The original format of the Birth Date field was Medium Date, the format also used with the Hire Date field.

You need to expand the width of the Birth Date field to accommodate the additional characters in the Long Date format. You increase the width of the field by dragging the right vertical bar of the field name header to the right to display the entire field. Date fields are right-justified in Access.

PICTURE
expression

The time of birth is displayed as 00:00, because the decimal fraction that determines time is 0 for all entries in the Birth Date field.

Custom formats in Access are more flexible than the PICTURE expressions of xBase and Paradox, because you can assign one format if the value of numeric field data is positive, a second if it is negative, a third if it is zero, and a fourth if it is Null. You separate the formats for the four conditions with semicolons.

PICTURE
expression

Last Name	First Name	Title	Birth Date	Hire Date	Ad
Davolio	Nancy	Sales Representative	December 08, 1948 - 00:00	01-Apr-87	507 - 20th A
Fuller	Andrew	Vice President, Sales	February 19, 1942 - 00:00	15-Jul-87	908 W. Cap
Leverling	Janice	Sales Representative	August 30, 1963 - 00:00	01-Mar-88	722 Moss B
Peacock	Phyllis	Sales Representative	September 19, 1937 - 00:00	01-Apr-88	4110 Old R
Buchanan	B. L.	Sales Manager	March 04, 1955 - 00:00	15-Sep-89	14 Garrett H
Suyama	Michael	Sales Representative	July 02, 1963 - 00:00	15-Sep-89	Coventry H
King	Jonathan	Sales Representative	May 29, 1960 - 00:00	01-Dec-89	Edgeham H
Callahan	Linda	Inside Sales Coordinator	January 09, 1958 - 00:00	01-Feb-90	4726 - 11th
Dodsworth	Annabella	Sales Representative	January 27, 1966 - 00:00	15-Oct-91	7 Houndsto

Following is an example that formats negative numbers enclosed in
parentheses and replaces a Null entry with text:

```
$###,###,##0.00;$(###,###,##0.00);0.00;"No Entry Here"
```

The entries 1234567.89, -1234567.89, 0, and a Null default value would
appear as follows:

```
$1,234,567.89
$(1,234,567.89)
0.00
No Entry Here
```

A feature of Paradox and xBase that is missing in Access 1.0 is the capability to restrict entries in Text fields to numbers. The familiar PICT
"###-###-###" expression in xBase used to format telephone numbers
cannot be duplicated in Access, because Access's # symbol is restricted to numeric fields.

Using the Northwind Traders Sample Database

One of the fundamental problems with books about database management applications is the usual method of demonstrating how to create
a "typical" database. You are asked to type fictitious names, addresses,
and telephone numbers into a Customers table. Next, you must create
additional tables that relate these fictitious customers to their purchases of various widgets in assorted sizes and quantities. This process
is unrewarding for readers and authors, and few readers ever complete
the exercises.

Access is a new product, and it includes a comprehensive and interesting sample database; therefore, this book takes a different tack. Instead
of creating a new database at this point, you create a new table as an

addition to the Northwind Traders database. Adding a new table minimizes the amount of typing required and requires just a few entries in order to make it functional. The new Personnel Actions table demonstrates many of the elements of relational database design.

Adding a Table to an Existing Database

The Northwind Traders database includes an Employees table that provides most of the information about the employees of the firm that is typical of personnel tables. This chapter explains how to add a table called *Personnel Actions* to the database. The Personnel Actions table is a record of hire date, salary, commission rate, bonuses, performance reviews, and other compensation-related events for employees. Because Personnel Actions is based on information in the Employees table, the first step of this process is to review the structure of the Employees table to see how you can use it with your new table. The structure of tables is displayed in Design mode.

To open the Employees table in Design mode, follow these steps:

1. Close any document windows that you have open.

2. Click Employees in the Database window, and then click the Design button. You also can open the Employees table by double-clicking the Database window entry, and then clicking the Design button on the Tables toolbar.

3. The Design grid for the Employees table appears. Maximize the document window to the size of your Access window by clicking the document's Maximize button.

4. Close the Properties window, if it appears, by double-clicking its Window Control button. Alternatively, you can choose Table Properties from the View menu.

   The Table Properties command toggles the visibility of the Table Properties window. A check mark next to Table Properties indicates that the window is always visible in Table Design mode. At this point, your display resembles that shown in figure 4.11.

The table design window displays the field names and the field data types and provides a third column for an optional description of each field in the table. This display is called a *grid* rather than a *datasheet*, because the display doesn't contain data from a table. A scroll bar is provided, regardless of whether more fields exist in the table than can be displayed in the window. The Field Properties pane enables you to set additional properties of individual fields and provides a brief description of the purpose of each column of the grid and of the Field Properties entries as you choose them. You cannot resize this pane.

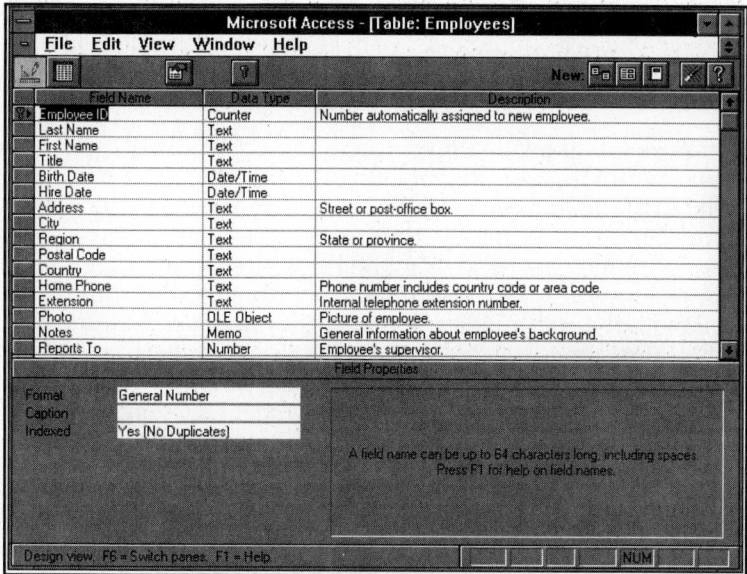

FIG. 4.11

The Employees
table of the
Northwind
Traders database
in Design mode.

One field is conspicuous by its absence: the Social Security number
that is used by most firms to identify their personnel in databases. The
Employee ID field is an adequate substitute for the Social Security number for an example table, because a unique sequential number is assigned to each employee. Click the Datasheet View button to display
the data in the Employee ID field, and then return to Design mode by
clicking the Design button.

Designing the Personnel Actions Table

You should place employee remuneration data in a table of its own,
rather than adding fields for entries (such as salary, commission rate,
and bonuses) to the Employees table for the following reasons:

■ Multiple personnel actions are taken for individual employees
over time. If these actions were to be added to records in the Employees table, you would be forced to create many additional
fields to hold an arbitrary number of personnel actions. If, for
example, quarterly performance reviews were entered, you would
be forced to add a new field for every quarter to hold the review
information. In this situation, flat-file managers encounter difficulties.

- Personnel actions can be categorized by type so that any action taken can use a common set of field names and field data types. This feature makes the design of the Personnel Actions table simple.

- Employees can be identified uniquely by their Employee ID numbers. Therefore, records for entries of personnel actions can be related to the Employees table by an Employee ID field. This feature eliminates the necessity of adding employee names and other information to the records in the Personnel Action table. You link the Employees table to the Personnel table by the Employee ID field, and the two tables are joined; they act as if they are a single table. Minimizing information duplication to only what is required in order to link the tables is your reward for choosing a relational, rather than a flat-file, database management system.

- Personnel actions usually are considered confidential information and are made accessible only to a limited number of people. Although Access enables you to grant permission for others to view specific fields, restricting permission to view an entire table is simpler.

The next step is to design the Personnel Actions table. Chapter 19, "Exploring Relational Database Design and Implementation," discusses the theory of database design and the tables that make up databases. Because the Personnel Actions table has an easily discernible relationship to the Employees table, the theoretical background isn't necessary for this example.

Determining What Information Should Be Included

Designing a table requires that you identify the type of information the table should contain. Information associated with typical personnel actions might consist of the following items:

- *Important dates:* The date of hire and termination, if applicable, are important dates, but so are the dates on which salaries are adjusted, commission rates are changed, and bonuses are granted. Each action should be accompanied by the date on which it was scheduled to occur and the date on which it actually occurred.

■ *Types of actions:* Less typing is required if personnel actions are identified by a code character, rather than a full-text description of the action. This feature saves valuable disk space, too. First-letter abbreviations used as codes, such as *H* for *hired*, *T* for *terminated*, *Q* for *quarterly review*, and so on, are easy to remember.

■ *Initiation and approval of actions:* As a rule, the employee's supervisor initiates a personnel action, and the supervisor's manager approves it. The Employee ID number for a supervisor and manager must be included, therefore.

■ *Amounts involved:* Salaries are assumed to be based on monthly payment, bonuses are paid quarterly with quarterly performance reviews, and commissions are paid on a percentage of sales made by the employee.

■ *Performance rating:* Rating employee performance by a numerical value is a universal, but somewhat arbitrary, practice. Scales of 1 to 9 are common, with exceptional performance ranked as 9 and candidacy for termination as 1.

■ *Summaries and comments:* Provision should be made for a summary of performance, explanation of exceptionally high or low ratings, and reasons for adjusting salaries or bonuses.

If you are involved in personnel management, you probably can think of additional information that might be included in the table, such as accruable sick leave and vacation hours per pay period. The Personnel Actions table is just an example; it isn't meant to add full-scale human resources development capabilities to the database. The limited amount of data described serves to demonstrate several uses of the new table in this and succeeding chapters.

Assigning Information to Fields

After you determine the types of information, called *data entities* or *entities*, to be included in the table, you must assign each data entity to a field of the table. This process involves choosing a field name that must be unique within the table. Table 4.6 lists the candidate fields for the Personnel Actions table. *Candidate fields* are written descriptions of the fields that are proposed for the table. Data types have been assigned from those listed in table 4.7 in the following section.

Table 4.6. Candidate Fields for the Personnel Actions Table

Field Name	Data Type	Function of Field
PA ID	Number	Identifies the employee to whom the action applies. PA ID numbers are assigned based on the Employee ID field of the Employee table (to which the Personnel Table is linked).
PA Type	Text	Code for the type of action taken. H=hired, C=commission rate adjustment, Q=quarterly review, Y=yearly review, S=salary adjustment, B=bonus adjustment, and T=terminated.
PA Initiated By	Number	Employee ID number of the supervisor who initiates or is responsible for recommending the action.
PA Scheduled Date	Date/Time	The date on which the action is scheduled to occur.
PA Approved By	Number	Employee ID number of the manager who approves the action proposed by the supervisor.
PA Effective Date	Date/Time	The date on which the action occurred. The effective date remains blank if the action has not occurred.
PA Rating	Number	Performance on a scale of 1 to 9, with higher numbers indicating better performance. A blank indicates no rating; 0 is reserved for terminated employees.
PA Amount	Currency	Salary per month, bonus per quarter, commission rate as a percent of the amount of the order, expressed as a decimal fraction.
PA Comments	Memo	Abstracts of performance reviews and comments on actions proposed or taken. No limit exists for the length of the comments; the supervisor and manager can contribute to the comments.

Use distinctive names for each field. In this example, each field name is preceded by the abbreviation PA to identify the field with the Personnel Actions table. When designing xBase databases, for example, a common practice is to use the same name for fields that contain identical data but are located in different tables. Because of the way Access uses these names in expressions for validating data entry and calculating field values (discussed later in this chapter and in Chapter 7), a better practice is to assign related, but distinctive, names to such fields.

Creating the Personnel Actions Table

Now you can put to work what you have learned about field names, data types, and formats by adding the Personnel Actions table to the Northwind Traders database. The field names, taken from table 4.6, and the set of properties you assign to the fields are shown in table 4.7. The text in the Caption property column substitutes for the Field Name property that otherwise would be displayed in the field header buttons.

Table 4.7. Field Properties for the Personnel Actions Table

Field Name	Caption	Data Type	Field Size	Format
PA ID	ID	Number	Long Integer	General Number
PA Type	Type	Text	1	@> (all caps)
PA Initiated By	Initiated By	Number	Integer	General Number
PA Scheduled Date	Scheduled	Date/Time	N/A	Short Date
PA Approved By	Approved By	Number	Integer	General Number
PA Effective Date	Effective	Date/Time	N/A	Short Date
PA Rating	Rating	Number	Integer	General Number
PA Amount	Amount	Currency	N/A	##,##0.00#
PA Comments	Comments	Memo	N/A	None

The Field Size property of the PA ID field must be set to the Long Integer data type, although you might not expect Northwind Traders to have more than the 32,767 employees that would be allowed by an integer. You need to use the Long Integer data type because the Counter field data type of the Employee ID field of the Employees table is a Long Integer. The reason that the data type of PA ID must match that of the Employee ID number field of the Employees table is explained in the "Maintaining Referential Integrity" section later in this chapter.

To add the new Personnel Actions table to the Northwind Traders database, complete the following steps:

1. Close the Employees table, if it is open, by double-clicking the Document Control button.

2. Click the Table button of the Database window, if it isn't selected, and then click the New button. Access enters Design mode automatically and opens a blank grid in which you enter field names, data types, and optional comments. The first cell in the grid is selected automatically by Access.

3. Enter **PA ID** as the first field name. Press Enter to accept the field name (see fig. 4.12). The caret moves to the Data Type column; Access adds the default field type, Text.

4. Press F4 to open the Data Type list box. The function keys, rather than the mouse, are used here because your entries are from the keyboard.

5. Use the arrow keys to choose the Number data type and press Enter to accept your selection.

6. Press F6 to move to the Field Size text box in the Field Properties window. Access has entered Double as the default Field Size property. To learn more about the Field Size property, press F1 for help.

7. Press F4 to open the Field Size list box. Choose Long Integer and press Enter (see fig. 4.13).

8. Press the down arrow to choose the Format text box. You can press F1 for context-sensitive help on the Format property.

9. Press F4 to open the Format list box, choose General Number from the list, and press Enter (see fig. 4.14).

10. Press the down-arrow key twice to bypass Decimal Places and select the Caption text box. Integers cannot have decimal fractions, so Decimal Places can remain set to Auto.

11. Enter **ID** as the caption and press Enter. ID is used as the Caption property to reduce the column width necessary to display the PA ID number.

12. Press F6 to return to the Table Design grid. The caret is located in the Comments column. The remaining properties for each field will be completed after the basic properties shown in table 4.7 have been completed.

13. Comments are used to create prompts that appear in the status bar when you are adding or editing records in Run mode's Datasheet view. Although comments are optional, a good database design practice is to enter the purpose of the field if its use isn't obvious from its Field Name or Caption property. You can skip the Caption property entries now, and then refer to table 4.7 and enter the captions as a group when you have completed the basic steps described here.

14. Press the down-arrow key to choose the next row of the grid.

15. Repeat steps 3 through 13, entering the values shown in table 4.7 for each of the eight remaining fields of the Personnel Action table. N/A means that the entry in table 4.7 isn't applicable to the data type for the field.

Your Table Design grid now appears as shown in figure 4.15. You can double-check your properties entries by selecting each field name with the arrow keys and reading the values shown in the properties text boxes of the Field Properties window.

FIG. 4.15

The initial design of the Personnel Actions table.

Field Name	Data Type	Description
PA ID	Number	Linked to Employee ID of Employees table
PA Type	Text	H = hired, S = salary adjustment, Q = quarterly review, Y =
PA Initiated By	Number	Employee number of supervisor
PA Scheduled Date	Date/Time	Date on which action is scheduled to occur
PA Approved By	Number	Employee number of approving manager
PA Effective Date	Date/Time	Date action is to be effective (requires approval)
PA Rating	Number	Employee performance rating, 0 to 9, 0 for terminated empl
PA Amount	Currency	Amount of increase (or decrease) in salary, bonus or comm
PA Comments	Memo	Comments by supervisor or manager

 Click the Datasheet toolbar button to return to Datasheet view in Run mode to view the results of your work. A Save As dialog box appears, with the default table name, Table1, requesting that you give your table a name. Type **Personnel Actions**, as shown in figure 4.16, and press Enter or choose OK.

FIG. 4.16

The dialog box for naming the Personnel Actions table.

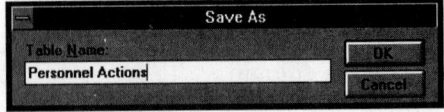

Save As

Table Name:
Personnel Actions

OK
Cancel

You haven't yet assigned Personnel Actions a primary key field because key fields and indexes are subjects of sections that follow in this chapter. The dialog box shown in figure 4.17 notifies you that no primary key has yet been defined. Click No, because the primary key will be assigned later.

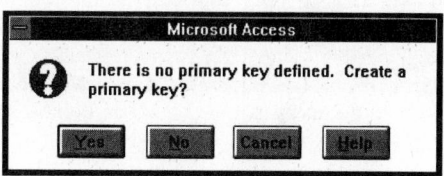

The Datasheet view of your table appears, with its first default record. To view all the fields of your new table, narrow the field name header buttons by dragging to the left the right vertical bar that separates each of the headers. When you have finished adjusting the display widths of your fields, your Datasheet view of the Personnel Actions table appears as in figure 4.18.

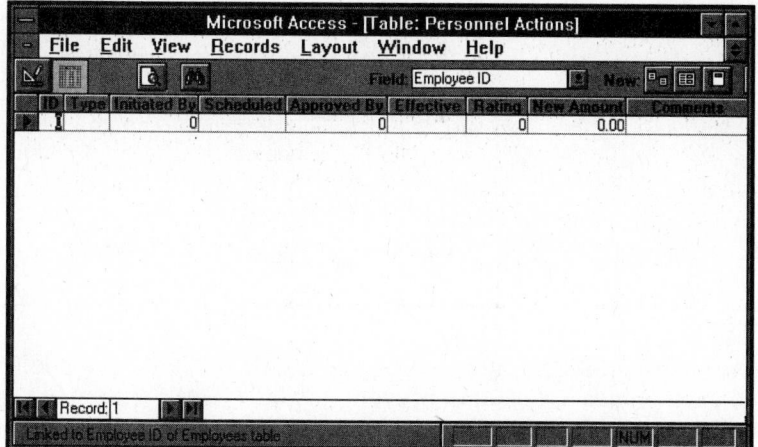

Setting Default Values of Fields

Access has assigned your fields the default values that are usually appropriate for the addition of new records to a table. Access's default value for Number, Currency, and Yes/No fields is always 0, which is equal to No in the case of Yes/No fields. Text, Memo, and Date fields are empty by default. You can save data entry time by establishing your own default values for fields. The default values for the fields of the Personnel Actions tables are listed in table 4.8.

Table 4.8. Default Field Values for the Personnel Actions Table

Field Name	Default Value	Comments
PA ID	No entry	0 is not a valid Employee ID number.
PA Type	Q	Quarterly performance reviews are the most common personnel action.
PA Initiated By	No entry	0 is not valid.
PA Scheduled Date	=Date( )	The expression to enter today's (DOS) date.
PA Approved By	No entry	0 is not valid.
PA Effective Date	=Date( )	Today's (DOS) date.
PA Rating	No entry	In many cases, a rating will not be applicable. A zero rating is reserved for terminated employees.
PA Amount	No entry	If a salary, bonus, or commission has no change, no entry should appear. 0 would indicate no salary, for example.
PA Comments	No change	For now, Access's default is adequate.

No entry in the Default Value text box creates a Null default value. The Null default values are used to prevent invalid values (0 in the five No Entry fields of table 4.8) from being used as defaults. Null values can be used for testing whether a value has been entered into a field to ensure that required data has been entered. (This subject is discussed in the following section.) The =Date() default is an *expression* that returns the DOS date. Expressions are used to enter values in fields, make calculations, and perform other useful duties, such as validating data entries. Expressions are discussed briefly in the next section and in greater detail in Chapter 7. Expressions used to establish default values always are preceded by an equal sign.

To assign the new default values from those of table 4.8 to the fields of the Personnel Actions table, complete these steps:

1. Change to Design mode by choosing Table **D**esign from the **V**iew menu. The PA ID field is selected automatically.

2. Press F6 to switch to the Field Properties window, and then move the caret to the Default Value text box. The value in the text box is selected automatically.

3. Deleting the default value, if one appears, assigns a null default value to the field. Press the Delete key.

4. Press F6 to switch back to the Table Design grid. Move to the next field and press F6 again.

5. Create the default values for the eight remaining fields from the entries shown in table 4.8, repeating steps 2 through 4. Enter the letter **Q** for the PA Type field, enter **=Date( )** for the AP Scheduled Date and AP Effective Date fields, and delete the default values for the other fields.

6. When you have completed your default entries, choose Datasheet from the View menu to return to Run mode. A dialog box requesting confirmation of the changes you made appears, as shown in figure 4.19.

7. Press Enter or choose OK.

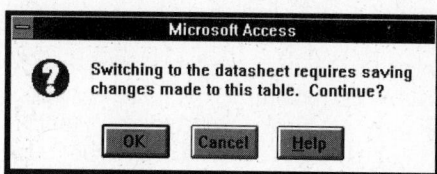

FIG. 4.19

Confirming your changes to the design of a table.

You are warned again that no key field has been selected. Click No, because you will select the key field in a later section. The Design view of the Personnel Actions table now appears as shown in figure 4.20 with the new default entries you have assigned.

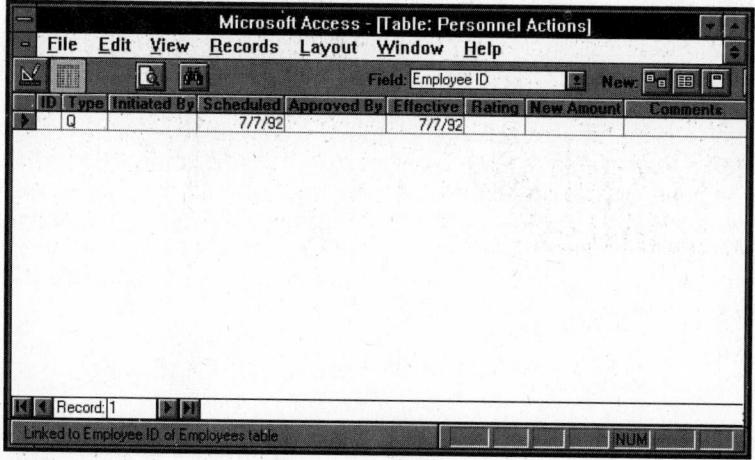

FIG. 4.20

The first record of the Personnel Actions table with the new default entries.

Validating Data Entry

The data entered in tables must be accurate if the database is to be valuable to you or your organization. Even the most experienced data entry operators occasionally enter incorrect information. You can add simple tests for the reasonableness of entries by adding short expressions to the Validation Rule text box. If the data entered fails to conform to your validation rule, a message box informs the operator that a violation has occurred.

Expressions are the core element of computer programming. Access enables you to create expressions without requiring that you be a programmer, although some familiarity with a programming language is helpful. Expressions are statements used to calculate values, using the familiar arithmetic symbols, +, -, * (multiply), and / (divide). These symbols are called *operators*, because they operate on (use) the values that precede and follow them. The values operated on by operators are called *operands*.

You can use operators to compare two values; the < (less than) and > (greater than) symbols are examples of *comparison operators*. AND, OR, IS, NOT, BETWEEN, and LIKE are called *logical operators*. Comparison and logical operators result in (return) only true, false, and unknown (the null value). The & operator combines two text entries (character strings or just strings) into a single string; & is the equivalent of the + used to join (concatenate) character strings in xBase, Excel, and other related applications. To qualify as an expression, at least one operator must be included. You can construct complex expressions by combining the different operators according to rules that apply to each of the operators involved. The collection of these rules is called *operator syntax*.

Data validation rules use expressions that result in one of three values: true, false, or null. Entries in a data cell are accepted if the result of the validation is true and rejected if it is false. If the data is rejected by the validation rule, the text you enter in the Validation Text text box appears in a message box. You have the option of deciding whether the unknown condition, represented by the null value, is treated as the true or false condition. Table 4.9 lists the simple validation rules that will be used for some of the fields of the Personnel Actions table. Chapter 7, "Understanding Operators and Expressions in Access," explains the syntax of Access validation expressions.

Table 4.9. Validation Criteria for the Fields of the Personnel Actions Table

Field Name	Validation Rule	Validation Text
PA ID	>0	Please enter a valid
PA Type	"H" Or "S" Or "Q" Or "Y" Or "B" Or "C"	employee ID number. Only H, S, Q, Y, B, and C codes can be entered.
PA Initiated By	>0	Please enter a valid
PA Scheduled Date	Between Date( ) -3650 And Date( ) +365	supervisor ID number. Scheduled dates cannot be more than 10 years ago or more than one year from now.
PA Approved By	>0 Or Is Null	Please enter a valid manager ID number or leave blank if not approved.
PA Effective Date	>=[PA Scheduled Date] Or Is Null	Effective date must on or after scheduled date or left blank.
PA Rating	Between 0 And 9 Or Is Null	Rating range is 0 for terminated employees, 1 to 9, or blank.
PA Amount	N/A	N/A
PA Comments	N/A	N/A

The validation rules for fields that require employee ID numbers are not, in their present form, capable of ensuring that a valid ID number has been entered. You could enter a number greater than the total number of employees in the firm. The validation rule for the PA ID field should test the Employee ID number field of the Employees table to determine whether the PA ID number is present. You don't need to create this test, because the rules of referential integrity, discussed in a later section, "Maintaining Referential Integrity", perform this validation for you. Validation rules for PA Initiated By and PA Approved By require tests based on entries in the Employees table.

To add the validation rules to the Personnel Actions table, follow these steps:

1. Return to Design mode by clicking the Design View button. The PA ID field is selected.

2. Press F6 to switch to the Field Properties window, and then move to the Validation Rule text box.

3. Enter **>0**. Press Enter to accept the entry and move to the Validation Text text box.

4. Type **Please enter a valid employee ID number.** in the Validation Text text box. The text scrolls to the left when it becomes longer than can be displayed in the text box. To display the beginning of the text, press Home. Press End to position the caret at the last character. Figure 4.21 shows your entries in the Field Properties text boxes.

FIG. 4.21

The Field Properties text boxes showing your entries.

Field Properties		
Field Size	Long Integer	
Format	General Number	
Decimal Places	Auto	The error message that appears when you enter a value prohibited by the validation rule. Press F1 for help on validation text.
Caption	ID	
Default Value		
Validation Rule	>0	
Validation Text	Please enter a valid employee ID	
Indexed	No	

5. Press F6 to switch back to the Table Design grid. Move to the next field and press F6 again.

6. Enter the validation rule and validation text for the six remaining fields listed in table 4.9 that use data entry validation, repeating steps 2 through 5. Square brackets ([]) are used to enclose field names that include punctuation or spaces.

You test your validation rule entries "Adding Records to a Table," later in this chapter.

FROM HERE...

For Related Information:

▸▸ "Understanding the Elements in Expressions," p. 266.

Working with Relations, Key Fields, and Indexes

Your final tasks before adding records to the Personnel Actions table are to determine the relationship between Personnel Actions and an existing table in the database, assign a primary key field, and add indexes to your table.

Establishing Relationships between Tables

Relationships between existing tables and your new table determine the field used as the new table's primary key. The following four possibilities exist for relationships between tables:

- *One-to-one* relationships require that the value of the key field in one and only one record in your new table match a corresponding value of the related field in the existing table. In this case, the key field in your new table must be unique; duplicate values aren't allowed in the key field. A one-to-one relationship is the equivalent of a table that contains all the fields of the existing table and the new table. Tables with one-to-one relationships are uncommon.

- *Many-to-one* relationships allow your new table to have more than one value in the key field corresponding to a single value in the related field of the existing table. In this case, duplicate key field values are allowed. Many-to-one relationships are the most common type you will find; the capability to create many-to-one relationships is the principal reason for choosing a relational system, rather than a flat-file application, to manage your databases.

- *One-to-many* relationships require that your new table's key field be unique, but the values in the key field of the new table can match many entries in the related field of the existing database. In this case, the related field of the existing database has a many-to-one relationship with the key field of the new database.

- *Many-to-many* relationships are a free-for-all in which no unique relationship exists between the key fields in the existing table or the new table, and both of the tables' key fields contain duplicate values.

Keep in mind that the many-to-one and one-to-many relationships apply to how your new table relates to an existing table. When viewed from the existing table's standpoint, the relationships to your new table are one-to-many and many-to-one, respectively. Chapter 19, "Exploring Relational Database Design and Implementation," provides a more comprehensive explanation of the four types of relations.

Many entries in the Personnel Actions table may apply to a single employee whose record appears in the Employees table. A record is created in Personnel Actions when the employee is hired, and a record is created for each quarterly and yearly performance review. Also, any changes made to bonuses or commissions other than as the result of a performance review are entered, and employees may be terminated. Over time, the number of records in the Personnel Actions table is likely to be greater by a factor of 10 or more than the number of records in the Employees table. Thus, the records in the new Personnel table will have a many-to-one relationship with the records in the Employees table. Establishing the relationships between the new and existing tables when you create the new table enables Access to reestablish the relationship automatically when you use the tables in queries, forms, and reports.

Access requires that the two fields participating in the relationship have exactly the same data type. In the case of the Number field data type, the Field Size property of the two fields must be identical. You cannot, for example, create a relationship between a Counter type field (which uses a Long Integer data type) and a field containing Byte, Integer, Single, Double, or Currency data. On the other hand, Access enables you to relate two tables by text fields of different lengths. Such a relationship, if created, can lead to strange behavior when you create queries, which is the subject of Chapters 6 through 8. As a rule, the relationships between text fields should use fields of the same length.

To establish the relationships between two tables using Access's Relationships dialog box, follow these steps:

1. Close the Personnel Actions table by double-clicking the Document Control button. If the Employees table is open, close it. You cannot create or modify relationships between tables that are open. The Relationships option is accessible only when all tables are closed.

2. If the Database window isn't the active window (indicated by a colored title bar), click the Database window or choose Database from the **W**indows menu. Up to nine of the windows for database objects you have opened appear as numbered choices in the **W**indows menu. (The Database window is always number 1.) Press 1 to choose the Database window. The Database window must be active in order to establish relationships.

3. Choose **R**elationships from the **E**dit menu. The Relationships dialog box appears.

4. Open the Primary Table drop-down list box by clicking the down arrow or by pressing the F4 key. Choose the Employees table by clicking Employees or by using the arrow keys to select Employees and press F4 again. Employees is the existing table with which you will create the new relationship. The primary key field name of the primary table, Employee ID, appears below the Primary Key Fields header.

5. You choose the type of relationship with the Type option buttons. Many is the default because it is the most common relationship. Click the Many option button if it is not selected for you.

6. Open the Related Table list box and choose the Personnel Actions table in the same manner as in step 4.

7. Open the Select Matching Fields list box. Because only one field (PA ID) exists in the Personnel Actions table with a data type (Long Integer) matching the data type of the key field of the primary table (Employee ID), PA ID is the only choice offered. The Relationships dialog box now appears as shown in figure 4.22. Choose PA ID by clicking it or by pressing the down-arrow key. Then close the list box.

FIG. 4.22

The Relationships dialog box before selecting the matching field to establish a many-to-one relationship.

8. The Enforce Referential Integrity check box is provided so that Access can perform validation testing for you and accept entries in the PA ID field that correspond to values for Employee IDs in the Employees table. This process is called *enforcing* (or maintaining) referential integrity. Referential integrity is discussed in the following section. Enforced referential integrity is required here, so make sure that the box is checked.

9. After you select the matching field, the Add button is active. Click Add to accept the new relationship.

10. Click Close to return to the Database window.

xBase

SET RELATION TO

The relationship you have created will be used by Access when you create queries and design forms and reports that require data in the Personnel Actions table.

The relationship is equivalent to that which would be created by the following xBase statements:

```
SELECT 2
USE pers_act
SELECT 1
USE employee INDEX emp_idno
SET RELATION TO emp_idno INTO 2
```

The difference between Access and xBase relationships is that the related table in xBase, pers_act, must be indexed on the key expression of the primary table, Employee ID, but Access does not require that the related table be indexed.

FROM HERE...

For Related Information:

▶▶ "Types of Relationships," p. 801.

Maintaining Referential Integrity

The ability to automatically enforce referential integrity is an important feature of Access; few other PC relational database managers include this feature. Referential integrity prevents the creation of "orphan records" that have no connection to a primary table. An example of an orphan record is a record for a personnel action for PA ID 10 when you have records in the Employees file only for employees numbered 1 through 9. You would never know who employee 10 might be until you entered the next employee hired. Then the orphan record, intended for some other employee, would be attached, improperly, to the new employee's record.

Referential integrity prevents you from deleting a primary record on which related records depend. If you terminate an employee, and then try to delete the employee's record from the Employees table, Access prevents you from doing so. Access displays a message box informing you that you must delete all records related to the record in the primary table before you can delete the primary record.

Selecting a Primary Key

You do not need to designate a primary key field for a table that is never used as a primary table. A *primary table* is a table that contains information representing a real-world object, such as a person or an invoice, and has just one record that is uniquely associated with that object. The Personnel Actions table can qualify as a primary table because it identifies an object—in this case, the equivalent of a paper form representing the outcome of two actions: initiation and approval. Personnel Actions, however, probably would not be used as a primary table in a relationship with another table.

Using a key field is a simple method of preventing the duplication of records in a table. Access requires that you specify a primary key if you want to create a one-to-one relationship or update two or more tables at the same time; this subject is covered in Chapter 8, "Creating Queries and Joining Tables."

The primary table participating in relations you set with the Relationships dialog box must have a primary key. Access considers a table without a primary key field to be an oddity; therefore, you often are prompted—*nagged* may be a more apt description—by a message that a key field hasn't been created when you make changes to the table and return to Run mode. You may want to create a key field just to stifle these messages.

Primary keys can be created on more than one key. In the case of the Personnel Actions table, a primary key that prevents duplicate records must consist of more than one field, because more than one personnel action for an employee can be scheduled or approved on the same date. If you establish the rule that no more than one type of personnel action for an employee can be scheduled for the same date, you can create a primary key that consists of the PA ID, PA Type, and PA Scheduled Date fields. When you create a primary key, Access creates an index based on the primary key. Indexes are the subject of the next section and are discussed in detail in Chapter 19, "Exploring Relational Database Design and Implementation."

To create a multiple-field primary key and index for the Personnel Actions table, follow these steps:

Design

1. Open the Personnel Actions table from the Database window in Design mode.

2. Click the selection button for the PA ID field.

3. Hold down the Ctrl key and click the selection button for the PA Type field. In most instances, when you hold down Ctrl and click a selection button, you can make multiple selections.

4. Hold down Ctrl and click the selection button for the PA Scheduled Date field.

   If you accidentally choose one of the other fields, release Ctrl and click the field's selection button to deselect it.

5. Click the Key Field button on the toolbar. Symbols of keys appear in each of the selected fields, as shown in figure 4.23, indicating their inclusion in the primary key.

6. To determine the sequence of the fields in the primary key, click the Table Properties button to display the Table Properties window. Expand the size of this window, as shown in figure 4.23, so that you can see the entire primary key.

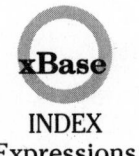

xBase

INDEX
Expressions

The semicolons in the primary key description function in the same way the + operator does when you are creating an xBase index for Character fields. In Access, however, you can create multiple-field primary keys and indexes with fields of different data types, without resorting to xBase-type changing functions. The entry in the primary key text box is the equivalent of the following xBase statement:

```
INDEX ON STRZERO(pa_id,2) + pa_type + DTOS(pa_sced)
TO whatever
```

The capability to concatenate different data types to form an index instruction or a string is the result of Access's Variant data type discussed in Chapter 23, "Exchanging Data with Access Basic DDE."

7. While the Table Properties window is open, you may want to add an optional description of the Personnel Actions table in the Description text box.

You now have a multiple-field primary key and a corresponding index to the Personnel Actions table that precludes the addition of records that duplicate records with the same primary key.

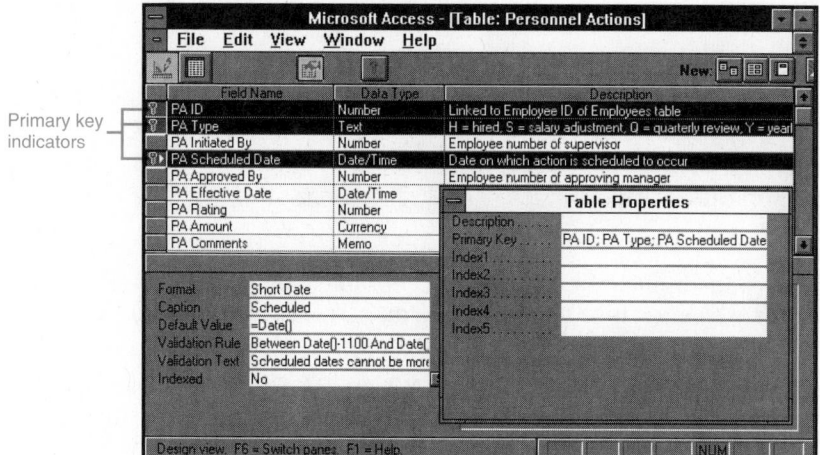

Primary key indicators

FIG. 4.23

Setting a multiple-field primary key for the Personnel Actions table.

Adding Indexes to Tables

Although Access creates an index on the primary key, you may want to create an index on some other field or fields in the table. Indexes speed searches for records that contain specific types of data. You may want to find all personnel actions that occurred in a given period and all quarterly reviews for all employees in PA Scheduled Date sequence, for example. If you have many records in the table, an index will speed up the searching process. A disadvantage of multiple indexes is that data entry operations are slowed by the time it takes to update the additional indexes. You can create up to 32 indexes for each Access table, and five of those can be of the multiple-field type. Each multiple-field index can include up to 10 fields.

To create a single-field index for the Personnel Actions table based on the PA Effective Date field, and a multiple-field index based on the PA Type and the PA Scheduled Date fields, follow these steps:

1. Choose the PA Effective Date field by clicking its selection button.

2. Choose the Indexed text box in the Field Properties window.

3. Open the Indexed drop-down list box by clicking the arrow button or pressing F4. The list box appears as shown in figure 4.24.

FIG. 4.24

Creating a single-field index on the PA Scheduled Date field.

4. In this case, duplicate entries are acceptable, so choose Yes (Duplicates OK) and close the list box. You can create only a single-field index by using this method.

5. Choose the Index1 text box. Type **PA Type;PA Scheduled Date** to create a multiple-field index on these two fields, as shown in figure 4.25. You do not need to enclose field names containing spaces within square brackets when defining indexes. Multiple-field indexes can be created only in the Index1...Index5 text boxes.

FIG. 4.25

Creating a multiple-field index on the PA Type and PA Scheduled Date fields.

6. Press Enter or move to Primary Key. When you press Enter and move from the Index1 text box, Access tests your entry to make sure that you have spelled the field names correctly. If you have a misspelling, a message box appears advising you of the problem.

7. Click the Datasheet button to return to Run mode. Choose OK when the messages in the status bar indicate that the new indexes are being created as you leave Design mode.

You now have three indexes for the Primary Key table: the index automatically created for the primary key, the single-key index on PA Effective Date, and the multiple-key index on PA Type and PA Scheduled Date.

Adding Records to a Table

Now you have a chance to test your work in creating the Personnel Actions table and to check whether Access is enforcing referential integrity. The initial entries for each of the nine employees of Northwind Trading is shown in table 4.10. The entries for PA Scheduled Date and PA Effective Date were taken from the Hire Date field of the Employees table. The Hire Date field of the Employees table now is superfluous, because it duplicates the data in the Personnel Actions table. You will delete the Hire Date field in a later chapter. Feel free to be as generous or as parsimonious as you want with the monthly salaries shown in the PA Amount field.

Table 4.10. First Nine Entries for the Personnel Actions Table

ID	Type	Initiated By	Scheduled	Approved By	Effective	Rating	New Amount	Comments
1	H		01-Apr-87		01-Apr-87		2,000	Hired
2	H		15-Jul-87		15-Jul-87		3,500	Hired
3	H	2	01-Mar-88	2	01-Mar-88		2,250	Hired
4	H	2	01-Apr-88	2	01-Apr-88		2,250	Hired
5	H	2	15-Sep-89	2	15-Sep-89		2,500	Hired
6	H	5	15-Sep-89	2	15-Sep-89		4,000	Hired
7	H	5	01-Dec-89	2	01-Dec-89		3,000	Hired
8	H	2	01-Feb-90	2	01-Feb-90		2,500	Hired
9	H	5	15-Oct-91	2	15-Oct-91		3,000	Hired

Entering historical information in a table in Datasheet view is a relatively fast process for an experienced data entry operator. This process also gives you a chance to test your default entries and Format properties for each field. You can enter bogus values that don't comply with your validation rules to verify that your rules are operational. To add the first nine historical records to the Personnel Actions table using the data from table 4.10, follow these steps:

1. Click the Datasheet button on the toolbar to return to Datasheet view in Run mode. The caret will be positioned in the PA ID field of the default first record.

2. Enter the PA ID of the employee. Press Enter, Tab, or the right-arrow key to move to the next field. When you do this, a new default blank record is added to the view, but not the content, of the table. A new record is added to the table only when a value is entered in one of the fields of the default blank record.

3. If a value is in the table for PA Initiated By, type the value. Press Enter, Tab, or the right-arrow key to move to the next field.

4. Type the PA scheduled date. You don't need to delete the default date value. When you type a new date, it replaces the default value. Then press Enter, Tab, or the right-arrow key.

5. If a value is in the table for PA Approved By, type the value. Then press Enter, Tab, or the right-arrow key.

6. Type the PA effective date. Press Enter, Tab, or the right-arrow key twice to skip the Rating field, which is inapplicable to newly hired employees.

7. Enter the PA amount of the monthly salary at the time of hiring. Press Enter, Tab, or the right-arrow key.

8. Type **Hired** in the PA Comments field, or any other comment you care to make. Press Enter, Tab, or the right-arrow key. The caret moves to the PA ID field.

9. Press the down-arrow key to move the caret to the default blank record.

10. Repeat steps 2 through 9 for each of the eight remaining employees in table 4.10.

When you complete your entries, your table appears as shown in figure 4.26. If Access displays error message boxes during data entry, edit or reenter the data to conform to the data types and validation rules. Error messages that appear when you have entered the data correctly indicate that something is amiss with your validation rules. In this case, change to Design mode and review your validation rules for the offending fields against those listed in table 4.9. Return to Run mode to continue with your entries.

FIG. 4.26

The first nine records of the Personnel Actions table.

Editing Table Data and Testing Validation Rules

You can experiment with editing table data and testing your validation rules at the same time. Testing database applications often requires much more time and effort than creating them. The following basic tests are required to confirm your validation rules:

■ *Referential integrity:* Type **10** in the PA ID field of the default blank record, record number 10, and then press the up-arrow key. Pressing the up-arrow key tells Access that you are finished with the current record and to move up to the preceding record with the caret in the same field. Access then tests the primary key integrity before enabling you to leave the current record. The message box shown in figure 4.27 appears. Choose OK or press Enter.

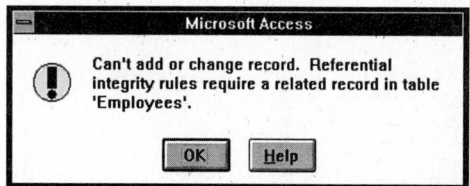

FIG. 4.27

The message box indicating that an entry violates referential integrity rules.

■ *No duplicates restriction for primary key:* In the record just added, attempt to duplicate exactly the entries for record number 9, and then press the up-arrow key. You see the message box shown in figure 4.28. Choose OK or press Enter.

■ *PA Type validation:* Type **x** and press the right-arrow key to display the message box with the validation text you entered for the PA Type field, shown in figure 4.29. Choose OK or press Enter.

Type **q**, and then move to the PA Initiated By field. When the caret leaves the PA Type field, the q changes to Q because of the > format character used. Type **0** (an invalid employee ID number) and press the right-arrow key to display the message box shown in figure 4.30. Choose OK or press Enter.

FIG. 4.28

The message box
that appears
when a record
with a duplicate
key is added to
a field indexed
with the No
Duplicates
option.

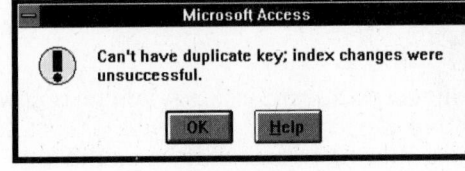

FIG. 4.29

A message box
created by an
entry that violates
a validation rule.

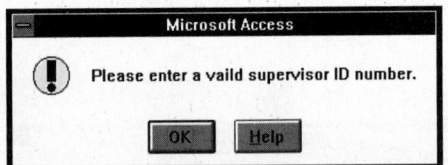

FIG. 4.30

The message box
that appears in
response to an
invalid employee
ID number entry.

Continue with the testing. Type a date, such as **1/1/80**, for the PA
scheduled date and type the same date for the PA effective date to display the error message boxes with the validation text you entered. Enter a valid date after the test. To edit a field rather than retype it, press
F2 to deselect the entire field and display the caret for editing. F2
toggles selection and editing operations.

When you have finished your testing, click the selection button of the
added field, and then press Del. The confirmation message box shown
in figure 4.31 appears.

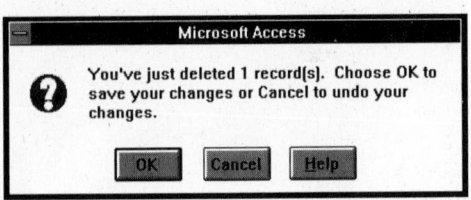

FIG. 4.31

The confirmation
box for deletion
of one or more
records.

Altering Fields and Relationships

When you are designing your own database, you often will discover that the original choices you made for the sequence of fields in a table, data types, or relationships between tables must be altered. One of the reasons for adding substantial numbers of records to tables during the testing process is to discover any changes that are necessary before putting the database into daily use.

You can change formats, change validation rules and text, change lengths of Text fields, and make other minor modifications to the table by changing to Design mode, selecting the field to modify, and making the changes in the properties boxes. Changing data types can cause a loss of data, however, so be sure to read "Changing Field Data Types and Sizes," later in this chapter, before you attempt to make these changes. Changing relationships between tables is considered a drastic action if you have entered a substantial amount of data, so this subject also is covered in a later section, "Changing Relationships between Tables."

Avoid changing field names if you have created data entry forms or reports that use the data in the field. Although Access performs many operations automatically, it does not change the field names that you have assigned to text boxes and other objects in forms or the groups in reports. The time to finalize field names is while creating your tables; a bit of extra thought at this point saves hours of modification when you are well into creation of a complex application.

Rearranging the Sequence of Fields in a Table

If you are manually entering historical data in Datasheet view, you can find that the sequence of entries isn't optimum. You may, for example, be entering data from a printed form with a top-to-bottom, left-to-right sequence that doesn't correspond to the left-to-right sequence of the corresponding fields in your table. Access makes rearranging the order of fields in tables a matter of dragging and dropping fields where you want them. You can choose whether to make the revised layout temporary or permanent when you close the table.

To rearrange the fields of the Personnel Actions table, follow these steps:

1. Choose Datasheet view in Run mode. This is the only table design change you can implement in Access's Datasheet view.

2. Click the field name button of the field you want to move. This action selects the field name button and all the data cells of the field.

3. Place the mouse pointer on the field name button and press the left mouse button. The mouse pointer turns into the drag-and-drop symbol, and a heavy vertical bar marks the far left position of the field. Figure 4.32 shows the PA Scheduled Date field being moved to a position immediately to the left of the PA Effective Date field.

4. Move the mouse pointer and vertical bar combination to the new position for the selected field and release the mouse button. The field assumes the new position shown in figure 4.33.

ID	Type	Initiated By	Scheduled	Approved By	Effective	Rating	New Amount	Comments
1	H		4/1/87		4/1/87		2,000.00	Hired
2	H		7/15/87		7/15/87		3,500.00	Hired
3	H	2	3/1/88	2	3/1/88		2,250.00	Hired
4	H	2	4/1/88	2	4/1/88		2,250.00	Hired
5	H	2	9/15/89	2	9/15/89		2,500.00	Hired
6	H	5	9/15/89	2	9/15/89		4,000.00	Hired
7	H	5	12/1/89	2	12/1/89		3,000.00	Hired
8	H	2	2/1/90	2	2/1/90		2,500.00	Hired
9	H	5	10/15/91	2	10/15/91		3,000.00	Hired
	Q		7/9/92		7/9/92			

FIG. 4.32

Dragging a field to a new position in Run mode.

5. When you close the Personnel Actions table, you see the familiar Save Changes message box. To make the modification permanent, choose OK; otherwise, click No.

MODIFY STRUCTURE

Dragging and dropping fields to a new location is a vastly simpler process than the MODIFY STRUCTURE operations required by xBase to achieve the same result. You can reposition fields in Design mode by clicking the select button of the row of the field to be moved, and then dragging the row vertically to a new location. Changing the position of a field in a table doesn't change any of its other properties.

	Microsoft Access - [Table: Personnel Actions]	
□	**File Edit View Records Layout Window Help**	

Field: PA Scheduled Date   New

ID	Type	Initiated By	Approved By	Scheduled	Effective	Rating	New Amount	Comments
1	H			4/1/87	4/1/87		2,000.00	Hired
2	H			7/15/87	7/15/87		3,500.00	Hired
3	H	2	2	3/1/88	3/1/88		2,250.00	Hired
4	H	2	2	4/1/88	4/1/88		2,250.00	Hired
5	H	2	2	9/15/89	9/15/89		2,500.00	Hired
6	H	5	2	9/15/89	9/15/89		4,000.00	Hired
7	H	5	2	12/1/89	12/1/89		3,000.00	Hired
8	H	2	2	2/1/90	2/1/90		2,500.00	Hired
9	H	5	2	10/15/91	10/15/91		3,000.00	Hired
*	Q			7/9/92	7/9/92			

Record: 1

Date on which action is scheduled to occur   NUM

FIG. 4.33

The PA Sched-
uled Date field
dropped into a
new position in
Datasheet view.

Changing Field Data Types and Sizes

You may find it necessary to change a field data type as the design of your database develops or if you import tables from another database, a spreadsheet, or a text file. If you import tables, the data type automatically chosen by Access during the importation process cannot be what you want, especially with Number fields. Importing and exporting tables and data from other applications is the subject of Chapter 5. Another example of altering field properties is changing the number of characters in fixed-length Text fields to accommodate longer than expected entries, or converting variable-length Text fields to fixed length.

Before making changes to the field data types of a table that contains substantial amounts of data, make a backup copy of the table by copying or exporting it to a backup Access database. If you accidentally lose parts of the data contained in the table, such as decimal fractions, when you make the conversion, you can import the backup table to your current database. The simple and quick process of exporting Access tables is covered in Chapter 5. After you create a backup database file, you can copy a table to Windows Clipboard, and then paste it to the backup database. Copying and pasting tables to and from the Clipboard is discussed later in this chapter, in the section "Copying and Pasting Fields, Records, and Tables."

Numeric Fields

Changing a data type to one that requires a larger number of bytes of storage is, in almost all circumstances, safe. You will not sacrifice the accuracy of your data. Changing a numeric data type from Byte to Integer to Long Integer to Single and, finally, to Double, will not affect the value of your data because each change, with the exception of Long Integer to Single, requires more bytes of storage for a data value. Changing from Long Integer to Single and Single to Currency involves the same number of bytes and only decreases the accuracy of the data in exceptional circumstances. The exceptions can occur when you are using very, very large numbers or extremely small decimal fractions, such as in some scientific and engineering calculations.

On the other hand, your data may be truncated if you change to a data type with fewer data bytes required to store it. If you change from a fixed-point format (Currency) or floating-point format (Single or Double) to Byte, Integer, or Long Integer, any decimal fractions in your data will be truncated. *Truncation* means reducing the number of digits in a number to fit the new Field Size property you choose. If you change a numeric data type from Single to Currency, for example, data in the fifth, sixth, and seventh decimal places (if any exists) of your Single data will be lost, because Single provides up to seven decimal places and Currency provides only four.

RECNO(),
PACK

You cannot convert any type of field to a Counter type field. The Counter field is restricted to use as a record counter and enables entry only by the appending of new records; you cannot edit a record number field. When you delete a record in Access, the Counter values of the higher numbered records are immediately reduced by 1. Record numbers are assigned to records in the order of the primary key, not in the order in which the records were entered. If your table doesn't have a primary key, the record numbers represent the order in which the records were created.

Text Fields

You can convert Text fields to Memo fields without Access truncating your text. Converting a Memo field to a Text field, however, truncates characters beyond the 255 limit of Text fields. Similarly, if you convert a variable-length Text field to fixed length, and some records contain character strings that exceed the length you chose, these strings will be truncated.

Conversion between Number, Date, and Text Field Data Types

Access makes many conversions between Number, Date, and Text field data types for you. Conversion from Number or Date to Text field data types does not follow the Format property you assigned to the original data type. Numbers are converted using the General Number format, and dates use the Short Date format. Access is quite intelligent in the methods it uses to convert suitable Text fields to Number data types. Access accepts dollar signs, commas, and decimals during the conversion, for example. Access ignores trailing spaces. Access converts dates and times in the following Text formats to internal Date/Time values that you then can format the way you want:

```
1/4/93 10:00 AM
04-Jan-92
January 4
10:00
10:00:00
```

You cannot change the Data Type or Field Size property of a field designated as the primary key field, included in a composite primary key, or having a designated relationship with a field in another table. If you try to change a Data Type or Field Size in this case, you receive the message shown in figure 4.34.

FIG. 4.34

Attempting to change a data type or field.

Changing Relationships between Tables

Adding new relationships between tables is a straightforward process, but changing relationships can require you to change data types so that the related fields have the same data type. To change a relationship between two tables, complete the following steps:

1. Close the tables that are involved in the relationship.

2. If the Database window is not active, click it to choose it, or choose Database from the **W**indows menu.

3. Choose Relationships from the Edit menu.

4. Choose the primary table in the relationship from the Primary Table drop-down list box.

5. Choose the related table from the Related Table drop-down list box.

   The field in the related table on which the relationship is based, if a relationship has been established, appears as shown in figure 4.35.

6. Click Delete to clear the existing relationship.

7. If you are changing the data type of a field that constitutes or is a member field of the primary key of the primary table, delete all other relationships that exist between the primary table and every other table to which it is related.

8. Change the data types of the fields in the tables so that the data types will match in the new relationships.

9. Re-create the relationships, using the procedure described in the earlier section, "Establishing Relationships between Tables."

Copying and Pasting Fields, Records, and Tables

You can copy a complete table or records of a table to the Windows Clipboard with the methods applicable to most other Windows applications. You will use Clipboard operations extensively when you reach Part III of this book, "Integrating Access with Other Applications." You can copy tables into other databases, such as a general-purpose back-up database, by using the Clipboard; however, exporting a table to a temporary database file, described in the next chapter, is a more expeditious method.

To copy a table to another Access database, a destination database must exist. To create a backup database and copy the contents of the Personnel Actions table to the database, follow these steps:

1. Make the Database window active by clicking it, if it is accessible, or by choosing Database from the **W**indows menu.

2. Click the Tables button, if necessary, to display the list of tables.

3. Choose the table you want to copy to the new database.

4. Press Ctrl+C or choose **C**opy from the **E**dit menu.

5. If you plan to copy the table to your current database, skip to step 8.

6. If you have created a destination backup database, choose **O**pen from the **F**ile menu and open the database; then skip to step 8.

7. To create a backup database, choose **N**ew from the **F**ile menu and type **backup.mdb** or another appropriate file name in the Files combo box, and then choose OK. Access creates your BACKUP.MDB database, which occupies 64K without any tables (this is called 64K of overhead). Your new database now is active.

8. Press Ctrl+V to choose **P**aste from the **E**dit menu. The Paste Table As dialog box shown in figure 4.36 appears.

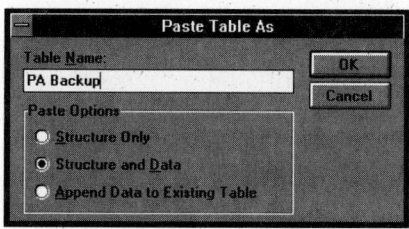

FIG. 4.36

The Paste Table As dialog box used to create a backup table.

9. You have three options for pasting the backup table to the destination database. You can create a new table or replace the data in a table of the name you enter in the Table Name text box by selecting Structure and Data, which is the most common choice. You can paste the structure only, and then append data to the table later by selecting Structure Only. Or, you can append the records to an existing table of the name you enter. For this example, choose the default, Structure and Data.

10. Your current or backup database now has a copy of the table you selected, and the name you entered appears in the backup's Database window. You can save multiple copies of the same table under different names if you are making a series of changes to the table that may affect the integrity of the data it contains.

To delete a table from a database, choose the table name in the Database window, and then press the Del key. A confirmation message box appears. Choose OK to delete the table forever. You cannot choose Edit Undo after you have deleted a table.

Version 1.0 of Microsoft Access makes no provision for copying a specific group of fields within a group of records similar to Excel's capability to copy a rectangular range of spreadsheet cells. If you select individual or contiguous groups of fields (by dragging the mouse across the field name buttons) in Datasheet view and display the Edit menu, you will see that the Copy option is inactive (grayed). You can select an individual record in Datasheet view (by clicking its selection button) or a contiguous group of records (by dragging the mouse across the record select buttons), but all the fields of the selected records are copied. You cannot then deselect records or fields within a group by holding down Ctrl while you click selection buttons.

You quickly can copy all data in the table to the Clipboard by choosing Select All Records from the Edit menu then choosing Edit Copy. You can paste copied records back into your table. To replace records with data from other records, follow these steps:

1. Copy to the Clipboard the records to be used for replacement.

2. Select the records that are to be replaced.

3. Choose Paste from the Edit menu or press Ctrl+V. The pasted fields or records overwrite the contents of the data cells, starting from the first selected record.

Choosing Paste Append from the Edit menu adds the data cells in the Clipboard to your table. If the pasting operation would violate referential integrity or result in duplicate data in a field in which no duplicates are allowed, you see a message box informing you of the problem. Any records or fields that cannot be pasted into the table are, instead, added to a table called Paste Errors that Access creates for you. You then can examine the entries that didn't replace or append by opening the Paste Errors table.

Chapter Summary

Tables are the core elements of the databases you create. The capability to segregate data of different types into individual tables, and then relate the tables by common fields or combinations of fields is central to the concept of relational databases.

The techniques you used in this chapter to add the Personnel Actions table to the Northwind Traders database are typical of those techniques you will use when you create databases from the information you have stored in other types of database, spreadsheet, or text files, or from information that you or others enter manually.

Most purchasers of Access will have existing data in one of the forms mentioned in the preceding paragraph. The next chapter describes how to import existing data into Access tables, how to attach files created by common PC database managers so that they retain their original formats, and how to export files from Access in the formats it supports. Dealing with files created by client-server database management systems is discussed in Chapter 21, "Using Access in a Network Environment."

Attaching, Importing, and Exporting Tables

U ndoubtedly, more than 90 percent of the users of personal computers have data that can be processed by database management techniques. Any data that a computer can arrange in tabular form, even tables in word processing files, can be converted to database tables. The strength of a database manager (DBM) lies in its capability to handle large numbers of individual pieces of data stored in tables and to relate the pieces of data in a meaningful way.

PC users acquire DBMs when the amount of data created exceeds the application's capability to manipulate the data effectively. One of the most common examples of this situation is a large mailing list created in a word processing application. As the number of names in the list increases, using the word processor to make selective mailings and maintain histories of responses to mailings becomes increasingly difficult. A PC DBM is the most effective type of application for manipulating large lists.

One of Access for Windows' strong points is its capability to transform existing database table, spreadsheet, and text files created by other

DOS and Windows applications into the Access .MDB format—a process called *importing* a file. Access can *export* (create) table files in any format that it can import the files. Most PC DBMs share this capability, but Access can import and export Borland Paradox files while most other systems cannot. Most client/server database management systems can import and export only text type files.

Access for Windows can *attach* a database table file created by another DBM to your Access database; Access then acts as a database front end. Because Access has an attaching capability, it can use a file created by another DBM in its native form. This capability is far less common in other PC and client/server DBMs. When you attach a database table from a different DBM, you can display and update the attached table as if it were an Access table contained in your .MDB file. If the file containing the table is shared on a network, other users can use the file with their applications while it is attached to your database. This capability to attach files is an important feature for two reasons: you can have only one Access database open at a time, and you can create new applications in Access that can coexist with applications created by other database managers.

This chapter deals primarily with what are called *PC database managers*—a term used to distinguish them from client/server DBMs, such as Microsoft SQL Server and Oracle. (Client/server DBMs are designed specifically for use with networked PCs and require you to set aside a PC for use as a file server.) PC DBMs, such as dBASE and Paradox, are much more widely used than client/server systems. The majority of PC DBMs can share files on a network, but several publishers require that you purchase a special multiuser version of the DBM to do so. Multiuser PC DBMs, while accommodating the workstation-server configuration required by conventional networks such as Novell NetWare and Microsoft LAN Manager, are especially well-suited to the peer-to-peer networks discussed in Chapter 1, such as Windows for Workgroups, NetWare Lite, and LANTastic. Chapter 21 explains how to use Access with shared database files in general and client/server databases in particular.

FROM HERE...

For Related Information:
◄◄ "Importing and Attaching Existing Files," p. 28.

Learning How Access Handles Tables in Other Database File Formats

Conventional PC database managers maintain each table in an individual file. Each file contains a *header* followed by the data. A header is a group of bytes that provides information on the structure of the file, such as the names and types of fields, the number of records in the table, and the length of the file. When you create a table file in dBASE or Paradox, for example, the file contains only a header. As you add records to the file, the file grows by the number of bytes required for one record, and the header is updated to reflect the new file size and record count. Novell Btrieve files are slightly different than the files created by dBASE and Paradox because Btrieve files use variable-length records for storing text data.

PC DBMs create a variety of supplemental files—some of which are required to import, attach, or export DBMs:

- Paradox stores information about the primary key index file (.PX) in the associated table (.DB) file; the .PX file for the .DB file must be available in order for Access to open a Paradox .DB file. Access attaches the .PX file automatically.

- dBASE stores its Memo type data in a separate .DBT file. If a dBASE table file contains a Memo field, the .DBT file must be available, but use of .NDX (dBASE III) and .MDX (dBASE IV) index files is optional. You should always use .NDX or .MDX files when you have them.

- Opening Btrieve files requires having a .DDF data dictionary for the database that contains the table file.

All supplemental files must be in the same directory as the related database file to be used by Access.

The header of an Access .MDB file differs from conventional PC DBM files in that an .MDB header contains information on all the tables, indexes, macros, and Access Basic functions and procedures stored in a single Access file. The Access file header also contains information on the location and characteristics of other PC DBM files that you have attached to your Access database.

FROM HERE...

For Related Information:

◄◄ "Understanding Relational Databases," p. 123.

Identifying PC Database File Formats

Access can import, attach, and export the following types of database table files used by the most common PC database managers:

- *dBASE .DBF table and .DBT memo files, and dBASE III .NDX and dBASE IV .MDX index files:* dBASE III files and indexes are the standard language of the PC DBM industry. The majority of PC DBMs, as well as all common spreadsheet applications, can import and export .DBF files. Most of these DBMs can update existing .NDX index files, and some DBMs can create these files.

  The .DBF file structure is native to xBase clones such as FoxPro, but not all these DBMs create fully compatible dBASE file structures. Compilers like CA-Clipper and Arago have their own native index file structures, but they can use .NDX indexes when necessary. The capability to use .MDX multiple-index files is less widespread.

  Access can attach, but not create, .NDX and .MDX files. Access updates both types of dBASE index files when you edit or add records to an attached .DBF file. The section "Setting Primary Keys and Using Index Files," later in this chapter, discusses index files in attached tables. When you export an Access table with a Memo type field, a .DBT memo file with the same name you assign to the dBASE file is created.

- *FoxPro 2.0 .DBF table files:* You can import and export FoxPro 2.0 .DBF files and files created by earlier versions of FoxPro. The procedures for importing FoxPro 2.0 .DBF files are the same as those for dBASE III and IV. You cannot attach FoxPro 2.0 files as Access tables.

- *Paradox 3.0 and 3.5 .DB table and .PX primary key files:* Tests indicate that files created by beta copies of Paradox 4.0 and Paradox for Windows can be imported and attached to Access tables. The next section presents the specific limitations applicable to Paradox files.

■ *Btrieve table and .DDF data definition files:* The Btrieve file structure was one of the first DBMs to be used by PC applications written in the C language. The Btrieve table file contains the indexes;
they are not in separate files. A number of PC-based accounting
applications use Btrieve files, but do not advertise this fact. If the
application you are using creates databases and the files are not
dBASE or Paradox files, they may be Btrieve files. If the directory
containing the database files includes a .DDF file, you probably
can attach the tables to an Access database. If the directory does
not contain a .DDF file, you can contact the publisher of the application to determine whether the files are in Btrieve format and
whether a data definition file with a disguised extension exists.

The majority of applications that use table and index files also use the
standard file extensions presented in the preceding paragraphs. The
dBASE memo file, for example, requires a standard extension. Using the
standard extensions for all types of files, however, is not a requirement.
Some developers of xBase applications disguise their files by using
arbitrary extensions. You may have to do a bit of detective work to
determine which files contain data and which are indexes.

If you are working in a multiuser environment, you must have
exclusive access to the file you intend to import. No other user
can have that file open when you initiate the importing process,
and other users are denied access to the file until you close the
Import dialog box.

Make sure that you work on a backup copy of the attached file,
not the original, until you are certain that your updates to the
data in the attached table are valid for the existing database
application.

To attach or import an xBase, Paradox, or Btrieve file as a table in an
Access database, follow these steps:

1. Close all open tables so that only the Database window remains
   open. Access does not require that all open tables be closed before you attach or import a table.

2. If you have created a test database that can be used for this procedure, choose **O**pen Database from the **F**ile menu, select the test
   database, open it, and skip to step 5.

3. If you have not created a test database, create a sample to use
   throughout this chapter. From the **F**ile menu, choose **N**ew Database.

4. In the File Name text box, type a name, such as **MDB_TEST.MDB**, for your test database and choose OK. You must wait while Access creates and tests the new database.

5. In this example, you are attaching a table. From the File menu, choose **A**ttach Table. The Attach dialog box appears (see fig. 5.1). If you choose Import Table, the Import dialog box appears.

6. Use the arrow keys or the scroll bar slider to choose the data source. (If you have a suitable Paradox table to attach, choose Paradox. Otherwise, choose dBASE III, dBASE IV, or Btrieve as appropriate to the format of your table file.) Choose OK. The Select File dialog box appears (see fig. 5.2).

7. From the list in the File Name combo box, choose the table you want to attach or import. Access supplies the standard extensions for dBASE and Paradox table files and the .DDF extension for Btrieve data definition files. Click the Attach button.

   If you are attaching a Btrieve file, the Attach Tables dialog box appears (see fig. 5.3). Choose the table to attach and then click the Attach button.

FIG. 5.1

Selecting the type of file to attach as an Access table.

FIG. 5.2

Choosing the file to attach.

8. If the file you have chosen is encrypted (coded) and requires a password to decrypt it, the Password Required dialog box appears (see fig. 5.4). Type the password in the box and press Enter.

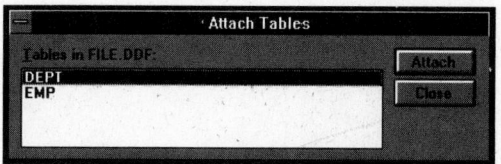

FIG. 5.3

Choosing the
Btrieve tables
to attach.

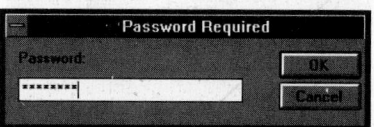

FIG. 5.4

The Password
Required dialog
box for en-
crypted database
files and tables.

9. After you successfully attach or import the file, a dialog box appears confirming this operation (see fig. 5.5).

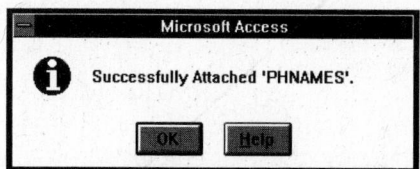

FIG. 5.5

Confirming that
Access has
attached a table.

10. From the Select File dialog box, choose Close. The selected table
now is listed in the Database window. If you attached a file, Access
superimposes an arrow over the icon for the corresponding table.

11. Click the Open button to display the records in the table document window (see fig. 5.6).

Open

After you attach an external file as a table, you can use it almost as if it
were a table in your own database. The only general limitation is that
you cannot change the structure of an attached table: field names, field
data types, or the FieldSize properties. In attached Paradox files,
Access prevents you from changing a table's primary key field that
has been defined, because this property determines the contents of the
associated .PX index file.

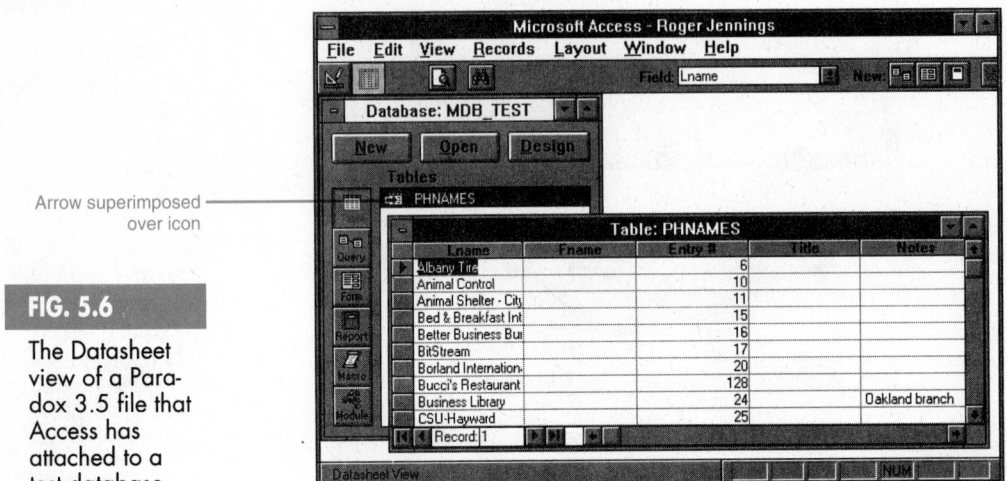

Arrow superimposed over icon

The Datasheet view of a Paradox 3.5 file that Access has attached to a test database.

Solving Problems with Importing or Attaching Files

Access detects problems with attached or imported tables that will cause errors when you try to use the tables with Access. The following sections describe these problems and how to overcome most of them.

The Incorrect Password Dialog Box

If you enter a wrong password or just press Enter, Access informs you that it cannot decrypt the file, and it gives you another opportunity to enter the password or to choose Cancel to terminate the attempt (see fig. 5.7).

The dialog box resulting from an incorrect password entry.

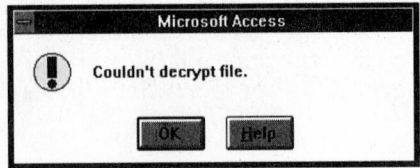

The Null Value in Index Dialog Box

Occasionally, Paradox .PX index files do not have an index value for a record; when this happens, you receive a warning dialog box (see fig. 5.8). In most cases, you can disregard the message and continue attaching or importing the file. The offending record, however, may not appear in the table; fixing the file in Paradox and starting over is better than ignoring the message.

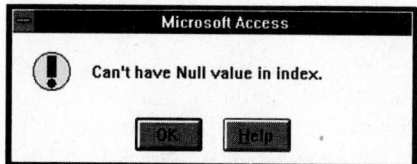

FIG. 5.8

The dialog box indicating a null value in a Paradox primary key index file.

The Missing Memo File Dialog Box

If Access cannot open a dBASE memo file because it does not exist, because it is not in the same directory as the .DBF file with which it is associated, or because it contains nontext data, a dialog box appears, and Access cancels the attachment or importation (see fig. 5.9).

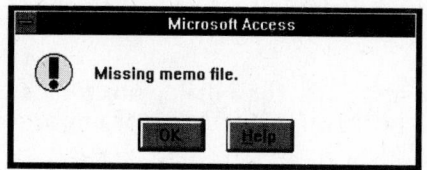

FIG. 5.9

The dialog box that appears if Access cannot open a required dBASE memo file.

The Graphics Field Type Restriction

If the successful attachment dialog box does not appear, your table or its accompanying dBASE memo file probably contains a graphics field type. The following section discusses modifying files with graphics content so that you can attach them or import them as Access tables.

Dealing with Graphics in External Files

Most database managers designed for Windows include some form of graphics field data type. Superbase IV, Paradox 4.0, and Paradox for

Windows provide a special field data type for graphics. Although dBASE IV Version 1.5 does not have a field data type for graphics, third-party software firms publish applications that enable you to store graphic images in dBASE memo fields. A variety of add-on applications enable CA-Clipper programmers to display and edit graphic images. The images are usually in individual files, but a few third-party applications place images in memo files. CA-dbFast, for example, can display, but not edit, images stored in Windows bit-map (.BMP) files. CA-dbFast does not add a graphics field type to store bit-mapped data within tables.

When you attempt to import or attach Paradox 4.0, Paradox for Windows files, or dBASE .DBT files that contain images or other binary data, you receive an error message that the memo file has been corrupted or a message that you cannot import the .DB or .DBF file that contains the offending memo or graphics field (see fig. 5.10). In rare cases, usually involving tiny images, you can import the .DBF and .DBT files, but you will see random characters in the Access memo field.

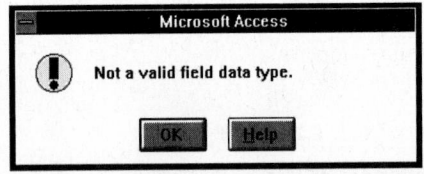

If the dialog box in figure 5.10 (or a dialog box indicating a similar type of problem) appears, the attachment or importation process is canceled.

The following recommendations can help you deal with graphic images processed with other DBMs and add-on applications:

- Use add-on applications for xBase clones and compilers that operate with the original graphics files in their native format, such as .TIF, .PIX, .GIF, or .TGA. In nearly all cases, the original graphics file is on your computer's fixed disk or on a file server. You can link or embed the graphics file in an Access OLE Object field by using the techniques described in Chapter 13, "Using the OLE Field Data Type for Graphics."

■ Do not use add-on applications that incorporate graphics in .DBT files. If you are committed to this approach, use the method that follows to place the offending memo file in a new file.

■ If you are using Paradox 4.0 or Paradox for Windows with application development in Access, maintain files with graphics fields (as well as any OLE fields in Paradox for Windows tables) in files separate from those containing conventional data types.

■ Use an OLE server that can process the graphics file type of the original image. Windows Paintbrush is limited to Windows bit-map files (.BMP and .DIB) and .PCX files. To display the image in a form or report, you can create a reduced-sized, 16-color or 256-color, Windows bit-map file to be displayed as a bound object. Chapter 13 discusses methods of handling images in this way.

In order to attach or import an xBase file containing a memo field or a Paradox file containing graphics fields, you must be familiar with file-restructuring methods for dBASE or Paradox. To restructure an xBase file with a memo file containing graphic images, follow these steps:

1. Make a copy of the file and give the file a new name.

2. Modify the structure of the original file by deleting all but the relating fields and the memo or graphics field of the original file. Modifying the new file with Modify Structure creates a backup of the original file with a .BAK extension.

3. Modify the structure of the new file by deleting the memo or graphics field.

4. Add a field for the path and file name of the original graphics file, if it is not already included. Access then can use the location of the original graphics file to pass the file name to an OLE server. You must write a bit of Access Basic code to do this, however. See Chapter 22 for examples of writing Access Basic code.

5. Modify the source code of your original application, establishing a one-to-one relationship between the new files.

For Related Information:

▶▶ "Embedding and Linking Graphics Files in Tables," p. 546.

▶▶ "Obtaining Graphics Files To Embed or Link," p. 549.

FROM HERE...

Converting Field Data Types to Access Data Types

When you import or attach a file, Access reads the header of the file and converts the field data types to Access data types. In most cases, Access is quite successful in this conversion; Access offers a greater variety of data types than any other widely used PC DBM. Table 5.1 shows the correspondence of field data types between dBASE, Paradox, Btrieve, and Access files.

Table 5.1. Field Data Type Conversion between Access and DBMs

dBASE III/IV	Paradox 3.0 and 3.5	Btrieve	Access
Character	Alphanumeric	String, lstring, zstring	Text (Specify Size property)
Numeric, Float*	Number, Currency	Float or bfloat (8-byte)	Number (Double)
		Float or bfloat (4-byte)	Number (Single)
		Integer (1-byte)	Number (Byte)
	Short Number	Integer (2-byte)	Number (Integer)
		Integer (4-btye)	Number (Long)
Logical			Yes/No
Date	Date		Date/Time
Memo			Memo

*Sometimes two types of field data, separated by commas, are shown within a single column in table 5.1. When Access exports a table containing a data type that corresponds with one of the two field data types, the first of the two data types is assigned to the field in the exported table. The Float data type is available only in dBASE IV.

If you are importing tables, you can change the field data type and the FieldSize property so that they are more suitable to the type of information contained in the field. When you change a data type or FieldSize, however, follow the precautions noted in Chapter 4. Remember that you cannot change the field data type or FieldSize property of attached tables. You can use the Format property with imported or attached tables, however, to display the data in any format that is compatible with the field data type of imported or attached files. You can change any remaining properties applicable to the field data type, such as validation rules and text. Using the Caption property, you can give the field a new and more descriptive name.

You can create Access indexes for both imported and attached files. With attached files, Access simultaneously updates the internal Access index and any external indexes that Access or you identify.

For Related Information:

◀◀ "Choosing Field Data Types, Sizes, and Formats," p. 133.

◀◀ "Adding Indexes to Tables," p. 167.

FROM HERE...

Setting Primary Keys and Using Index Files

Methods of setting primary keys and creating indexes differ according to the type of file you use to attach a table. Tables based on Paradox, Btrieve, and client/server DBM files usually have predefined primary key fields and are indexed on the key fields. Files based on dBASE structures, however, define key fields through index files. The following two sections discuss the effects these differences have on the tables you create.

Establishing Key Fields in Attached Paradox and Btrieve Tables

When you attach or import a Paradox or Btrieve table that has a primary key index, Access establishes this primary key as the primary key for the new table. To verify that Access has established a primary key for an attached Paradox or Btrieve table, click the Design mode button on the toolbar. A dialog box informs you that you cannot modify some of the properties of the table (see fig. 5.11). Choose OK.

The table appears in Design mode. If the Table Properties window is not displayed, choose Table Properties from the View menu.

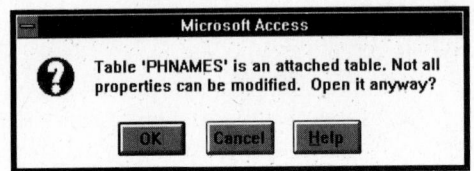

When you attach a Paradox .DB table file that has a primary key, Access uses the Paradox .PX file to establish the primary key. (With Btrieve, Access uses the .DDF and database files.) If you modify the values in a key field, the .DB and .PX files simultaneously reflect that modification. The Table Properties window text box shows the primary key.

Attaching dBASE Index Files

Key field indexing is not automatic with dBASE files attached as tables; dBASE file headers do not include data about the indexes used by the application that has the .DBF file. The first time you attach the .DBF file as an Access table, you must manually attach the index files associated with a dBASE file. Then when you open the Access database with the attached table again, Access attaches the indexes you specify.

Access cannot open or update index files in proprietary formats of xBase clones and compilers. You cannot, for example, attach CA-Clipper .NTX files or FoxPro .CDX or .IDX files to Access databases. Current versions of CA-Clipper (5+) and FoxPro, however, can create and maintain .NDX files, as an addition to or a substitute for their original index structures. Access cannot use secondary indexes of Paradox tables. If you have created or commissioned custom database applications that use nonstandard or secondary indexes and you plan to use Access to update these files while they are attached, you must modify your applications so that they use only .NDX or .PX indexes. You probably will not have to make a major revision of the source code, but you may find that your present applications run more slowly with .NDX indexes.

When you attach a dBASE file as a table in your database and choose the file name for the table, Access displays a Select Index Files dialog box (see fig. 5.12). When you import a dBASE file, this dialog box does not appear.

If you choose a dBASE III source file, Access supplies the default .NDX file extension. Your dBASE III file may have one or more .NDX index files associated with it.

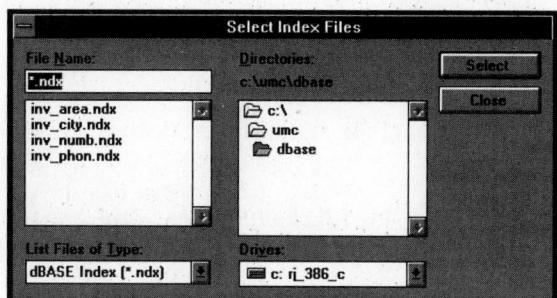

FIG. 5.12

The dialog box for selecting dBASE III index files.

dBASE IV can create a multiple-index (.MDX) file that includes all the indexes associated with the .DBF file. The .MDX file usually has the same file name as the .DBF file. Access supplies both .MDX and .NDX as default index-file extensions when you choose a dBASE IV file.

To attach index files to tables created from dBASE files, follow these steps:

1. From the list in the File Name combo box of the Select Index Files dialog box, choose the index file name and then choose Select. A dialog box appears, prompting you to confirm the addition (see fig. 5.13).

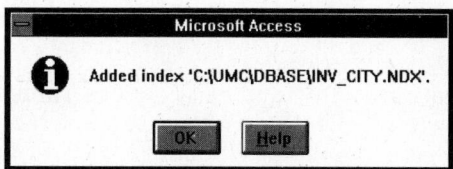

FIG. 5.13

The dialog box confirming that Access has added an attached index to an attached table.

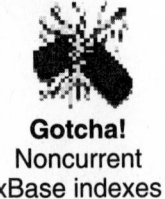

Gotcha!
Noncurrent
xBase indexes

Access does not test to determine whether the table's .NDX or .MDX index file matches the structure of its associated Access .DBF file. If the index file does not match the Access file, Access does not update the index file. Unfortunately, Access does not advise you that it is ignoring the nonconforming index. If you add records to the table in Access and then attempt to use the table with an xBase application that uses the proper index, you receive the following error message:

```
Index does not match database
```

You then must reindex the .DBF file.

If more than one index file is associated with the dBASE.DBF file, you must repeat this step for each .NDX file.

When you attach a dBASE III file used by another application, you *must* select *all* indexes associated with that file if your Access application modifies fields in the index expressions of each index file. If you do not update all the associated index files while updating the .DBF file with Access, the other application may display the following error message:

```
Index does not match file
```

Or, worse yet, the application may produce erroneous or unpredictable results. If the message or errors occur, you must reindex the file in the other application.

2. After you add the names of all the indexes required for your Access table, click the Close button in the Select Index Files dialog box.

3. Click the Close button in the Select File dialog box.

4. Click the Design button in the Database window to display the structure of your attached dBASE table.

5. If the Table Properties window is not already visible, click the Properties button on the toolbar or choose Table Properties from the View menu. The field names that are the basis for any attached single- or multiple-field indexes appear in the Index1 through Index9 properties text boxes of the Table Properties window (see fig. 5.14).

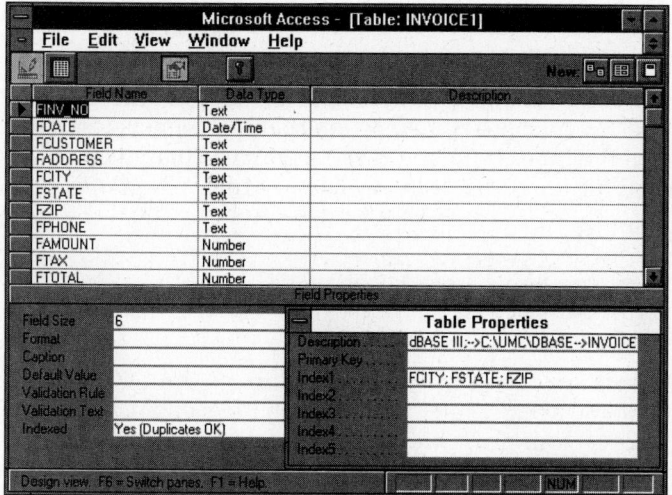

FIG. 5.14

An Access table
with an attached
dBASE file and
its associated
index files.

Access does not distinguish between dBASE indexes created with
SET UNIQUE ON and SET UNIQUE OFF. In the case of the Invoice
database of figure 5.14, the index on the FINV_NO field was created with SET UNIQUE ON. Access indicates, however, that duplicates are OK in the Indexed text box. You can create a validation
rule to prevent entering duplicate values by setting FINV_NO as
the primary key field in Access.

If you try to change the data type or the FieldSize property of an attached table and then choose the Datasheet view in Run mode, Access
displays a dialog box (see fig. 5.15). Choose OK. (Choosing Cancel restores the original values.) Access does not change the properties in
the attached file, although the Design and Datasheet windows display
the changes.

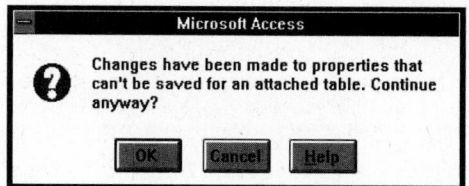

FIG. 5.15

The dialog box
indicating that
Access is
ignoring
changes made
to restricted table
properties.

Creating Access .INF Files for dBASE Indexes

When you attach one or more indexes to a table created from a dBASE file, Access creates a file with the same file name as the .DBF file but with an .INF extension. The *FILENAME*.INF file contains the path and the file name of the index you have attached in a format identical to the format used for Windows .INI files, such as this WIN.INI file:

```
[dBASE III]
NDX1=C:\UMC\DBASE\INV_AREA.NDX
NDX2=C:\UMC\DBASE\INV_CITY.NDX
NDX3=C:\UMC\DBASE\INV_NUMB.NDX
NDX4=C:\UMC\DBASE\INV_PHON.NDX
```

The .INF file is located in the same directory as the .DBF file you are attaching. If you accidentally try to attach the same index file twice, Access ignores your error initially, but when you close the Select Index File dialog box, you receive the error message Invalid .INF file. (see fig. 5.16).

If you create an invalid .INF file, Access terminates the current attach operation, and you must attach the dBASE file again. When you reattach index files to correct a prior error, a dialog box indicates that an .INF file exists (see fig. 5.17). Choose Yes to create a new .INF file.

FIG. 5.16

The dialog box informing you of a duplication in an attachment of a dBASE index file.

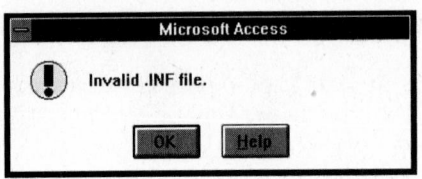

FIG. 5.17

The dialog box warning that you already have attached indexes for an attached dBASE file.

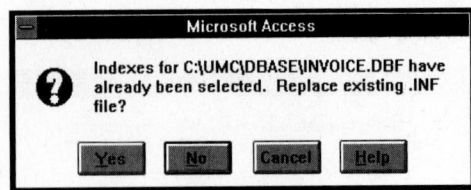

Attaching Tables from Other Access Databases

The procedure for attaching a table from one Access database to another Access database is like the procedure for attaching other tables. If you want to attach a table from NWIND.MDB to your test database, for example, follow these steps:

1. Choose Access Table, the default, from the Attach dialog box. The Attach Tables dialog box appears.

2. Choose the name of the table you want to attach from the Attach Table list box that displays the names of tables in the other Access database. Then choose Attach (see fig. 5.18). The Select Files dialog box appears.

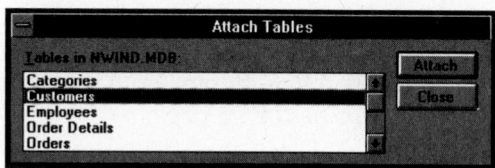

FIG. 5.18

The dialog box for choosing another Access database table to be attached to the current Access database.

3. Choose Close from the Select Files dialog box. The name of your attached Access table appears in the Database window.

Access maintains a record of the drive and directory containing the files responsible for your attached tables. If you rename or change the location of a file that you have attached as a table, Access is no longer able to find the file and displays the error dialog box (see fig. 5.19).

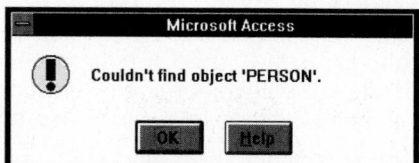

FIG. 5.19

The dialog box indicating that Access cannot find an attached file.

Importing Versus Attaching Database Files as Tables

The preceding examples demonstrate the differences between the behavior of Access with attached and imported database files. You should attach tables contained in another database file if any of the following conditions are present:

■ You are sharing the file with other users who are allowed to update the file, or you are making your updates of the file available to other users.

■ You are using another DBM to modify the file in any way.

■ The file is resident on another computer, such as a server, and its size is larger than fits comfortably on your fixed disk.

You should import a table when one of the following conditions is present:

■ You are developing an application and want to use data types or FieldSize properties that are different from those chosen for you by Access.

■ You or the users of your application do not have on-line access to the required database files and cannot attach them.

■ You want to use a different key field than the field specified in a Paradox, Btrieve, or client/server table or used as an index by a dBASE file. This situation may occur when the structure of one or more of the files you plan to use seriously violates one or more of the normalization rules described in Chapter 19, "Exploring Relational Database Design and Implementation."

■ You need Access to allow duplicate values in your table when a primary key field precludes the values.

If you decide to use a temporarily imported table in an application that, when completed, also will use an attached table, make sure that you do not change any of the field names, field data types, or FieldSize properties after you import the table. If you change FieldName properties, you may have to make many changes to forms, reports, macros, and Access Basic code when you change to an attached table. If your application involves Paradox, Btrieve, and client/server database tables, do not change the primary key fields of these tables. With dBASE tables, make sure that the indexes you create correspond to those of the associated .NDX or .MDX files.

Importing Spreadsheet Files

Access can import files created by spreadsheet and related applications, such as project management systems, in the following formats:

- Excel 2.x, 3.0, and 4.0 .XLS files and task and resource files created by Microsoft Project for Windows 1.0 and 3.0 in .XLS format.

- Lotus 1-2-3 .WKS (Release 1 and Symphony), .WK1 (Release 2) and .WK3 (Release 3) files. Most spreadsheet applications can export files to at least one of these Lotus formats.

You can embed or link charts created by Microsoft Excel that are stored in files with an .XLC extension. Copy the contents of the file to the Windows Clipboard (either from Excel or the Windows 3.1 Object Packager). Then embed or link the chart in fields of the OLE object type and display the chart on a form or print it on a report as an unbound object. Similarly, you can embed or link views displayed in Project for Windows 3.0, which also uses the Microsoft Chart applet, except task and resource forms and the Task PERT chart. Chapters 13 through 15 describe linking and embedding techniques.

Figure 5.20 illustrates the preferred format for exporting data from Excel and other spreadsheet applications to Access tables. Most spreadsheet applications refer to the format as a *database*. The names of the fields entered in the first row and the remainder of the database range consist of data. The type of data in each column must be consistent within the database range you choose.

FIG. 5.20

Invoice data in a Microsoft Excel spreadsheet.

All the cells that comprise the range of the worksheet to be imported into an Access table must have *frozen values*. Frozen values substitute numeric results for the Excel expressions that were used to create the values. When cells include formulas, Access imports the cells as blank data cells. Freezing values causes Access to overwrite the formulas in your spreadsheet with the frozen values. If the range to be imported includes formulas, save a copy of your .XLS file with a new name. Using the worksheet window with the new file name, select the range to be imported and freeze the values by choosing **E**dit **C**opy or pressing Ctrl+C. Choose **E**dit Paste **S**pecial, choose the Values command, and choose OK. Save the new spreadsheet by its new name and use this file to import the data. The section "Using the Clipboard To Import Data," later in this chapter, presents an alternative to this procedure.

To import data from an Excel spreadsheet in to an Access table, follow these steps:

1. Launch Excel and open the .XLS file that contains the data you want to import.

2. Add field names above the first row of the data you plan to export (if you have not done so). Field names cannot include periods (.), exclamation points (!), or brackets ([ ]). You cannot have duplicate field names. If you include improper characters in field names or use duplicate field names, you receive an error message.

3. If your worksheet contains cells with data that is not to be included in the imported table, select the range that contains the field names row and all the rows of data needed for the table. Choose **D**efine Name from the **F**ormula menu and name the range.

Access does not accept Excel's database range name for importing table data. If you previously defined the range that you want to import as an Excel database, select the same range of cells and define a new range name for the field names and data. If you try to import Excel's database named range, you receive an Invalid Range message box.

4. If the worksheet cells include expressions, freeze the values as described in the warning preceding these steps.

5. Save the Excel file (using a different file name if you froze values) and exit Excel to conserve Windows resources for Access if your computer has less than 4M of memory.

6. Launch Access, if it is not running, and open the database to which you want to add the new table. The Database window must be active (with a dark title bar, usually blue) in order for you to be able to import a file.

Access

7. Choose **I**mport from the Access **F**ile menu. The Import dialog box appears (see fig. 5.21). The Data Source list box provides several more formats for importing tables than it provides for attaching files.

8. Choose Microsoft Excel from the list box and choose OK.

9. Choose the drive, directory, and file name of the spreadsheet to import from the Select File dialog box and then choose OK. The Import Spreadsheet Options dialog box appears (see fig. 5.22).

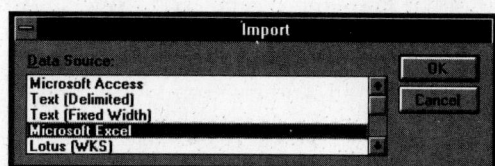

FIG. 5.21

The dialog box for selecting an Excel spread-sheet as the im-port file source.

FIG. 5.22

The dialog box for selecting options for importing spreadsheets.

10. Your spreadsheet range contains field names in the first row, so choose the First Row Contains Field Names box. You have the option of creating a new table or appending records from the spreadsheet to an existing table. Create New Table is the default. If you have named the range in your spreadsheet that contains the data to import, enter the range name in the Spreadsheet Range text box. Or, you may enter the range in standard row-column format. Then choose OK.

11. Access imports the field names and data from the .XLS file. When the operation is complete and error-free, the Import Results dialog box displays a message confirming the importation and telling you how many records were imported (see fig. 5.23).

FIG. 5.23

The Import
Results dialog
box when no
errors occur.

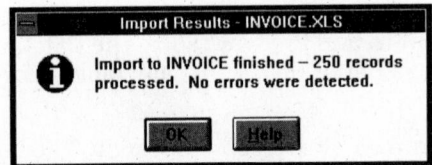

If every cell in a column has a numeric or date value, the columns convert to Number and Date/Time field data types, respectively. A single
text entry in a column of your spreadsheet causes Access to display a
message reporting that errors occurred and to change the field data
type to Text (see fig. 5.24). The five errors reported were deliberately
introduced in another imported Excel file named INV_ERRS.XLS.

If you received an error message similar to the one shown in figure
5.24, Access creates an Import Errors table with one record for each
error (see fig. 5.25). You can review this table, select the records in
which the errors are reported, and fix them. A better approach, however, is to correct the cells in the spreadsheet, resave the file, and import the corrected data.

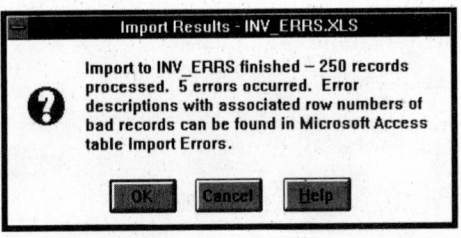

FIG. 5.24

The Import
Results dialog
box that reports
errors.

FIG. 5.25

The Import Errors
table that Access
creates when
inconsistent field
data types occur.

The Database window now contains a new table with the name of your
file, minus the extension as the default. If you import another file with
the same name as your spreadsheet file name, Access adds the number
1 to the file name.

To verify that you obtained the result you wanted, double-click the
name of the imported table in the Database window to display the new
table in Datasheet view. Figure 5.26 illustrates a portion of the Access
table created from the INVOICE.XLS spreadsheet file of figure 5.20.

Invoice	Date	Customer	Address	City	STA	Zip Cod	Phone
1001	7/9/92	John Sayers	887 Oak St.	Kensington	CA	94707	415-837-2262
1002	7/9/92	Bill Colburn	2723 Barnard Stree	Fremont	CA	94536	415-934-8467
1003	7/9/92	De Marco	4907 Antioch St.	Danville	CA	94526	415-651-2733
1004	7/9/92	Joe Mock	550 Freitas Rd.	Alamo	CA	94507	415-866-1727
1005	7/9/92	Richard Cox	2032C Ascott Dr.	Alamo	CA	94507	415-254-7043
1006	7/9/92	Anna Hennessy	363 Reed Dr.	Concord	CA	94518	415-284-5110
1007	7/9/92	Patricia Washburn	34 Sherwood Ct.	El Sobrante	CA	94803	415-820-2885
1008	7/9/92	Chuck Pickens	2000 Norris Rd.	Walnut Creek	CA	94598	415-827-3746
1009	7/9/92	Ellinwood HOA	353 Conifer Court	Walnut Creek	CA	94598	415-223-5168
1010	7/10/92	Axel Hoffmann	1940 Blackstone D	Lafayette	CA	94549	415-687-5084
1011	7/10/92	Diane Wood	1311 Hampshire Ct	Fremont	CA	94536	415-938-7044
1012	7/10/92	David Krumboltz	43438 Newport	Antioch	CA	94509	415-635-1794
1013	7/10/92	Rudolf Storz	1347 New Hampsh	San Ramon	CA	94583	415-939-2599
1014	7/10/92	Vincent Andrade	3363 Springhill Rd.	Concord	CA	94518	415-337-1496
1015	7/10/92	Roger Cornwall	3155 Henderson D	Antioch	CA	94509	415-829-3393
1016	7/10/92	Wes Dodd	24450 Alves Rd.	Concord	CA	94518	415-937-2967
1017	7/10/92	Mary Radley	35531 Woodbridge	Concord	CA	94520	415-462-8475
1018	7/10/92	Nell Spamm	5160 Myrtle Drive	Hayward	CA	94541	415-237-5063
1019	7/10/92	Juan Gutierrez	2464 Wimbledon L	Pinole	CA	94564	415-490-2897
1020	7/13/92	Charles Trombetta	1781 Margo Dr.	Richmond	CA	94801	415-743-1917

FIG. 5.26

The Excel
spreadsheet data
of figure 5.20
imported to the
Invoice table.

To display the .XLS file data types that Access has chosen, click the
Design mode button on the toolbar. Figure 5.27 shows the structure of
the new Invoice table.

To change the table name from the default assigned by Access, close all
open tables and activate the Database window, if necessary. Choose
Rename from the File menu. The Rename dialog box appears with the
default table name (see fig. 5.28). In the text box, type the new name for
the table and then press Enter or choose OK. You cannot rename an
open table, and you cannot rename a table that is created from an
attached file.

After you successfully import the table, you may want to change the
properties of the fields. Unlike its procedure with attached files, Access
places no restrictions on altering the field properties of imported files.
The section "Modifying Attached and Imported Tables," later in this
chapter, discusses changing the default field data types of tables created by imported files.

FIG. 5.27

The structure of
the Invoices table
imported from
Excel.

FIG. 5.28

Renaming a
table.

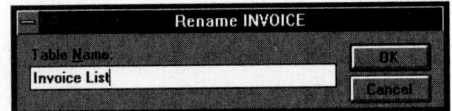

Importing Text Files

If the data you want to import into an Access table was developed in a
word processing, database, or other application that cannot export the
data as a .DBF, .WK?, or .XLS file, you need to create a text file in one
of the text formats supported by Access. (A *text file* is a file with data
consisting of characters that you can read with a text editor, such as
Windows Notepad or the DOS 5 text editor, EDIT.COM.) Most DOS-
compatible data files created from data in mainframe computers and
files converted from nine-track magnetic tapes are text files, and Access
imports these files in various formats.

Access refers to the characters that separate fields as *delimiters* or
separators. In this book, the term *delimiter* refers to characters that
identify the end of a field; the term *text identifiers* refers to the single
and double quotation marks that you can use to distinguish text from
numeric data.

The following list details the formats that Access supports:

Format	Description
Comma-delimited text files (also called CSV [Comma-Separated Value] files)	Commas separate (delimit) fields. The *newline pair*, carriage return (ASCII character 13) and line feed (ASCII character 10), separate records. Some applications enclose all values within double quotation marks; this format is often called *mail-merge* format. Other applications enclose only text (strings) in quotation marks to differentiate between text and numeric values, the standard format for files created by the xBase command COPY TO *FILENAME* DELIMITED.
Tab-delimited text files (also called ASCII files)	These files treat all values as text and separate fields with tabs. Records are separated by newline pairs. Most word processing applications use this format to export tabular text.
Space-delimited files	Access can use spaces to separate fields in a line of text. The use of spaces as delimiter characters is uncommon because it can cause fields, such as names and addresses, to be divided inconsistently into different fields.
Fixed-width text files	Access separates (parses) the individual records into fields based on the position of the data items in a line of text. Newline pairs separate records; every record must have exactly the same length. Spaces pad the fields to a specified fixed width. Using spaces to specify field width is the most common format for data exported by mainframes and minicomputers on nine-track tape. Unlike the delimited and tab-separated files, Access requires that you create an import/export specification before you import a fixed-width text file.

Access requires that you define how text files are to be imported. For delimited files of any type, you first can choose the file and then provide the setup parameters. Fixed-width files, however, require that you prepare and save a setup specification before you select the text file to import.

To create an import specification before you select the text file to import, complete the following steps:

1. Activate the Database window to make the import/export commands appear in the File menu.

2. Choose Imp/Exp **S**etup from the **F**ile menu. The Import/Export Setup dialog box appears (see fig. 5.29).

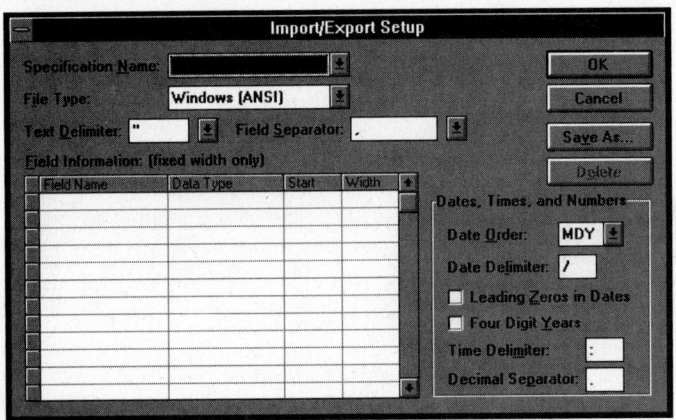

FIG. 5.29

Using Import/Export Setup dialog box to specify parameters for imported text files.

3. From the drop-down list boxes, choose the values applicable to each of the parameters that affect the type of file you are importing. For comma-delimited files, choose the quotation mark (") as the text delimiter and the comma (,) as the field separator.

4. If you are importing a fixed-width text file (also called *fixed-length* text file), you are required to assign field names, data types, starting positions, and field widths at this point. Text-delimiter and field-separator characters are ignored when fixed-width text files are imported.

5. Choose Save As. The Save Specification As dialog box appears (see fig. 5.30).

FIG. 5.30

Assigning names to import/export specifications.

6. Enter a descriptive name for the specification in the dialog box. Then choose OK.

After you create and save an import/export setup, you can reuse the setup by choosing Import/Export Setup from the File menu to display the Import/Export Setup dialog box. This dialog box is the only place where you can select or delete an existing specification that you have created. You can select one of your customized setups from the Specification Name drop-down list.

The specific values of the parameters to be used and the method of calculating field starting points for delimited and fixed-width text file types are described in the two sections that follow.

Using Delimited Text Files

Delimited files can accept a wide variety of field and record delimiting characters. The native format (used by files created within WordPerfect) of WordPerfect secondary merge files, for example, uses control characters to separate fields and records. Access provides commas, tabs, and spaces as standard field delimiters. You can type any printable character (such as an asterisk or a dollar sign) in the text box as a delimiter. Because spaces and other special-character delimiting seldom is used, only comma-delimited (CSV) and tab-delimited files are presented in this chapter.

Word processing applications use both commas and tabs as delimiters in the mail-merge files that they or other applications create for personalized documents. The newline pair is universally used to indicate the end of a record in mail-merge files; a record always consists of a single line of text.

Comma-Delimited Text Files without Text-Identifier Characters

Comma-delimited files come in two styles: with or without quotation marks surrounding text fields. The quotation marks, usually the standard double quotation marks ("), identify the fields within them as having the Text data type. Fields without quotation marks are processed as numeric values. Not all applications offer this capability; for example, CSV files exported by Excel do not enclose text within quotation marks. Figure 5.31 shows a typical Excel CSV file opened in the Windows Notepad applet.

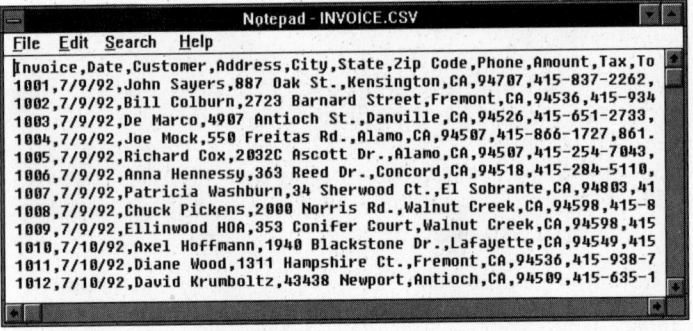

FIG. 5.31

A comma-
delimited Excel
file displayed in
the Windows
Notepad applet.

Using Notepad to view files that fit within its 60K file size limitation is a quick way to determine the type of text file with which
you are dealing. If the file is longer than 60K, you can use Windows Write to view the file. Make sure, however, that you do not
save the file as a .WRI file after you view or edit it. If you used
Write to edit the file, choose **File Save As** and specify a .TXT file.

To import values in a comma-delimited (CSV) file into an Access table,
follow these steps:

1. Activate the Database window, making the **File** menu import
   commands available.

2. Choose **Import** from the **File** menu. The Data Source list box
   appears.

3. Choose Text (Delimited) and then choose OK. The Select File dialog box appears.

4. Choose the drive, directory, and file name of the CSV file from
   which the values are to be imported. Then choose OK. The simplified version of the Import Text Options dialog box appears (see
   fig. 5.32).

5. If your text file uses commas as the field-delimiting character and
   either no quotation marks or double quotation marks to identify
   text fields, you can accept the defaults and choose OK. For this
   example, however, click the Options >> button. The detailed version of the Import Text Options dialog box appears (see fig. 5.33).

6. Because the CSV file includes the field names, choose the First
   Row Contains Field Names check box. Access offers to append
   records to an existing table, INVOICE. (In this example, Access
   does not have an existing table and creates a new table.)

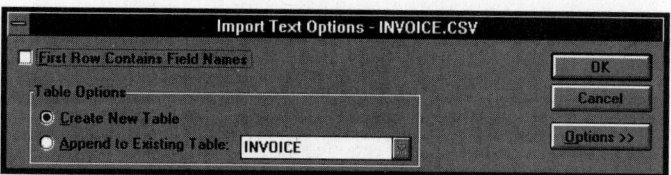

FIG. 5.32

Importing files with Access defaults as field separators and text identifiers.

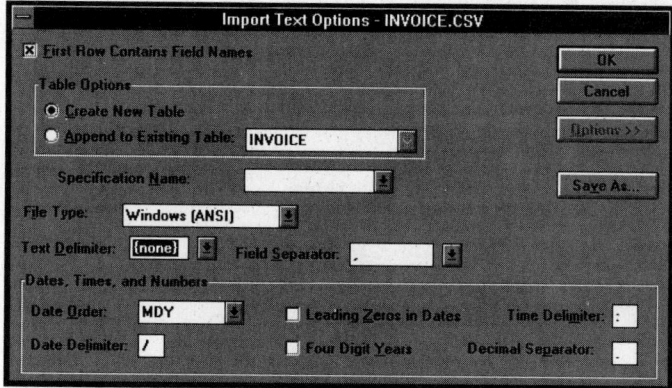

FIG. 5.33

The detailed version of the Import Text Options dialog box.

7. Accept the default. You have not created any specification names at this point, so you cannot select a previously defined specification for importing.

8. Because this CSV file does not use quotation marks as text identifiers, open the Text Delimiter drop-down list and choose None. The other settings are standard, and you do not need to change them.

9. Click the Save As button. The Save Specification As dialog box appears (see fig. 5.34).

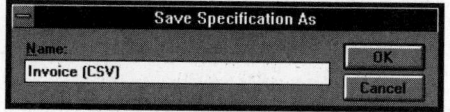

FIG. 5.34

The Save Specification As dialog box.

From this point, the procedure for importing text files is the same as the procedure for importing spreadsheet files. If no errors occur during importation, you receive the Import Results dialog box with

214

the number of records imported. Errors in field data types are likely to occur only if you have incorrectly edited the text identifiers of the files.

Comma-Delimited Text Files with Text-Identifier Characters

The default delimited text file type of dBASE, created by the COPY TO *FILENAME* DELIMITED command, creates comma-delimited files with text fields surrounded by double quotation marks. (Date and Numeric field types do not have quotation marks.) This type of delimited file is standard in many other database systems, as well as project and personal information management applications. Figure 5.35 shows an example created by dBASE III+.

The specification for double quotation marks as the text identifier is the only difference between the Import Text Options dialog box entries of the INVOICE.CSV and INVOICE.DEL files (see figs. 5.33 and 5.36).

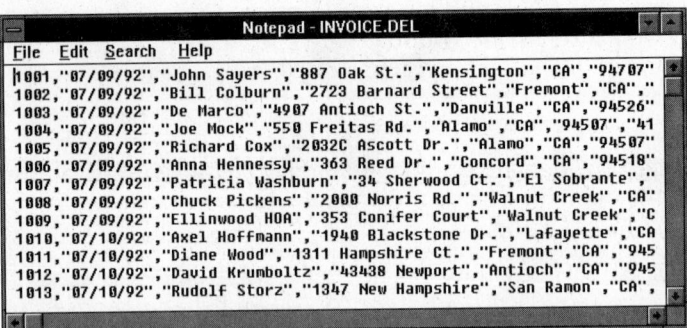

FIG. 5.35

A comma-delimited text file with text identifiers using double quotation marks.

Tab-Delimited Text Files

Word processing applications often use tab characters to separate fields in mail-merge files. These tab characters usually define the fields of tables when you convert conventional text to tabular format (and *vice versa*) in word processors such as Word for Windows. Tab-delimited files rarely use text-identifier characters. Figure 5.37 shows a tab-delimited text file in Windows Notepad.

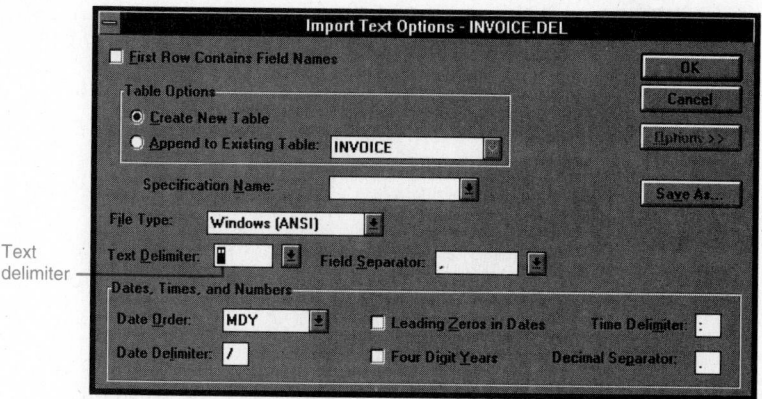

FIG. 5.36

The Import Text Options dialog box for files with text identification characters.

The Word for Windows 2.0 merge data file that created the tab-delimited text file in figure 5.37 is shown in figure 5.38. Many organizations acquire DBMs because the amount of their data becomes too large for their word processing application to maintain mailing lists for direct-mail advertising and other promotional and fund-raising purposes. DBMs also enable you to create specialized merge data files for specific types of customers, ranges of ZIP codes, and other parameters you select.

```
Notepad - INVOICE.TXT
 File   Edit   Search   Help
Invoice Date     Customer        Address City     State     Zip Code
1001    7/9/92   John Sayers     887 Oak St.    Kensington     CA
1002    7/9/92   Bill Colburn    2723 Barnard Street     Fremont CA
1003    7/9/92   De Marco        4907 Antioch St.        Danville
1004    7/9/92   Joe Mock        550 Freitas Rd. Alamo   CA      94507
1005    7/9/92   Richard Cox     2032C Ascott Dr.        Alamo   CA
1006    7/9/92   Anna Hennessy   363 Reed Dr.    Concord CA      94518
1007    7/9/92   Patricia Washburn      34 Sherwood Ct. El Sobrante
1008    7/9/92   Chuck Pickens   2000 Norris Rd. Walnut Creek   CA
1009    7/9/92   Ellinwood HOA   353 Conifer Court       Walnut Creek
1010    7/10/92  Axel Hoffmann   1940 Blackstone Dr.     Lafayette
1011    7/10/92  Diane Wood      1311 Hampshire Ct.      Fremont CA
1012    7/10/92  David Krumboltz 43438 Newport   Antioch CA      94509
```

FIG. 5.37

A tab-delimited text file displayed in the Notepad applet.

Fortunately, Access has a simple process for converting the merge data files used by most word processors to text files that can be imported and maintained by an Access database application. In Word for Windows, for example, you simply open the merge data file in whatever format you use (usually the native .DOC) and save the document in Text Only (.TXT) format with a different file name. WordPerfect 5+ (using CONVERT.EXE) and WordPerfect for Windows offer a variety of export formats for their secondary merge files. Unless you have a specific file type in mind, choose the tab-delimited format for these files.

216

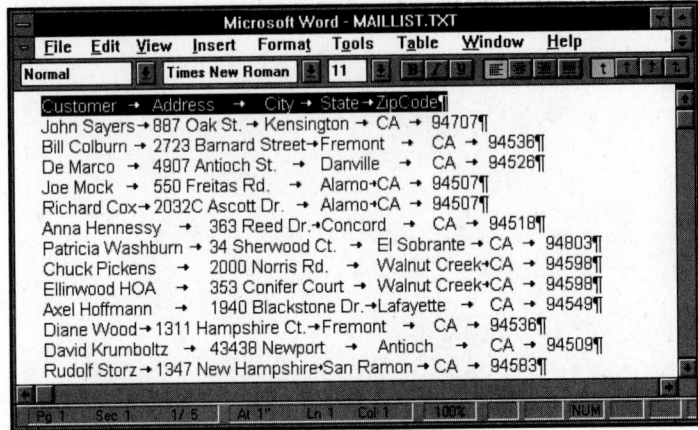

A Word for Windows 2.0 data file used for customizing merge documents.

Handling Fixed-Width Text Files

If you have a choice of text file formats for the data you plan to import into Access, avoid using fixed-width text files by choosing a delimited file format. Fixed-width text files require that you enter a complete specification for the location and width of each field. In addition, you must name the fields, rather than rely on the first line of the text file to provide names for you. Fixed-width text files seldom come with a field name header in the first line.

A fixed-width text file looks like the file in figure 5.39. Fixed-width text files often contain more spaces than data characters. In a tab-delimited file, the spaces between fields are not included in the file itself, but are added by the text editor (see the Notepad in figure 5.37) when tab characters (ASCII character 9) are encountered. In a fixed-width file, each space is represented by ASCII character 32.

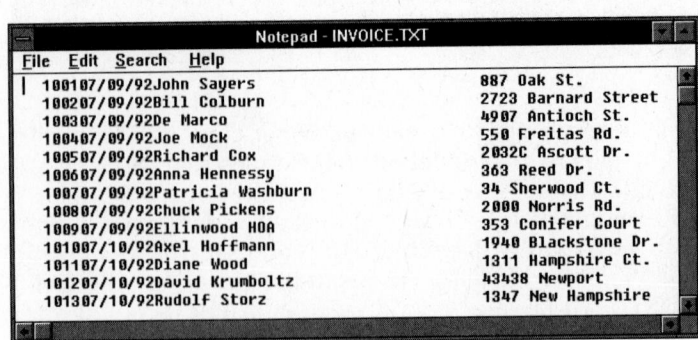

FIG. 5.39

A fixed-width text file displayed in Notepad.

To import a fixed-width text file into an Access table, complete the following procedure:

1. Choose Import/Export Setup from the File menu. The Import/Export Setup dialog box appears without the Field Information entries (see fig. 5.40). Access requires an import specification before you can select the fixed-width text file for importing.

File specification entries required for importing fixed-width text.

You can disregard the field delimiters and text-identification characters when you are working with fixed-width text files. Figure 5.40 shows the delimiter as None and the text-identification character as Space only to emphasize that these characters can be disregarded. The other default values offered in the dialog box are acceptable, except on rare occasions.

2. In the Field Information text boxes, enter the field name and data type for each field contained in the records. With fixed-width fields, you may select data types from a drop-down list that includes the standard field data types and those defined by the FieldSize property, such as Integer.

3. In the Start box, enter the beginning position of the first character of the field. Then, in the Width text box, enter the number of characters in the field. You often can obtain the required entries from a file-specification sheet provided with the disk or tape on which the file was stored originally. If you do not have a specification sheet, add the values of the starting position to the field width of the last field you entered in order to find the starting position of the next field.

4. Repeat steps 2 and 3 until you have fully specified each field.

5. Save your import specification by clicking the Save As button. The Save Specification As dialog box appears.

> If you do not save your specification, you will lose all your work.

6. In the Save Specification As dialog box, enter an appropriate name.

7. Choose Import from the File menu. The Import dialog box appears.

8. Choose Text (Fixed Width) from the Data Source list box of the Import dialog box. Another variation of the Import/Export Options dialog box appears—this time with a Specification Name drop-down list box (see fig. 5.41).

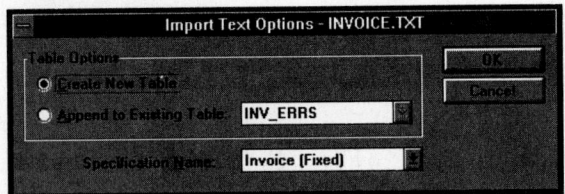

9. Select the name you assigned to the import specification for the fixed-width file and choose OK.

From this point, the import procedure is the same as that for spreadsheets and delimited text files. If your fields don't import properly or you receive a substantial number of error messages, you may have miscalculated one or more of the starting positions of a field. Locate the first field name with a problem; the names following it usually have problems, too. Choose Import/Export Setup from the File menu to correct the errors in field position. Close all open tables. From the Database window, choose the table you imported and press the Del key. If you have an Errors table, delete it, too. You cannot delete an open table.

Appending Text Data to an Existing Table

If the data you are importing is provided on a floppy disk, you may need several disks to store the data. Fixed-width text files especially require more floppy disks because they usually are derived from data on mini- and mainframe computers, and the fixed-width format is quite inefficient. If you have imported multiple-disk data into dBASE files, for example, you probably have learned that you must concatenate all the files on your hard disk into one large text file. You concatenate files by using the DOS COPY *file1+file2 file3* command or by appending each file to a separate dBASE file and then appending the remaining BASE files to the file created from the first disk. This is a very tedious process.

Access enables you to append data from text files to an existing table. In addition to simplifying the process described in the preceding paragraph, you can update an imported file with new text data by appending it directly from the source text file, rather than by creating a new Access table and then appending the new table to the existing one.

If you saved the import/export specifications when you first created the table from a text file, you can append a text file to an existing table by following these steps:

1. Make a backup copy of your table in the same database or another database in case an error occurs during the Append operation.

2. Choose Import from the File menu.

3. Choose the type of source data from the Import dialog box.

4. From the Import Options dialog box, choose Append to Existing Table.

5. From the drop-down list of existing tables, select the table to which you want to append the data.

6. Open the Specification Name drop-down list, select the import specification that applies to the table, and then choose OK.

At the end of the appending process, a message box appears, reporting the number of new records added to your table. The Import Errors table displays any errors made.

Maintaining a backup copy of the table to which you are appending files is very important. If you accidentally choose the wrong import specification for the file, you can end up with one error for each appended record. Then, if you do not have a backup file, you must delete the appended records and start over. To use a backup table file, close and delete the damaged table. Then choose Rename from the File menu to change the name of the backup table to the name of the damaged table.

Using the Clipboard To Import Data

If another Windows application generates the data you want to import, you can use the Windows Clipboard to transfer the data without having to create a file. This technique is especially useful for making corrections to a single record with many fields or for appending new records to a table. This process requires a table with the proper field structure so that you can paste the data copied to the Clipboard in the other application. Pasting rows from an Excel spreadsheet, for example, requires a table with fields containing data types that correspond to those of each column that you copy to the Clipboard. Other Windows applications that can copy tabular data to the Clipboard use similar techniques.

Pasting New Records to a Table

To import data from the Clipboard and then append the data to an existing table or table structure, use the following procedure:

Microsoft

1. Open the application you will be using to copy the data to the Clipboard—in this case, Microsoft Excel. Then open the file that contains the data. If you have less than 3M of memory, you may have to close Access before you can open Excel.

2. Select the range to be appended to the table (see fig. 5.42). The Excel columns you select must start with the column that corresponds to the first field of your Access table. You do not, however, need to copy all the columns that correspond to fields in your table. Access supplies blank values in the columns of your appended records that are not included in your Excel range. Remember that, if any of the columns you select contain formulas, the values must be frozen.

3. Press Ctrl+C, or choose Copy from the Edit menu, to copy the selected cells to the Clipboard.

Microsoft

Access

4. Launch Access and open the table to which you are appending the records in Datasheet view.

5. Choose Paste Append from the Access Edit menu. If no errors occur during the pasting process, a message box reports how many new records you added (see fig. 5.43). Choose OK. The records are appended to your Access table (see fig. 5.44).

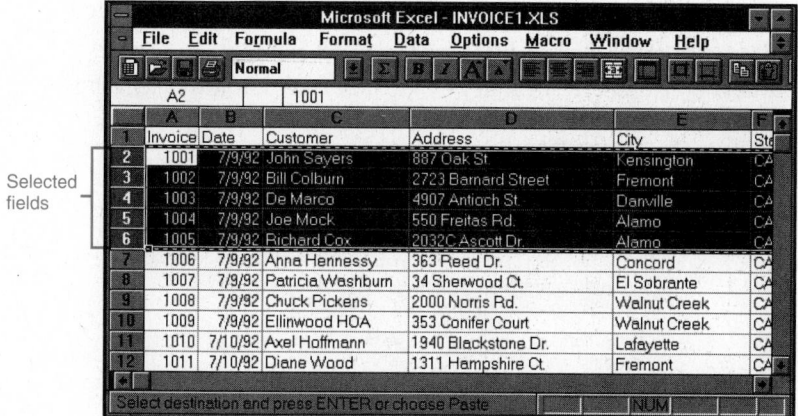

FIG. 5.42

Fields selected in Excel to be appended to an Access table using the Clipboard.

FIG. 5.43

The dialog box that follows a successful appending operation.

FIG. 5.44

Records appended to an Access table.

Errors usually occur during the Paste/Append process for one of two reasons: the data types in the Excel cells do not match those in the corresponding fields of your Access table, or you attempted to paste records with data that duplicates information in key fields of the table. Both types of errors result in Access creating a Paste Errors table containing information on the records with the errors. The Paste Errors table for field type mismatches is similar in purpose and appearance to the Import Errors table described earlier in this chapter.

 Errors caused by duplicate primary key violations result in the following series of cascading dialog boxes:

■ Figure 5.45 shows the first message you receive. Access does not offer a Cancel option; therefore, you must choose OK.

FIG. 5.45

The dialog box indicating that an attempt has been made to paste a record with a duplicate key value.

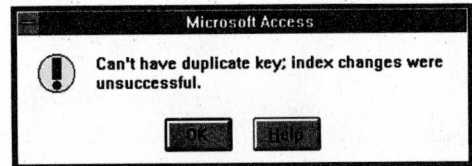

■ Next, a dialog box appears enabling you to suppress further error messages (see fig. 5.46). If you want to cancel the append operation, choose Cancel. Otherwise, choose Yes to attempt to paste the remaining records without reporting further errors. If you want to see which errors occur as they are encountered, choose No.

FIG. 5.46

The dialog box enabling you to continue pasting records without reporting errors.

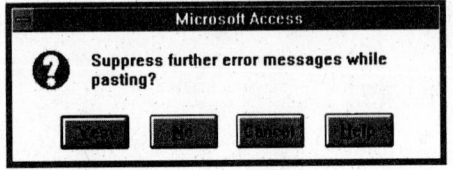

■ A dialog box reports how many records were successfully pasted (see fig. 5.47). Choose OK.

FIG. 5.47

The dialog box indicating that some records were pasted.

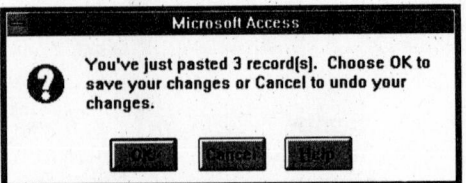

■ Finally, a dialog box reports where the records that couldn't be pasted were placed (see fig. 5.48). Choose OK.

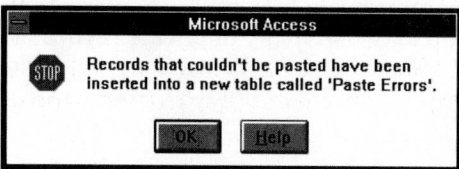

FIG. 5.48

The message that some records could not be pasted.

Figure 5.49 illustrates the result of this Pandora's box of messages. The set of five records copied to the Clipboard from Excel contained two records that duplicated key field values in the existing table. Access pasted the remaining three records and inserted the two records with duplicate key values into a Paste Errors table.

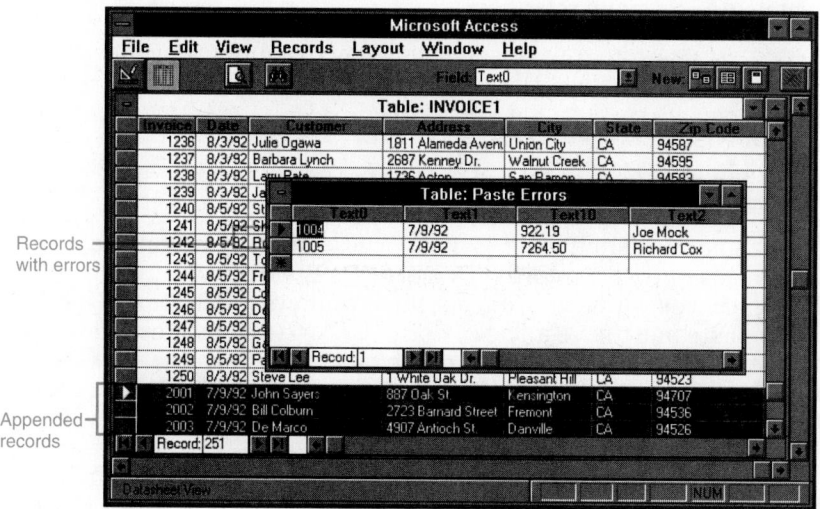

FIG. 5.49

Tables showing pasted records and key field index errors.

If you have specified one or more primary key fields for your table, records that duplicate key field values are not appended. Tables without primary key fields do not preclude adding duplicate records. The capability to index a nonkey field with the condition "no duplicates allowed" is useful when you have made new entries into a spreadsheet or word processing document, and you want to append the new entries as records to a table. You preserve the uniqueness of the records by preventing the addition of records that duplicate records already in your table.

When pasting or importing large numbers of records to a table, you must specify primary key fields or a no-duplicate index for fields that later may become the primary key *before* you import *any* data. If you import the data before you create the primary key fields index, you may find many duplicate records in the table. Then when Access attempts to create a no-duplicates index on the key fields, you receive the following message:

```
Can't have duplicate key
```

You must manually review all the added records for duplicates because Access does not create an Errors table in this case. If, on the other hand, the data you are importing contains redundant information that you ultimately will be removing to one or more secondary tables, you must import *every* record. Do not assign key fields or no-duplicates indexes in this case. The section "Deleting Redundant Fields in Imported Tables," later in this chapter, discusses the requirement to import every record when records contain one-to-many relations.

Replacing Records by Pasting from the Clipboard

You can replace existing records in an Access table by pasting data in the Clipboard over the records. This process is useful when you are updating records with data from another Windows application. The data you paste must have a one-to-one column-to-field correspondence and must begin with the first field of the table. You need not, however, paste new data in all the fields. If no data is pasted in a field that is not included in the copied data's range, that field retains its original values.

To use data in the Clipboard to replace existing records in a table, follow this procedure:

1. Select and copy the data from the other application that you want to paste to the Clipboard, using the method previously described for appending records from Clipboard data.

If you choose more than one row of data in Excel, for example, the rows must have a one-to-one correspondence with the records to be replaced in the Access table. The one-to-one correspondence is likely to occur only if the table is indexed and the source data you·are copying is sorted in the same order as the index. You can paste only contiguous rows from Excel.

2. Open your Access table. To select the records to be replaced by the Clipboard data, click the selection button for a single record or drag the mouse across the buttons for multiple records.

Access

If you are replacing multiple records, the number of records you select must be equal to or exceed the number of rows you copied to the Clipboard. If the number of records selected is less than the number of rows, the remaining rows are ignored.

If you are replacing records in a table with key fields or a no-duplicates index, the columns of the replacement data corresponding to the key or indexed fields of the table must match exactly the key fields of the selected records. Otherwise, you receive the key duplication error message sequence.

3. From the Access **Edit** menu, choose **Paste**. In this case, instead of appending the records, the contents of the existing records are overwritten, and you see a dialog box telling you how many records were replaced successfully.

When you use **Paste** for a replacement record rather than Paste Appen**d** for a new record with an identical key field value, Access suppresses the key violation error messages.

If you do not select one or more records to be replaced by the Pasting operation, and the caret is located within a data cell of one of your records or a data cell is selected, Access attempts to paste all the data in the Clipboard to this single cell, rather than to the records. If the data does not create a mismatch type error or exceed 255 characters (if the caret is in a Text field), you do not receive a warning message. If you notice unexpected data values in the cell, Access has pasted all the data to a single cell. Press Esc before selecting another record; Access restores the original value of the data cell.

Modifying Attached and Imported Tables

Access provides a great deal of flexibility in the presentation of the Datasheet view of tables. You can rearrange the sequence of fields in Datasheet view without changing the underlying structure of the database. You also can alter the Caption property of the fields to change the names of the field name buttons. Although you cannot modify the field names, field data types, or FieldLength properties of attached tables, you can use the Format property to display the data in attached or imported tables in various ways.

Restructuring the Presentation of Tables

The basic structure of the tables you attach or import is controlled by the structure of the files from which the table was created. The original structure, unfortunately, may not be in the sequence you want to use for data entry. Database design, for example, often displays the key fields in a left-to-right sequence, starting with the first field. This sequence may not be the best sequence for entering data. You can change the order of the fields displayed by dragging and dropping the field name buttons of attached or imported tables to new locations, using the method described in Chapter 4.

Adding Fields to Tables with Imported Data

You can add fields to tables that use imported data. During the development of your database application, you may need to repeatedly import data into your table. Therefore, you should append new fields to the end of the field list in Design view rather than insert them between existing fields. The imported data fills the fields in the sequence of the rows in the field list, and the added fields contain null values. You then can rearrange the display position of the new fields in Design view, as described in the preceding section.

Changing Field Data Types of Imported Files

Access converts all numeric data within imported files to the Double data type. The only exception is Btrieve files, where Access assigns Byte, Integer, Long Integer, and Single data types when you attach or import Btrieve files that include these data types. The following list contains recommendations for field data type changes for data imported from any type of source file:

- Use *Integer* or *Long* data types for numeric fields that do not require decimal values. Your database files will consume less disk space, and your applications will run faster.

- Change the data type of values that represent money to the data type *Currency* in order to eliminate rounding errors.

■ Assign *FieldLength* properties to Text type fields. You should assign FieldLength values that are no greater than the longest text entry you expect to make. If you assign a FieldLength value less than the number of characters in the field, characters in positions beyond the FieldLength value are lost irretrievably.

Because Paradox 3+ does not provide a Memo field data type, you often can find comments in large, fixed-width alphanumeric fields. If you are importing Paradox files that contain fields of comments, you should convert the fields to Memo fields unless you plan to export the data back to a Paradox 3+ file. (You cannot export a table containing a Memo type field to Paradox 3+ files.) The same recommendation applies to comments in variable-length string fields of Btrieve files.

Adding or Modifying Other Field Properties

The following list includes properties of both attached and imported tables that you may change:

Property	Description
Caption	Use this property to change the caption of the field name buttons when using attached files. You can assign any FieldName property to imported tables.
DecimalPlaces	You can specify the number of decimal places to be displayed for numeric values other than Byte, Integer, and Long Integer.
DefaultValue	Default values are substituted for data elements missing in the imported or attached file. The default values, however, do not replace zeros and blank strings that represent no entry in the fields of most PC database files.
Format	You can create custom formats to display the data in the most readable form.
ValidationRule	Validation rules do not affect importing data; they affect only editing the data or appending new records in Access. You cannot use a validation rule to filter imported records. *Filtering*, in this case, means importing only those records that meet the validation rule.
ValidationText	Prompts created from validation text assist data entry operators when they begin using a new table.

Deleting Redundant Fields
in Imported Tables

The purpose of a relational database is to eliminate redundant data in tables. If you are designing a database that does not use data imported or attached from existing databases, you can eliminate data redundancy by following the normalization rules of relational database design described in Chapter 19. When you attach files, however, you are at the mercy of the database designer who originally created the files. Any redundant data the attached file contains is likely to remain a permanent characteristic of the file. Existing database structures are substantially inert; developers of applications that work usually are reluctant to make changes. Changes may introduce new problems that may come back to haunt the developers later.

If you import table data from a file or append records by pasting from the Clipboard, you can eliminate data redundancy by restructuring the resulting tables. The Invoice tables that have been used for the examples of this chapter contain one record for each invoice. When a customer makes more than one purchase, the customer information is duplicated in the invoice file for each purchase. You need to create separate tables for customers and invoices. The Customer table should contain one record per customer, with name and address information. The Invoice table should contain one record per customer with date, amount, and other information specific to the transaction.

The process of removing redundancy from existing tables by dividing them into two or more related tables is not a simple task. You must create a query that establishes the relationship between two tables that contain one record for each invoice based on a new primary key field. Then you delete the duplicate records from the Customer table. Fortunately, the Import Errors table can do much of the work for you; import the data into a new table with primary key fields or a no-duplicate index on the customer name and address.

Another type of redundancy is the presence of fields in tables that have values calculated from other fields, either within the table itself or in the fields of related tables. Any field with values derived from combinations of values within the table or accessible in any other related table within the database or attached to the database contains redundant data. In this case, you simply can remove the redundant field and perform the calculation with a query. You should not remove redundant fields, however, until you verify that your calculated values match those in the redundant field to be replaced.

You need to learn about queries and joining tables, the subject of the next three chapters, to know how to eliminate redundancy in imported tables. The point of this discussion is to let you know that you can

perform much of the restructuring by using specialized Access operations, and to caution you not to prematurely attempt to remove duplicate data from imported tables.

For Related Information:

▶▶ "Joining Tables To Create Multitable Queries," p. 306.

FROM HERE...

Exporting Data from Access Tables

You can export data contained in Access tables in any format you can
use to import data. The most common export operation with PC DBMs
is the creation of mail-merge files, used with word processing applications and spreadsheet files, for data analysis. In most cases, you may
want to export the result of a query, enabling you to select specific
records to export rather than the entire contents of a file. Exporting
tables created from action queries is discussed in Chapter 8.

Exporting Data through the Windows Clipboard

If a Windows application will be using your exported data, the simplest
method to export data is to copy the records you want to export to the
Windows Clipboard and then paste the data into the other application.
You can copy specific groups of contiguous records to the Clipboard
by using the techniques described in Chapter 4.

To create a merge data file from the Customers table of the Northwind
sample database for use with Word for Windows, follow these steps:

1. Activate the Database window and then open the NWIND.MDB
   database.

2. Open the Customers table from the table list.

Table

3. Rearrange the display of the fields of the Customers table by
   selecting and then dragging and dropping the Customer ID field to
   the right of the Country field, and the Contact Name and Contact
   Title fields to the left of the Company Name field.

4. Select the records you want to copy by dragging the mouse down the column of selection buttons. The Datasheet view should look like the window in figure 5.50. If you want to select all records in the table, choose Select All Records from the Edit menu.

5. Press Ctrl+C or choose Copy from the Edit menu to copy the selected records to the Clipboard.

6. Open Word for Windows and choose New from the File menu to create a new window for your merge data file.

7. Press Ctrl+V or choose Paste from the Edit menu to paste the records from the Clipboard into your new document. Tabs separate the fields and the newline pairs—the records (see fig. 5.51). The highlighted line in figure 5.51 shows the effect of including a newline pair (created by pressing Ctrl+Enter) within a field. This file uses quotation marks to identify place names as addresses typical of rural addresses in the United Kingdom.

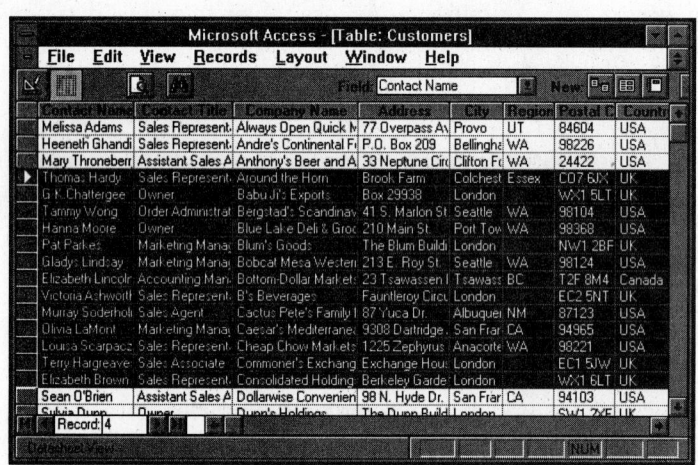

FIG. 5.50

Customer records selected for copying to the Clipboard.

8. You can remove the quotation marks with the Word for Windows Find and Replace function; however, you must manually remove the newline pairs separating structure names from place names in United Kingdom addresses. As a rule, including newline pairs within fields is not wise. A better approach, if you want to place the names on separate lines on an envelope or in an internal address of a letter, is to add a field for the second line of United Kingdom addresses.

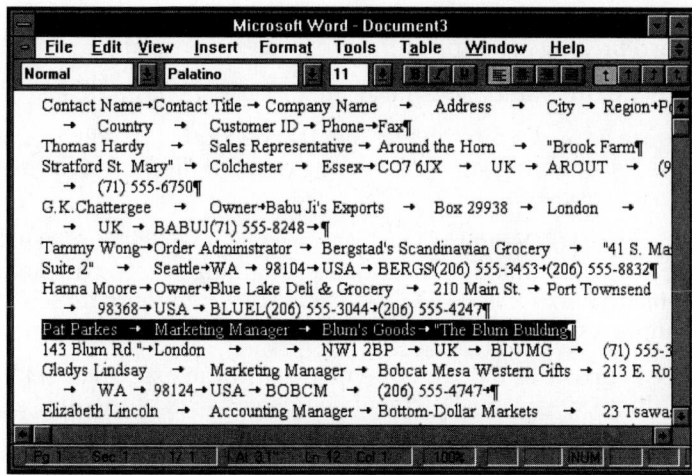

FIG. 5.51

Data in figure 5.50 imported into a Word for Windows document.

When you copy Access records to the Clipboard, the first line contains field names, no matter what group of records you select. If you append individual records or groups of records to those already pasted to a document in another application, you must manually remove the duplicated field names.

The field names pasted into the Word for Windows documents contain spaces. Spaces, however, are not allowed in the first (field names) row for merge data documents. Delete the spaces or replace them with underscores so that Word for Windows accepts the names. If you do not remove the spaces, you receive an error message when you try to use the document during the Merge operation.

For Related Information:

◄◄ "Copying and Pasting Fields, Records, and Tables," p. 178.

FROM HERE...

Exporting Data in a File

Exporting a table involves a sequence of operations quite similar to importing a file with the same format. To export a table as a comma-delimited file that you can use as a merge file with a wide variety of word processing applications, complete these steps:

1. Activate the Database window.

2. Choose Export from the File Menu. The Export dialog box appears, enabling you to select the type of file to which the table is to be exported (see fig. 5.52).

3. Choose Text (Delimited) and choose OK. The Select Microsoft Access Object dialog box appears, enabling you to choose the table to export (see fig. 5.53). Select the Customers table for this example and choose OK.

   Access provides a default file name with the extension .TXT for all text files (see fig. 5.54). The file name consists of the first eight characters of the table name, with any spaces or other punctuation (except underscores) removed.

FIG. 5.52

The dialog box for choosing the file format of an exported table.

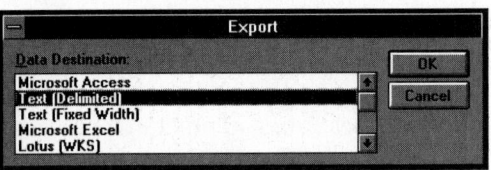

FIG. 5.53

The dialog box for selecting the table to export.

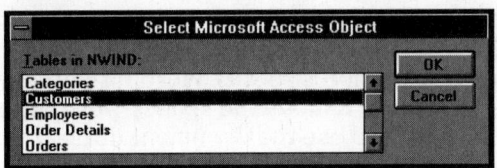

FIG. 5.54

The File Save As dialog box disguised as the Export to File dialog box.

4. Edit the file name, if necessary, to properly identify the file and choose the destination drive and directory. Then choose OK. The abbreviated Export Text Options dialog box appears.

5. Click the Options >> button to display the full Export Text Options dialog box (see fig. 5.55). The defaults shown in the Export Text Options dialog box are standard for comma-delimited files with text identification characters.

6. Choose OK. Access creates the comma-delimited file, consisting of all records in the table. A portion of a comma-delimited file exported from the Customers table and displayed in the Notepad applet is shown in figure 5.56.

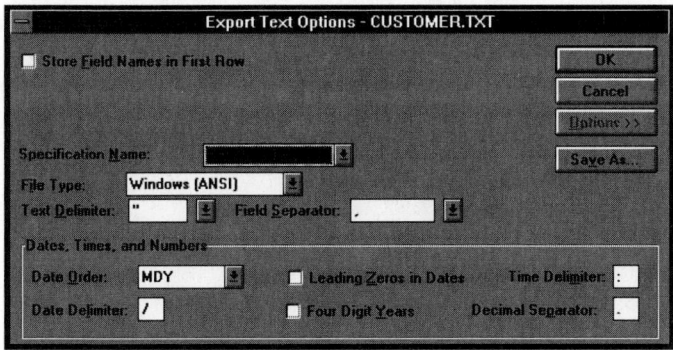

FIG. 5.55

The full Export Text Options dialog box for delimited files.

FIG. 5.56

The comma-delimited file created from Northwind's Customers table.

The records in files created by Access are exported in the order of the primary key. Any other order you may have created is ignored. If you do not assign primary key fields, the records are exported in the sequence that you entered them into the table.

Text files created from tables with fields that include newline pairs share the problem described in the preceding section on exporting data from the Clipboard; any field containing a newline pair results in the creation of a new record at the position of the newline character. Unnecessary newline characters in the resulting text file must be removed manually.

 When you export a dBASE file, Access does not create .NDX files corresponding to the primary key or any additional indexes you may have created in Access. Similarly, exporting a Paradox .DB file does not create an associated .PX file to accompany it. You must use dBASE, one of its clones, or Paradox to re-create any index files required for your application in the other DBMs.

Chapter Summary

Importing data created by other applications is one of the most important subjects when explaining how to use a DBM with a new and, for PC DBMs, unusual file structure. Access is a new combatant in the PC database war. Unlike Paradox for Windows, which can use files that were created by prior versions of Paradox, no prior version of Access exists. You, like every other user of Access, have no existing library of data in the Access native .MDB file format.

Fortunately, with Access you can attach dBASE, Paradox, and even Btrieve files; Btrieve file compatibility is uncommon in PC DBMs. Once you create your database applications using Access forms, reports, and macros and change over to Access as your primary DBM, you probably will choose to import all your files into the Access native .MDB structure.

The next three chapters deal with *queries*—the method used by Access to enable you to select the specific data you need from one or more tables. A few of these chapters will be extensive; you don't have to remember all the nuances of these chapters. You do need to remember where the instructions for performing specific types of operations were presented so that you can return to that point in the book when you create your initial database applications.

PART

II

OUTLINE

Using Queries, Forms, and Reports

Using Query by Example: A Quick Start

Query by Example, usually abbreviated QBE, was originally
developed to enable users of mainframe-computer database
applications to find and display pieces of data (or collections of data)
without requiring them to know a computer language. Many database
management systems eventually came to use QBE in one form or another. (In fact, dBASE, the first commercially successful PC database
manager, uses a variant of QBE for its dot-prompt commands.)

At dBASE's dot prompt, for example, QBE users entered such statements as

```
LIST ALL LASTNAMES LIKE LIN* WITH STATE IL IN USHISTORY
```

(These are known as *give me an example of* statements.) The QBE application program then searched the LASTNAMES field of the
USHISTORY file for all names beginning with LIN. The program disregarded the remaining characters in the names and displayed only those
records having a STATE field containing the value IL.

As computer display terminals became more sophisticated, *graphical
QBE* developed as the preferred method of creating queries. Graphical
QBE displays the field names of one or more database tables as headers
of a column. Users can type partial example statements, or *expressions*,

in these columns to create a query. Because terminals capable of displaying actual graphics were a rarity when graphical QBE was developed, the standard 80-character by 25-line text mode was used. The term *graphical* is a misnomer, therefore, in today's world of truly graphical user environments like Windows. In the original version of graphical QBE, the preceding example statement might resemble the following display:

LASTNAME	FIRSTNAME	ADDRESS	CITY	STATE
Like LIN*				IL

Fields that correspond to the columns in which no expressions are entered are not checked for compliance with the query.

After the designated fields are checked and all matches within the searched file are found, the application displays those addresses containing matching values. The parts of each address appear in their respective columns, as in the following:

LASTNAME	FIRSTNAME	ADDRESS	CITY	STATE
Lincoln	Abraham	123 Elm St.	Springfield	IL
Lincoln	Mary Todd	123 Elm St.	Springfield	IL
Lincoln	Todd	123 Elm St.	Springfield	IL

Learning to type query expressions in graphical QBE columns proved easier for most computer users than typing QBE expressions at a prompt. The user had to know the syntax of only a few expressions to create relatively complex queries. The use of graphical QBE was one feature that made Ansa Software's original Paradox DBM a success in the PC DBM market, dominated at the time by dBASE.

The advent of Microsoft Windows introduced a graphical user environment ideally suited to a truly graphical QBE database management system. Microsoft has taken full advantage of the wide range of graphical features incorporated in Windows 3.1, as you see when you create your first Access query.

Creating Your First Query

Access includes several sample forms and reports created by Microsoft to demonstrate its DBM's prowess. Access also contains sample databases. In this quick start, for example, you use the sample Northwind Traders database. This database features a number of prefabricated queries normally used with the program's sample forms and reports. A quick start may be made quicker by using one of these queries, but you actually can learn far more by creating your own query with simple expressions. This quick start chapter, therefore, teaches you to do just that.

To devise a simple query that enables you to create mailing lists to selected customers, for example, follow these steps:

1. Open the Northwind Traders database (file name NWIND.MDB). The Database window appears.

2. Click the Query button in the Database window, and then click the New button.

   A new Query Design window appears, with the Add Table dialog box superimposed on the window, as shown in figure 6.1. The Table/Query list box in the Add Table dialog box contains all existing tables and queries, because you can base a new query on a previously entered table or query. (The tables and queries listed in the Add Table list box come with Access as samples for the Northwind Traders database.)

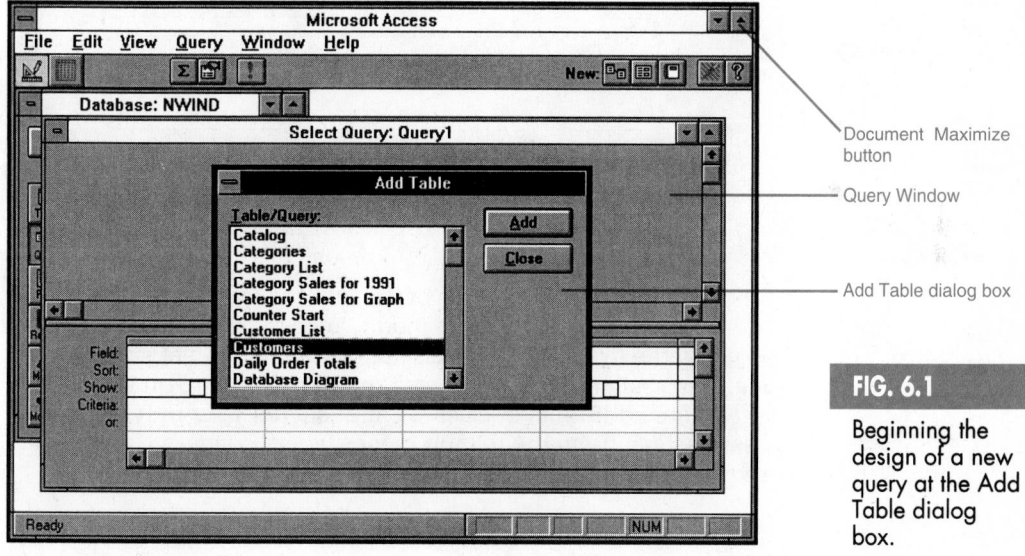

FIG. 6.1

Beginning the design of a new query at the Add Table dialog box.

3. For this quick start example, click Customers in the Add Table list (or use the down-arrow key) to select the Customers table, and then click the Add button. You also can double-click Customers to add a table to the query. You can use more than one table in a query by choosing another table name from the list and clicking Add again. In this example, however, only one table is used, so click Close now. The Add Table dialog box disappears, leaving only the blank Query Design window on-screen.

4. Now maximize the size of the Query Design window by clicking the Document Maximize button in the window's upper right corner. The Field list box for the Customers table appears at the left in the upper pane of the Query Design window, and a blank Query Design grid appears in the lower pane, as shown in figure 6.2. The Field list box displays all the names of the fields listed in the Customers table.

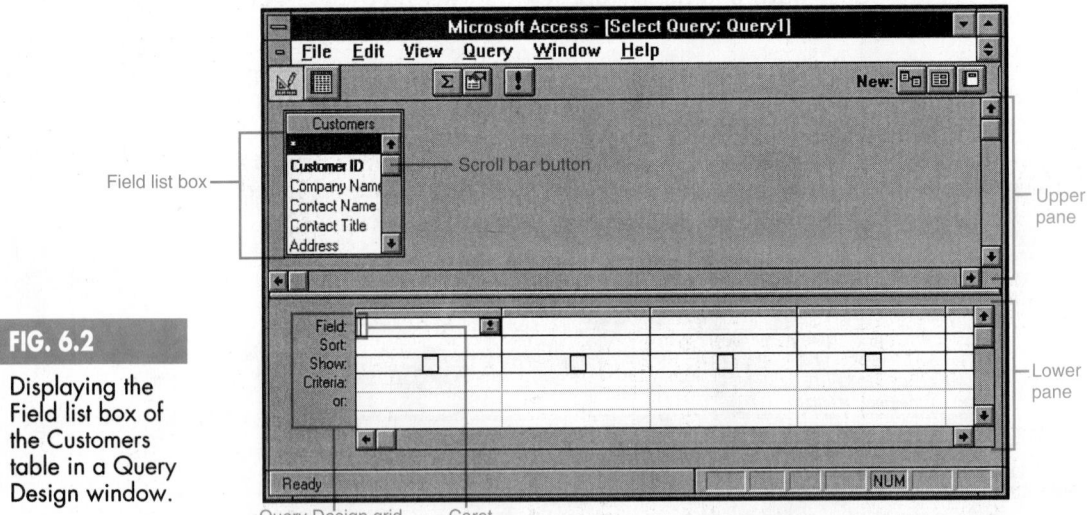

FIG. 6.2

Displaying the Field list box of the Customers table in a Query Design window.

By clicking the Query and New buttons in the Database window, you entered Access's Query Design mode. Access assigns a default name, Query1, to the first query you create (but have not yet saved) in this mode. You assign your own names to queries when you save them. If you create additional queries without saving your first query, Access assigns them the default names Query2, Query3, and so on, in sequence.

Choosing Fields for Your Query

After you choose a table from the Add Table dialog box, your next step is to decide which of the table's fields to include in your query. Because you will use this query to create a customer mailing list, you must include the fields that make up a personalized mailing address.

As explained in the introduction to this chapter, the first row of any graphical QBE query contains the names of each field involved in the query. (These field names also are called *field headers*.) The sample query you are creating, therefore, must include in its first row the names of all the fields that constitute a mailing address.

To choose your fields for the Query Design grid, follow these steps:

1. When you open the Query Design window, the caret (the insertion point) is located in the Field row of the first column. Click the List Box button that appears in the right corner of the first column, or press F4, to open the Field Name list box (see fig. 6.3).

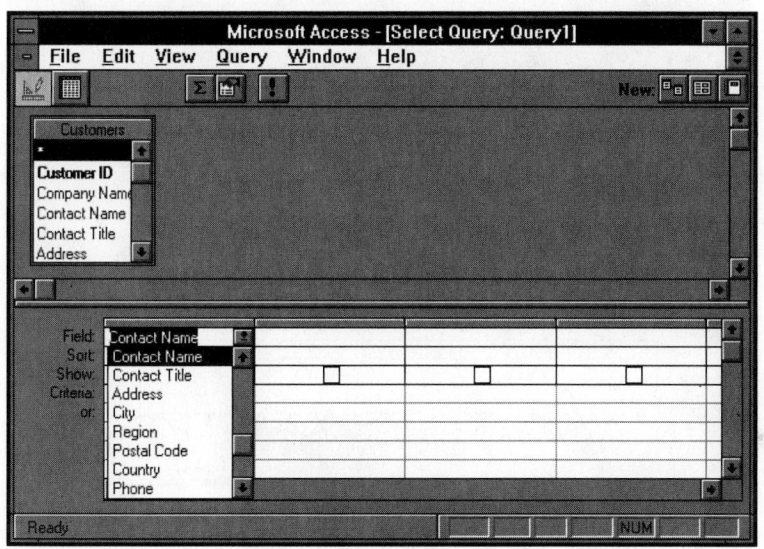

2. Click the Contact Name field to choose it as the first field header of the query, or use the down-arrow key to highlight the name and press Enter. The Field list box in the lower pane closes.

3. Move the caret to the second column by using the right-arrow or Tab key. (Notice that the List Box button has moved to the second column along with the caret.) Double-click Company Name in the Customers field list in the upper pane to add Company Name as the second field of your query. This is the second method Access uses to add fields to a query.

   Access also offers a third method of adding fields to your query: the *drag-and-drop* method. You can add the Address, City, and Region fields to columns 3 through 5, respectively, in one step by using the drag-and-drop method.

4. First you must select the fields. In the Customers field list in the upper pane of the Query Design Window, click Address, and then hold down the Shift or Ctrl key and click City and Region. Alternatively, you can select Address with the down-arrow key, and then hold down the Shift or Ctrl key and press the down-arrow key twice.

You have selected the Address, City, and Region fields, as shown in figure 6.4.

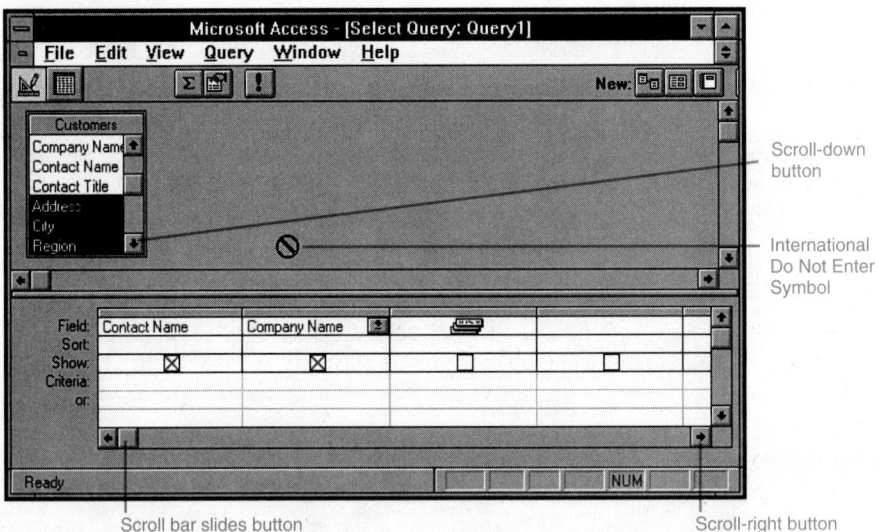

FIG. 6.4

Selecting multiple fields and using the drag-and-drop method to add the fields to the query.

Scroll-down button

International Do Not Enter Symbol

Scroll bar slides button

Scroll-right button

5. Position the mouse pointer over the selected fields and click the left mouse button. Your mouse pointer turns into a symbol representing the three selected field names. Drag the symbol for the three fields to the third column of your query's Field row, as shown in figure 6.4, and release the left mouse button.

Access adds the three fields to your query, in sequence, starting with the column in which you drop the symbol. While the mouse pointer is in an area where you cannot drop the fields, it becomes the international Do Not Enter symbol shown in the upper pane of the Query Design window.

6. The Query Design grid in the lower pane can display a maximum of five fields at a time when both Access's main window and the Query Design window are maximized. This query uses seven

fields, so you need to move the grid's display to expose two additional empty fields. Click the scroll-right button (on the horizontal scrollbar at the bottom of the window) twice to display two blank fields. Or you can drag the scroll bar slider button to the right to expose empty fields as necessary.

7. Click the scroll-down button in the Customers field list to display the Postal Code and Country fields. Hold down the Shift or Ctrl key and select Postal Code and Country. Drag the symbol for these two fields to the first empty field cell (column 6), and drop the two fields there. Your Query Design window appears similar to that shown in figure 6.5. (Notice that the check boxes in the Show row columns that contain a field name now are marked.)

Field:	City	Region	Postal Code	Country	
Sort:					
Show:	☒	☒	☒	☒	
Criteria:					
or:					

Ready   NUM

FIG. 6.5

The last four field names included in the query.

Many figures in this book are created with Access's main window in *Normal* style (which occupies a portion of the display), rather than *Maximized* style (which occupies all of the display). Normal style is used so that figures can be reproduced on a larger scale, which improves legibility.

8. Click the Query Datasheet View button on the toolbar to enter Run mode. Expect a brief waiting period while Access processes your query on the Customers table. Or, you can click the Run Query button on the toolbar to run your query against the Customers table.

Because you have not yet entered any selection criteria in the Criteria row of the Query Design grid, your query results in a display of all records in the Customers table. These records appear in the order of the primary key index on the Customer ID field because you have not specified a sorting order in the Sort row of the design. (The values in the Customer ID field are alphabetic codes derived from the Company Name field.) The result of your first query is shown in figure 6.6.

FIG. 6.6

A list of all records contained in the table.

For Related Information:

◄◄ "Working with Relations, Key Fields, and Indexes," p. 161.

FROM HERE...

Selecting Records by Criteria and Sorting the Display

The mailing for which you are creating a list with your sample query is to be sent to U.S. customers only, so you want to include in your query only those records with USA in their Country fields. Selecting records based on the values of fields—that is, establishing the criteria for the records to be returned (displayed) by the query—is the very heart of the query process.

Perform the following steps to establish criteria for selecting the records to comprise your mailing list:

1. Click the Design Mode button on the toolbar to return to Design mode. The partially filled Query Design grid replaces the mailing list on-screen.

2. To restrict the result of your query to firms in the United States, type the expression **=USA** in the Criteria row of the Country column. The equal sign indicates that the value of the field must match the value of the expression USA. You do not need to add quotation marks to the expression, because Access adds them for you (see the Country column in fig 6.7).

3. Click the Show check box in the Country column to remove the X mark that appeared when you named the column. After you deactivate the Show check box, the Country field is not displayed when you run your query. (You do not need to include the Country column in your mailing list address if you are mailing from a U.S. location to other U.S. locations.) If a Show check box is not deactivated, all fields in the query display by default.

4. Move the caret to the Sort row of the Postal Code column, and press F4 to display your sorting options for that field: Ascending, Descending, and (not sorted). Choose the Ascending option to sort the query by Postal Code from low codes to high.

   At this point, the Query Display grid appears as shown in figure 6.7.

FIG. 6.7

Adding the Ascending sort order to the Postal Code field.

5. Click the Query Datasheet View button on the toolbar to display the result of your criterion and sorting order. Use the horizontal scroll bar to display additional fields.

Figure 6.8 displays the query result Access calls a *dynaset*. A dynaset is a temporary table stored in your computer's memory, but it is not a permanent component of the database file. Only the design specifications of your query, and not the values the query contains, are saved in the NWIND.MDB (the Northwind Traders database) file after you save the query.

Creating More Complex Queries

To limit your mailing to customers in a particular state or group of states, you can add a Criteria expression to the Region or Postal Code field. To restrict the mailing to customers in California, Oregon, and Washington, for example, you can specify that the value of the Postal Code field must be equal to or greater than 90000. Alternatively, you can specify that Region values must be CA, OR, and WA. (Notice that the Postal Code values for Clifton Forge and Granville, Washington, are incorrect in the mailing list shown in fig. 6.8, so using the Region values is the better choice for this example.)

Microsoft Access - [Select Query: Query1]

File   Edit   View   Records   Layout   Window   Help

Field: Contact Name   New:

Contact Name	Company Name	Address	City	Region	Postal C
Nelda Jamison	Quality Plus Foods	180 Park Avenue	New York	NY	10021
Norman Jones	Highbridge Gourmet Shoppe	361 Pitt St.	Jamaica	NY	11451
Margaret Morgan	Walnut Grove Grocery	33 Upper Arctic Dr.	Buffalo	NY	14240
Bill Blandings	Sawyer Hill General Store	234 Samuel Pl.	Ithaca	NY	14853
Mary Throneberry	Anthony's Beer and Ale	33 Neptune Circle	Clifton Forge	WA	24422
April Cienkewicz	Family Corner Market	4242 Maple Blvd.	Granville	WA	43023
Roberto Martinez	Silver Screen Food Gems	12 Meikeljohn Ln.	Helena	MT	59601
Chiara Santorini	Morning Star Health Foods	45 N. Terminal Way	Helena	MT	59601
Liu Wong	The Cracker Box	55 Grizzly Peak Rd.	Butte	MT	59801
Marie Dubois	Parisian Specialties	716 Clancy Street	Chicago	IL	60608
Sandy Lapworth	ValuMax Food Stores	P.O. Box 10029	Austin	TX	78759
David Oberhofer	Margot's Fromagerie	340 Mile High Blvd.	Denver	CO	80202
Katrina Jefferson	Tommy's Imported Specialties	Thompson Building	Denver	CO	80227
Art Braunschweiger	Split Rail Beer & Ale	P.O. Box 555	Lander	WY	82520
Morris Borinski	Reggie's Wine and Cheese	612 E. 2nd St.	Pocatello	ID	83201
Bill Lee	Frugal Purse Strings	418 Datablitz Ave.	Pocatello	ID	83201
Alan Butterworth	Witanowski's East-West Mart	7775 S.W. Clinton Ave.	Lewiston	ID	83501
Jose Pavarotti	Save-a-lot Markets	187 Suffolk Ln.	Boise	ID	83720
Melissa Adams	Always Open Quick Mart	77 Overpass Ave.	Provo	UT	84604

Record: 1

Datasheet View   NUM

Incorrect Postal Code Values

FIG. 6.8

Sorting the query in numeric order by Postal Code values.

Follow these steps to restrict your mailing to customers in California, Oregon, and Washington:

1. Click the Query Design View button on the toolbar to return to Query Design mode.

2. Use the right-arrow or Tab key to move the caret to the Region column. If the Region column is not on-screen, click the scroll-right button until that column appears.

3. Type **=CA** in the first criteria row of the Region column. Access adds the quotation marks around CA, as it did when you restricted your mailing to U.S. locations with the =USA criterion.

4. Press the down-arrow key to move to the next criteria row in the Region column. Type **=OR**, and then move to the third criteria row and type **=WA**. Your query design now appears as shown in figure 6.9. Access adds the required quotation marks to these criteria also.

FIG. 6.9

Adding criteria to the Region field of the Query Design grid.

After you type a criterion on the same line as a previously entered criterion in another field, only those records that meet both criteria are selected for display. In the preceding example, therefore, only those records with Region values equal to CA and Country values equal to USA are displayed. Records for Region values OR and WA need not have Country values equal to USA to be displayed, because the USA criterion is missing from the OR and WA rows. This omission does not really affect the selection of records in this case, because all OR and WA records are also USA records.

(Note that the remaining criteria rows in the different columns on the Query Design grid enable you to enter additional criteria to further qualify which records are displayed. In the current example, no additional criteria are needed, so these cells are left blank.)

5. Click the Query Datasheet View or Run Query button on the toolbar to return to Run mode. The query result table appears, as shown in figure 6.10. (Use the vertical scroll bar button or the record position buttons to display additional query records in the mailing list that do not fit within the screen window.)

Editing Table Data in Query View

You can edit the data in any visible fields of the table in the query display. The postal codes for the two cities in Washington, for example, need to be corrected, so you must edit the data in these fields. To edit the Postal Code fields, perform the following steps:

1. Use the right-arrow or Tab key to move the caret to the Postal Code field. Then use the down-arrow key to move to the Granville row.

Microsoft Access - [Select Query: Query1]					
File **Edit** **View** **Records** **Layout** **Window** **Help**					
			Field: Contact Name		New:
Contact Nam	Company Name	Address	City	Region	Postal Code
Mary Throneber	Anthony's Beer and Ale	33 Neptune Circle	Clifton Forge	WA	24422
April Cienkiewicz	Family Corner Market	4242 Maple Blvd.	Granville	WA	43023
Gyorgy Ghiorgh	Village Food Boutique	2782 - 92nd Ave.	Los Angeles	CA	90071
Rob Petri	La Tienda Granda	12345 - 6th St.	Los Angeles	CA	91406
Michael Hsu	Rite-Buy Supermarket	P.O. Box 4421	Berkeley	CA	92701
Sean O'Brien	Dollarwise Convenience	98 N. Hyde Dr.	San Francisco	CA	94103
Jaime Yorres	Let's Stop N Shop	87 Polk St.	San Francisco	CA	94117
Susan Hayes	Gruenewald Delikatesse	3344 Byerly St.	Berkeley	CA	94701
Olivia LaMont	Caesar's Mediterranean I	9308 Dartridge Ave.	San Francisco	CA	94965
George Eddingt	Oceanview Quickshop	Franklin Mall	Aloha	OR	97006
Liz Nixon	The Big Cheese	89 Jefferson Way	Portland	OR	97201
Judy Pamona	Lillegard's Old Country D	89 Rain Way	Portland	OR	97219
Fran Wilson	Lonesome Pine Restaura	89 Chiaroscuro Rd.	Portland	OR	97219
Alan Thompson	Live Oak Hotel Gift Shop	7384 Washington Av	Portland	OR	97229
Rita Morehouse	Lee's Oriental Food Mart	44 McKnight Rd.	Portland	OR	97229
Howard Snyder	Great Lakes Food Marke	2732 Baker Blvd.	Eugene	OR	97403
Rona Rumalski	Frugal Feast Comestibles	Evans Plaza	Eugene	OR	97403
Hank Proudfit	O'Connor's Town Store	45 E. 23rd St.	Drain	OR	97435
Melinda Overmir	Gorham Street Co-op	511 Lincoln Ave.	Burns	OR	97720
Yoshi Latimer	Hungry Coyote Import St	City Center Plaza	Elgin	OR	97827
Record: 1					
Datasheet View					NUM

FIG. 6.10

Running the query for customers in California, Oregon, and Washington.

2. Press F2 to deselect the field and to enter Edit mode.

3. If the caret is not at the first position in the Postal Code column, press Home to get it there, and then change the first two digits for Granville to **98**.

4. Move the caret to the next line by pressing the down-arrow key, and then press F2 to deselect this field and to enter Edit mode. Change the first two digits of Clifton Forge's postal code to **98**.

5. Press Enter or move the caret down another line to make the change for Clifton Forge permanent. (Data in the underlying table is not changed until you press Enter or move to a different record.)

xBase

Edits on Indexed Values

Unlike edits made to values in indexed fields in dBASE's Browse mode, changes made to sorted fields in Access do not actually move the edited records to their correct locations in the query tables until after you press Shift+F9 to rerun the query.

6. To update the query and re-sort the records in their correct postal code order, press Shift+F9 to rerun the query.

You can scroll down the records to verify that Granville and Clifton Forge now are in their proper postal code order, as shown in figure 6.11.

FIG. 6.11

Rerunning the query after correcting the Postal Codes of two records.

— Revised and reordered postal codes

Changing the Names of Field Headers

You can substitute the field header names in a query with the header names of your choice. If you are a U.S. firm, for example, you may want to change Region to State and Postal Code to Zip Code. (Canadian firms need only change Region to Province.)

To change the field header names, perform the following steps:

1. Switch to Query Design mode by clicking the Query Datasheet View button. Then use the right-arrow or Tab key to move the caret to the Field column containing the field header name you want to change—in this case, the Region field.

2. Press F2 to deselect the field, and then press Home to move the caret to the first character position.

3. Type the new name for the field, and follow the name with a colon (no spaces): **State:**. The colon separates the name you type from the existing field name, which shifts to the right to make room for your addition. The result, in this example, is `State:Region` (see fig. 6.12).

4. Now use the arrow key to move to the Postal Code field and repeat steps 2 and 3, typing **Zip Code:** as the header's new name. The result, as shown in figure 6.12, is `Zip Code:Postal Code`.

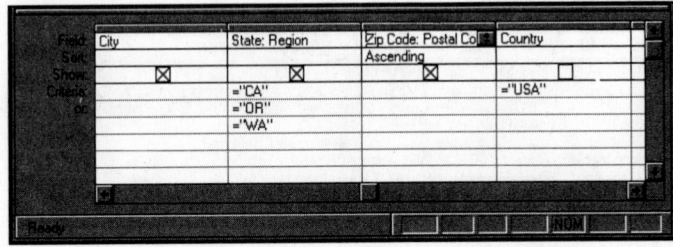

FIG. 6.12

Changing the
names of the
Region and
Postal Code field
headers.

5. Click the Query Datasheet View or Run Query button to return to Run mode, and verify that the change or changes have been made by using the scroll bar to scroll to the right, displaying the State and Zip Code field headers.

If you are creating data for a merge data document in Word for Windows, for example, you must rename the field headers so that the names do not contain spaces or other punctuation. To rename the headers, follow these additional steps:

1. Use the arrow key to move the caret in the Field row to the Contact Name column, and press F2 to deselect the field.

2. Press Home to move the caret to the first character of the field header, and edit the header to read Contact:Contact Name.

3. Move to the next field and edit the field header to read Company:Company Name. Follow the same procedure for any additional headers that must be changed. To avoid spaces in header names, the corrected Zip Code field must be edited to read ZipCode:Zip Code.

4. Click the Query Datasheet View or Run Query button to return to Run mode, and verify that the change or changes have been made by using the scroll bar to scroll to the right.

If you already have a main document for the merge operation, substitute the field names of the main merge document for the table's field header names in your query.

Printing Your Query as a Report

Previewing the appearance of your query table, to see how the table will appear when printed, is generally a good idea. After you determined from the preview that everything in the table is correct, you can print your finished query table.

To preview a query table prior to printing, follow these steps:

1. In Query Datasheet view, click the Print Preview button on the toolbar. A miniature version of the query table now appears in Report Preview mode.

2. Position the *Zoom mouse pointer* (the magnifying glass button) at the upper left corner of the miniature table, and click the left mouse button or the Zoom button above the window to view the report at approximately the scale at which it will print.

3. Use the vertical and horizontal scroll bar buttons to position the preview in the window (see fig. 6.13).

Contact	Company	Address	City
Gyorgy Ghiorghu	Village Food Boutique	2782 - 92nd Ave.	Los Angel
Rob Petri	La Tienda Granda	12345 - 6th St.	Los Angel
Michael Hsu	Rite-Buy Supermarket	P.O. Box 4421	Berkeley
Sean O'Brien	Dollarwise Convenience Store	98 N. Hyde Dr.	San Franc
Jaime Yorres	Let's Stop N Shop	87 Polk St.	San Franc
Susan Hayes	Gruenewald Delikatessen	3344 Byerly St.	Berkeley
Olivia LaMont	Caesar's Mediterranean Imports	9308 Dartridge Ave.	San Franc
George Eddington	Oceanview Quickshop	Franklin Mall	Aloha
Liz Nixon	The Big Cheese	89 Jefferson Way	Portland
Fran Wilson	Lonesome Pine Restaurant and Gift Sho	89 Chiaroscuro Rd.	Portland
Judy Pamona	Lillegard's Old Country Deli	89 Rain Way	Portland
Rita Morehouse	Lee's Oriental Food Mart	44 McKnight Rd.	Portland
Alan Thompson	Live Oak Hotel Gift Shop	7384 Washington Ave.	Portland
Howard Snyder	Great Lakes Food Market	2732 Baker Blvd.	Eugene
Rona Rumalski	Frugal Feast Comestibles	Evans Plaza	Eugene
Hank Proudfit	O'Connor's Town Store	45 E. 23rd St.	Drain
Melinda Overmire	Gorham Street Co-op	511 Lincoln Ave.	Burns
Yoshi Latimer	Hungry Coyote Import Store	City Center Plaza	Elgin

FIG. 6.13

A preview of the Mailing List query table in zoomed scale.

Field width in the query table is based on the column width you last established in Query Run mode. If the width of the query data exceeds the available printing width (the paper width minus the width left and right margins), Access prints two or more sheets for each page of the report.

4. Click the Cancel button, and then reduce the width of the columns in the Query Run mode so that all seven columns of your query fit on-screen when you preview the report (and on one sheet of paper when you print it). Return to Report Preview mode after you finish this process.

You adjust the displayed width of query fields in the same manner that you adjust table fields (described in Chapter 4). Query display field widths are not stored as properties of the query; therefore, they revert to their default values when you change to Query Design mode.

To print a query table after you have previewed it and determined that all the data is correct, follow these steps:

Print...

1. Click the Print button while you are in Report Preview mode. The standard Print dialog box appears.

   To change the default printing margins of one inch on all sides of the sheet (or any revised defaults you may have set earlier by choosing the **O**ptions command from the **V**iew menu), or to print only data (but not field header names), follow steps 2 and 3. If you don't want to change anything, skip to step 4.

Setup...

2. Click the Setup button. The Print Setup dialog box appears, as shown in figure 6.14.

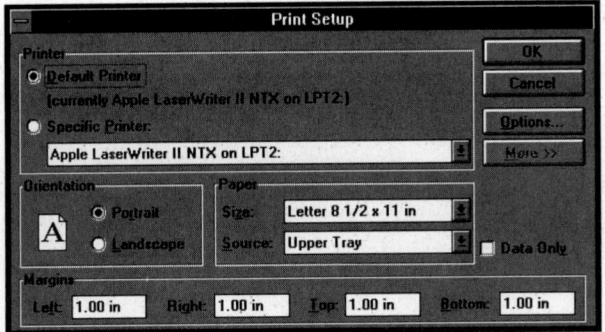

FIG. 6.14

The Print Setup dialog box.

3. Enter any changes you want to make to the margins, and click the Data Only check box if you do not want to print the field header names. Then choose OK.

   You return to Print Preview mode, where you can click the Print button to display the Print dialog box.

4. Click the Print button in the Print dialog box to print your query data.

5. Press Esc to return to Query Datasheet view after you have printed your query table.

For Related Information:

◄◄ "Printing Options," p. 104.

FROM HERE...

Using the Data from Your Query

Occasionally, you may want to use data from your query as part of a different Windows application. The simplest technique for transferring data in your query to another Windows application is to use the Clipboard. Clipboard operations for data in query tables are identical to those operations for tables described in Chapter 5, "Attaching, Importing, and Exporting Tables."

To create a merge data file for Word for Windows, for example, follow these steps:

1. In Query Datasheet view, choose Select **A**ll Records from the **E**dit menu.

   For a partial mailing, such as to firms in California only, you can choose the individual records by dragging the mouse over the records' selection buttons.

2. Press Ctrl+C or choose **C**opy from the **E**dit menu to copy the selected records to the Clipboard.

3. Now run Word for Windows. Press Ctrl+Esc to display the Windows Task Manager's list. If Word is running, double-click its name to display its window. If Word is not running, double-click Program Manager to launch Word. Choose **N**ew from the **F**ile menu to open a new window.

4. Press Ctrl+V or choose **P**aste from the Word for Windows **E**dit menu. Your Access mailing records are added to the Word for Windows file. A portion of the resulting merge data document is shown in figure 6.15.

   Some of the records of this query also contain *newline pairs* (paragraph marks) embedded in fields that result in premature ends of these records. An example of a spurious newline pair is highlighted in figure 6.16. Replace the extra newline pairs with commas and spaces, and delete the quotation marks that enclose fields containing extra headline pairs before using the document in a merge operation.

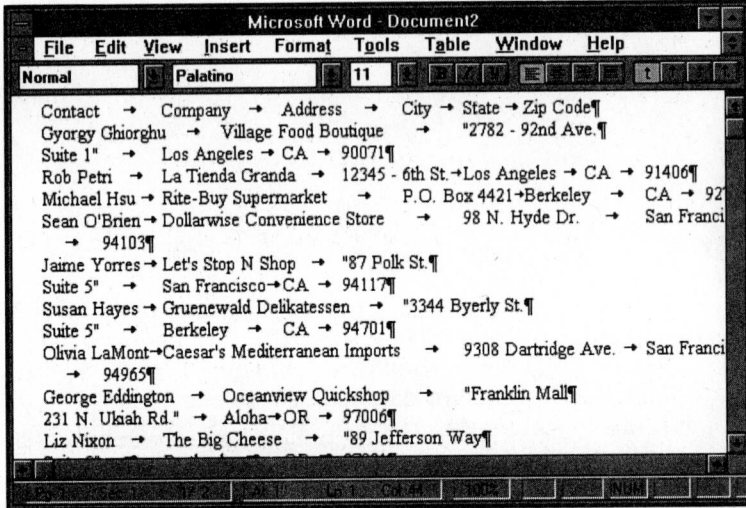

FIG. 6.15

Part of the Word for Windows merge data document.

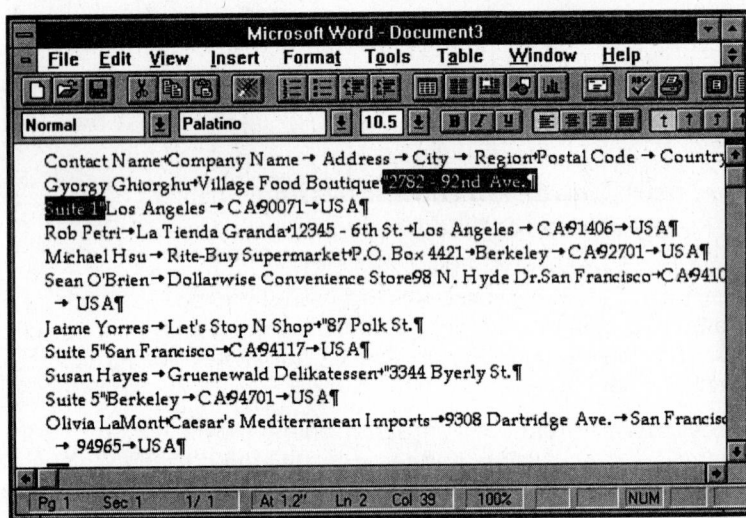

FIG. 6.16

A Word for Windows merge data file with extra newline pairs embedded.

If you use a DOS word processor and want to import query data into a merge data file, you must save your query in the form of a table and then export the table as a file in a format compatible with that of your word processor. This process requires that you create an Action query to create a table. You then export the data from the table in a compatible format, as described in Chapter 5. Action queries are discussed in a later section, "Creating and Using a Make Table Action Query," and in Chapter 8, "Creating Queries and Joining Tables."

Saving and Naming Your Query

After completing your query, you need to save it as an element of your database file, giving the query its own descriptive name.

Follow these steps to save and name your query:

1. Close your query by double-clicking the Document Control button. Access prompts you with a message box to save the new or modified query, as shown figure 6.17.

2. Click the Yes button in the message box to save your query. Because Access has assigned a default name to your query, the Save As dialog box now appears, as shown in figure 6.18. If you choose Cancel or press Esc, Access does not save your query.

3. Type a descriptive name for your query in the Query Name text box, and press Enter or choose OK. Your query now is saved under the name you have assigned it rather than the default name.

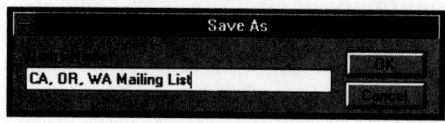

FIG. 6.17

The message box reminding you to save a newly created or modified query.

FIG. 6.18

The Save As dialog box.

As an alternative, you can save your query by choosing Save As from the File menu.

To rename your saved query, follow these steps:

1. Close the query by double-clicking the Document Control button.

2. Select the query you want to rename in the Database window.

3. Choose Rename from the File menu.

4. Type the new name in the text box of the Rename dialog box that appears after you choose Rename.

5. Press Enter or choose OK. Access saves your query with the new name you assigned it.

Creating Other Types of Queries

Access enables you to create the following four types of queries to achieve different objectives:

- *Select:* Extracts data from one or more tables and displays the data in tabular form.

- *Crosstab:* Summarizes data from one or more tables in the form of a spreadsheet. Crosstab queries are very useful for analyzing data and creating graphs or charts based on the sum of the numeric field values of many records.

- *Action:* Creates new database tables from query tables or makes major alterations to a table. Action queries enable you to add or delete records from a table or to make changes to records based on expressions you enter in a query design.

- *Parameter:* Repeatedly uses a query and makes only simple changes to its criteria. The mailing list query you created in the preceding example is an excellent candidate for a Parameter query, because you can change the criterion of the Region field for mailings to different groups of customers. When you run a Parameter query, Access prompts you with a dialog box for the new criterion. Parameter queries are not actually a separate query type, because you can add the parameter function to Select, Crosstab, and Action queries.

Chapter 8, "Creating Queries and Joining Tables," explains how to create each of the four query types. Creating a table from your mailing list query to export to a mail merge file is an example of an Action query. (In fact, this is the simplest example of an Action query and also the safest, because Make Table queries do not modify data in existing tables.)

Creating and Using a Make Table Action Query

To create a table from your mailing list query, you first must convert the query from a Select to an Action query. Follow these steps:

| Design |

1. Open your mailing list query in Design mode by selecting the name you gave the query in the Database window and clicking the Design button.

2. Choose Make Table from the **Query** menu. (The Query menu is accessible only in Query Design mode.) The Query Properties dialog box appears, as shown in figure 6.19.

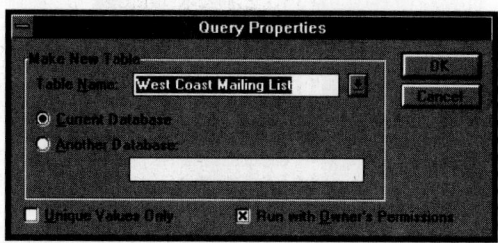

FIG. 6.19

The Query Properties dialog box.

3. Type a descriptive table name for your query table in the Table Name text box.

   The Query Properties dialog box enables you to further define your query table's properties in several ways. You can add the table to the Northwind Traders database by choosing the Current Database option, which is the default value. Or, you can choose the Another Database option to add the table to a different database. You also can choose to eliminate any duplicate records by marking the Unique Values Only check box. The Run with Owner's Permissions check box is marked as the default option when the dialog box appears. You are considered the owner of all databases resident on your computer's fixed disk, so accept the default. (Permissions are explained in Chapter 21, "Using Access in a Network Environment.")

4. Choose OK. Access converts your Select query to the Make Table type of Action query. The Datasheet view of your query no longer is available, as indicated by the inactive status (gray color) of the Query Datasheet View button on the toolbar.

5. Close your query by double-clicking the Document Control menu box. Your query name in the Database window now is prefixed by an exclamation point, as shown in figure 6.20. An exclamation point indicates that the query is an Action query.

Now that you have converted your query from a Select query to an Action query, you can create your new West Coast Mailing List table. To create the table, follow these steps:

1. Run the newly converted Action query table to create your mailing list by double-clicking its name in the Queries list of the Database window.

Exclamation point indicating an Action query

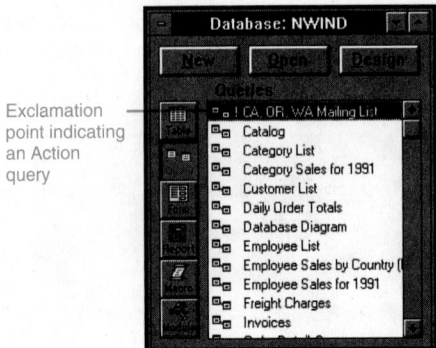

FIG. 6.20

A highlighted Action query in the list of queries.

After you open an Action query table, it performs the desired action—in this case, creating the West Coast Mailing List table—instead of simply displaying a Select query table. Before Access carries out the action, however, a message box appears and warns you that the data in the West Coast Mailing List will be modified (see fig. 6.21).

2. Choose OK to dismiss the message box and continue the operation. (You can choose **O**ptions from the **V**iew menu and then choose Query Design from the Category list box to turn off this warning message so that it doesn't appear when you open an Action query table.)

A second warning message box, shown in figure 6.22, now appears to tell you what will happen after you execute the Action query.

FIG. 6.21

The message box that appears after you open an Action query.

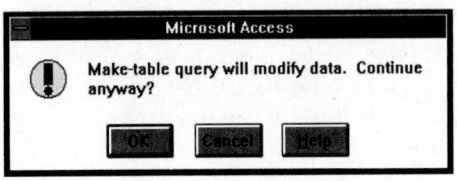

FIG. 6.22

A second warning message that indicates the effects of running the Action query.

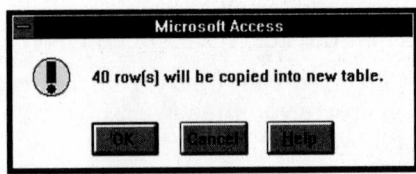

3. Choose OK. Because you have not run this Action query before, running it now creates the new West Coast Mailing List table.

4. Click the Table button in the Database window. Access adds the new West Coast Mailing List table to the list of tables in the NWIND database, as shown in figure 6.23.

5. Open the West Coast Mailing List table. Its contents may appear as they do in figure 6.24.

Access has rearranged the fields, making ZipCode the first field, because the query that created the table is set up to sort by ZIP code. You can move the ZipCode field to its usual position in an address table by clicking the ZipCode header name and then dragging the selected ZipCode field past the State field and dropping the ZipCode field there.

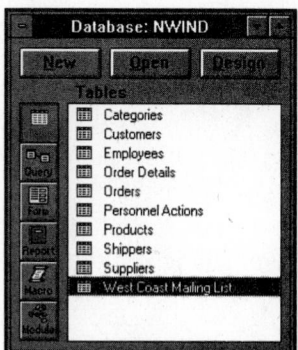

FIG. 6.23

The new table added to the NWIND database's table list.

FIG. 6.24

Running a Datasheet view of the records in the new table.

After you create the new table, you can export its data to any of the other file formats supported by Access by using the methods described in Chapter 5, "Attaching, Importing, and Exporting Tables."

For Related Information:

FROM HERE...

◄◄ "Setting Default Options," p. 101.

►► "Converting to a Parameter Query," p. 337.

Adding a Parameter to Your Make Table Query

A simple modification to your mailing list query enables you to enter a selection criterion, called a *parameter*, from a prompt created by Access. Follow these steps:

1. Close the West Coast Mailing List table by double-clicking the Document Control box, and click the Query button in the Database window.

2. Choose the CA, OR, WA Mailing List query, and then click the Design button to display your Make Table Action query in Design mode.

3. Use the arrow keys to move the caret to the State column, and then delete the three existing entries—="CA", ="OR", and ="WA". You will enter the state abbreviation as a query parameter.

4. Type **[Enter the state code:]** in the first criteria row of the State: Region column, as shown in figure 6.25. The enclosing square brackets indicate that the entry is a prompt for a parameter after you run the Action query.

FIG. 6.25

Entering a parameter prompt as a criterion in Query Design view.

Field:	Address	City	State: Region	Country
Sort:				
Show:	☒	☒	☒	☐
Criteria:			[Enter the state code:]	"USA"
or:				

5. Close the Action query, select the West Coast Mailing list, and then choose Rename from the File menu. The Rename dialog box appears.

6. Rename your query by typing **Mailing List by State** in the text box and choosing OK.

7. Choose the renamed Mailing List by State query from the list in the Database window, and then click the Open button. You receive the message box indicating that data will be modified (refer to fig. 6.21).

Open

8. Choose OK, and another message box appears. This box's message warns you that you are about to overwrite the data in the table created by the last execution of your query (see fig. 6.26).

9. Click the Yes button. Access displays the Enter Parameter Value dialog box. This dialog box contains a prompt for you to enter the State criterion, as shown in figure 6.27.

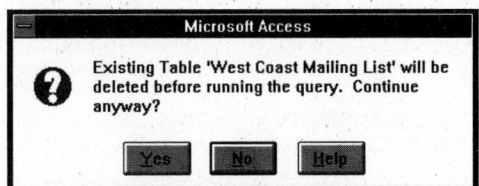

FIG. 6.26

The message box warning that data is about to be overwritten.

FIG. 6.27

The text box for entering a parameter to be used as a select criterion.

10. Type **CA**, and press Enter or choose OK. (You do not need to type an equal sign before the state code here because Access enters the equal sign for you.)

Another message box appears, similar to the one in figure 6.22, indicating the number of records in the new version of the West Coast Mailing List table that have a value in the Regions field matching your state parameter entry.

11. Choose OK. The message box is replaced by the Database window, showing Mailing List by State as one of its options.

12. Click the Table button in the Database window, and choose Mailing List by State. Then click the Open button. Records for customers in California now appear in the table.

You can delete the new table from the Northwind Traders database by closing the table, selecting the West Coast Mailing List table in the Database window, and then pressing the Del key. (Access requests that you confirm your deletion. Choose OK, and Access removes the table from the database.)

Translating Graphical QBE to Structured Query Language

Structured Query Language, or SQL, is a standard set of English words used to describe a query. Access translates the QBE expressions you type in the Query Design grid into a series of statements in Structured Query Language. Access then carries out these instructions on any tables that contain fields matching those specified in your query.

Access's use of SQL is important when you are dealing with client-server databases that process SQL statements on the server's computer. After the query is processed, the server sends the data for the query result table to your Access client application for further processing.

To display the SQL statements created from your mailing list query, perform the following steps:

1. Open the mailing list query in Design mode by selecting the name you gave the query in the Database window and clicking the Design button.

2. Choose **SQL** from the View menu.

3. The SQL dialog box, which contains a multiline text box, appears, as shown in figure 6.28.

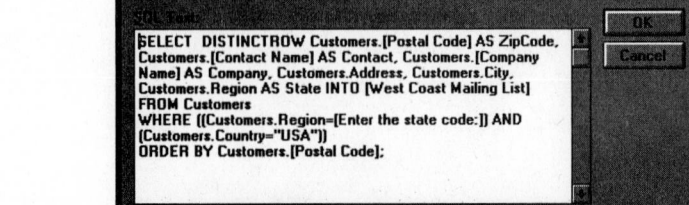

FIG. 6.28

Graphical QBE expressions translated by Access into SQL.

SQL *keywords* are displayed in uppercase letters. SQL keywords are the instructions or the actions to be performed by the query. The names of the objects in your query appear in upper- and lowercase letters. The meanings of the keywords used in your query (as shown in fig. 6.28) are explained in the following list:

- *SELECT* is usually the first keyword in an SQL statement. The expressions that follow specify the fields involved in the query. Fields are identified by the name of the table, followed by a period and the name of the field.

- *DISTINCTROW* causes only unique records to be included in the query result table.

- *AS* establishes the alias for the field name preceding the alias. ZipCode, for example, is the *alias* for the Postal Code field. The alias is the caption that appears in the field header for the Postal Code field.

- *INTO* specifies the name of the table into which the results of the query are to be placed. INTO is applicable only to Action queries.

- *FROM* is the name of the table in which the fields are located.

- *WHERE* identifies the expressions that follow as the selection criteria for the query.

- *AND* is a logical operator that results in records that meet both the criterion that precedes the AND and the criterion that follows the AND.

- *ORDER BY* specifies the field(s) by which the query result table is to be sorted.

When you are finished viewing the SQL statements, close the SQL dialog box by choosing Cancel.

Only a brief glimpse of SQL is provided in this quick start, and only a small cross-section of the reserved words of SQL are used in this example. The syntax used to edit and create SQL statements is explained in detail in Chapter 20, "Working with Structured Query Language."

For Related Information:

◄◄ "Client-Server Front Ends," p. 63.

►► "What Is Structured Query Language," p. 830.

FROM HERE...

Chapter Summary

This quick start gave you insight into the methods used by Access to choose data from tables and to organize the selected data into query tables (called *dynasets* by Access). Most of the forms and reports you create in Chapter 9, "Creating and Using Forms," and Chapter 10, "Designing Custom Forms," use such queries rather than tables as data sources. Even when you are not concerned with creating forms and reports, however, you can use queries to display data in tabular form for analysis or to export to other Windows and DOS applications.

To create more sophisticated queries than those covered in this chapter, you must learn more about the syntax of the expressions you need in order to choose records. As you become increasingly specific in the selection of records for your queries, the complexity of these expressions increases. For this reason, the next chapter, "Understanding Operators and Expressions in Access," precedes the chapter in which you actually learn the detailed procedures for creating and optimizing your queries.

The remaining chapters in Part II of this book show you how to use your queries with custom-designed forms for data entry and with reports that summarize the data.

Understanding Operators and Expressions in Access

You were introduced briefly to operators and the expressions that use them in Chapter 4, "Working with Access Databases and Tables," when you added validation rules to table fields. Expressions were touched on again in Chapter 6, "Using Query by Example: A Quick Start," when you devised selection criteria for the query you created. You must use expressions with the forms (Chapters 9 and 10), reports (Chapter 11), and macros (Chapters 16 through 18) you combine in creating custom Access applications; furthermore, expressions are used extensively in programming with Access Basic (Chapters 22 and 23). To work effectively with Access, therefore, you must know how to create simple expressions that use Access's group of operators.

If you use spreadsheet applications such as Excel or 1-2-3, you may be familiar with using operators to create expressions. In spreadsheet applications, expressions are called *formulas*. As discussed in Chapter 4, the syntax for expressions that create default values, such as

=Date( ), is very similar to formula entries in Excel. Conditional expressions that use the =IF( ) function in Excel, however, are usually handled differently in Access. Access also provides the IIf( ) function to duplicate Excel's =IF( ) function, however.

Much of this chapter is devoted to describing the functions available in Access for manipulating Numeric and Text field data. Functions play important roles in every element of Access, from validation rules for fields in tables to the control of program flow in Access Basic. You use functions in the creation of queries, forms, reports, and macros. To use Access effectively, therefore, you must know functions are available to you.

Understanding the Elements in Expressions

An *expression* is a statement of intent. If you want an action to occur after meeting a specific condition, your expression must specify that condition. To select records in a query that contains Zip Code field values of 90000 or higher, for example, you type the expression **Zip Code >= 90000**. You also can use expressions in arithmetic calculations. If you need an Extended Amount field in a query, for example, you type **Extended Amount: Quantity * Unit Price** as the expression in order to create calculated values in the data cells of the Extended Amount column.

To qualify as an expression, a statement must have at least one operator and at least one literal, identifier, or function. The following list describes these elements:

■ *Operators* include the familiar arithmetic symbols +, –, * (multiply), and / (divide), as well as many other symbols and abbreviations. Most other operators available in Access are equivalent to those operators found in traditional programming languages, such as BASIC, but some are specific to Access or SQL, such as the Between, In, Is, and Like operators.

■ *Literals* consist of values you type, such as 12345 or ABCDE. Literals are used most often to create default values and, in combination with field identifiers, to compare values in table fields.

■ *Identifiers* are the names of objects in Access (such as fields in tables) that return distinct numeric or text values. The term *return*, used with expressions, means that the present value of the identifier is substituted for its name in the expression. As an example, the field name identifier [Company Name] in an expression returns the value (a name) of the Comany Name field for the currently selected record. Access has five predefined named constants that also serve as identifiers: True, False, Yes, No, and Null. Named constants and variables you create in Access Basic also are identifiers.

■ *Functions*, such as Date( ) and Format( ), which are used in the examples in Chapter 4, return a value in place of the function name in the expression. Unlike identifiers, most functions require that you supply with parentheses an identifier or a value as an argument. Functions and their arguments are explained in the "Functions" section later in this chapter.

When literals, identifiers, or functions are used with operators, these combinations are called *operands*. These four elements of expressions are described more thoroughly in the following sections.

Operators

Access provides six categories of operators that you can use to create expressions:

■ *Arithmetic operators* perform addition, subtraction, multiplication, and division.

■ *Assignment and comparison operators* set values and compare values.

■ *Logical operators* deal with values that can be true or false only.

■ *Concatenation operators* combine strings of characters.

■ *Identifier operators* create unambiguous names for database objects so that you can assign the same field name, for example, in several tables and queries.

■ *Other operators* simplify the creation of expressions for selecting records with queries.

Operators in the first four categories are available in almost all programming languages, including xBase and PAL. Identifier operators are specific to Access, and the other operators of the last category are provided only in DBMs that create queries using QBE or SQL. The following sections explain how to use each of the operators in these categories.

Arithmetic Operators

Arithmetic operators operate only on numeric values and must have two numeric operands, with the following exceptions:

■ When the minus sign (–) changes the sign (negates the value) of an operand. In this case, the minus sign is called the *unary minus*.

■ When the equal sign (=) assigns a value to an Access object or an Access Basic variable identifier.

Table 7.1 lists the arithmetic operators that you can use in Access expressions.

Table 7.1. Arithmetic Operators

Operator	Description	Example
+	Adds two operands	[Subtotal] + [Tax]
–	Subtracts two operands	Date( ) – 30
– (unary)	Changes sign of operand	–12345
*	Multiplies two operands	[Units] * [Unit Price]
/	Divides one operand by another	[Quantity] / 12.55
\	Divides one integer operand by another	[Units] \ 2
Mod	Returns remainder of division by an integer	[Units] Mod 12
^	Raises an operand to a power (exponent)	[Value] ^ [Exponent]

Access operators are identical to those operators used in Microsoft QuickBASIC, QBasic (supplied with DOS 5.0), and Visual Basic. If you aren't familiar with Basic programming, the following operators deserve further explanation:

■ \, the integer division symbol, is the equivalent of "goes into," as used in the litany of elementary school arithmetic: "Three goes into 13 four times, with one left over." When you use integer division, operators with decimal fractions are rounded to integers, but any decimal fraction in the result is truncated.

■ Mod, an abbreviation for *modulus*, returns the "left over" value of integer division. Therefore, 13 Mod 4, for example, returns 1.

■ ^, the exponentiation operator, raises the first operand to the power of the second. Therefore, 2 ^ 4, or two to the fourth power, for example, returns 16 (2*2*2*2).

These three operators seldom are used in business applications, but often are used in Access Basic program code.

Assignment and Comparison Operators

The equal sign associated with arithmetic expressions is missing from table 7.1 because it is used in two ways in Access—neither of which falls into the arithmetic category. The most common use of the equal sign is as an assignment operator; = assigns the value of a single operand to an Access object or to a variable or constant. When you use the expression = "Q" to assign a default value to a field, the equal sign acts as an assignment value. Otherwise, = is a comparison operator that determines whether one of two operands is equal to the other.

Comparison operators compare the values of two operands and return logical values (True or False), depending on the relationship between the two operands and the operator. An exception is when one of the operands has the Null value. In this case, any comparison returns a value of Null; because Null represents an unknown value, you cannot compare an unknown value with a known value and come to a valid True or False conclusion.

Table 7.2 lists the comparison operators available in Access.

Table 7.2. Comparison Operators

Operator	Description	Example	Result
<	Less than	123 < 1000	True
<=	Less than or equal to	15 <= 15	True
=	Equal to	2 = 4	False
>=	Greater than or equal to	1234 >= 456	True
>	Greater than	123 > 123	False
<>	Not equal	123 <> 456	True

The principal uses of comparison operators are creating validation rules, establishing criteria for record selection in queries, determining actions taken by macros, and controlling program flow in Access Basic.

Logical Operators

Logical operators (also called *Boolean operators*) are used most often to combine the results of two or more comparison expressions into a single result. Logical operators can combine only expressions that return the logical values True, False, or Null. With the exception of Not, which is the logical equivalent of the unary minus, logical operators always require two operands.

Table 7.3 lists the Access logical operators.

Table 7.3. Logical Operators

Operator	Description	Example 1	Result 1	Example 2	Result 2
And	Logical and	True And True	True	True And False	False
Or	Inclusive or	True Or False	True	False Or False	False
Not	Logical not	Not True	False	Not False	True
Xor	Exclusive or	True Xor False	True	True Xor True	False

The logical operators And, Or, and Not are used extensively in Access expressions. Xor seldom is used in Access, and Eqv (equivalent) and Imp (implication) are rarely seen, even in programming code, so these two operators are not included in the table.

Concatenation Operators

Concatenation operators combine two text values into a single string of characters. If you concatenate ABC with DEF, for example, the result is ABCDEF. The ampersand (&) is the preferred concatenation operator in Access because & is the standard concatenation symbol in SQL. You can use the + operator to link two strings of characters as in Basic; however, using the + operator for concatenation can lead to ambiguities, because the operator's primary purpose is adding two operands.

Identifier Operators

The identifier operators, ! and . (the period, called the *dot operator* in Access), perform the following operations:

■ Combine the names of object classes and object names to select a specific object or property of an object. For example,

```
Forms![Personnel Actions]
```

identifies the Personnel Actions form. This identification is necessary because you may have a table called Personnel Actions.

■ Distinguish object names from property names. In the expression

```
TextBox1.FontSize=8
```

TextBox1 is a control object and FontSize is a property.

■ Identify specific fields in tables, as in

```
Customers.[Company Name]
```

This specifies the Company Name field of the Customers table.

This book uses only the dot operator until Chapter 9, "Creating and Using Forms," which uses the ! operator.

Other Operators

The remaining Access operators are related to the comparison operators. These operators return True or False, depending on whether the value in a field meets the chosen operator's specification. A True value causes a record to be included in a query; a False value rejects the record. When used in validation rules, entries are accepted or rejected based on the logical value returned by the expression.

Table 7.4 lists the four other operators used in Access.

Table 7.4. Other Operators		
Operator	Description	Example
Is	Used with Null to determine whether a value is Null or Not Null	Is Null Is Not Null
Like	Determines whether a string value begins with one or more characters. You need to add a wild card, *, or one or more ?s for Like to work properly.	Like "Jon*" Like "FILE????"
In	Determines whether a string value is a member of a list of values	In("CA", "OR", "WA")
Between	Determines whether a numeric value lies within a specified range of values	Between 1 And 5

The wild-card characters * and ? are used with the Like operator the same way they are used in DOS. The * (often called *star* or *splat*) takes the place of any number of characters. The ? takes the place of a single character. For example, Like "Jon*" returns True for values such as "Jones" or "Jonathon". Like "FILE????" turns True for "FILENAME", but not "FILE000" or "FILENUMBER". Wild-card characters may precede the characters you want to make, as in Like "*son" or "Like "????NAME".

With the exception of Is, the operators in the other category are equivalent to the reserved words LIKE, IN, and BETWEEN in SQL and are included in Access to promote compatibility with SQL. You can create each of these operators by combining other Access operators or functions. Like "Jon*" is the equivalent of Access Basic's InStr(Left$(FieldName, 3), "Jon"), and In("CA", "OR", "WA") is similar to InStr(FieldName,"CAORWA"), except that no matches occur for the ambiguous "AO" and "RW". Between 1 And 5 is the equivalent of >= 1 And <= 5.

Literals

Access provides three types of literals that you can combine with operators to create expressions. The following list describes these types of literals:

- *Numeric literals* are typed as a series of digits, including the arithmetic sign and decimal point, if applicable. You don't need to prefix positive numbers with the plus sign; positive values are assumed unless the minus sign is present. Numeric literals can include *E* or *e* and the sign of the exponent to indicate an exponent in scientific notation—for example, –1.23E–02.

- *Text literals* (or *string literals*) can include any printable character, plus unprintable characters returned by the Chr$( ) function. The Chr$() function returns the characters specified by a numeric value from the ANSI character table (similar to the ASCII character table) used by Windows. For example, Chr$(9) returns the Tab character. Printable characters include the letters A through Z, numbers 1 through 0, punctuation symbols, and other special keyboard symbols such as the tilde (~). Access expressions require that string literals be enclosed within double quotation marks (""). Combinations of printable and unprintable characters are concatenated with the ampersand; the expression

```
"First line" & Chr$(13) & Chr$(10) & "Second line"
```

separates the two strings with a newline pair. Chr$(13) is the carriage return (CR), and Chr$(10) is the line feed (LF) character; together they form the # newline pair. When you enter string literals in the cells of tables and Query Design grids, Access adds the quotation marks for you. In other places, you must enter the quotation marks yourself.

■ *Date/time literals* are enclosed within number or pound signs (#), as in the expressions #1-Jan-80# or #10:20:30#. Access adds the enclosing pound signs if the program detects that you are typing into a Design grid a date or time in one of the standard Access date/time formats.

Numeric and string literals have exact equivalents in BASIC, xBase, and PAL, but the date/time literal is a literal data type defined by Access.

Identifiers

An identifier is usually the name of an object; databases, tables, fields, queries, forms, and reports are objects in Access. Each object has a name that uniquely identifies that object. Sometimes, to identify a sub-object, an identifier name consists of a *family name* separated from a *given name* by a period (an identifier operator). The family name of the identifier comes first, followed by the period and then the given name. An example of an identifier in an SQL statement is

```
Customers.Address;
```

the identifier for the Address field object is contained in the Customers table object. *Customers* is the family name of the object (the table), and *Address* is the given name of the subobject (the field). If an identifier contains a space or other punctuation, you enclose the identifier within square brackets, as in

```
[Personnel Actions].[PAID]
```

You cannot include periods or exclamation points within the names of identifiers; [PA!ID], for example, is not allowed.

In simple queries that use only one table, identifiers are usually the name of a field. You use identifiers to return the values of fields in form and report objects. The specific method of identifying objects within forms and reports is covered in Chapters 9 through 11.

Functions

Functions return values to their names; therefore, functions can take the place of identifiers in expressions. One of the most common functions used in Access expressions is Now( ), which returns to its name the date and time from your computer's internal clock. If you type =NOW( ) as the Default Value property of a Date/Time field of a table, for example, 1/30/93 9:00 appears in the field when you change to Datasheet view (at 9:00 a.m. on January 30, 1993). Access has defined about 140 individual functions. The following list groups functions by purpose:

- *Date and time functions* manipulate date/time values in fields or date/time values you enter as literals. You can extract parts of dates (such as the year or day of the month) and parts of times (such as hours and minutes) with date and time functions.

- *Text manipulation functions* are used for working with strings of characters.

- *Data type conversion functions* enable you to specify the data type of values in Numeric fields, instead of depending on Access to pick the most appropriate data type.

- *Mathematic and trigonometric functions* perform on numeric values operations beyond the capability of the standard Access arithmetic operators. You can use simple trigonometric functions, for example, to calculate the length of the sides of a right triangle (if you know the length of one side and the included angle).

- *Financial functions* are similar to functions provided by 1-2-3 and Excel. Financial functions calculate depreciation, values of annuities, and rates of return on investments. To determine the present value of a lottery prize paid out in 25 equal yearly installments, for example, you can use the PV( ) function.

- *General purpose functions* don't fit any of the preceding classifications—you use these functions in creating Access queries, forms, and reports.

- *Other functions* include functions to perform Dynamic Data Exchange (DDE) with other Windows applications, domain aggregate functions, SQL aggregate functions, and functions used primarily in programming with Access Basic.

The following sections describe these functions more fully.

You can create user-defined functions by defining them with Access Basic programming code. Creating user-defined functions is the subject of Chapter 17, "Understanding Access Macros."

For Related Information:

▶▶ "Using the SQL Aggregate Functions," p. 326.

▶▶ "Using DDE Links with Excel," p. 676.

▶▶ "Modules, Functions, and Procedures," p. 926.

FROM HERE...

Using the Immediate Window

When you write Access Basic programming code in a module, the Immediate window is available to assist you in debugging your code. You also can use the module's Immediate window to demonstrate the use and syntax of functions.

To experiment with some of the functions described in the following sections, perform these steps:

1. Click the Module button in the Database window.

2. Click the New button to create a temporary module. Access assigns the default name Module1 to the temporary module.

3. Click the Document Maximize button in the upper right corner of the Module window, if the window is not maximized.

4. Choose the Immediate Window command from the View menu. The Immediate window appears, as shown in figure 7.1.

   The entries shown in figure 7.1 aren't visible at this point. You can create similar entries by using the functions for date and time described later in this chapter.

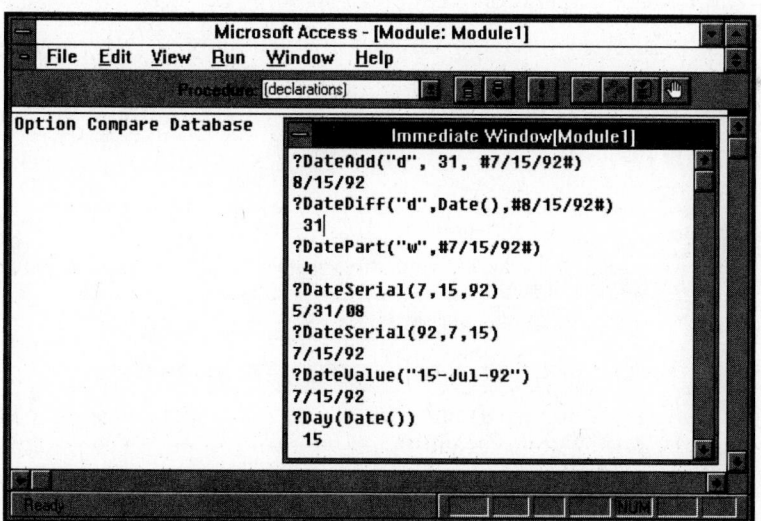

FIG. 7.1

Using the Immediate window of a temporary module to experiment with functions.

5. Type **?Now()** and press Enter. The date and time from your computer's clock appear on the next line. The ? is shorthand for the Print statement (which displays the value of a function or variable) and must be added to the Now( ) function to display the value of the function.

6. If you neglected to precede the function entry with ? or Print, an error message appears, indicating that Access expected you to type a statement or an equal sign. Choose OK and then type **?** before the function name in the Immediate window. Press End to return the caret to the end of the line; then press Enter to retry the test.

The following sections contain descriptions of the various functions available to Access users and provide the correct syntax for these functions. This information is designed to help acquaint you with the use of functions with queries, forms, and reports. These descriptions and syntax examples are brief compared to the information available from the Access on-line Help system and in the *Microsoft Access Language Reference*.

One way to learn more about functions is to choose **Search** from the **Help** menu and then type the name of the function for which you want more information in the text box of the Search dialog box. For a faster method to learn more about a particular function, however, follow these steps:

1. Click the surface of the Module1 window anywhere outside the Immediate window to make the Module1 window active. (This procedure is commonly called *giving it the focus*.)

2. Press Enter to move the caret to the beginning of a new line.

3. Type the name of the function; then select the name by clicking it or by pressing Shift+Left arrow key (as shown for the Format function in fig. 7.2).

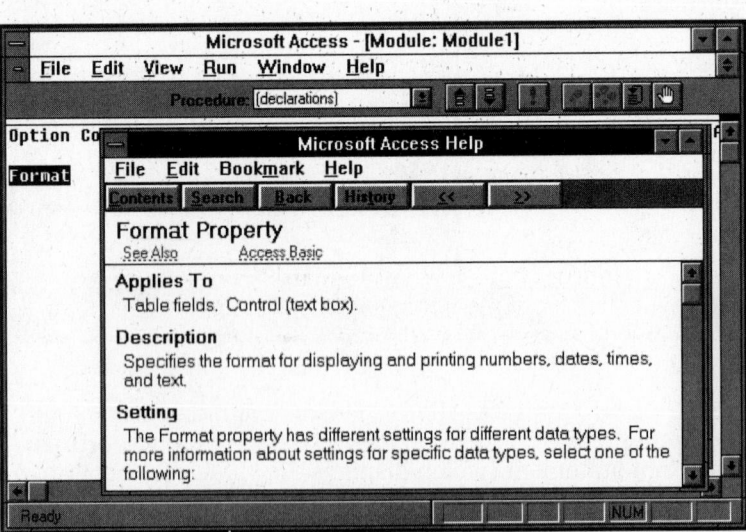

4. Press F1. The Help window opens. If a function and a property share the same name, as is the case with Format, an intermediate Help window appears that enables you to choose the function or the property. Click Format Function. The Format, Format$ Functions Help screen appears as shown in figure 7.3.

5. Click See Also. Related Help topics appear in a pop-up window (see fig. 7.4). Click the See Also window to make the window disappear.

6. After you review the syntax and other information concerning the function, close the Help window by double-clicking its Application Control menu box. Then press Del to delete the selected function name. (This step prevents any error messages that may result from leaving an incomplete line of code in the Module1 window.)

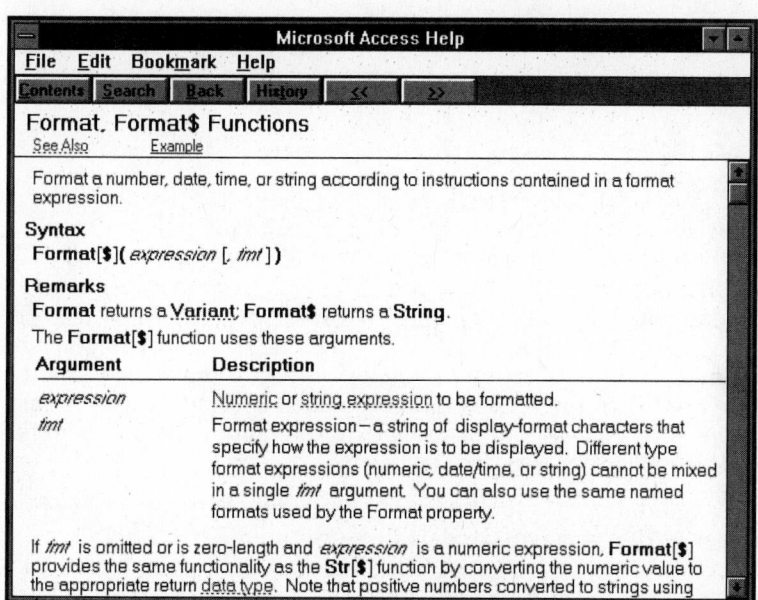

FIG. 7.3

The Format, Format$ Functions Help screen.

Help windows for functions have a standard format, as shown in figure 7.3. If you click Example in any functions Help window, another window displays an example of the function used in Access Basic code. These examples show the syntax of the functions and appropriate arguments.

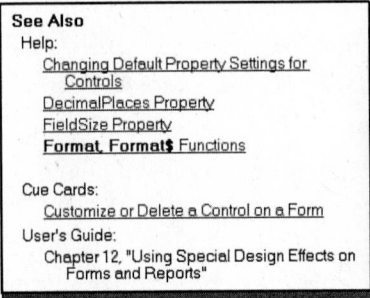

See Also

Help:
    Changing Default Property Settings for
      Controls
    DecimalPlaces Property
    FieldSize Property
    Format, Format$ Functions

Cue Cards:
    Customize or Delete a Control on a Form
User's Guide:
    Chapter 12, "Using Special Design Effects on
      Forms and Reports"

FIG. 7.4

The See Also
pop-up window.

For Related Information:

◄◄ "The Code Editor," p. 53.

The Variant Data Type in Access

xBase

PDOX

Concatenating
different data
types

The Variant data type is a special data type unique to Access and
Visual Basic 2.0. No equivalent of the Variant data type exists in xBase,
Paradox 3+, or other BASIC dialects. The variant data type enables you
to concatenate values that ordinarily would have different data types,
such as an integer and a character string. The capability to concatenate
different data types is called *turning off data type checking*. Variant values are related to the As Any data type used by Visual Basic to turn off
data type checking when declaring external functions contained in Windows Dynamic Link Libraries (DLLs).

The Variant data type enables you to concatenate field values of tables
and queries that have unlike data types without Basic's data type conversion functions such as Str$() or xBase's DTOC(). (Str$() converts
numeric values to the String data type, and DTOC() converts xBase
date values to the character (String) data type.) The Variant data type
also simplifies expressions that combine field values to create concatenated indexes. Specifying a composite (concatenated) index on customer number (Long) and date (Date/Time) with Access's Customer ID;
Order Date expression, for example, is much simpler than using the
expression STRZERO (Cust_Num,6) + DTOC(Order_Date) required to
create a similar index in xBase. The Variant data type also accommodates the Structured Query Language requirement that values of different data types can be concatenated with the & symbol.

Table 7.5 lists the nine subtypes of the Variant data type.

Table 7.5. Subtypes of the Variant Data Type

Subtype	Corresponds To	Stored As
0	Empty (uninitialized)	Not applicable
1	Null (no valid data)	Not applicable
2	Integer	2-byte integer
3	Long	4-byte long integer
4	Single	4-byte single-precision floating point
5	Double	8-byte double-precision floating point
6	Currency	4-byte fixed point
7	Date	8-byte double-precision floating point
8	String	Conventional string variable

You can concatenate Variant values with any of the nine Variant subtypes listed in table 7.5. You can concatenate a subtype 8 Variant (String) with a subtype 5 Variant (Double), for example, without receiving the Type Mismatch error message from Access if you attempted this with conventional String (Text) and Double data types. Access returns a value with the Variant subtype corresponding to the highest subtype number of the concatenated values. This example, therefore, returns a subtype 8 (String) Variant because 8 is greater than 5, the subtype number for the (Double) value. If you concatenate a subtype 2 (Integer) value with a subtype 3 (Long) value, Access returns subtype 3 Variant data.

Distinguishing between the Empty and Null Variant subtypes is important. Empty indicates that a variable you create with Access Basic code has a name, but doesn't have an initial value. Empty applies only to Access Basic variables (see Chapter 22, "Writing Access Basic Code"). Null indicates that a data cell doesn't contain an entry. You can assign the Null value to a variable, in which case the variable is initialized to the Null value, subtype 1.

You can experiment with Variant subtypes in the Immediate window to become more familiar with using the Variant data type. Access provides a function, VarType( ), that returns the integer value of the subtype of its argument. Figure 7.5 shows the data subtype values returned by VarType( ) for four variables (A to D) and the result of the concatenation of these variables (E).

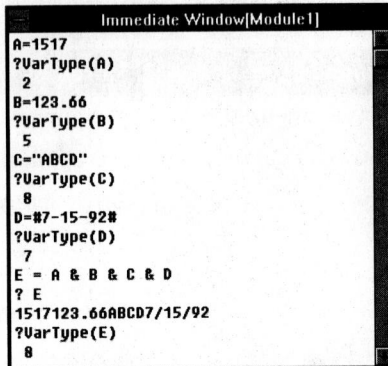

FIG. 7.5

The Variant subtype return values for four variables and the result of the concatenation.

For Related Information:

◄◄ "Choosing Field Data Types, Sizes, and Formats," p. 133.

◄◄ "Adding Indexes to Tables," p. 167.

Functions for Date and Time

Access offers a variety of functions for dealing with dates and times. If you have used Visual Basic, you probably recognize most of the functions applicable to Date/Time field data types, as shown in table 7.6. Access has added several new Date/Time functions, such as DateAdd( ) and DateDiff( ), to simplify the calculation of date values.

All date/time values are stored as double-precision values, but are returned as Variant subtype 7, unless you use the String form of the function. The String form is identified by the String data type identification character, $, appended to the end of the function name. Both ?VarType(Date$( )) and ?VarType(Time$( )) return a subtype 8 (String) Variant.

The Immediate window in figure 7.1 shows a few of the entries used to test the syntax examples of table 7.6.

Table 7.6. General-Purpose Access Functions

Function	Description	Example	Returns
Date(), Date$()	Returns the current system date and time as a subtype 7 date Variant or a standard date string subtype 8	Date()	7/15/92 15-Jul-92
DateAdd()	Returns a subtype 7 date Variant with a specified number of days ("d"), weeks ("ww"), months ("m"), or years ("y") added to the date	DateAdd("d",31, #7/15/92#)	15/Aug/92
DateDiff()	Returns an integer representing the difference between two dates, using the d/w/m/y specification	DateDiff("d",Date(),#8/15/92#) (assuming Date()=7/15/92)	31
DatePart()	Returns the specified part of a date, such as day, month, year, day of week, ("w"), and so on, as an integer	DatePart("w",#7/15/92#)	4 (Wednesday)
DateSerial()	Returns a subtype 7 variant that represents the number of days since December 31, 1899	DateSerial(92,7,15)	7/15/92
DateValue()	Returns a subtype 7 variant that corresponds to a date argument in a string format	DateValue("15-Jul-92")	7/15/92
Day()	Returns an integer between 1 and 31 (inclusive) that represents a day of the month from a date/time value	Day(Date()) (assuming the date is the 15th of the month)	15
Hour()	Returns an integer between 0 and 23 (inclusive) that represents the hour of the date/time value	Hour(#2:30 PM#)	14

continues

Table 7.6. Continued

Function	Description	Example	Returns
Minute( )	Returns an integer between 0 and 59 (inclusive) that represents the minute of a date/time value	Minute(#2:30 PM#)	30
Month( )	Returns an integer between 1 and 12 (inclusive) that represents the month of a date/time value	Month(#15-Jul-92#)	7
Now( )	Returns the date and time of a computer's system clock as a Variant of subtype 7	Now( )	7/15/92 11:57:28 AM
Second( )	Returns an integer between 0 and 59 (inclusive) that represents the minute of a date/time value	Second(Now( ))	28
Time( ), Time$( )	Returns time portion of date/time value from system clock	Time( ) (returns subtype 7) Time$( ) (returns string)	11:57:20 AM
TimeSerial( )	Returns time serial value of time expressed in integer hours, minutes, and seconds	TimeSerial(11,57,20)	11:57:20 AM
TimeValue( )	Returns time serial value of time (entered as string value) as a subtype 7 Variant	TimeValue("11:57")	11:57
Weekday( )	Returns day of week (Sunday=1) corresponding to date as an integer	Weekday(#7/15/92#)	4
Year( )	Returns year of date/time value as an integer	Year(#7/15/92#)	1992

Text Manipulation Functions

Table 7.7 lists the functions that deal with the Text field data type, corresponding to the String data type or Variant subtype 8. Most of these functions are modeled on basic string functions and have similarly named equivalents in xBase and PAL.

Table 7.7. Functions for String and Subtype 8 Variant Data Types

Function	Description	Example	Returns
Asc()	Returns ANSI numeric value of character as an integer	Asc("C")	67
Chr(), Chr$()	Returns character corresponding to numeric ANSI value as a string	Chr(67) Chr$(10)	C (Line feed)
Format(), Format$()	Formats an expression in accordance with appropriate format strings	Format(Date(),"dd-mm-yy")	15-Jul-92
InStr()	Returns position of one string within another	InStr("ABCD","C")	3
LCase(), LCase$()	Returns lowercase version of a string	LCase("ABCD")	abcd
Left(), Left$()	Returns leftmost characters of a string	Left("ABCDEF",3)	ABC
Len()	Returns number of characters in string as an integer	Len("ABCDE")	5
LTrim(), LTrim$()	Removes leading spaces from string	LTrim(" ABC")	ABC
Mid(), Mid$()	Returns a portion of the string from a string	Mid("ABCDE",2,3)	BCD
Right(), Right$()	Returns rightmost characters of string	Right("ABCDEF",3)	DEF

continues

Table 7.7. Continued

Function	Description	Example	Returns
RTrim(), RTrim$()	Removes trailing spaces from string	RTrim("ABC ")	ABC
Space(), Space$()	Returns string consisting of a specified number of spaces	Space(5)	
Str(), Str$()	Converts numeric value of any data type to a string	Str(123.45)	123.45
StrComp()	Compares two strings for equivalence and returns the integer result of comparison	StrComp("ABC", "abc")	0
String(), String$()	Returns a string consisting of specified repeated characters	String(5,"A")	AAAAA
Trim(), Trim$()	Removes leading and trailing spaces from a string	Trim(" ABC ")	ABC
UCase(), UCase$()	Returns uppercase version of a string	UCase("abc")	ABC
Val()	Returns numeric value of a string in data type appropriate to the format of the argument	Val("123.45")	123.45

Two versions of most of the functions are shown in table 7.7: one with and one without a string-identifier character ($). In these cases, the function without the $ returns a Variant subtype 8 (string), and the function with the $ returns a Text data type (string in Basic). Figure 7.6 shows tests of a few of the string functions in the Immediate window.

Access's Format() and Format$() functions are identical to the Format$() function of Visual Basic (see Chapter 4, "Working with Access Databases and Tables," for the arguments for these functions). Access Basic programming uses Format() and Format$() primarily because the Format property of tables, which uses the same arguments as Format(), takes the place of the function. Table 7.7 doesn't include the Tab() and Spc() functions (included in Visual Basic) because these functions format the display and printing of text strings and are used exclusively by Access Basic.

```
Immediate Window[Module1]
?Asc("C")
 67
?Chr(67)
C
?Format(Date(),"dd-mm-yy")
15-07-92
?InStr("ABCD","C")
 3
?LCase("ABCD")
abcd
?Left("ABCDEF",3)
ABC
?Len("ABCDE")
 5
```

FIG. 7.6

Testing the string functions.

Numeric Data Type Conversion Functions

You can assign a particular data type to a numeric value with any of the data type conversion functions. After you "freeze" a data type with one of the numeric data type conversion functions, you cannot concatenate that data type with the String data type or data Variant subtype 7. Table 7.8 lists the eight numeric data type conversion functions.

Table 7.8. Data Type Conversion Functions for Numeric Values

Function	Description	Syntax
CCur()	Converts numeric value to Currency data type	CCur(NumValue)
CDbl()	Converts numeric value to double-precision data type	CDbl(NumValue)
CInt()	Converts numeric value to Integer data type	CInt(NumValue)
CLng()	Converts numeric value to Long Integer data type	CLng(NumValue)
CSng()	Converts numeric value to Single-Precision data type	CSng(NumValue)
CStr()	Converts numeric value to String data type	CStr(NumValue)

continues

Table 7.8. Continued

Function	Description	Syntax
CVar()	Converts numeric value to Variant data type	CVar(NumValue)
CVDate()	Converts numeric value to Variant subtype 7	CVDate(NumValue)

Mathematical and Trigonometric Functions

Access provides a sufficient number of mathematical and trigonometric functions to meet most scientific and engineering requirements. You can create additional trigonometric functions with more complex expressions. If you are interested in more obscure transcendental functions, such as cosecants or hyperbolics, choose the **S**earch command from the **H**elp menu, enter math functions, and then click Derived Math Functions from the Math Functions Help menu. Table 7.9 lists the mathematical and trigonometric functions available in Access.

Table 7.9. Mathematical and Trigonometric Functions

Function	Description	Example	Returns
Abs()	Returns absolute value of numeric value	Abs(–1234.5)	1234.5
Atn()	Returns arctangent of numeric value, in radians	Atn(1)	.7853982
Cos()	Returns cosine of angle represented by numeric value, in radians	Cos(π/4)	.707106719949
Exp()	Returns exponential (antilog) of numeric value	Exp(2.302585)	9.9999990700 (rounding errors)
Fix()	Identical to Int() except for negative numbers	Fix(–13.5)	13

Function	Description	Example	Returns
Int()	Returns numeric value with decimal fraction truncated; data type isn't changed unless argument is a string	Int(13.5) Int(−13.5)	13 14
Log()	Returns natural (Naperian) logarithm of numeric value	Log(10)	2.302585
Rnd()	Creates random single-precision number between 0 and 1 when no argument is supplied	Rnd()	.533424 (varies)
Sgn()	Returns sign of numeric value: 0 if positive, −1 if negative	Sgn(−13.5)	−1
Sin()	Returns sine of numeric value, in radians	Sin(π/4)	.707106842423
Sqr()	Returns square root of numeric value	Sqr(144)	12
Tan()	Returns tangent of numeric value, in radians	Tan(π/4)	1.0000001732 (fraction due to rounding)

The angles returned by the trigonometric functions are expressed in radians, as is the argument of the arctangent (Atn( )) function shown in the table. In the examples, the expression Pi = 3.141593 was typed in the Immediate window prior to entering the syntax example expressions. The returned values of the trigonometric functions are for an angle of approximately 45 degrees, corresponding to π/4 radians.

Because a circle of 360° contains 2π radians, you convert radians to degrees with the expression radians * 360/2π. Because Pi is a rounded value of π and the trigonometric functions round results, you usually obtain values with rounding errors. The cosine of 45°, for example, is 0.7070707..., but Access returns 0.7071067.... These rounding errors are not significant in most applications.

Int() and Fix() differ in the following way: Fix() returns the first negative integer *less than or equal to* the argument, and Int() returns the
first negative integer *greater than or equal to* the argument. Int() and
Fix(), unlike other mathematical and trigonometric functions, return
the integer value of a string variable, but not the value of a literal string
argument. ?Int("13.5"), for example, returns a data type error message;
however, if you type **A=13.5** and then **?Int(A)**, Access returns 13.

Financial Functions

You may be interested in the financial functions of Access because you
have used similar functions in Excel or 1-2-3 spreadsheets. The financial functions of Access (listed in table 7.10) are identical to their capitalized counterparts in Excel and employ the same arguments. If you
have a table of fixed asset records, for example, you can use the depreciation functions to calculate monthly, quarterly, or yearly depreciation
for each asset and then summarize the depreciation schedule in an
Access report.

A full description of the use and syntax of these functions is beyond the scope of this book. If you are interested in more details
about these functions, choose **S**earch from the **H**elp menu and
enter the function name.

Table 7.10. Financial Functions for Calculating Depreciation and Annuities

Function	Description
DDB()	Returns the depreciation of a fixed asset over a specified period by using the double-declining balance method
FV()	Returns the future value of an investment based on a series of constant periodic payments and a fixed rate of interest
IPmt()	Returns the amount of interest for an installment payment on a fixed-rate loan or annuity
IRR()	Returns the internal rate of return for an investment consisting of a series of periodic incomes and expenses
MIRR()	Returns the modified internal rate of return for an investment consisting of a series of periodic incomes and expenses

Function	Description
NPer()	Returns the number of payments of a given amount required to create an annuity or to retire a loan
NPV()	Returns the net present value of an annuity paid out in equal periodic installments
Pmt()	Returns the amount of the periodic payment that must be made to create an annuity or to retire a loan
PPmt()	Returns the amount of principal in an installment payment on a fixed-rate loan or annuity
PV()	Returns the present value of an annuity paid out in equal periodic installments
Rate()	Returns the interest rate of a loan or annuity based on a constant interest rate and equal periodic payments
SLN()	Returns the depreciation of a fixed asset over a specified period by using the straight-line method
SYD()	Returns the depreciation of a fixed asset over a specified period by the sum-of-the-years digits method

General-Purpose Functions

Access provides seven functions that don't fit in any of the preceding categories but that you can use for creating queries, validating data entries, or with forms, reports, and macros. Table 7.11 lists these general-purpose functions.

Table 7.11. General-Purpose Access Functions

Function	Description	Syntax
Choose()	Returns a value from a list of values, based on the position of the value in the list	Choose([Unit of Measure], "Each", "Dozen", "Gross")
IIF()	Returns one value if the result of an expression is True, another if the result is False	IIf([Order Quantity] Mod 12 = 0, "Dozen", "Each")

continues

Table 7.11. Continued

Function	Description	Syntax
IsDate()	Returns True if argument is the Date /Time field data type; otherwise, returns False	IsDate(*FieldName*)
IsEmpty()	Returns True if argument is a noninitialized variable; otherwise, returns False	IsEmpty(*FieldName*)
IsNull()	Returns True if argument is Null; otherwise, returns False	IsNull(*FieldName*)
IsNumeric()	Returns True if argument is one of the Numeric field data types; otherwise, returns False	IsNumeric(*FieldName*)
Partition()	Returns string value indicating number of occurrences of a value within a range of values	Partition(*Number,Start, Stop, Interval*)
Switch()	Returns value associated with first of a series of expressions evaluating to True	Switch([Unit of Measure], "Each", 1, "Dozen", 12, "Gross", 144)

Choose( ) creates a lookup table that returns a value corresponding to a position from a list of values you create. Choose( ) is related closely to the Switch( ) function, which returns a value associated with the first of a series of expressions evaluating to True. In the Choose( ) example of table 7.11, if the value of the Unit of Measure field is 1, Each is returned; if the value is 2, Dozen is returned; and if the value is 3, Gross is returned. Otherwise, Null is returned.

The Switch( ) example returns a divisor value for an order. If the value of the Unit of Measure field is Each, Switch( ) returns 1. If Unit of Measure is Dozen, 12 is returned; and 144 is returned if Unit of Measure is

Gross. Null is returned for no matching value. Choose() and Switch() have similarities to the Select Case statement in Access Basic and other BASIC dialects (Null is the Case Else value). Examples of Choose() and Switch() are included in Chapter 9, "Creating and Using Forms."

The IIf() function is called "in-line If" because it substitutes for the multiline If ... Then ... Else ... End If structure of the Access Basic conditional expression. In the example shown in table 7.11, the IIf() function returns Dozen if the quantity ordered is evenly divisible by 12; otherwise, the function returns Each.

The Partition() function creates histograms. A *histogram* is a series of values (usually displayed in the form of a bar chart) representing the frequency of events that can be grouped within specific ranges. A familiar histogram is a distribution of school examination grades, indicating the number of students who received grades A, B, C, D, and F. The grades may be based on a range of test scores from 90 to 100, 80 to 89, 70 to 79, 60 to 69, and less than 60. You establish the upper and lower limits of the data and then add the partition value.

Effective use of the Partition() function requires typing or editing an SQL statement, and the result of the query is most useful if presented in graphical form. Adding a histogram chart to a form is much easier than using the Partition() function.

The four Is*DataType*() functions determine the type or value of data. You can use IsNull() in validation rules and query criteria of one field to determine whether another field—whose field name is used as the argument—contains a valid entry. Although *FieldName* is the argument in the example syntax in table 7.11, you can substitute an Access Basic variable name.

For Related Information:

▶▶ "Creating a Preview Graph or Chart from a Crosstab Query," p. 347.

▶▶ "Adding Graphs to Forms and Reports," p. 610.

FROM HERE...

Other Functions

Descriptions and syntax for special purpose functions are explained in the chapters covering the Access database object in which the following special purpose functions are used:

- *SQL aggregate functions* are described in Chapter 8, "Creating Queries and Joining Tables," because these functions are used most often with forms. SQL aggregate functions return statistical data on the records selected by a query. You cannot use these functions in macros or call them from Access Basic modules.

- *Domain aggregate functions* perform the same functions as the SQL aggregate functions, but on calculated values rather than the values contained in query fields. Chapter 9, "Creating and Using Forms," covers these functions. You cannot use domain aggregate functions in queries. One domain aggregate function, DCount( ), is quite useful in validating entries in tables; this function is explained later in "Expressions for Validating Data."

- The two dynamic data exchange functions, DDE( ) and DDESend( ), are used to transfer data from and to other applications, respectively. The use of DDE( ) and DDESend( ) functions are covered in Chapter 15, "Using Access with Microsoft Excel."

- The remaining Access functions are used exclusively or almost exclusively in Access Basic modules, and are described in Part VI of this book, "Programming with Access Basic."

Constants

As mentioned earlier, Access Basic has five predefined named constants. The names of these constants are considered keywords because you cannot use these names for any purpose other than returning the value represented by the names: –1 for True and Yes, 0 for False and No. (*True* and *Yes* are synonyms, as are *False* and *No*, and can be used interchangeably.) Null indicates a field with no valid entry.

Named constants return a single, predetermined value for the entire Access session. You can create constants for use with forms and reports by defining them in the declarations section of an Access Basic module. Chapter 22, "Writing Access Basic Code," describes how to create and use constants such as π (used in the examples of trigonometric functions).

Creating Access Expressions

Chapter 4, "Working with Access Databases and Tables," uses several functions to validate data entry for most fields in the Personnel Actions table. Chapter 5, "Attaching, Importing, and Exporting Tables," uses an expression to select the states to be included in a mailing list query. These examples provide the foundation on which to build more complex expressions that can define more precisely the validation rules and query criteria for real-life database applications.

The topics that follow provide a few examples of typical expressions for creating default values for fields, validating data entry, creating query criteria, and calculating field values. The examples demonstrate the similarity of syntax for expressions with different purposes. The remaining chapters of Part II provide additional examples of expressions designed for use in forms and reports, and Part IV explains the use of expressions with macros.

Expressions for Creating Default Values

Expressions that create default field values can speed the entry of new records. Assignment of values ordinarily requires you to use the assignment operator (=). When you are entering a default value in the Properties pane for a table in Design mode, however, you can enter a simple literal. An example is the Q default value assigned to the PA Type field in Chapter 4. In this case, Access infers the = assignment operator and quotation marks surrounding the Q. To adhere to the rules of creating expressions, the default value entry must be = "Q". Access often enables you to use shorthand techniques for typing expressions by inferring the missing characters. If you enter = **"Q"**, you achieve the same result; Access doesn't infer the extra characters.

You can use complex expressions for default values if the result of the expression conforms to or can be converted by Access to the proper field data type. You can enter **=1** as the default value for the PA Type field, for example, although 1 is a Numeric field data type and PA Type is a Text type field.

Expressions for Validating Data

The Personnel Actions table used a number of expressions to validate data entry. The validation rule for the PA ID field is > 0; the rule for the PA Type field is S Or Q Or Y Or B Or C; and the rule for the PA Approved By field is >0 or Is Null. The validation rule for the PA ID field is equivalent to the following imaginary in-line IIf() function:

```
IIf(DataEntry > 0, [PA ID] = DataEntry, MsgBox("Please enter a
valid employee ID number."))
```

Access tests *DataEntry* in the validation rule expression. If the validation expression returns True, the value in the field of the current record is replaced by the value of *DataEntry*. If the expression returns False, a message box displays the validation text you typed. MsgBox() is a function used in Access Basic programming to display a message box on-screen. You cannot type the imaginary validation rule just described; Access infers the equivalent of the imaginary IIf() expression after you add the ValidationRule and ValidationText properties by entries in the two text boxes for the PA ID field.

The validation rule for the PA ID field isn't a valid test because you can type a value greater than the number of employees in the firm. You can determine the number of employees only from the Employees table. One way you can test for a valid PA ID number entry is to retain the > 0 restriction and make sure that the maximum value of the entry is less than or equal to the number of records in the Employees table. This procedure is close to a valid test because the Employee ID field of the Employees table is of the Counter field data type, which numbers appended records consecutively. But how do you determine the number of employees in the Employees table?

The domain aggregate function DCount() is useful for performing validations that involve testing entries in other tables. DCount() returns the number of records in a *domain* that meet a particular criterion. A domain can be a table or the result of a query. The syntax of the DCount() function follows:

```
DCount("[FieldName]", "DomainName", "Criterion")
```

FieldName is the name of the field to be tested—in this case, Employee ID. *DomainName* is the name of the table containing the Employees field. *Criterion* is an optional expression you can use to count records containing values that cause the expression to return True. If you need to count only the number of entries in the Employee ID field, you can omit the *Criterion* argument. After you use DCount(), the function creates and runs the following SQL statement:

```
SELECT Count([FieldName]) FROM DomainName WHERE Criterion
```

Although SQL is the subject of Chapter 20, "Working with Structured Query Language," examples of simple SQL statements are shown here so that you can become familiar with the syntax of these statements. If you program with Clipper, you can see that the use of DCount() is much simpler than VALID *UserFunction()*, which requires you to write a user-defined function to count the records.

To improve the validation rule for PA ID, follow these steps:

1. Open the NWIND database, if necessary; then open the Personnel Actions table in Design mode.

2. The PA ID field is selected after you enter Design mode. Because

   ```
   Between Value 1 And Value 2
   ```

   is a more expressive syntax for

   ```
   >= Value1 And <= Value2
   ```

   replace >0 in the Validation Rule text box with

   ```
   Between 1 And DCount("[Employee ID]", "Employees")
   ```

3. Typing this entry fills the Validation Rule text box. Access has a solution for this problem: the Zoom box for expressions. Press Shift+F2 to open the Zoom box (see fig. 7.7).

4. Complete the expression in the Zoom box. Then choose OK to move the completed entry into the Validation Rule text box.

5. The new validation rule isn't tested for syntax errors until you change to Run mode. Click the Datasheet button on the toolbar.

   If you make spelling errors or miss quotation marks when you type the validation rule, a Syntax Error message box appears. Open the Zoom box to correct the entry.

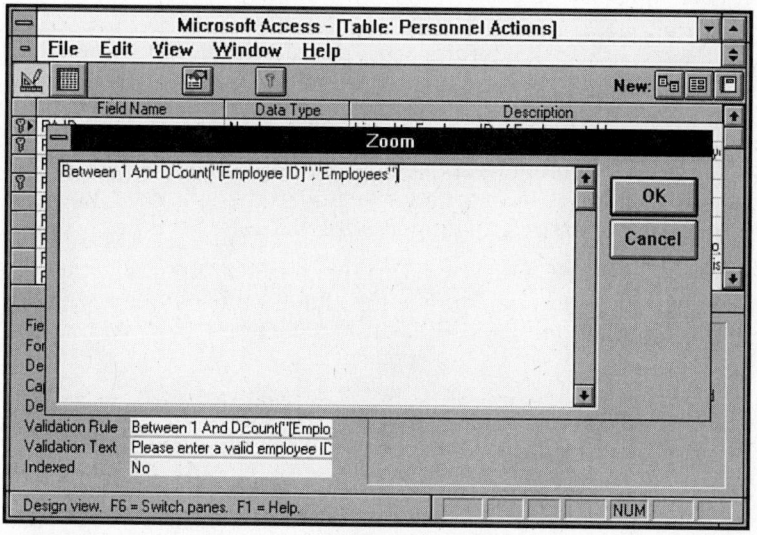

FIG. 7.7

The Zoom box for entering complex expressions.

6. The field and table names you type in the validation rule aren't tested until you create a new record or edit an existing record. Type a valid Employee ID number in the field to test the operation of the validation rule. The DCount( ) function opens the Employees table, counts the number of records with Not Null values in the Employee ID field, and returns the count to the expression.

Gotcha!
Invalid reference to a nonexistent table or field.

FIG. 7.8

'A message box announcing an error in the syntax of an expression.

If you made an error in the field name or the table name, an invalid reference message box appears (similar to the one shown in fig. 7.8) when you attempt to enter a new record in Run mode. When this kind of message appears, you are in what programmers call a *trap*. To correct the invalid reference, you must switch to Design mode to fix the error—but you cannot return to Design mode by clicking the Design View button on the toolbar or by choosing Table **D**esign from the **V**iew menu. The only solution is to close the table without saving the changes; then reopen the table in Design mode and make the necessary corrections.

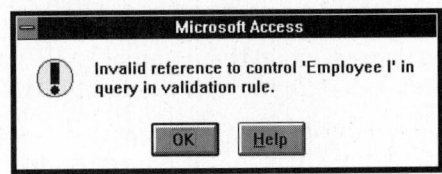

For this exercise, try entering employee ID numbers such as 0 and 15, which are outside the valid range. You receive the message box containing the validation text

    Please enter a valid employee ID number.

Using DCount( ) to validate employee numbers doesn't provide a foolproof test. If you delete records for employees terminated from your employee list, for example, some employee numbers will be missing and a count no longer gives the proper upper limit for employee numbers. If you don't delete records for terminated employees, you can enter actions for persons no longer employed.

The expression S Or Q Or Y Or B Or C used to test the PA Type field is another candidate for change. The In( ) function provides a simpler expression that accomplishes the same objective:

    In("S", "Q", "Y", "B", "C").

Alternately, you can use the validation expression

    InStr("SQYBC",[PA ID]) > 0.

Both expressions give the same result.

Expressions for Query Criteria

When creating the Western States Mailing List query (in Chapter 6, "Using Query by Example: A Quick Start") to select records from the states of California, Oregon, and Washington, you enter **="CA"**, **="OR"**, and **="WA"** on separate lines. A better expression is In("CA", "OR", "WA"), entered on the same line as the ="USA" criterion for the Country field. This expression corrects the failure to test the Country field for a value equal to USA for the OR and WA entries.

You can use a wide range of other functions to select specific records to be returned to a query table. Table 7.12 shows some typical functions used as query criteria applicable to the Northwind Traders tables.

Table 7.12. Typical Expressions Used as Query Criteria

Table	Field	Expression	Records Returned
Customers	Country	Not "USA" And Not "Canada"	Firms other than those in the U.S. and Canada
Customers	Country	Not ("USA" Or "Canada")	Same as preceding; the parentheses apply the Not condition to both literals
Customers	Company Name	Like "[N-Z]*"	Firms with names beginning with N through Z, outside the U.S.
Customers	Company Name	S* Or V*	Firms with names beginning with S or V (Access adds Like and quotation marks)
Customers	Company Name	Like "*shop*"	Firms with *shop*, *Shop*, *Shoppe*, or *SHOPPING* in the firm name
Customers	Postal Code	>=90000	Firms with postal codes greater than or equal to 90000
Orders	Order Date	Year([OrderDate]) = 1992	Orders received to date, beginning with 1/1/1992
Orders	Order Date	Like "*/*/92"	Same as preceding; using wild cards simplifies expressions

continues

Table 7.12. Continued

Table	Field	Expression	Records Returned
Orders	Order Date	Like "1/*/92"	Orders received in the month of January, 1992
Orders	Order Date	Like "1/?/92"	Orders received from the 1st to the 9th of January, 1992
Orders	Order Date	Year([OrderDate] = 1992 And DatePart("q", [OrderDate]) = 1	Orders received in the first quarter of 1992
Orders	Order Date	Between #1/1/92# and #3/31/92#	Same as preceding
Orders	Order Date	Year([OrderDate] = 1992 And DatePart("ww", [OrderDate]) = 10	Orders received in the 10th week of 1992
Orders	Order Date	>= DateValue ("1/15/92")	Orders received on or after 1/15/92
Orders	Shipped Date	Is Null	Orders not yet shipped
Orders	Order Amount	>= 5000	Orders with values greater than or equal to $5,000
Orders	Order Amount	Between 5000 and 10000	Orders with values greater than or equal to $5,000 and less than or equal to $10,000
Orders	Order Amount	< 1000	Orders less than $1,000

The wild-card characters used in Like expressions simplify the creation of criteria for selecting names and dates. As in DOS, the asterisk (*) substitutes for any legal number of characters and the question mark (?) substitutes for a single character. When a wild-card character prefixes or appends a string, the matching process loses its default case sensitivity. If you want to match a string without regard to case, use the following expression:

```
UCase(FieldName) = "MATCH STRING"
```

To experiment with query criteria expressions, follow these steps:

1. Click the Query button in the Database window then click the New button to open a new query.

2. Select the Customers table from the Add Table list box and click the Add button.

3. Select the Orders table from the list box and click the Add button. Click the Close button to close the Add Table dialog box. The Customer ID fields of the Customers and Orders table are joined; joins are indicated by a line between the fields of the two tables. (The next chapter covers joining multiple tables.)

4. Add the Company Name, Postal Code, and Country fields of the Customers table to the query. You can add fields by selecting them from the field drop-down list in the Query Design grid or by clicking a field in the Customers Field list above the grid and dragging the field to the desired Field cell in the grid.

5. Add the Order Date, Shipped Date, and Order Amount fields of the Orders table to the query. Use the horizontal scroll bar slider under the Query Design grid to expose additional field columns as necessary. Your query appears similar to that shown in figure 7.9.

6. In the first Criteria row of the designated field, type one of the expressions from table 7.12. Figure 7.10 shows the example expression Like "*shop*" entered in the Criteria row of the Company Name column.

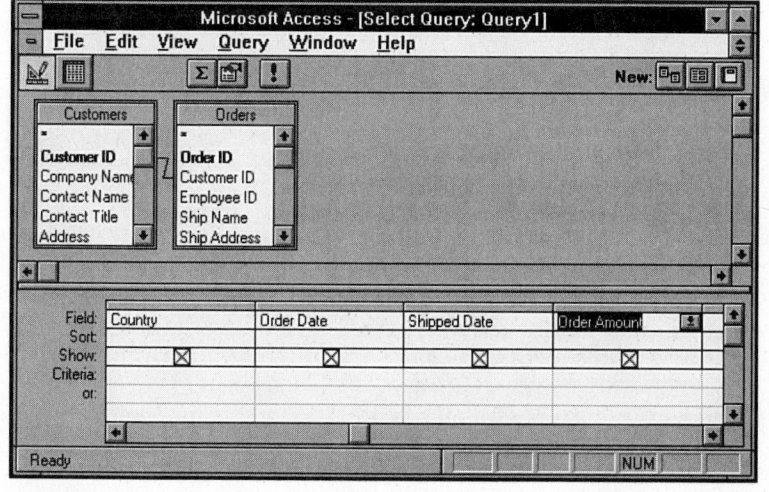

FIG. 7.9

The query design for testing the use of expressions to select records with values that meet criteria.

FIG. 7.10

Entering a criterion to display only records with company names that include the word *shop*.

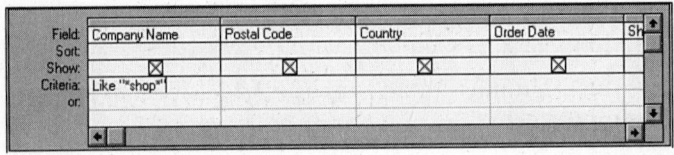

7. Click the Run Query button on the toolbar to test the expression. The query result for the example in figure 7.10 appears as shown in figure 7.11.

8. Return to Query Design mode; then select and delete the expression by pressing the Del key.

FIG. 7.11

The query dynaset resulting from adding the Like "*shop*" criteria to the Company Name field.

Company Name	Postal Code	Country	Order Date	Shipped Date	Order Amount
Let's Stop N Shop	94117	USA	20-Dec-89	10-Jan-90	$1,485.00
Let's Stop N Shop	94117	USA	22-May-91	31-May-91	$317.75
Let's Stop N Shop	94117	USA	23-Sep-91	02-Oct-91	$844.25
Let's Stop N Shop	94117	USA	07-Oct-91	18-Oct-91	$536.40
Let's Stop N Shop	94117	USA	09-Jan-92	10-Jan-92	$1,378.07
Live Oak Hotel Gift Shop	97229	USA	01-Jun-89	05-Jun-89	$1,057.60
Live Oak Hotel Gift Shop	97229	USA	24-Jul-89	02-Aug-89	$1,816.02
Live Oak Hotel Gift Shop	97229	USA	06-Oct-89	10-Oct-89	$127.36
Live Oak Hotel Gift Shop	97229	USA	14-Feb-90	16-Feb-90	$981.00
Live Oak Hotel Gift Shop	97229	USA	03-Dec-90	19-Dec-90	$400.00
Live Oak Hotel Gift Shop	97229	USA	19-Feb-91	25-Feb-91	$1,584.00
Live Oak Hotel Gift Shop	97229	USA	17-Jul-91	29-Jul-91	$2,720.05
Live Oak Hotel Gift Shop	97229	USA	04-Sep-91	10-Sep-91	$805.43
Live Oak Hotel Gift Shop	97229	USA	01-Oct-91	11-Oct-91	$1,850.00
Live Oak Hotel Gift Shop	97229	USA	29-Nov-91	05-Dec-91	$852.00
Live Oak Hotel Gift Shop	97229	USA	16-Dec-91	20-Dec-91	$1,938.38
Live Oak Hotel Gift Shop	97229	USA	16-Dec-91	13-Jan-92	$211.20

9. Repeat steps 5 through 7 for each expression you want to test. When you are testing expressions using date/time functions, sort the Order Date field in ascending order. Similarly, sort on the Order Amount field when queries are based on amount criteria. You can alter the expressions and try combinations with the implied And condition by entering criteria for other fields in the same row. Access warns you with an error message if you make a mistake in the syntax for an expression.

10. After you finish experimenting, double-click the Document Control menu box to close the query and do not save it.

Expressions for Calculating Query Field Values

You can use expressions to create new, calculated fields in query tables. Calculated fields display data that is computed based on the values of other fields in the same row of the query table. Table 7.13 shows some representative expressions you can use to create calculated query fields. To create a query containing calculated fields, follow these steps:

1. Create a new query and add the Orders table to the query.

2. Add the Order ID, Order Amount, and Freight fields to the query.

3. In the next blank field, type the field name shown in table 7.13, followed by a colon and then the expression. Press Shift+F2 to use the Zoom box to enter the expression, as shown in figure 7.12. If you don't type the field name and colon, Access provides the default Expr1 as the calculated field name.

4. Run the query. The resulting dynaset for the query with the calculated field appears as shown in figure 7.13.

5. Repeat steps 3 and 4 for each of the four examples in table 7.13.

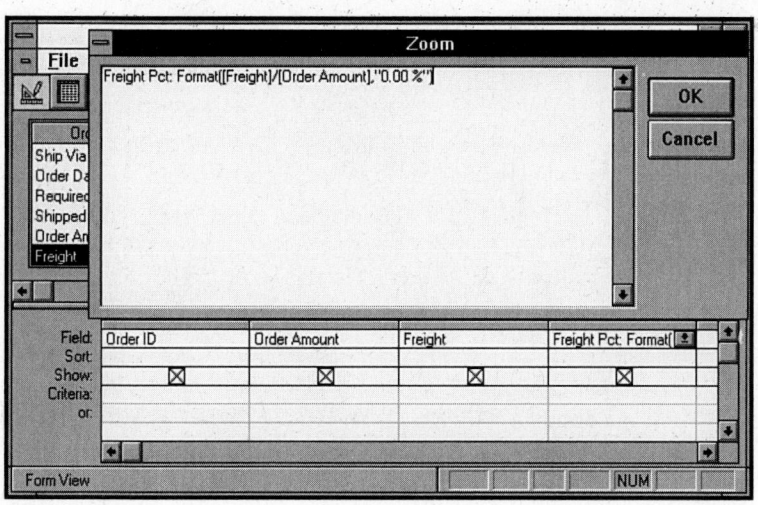

FIG. 7.12

Entering an expression to create a calculated field in a query.

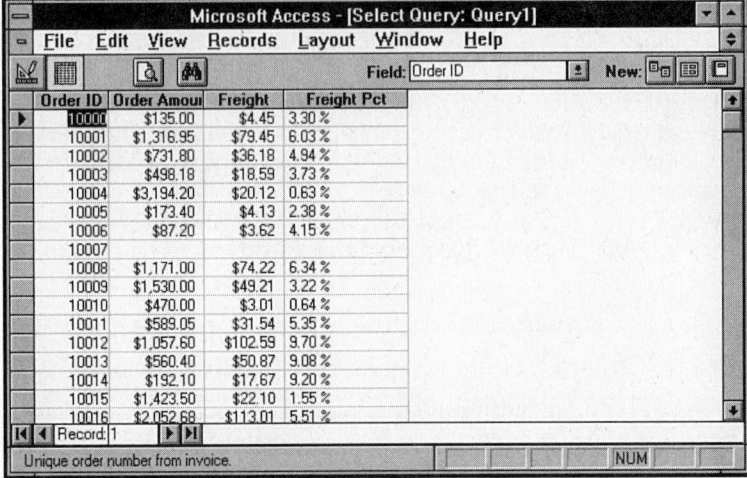

FIG. 7.13

The query dynaset with a calculated field displaying freight charges as a percent of order amount.

Table 7.13. Typical Expressions To Create Calculated Query Fields

Field Name	Expression	Values Calculated
Total Amount	[Order Amount] + Freight	Sum of Order Amount and Freight fields
Freight Percent	100 * Freight/[Order Amount]	Freight charges as a percentage of the order amount
Freight Pct	Format([Freight]/[Order Amount],"0.00 %")	Same as above, but with formatting applied
Sales Tax	Format([Order Amount] * 0.05, "$#,###.00")	Sales tax of 5 percent of the amount of the order added with display similar to the Currency data type

You use the Format( ) function with your expression as its first argument to display the calculated values in a more readable form. When you add the percent symbol (%) to a format expression, the value of the expression argument is multiplied by 100, and the percent symbol preceded by a space is appended to the displayed value. Figure 7.14 shows the SQL statement that creates the query with all four calculated fields. Note that you cannot include periods indicating abbreviations in field names. Periods and exclamation points are identifier operators, so they cannot be included within identifiers.

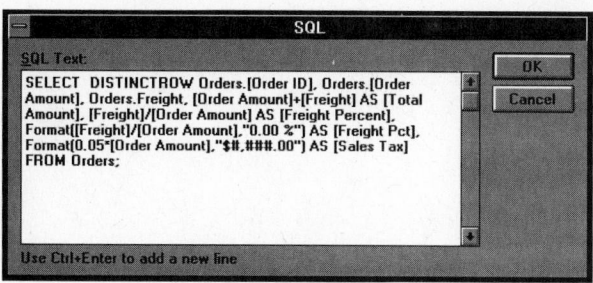

FIG. 7.14

The SQL state-
ment used to
create a query
with four cal-
culated fields.

Other Uses for Expressions

You can use expressions with update queries, as conditions for the execution of a macro action, or as an argument for an action such as RunMacro (see Chapter 17, "Understanding Access Macros"). Expressions are used in SQL SELECT statements, such as the following:

```
WHERE [Birth Date] >= #1/1/60#
```

see Chapter 20, "Working with Structured Query Language," for more information. Expressions also are used extensively in Access Basic code to control program flow and structure. These uses for expressions are described in the chapters devoted to macros, SQL, and Access Basic programming (Parts IV and V).

Chapter Summary

Expressions you create with Access operators, identifiers, constants, and functions; and the literals you supply are used in every aspect of an Access database application. Although the emphasis in this chapter is on using expressions to validate data entry in tables and creating query tables, expressions are basic elements of forms, reports, macros, and modules.

Now that you have a firm foundation in the use of expressions, you are ready to learn how to create more complex queries that join multiple tables, cross-tabulate query data, create new tables, and append entries to existing tables. Chapter 6 previewed Action queries and this chapter covered joining tables; the next chapter tells you how to create queries that return precisely those records you want.

The remaining chapters in Part II of this book cover the basics of creating forms, printing reports, and using macros to automate your applications. More advanced methodology for the subjects covered in Part II is described in Part IV, "Powering Access with Macros."

Creating Queries and Joining Tables

Your purpose in acquiring Access is undoubtedly to take advantage of this application's relational database management capabilities. To do so requires that you be able to link related tables, based on key fields that have values in common, a process known as a *join* in database terms. Chapters 6 and 7 showed you how to create simple queries based on a single table. If you tried the examples in Chapter 7, you saw a glimpse of a multiple-table query when you added the Orders table to the test query, which was based on the Customers table. The first part of this chapter deals exclusively with queries created from multiple tables related through joins.

This chapter provides examples of queries that use each of the four types of joins you can create in Access's Query Design mode: equi-joins, outer joins, self-joins, and theta joins. Some of the example queries in this chapter use the Personnel Actions table you created in Chapter 4, "Working with Access Databases and Tables." If you didn't create the Personnel Actions table, refer to the "Creating the Personnel Actions Table" section of Chapter 4 or to Appendix E, "Data Dictionary for the Personnel Actions Table," for instructions to build this table. Other example queries build on queries you create in preceding sections. You will find, therefore, that reading the chapter and creating the example queries sequentially, as the queries appear in text, is more efficient.

This chapter also includes descriptions and examples of the five categories of queries that you can create with Access: select, summary, parameter, crosstab, and action queries. Near the end of the chapter, you create an Access form that incorporates a graph of the data supplied by a crosstab query, a special form of summary query unique to Access. Four types of action queries exist that you can use to create or modify data in tables: make table, append, delete, and update. The chapter presents typical applications for and examples of each type of action query.

Joining Tables To Create Multitable Queries

Before you can create joins between tables, you must know the contents of the fields of the tables and which fields are related by common values. As mentioned in Chapter 4, assigning identical names to fields in different tables that contain related data is a common practice. This approach was followed when Microsoft created the Northwind Traders database and makes determining relationships and creating joins between tables easier. The Customer ID field of the Customers table and the Customer ID field of the Orders table, for example, are used to join orders with customers. The structure of the Northwind Traders database, together with a graphical display of the joins among the tables, is shown in figure 8.1. Joins are indicated in Access query designs by lines between field names of different tables. Primary key fields are indicated by boldface type. At least one primary key field usually is involved in each join.

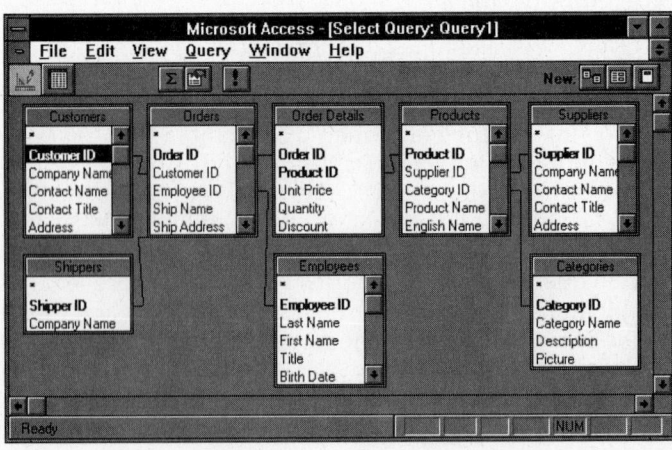

FIG. 8.1

The joins among the tables of the Northwind Traders sample database.

You can display the structure of the joins between the tables in the Northwind Traders database on-screen by clicking the Query button in the Database window, selecting the Database Diagram query, and clicking Design. (If you open the Database Diagram in Datasheet view, only a single field header appears; this query was designed as a diagram, not to be run.)

Four types of joins are supported by Access in the graphical QBE Design mode:

- *Equi-joins* are the most common join in creating select queries. Equi-joins display all the records in one table that have corresponding records in another table. The correspondence between records is determined by identical values (= in SQL) in the fields that join the tables. In most cases, joins are based on a unique primary key field in one table and a field in the other table in a one-to-many relationship. If no records in the table that act as the *many* side of the relationship have field values that correspond to a record in the table of the *one* side, the corresponding records in the *one* side don't appear in the query result.

  Access creates the joins between tables if the tables share a common field name and this field name is a primary key of one of the tables or if you previously specified the relationships between the tables in the Relationships dialog box.

- *Outer joins* are used in database maintenance to remove orphan records and to remove duplicate data from tables by creating new tables that contain records with unique values. Outer joins display records in one member of the join, regardless of whether corresponding records exist on the other side of the join.

- *Self-joins* relate data within a single table. You create a self-join in Access by adding a duplicate of the table to the query (Access provides an alias for the duplicate) and then creating joins between the fields of the copies.

- *Theta joins* relate data by using comparison operators other than =. Theta joins include *not-equal joins* (<>) used in queries designed to return records that lack a particular relationship. Theta joins are implemented by WHERE criteria rather than by the SQL JOIN reserved word. Theta joins aren't indicated by lines between field names in the Query Design window.

For Related Information:

◄◄ "Establishing Relationships between Tables," p. 161.

FROM HERE...

Creating Conventional Single-Column Equi-joins

Joins based on one column in each table are known as *single-column equi-joins*. Most relational databases are designed to employ single-column equi-joins only in one-to-many relationships. The basic rules for creating a database that enables you to use simple, single-column equi-joins for all queries are detailed in the following list:

- Each table on the *one* side of the relationship must have a primary key with a No Duplicates index to maintain referential integrity. Access creates a No Duplicates index on the primary key field of a table.

- Many-to-many relationships, such as the relationship of Orders to Products, are implemented by an intermediary table (here, Order Details) having a one-to-many relationship (Orders to Order Details) with one table and a many-to-one relationship (Order Details to Products) with another.

- Duplicated data in tables, where applicable, is extracted to a new table that has a primary-key, no-duplicates, one-to-many relationship with the table from which the duplicate data is extracted. Using a multicolumn primary key to identify extracted data uniquely often is necessary because individual key fields may contain duplicate data. The combination (also known as *concatenation*) of the values of the key fields, however, must be unique. Extracting duplicate data from tables is described in the "Creating New Tables with Action Queries" section later in this chapter.

All the joins in the Northwind Traders database, shown by the lines that connect field names of adjacent tables in figure 8.1, are single-column equi-joins. Access uses the SQL reserved words INNER JOIN to identify conventional equi-joins, and LEFT JOIN or RIGHT JOIN to specify outer joins.

Among the most common applications for queries based on equi-joins is matching customer names and addresses with orders received. You may want to create a simple report, for example, that lists the customer name, order number, order date, and amount. To create a conventional one-to-many single-column equi-join query that relates Northwind's customers to the orders the customers place, sorted by company and order date, follow these steps:

1. If NWIND.MDB is open, close all windows except the Database window by double-clicking the Document Control Menu box. Otherwise, open Access' File menu and click NWIND.MDB to open the Northwind Traders database.

2. Click the Query button of the Database window and then click New to create a new query. Access displays the Add Table dialog box superimposed on an empty Query Design window.

3. Select the Customers table from the Add Table list box and click the Add button. Instead, you can double-click the Customers table name to add the table to the query. Access adds the Field Names list box for Customers to the Query Design window.

4. Double-click the Orders table in the Add Table list box, and then click the Close button. Access adds the Field Names list box for Orders to the window, plus a line that indicates a join between the Customer ID fields of the two tables, as shown in figure 8.2. The join is created automatically, because Customer ID is the key field of the Customers table, and Access found a field with the same field name in the Orders table.

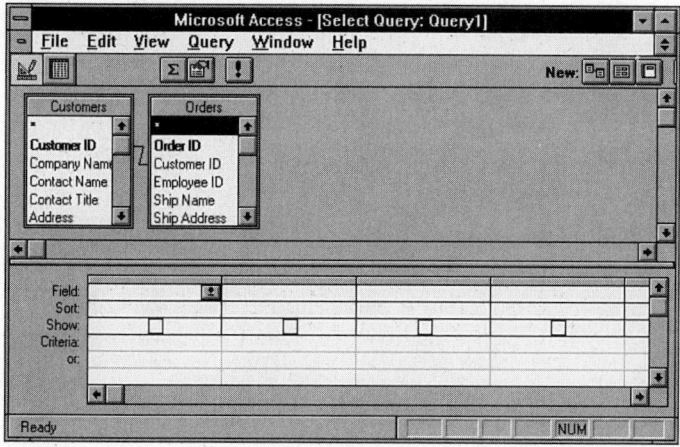

FIG. 8.2

A join between fields of two tables with a common field name, created by Access.

5. To identify each order with the customer's name, select the Company Name field of the Customers table and drag the field symbol to the Field row of the first column of the Query Design grid.

6. Select the Order ID field of the Orders table and drag the field symbol to the Field row of the second column.

7. Repeat step 6 for the Order Date and Order Amount fields of the Orders table. To make the information displayed by the query more meaningful, click the Sort row of the Company Name field, open the Sort list box, and select an Ascending sort. Access displays the company names in alphabetical order. Perform the same process for the Order Date field so that orders for each customer are displayed in date sequence. The query design appears as shown in figure 8.3.

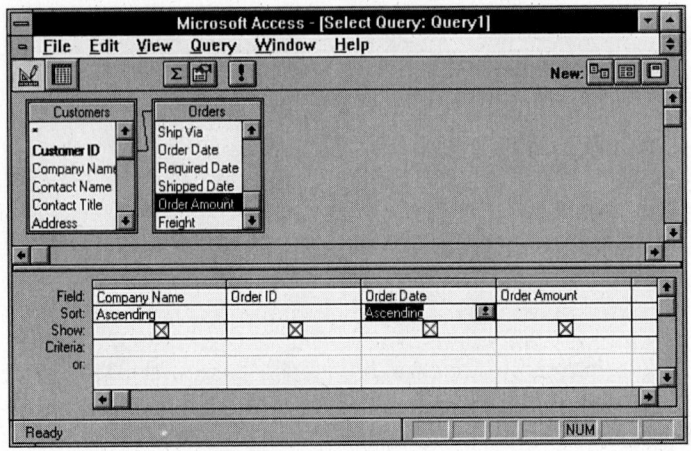

FIG. 8.3

Designing a
query to display
orders placed by
customers, sorted
by customer
name and date.

8. Click the Run Query button to display the result of the query, the
   dynaset shown in figure 8.4.

Access sorts the results queries that contain more than one sorted field
with left to right precedence. Because Company Name is the farthest
left sorted field, the query dynaset displays all orders for a single company in sequence. Order Date is to the right of Company Name, so orders for a single company next are sorted by order date.

Company Name	Order ID	Order Date	Order Amount
Always Open Quick Mart	10062	24-Aug-89	$855.38
Always Open Quick Mart	10643	22-Jul-91	$814.50
Always Open Quick Mart	10692	30-Aug-91	$878.00
Always Open Quick Mart	10702	09-Sep-91	$330.00
Always Open Quick Mart	10835	12-Dec-91	$845.80
Always Open Quick Mart	10952	10-Feb-92	$471.20
Always Open Quick Mart	11011	05-Mar-92	$933.50
Andre's Continental Food Market	10308	15-Aug-90	$88.80
Andre's Continental Food Market	10625	05-Jul-91	$479.75
Andre's Continental Food Market	10759	25-Oct-91	$320.00
Andre's Continental Food Market	10926	29-Jan-92	$514.40
Anthony's Beer and Ale	10028	28-Jun-89	$970.00
Anthony's Beer and Ale	10044	25-Jul-89	$1,149.74
Anthony's Beer and Ale	10101	30-Oct-89	$437.48
Anthony's Beer and Ale	10137	28-Dec-89	$807.50
Anthony's Beer and Ale	10142	05-Jan-90	$330.00
Anthony's Beer and Ale	10218	24-Apr-90	$779.00

FIG. 8.4

The result of the
query design of
figure 8.3 that
joins the Custom-
ers and Orders
tables.

For Related Information:

◀◀ "Adding Indexes to Tables," p. 167.

FROM HERE...

Creating Queries from Tables with Indirect Relationships

You can create queries that return indirectly related records, such as the categories of products purchased by each customer. You need to include in the query each table that serves as a link in the chain of joins. If you are creating queries to return the categories of products purchased by each customer, for example, include each of the tables that link the chain of joins between the Customers and Categories tables. This chain includes Customers, Orders, Order Details, Products, and Categories. You don't need to add any fields, however, from the intermediate tables to the Query Design grid. Just the Company Name and the Category Name are sufficient.

To modify your customers and orders so that you create a query that displays fields of indirectly related records, follow these steps:

1. Delete the Order ID column of the query by clicking the thin bar above the Field row to select (highlight) the entire column. Then press Delete. Perform the same action for the Order Date and Order Amount columns, so that only the Company Name column contains entries.

2. Choose **A**dd Table from the **Q**uery menu and add the Order Details, Products, and Categories tables to the query, in sequence, then click the Close button of the Add Table dialog box. The upper pane of figure 8.5 shows the chain of joins that Access creates between Customers and Categories based on the primary key field of each table and the identically named field in the adjacent table.

3. Drag the Category Name from the Categories field list to the Field row of the second column of the grid. Add an ascending sort to this field.

4. If you want to see the SQL statement that Access uses to create the query, choose **S**QL from the **V**iew menu to display the SQL dialog box of figure 8.6.

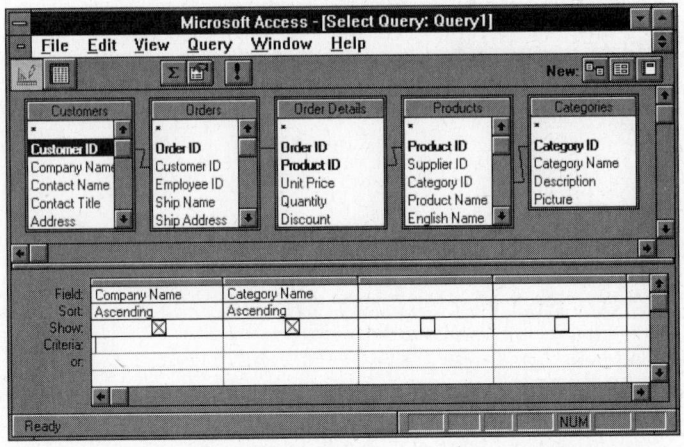

FIG. 8.5

The chain of joins required to create queries from tables that have an indirect relationship.

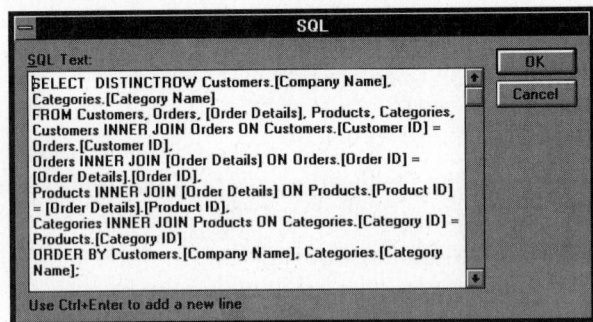

FIG. 8.6

The SQL statement that creates the query to determine customers purchasing categories of products.

5. Choose Cancel to close the SQL dialog box, then click the Run Query button on the toolbar. The query table or dynaset shown in figure 8.7 appears.

6. Click the End of Table button to determine the number of rows in the query table. When this chapter was written, the number of row (Records) was 638. Because databases are dynamic objects and Microsoft continued to add new records to the tables during the beta-testing process, the query may result in more rows.

7. Close the query by double-clicking the Document Control Menu box. This query is only an example, so you don't need to save the query.

Queries made on indirectly related tables are common, especially when you want to analyze the data with SQL aggregate functions or Access's crosstab queries. For more information, see the sections "Using the SQL Aggregate Functions" and "Creating Crosstab Queries" in this chapter.

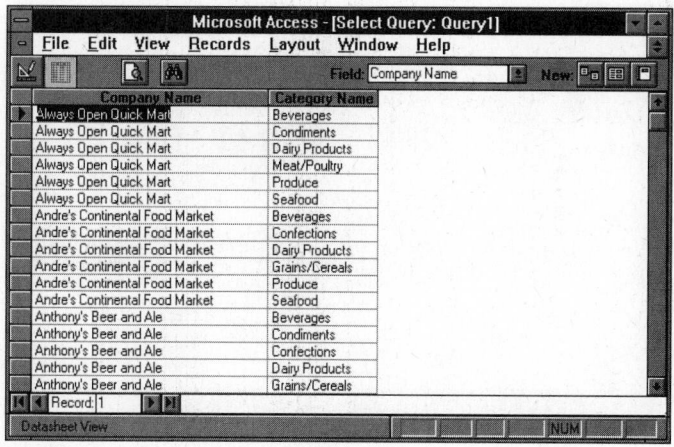

FIG. 8.7

The Customers-
Categories
dynaset, resulting
from the query of
figure 8.3.

Creating Multicolumn Equi-joins and Selecting Unique Values

You can have more than one join between a pair of tables. You may, for example, want to create a query that returns the names of customers for which the billing and shipping addresses are the same. The billing address is the Address field of the Customers table, and the shipping address is the Ship Address field of the Orders table. Therefore, you need to match the Customer ID fields in the two tables and Customers.Address with Orders.[Ship Address]. This task requires a *multicolumn equi-join*.

To create this example of an address-matching multicolumn equi-join, follow these steps:

1. Create a new query by clicking the Query button and then the New button in the Database window.

2. Add the Customers and Orders tables to the query by selecting each table in the Add Table dialog box and clicking the Add button. Click Close.

3. Click and drag the Address field of the Field List box for the Customers table to the Ship Address field of the Field List box for the Orders table. Another join is created, indicated by the new line between Address and Ship Address (see fig. 8.8).

4. Drag the Company Name and Address fields of the Customers table to the Field row of the first and second query columns and drop the fields. Drag the Ship Address field of the Orders table to the third column of the query and drop the field in the Field row.

Query

New

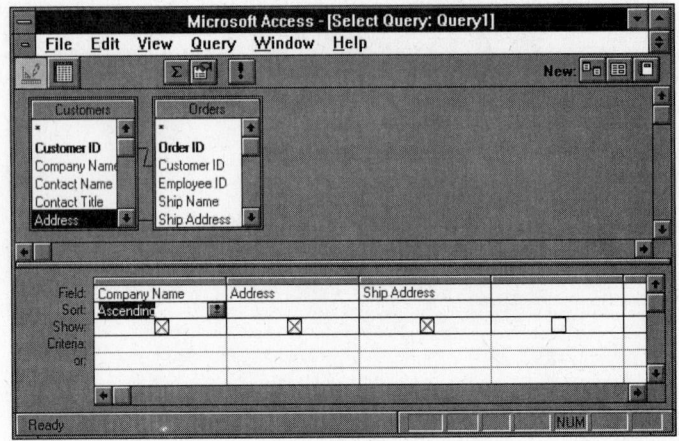

FIG. 8.8

Creating a multi-column equi-join by dragging one field name to a field in another table.

5. Add an ascending sort to the Company Name column.

6. Click the Run Query button on the toolbar. The result of the query is shown in figure 8.9.

7. To eliminate the duplicate rows, you must use the Query Properties dialog box's Unique Values Only option. To display this dialog box, which is shown in figure 8.10, click the Design mode button, and then click the Properties button on the toolbar.

8. Mark the Unique Values Only check box; then choose OK to close the dialog box.

9. Click the Run Query button on the toolbar. The dynaset no longer contains duplicate rows, as demonstrated by figure 8.11.

10. Double-click the Document Control Menu box to close it, without saving the query. You then avoid cluttering the Queries list of the Database window with obsolete query examples.

Because most of the orders have the same billing and shipping addresses, a more useful query is to find the orders for which the customer's billing and shipping addresses differ. You cannot create this query with a multicolumn equi-join, however, because the INNER JOIN reserved word in Access SQL doesn't accept the <> operator. Adding a not-equal join uses a criterion rather than a multicolumn join, as explained in section "Creating Not-Equal Theta Joins with Criteria" later in this chapter.

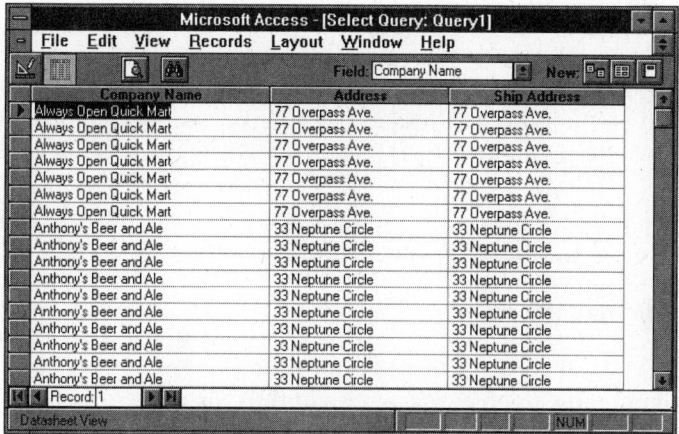

FIG. 8.9

A dynaset of orders for customers who have the same billing and shipping addresses.

FIG. 8.10

Using the Query Properties dialog box to display only rows with unique values.

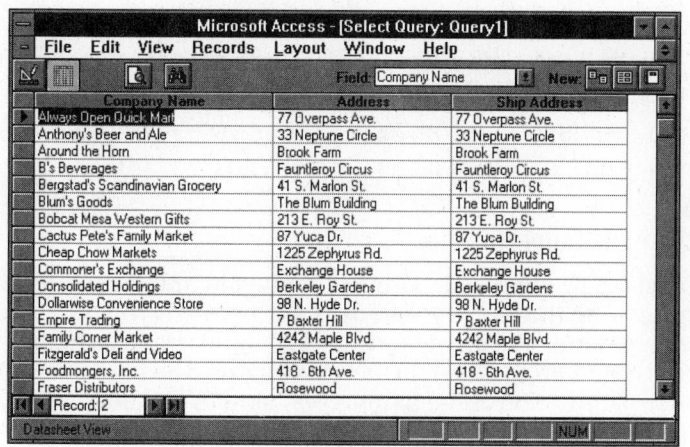

FIG. 8.11

The dynaset after duplicate rows are removed.

Creating Outer Joins

Outer joins enable you to display fields of all the records in a table participating in a query, regardless of whether corresponding records exist in the joined table. With Access, you can select between left and right outer joins.

In diagramming database structures, a subject of Chapter 21, the primary *one* table traditionally is drawn to the left of the secondary *many* table. A left outer join (LEFT JOIN or *= in SQL) query in Access, therefore, displays all the records in the table with the unique primary key, regardless of whether matching records exist in the *many* table. Conversely, a right outer join (RIGHT JOIN or =*) query displays all the records in the *many* table, regardless of the existence of a record in the primary table. Records in the *many* table without corresponding records in the *one* table usually, but not necessarily, are orphan records; these kinds records may have a many-to-one relationship to another table.

Neither Access nor SQL includes all provisions to create an *ambidextrous* join (conceptually, *=*) that results in the selection of all records of both tables; neither do you have a use for this kind of join in a relational DBM.

To practice creating a left outer join, follow these steps to detect whether records are missing for an employee in the Personnel Actions table:

1. Click the Tables button of the Database window and open the Employees table.

2. Move the caret to the blank append record, type **Test** or a false employee name, then move the caret up to record 9 to save the new record 10.

3. Close the Employees table.

4. Open a new query and add the Employees and Personnel Actions table. Drag the Employee ID field symbol to the PA ID field of Personnel Actions to create an equi-join between these fields, if Access didn't create the join. Select and drag the Last Name and First Name fields of the Employees table to columns 1 and 2 of the Query Design grid. Select and drag the PA Type and PA Scheduled Date fields of the Personnel Actions table to columns 3 and 4.

5. Click the *line* joining Employee ID with PA ID to select it. The thickness of the line increases to indicate the selection, as shown in figure 8.12.

6. Choose Join Properties from the View menu. (The Join Properties command is active only after you select an individual join with a mouse click.) You also can double-click the join line. The Join Properties dialog box of figure 8.13 appears. Type 1 is an inner join, type 2 is a left join, and type 3 is a right join.

FIG. 8.12

Selecting a join to change the join's property from an inner to a left or right outer join.

FIG. 8.13

The Join Properties dialog box for choosing inner, left, or right joins.

7. Choose a type 2 join, a left join, by clicking the 2 button. Choose OK to close the dialog box.

   Note that an arrowhead is added to the line that joins Employee ID and PA ID. The direction of the arrow, left to right, indicates that a left join between the tables was created.

8. Click the Run Query button on the toolbar to display the result of the left join query. The test employee without a record in Personnel Actions appears in the last row of the result table, as illustrated by figure 8.14.

Microsoft Access - [Select Query: Query1]			
File Edit View Records Layout Window Help			
Last Name	First Name	PA Type	PA Scheduled Date
Davolio	Nancy	H	4/1/87
Fuller	Andrew	H	7/15/87
Leverling	Janice	H	3/1/88
Peacock	Phyllis	H	4/1/88
Buchanan	B. L.	H	9/15/89
Suyama	Michael	Q	7/18/92
King	Jonathan	H	9/15/89
Callahan	Linda	H	12/1/89
Dodsworth	Annabella	H	10/15/91
Test	Employee		

FIG. 8.14

Creating a left join between the ID fields of the Employees and Personnel Actions tables.

9. Close, but don't save, the query. You can leave the false record in the Employees table. If you delete the record and later decide to add another *real* employee, the next Employee ID will be 11, not 10. You cannot update a value in a Counter field data type, even if no corresponding records exist in other tables. The inability to correct a mistake is a good reason *never* to use the Counter field data type.

If you could add a personnel action for a nonexistent Employee ID (the validation rule you added in Chapter 7 prevents you from doing so), a right join shows the invalid entry with blank employee name fields.

Creating Self-Joins

Self-joins relate values in a single table. Creating a self-join requires that you add a copy of the table to the query and then add a join between the related fields. An example of the use of a self-join is to determine whether supervisors have approved personnel actions that they initiated, which is prohibited by the imaginary personnel manual for Northwind Traders.

To create this kind of self-join for the Personnel Actions table, follow these steps:

1. Open a new query and add the Personnel Actions table.

2. Add another copy of the Personnel Actions table to the query by clicking the Add button again. Access names the copy Personnel Actions_1.

3. Drag the PA Initiated By field of the original table to the PA Approved By field of the copied table. The join appears as shown in the upper pane of figure 8.15.

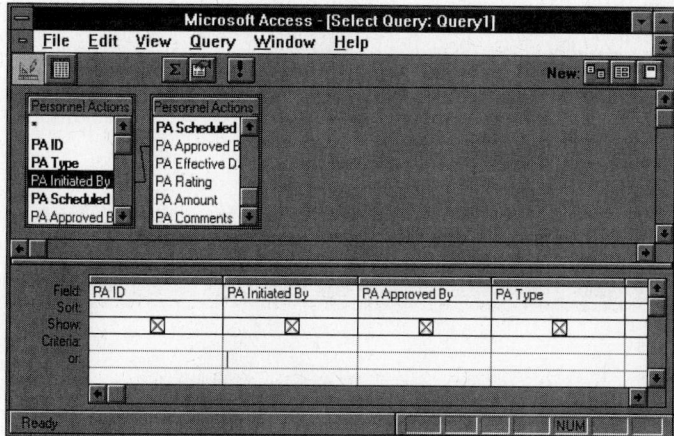

FIG. 8.15

Designing the query for a self-join on the Personnel Actions table.

4. Drag the PA ID and PA Initiated By fields of the original table, and the PA Approved By and PA Type fields of the copy of Personnel Actions, to the Field row of columns 1 through 4, respectively, of the Query Design grid.

5. With self-joins, you must specify that only unique values are included. Click the Properties button on the toolbar and choose the Unique Values Only check box in the Query Properties dialog box.

6. Click the Run Query button on the toolbar to display the records in which the same employee initiated and approved a personnel action, as shown in figure 8.16. In this case, Employee ID 2 is a vice-president and can override personnel policy.

In this example, you can add the Employees table to the query to display the employee name. Adding the Employees table creates an additional join between the PA ID field of the original Personnel Actions table and the Employee ID field of the Employees table. You then need to drag the Last Name field to the fifth column of the Query Design grid. Because this join includes a primary key field, Employee ID, the default DISTINCTROW process yields unique values. To verify that the values are unique, click the Properties button on the toolbar, choose the Unique Value Properties check box to remove the check mark, and then rerun the query.

Self-joins are seldom used in full-fledged relational database applications because the types of problems self-joins can detect can be (and should be) eliminated by validation criteria.

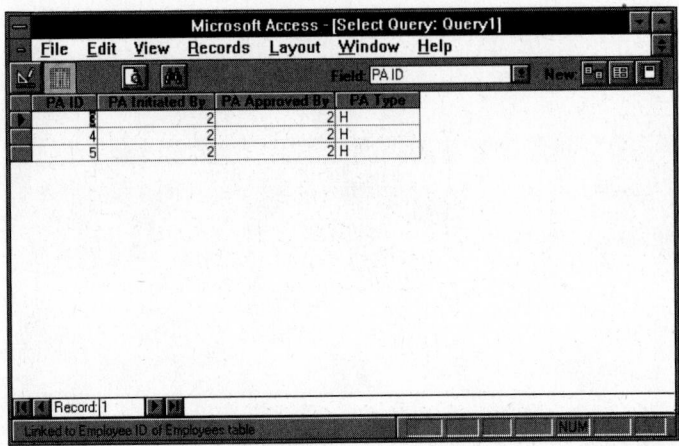

FIG. 8.16

The result of a self-join that tests for supervisors approving personnel actions they initiated.

Creating Not-Equal Theta Joins with Criteria

Most joins are based on fields with equal values, but sometimes you need to create a join on unequal fields. Joins you create with graphical QBE in Access are restricted to conventional equi-joins and outer joins. You can create the equivalent of a not-equal theta join by applying a criterion to one of the two fields you want to test for not-equal values.

Finding customers that have different billing and shipping addresses, as mentioned previously, is an example in which a not-equal theta join is useful. To create the equivalent of this join, follow these steps:

1. Create and add the Customers and Orders tables to a new query.

2. Select and drag the Company Name and Address fields from the Customers table, and the Ship Address field from the Orders table, to the first three columns of the Query Design grid, respectively.

3. In the Criteria row of the Address column, type **<> Orders.[Ship Address]**. (Square brackets must surround table and field names that include spaces or other punctuation.) The query design window appears as shown in figure 8.17. (Typing **<> Customers.Address** in the Ship Address column gives an equivalent result.) This criterion adds a WHERE Customers.Address <> Orders.[Ship Address] clause to the SQL SELECT statement.

4. Choose Query Properties from the **Query** menu to open the Query Properties dialog box. Choose Unique Values Only.

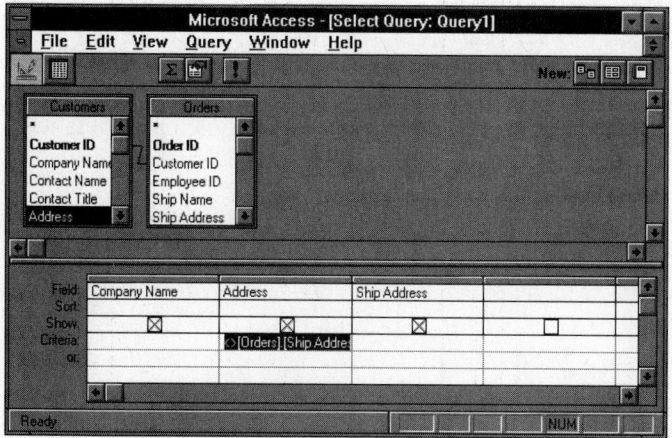

FIG. 8.17

Designing the
query for the
equivalent of a
not-equal join.

5. Run the query. Only the records for customers that placed orders
with different billing and shipping addresses appear, as shown in
figure 8.18. Note that the appearance of Bottom-Dollar Markets in
the result is due to a spelling error in the Ship Address field.

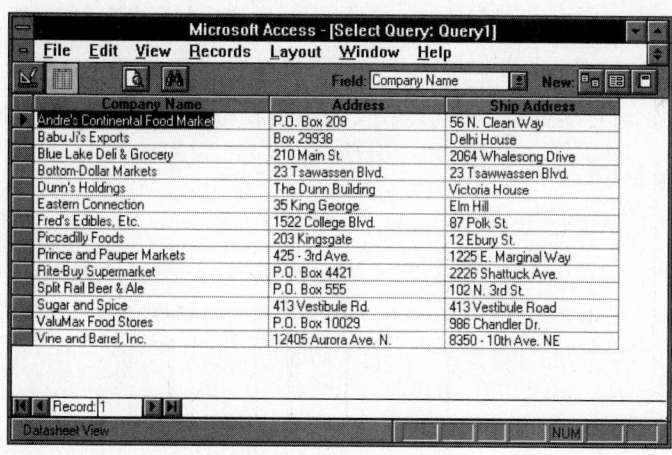

FIG. 8.18

The result of a
not-equal join
designed to iden-
tify different bil-
ling and shipping
addresses.

Being able to delete the extra w in the Ship Address column of the
Bottom-Dollar Markets row, now that the misspelling is exposed, is
desirable. But you cannot update a query unless you see the blank append record (with the asterisk in the select button) at the end of the
query result table. The conditions under which you can append a new
record or update a record of a table included in a query are the subject
of the following section.

Updating Tables with Queries

Adding new records to tables or updating existing data in tables included in a query is a definite advantage in some circumstances. Correcting data errors that appear when you run the query is especially tempting. Unfortunately, however, you cannot append or update records in most of the queries you create. The following properties of a query *prevent* you from appending and updating records:

- Unique values are set with the check box in the Query Properties dialog box.

- Self-joins are used in the query.

- SQL aggregate functions are employed in the query.

- **Crosstab** was chosen from the **Query** menu.

- No primary key fields exist for the *one* table in a one-to-many relationship.

- No unique (No Duplicates) index exists on the *one* table in a one-to-many relationship.

When designing a query to use as the basis of a form for data entry or editing, make sure that none of the preceding properties apply to the query.

If none of the preceding properties apply to the query or to all tables within the query, you can append records to and update fields in the following listing:

- A single-table query

- Both tables in a one-to-one relationship

- The *many* table in a one-to-many relationship

- The *one* table in a one-to-many relationship if none of the fields of the *many* table appear in the query

Updating the *one* table in a one-to-many query is a special case in Access. To enable updates to this table, follow these steps:

1. Add the primary key field(s) of the *one* table and additional fields to update to the query.

2. Add the field of the *many* table that corresponds to the key field(s) of the *one* table, which is required to select the appropriate records for updating.

3. Add to the fields chosen in step 2 the criteria to select the records for updating.

4. Click the Show box so that the *many* table field(s) doesn't appear in the query.

After following these steps, you can edit the *nonkey* fields of the *one* table. You cannot, however, alter the values of key fields that have relationships with records in the *many* table. Such a modification would violate referential integrity. You also cannot update a calculated column of a query; calculated values are not allowed in tables.

Making All Fields of Tables Accessible

Most queries you create include only the fields you specifically choose from the drop-down list in the Field row of the Query Design grid or by dragging the field names from the field lists to the appropriate cells in the Field row. You can, however, include in a query all the fields of a table. Access provides three methods, which are covered in the following sections.

Using the Field List Title Bar To Add All Fields of a Table

One way to include all the fields of a table in a query is to use the field list title bar or asterisk. To use this method to include all fields, together with their field name headers, in your query, follow these steps:

1. Open a new query and add the required tables.

2. Double-click the title bar of the field list of the table for which all fields are to be included. All the fields in the field list are selected.

3. Click and drag a field name to the Field cell of the Query Design grid and drop the field name where you want the first field to appear. An example of the result of the preceding steps for the Customers table is shown in figure 8.19.

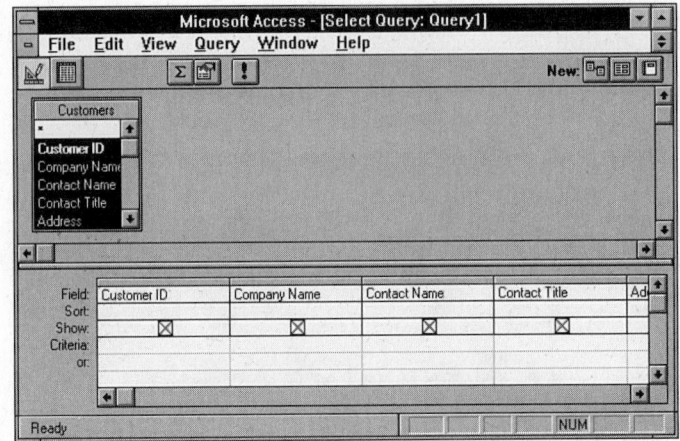

FIG. 8.19

Adding all fields of the Customers table to a query by double-clicking the header of the Customers Field List box.

Using the Asterisk To Add All Fields Without Field Names

To include in the query all fieldsof the table without displaying their field names, click and drag the asterisk to the first Field cell of the Query Design grid and drop the asterisk where you want all the fields to appear in the query result table. The asterisk column is equal to the Access SQL statement SELECT DISTINCTROW * FROM *TableName*.

You cannot sort on a column with an asterisk in the Field cell, nor can you establish criteria. If you choose the asterisk approach, you can sort or apply criteria to one or more fields in the table by following this technique:

1. After you add the asterisk to the Field cell, drag and drop the name of the field you want to sort or to which you want to apply a criterion to the Field row of the adjacent column.

2. Add the sort specification to the Sort cell or the criterion to the Criteria cell.

3. Click the Show box, which removes the check mark, so that the field doesn't appear twice in the query. The resulting query design with the Customers table is shown in figure 8.20.

You can use this method to add to the query as many columns from the asterisk table as you need. The field on which you sort the data is added to the SQL statement as a SORT BY *TableName.FieldName* clause, and a criterion is added in a WHERE *CriterionExpression* clause.

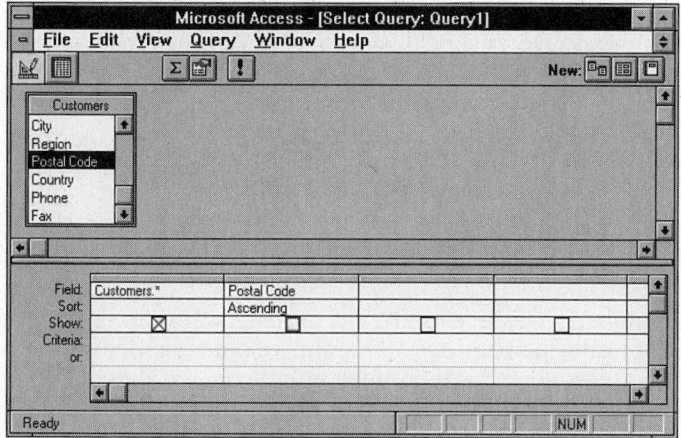

FIG. 8.20

Adding all fields of the Customers table with the asterisk field and providing a hidden column for sorting by Postal Code.

Selecting All Fields by Removing the Restrict Available Fields Option

Usually, only the fields whose names appear in the query are available for updating in forms or including in reports. All other fields are excluded from the dynaset. You can make all the fields in the tables used in the query available to the forms and reports you create—even though the fields are not included by name in the query design—by turning off the Restrict Available Fields option (turned on by default) in the Query Properties dialog box. To use this method to make all table fields available, follow these steps:

1. Open a new query and add the table(s) that participate in the query.

2. Click the Properties button on the toolbar.

3. In the Query Properties dialog box, unmark the Restrict Available Fields check box to turn off this default option.

4. If the Unique Values Only check box is checked, unmark this option. You cannot update fields if the Unique Values Only option is chosen.

5. Choose OK to close the Query Properties dialog box.

Turning off the Restrict Available Fields option adds an all-fields asterisk to the list of specified fields in the SQL statement, as in the following example:

```
SELECT DISTINCTROW Customers.[Company Name],
Categories.[Category Name], *
```

When you include all fields in your queries, you may find that running the query takes longer, especially with queries that create a large number of rows in the dynaset.

Making Calculations on Multiple Records

One of the most powerful capabilities of QBE is the capability of obtaining summary information almost instantly from specified sets of records in tables. Summarized information from databases is the basis of virtually all management information systems (MIS). Management information systems usually answer questions, such as "What are our sales to date for this month?" or "How did last month's sales compare with the same month last year?" To answer these questions, you must create queries that make calculations on field values from all or selected sets of records in a table. Making calculations on table values requires that you create a query that uses the table and employ Access's SQL aggregate functions to perform the calculations.

Using the SQL Aggregate Functions

Summary calculations on fields of tables included in query result tables use the SQL aggregate functions listed in table 8.1, which are known as *aggregate functions* because these functions apply to groups (aggregations) of data cells. The SQL aggregate functions satisfy the requirements of most queries needed for business applications. You can write special, user-defined functions with Access Basic code to apply more sophisticated statistical, scientific, or engineering aggregate functions to your data.

Table 8.1. SQL Aggregate Functions

Function	Description	Field Types
Avg( )	Average of values in a field	All except Text, Memo, and OLE Object
Count( )	Number of Not Null values in a field	All field types
First( )	Value of field of the first record	All field types

Function	Description	Field Types
Last( )	Value of field of the last record	All field types
Max( )	Greatest value in a field	All except Text, Memo, and OLE Object
Min( )	Least value in a field	All except Text, Memo, and OLE Object
StDev( ), StDevP( )	Statistical standard deviation of values in a field	All except Text, Memo, and OLE Object
Sum( )	Total of values in a field	All except Text, Memo, and OLE Object
Var( ), VarP( )	Statistical variation of values in a field	All except Text, Memo, and OLE Object

StDev( ) and Var( ) evaluate population samples. You can choose these functions from the drop-down list in the Total row of the query design table. StDevP( ) and VarP( ) evaluate populations and must be entered as expressions. If you are familiar with statistical principals, you recognize the difference in the calculation methods of standard deviation and variance for populations and samples of populations. The method of choosing the SQL aggregate function for the column of a query is explained in the following section.

Making Calculations Based on All Records of a Table

Managers, especially sales and marketing managers, are most often concerned with information about orders received and shipments made during specific periods of time. Financial managers are interested in calculated values, such as the total amount of unpaid invoices and the average number of days between the invoice and payment dates. Occasionally, you may want to make calculations on all the records of a table, such as finding the historical average value of all invoices issued by a firm. Usually, however, you apply criteria to the query to select specific records that you want to total.

Access considers all SQL aggregate functions to be members of the Totals class of functions. You create queries that return any or all SQL aggregate functions by clicking the Totals button (with the Greek sigma, which represents summation) on the toolbar.

To create a sample query that uses the SQL aggregate functions to display the total number of order, total sales, average order value, and maximum order value, follow these steps:

Query

New

Σ

1. Create, and add the Orders table to, a new query.

2. Drag the Order ID field to the first column of the Query Design grid, and then drag the Order Amount field to the next three columns.

3. Click the Totals button on the toolbar. A new row, Total, is added to the Query Design grid. Access adds Group By, the default action, to each cell in the Totals row. The following section discusses the use of Group By.

4. Move to the Total row of the first column and press F4 or click the Open symbol to display the drop-down list of SQL aggregate functions. Choose Count as the function for the first column, as shown in figure 8.21.

5. Move to the second column, open the list box, and choose Sum from the Total drop-down list. Repeat the process, choosing Avg for the third column and Max for the fifth.

6. Click the Run Query button on the toolbar to display the result of the query. You haven't specified criteria for the fields, so the result shown in figure 8.22 is for the table as a whole. Notice that each field name button caption is prefixed with the name of the function employed. (The values in the result may differ from the values in figure 8.22 because of records added by Microsoft to the sample database after this book was written.)

FIG. 8.21

Choosing the SQL aggregate function for calculations based on multiple records in a table.

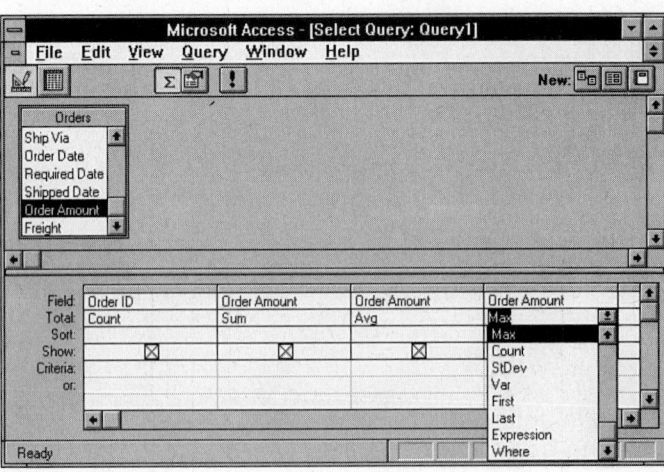

FIG. 8.22

CountOfOrder ID	SumOfOrder Amount	AvgOfOrder Amount	MaxOfOrder Amount
1078	$1,524,577.64	$1,415.58	$16,387.50

The result of the all-records query of figure 8.21.

Making Calculations Based on Selected Records of a Table

The preceding example performed calculations on all orders received by Northwind Traders that were entered in the Orders table. Usually, you are interested in a specific set of records—a range of dates, for example—from which to calculate values. To restrict the calculation to orders Northwind received in March 1992, follow these steps:

1. Click the Design button on the toolbar to return to Design mode so that you can add criteria to select a specific group of records based on the date of the order.

2. Move to or click the Field row of the fourth column of the Query Design grid. To replace Order Amount, open the Field drop-down list and choose Order Date. The Order Date field is needed to restrict the data to a range of dates.

3. Open the Total drop-down list in the Order Date column and choose Where to replace Max.

4. Click the Show box in the fourth column so that the Order Date field doesn't appear. If you forget to turn off the Show property, you see a message box that says you cannot display values in this field.

5. Move to the Criteria row of the fourth column and type **Like "3/*/ 92"** to restrict the totals to orders received in the month of March 1992 (see fig. 8.23). When you use the Like criterion, you must type the quotation marks. If you don't type the quotation marks, Access places the opening quotation mark in the wrong position (before the asterisk).

   The Where instruction you type in the Total row adds a WHERE clause to the SQL statement, here WHERE ((Orders.[Order Date] Like "3/*/92")), to restrict the totaled records to the records for the date range specified. The parentheses are added because this WHERE clause contains required spaces in the syntax. If you don't add the Where instruction to the Total row, the query result consists of rows with the totals of orders for each day of March 1992, not the entire month.

6. Click the Run Query button on the toolbar to display the result: the count, total, and average value of orders received during the month of March 1992 (see fig. 8.24).

Determining the Sequence of Record Selection and Totaling

The Where instruction causes records to be selected for display in accordance with the criterion expression you add *before* the totals are calculated. In the preceding example, all records for orders placed in March 1992 were selected; then the total was calculated for the selected records. This limits the query to returning only one row in the resulting dynaset.

The Group By instruction causes records to be selected for display *after* the totals are calculated in accordance with the criterion expression. In this case, each unique value of the field to which the Group By instruction is applied is totaled; then one record is displayed for each unique value. Group By returns as many rows to the query dynaset as the number of different values found in the Group By field. To see the difference between the use of Where and Group By, follow these steps:

1. Return to Design mode and change the Total cell of the Order Date column to Group By.

2. Click the Show box so that the values of Order Date are displayed, as shown in figure 8.25.

3. On the toolbar, click the Run Query button. The result, shown in figure 8.26, is based on the total number of orders received on each day of March 1992.

FIG. 8.25

Using Group By to select records for display, after totaling values.

FIG. 8.26

The result of changing the Where instruction to the Group By instruction.

The Where instruction gives you the immediate ability to answer ad hoc summary inquiries, usually from members of sales management, that begin "How are orders doing ... ?" or "How many orders have we gotten from ... ?" The Group By instruction provides the next level of detail behind the summary provided by the Where instruction. This approach is known as *drilling down* in management information system terminology. You drill through the summary and then continue to drill progressively down through the levels of detail that make up the summary. You stop drilling when you reach the maximum level of detail, a query consisting of each individual record in the highest summary level.

Using the Group By Instruction To Make Calculations on Multiple Groups of Records

As you learned in the preceding section, the Group By instruction enables you to create queries that summarize data in the "many" side of a relationship at an intermediate level of detail. A marketing manager, for example, may ask, "For what products did we receive the most orders in March?" You can come up with the answer in a couple of minutes by using the Where instruction to limit the orders to the orders in March 1992 and the Count instruction to total the number of orders that included each product.

To create a query that exactly answers the marketing manager's question, follow these steps:

1. Close the current example query and open a new query.

2. The target of the query is a list of Product ID values, followed by the number of times each Product ID appears in orders received in March. Therefore, the first column of the query is Product ID. The table that contains unique values for Product ID is the Products table, so add the table to the query and close the Add Table dialog box. Drag the Product ID field to the first column of the query.

3. Marketing managers aren't known for memorizing numbers, so you need to identify each product by name. The Products table has this information, so drag the English Name field to the second column of the query.

4. You need to count the number of times the product appeared in orders. The only table from which this information is available is Order Details. Choose **A**dd Table from the **Q**uery menu and choose the Order Details table. Close the Add Table dialog box and drag the Product ID field of the Order Details table to the third query column.

5. More than one table is involved in the query, so it is helpful to display the name of the table from which the field is selected. To add a row that displays the table names, choose Table **N**ames from the **V**iew menu.

6. The Orders table contains the dates that the orders were received, so again choose **A**dd Table from the **Q**uery menu and select the Orders table. Close the dialog box and drag the Order Date field to the fourth query column.

Now that you have added all the needed tables, you are ready to fine-tune the query to give you the information you want. Follow these steps:

1. Because this query is based on calculated values, click the Totals button on the toolbar. The upper pane of the Design mode view of the query appears as shown in figure 8.27.

    All the Total cells default to the Group By instruction, which is satisfactory for the first two columns because the Product ID and English Name columns have a one-to-one correspondence. However, you need to change the third and fourth columns.

FIG. 8.27

The fields and joins of a multiple-group summary query.

2. To limit the range of the query to orders received in March 1992, move to the Total cell of the Order Date column and replace the default Group By with the Where instruction.

3. Click the Show box to turn off the display of Order Date values. Type the date-limiting criterion **Like "3/*/92"** in the Criteria row of the Order Date column.

4. Because you need to count the number of times an individual product ID appears in the Order Details list, move to the Order Details column and select Count for the Total cell.

5. The more popular products are of the most interest, so move down to the Sort row of the third (Product ID) column and choose Descending sort order.

6. Marketing managers often take the *broad-brush* approach, so you can restrict the list to products for which more than three orders were received. This way, you can minimize extraneous detail. Type **>3** in the Criteria row of the Product ID column 3.

   The bottom pane of the query now appears as shown in figure 8.28.

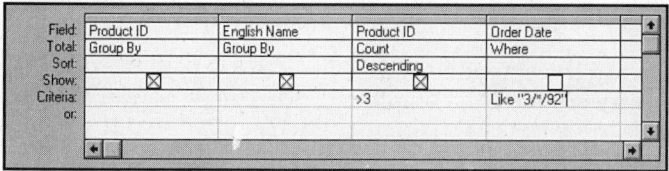

FIG. 8.28

An order frequency query table.

7. The SQL statement for this query is complex. If you want to see the translation, choose **SQL** from the **View** menu.

8. Click the Run Query button on the toolbar to display the result.

Grouping Data by Calculated Values

The result shown in figure 8.28 isn't exactly what the marketing manager wants. The manager wants products ranked, not by the number of orders in March, but by total dollar sales of each product. To rank the groups in this manner, you need to add to the query a calculated field with values created by an expression that multiplies units ordered by unit price.

 Before you begin modifying the query, return to Query Design mode and save the query by choosing **S**ave Query As from the **F**ile menu. Assign the query an appropriate name in the Save As dialog box, such as **Product Order Value**.

 When creating a complex query, saving the query periodically during the design and testing process is a good idea. This safeguard prevents loss of work in a power failure, a hardware glitch, or a problem, such as an out-of-memory condition with Access. If you make a serious error when revising the design of a query, you can close without saving the edited version, open the last version you saved, and restart the editing process.

To modify the example query to create the ranking, based on dollar sales of each product, follow these steps:

1. Move to the Field row of the first empty column and type an appropriate calculated field name, followed by a colon, such as **March Sales:**.

2. Because the expression is used to create totals, it must take the form of the SQL aggregate function Sum( ). Because the entry is long, press Shift+F2 to use the Zoom text box.

3. To create the extended value of the Order line, continue with the entry so that the complete expression is **March Sales: Sum([Order Details].[Quantity]*[Order Details].[Unit Price])**. Choose OK to update the expression.

The sales manager also is interested in the average order value for the products with the highest sales volume, so an average sales column is necessary. You can use the March Sales expression to help build the new expression.

 When you create calculated fields that use similar expressions, copy the expression part of the calculated field description to the Clipboard and then paste the expression to the field description of the next column. Change the field name and then edit the expression as required for the second field. This method saves much typing when several fields are calculated by similar expressions.

4. Press F2 to select the expression; then press Ctrl+C to copy the expression to the Clipboard.

5. Move to the Field row of the next blank column and press Ctrl+V to paste a copy of the March Sales expression that you can edit to create the average column. Access detects that you created a calculated column and places the Expression instruction in the Total row.

6. Change March Sales to Order Size and change Sum to Avg.

7. Move to the Sort row of the Product ID column and choose (not sorted) from the drop-down list. Move to the March Sales column and choose a Descending sort sequence.

8. Minimize the display of relatively unpopular products by limiting the March Sales column to products with $2,500 or more of orders. To do so, add the criterion >=2500 in the Criteria row. The Query Design grid pane appears as shown in figure 8.29.

9. The SQL statement for this query is even more complex than the preceding example. Choose **SQL** from the **View** menu to view the translation of the QBE example. The HAVING clause of the SQL statement creates the criterion for the calculated field.

10. Click the Run Query button on the toolbar to view the result of the revised query, which is shown in figure 8.30.

Field:	Product ID	Order Date	March Sales: Sum([I	Order Size: Avg([Ord
Table:	Order Details	Orders		
Total:	Count	Where	Expression	Expression
Sort:			Descending	
Show:	☒		☒	☒
Criteria:		Like "3/*/92"	>=2500	
or:				

| Ready | | NUM | |

FIG. 8.29

A summary query design to rank the result by values of a calculated field.

Product ID	English Name	CountOfProduct	March Sales	Order Size
59	Courdavault Raclette Cheese	6	$16,720.00	$2,786.67
29	Thüringer Sausage	3	$8,912.88	$2,970.96
38	Côte de Blaye (Red Bordeaux wine)	1	$6,587.50	$6,587.50
64	Wimmer's Delicious Bread Dumplings	3	$5,818.75	$1,939.58
60	Pierrot Camembert	7	$5,780.00	$825.71
51	Manjimup Dried Apples	4	$5,194.00	$1,298.50
28	Rössle Sauerkraut	3	$4,468.80	$1,489.60
43	Malaysian Coffee	3	$4,416.00	$1,472.00
71	Flotemysost Cream Cheese	6	$4,235.50	$705.92
7	Uncle Bob's Organic Dried Pears	5	$4,170.00	$834.00
17	Alice Springs Lamb	2	$3,471.00	$1,735.50
53	Perth Meat Pies	3	$3,444.00	$1,148.00
2	Tibetan Barley Beer	6	$3,401.00	$566.83
18	Carnarvon Tiger Prawns	3	$3,312.50	$1,104.17
55	Shepard's Pie	5	$2,880.00	$576.00
1	Dharamsala Tea	8	$2,592.00	$324.00
26	Gumbär Gummy Bears	3	$2,529.63	$843.21

FIG. 8.30

Products ranked by sales volume for March 1992.

You can give the sales manager a printout of the new query simply by clicking the Preview button on the toolbar and then clicking the Print button.

If you are experienced with creating spreadsheets, now is a good time to sit back and consider the relative ease with which Access can answer questions similar to those that created this example query. Even if you had the required information in database format in multiple Excel spreadsheets, a complex macro is needed to select and present the required data in easily readable form. After you have a bit of practice with the use of SQL aggregate functions in Access, you can create complex queries in just minutes. No macros, forms, or reports are needed; just design a query and then print the result.

Verifying the Result of a Summary Query

Verifying during the query design process that the values shown in summary queries are correct is a good idea. Verification is important when calculated fields are involved in the query, because errors may exist in the expressions used to make the calculations. Verification of the query you created in the preceding example requires that you check one or two of the counts and totals against the records in the Order Details table. You need a simple query on the Order Details table, therefore, to display the records for one of the products that appears in the result table of your summary query.

To create a temporary query to validate the result of the preceding query design, follow these steps:

1. Choose the Database window from the **Window** menu. Click the New button to create a new query. You don't need to close the prior query.

2. Add the Orders and Order Details tables to the query.

3. Drag the Order Date field of the Orders table, and the Product ID, Unit Price, and Quantity fields of the Order Details table, to the Field row of the first four columns of the Query Design grid.

4. Add a calculated field to the fifth column by typing **Amount:[Unit Price] * Quantity** in the Field row to determine the dollar amount of the order for the product.

5. Type **Like "3/*/92"** in the Criteria row of the Order Date column and a product number, such as **59**, in the same row of the Product ID column. This step creates the equivalent of an And operator between the two expressions. The records selected must be for orders received in March 1992 *and* for the specified product number.

6. Click the Run Query button on the toolbar. The result of the verification query is shown in figure 8.31.

   This query result confirms that six orders are included for Product ID 59 in March 1992, with a total value of $16,720. (Use the Windows Calculator to obtain the sum of the Amount column.) Disregard the blank append record that indicates that you may update values in this query.

Order Date	Product ID	Unit Price	Quantity	Amount
08-Mar-92	59	$55.00	10	$550.00
09-Mar-92	59	$55.00	110	$6,050.00
12-Mar-92	59	$55.00	24	$1,320.00
13-Mar-92	59	$55.00	100	$5,500.00
13-Mar-92	59	$55.00	30	$1,650.00
16-Mar-92	59	$55.00	30	$1,650.00
			1	

FIG. 8.31

Verifying the order count and dollar sales amount for one of the products.

7. Checking one or two other results is simple. Return to Design mode, change the Product ID criterion to another value from the summary query, and run another test.

8. Close—but don't save—the query, because this query is useful only for test purposes.

One reason for leaving the CountOfProduct ID field in the query you created in the example shown in figure 8.30 is to verify that the Order Size column has reasonable values. Dividing March Sales by CountOfProduct ID verifies that the average values are reasonable.

Converting to a Parameter Query

If you expect to run a summary or another type of query repeatedly with changes to the criteria, you can convert the query to a *parameter query*. Parameter queries, explained briefly in Chapter 6, enable you to enter criteria with the Enter Parameter Value dialog box. You are prompted for each parameter required. For the example Product Order Value query you created previously in this chapter (see "Grouping Data by Calculated Values"), the only parameter likely to change is the range of dates for which the product sales volume ranking is to be generated.

To convert the Product Order Value summary query to a parameter query, you need to begin by creating prompts for the Enter Parameter Value dialog boxes that appear when the query is run. Parameter queries are created by substituting the text with which to prompt, enclosed within square brackets, for actual values. Follow these steps:

1. Open the Product Order Value query from the Database window in Design mode.

2. Move to the Criteria cell of the Order Date column and press Shift+F2 to open the expression Zoom text box.

3. Press Delete to erase the existing Like statement currently selected in the Zoom box.

4. Because in this example, you want to determine product sales for any valid range of dates, the Between ... And ... expression is the best choice for parameter entry. Type the following line in the text box (see fig. 8.32):

   ```
   Between [Enter the starting date:] And [Enter the ending
   date:]
   ```

   Then choose OK or press Enter. The two prompts to display are enclosed within square brackets.

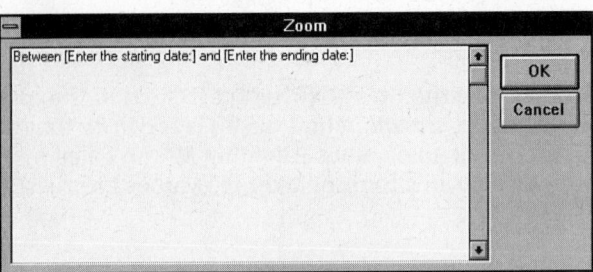

FIG. 8.32

The expression to create Enter Parameter Value dialog boxes for starting and ending dates.

Next, you need to assign data types to the entries that will be made through the two Enter Parameter Value dialog boxes created by the bracketed prompts. Data types for values entered as parameters are established in the Query Parameters dialog box. Follow these steps:

1. Use the mouse to select Enter the starting date: in the Criteria cell of the Order Date column (without the square brackets) and copy the text of the prompt to the Clipboard by pressing Ctrl+C.

2. Choose Parameters from the Query menu to display the Query Parameters dialog box.

3. To insert the first prompt in the Parameter column of the dialog box, press Ctrl+V. The prompt entry in the Parameter column must match the prompt entry in the Criteria field exactly; copying

and pasting the prompt text ensures an exact match. The square brackets are not included in the Parameter column.

4. Press Tab to move to the Data Type column, press F4 to open the Data Type drop-down list, and choose Date/Time.

5. Press Tab to move to the next Parameter cell. Press Ctrl+V to add the prompt again. Change starting to ending. Repeat step 4 to assign the Date/Time data type. The Query Parameters dialog box now should resemble figure 8.33. Choose OK or press Enter.

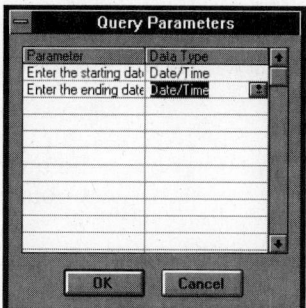

Running the query and entering the appropriate parameters are simple procedures. To perform this process, follow these steps:

1. Click the Run Query button on the toolbar. The first Enter Parameter Value dialog box, shown in figure 8.34, appears.

2. Enter the starting date for which you want to include records in the query. You can enter dates in any valid format, including 3-1-92, 3/1/1992, or 1-Mar-92. Choose OK or press Enter.

3. When the second Enter Parameter Value dialog box appears, enter the ending date for the query, and then choose OK or press Enter (see fig. 8.35).

   Here, the query table created by the parameters you enter gives the same result as when you use the Like "3/*/92" expression as the date parameter. As you can see, however, because you can enter any valid starting and ending dates in the Enter Parameter Value dialog boxes, your parameter query is far more flexible than the summary query. You would change the name of the March Sales field to a more generic name, such as Sales for Period, if this query were a real-life parameter query.

4. Save the changes to but don't close the query. This query forms the foundation for the crosstab query you learn how to create in the following section.

Complete your query design and testing before you convert any type of query to a parameter query. Using fixed criteria with the query maintains consistency during the testing process, and re-peated changes between Design and Run mode are speeded if you don't have to enter one or more parameters in the process. After you complete testing the query, edit the criteria to add the Enter Parameter Value dialog boxes.

The parameter conversion process described in this section applies to all types of queries you create, providing that one or more of the query columns includes a criterion expression. The advantage of the param-eter query is that you or a user of the database can run a query for any range of values, in this case dates, such as the current month to date, a particular fiscal quarter, or an entire fiscal year.

Creating Crosstab Queries

Crosstab queries are summary queries that enable you to determine exactly how the summary data appears on-screen. Crosstab queries display summarized data in the traditional row-column form of spread-sheets. Crosstab queries use the SQL TRANSFORM keyword to indicate that the statements that follow the keyword are for a crosstab query. With crosstab queries, you can perform the following processes:

■ Specify the field that creates labels (headings) for rows by using the Group By instruction. You can use only the first column for row headings.

■ Determine the field or fields that create column headers and the criteria that determine the values appearing under the headers.

■ Assign calculated data values to the cells of the resulting row-column grid.

The following list details the advantages of using crosstab queries:

■ You can display a substantial amount of summary data in a compact format familiar to anyone who uses a spreadsheet application or a columnar accounting form.

■ The summary data is presented in a format ideally suited for creating graphs and charts automatically with the Access GraphWizard.

■ Designing queries to create multiple levels of detail is quick and easy. Queries with identical columns but fewer rows can represent increasingly summarized data. Highly summarized queries are ideal to begin a drill-down procedure by instructing the user, for example, to "Click the Details button to show sales by product." You create a form that implements drill-down techniques in the following chapter.

The only restriction imposed by using crosstab queries is that you cannot sort your result table on calculated values in columns. You cannot, therefore, create the equivalent of the query in the previous section in which products are ranked by sales volume. Columns are likely to have values that cause conflicts in the sorting order of the row. You can choose an ascending sort, a descending sort, or no sort on the row label values in the first column.

To create a typical crosstab query that displays products in rows and monthly sales volume for each product in the corresponding columns, begin by changing the query type and removing the unneeded columns. To perform this process, follow these steps:

1. Choose Save Query **As** from the **F**ile menu and save this copy of the query you created in the preceding section with the temporary name **Query1**. You then eliminate the risk of accidentally overwriting the previous version of the query.

2. Choose Parameters from the **Q**uery menu. Delete all entries in the Parameter and Data Type columns so that the grid of the Query Parameters dialog box contains only blank cells. (If you delete the criterion with the parameters from the query design, you don't remove the parameters list.) Choose OK or press Enter to close the dialog box.

3. Choose **Crosstab** from the **Query** menu. The title bar of the query changes from Select Query: Query1 to Crosstab Query: Query1, and another row, Crosstab, is added to the Query Design grid.

4. Click the selection bar of the first Product ID column to select the entire column. Press Delete to delete this column from the query. Remember that you can use only one field to provide row headers, and English Name is a better choice than Product ID numbers.

5. Click the selection bar of the other Product ID column and press Delete to delete this column from the query. Order counts are not used in this query.

6. Click the selection bar of the Order Size column and press Delete to delete this column from the query. The Query Design grid now consists of three columns: English Name, March Sales, and Order Date.

The following steps involve fine-tuning the design and choosing the appropriate entries for the new Crosstab row. A crosstab query must have one field to act as the source of row labels and at least one field to act as the source for column headings and cell values. If you want to establish limiting criteria, an extra column for the field on which each criterion is based is needed, which you add by following these steps:

1. Edit the March Sales field name to read Sales but don't change any other characters (retain the colon and the Sum( ) expression).

2. In the Field row of the fourth column, type **Format([Order Date], "mmmm")**. Access adds a default field name, Expr1:. Accept the default, because the Format( ) function you added creates the column names, the months of the year spelled in full ("mmmm" format), when you run the query.

3. Group By, the default instruction in the Total cell of the fourth column, causes the data for the columns to group by month. Move down to the Crosstab cell, press F4 to open the drop-down list, and select Column Heading.

4. Move left to the Crosstab cell of the Sales column. Press F4 and select Value. Total dollar product sales values is used to fill the cells of the crosstab query.

5. Move left again to the Crosstab cell of the English Name column. Press F4 and select Row Heading.

6. If you don't restrict the date range of the Order Date field, you will have as many columns as you have months in which records for orders received are entered in the Orders table. Delete the current criteria that calls for user-supplied parameters and substitute

>= **1/1/92** to create a year-to-date query for 1992. The Query Design grid now resembles figure 8.36; Access adds the # signs that surround 1/1/92 to identify the value as a date. Do not enter table names for the two calculated fields, Sales and Expr1. If you add table names, you see a message box that states the expression includes a syntax error.

Field:	English Name	Sales: Sum([Order C	Order Date	Expr1: Format([Orde
Table:	Products		Orders	
Total:	Group By	Expression	Where	Group By
Crosstab:	Row Heading	Value		Column Heading
Sort:	Ascending			
Criteria:			>=#1/1/92#	
or:				

Ready   NUM

FIG. 8.36

The Query Design grid for a crosstab query that results in a table of year-to-date sales.

To run the query, click the Run Query button on the toolbar. A period of disk activity occurs, followed by a display of the result of the crosstab query, shown in figure 8.37. (You may have more columns than shown here because orders may have been added to the sample database since this book was written.)

English Name	April	February	January	March
Alice Springs Lamb		$468.00	$2,652.00	$3,471.00
Angelo Ravioli		$292.50	$975.00	$936.00
Bean Curd	$465.00			
Boston Crab Meat		$184.00	$2,263.20	$1,012.00
Cabrales Cheese		$1,050.00	$1,932.00	$420.00
Carnarvon Tiger Prawns		$1,125.00	$1,562.50	$3,312.50
Chef Anton's Cajun Seasoning		$110.00	$660.00	$550.00
Chef Anton's Gumbo Mix		$427.00		$2,135.00
Cloudberry Liqueur	$36.00	$3,672.00	$630.00	$1,008.00
Côte de Blaye (Red Bordeaux wine)		$17,127.50	$10,540.00	$6,587.50
Courdavault Raclette Cheese		$1,210.00	$2,200.00	$16,720.00
Dharamsala Tea		$378.00	$2,340.00	$2,592.00
Escargots from Burgundy			$795.00	$530.00
Fish Roe		$1,705.00	$3,100.00	$744.00
Flotemys Cream Cheese		$752.50	$1,182.50	$4,235.50
Giovanni's Mozzarella		$2,679.60	$904.80	$1,218.00
Goat Cheese		$55.00	$175.00	$137.50
Gorgonzola Telino		$1,912.50	$437.50	$437.50

FIG. 8.37

The first result table from the crosstab query design of figure 8.36.

Notice that the crosstab query result contains two defects. First, a partial month (only a few orders were entered for April) is included. Correct this problem by changing the criterion for Order Date from >= 1/1/92 to **Between #1/1/92# And #3/31/92#**. If the data is available, use a later ending date. The second problem is that the columns are arranged in alphabetical order by month name rather than in calendar order. You can solve this problem by using fixed column headings, which you learn about in the following section.

For Related Information:

◄◄ "Functions for Date and Time," p. 280.

Using Fixed Column Headings with Crosstab Queries

Access uses an alphabetical or numerical sort on column headings to establish the sequence of appearance in the crosstab query result table. For this reason, if you use short or full names for months, the sequence is in alphabetic rather than calendar order. You can correct this problem by assigning fixed column headings to the crosstab query. Follow these steps to modify and rerun the query:

1. Return to Query Design mode and click the Properties button on the toolbar. The Query Properties dialog box has another option only for crosstab queries: Fixed Column Headings.

2. Choose the Fixed Column Headings check box to turn on the option, and type the full names of all 12 months of the year in the text box below the option, as illustrated by figure 8.38. You must spell out the names of the months correctly; data for months with spelling mistakes do not appear. You can separate entries with commas or semicolons or use the Ctrl+Enter key combination to place each entry on a separate line. You don't need to type quotation marks because Access adds them. Spaces are unnecessary and undesirable between the Column Headings values. After you complete all 12 entries, choose OK or press Enter.

. FIG. 8.38

Entering fixed column headings in the crosstab Query Properties dialog box.

3. Click the Run Query button on the toolbar. Now the result table, shown in figure 8.39, includes columns for all 12 months, but only January through March (or the month of the limiting date you

entered) have values. If the crosstab appears different, check to see if you entered the Fixed Column Headings in the Query Properties dialog box properly. A misspelled month causes errors.

English Name	January	February	March	April
Alice Springs Lamb	$2,652.00	$468.00	$3,471.00	
Angelo Ravioli	$975.00	$292.50	$936.00	
Boston Crab Meat	$2,263.20	$184.00	$1,012.00	
Cabrales Cheese	$1,932.00	$1,050.00	$420.00	
Carnarvon Tiger Prawns	$1,562.50	$1,125.00	$3,312.50	
Chef Anton's Cajun Seasoning	$660.00	$110.00	$550.00	
Chef Anton's Gumbo Mix		$427.00	$2,135.00	
Cloudberry Liqueur	$630.00	$3,672.00	$1,008.00	
Côte de Blaye (Red Bordeaux wine)	$10,540.00	$17,127.50	$6,587.50	
Courdavault Raclette Cheese	$2,200.00	$1,210.00	$16,720.00	
Dharamsala Tea	$2,340.00	$378.00	$2,592.00	
Escargots from Burgundy	$795.00		$530.00	
Fish Roe	$3,100.00	$1,705.00	$744.00	
Flotemys Cream Cheese	$1,182.50	$752.50	$4,235.50	
Giovanni's Mozzarella	$904.80	$2,679.60	$1,218.00	
Goat Cheese	$175.00	$55.00	$137.50	
Gorgonzola Telino	$437.50	$1,912.50	$437.50	
Gramma Alice's Dumplings	$1,406.00	$1,140.00	$950.00	

FIG. 8.39

The result table from the crosstab query design with fixed column headings and a date limiting criterion.

4. Choose Save Query **As** from the **F**ile menu and save the query with an appropriate name, such as **Year-to-Date Sales by Product**.

You can produce a quick printed report from the query by clicking the Print Preview button on the toolbar and then clicking the Print button.

You may want to use fixed column headings if you use the Group By instruction with country names. U.S. users will probably place USA first, and Canadian firms undoubtedly will choose Canada as the first entry. If you add a record with a new country, you need to remember to update the list of fixed column headings with the new country value. Fixed column headings have another, hidden benefit of usually speeding the operation of crosstab queries.

Decreasing the Level of Detail in Crosstab Queries

The result table created by the preceding example query has a row for every product for which Northwind Traders received an order in the first three months of 1992. Higher-level management usually wants information in the form of a graph or chart to use to analyze trends in the data. You therefore need to reduce the number of rows so that you can create a readable graph from the values in the query result table.

Don't try to display more than four sets of values in one graph or chart. Each product that Northwind Traders sells is assigned to one of eight product categories, so the graph needs to display eight sets of values: total sales for each product category. This design violates the graph maxim, but no other one-to-many relationship exists in the product-related tables that you can use to reduce the number of rows. Fortunately, a graph that displays monthly sales of eight product categories can be readable if it occupies all of a maximized window or is scaled to the width of a printed page.

To create a summary query that returns year-to-date total sales of products by category (rather than by Product ID) and can be used to create a graph, follow these steps:

1. Choose Save Query As from the File menu and save a copy of the query you created in the preceding section with the temporary name **Query1**.

2. Choose Add Table from the **Query** menu and add the Categories table to the query.

3. To make the relationships among the tables more clear, click the title bar of each of the field lists in the upper pane and drag these title bars to the positions shown in figure 8.40.

FIG. 8.40

The design of a summary query for year-to-date sales by product category.

4. Drag and then drop the Category Name field of the Categories field list into the Field cell of the first column, which contains English Name. A new Category Name column is added to the query. Move down to the Crosstab cell and choose Row Heading from the drop-down list.

5. Click the selection bar above the English Name cell of the second column, and then press Delete to delete this column. The crosstab Query Design grid then appears as shown in figure 8.41.

FIG. 8.41

The query design grid for the sales by product category cross-query.

6. Click the Run Query button on the toolbar. The query result table appears as shown in figure 8.42.

7. Choose Save Query **As** from the **F**ile menu and give the query a descriptive name, such as **Year-to-Date Sales by Category**.

Category Name	January	February	March	April
Beverages	$20,796.25	$29,481.00	$24,321.50	
Condiments	$9,533.20	$10,565.80	$8,748.00	
Confections	$14,959.05	$20,019.95	$10,540.78	
Dairy Products	$13,413.80	$15,649.60	$34,116.50	
Grains/Cereals	$4,971.75	$3,366.50	$9,411.75	
Meat/Poultry	$24,892.06	$10,702.56	$18,931.38	
Produce	$2,570.80	$13,855.00	$13,832.80	
Seafood	$12,595.48	$8,474.45	$10,293.76	

Creating a Preview Graph or Chart from a Crosstab Query

Designing effective graphs and charts that you incorporate in forms and reports is the subject of chapters that follow in this book. But when you design a query for creating a graph or chart, previewing a sample graph created from the query can be helpful. A preview can verify that the query provides readable results with the type of graph that gives the clearest presentation. You also can use a preview graph to confirm the query and graph design with the user of the application before you spend time designing forms and reports that incorporate the graph.

Access provides a GraphWizard feature that does almost all the detail work involved in creating a preview graph. The GraphWizard is a member of the FormWizards family, which is used to automate the creation of data entry and editing forms. Using the GraphWizard requires that you first create a form on which the chart can be displayed. Only forms and reports can display and print charts.

To use the GraphWizard to create a preview graph from the crosstab summary query of the preceding section, follow these steps:

1. Choose the Database: NWND window from the **W**indow menu.

2. Click the Forms button in the Database window; then click New to create a new, temporary form. The New Form dialog box appears. Open the Select a Table/Query drop-down list and choose the Year-to-Date Sales by Category crosstab query you designed in the preceding section. The New Form dialog box now appears as shown in figure 8.43.

3. Click the FormWizards button to display the list of available FormWizards shown in figure 8.44.

4. Choose Graph from the list box; then choose OK or press Enter. A dialog box appears from which you can choose the graph type (see fig. 8.45).

5. An area chart, the first chart type in the selection dialog box, is the best type to use for displaying data in which the data in the rows creates a meaningful total. Area charts enable you to observe quickly the contribution of each data item in the cell of a column to the total of the column. Click the symbol for an area chart; then click Next > to display the field selection dialog box of figure 8.46.

FIG. 8.43

Using the New Form dialog box to access the FormWizards.

FIG. 8.44

Choosing a GraphWizard from the Microsoft FormWizard dialog box.

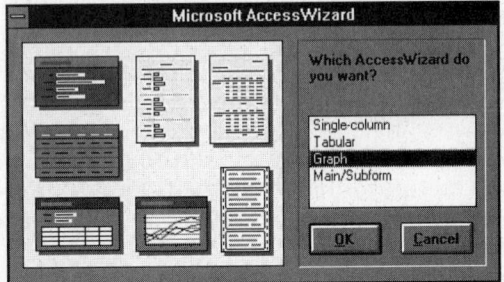

FIG. 8.45

Choosing a graph type for the summary query.

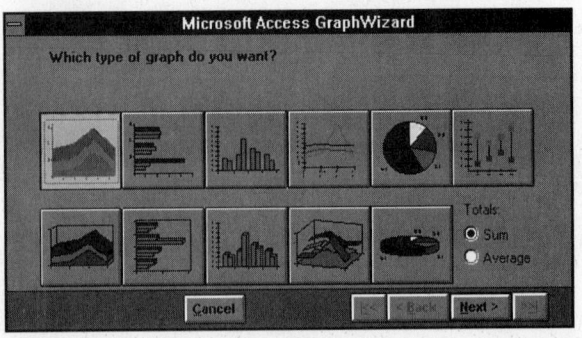

6. Your chart uses only the fields for which data is available. Choose Category Name in the Available Fields list; then click the Next > button to add this field to the Fields for Graph list. Do the same for January, February, and March. If the crosstab query has data for more months, add these months to the Fields for Graph list. Then click Next > to display the label selection dialog box shown in figure 8.47.

7. The column headings are used as labels for the horizontal (X) axis of the chart. Add each column heading in the Available Fields list to the Labels for Graph list by choosing a column heading and then clicking the > button.

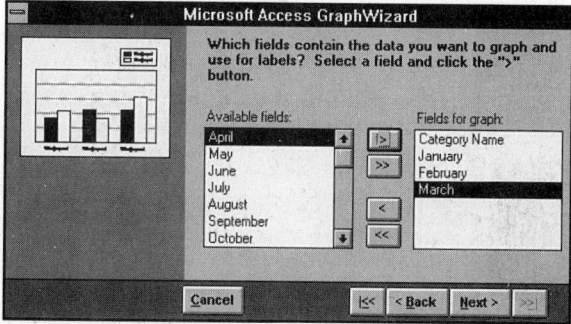

FIG. 8.46

The Graph-Wizard's field selection dialog box.

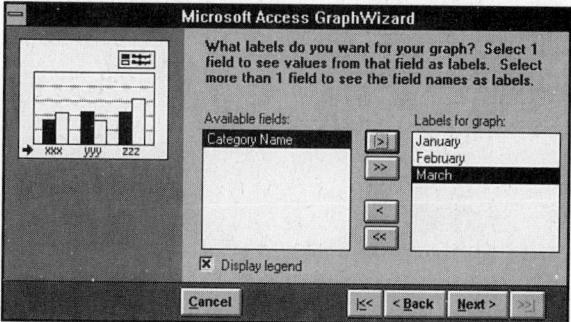

FIG. 8.47

The label selection dialog box for the horizontal (X) axis of the chart.

8. Click the Next > button to display the dialog box that enables you to add a title to the graph (see fig. 8.48). The name of your query is provided as the default title.

9. To create the graph, click Open. The GraphWizard runs the Year-to-Date Sales by Category query and then starts sending Microsoft Graph the data from the query, combined with the instructions you entered in the GraphWizard dialog boxes. After some intense disk activity, the graph shown in figure 8.49 appears.

FIG. 8.48

The Graph-Wizard's title selection dialog box.

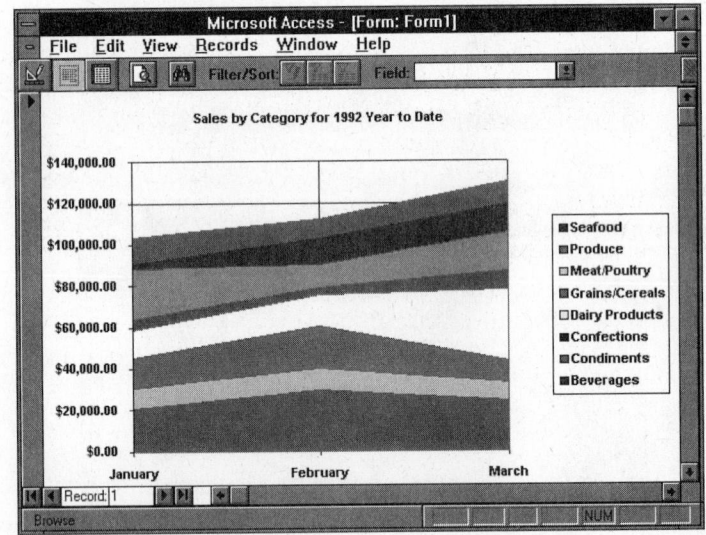

FIG. 8.49

The preview graph of the crosstab query for year-to-date sales by product category.

10. You can print a copy of the graph by clicking the Print Preview button on the toolbar and then clicking the Print button.

11. Close the form with the Document Control menu. Do not save the form because the graph you designed is only a preview, not a final product.

Using Action Queries

Action queries create new tables or modify the data in existing tables. Four types of action queries are available in Access:

- *Make-table queries* create new tables from the data contained in dynasets. The most common application for make-table queries is creating tables to export for use by other applications. A make-table query is a convenient way of copying a table to another database. In some cases, you can use make-table queries to speed the generation of multiple forms and reports based on a single, complex query.

- *Append queries* add new records to tables with data created by the query.

- *Delete queries* delete records from tables that correspond to the rows of the query dynaset.

- *Update queries* change the values of existing fields of records corresponding to rows of the query dynaset.

In the following section, you learn how to use action queries to create a new table, Shipping Address, for customers that have different shipping and billing addresses. This process allows the deletion of the shipping address data that, in most of the records in the Orders table, duplicates the address data in the Customers table. Removing duplicated data to new tables is an important step when you are converting data contained in a flat (nonrelational) database to a relational database.

Always make a backup copy of a table that you are going to modify by an action query. Changes made to table data by action queries are permanent; an error can render a table useless. Invalid changes made to a table with an action query that contains a design error often are difficult to detect.

Creating New Tables with Action Queries

An example of an action query that creates new tables for use by other applications is included in the quick start chapter for QBE. The following example extracts data from the Orders table based on data in the Customers table and creates a new table, Shipping Address. A modification of the previous query you created in this chapter by using the not-equal criterion generates the data for the new table. As mentioned previously, make-table queries are useful in converting flat-file tables that contain duplicated data, including tables created by spreadsheet applications, to relational form.

To create the new Shipping Address table from the data in the Orders table, first you need to build the query. To build the query, follow these steps:

1. Create a new query, and add the Customers and Orders tables to it.

2. Choose Table **N**ames from the **V**iew menu if the Table row doesn't appear in the Query Design grid.

3. Drag the Customer ID field from the Customers table and drop it in the first column of the query. The Customer ID field is the field that links the Shipping Address table with the Orders table.

4. Drag the Ship Name, Ship Address, Ship City, Ship Region, Ship Postal Code, and Ship Country fields and drop them in columns 2 through 7, respectively. You use these fields, in addition to Company ID, to create the new Shipping Address table.

   Next, you want to add only the records of the Orders table for which the Ship Name doesn't match the Company Name or the Ship Address doesn't match the Address of the Customers table.

5. In the first Criteria row of the Ship Name column, type

   <>[Customers].[Company Name].

6. Move to the next lower row of the Ship Address column and type

   <>[Customers].[Address]

   in the cell. This entry must be in a different Criteria row than the Company Name criterion so that the Or operator is applied to the two criteria. The Query Design grid appears as shown in figure 8.50.

   A more precise approach is to add additional Or criteria to test for not-equal cities, regions, postal codes, and countries. A customer having exactly the same address in two different cities, however, is highly improbable.

7. Click the Properties button on the toolbar to open the Query Properties dialog box. Choose Unique Values Only to turn on the check box.

8. Click the Run Query button to run the select query. Data for customers that placed orders with different billing and shipping addresses appears, as shown in figure 8.51. Bottom-Dollar Markets doesn't appear in this list because the spelling errors in the Ship Address and Ship City fields of the records for the firm were corrected previously.

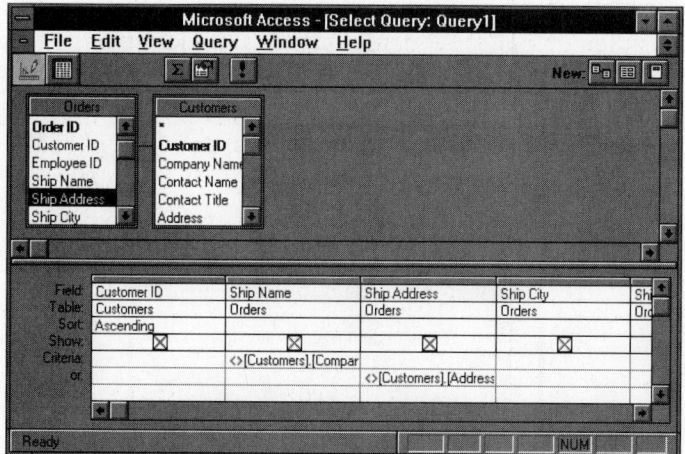

FIG. 8.50

Creating the make-table query for the new Shipping Address table.

Customer ID	Ship Name	Ship Address	Ship City	Ship Reg	Ship Postal	Ship Country
ANDRC	Andre's Continenta	56 N. Clean Way	Bellingham	WA	98226	USA
BABUJ	Babu Ji's Exports	Delhi House	London		WX1 5LT	UK
BLUEL	Blue Lake Deli & G	2064 Whalesong	Port Townser	WA	98368	USA
DUNNH	Dunn's Holdings	Victoria House	London		SW1 0NR	UK
EASTC	Eastern Connectio	Elm Hill	Needham Ma	Suffolk	SUB JXK	UK
FREDE	Let's Stop N Shop	87 Polk St.	San Francisc	CA	94117	USA
PICAF	Picadilly Foods	12 Ebury St.	London		SW1 0JR	UK
PRINA	Prince and Pauper	1225 E. Margina	Seattle	WA	98119	USA
RITEB	Rite-Buy Superma	2226 Shattuck A	Berkeley	CA	92701	USA
SPLIR	Split Rail Beer & Al	102 N. 3rd St.	Lander	WY	82520	USA
SUGAA	Sugar and Spice	413 Vestibule Rd	London		TN14 5EP	UK
VALUF	ValuMax Food Sto	986 Chandler Dr.	Austin	TX	78759	USA
VINEA	Vine and Barrel, In	8350 - 10th Ave.	Seattle	WA	98117	USA

FIG. 8.51

The data to be added to the new Shipping Address table.

Now that you have the necessary data, you can create the table from the query. To create the table, follow these steps:

1. Choose Ma**k**e Table from the **Q**uery menu. A variation of the Query Properties dialog box appears. Type the name of the table, **Shipping Address**, in the Table Name text box (see fig. 8.52). The default settings of Current Database, Unique Values Only, and Run with Owner's Permissions are suitable for this table. Choose OK.

FIG. 8.52

The Query Properties dialog box for make-table queries.

2. Click the Run Query button on the toolbar. A message box confirms the number of records that you are adding to the new table (see fig. 8.53). Choose OK to create the new Shipping Address table.

3. Choose Database: NWND from the **W**indow menu, click the Table button, and open the new Shipping Address table. The entries appear as shown in figure 8.54.

FIG. 8.53

The confirmation message box that precedes creation of the new table.

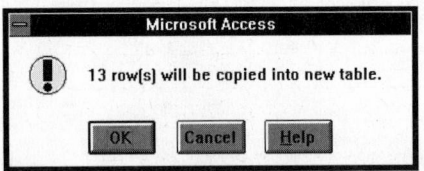

FIG. 8.54

The Shipping Address table created from the make-table query.

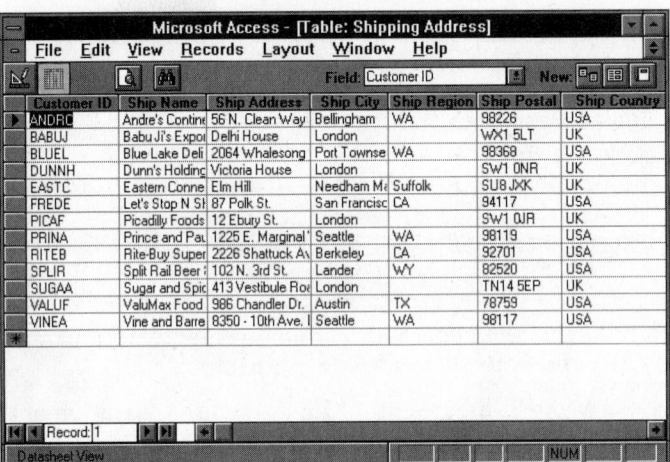

Now, complete the design of the new Shipping Address table by following these steps:

1. Click the Design button on the toolbar. The basic design of the table is inherited from the properties of the fields of the tables used to create the new table. Shipping Address does not, however, inherit the primary key assignment from the Customer ID field of the Customers table.

2. Click the Properties button on the toolbar to display the properties window. Type **Shipping addresses other than billing addresses** as the Description in the Table Properties window, as shown in figure 8.55.

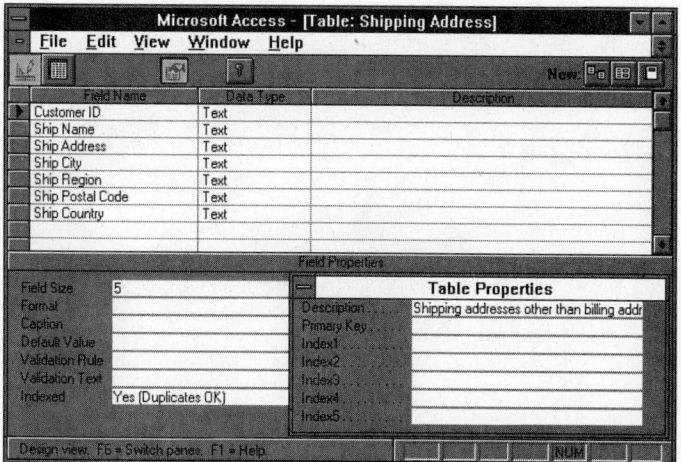

FIG. 8.55

The design of the newly created Shipping Address table.

3. The Shipping Address table presently has a one-to-one relationship with the Customers table because only one shipping address record exists for each customer who has different shipping and billing addresses. Customers may have a number of different shipping addresses, however, so the relationship of Customers to Shipping Address is one-to-many, and duplicate values in the Customer ID field of Shipping Address must be allowed. You cannot, therefore, create a primary key for the Shipping Address table unless you include three fields—Customer ID, Ship Name, and Ship Address—to make multiple entries for one customer unique. In this example, no primary key is used. Choose the Customer ID field, open the Indexed drop-down list, and choose Yes (Duplicates OK).

4. Close the table and choose No when the message box informs you that no primary key was selected.

5. Make the Database window active and choose **R**elationships from the **E**dit menu to open the Relationships dialog box that establishes the default relationships between tables (see fig. 8.56). Choose Customers from the Primary Table drop-down list, Shipping Address from the Related Table list, and Customer ID from the Select Matching Fields list.

6. Choose Add, then Close, then Yes when asked whether you want to save the changes.

You use this new Shipping Address table in the following chapter with forms used for data entry and editing.

FIG. 8.56

Establishing relationships for the Shipping Address table.

After creating a new table from a make-table query, you must take care of the following "housekeeping" chores:

■ Do not delete fields that contain duplicate data that was extracted to a new table until you confirm that the extracted data is correct and modify all the queries, forms, and reports that use the table.

■ Add the new table to any queries that require the extracted information.

■ Change references to fields in the original table in forms and reports to refer to fields in the new table.

During this process, you have the opportunity to test the modification before deleting the duplicated fields from the original table. Making a backup copy of the table before you delete the fields also is a low-cost insurance policy.

Creating Action Queries To Append Records to a Table

A make-table query creates the new table structure from the structure of the records that underlie the query. Only the fields of the records that appear in the query are added to the new table's structure. If you design and save a Shipping Address table before extracting the duplicated data from the Orders table, you can use an *append query* to add the extracted data to the new table.

Another situation in which append queries are useful is during the process of removing duplicate data from a table currently in use. In this case, you use make-table queries to create the related tables and then

change them to append queries. You change the type of query by
choosing **S**elect, **C**rosstab, Ma**k**e Table, **A**ppend, or **D**elete from the
Query menu while in Design mode.

If the field names of your query are identical to the field names
of the table to which records are to be appended, a simpler and
faster method is to select all or a particular set of records in the
query, copy the records to the Clipboard with Ctrl+C, and then
choose Paste Appen**d** from the **E**dit menu to add the records to
the table.

An append query differs from a make-table query because an append
query may have fewer fields than the table to which the data is to be
appended. Otherwise, the make-table and append processes are basically identical. To append records to the Shipping Address table, for
example, follow these steps:

1. Open your make-table query from the Database window (or
   choose it from the **W**indow menu if it is open).

2. Click the Design button on the toolbar to return to Design mode.

3. Choose **A**ppend from the **Q**uery menu. The append variant of the
   Query Properties dialog box appears.

4. Choose the table, Shipping Address, to which you want to append
   the records from the Table Name drop-down list, as shown in
   figure 8.57. Choose OK to accept the other default settings and
   exit the dialog box.

The Query Prop-
erties dialog box
for an append
query.

To append data to a table, the field names of the query and those
of the table to which the records are to be appended must be
identical; data will not be appended to fields in which the field
name differs by even a single space character. The Query Design
grid for append queries has an additional row, Append To, shown
in figure 8.58, that Access attempts to match by comparing field
names of the query and the table. Default values appear in the
Append To row of columns for which a match occurs.

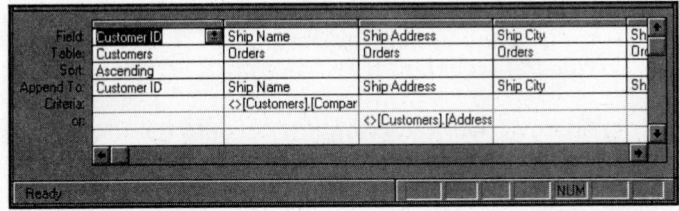

FIG. 8.58

The Append
Query Design
grid with the
Append To
row added.

5. If any of the field names of the table differ from those of the query, you can insert the proper table field name by selecting the Append To cell, opening the drop-down list of fields in the table, and choosing the field name from the list.

6. To add a set of duplicate records to the Shipping Address table as an example of the Append query process, click the Run Query button and then choose OK in response to the message box that confirms the number of records that will be added. (You can delete the duplicate records using a Delete query similar to the one described in the following section.)

7. Open the Shipping Address table to verify that the additional records have been added.

The Unique Values Only test that you specified in the Query Properties dialog box applies only to the query, not to the table to which the records are being appended. If you want to exclude the possibility of appending duplicate records, you must create the three-field primary key, discussed in the preceding section, and then create a No Duplicates index on the primary key.

If you attempt to append records that contain values which duplicate the values of the key fields in existing records, these records aren't appended. You see a message that indicates the number of records that cause key field violations. Unlike the Paste Append operation described in previous chapters, however, an Errors table that contains the unappended records isn't created.

Deleting Records from a Table with an Action Query

Occasionally, you may need to delete records from a table. You may, for example, want to delete records for orders that were canceled or records for customers that have made no purchases for several years.

Deleting records from a table with a *delete query* is the reverse of the append process. You create a select query with all fields (using the * choice from the field list) then add the individual fields to be used to specify the criteria for the deletion of specific records. If you don't specify any criteria, all the records in the table are deleted when you convert the select query into a delete query and run it against the table.

To give you some practice at deleting records—you stop short of actual deletion in this case, however—suppose that the credit manager for Northwind Traders has advised you that Empire Trading was declared insolvent and that any orders from Empire not yet shipped are to be canceled and deleted from the table. To design the query that selects all of Empire's open orders, follow these steps:

1. Choose Database: NWND from the **W**indow menu. Open a new query and add the Orders table to it.

New

2. Drag the * (all fields) item from the field list to the Field cell of the first column of the query.

3. Drag the Customer ID field to the Field cell of the second column. This field is required to provide record selection for a specific customer. The fields that comprise the query must be exactly those of the Orders table, so click the Show box to hide the Customer ID field. This field is included in the * (all fields) indicator in the first column.

4. Move to the Criteria cell of the Customer ID field and type = **"EMPIT"** to represent Empire's ID.

5. Orders that have not shipped are indicated by a Null value in the Ship Date field. Drag the Ship Date field from the field list to the Field cell of the third column. Click the Show box to hide the Ship Date field because it, too, is included in the first column.

6. Type **Is Null** in the Criteria cell of the Ship Date field. This criterion must be on the same line as the criterion for the Customer ID field so that only records for Empire Trading that have not been shipped are deleted. The select query design for the delete query should look like figure 8.59.

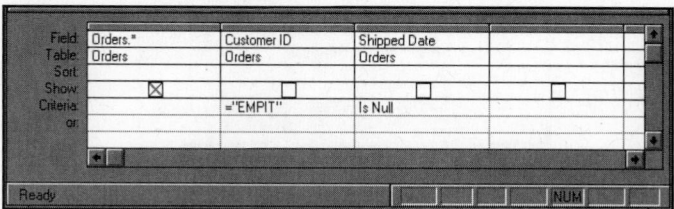

FIG. 8.59

The select query design for a delete query.

7. Run the select query to display the records to be deleted if you run the delete query.

To proceed with the deletion, follow these steps:

1. To provide insurance against the possibility that the information on Empire Trading was wrong, create a backup table that you can append to the Orders table if the need arises. Click the Design button on the toolbar, choose Make Table from the **Q**uery menu, type an appropriate name for the new table, such as **Empire Trading Canceled Orders**, and choose OK.

2. Click the Run Query button to create the backup table.

3. Choose **D**elete from the **Q**uery menu. The Sort and Show rows of the Select Query grid are replaced by the Delete row, as shown in figure 8.60. The From value in the first column of the Delete row, Orders, indicates that records that match the Field specification will be deleted from the Orders table. The Where values in the remaining two cells indicate fields in which the deletion criteria are specified.

FIG. 8.60

The delete query design created from the select query of figure 8.59.

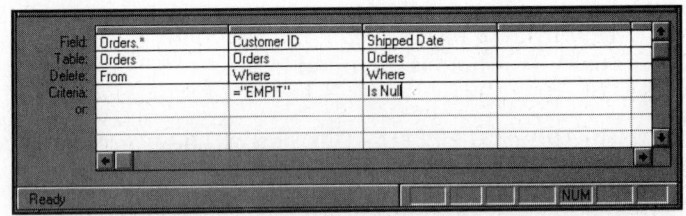

4. You want to duplicate exactly the make-table query that created the backup table, so you should make no changes to the delete query now.

5. Click the Run Query button. The message box shown in figure 8.61 appears, asking you to confirm the deletion of the rows. For this example, choose Cancel so that the records are not deleted.

FIG. 8.61

The deletion confirmation message box.

Deleting records in a *one* table when records corresponding to the deleted records exist in a related *many* table violates the rules of referential integrity; the records in the *many* table would be made orphans. In this situation, if the Enforce Referential Integrity check box is marked in the Relationships dialog box for the two tables, you see the message box shown in figure 8.62 when you attempt to delete the records.

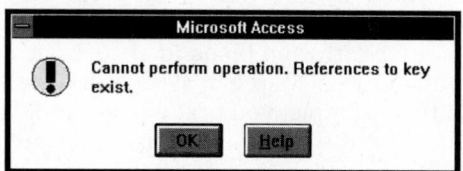

FIG. 8.62

The message box that indicates a violation of the rules of referential integrity.

If you accidentally delete records for Empire Trading, take the following steps:

1. Open the Empire Trading Canceled Orders table.

2. Select all the records in the table with the mouse or choose Select **A**ll Records from the **E**dit menu.

3. Press Ctrl+C to copy the records to the Clipboard.

4. Open the Orders table and choose Paste Appen**d** from the **E**dit menu. The message box confirms the addition of the deleted records from the backup table.

Before running a delete query, always make a backup table of the records you intend to delete from a table. Changing the select query to a make-table query to create the backup table involves only a few mouse clicks and the entry of a descriptive name. Re-creating the records you delete in error can take hours or days to reconstruct, even if a backup copy of the complete table or database exists. Table and database backup copies are seldom up-to-the-minute unless you made one or both of them yourself immediately before the deletion.

Updating Values of Multiple Records in a Table

Update queries change the values of data in a table. Update queries are useful when field values of a large number of records must be updated with a common expression. You may, for example, need to increase or decrease the unit prices of all products or products within a particular category by a fixed percentage.

To see how an update query works, suppose that the city in which Northwind Traders is located has imposed a gross receipts tax to fulfill a budget shortfall. The tax is 1 percent of sales, less freight charges, and is imposed as of March 1, 1992. Northwind forgot to notify its customers that the tax was to be added to invoices for products shipped after this date, but the company intends to send notices to all customers with open invoices. Northwind plans to absorb the cost of the tax for products shipped between March 1, 1992, and the date of the notice. To implement this example, you first need to modify the Orders table to include a field for the tax by following these steps:

1. Click the Tables button in the Database window and open the Orders table in Design mode.

2. Select the Freight field with the mouse and press Insert to add a new field between Order Amount and Freight. (Fields are inserted in tables above the selected field.)

3. Type **Gross Receipts Tax** as the field name, choose Currency as the field data type, and enter a brief description of the field. The table design pane appears as shown in figure 8.63 (the new field is shown selected).

4. Close the Orders table and save the changes.

Adding the Gross Receipts Tax field to the Orders table.

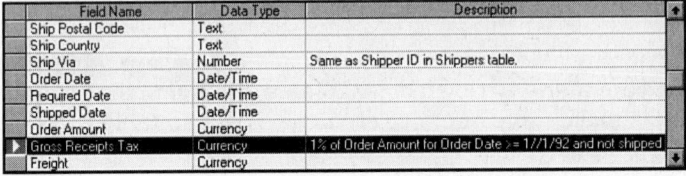

Field Name	Data Type	Description
Ship Postal Code	Text	
Ship Country	Text	
Ship Via	Number	Same as Shipper ID in Shippers table.
Order Date	Date/Time	
Required Date	Date/Time	
Shipped Date	Date/Time	
Order Amount	Currency	
Gross Receipts Tax	Currency	1% of Order Amount for Order Date >= 1/1/92 and not shipped
Freight	Currency	

Now you need to set up a query to select the orders to which you want to add the tax by following these steps:

1. Click the Query button in the Database window and open a new query. Add the Orders table to the query.

2. Drag the Order Date, Ship Date, and Gross Receipts Tax fields to columns 1 through 3, respectively, of the Query Design grid.

3. Type >=#3/1/92# in the Criteria cell of the Order Date field to restrict the selection to orders placed on or after March 1, 1992.

4. Type **Is Null** in the Criteria cell of the Shipped Date field so that only orders that were placed on or after March 1, 1992, *and* that

have not been shipped are selected. The Select Query Design grid appears as shown in figure 8.64.

FIG. 8.64

The select query to return orders placed after March 1, 1992, that have not been shipped.

5. Run the query to verify that the set of records to be updated is selected correctly.

After making sure that the appropriate records have been selected, you are ready to convert the select query to an update query by following these steps:

1. Return to Design mode and choose Update from the **Q**uery menu. A new Update To row replaces the Sort and Show rows of the Select Query Design grid.

2. Type **0.01*[Order Amount]** in the Update To cell of the Gross Receipts Tax column to calculate the amount of the 1 percent tax to be applied to the selected orders. The Update Query Design grid appears as shown in figure 8.65. The Update To cells of the first two fields remain blank, indicating that values in these fields are not to be updated.

FIG. 8.65

The completed Update Query Design grid.

3. Run the update query. The number of records that will be updated is indicated by a message box like the one shown in figure 8.66. (The query may return a different number of records because of additions to the database since this book was written.)

4. Choose Database: NWIND from the **W**indow menu and open the Orders table. Click the End of Table button and check to see that the Gross Receipts Tax values have been added correctly.

FIG. 8.66

The message box that indicates the number of records to which the tax will be added.

5. Switch to Design mode and delete the Gross Receipts Tax field from the table by selecting the row with the mouse and then pressing the Delete key. This action restores the table to its original design.

You can create a mailing list to notify the customers of the added tax by adding the Customers table to the query and then using the same selection criteria on the Orders table to select records from the Customers table. A make-table query that includes the fields required for a form letter provides the necessary merge data file for the word processing application.

Nesting Queries

The example queries presented so far in this chapter have been based exclusively on data contained in tables. You can, however, create queries based on data contained in a previously saved query. Queries based on data contained in other queries, rather than in tables, are known as *subqueries* or *inner queries* in SQL. Access calls subqueries *nested queries* and allows you to have up to 50 levels of nested queries. The initial query is the first level; a query based on the initial query is the second level; a query based on the second-level query is the third level; and so on.

Nested queries are especially useful for analyzing data created by summary queries. A nested query is useful, for example, in determining the level of current inventory for products included in orders that have not yet been shipped. If more units of a product are on order than are available from inventory, orders for the product must be placed with suppliers. The Northwind Traders database includes a Products and Suppliers query that relates the name of the supplier to each of the products Northwind sells. This query can be used as the first level query, because it includes the Product ID, English Name, supplier Company Name, and Quantity In Stock fields from which you need to display inventory levels by product. The design of the Products and Suppliers query is shown in figure 8.67.

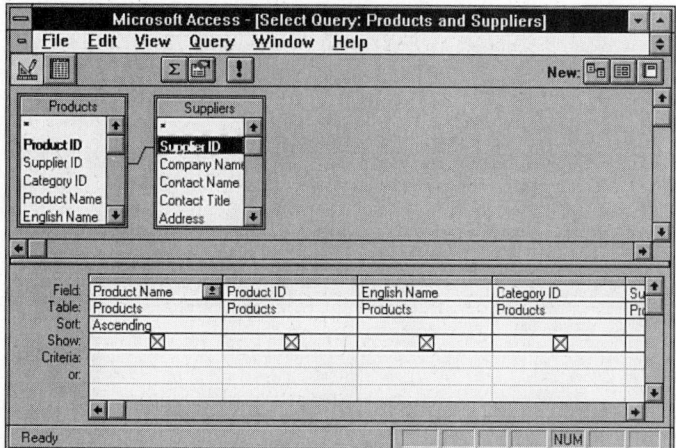

FIG. 8.67

The design of
the Products and
Suppliers query
of the North-
wind Traders
database.

You need to create a summary query that displays the number of units
of each product for which open orders exist, so that the quantity on
order can be compared to the quantity in stock. This second-level
query is a useful query in its own right, because it gives an overall comparison of open orders versus inventory levels. Finally, you need to
create a third-level select query with the criteria that displays only the
products whose inventory levels are insufficient to meet open order
requirements. To create the second-level summary query to compare
units in stock with units required for open orders, follow these steps:

1. Open a new query and add the Products and Suppliers query from
   the Add Tables dialog box. Add the Order Details table, because
   this table includes the Quantity Ordered field that you need to
   compare with the Quantity in Stock field of the Products and Suppliers query. Add the Orders table, because this table includes the
   Shipped Date field that has a Null value for orders that have not
   yet been shipped. Click the Close button.

2. Drag the Product ID field of the Products and Suppliers query to
   the Product ID field of the Order Details table to create the first
   join, and then drag the Order ID field of the Order Details table to
   the Order ID field of the Orders table to create the second join.
   The upper pane of the Query Design grid appears as shown in
   figure 8.68. Notice that none of the fields in the Products and Suppliers Field List box are in bold type, because queries don't have
   key fields.

3. Drag the Product ID, English Name, Company Name, and Units
   in Stock fields from the Products and Suppliers query to the
   Field row of columns 1, 2, 3, and 4 of the Query Design grid,

Query

New

respectively. Drag the Quantity On Order field of the Order Details table and the Shipped Date field of the Orders table to the Field row of columns 5 and 6 of the Query Design grid.

FIG. 8.68

The upper pane of the Query Design window for the second-level nested query.

4. Click the Summary Query button on the toolbar to create a summary query. You need a summary query because totals of the Quantity on Order field of the Order Details table are required for each product. The default Group By function is assigned to the Total row of each column of the grid.

5. In this example, aliases have been added to each Field cell to reduce the width of the field names. Select each field cell in sequence and prefix the field names with ID:, Product:, Supplier:, Stock:, and Orders:, from left to right. Shipped Date is not displayed, so this column does not need an alias.

6. Click the Total cell for the Stock:Units in Stock column, open the drop-down list box, and select Sum(), Avg(), Min(), Max(), First(), or Last() SQL aggregate function for this field. Each of these functions gives the same result because only one record exists for each product in the Products and Suppliers query. The first four columns of the query appear, as shown in figure 8.69.

FIG. 8.69

The first four columns of the Query Design grid for the second-level nested query.

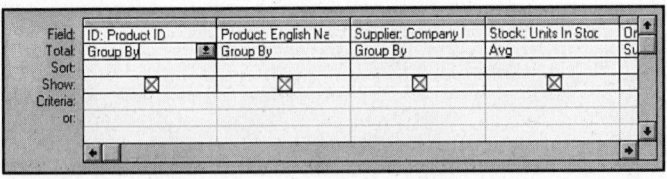

7. Click the Total cell for the Quantity On Order field and choose Sum from the drop-down list box, because you want to compare

the total of the units of a product ordered with the number of units in stock.

8. Click the Show check box of the Shipped Date column so that it is not displayed, and type **Is Null** in the Criteria row. The value of the Shipped Date field is Null for orders than have not been shipped. The last two columns of the Query Design grid appear as shown in figure 8.70.

9. Run the query. The inventory status of all products on order and not shipped is displayed, as shown in figure 8.71.

10. Close the query and save it with a descriptive name, such as Open Orders against Inventory, because it is a useful query that you will use as the data source for the next example query. You must save a query before it can be employed by a subquery.

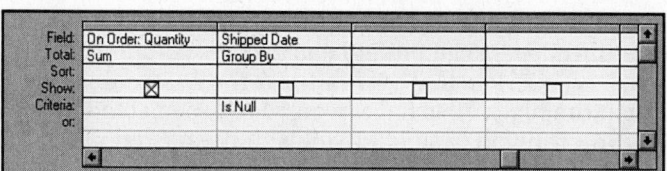

FIG. 8.70

Columns 5 and 6 of the Query Design grid for the second-level nested query.

ID	Product	Supplier	Stock	On Order
1	Dharamsala Tea	Exotic Liquids	39	40
2	Tibetan Barley Beer	Exotic Liquids	68	62
6	Grandma's Boysenberry Spread	Grandma Kelly's Homestead	120	20
7	Uncle Bob's Organic Dried Pears	Grandma Kelly's Homestead	15	15
11	Cabrales Cheese	Cooperativa de Quesos 'Las Cabras'	22	10
12	Manchego La Pastora Cheese	Cooperativa de Quesos 'Las Cabras'	86	4
13	Kelp Seaweed	Mayumi's	48	40
14	Bean Curd	Mayumi's	35	20
16	Pavlova Meringue Dessert	Pavlova, Ltd.	58	44
17	Alice Springs Lamb	Pavlova, Ltd.	0	12
19	Teatime Chocolate Biscuits	Specialty Biscuits, Ltd.	25	10
21	Sir Rodney's Scones	Specialty Biscuits, Ltd.	6	23
24	Guaraná Fantástica Soft Drink	Refrescos Americanas LTDA	40	30
28	Rössle Sauerkraut	Plusspar Lebensmittelgroßmärkte AG	78	98
30	Nord-Ost White Herring	Nord-Ost-Fisch Handelsgesellschaft mbH	10	4
31	Gorgonzola Telino	Formaggi Fortini s.r.l.	0	20
33	Goat Cheese	Norske Meierier	224	25
34	Sasquatch Ale	Bigfoot Breweries	111	90

FIG. 8.71

The query dynaset that compares units of products required to fill open orders with units in inventory.

The SQL syntax of nested queries created by Access differs from that for subqueries you create with SQL equi-joins using the WHERE clause. SQL uses a SELECT statement following the WHERE clause of a prior SELECT statement to create a subquery. Access, on the other hand, creates a dynaset that consists of the result of the first-level query. This dynaset acts as a table so that you can use Access's graphical QBE to create nested queries with joins to the fields of the dynaset. Access's method of creating nested queries also lets you choose a Sort property for fields of a nested query; SQL does not permit the equivalent ORDER BY statement to be used with subqueries. You can inspect Access's SQL syntax for nested queries by opening the Open Orders against Inventory query in Design mode and choosing SQL from the View menu.

Although you could review each of the records of the Open Orders against Inventory query to determine which products are in short supply, a simple third-level select query can do this. Another advantage of an Access nested query is that you can sort the nested query in a different order than the higher-level query on which the nested query is based. Also, you can add calculated fields to the nested query that may not be applicable in the higher-level queries.

To create a third-level nested query that limits the display to products for which the quantity on hand is less than the quantity on order, follow these steps:

1. Open a new query and add the Open Orders against Inventory table to the query.

2. Drag the * field (all fields) to the Field cell of the first column, and then drag the Stock and On Order fields to the second and third columns, respectively. You need to add these two fields so that you can compare their values. Click the Show button of the Stock and On Order columns to prevent their duplication in the query result dynaset.

3. Type <[On Order] in the criteria row of the Stock column. This expression selects only the product records of the Open Orders against Inventory dynaset where the inventory level is less than the outstanding orders.

4. Create a calculated field by typing **Shortage: [Open Orders] - Stock** in the fourth column, and then add a Descending Sort property so that the records for the largest shortages are displayed first. The addition of the Descending Sort property proves that Access can sort nested queries and demonstrates the use of calculated fields to sort any type of query. The query design appears as shown in figure 8.72.

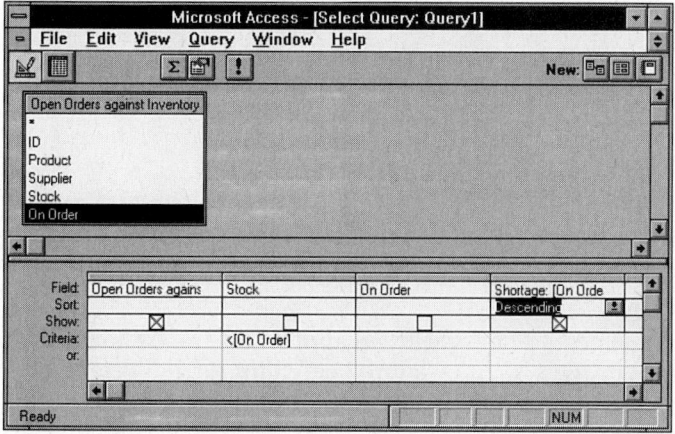

FIG. 8.72

The design for
the third-level
nested query that
displays products
with shortage
status.

5. Run the query. The resulting third-level subquery dynaset appears as shown in figure 8.73. The records are sorted in order of the severity of the shortage.

6. Click the Design Mode button and choose **S**QL from the **V**iew menu to display the SQL statements that create your third-level nested query, as shown in figure 8.74. The advantage of using nested queries is that Access's SQL syntax is much simpler than syntax required for ANSI SQL's chain of nested SELECT statements following WHERE clauses.

FIG. 8.73

The query result
of the third-level
nested query that
displays product
shortages sorted
by severity.

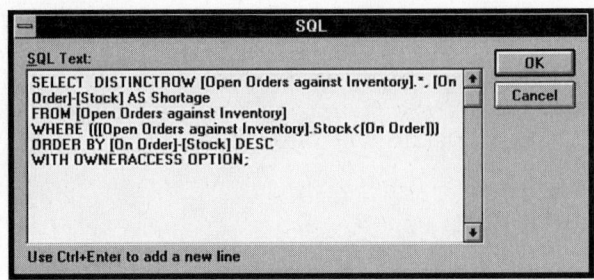

FIG. 8.74

The SQL statements that create your third-level nested query.

7. Save the nested query with an appropriate name, such as **Inventory Shortages**, if you want to keep it for further reference.

You should consider using nested queries whenever you create several queries based on the same or a similar set of records in more than one table. Nested queries save time when you create drill-down applications that progressively display more detail about categories of data. For example, you may create a parameter query that displays all orders for the month you enter as a parameter. You could then create several nested queries, based on the parameter query, to display additional details of the orders received for the month.

Chapter Summary

Queries are the foundation on which you build most of the forms and reports you design to create full-scale applications in Access. One of the principal features of Access, however, is its capability to select, display, and print both detailed and summary information without the need to design forms or reports. In many cases, a simple query can answer *ad hoc* requests for status reports. The printed output of the query does not have a slick format, but the data is what counts.

The section of this chapter on crosstab queries, for example, demonstrates that you can design a query to display and print a time-series area chart for trend analysis in less than five minutes. This area is where Access shines in comparison with spreadsheet applications; using Access, you can select and process the data required to produce a time-series chart in a tenth or so of the time required to produce the equivalent spreadsheet.

The following chapter shows you how to design Access forms that streamline data entry and display information in an attractive, professional-appearing format. If the tables contain graphic images, a form is the logical way to display them. You can let the Access FormWizard design forms, or you can use the toolbox to place text boxes, picture frames, and graphs where you want them on a custom-designed form. Forms also enable you to use more complex validation rules than can be applied to data entered directly into tables.

Creating and Using Forms

Access forms create the user interface to your tables. You use forms to enter, edit, display, and print data contained in Access tables. Although you can use table and query views to perform many of the functions provided by forms, forms offer the advantage of presenting data in an organized and attractive manner. You can arrange the location of fields on the form so that the data entry or editing operations for a single record follow a left-to-right, top-to-bottom sequence. Forms enable you to create multiple-choice selections for fields that use shorthand codes to represent a set of allowable values. A properly designed form speeds data entry and minimizes operator keying errors.

Forms are constructed from a collection of individual design elements, called *controls*. Controls are the components you see in the windows and dialog boxes of Access and other Windows applications. You use text boxes to enter and edit data, labels to hold field names, and picture boxes to display graphics. A form consists of a window in which you place a group of controls that display the data in your tables, and other controls that display static data that Access provides, such as labels or logos that you create.

As you learned in Chapter 8, you can display a graph of data from a crosstab query on a form. This chapter concentrates on creating forms that consist only of text-type controls. Chapters 13 and 14 provide explanations of object linking and embedding (OLE), the method used by Access to incorporate graphics in forms and reports.

Access forms are versatile; they enable you to complete tasks that you cannot complete in table or query views. You can validate entries based on information contained in a table other than the one you are editing. You can create forms that incorporate other forms. Forms can calculate values and display totals. This chapter shows you how to create a form using the Access FormWizard and how to modify the form to speed data entry. Chapter 10 explains how to use the form toolbox to add controls to forms and how to establish default values and validation rules with forms.

Identifying Types of Forms

The content and appearance of your form depends on its use in your database application. Database applications fall into three basic categories:

- *Transaction processing:* Add new records to the tables and edit existing records.

- *Decision-support applications:* Supply information in the form of graphs, tables, or individual data elements, but don't enable the user to add to or edit the data.

- *Database maintenance:* Administrative functions that relate to creating databases and the tables they contain, and to controlling database access by users, security assurance by encryption, periodic database compaction, and backup operations.

Forms are key elements in transaction processing and decision-support applications, which are described in sections that follow. Common database maintenance operations don't require forms, but forms can be useful for maintaining records of database maintenance activities.

Forms for Transaction Processing

Forms for transaction processing usually operate directly on tables when only one table is involved. If a single form is for adding or editing information in more than one table, you create a query that includes all the fields that you intend to add to or edit and then base the form on the query. Your primary form also can use a single table as its data source and use another form, incorporated in the basic form and called a *subform*, that has a related table as its data source. An example of a transaction processing form that uses the subform approach is the

Orders form of the Northwind Traders sample database (see fig. 9.1). The datasheet subform that appears below the Order ID text box is used to display and add line items to an invoice.

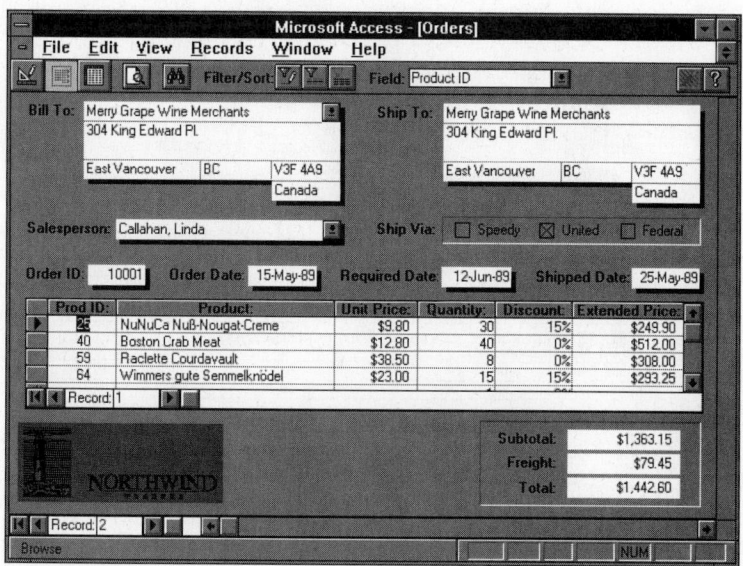

FIG. 9.1

The Orders form of the Northwind Traders database.

This chapter concentrates on forms used for transaction processing, but the techniques you learn are applicable to forms used for any other purpose.

Forms for Decision Support

Forms designed only to present information fall into the category of decision support; these forms provide historical data that managers and supervisors use to determine a course of action. You can design decision-support forms for long-range planning or for short-term (or *ad hoc*) decisions. Short-term decisions relate to a single action, such as granting a larger credit line to a customer or sending a sales representative to determine why the customer's purchases have declined. An example of a form to support a short-term decision is Northwind's Quarterly Orders form, which appears in figure 9.2.

The Quarterly Orders form consists of a main form that displays Customer ID, Company Name, City, and Country, and a subform that displays quarterly sales of products to the customer. The main form is based on the Customers table. The subform consists of the Quarterly

Orders subform (a separate form), which is based on the Quarterly Orders by Product crosstab query. Access enables you to include subforms within forms and even subforms within subforms. This feature is called *nesting*. You can nest forms in up to three levels: main, subform, and sub-subform.

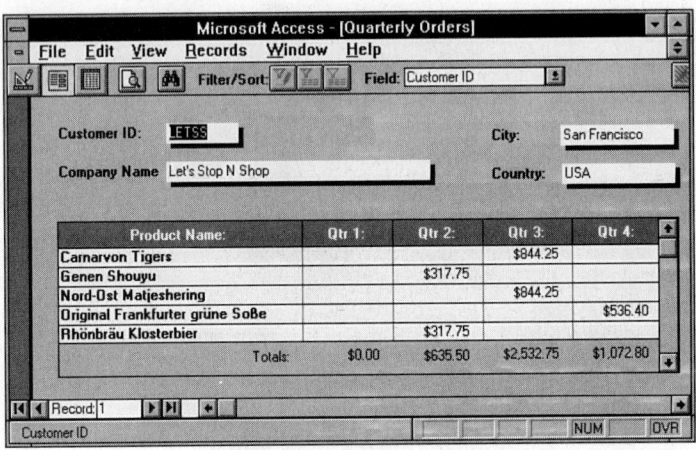

FIG. 9.2

The Quarterly Orders form.

Forms that support short-term decisions often are based on crosstab queries that summarize data in a time series, such as sales to a customer totaled by months, quarters, or years. A table used to support the decision to grant additional credit to a customer might list by quarters the number of invoices issued to the customer, total purchases, and average payment times in days.

Forms that support long-range management decisions most often are based on time-series graphs or charts derived from crosstab queries. Sometimes, however, other types of graphs, such as X-Y scatter charts that show relationships between data, are used. Figure 9.3 shows an example of a form with a graph, similar to the graph you created in Chapter 8 (but with the capability to display detailed data using drill-down techniques).

The decision-support form in figure 9.3 enables management to review sales by product category. You click an option button to choose a category, and then click the Category command button to display a graph of the year's sales for a single category. Click an option button for a month and then click the Month button. A list appears containing all orders that include products in the selected category. Click the Detail command button, and Access presents information on sales of individual products within the category. You click the Summary button to return to the format shown in figure 9.3.

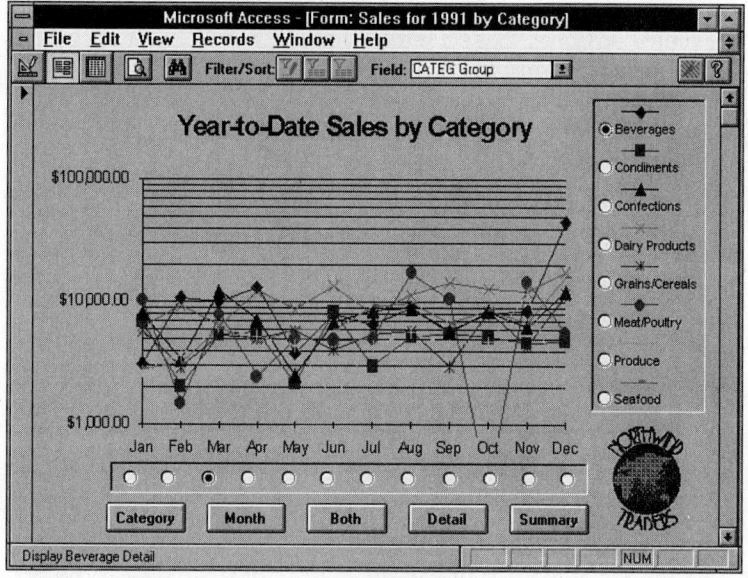

FIG. 9.3

The Quarterly
Sales by Product
form with drill-
down imple-
mented in a
subform.

Creating a Transaction Form
with the FormWizard

The form that you create in this example is typical of the transaction-
processing forms used to add new records to the many side of a one-to-
many relationship. Adding line items to an invoice is an example for
which a form of this kind, called a *many-to-one form*, is necessary. The
object of the Personnel Actions form is to add new records to the Personnel Actions table or enable you to edit the existing records. If you
didn't add the Personnel Actions table shown in figure 9.4 to the
Northwind Traders database in Chapter 4, you need to do so before
proceeding with this example. The structure of the Personnel Actions
table also is provided in Appendix E, "Data Dictionary for the Personnel
Actions Table."

Besides basic data entry and editing, the Personnel Actions form has a
subform that displays all the previous personnel actions for a given
employee. The majority of the forms found in common database applications are one-to-many forms, and most one-to-many forms require a
subform to display data from the many side of the relationship.

		Microsoft Access - [Table: Personnel Actions]					
ID	Type	Initiated By	Scheduled	Approved By	Effective	Rating	New Amount	Comments
1	H		4/1/87		4/1/87		2,000.00	Hired
2	H		7/15/87		7/15/87		3,500.00	Hired
3	H	2	3/1/88	2	3/1/88		2,250.00	Hired
4	H	2	4/1/88	2	4/1/88		2,250.00	Hired
5	H	2	9/15/89	2	9/15/89		3,000.00	Hired
6	H	5	8/28/91	2	9/1/91		2,750.00	Hired
7	H	5	9/15/89	2	9/15/89		4,000.00	Hired
8	H	5	12/1/89	2	12/1/89		3,000.00	Hired
9	H	5	10/15/91	2	10/15/91		3,000.00	Hired
	Q		11/2/92					

FIG. 9.4

The Personnel Actions table with a single entry for each employee.

You can take two approaches to designing a form that accomplishes the objectives of the Personnel Actions form:

■ Use the Employees table as the source of the data for the main form, and use the subform to display, add, and edit records of the Personnel Actions table. This method enables you to add a new employee to the Employees table, but the data of primary interest is relegated to a datasheet in the subform.

■ Use the Personnel Actions table as the source of data for the main form and the subform. In this case, you cannot add a new employee because the Employees table has a one-to-many relationship with the Personnel Actions table you are editing.

Because the Northwind Traders database includes an Employees form that you can use to add a new employee, this example form uses the Personnel Actions table as its primary source of data. If you were creating a full-scale human resources database application, you might choose the Employees table as the data source for the form and design a subform for editing the Personnel Actions table with the history displayed in a subform of the subform.

Creating the Query on Which To Base the Form

The Personnel Actions table identifies employees only by their ID numbers, located in the PA ID field. You need to display the employee's name and title on the form to avoid entering records for the wrong person. To obtain the employee's name and title data for the form, you need to create a many-to-one query that joins the Personnel Actions table (which may have many entries for one employee) with the Employees table (which has only one entry per employee).

To create the Personnel Actions query that serves as the data source for your main form, follow these steps:

1. Click the Query button in the Database window, and then click the New button. The Add Table dialog box appears, as shown in figure 9.5.

2. Choose the Personnel Actions table from the list of tables and queries, and then click the Add button.

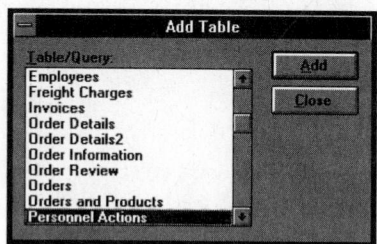

FIG. 9.5

The Add Table dialog box for the Personnel Actions query.

3. Choose the Employees table from the list, click the Add button, and then click Close. The Field List dialog boxes for the Personnel Actions and Employees tables appear in the upper pane of the Query Design window.

4. Click the PA ID field in the Personnel Actions Field List dialog box and drag it to the Employee ID field of the Employees Field List dialog box to create a join between these two fields (see fig. 9.6).

FIG. 9.6

The upper pane of the Query Design window for the Personnel Actions query.

5. Click the * field of the Personnel Actions table, drag it to the Query grid, and drop it in the Personnel Actions column.

6. Click the Employee ID field of the Employees table, drag it to the Query grid, and drop it in the Employee ID column.

7. From the Employees table, click and drag the Last Name, First Name, and Title fields, and drop them in columns 3, 4, and 5 of the Query grid, respectively, as shown in figure 9.7.

8. To simplify finding an employee, click the Sort cell of the Last Name column and choose an Ascending sort.

9. Close the new query. Click Yes when the dialog box asks if you want to save the query.

10. In the Save As dialog box, give the query a name, such as **Personnel Actions Query**, and then click OK (see fig. 9.8).

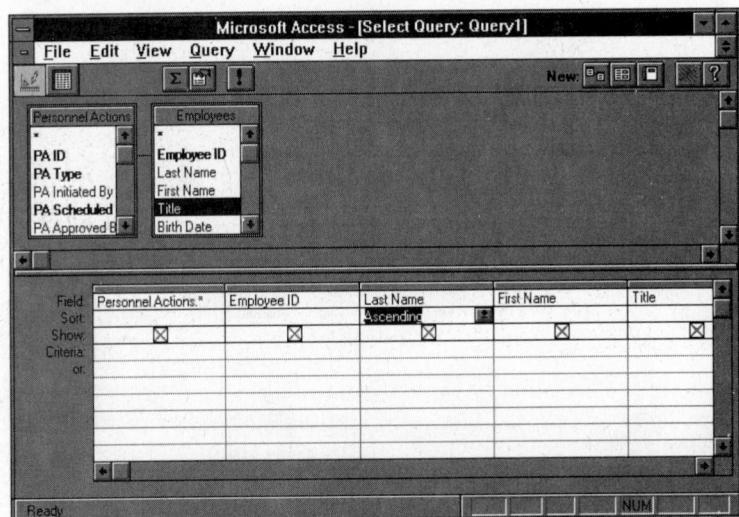

FIG. 9.7

The Query grid for the Personnel Actions query.

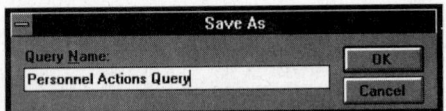

FIG. 9.8

The Save As dialog box.

If you didn't add records to the Personnel Actions table when you created it, you can add them with the Personnel Actions form you create with the assistance of Access's FormWizard.

Creating the Basic Form with the FormWizard

You were introduced to Access's FormWizard in Chapter 8, when you created the form with the time-series graph from the Product Sales by Category query. FormWizards create the basic design of the form and add the text box controls to display and edit the values of data items.

To create the Personnel Actions form with the FormWizard, follow these steps:

1. Click the Form button of the Database window, then click the New button. The New Form dialog box appears, as shown in figure 9.9.

2. Click the arrow to open the drop-down list box of existing tables and queries that may serve as a source of data for a form. The Personnel Actions Query that you just created is the basic source of data for your form, so choose it and then click the Form Wizards button. The AccessWizard dialog box appears, as shown in figure 9.10.

FIG. 9.9

The New Form dialog box.

FIG. 9.10

The types of forms the Form Wizard can create.

3. Because your form is to include a Personnel Actions history subform, choose Main/Subform and choose OK. (Single-column creates a simple data-entry form without a subform; Tabular creates a form with a row-column grid; and Graph uses the GraphWizard to add a graph or chart to your form.)

   The FormWizard dialog box appears and prompts you to choose the table or query that contains the data for the subform (see fig. 9.11).

4. Select Personnel Actions and click the Next > button. The next FormWizard dialog box appears and asks which Personnel Actions fields should be included on your main form (see fig. 9.12). You need to be able to edit all the fields of the Personnel Actions table.

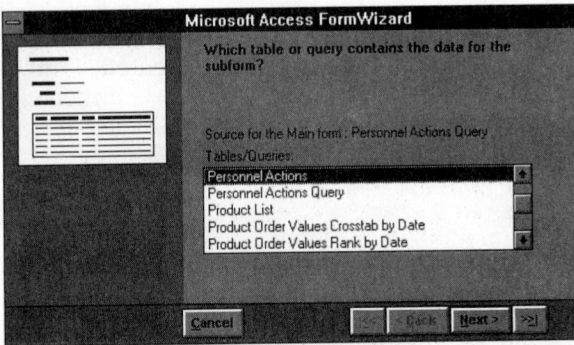

FIG. 9.11

Choosing the source of the data for the subform.

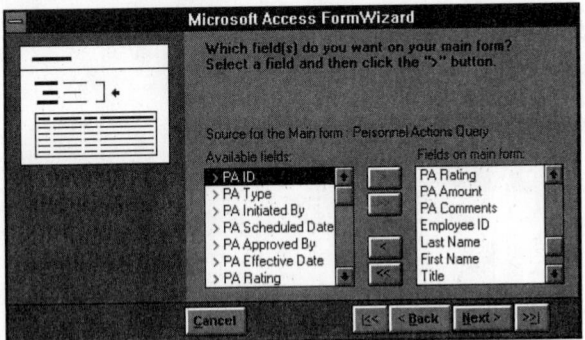

FIG. 9.12

Choosing the Personnel Actions fields to include on the main form.

5. Click the >> button to add all the fields, and then click the Next > button. The dialog box shown in figure 9.13 appears and asks you to choose the fields to appear on the subform.

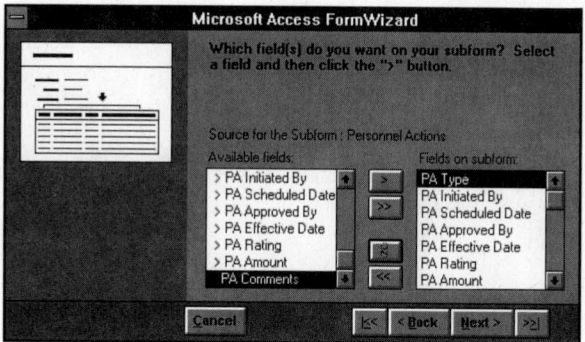

FIG. 9.13

Choosing the
Personnel Actions
fields to include
on the subform.

If you make an error or change your mind, you can click the
< Back button, when it is enabled, to modify your previous
choices. The |<< (rewind) button takes you to step 3 in the
FormWizard sequence. The >>| (fast forward) accepts de-
fault values for uncompleted selections and takes you to the
step immediately before creating the form. Using the >>|
button isn't recommended unless you are creating a simple
single-column form. Cancel takes you back to the Database
window without completing the form-creation process.

6. The PA ID field is included in the Personnel Actions query, so you
needn't include the PA ID field in the subform. For this example,
reviewing previous comments isn't necessary. To expedite the
addition of fields, click >> to add all the fields. Choose PA ID and
click the < button. Then choose PA Comments and click the < button again. This process removes the PA ID and PA Comments
fields from the subform.

   Double-check to verify that the fields on the subform are correct,
   then click the Next > button. The list of tables used in the forms
   appears, as shown in figure 9.14.

7. Access needs to know which of the two tables that supply data for
the form is the source of data for the main form and the subform.
Tables in subforms must be related to the main form. Choose Personnel Actions from the list of tables and click the Next > button.
The dialog box shown in figure 9.15 appears.

   This dialog box enables you to apply styles to your form. This
   form is for use by a data-entry operator and doesn't need special
   effects to highlight or decorate the fields.

FIG. 9.14

Specifying the table that contains the fields in the main form and the subform.

FIG. 9.15

Choosing the style for your form.

8. Choose Standard style and click the Next > button. A dialog box appears, as shown in figure 9.16, asking you for a title for your form. (A special area for the title is included at the top of the form.)

FIG. 9.16

Giving your form a title.

9. Type **Personnel Action Entry** as the title of the form. Click the Open button to allow the FormWizard to create the new form. If you click Design, you can change the design of the new form without viewing it.

A message box appears indicating that the main form must be able to open the subform before it appears in the Forms window (see fig. 9.17). Access cannot open a form that hasn't been saved.

10. Choose OK. The Save As dialog box appears (see fig. 9.18).

FIG. 9.17

The message box indicating that you must save your subform.

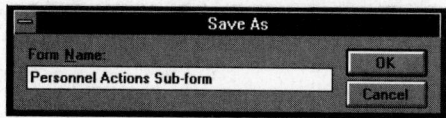

FIG. 9.18

The Save As dialog box used to name your subform.

11. Subforms are like any other main form; they are included in the list of forms displayed in the Database window. Enter a title for the subform, such as **Personnel Actions Subform**, in the Save As dialog box, and click OK. The new form created by the FormWizard appears as a normal-sized window (see fig. 9.19).

12. Click the Document Maximize button to expand the form's window to fill the available area.

The FormWizard creates a single column of controls—text boxes with associated labels for entering or editing the values of data items in each of the fields you specified in step 5. The vertical distance required for a single-column of text boxes causes the subform to be pushed below the bottom of the window. In the next section, you learn how to rearrange the controls created by the FormWizard so that all the controls, including the subform, fit in a single window.

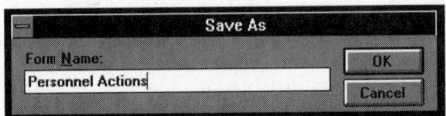

FIG. 9.19

The basic
Personnel Actions
form created by
the FormWizard.

13. Access gives your form the default name Form1. To give it a different name, choose Save Form **As** from the **File** menu and type **Personnel Actions** as the name of the form in the Save As dialog box
(see fig. 9.20). Choose OK to assign the new name to the form.

FIG. 9.20

Entering a name
for your main
form in the Save
As dialog box.

No matter how expert you become in the design of Access forms, using
the FormWizard to create the basic form design saves you time.

Using the Form Design Window

To modify the design of your new form, click the Design Mode button
on the toolbar. The Form Design window appears as shown in figure
9.21. The toolbox, at the right in the figure, usually appears to the left,
covering the labels for the field data entry text boxes. You use the
toolbox to add new control elements to the form, which is the subject

of a section later in this chapter. Click the bar at the top of the toolbox and drag it to the right, or click the window menu symbol at the upper left and choose Close to make the toolbox temporarily disappear.

The Personnel Actions form enables you to experiment with the methods of modifying forms and their content described in the sections that follow.

Do not save the form with the changes you make when following the instructions contained in this section. These changes are for demonstration purposes only. Saving the changes you make permanently modifies the form you created in the preceding section.

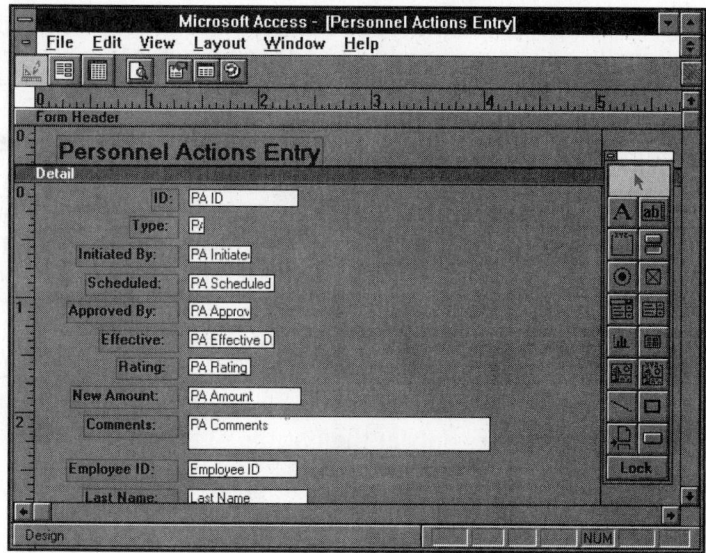

FIG. 9.21

The basic Personnel Actions form in Design mode.

Elements of the Form Design Window

Forms can be divided into three sections: Form Header, Detail, and Form Footer. Headers and footers are optional. The Form Design window includes the following basic elements:

- A toolbar with buttons that are shortcuts for menu selections in Form Design mode. The functions of the buttons and their equivalent menu choices are listed in tables in the next section.

- A set of vertical and horizontal rulers, calibrated in inches for the U.S. version of Access. Centimeters is the default for versions of Access supplied in countries where the metric system is used.

■ A vertical line, shown to the left of the toolbox in figure 9.21, that establishes the right margin of the form. You can move the margin indicator line by clicking and dragging it to the desired location.

■ A horizontal line (not shown in figure 9.21) that establishes the bottom margin of the form. You can drag the line to a new location with the mouse. Margins are important when you are designing a subform to fit within a rectangle of a predetermined size on the main form.

■ Vertical and horizontal scroll bars that enable you to view portions of the form that are outside the boundaries of the form window.

■ A Form Header bar that defines the height of the form's header section, if you choose to add a header and footer to your form. Headers and footers are added in pairs. The Form Header section contains static text, graphic images, and other controls that appear at the top of the form. If you print a multipage form, the Form Header appears only at the top of the first page.

■ A Form Detail bar that divides the Form Header from the rest of the form. Controls that display data from your tables and queries, plus static data elements such as labels and logos, are on the Form Detail bar.

■ A Form Footer bar (not shown in 9.21) that defines the height of the form's footer section. The Form Footer section is similar in function to the Form Header. If you print a multipage form, the Form Footer appears only at the bottom of the last page.

You can add a Form Header and Form Footer to the Personnel Actions form by choosing Form **H**dr/Footer from the **L**ayout menu. A dialog box warns you that you lose the content of the title in the current header when you take this action. Because you don't save the changes you make when following the instructions in this section, the temporary loss of the title text, if you try adding a header and footer, is not significant.

Form Design Toolbar Buttons and Menu Choices

The Form Design toolbar introduces two new buttons that apply only to the design of forms: the Field List and Palette buttons. Table 9.1 lists the function and equivalent menu choice for each of the standard toolbar buttons in Form Design mode.

Table 9.1. Standard Toolbar Buttons in Form Design Mode

Button	Function	Menu Choice
	Selects Form Design mode.	View Form **Design**
	Displays the form in Run mode.	View Form
	Displays the table or query that is the source of data for the main form.	View Datasheet
	Selects Print Preview to display how your form appears if printed. You can print the form from the Print Preview window.	File Print Preview
	Displays the Properties dialog box for one of the two sections of the form when you click the section bars, or displays the properties of a control when you select it.	View Properties
	Displays a list of fields in the query or table that is the data source for the main form.	View Field List
	Displays a palette from which you can choose the color of the text, background (fill), and border of a control. The palette also enables you to add special effects (raised or sunken) that affect the appearance of the control and enables you to choose the width of the control's border.	View Palette
	Returns the form to its state preceding the last modification.	Edit Undo
	Displays the Help menu for forms.	F1 key

The appearance of the Form Design window after clicking the Properties and Palette buttons is shown in figure 9.22.

You can close the palette and the Properties dialog box by double-clicking their Document Control menu boxes, or by clicking the appropriate buttons on the toolbar.

Properties dialog box

Palette

FIG. 9.22

The Form Design window with the palette and the Properties dialog box open.

Toolbar List Boxes To Format Text

When you choose a text-type control, such as a text box, two drop-down list boxes appear in the toolbar, with an additional set of seven toolbar buttons. The list boxes enable you to choose the desired typeface and type size for the text. The additional buttons, used to format the text, are similar to those buttons found on the toolbar ribbon of Microsoft Word for Windows and other Windows word processing applications. The default typeface for forms is the same as that for tables and queries, MS Sans Serif in an 8-point font. You may choose from a drop-down list of preset sizes or enter a size in points in the Size dialog box. The function of each of the toolbar's text-formatting buttons and its equivalent text-property setting is listed in table 9.2.

Table 9.2. Toolbar Buttons for Text Controls in Form Design Mode

Button	Function	Property and Value
B	Sets text style to bold (default for titles and labels).	Font Bold = Yes
I	Sets italic (or slanted) text style.	Font Italic = Yes
U	Underlines text.	Font Underline = Yes
≡	Left-justifies text within border.	Text Align = Left
≡	Centers text horizontally within border.	Text Align = Center

Button	Function	Property and Value
	Right-justifies text within border.	Text Align = Right
	General alignment (aligns text to the left and numbers to the right, the default).	Text Align = General

Default Values for Forms

You can change the default values that are used in the creation of all forms by choosing **O**ptions from the **V**iew menu and then choosing Form & Report design from the Categories list box. You can create a form to use as a template and to replace the standard template, determine whether objects control-snap to a 0.1-inch grid (visible or invisible) when you move them, and determine how objects are displayed when chosen.

You change the default values for the current form, section, or controls by choosing the object as described in the following section and then changing the default values displayed in the Properties dialog box for that object.

Background Colors

The background color of a form applies to all areas of the form except the areas occupied by control objects. The default background color of forms created by the FormWizard is light gray. This new standard is adopted by Microsoft for the background color of dialog boxes of Excel 4.0 and other applications introduced after the launch of Windows 3.1 in the spring of 1992. If you are creating a form that you intend to print, a gray background is distracting and consumes substantial amounts of laser printer toner. Data-entry operators may prefer a white background rather than a gray or colored background. Colored backgrounds do not aid text visibility.

To change the background color of a form, follow these steps:

1. Choose the section of the form (Header, Detail, or Footer) whose background color you want to change.

2. Click the Palette button on the toolbar to display the palette.

3. Click the box that contains the color you want to use in the Fill row of the palette.

Because the background color of each form section is independent, you must repeat the process for other sections of your form. The Clear check box option is disabled when a section is chosen because it isn't applicable to forms.

You choose the background color of a control object, such as a label, as you do for forms. In most cases, the chosen background color of labels is the same as that of the form. The default background color for text boxes is white so that text boxes contrast with the form's background color.

Selecting, Editing, and Moving Form Elements and Controls

The techniques for selecting, editing, and moving the elements that comprise Access forms were derived from the form-design system refined by Microsoft for Visual Basic 1.0. If you have used Visual Basic, you will find the selection, relocation, and sizing techniques for Access controls to be similar. Several subtle differences exist between Access and Visual Basic, however. These differences quickly become apparent when you edit your first form.

 The properties that apply to the entire form, each of the five sections into which an Access form can be divided, and each control object on the form are determined by the values shown in the Properties dialog box. To view the Properties dialog box for a control, click the Properties button on the toolbar. The sections of an Access form are shown in figure 9.23.

The following descriptions tell you how to choose and display the properties of the entire form, its sections, and its control objects:

■ *Form:* Click the area of the form to the right of the right-margin indicator line or choose Select Form from the Edit menu. Selecting the form enables you to set properties for the form as a whole by entering values from the properties listed in the Form Properties dialog box.

■ *Header section only:* Click the Form Header or Page Header bar. A set of properties applies to the Form Header or Page Header section only. A Form Header and Footer appear only if you choose Form Hdr/Ftr from the Layout menu. A Page Header and Footer appear if you choose Page Hdr/Ftr from the Layout menu. Page Headers and Footers are used primarily in conjunction with printing forms. You delete headers and footers by choosing Form Hdr/Ftr or Page Hdr/Ftr a second time.

■ *Detail section only:* Click the Detail bar. A set of properties that duplicates those of the Form Header section applies to the Detail section of the form.

■ *Footer section only:* Click the Form Footer or Page Footer bar. A set of properties identical to the Form Header apply. A Form Footer appears only if a Form Header has been added. The same applies to Page Headers and Footers.

■ *Control object (or both elements of a control with an associated label):* Click the surface of the control. Each type of control has its own set of properties. Choosing one or more control objects is the subject of a subsequent section.

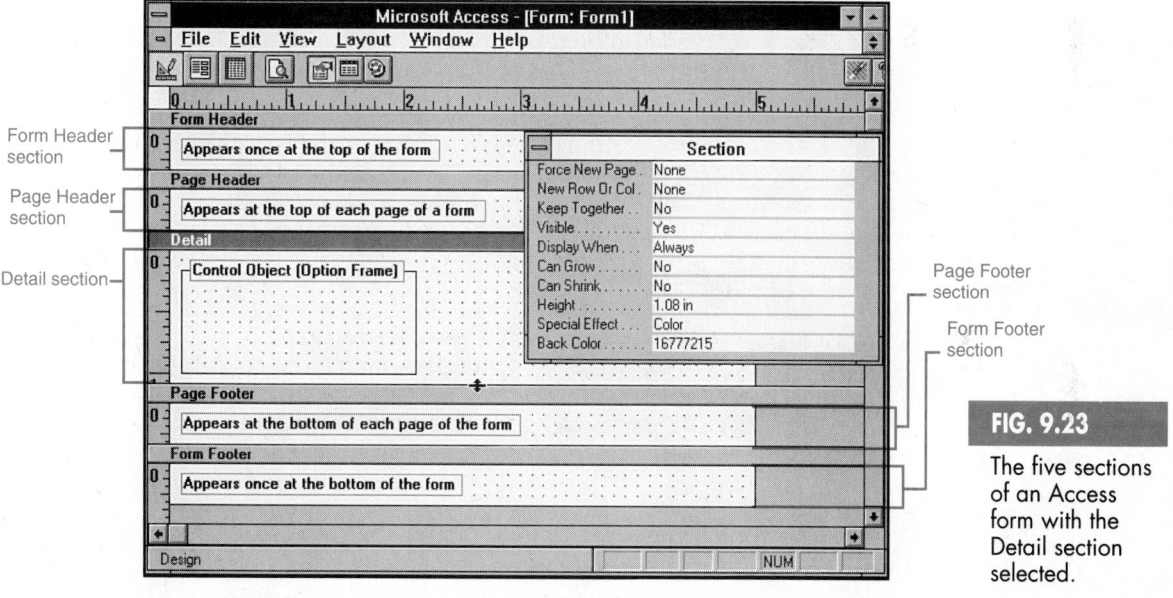

FIG. 9.23

The five sections of an Access form with the Detail section selected.

Changing the Size of the Form Header and Form Footer

You can change the height of the Form Header or Form Footer sections by dragging the Detail or Form Footer bar vertically with the mouse. When you position the mouse pointer at the top edge of a section divider bar, it turns into a line with two vertical arrows, as shown in figure 9.23. You drag the pointer with the mouse to adjust the size of the section above the mouse pointer.

The height of the Detail section is determined by the vertical dimension of the window in which the form is displayed, less the combined heights of the Form Header and Form Footer (and/or Page Header and Footer) sections, that are fixed in position. When you adjust the vertical scroll bar, only the Detail section scrolls.

Selecting, Moving, and Sizing a Single Control

When you select a control object by clicking its surface, the object is enclosed by a shadow line with an anchor rectangle at its upper left corner and five smaller rectangular sizing handles, as shown in figure 9.24. Text boxes, combo boxes, check boxes, and option buttons have an associated (attached) label. When you select one of these objects, the label and the object are selected as a unit.

FIG. 9.24

The appearance of a control object selected for relocation and resizing.

The following choices are available for moving or changing the size of a control object (the numbered choices correspond with the numbers in fig. 9.24):

1. *To select a control (and its associated label, if any):* Click anywhere on its surface.

2. *To move the control (and its associated label, if any) to a new position:* Move the mouse pointer within the outline of the object at any point other than the small resizing handles or within the confines of a text box (where the cursor becomes an editing caret). The mouse pointer becomes a symbol of a hand when it is on an area that you can use to move the control. Press the left mouse button while dragging the hand symbol to the new location for the control. If the control doesn't have an associated label, you can use the control's anchor handle to move the control. An outline of the control indicates its position as you reposition the mouse. Release the mouse button to drop the control in its new position.

3. *To move the elements of a control with an associated label separately:* Position the mouse pointer on the anchor handle of the control you want to move. The mouse pointer becomes a hand with an extended finger. Drag the individual element to its new position.

4. *To adjust the width and height of a control simultaneously:* Click the small sizing handle at one of the three corners of the outline. The mouse pointer becomes a diagonal two-headed arrow. Drag the two-headed arrow to the new position with the mouse.

5. *To adjust only the height of the control:* Click the sizing handle on one of the horizontal surfaces of the outline. The mouse pointer becomes a vertical two-headed arrow. Drag the two-headed arrow to the new position with the mouse.

6. Same as 5.

Selecting and deselecting controls is a *toggling* process. Toggling is repeating an action that causes the effect of the action to alternate between the on and off conditions. The Properties, Field List, and Palette buttons on the toolbar and their corresponding menu choices are toggles. The Properties dialog box, for example, appears and disappears as you repetitively click the Properties button.

Aligning Controls to the Grid

The form design window includes a grid consisting of one-pixel dots with a default spacing of 0.1 inch. When the grid is visible, you can use the grid dots to assist in maintaining the horizontal and vertical alignment of rows and columns of controls. Even if the grid isn't visible, as is the case with forms created by the FormWizard, you can cause controls to "snap to the grid" by choosing **S**nap to Grid from the **L**ayout menu. **S**nap to Grid is a toggle; when it is active, the menu choice is checked. When you move a control, the upper left corner of the object jumps to the closest grid dot.

You can cause the size of control objects to conform to grid spacing by toggling Size to **G**rid from the **L**ayout menu. You also can choose to have the size of the control fit its content by choosing Size to Fit from the **L**ayout menu.

If **S**nap to Grid is on and you want to locate or size a control without reference to the grid, press the Ctrl key when you move or resize the control.

Toggling the **G**rid command on the **V**iew menu controls the visibility of the grid. You can control whether the grid is visible or invisible when you create a new form by choosing **O**ptions from the **V**iew menu and setting the View Grid option of the Form & Report Design category to Yes or No. If the grid spacing is set to more than 16 per inch or 10 per centimeter, the dots aren't visible. To change the grid spacing for a form, follow these steps:

1. Choose Select Form from the Edit menu.

2. Click the Properties button on the toolbar to make the Properties dialog box appear.

3. Change the Grid X and Grid Y values to 16 dots per inch (if you want controls to align with ruler ticks) or 10 dots per inch (the default).

The default value of grid spacing when you use the FormWizard is 64 dots per inch; the grid dots don't appear on your form when you choose Grid from the View menu. Follow the preceding steps and adjust the Grid X and Grid Y values to 16 or less per inch (10 or less per centimeter).

Selecting and Moving a Group of Controls

You can select and move more than one object at a time by using one of the following methods:

■ Enclose the objects with a rectangle created by clicking the surface of the form outside the outline of a control object. Press the left mouse button while dragging the mouse pointer to create an enclosing rectangle that includes each of the objects you want to select (see fig. 9.25). Release the mouse pointer. You may move the group of objects by clicking and dragging the anchor handle of any one of them.

■ Select one object and hold down the Shift key while you use the mouse to select the next object.

■ Delete a member from the group by clicking its anchor with the mouse to deselect it. To deselect the group, click any inactive area of the form. An inactive area is an area outside the outline of a control.

FIG. 9.25

A collection of control objects enclosed with a selection rectangle.

If you select or deselect a control with an associated label, the label is selected or deselected with the control.

Aligning a Group of Controls

You can align selected individual controls or groups of controls to the grid or to each other by choosing **Align** from the Layout menu and completing the following actions:

- To align a selected control or a group of controls to the grid, choose To Grid from the fly-out submenu.

- To adjust the positions of controls within a selected columnar group so that their left edges fall into vertical alignment with the far-left control, choose Left from the submenu.

- To adjust the positions of controls within a selected columnar group so that their right edges align with the right edge of the far-right control, choose Right from the submenu.

- To align rows of controls by their top edges, choose Top from the submenu.

- To align rows of controls by their bottom edges, choose Bottom from the submenu.

Your forms will have a more professional appearance if you take the time to align groups of controls both vertically and horizontally.

Using the Windows Clipboard and Deleting Controls

All the conventional Windows Clipboard commands apply to control objects. You can cut or copy a selected control or group of controls to the Clipboard. You then can paste the control or group to the form by using Edit menu commands and relocate the pasted control(s) as desired. Access uses the new Windows 3.1 keyboard shortcut keys: Ctrl+X to cut and Ctrl+C to copy selected control(s) to the Clipboard, and Ctrl+V to paste the selected controls. The traditional Shift+Delete, Ctrl+Insert, and Shift+Insert commands perform the same operations.

You can delete a control by selecting it and then pressing the Delete key. If you accidentally delete a label associated with a control, select and copy another label to the Clipboard and then select the control with which the label is to be associated and paste the label to the control.

Changing the Color and Border Style of a Control

The default color for the text and border of controls is black. Borders are one pixel wide; some objects, such as text boxes, have default borders. Labels are *transparent* (clear) by default and other controls aren't. Transparent means that the background color appears within the control except in areas occupied by text or pictures. You control the color and border styles of a control from the Palette dialog box.

To change the color or border style of a selected control or group of controls, follow these steps:

1. Select the control(s) whose color you want to change.

 2. Click the Palette button on the toolbar to display the palette.

3. Click a color box in the Fill row to change the background color of the control(s) that aren't transparent (clear).

4. Click a color box in the Border row to change the color of the borders of the control(s) that have borders.

5. Click a border width to change the thickness of the border for control(s) whose borders are enabled.

6. Click a color box in the Text row to change the color of the text element of the control(s).

The DOS versions of dBASE and Paradox use reverse video as the default to indicate editable text. The general practice for Windows database entry forms is to indicate editable elements with borders and clear backgrounds. You can create the effect of reverse video by choosing black or a dark color for the fill of a text-box control and choosing a light color for its text. Reverse text is more difficult to read than normal text. If you decide to implement reverse text, you should use a larger font and the bold text attribute to ensure legibility.

Changing the Content of Text Controls

You can edit the content of text controls by using conventional Windows text-editing techniques. When you place the mouse pointer within the confines of a text control, the mouse pointer becomes the Windows text-editing caret (insertion point) that you use to insert or delete text. You can select text by pressing Shift and moving the caret with the mouse; all Windows Clipboard operations are applicable to text within controls. Keyboard text selection and editing techniques using the arrow keys in combination with the Shift key are applicable, also.

If you change the name of a field in a text box and make an error in naming the field, you receive a #Name?? error message in the offending text box when you select Run mode. Following is a better method of changing a text box with an associated label:

1. Delete the existing label.

2. Click the Field List button in the Properties bar to display the Field List dialog box.

3. Scroll the entries in the Field List dialog box until you find the field name you want.

4. Click the field name, press the left mouse button, and drag the field name to the location of the deleted control. Release the mouse button to drop the new control.

5. Close the Field List dialog box when you are finished.

You then can relocate the new field caption and text box and edit the caption as necessary.

Rearranging the Personnel Actions Form

The objective of the following set of instructions is to rearrange the controls on the Personnel Actions form so that all the elements of the form fit in a maximized window of a standard VGA display (640 × 480 pixels). When you complete the following steps, your form appears as shown in figure 9.26.

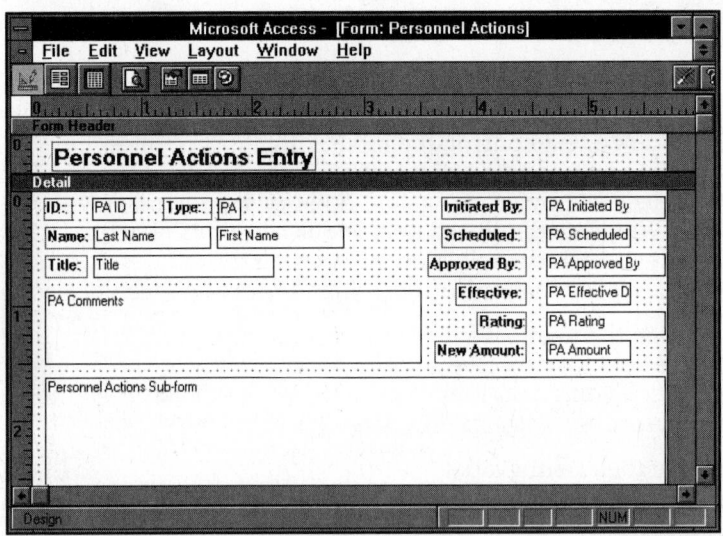

FIG. 9.26

The Personnel Actions form after relocating and resizing its control objects.

To rearrange the controls of the Personnel Actions form to correspond with the positions shown in figure 9.23, follow these steps:

1. Close the Personnel Actions form by double-clicking the Document Control menu box. Do not save the changes you made in the preceding section.

2. Choose Personnel Actions from the Forms list in the Database window and click the Open button.

3. Click the Design Mode button on the toolbar to display the form in Design view.

4. Click the Palette button on the toolbar to display the palette.

5. Click the Form Header bar to select the Form Header section, and click the white color square in the fill column to change the background color to white. Select the label and change the word *Query* to *Entry*, if you did not do so previously.

6. Click the Detail bar to select the Detail section and change its background color to white by the method used in step 5.

7. Choose Select Form from the Edit menu and then click the Properties button on the toolbar.

8. Scroll the entries in the Properties dialog box to display Grid X and Grid Y. Enter **16** for the Grid X and Grid Y values.

   Figure 9.27 shows the Personnel Actions Entry form after the background color changes and the addition of a 1/16-inch grid.

9. Close the Properties dialog box by clicking the Properties button again.

10. Place the mouse pointer at the upper left of the Initiated By control. Enclose Initiated By, Scheduled, Approved By, Effective, Rating, and New Amount by pressing the left mouse button and dragging the lower right corner of the rectangle. Release the mouse button when the six controls are enclosed.

11. Click the surface of one of the selected controls and drag the group to the upper right area of the form.

12. Delete the Employee ID control near the bottom of the form. This control duplicates the PA ID entry at the top of the form.

13. Delete the Comments label; the size of its text box is sufficient to identify it.

14. Drag the remainder of the controls to the positions shown in figure 9.26.

15. Delete the First Name label and edit the Last Name label to read Name:.

16. Adjust the widths of the labels and text boxes to suit their content. The Initiated By and Approved By boxes are made large enough to contain the names of the supervisor and manager, respectively, rather than just their ID numbers.

17. Select all the controls in the right column of the form, then choose **Align** from the **Layout** menu and click the Left submenu choice. All the left borders of the text boxes are aligned.

18. Choose **Save** from the **File** menu to save your changes to the Personnel Actions form.

You may need to adjust the sizes of some of the controls individually to make their appearance consistent with the other controls. When you have completed your rearrangement, click the Form Run Mode button. Your form appears as shown in figure 9.28.

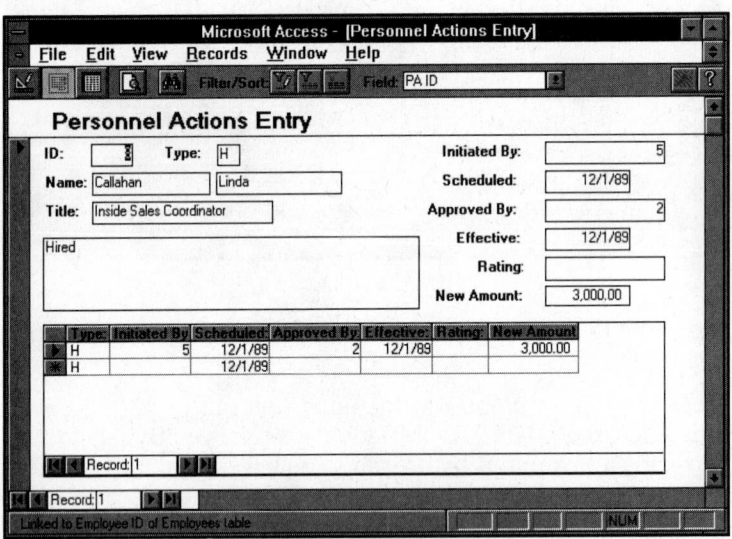

FIG. 9.28

The revised Personnel Actions form in Run mode.

Setting the Properties of a Subform

You can modify the properties of the subform used to create the history of prior Personnel Actions for an employee to suit its intended purpose. In this case, editing of entries in the subform should not be allowed. To change the properties of the Personnel Actions subform, follow these steps:

1. Close the Personnel Actions form.

2. Open the Personnel Actions Subform from the Database window to examine its appearance in Datasheet view.

3. Click the Design Mode button on the toolbar so that you can change the properties of the form. You need not be concerned with the design of the form; it will display in Datasheet view as a subform. (Datasheet view is the default view for subforms.)

4. Click the Properties button on the toolbar to display the Properties dialog box.

5. Scroll to the Default Editing entry, open the list box, and choose Read-Only.

6. Choose the Allow Editing entry, open the list box, and choose Unavailable. When you don't allow editing in a subform datasheet, the "tentative append" record no longer appears. Your Personnel Actions subform appears as shown in figure 9.29.

7. Close the Personnel Actions Subform and save your changes.

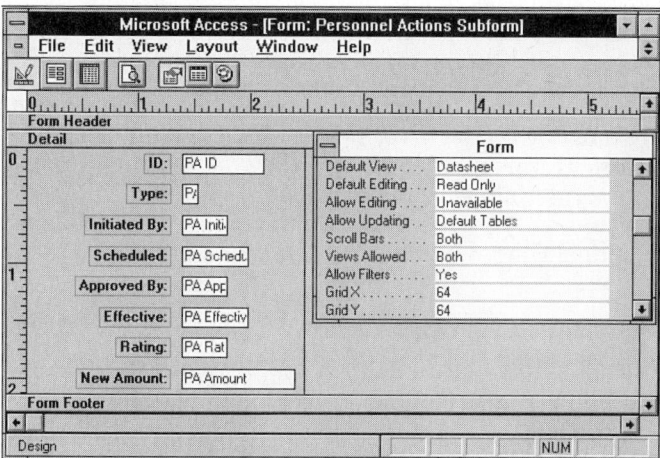

FIG. 9.29

The Personnel Actions subform shown in Design mode.

You can change the Default view of the subform to a Continuous form that you can modify to display the data in another format. When displaying historical data, the Datasheet view is usually the best choice because it is the easiest to implement.

Modifying Linkages between Main Forms and Subforms

When you add a subform to the main form, Access automatically creates links between the two forms if it can find a likely relationship. Relationships between main forms and subforms are based on the following factors:

- The relationship you have set between tables when both of the data sources are from tables.

- The primary-key field of the table that is the data source for the main form and any field with the same name in the subform.

- Each of a table's key fields that is used in the query for the main form if the data source of the subform is a table included in the main form's query or if the subform query has a table in common with the main form query.

In this example, the default linkage consists of the PA ID, PA Type and PA Effective fields because these three fields are key fields in the query used as the data source for the main form and the table acting as the data source for the subform. You selected these three fields when you designed the Personnel Actions table to preclude entries of duplicate actions. Multiple entries don't appear if you don't change the linkage because linkage by the three key fields results in a one-to-one relationship between records in the main form and the subform.

To display all the Personnel Actions records for the chosen employee, the linkage must be on the PA ID field only. Microsoft calls the main form the *Master* form and the subform the *Child* for the purposes of linkage. The term Child is used because the subform is a Windows multiple document interface (MDI) child window. MDI child windows are conventional windows you can open inside other windows, called *parent windows*.

To change the linkage between the main form and the subform's table or query, follow these steps:

1. Open the Personnel Actions form from the Database window.

2. Click the Design Mode button and choose the subform.

3. Click the Properties button to display the Subform/Subreport Properties dialog box for the subform.

4. Edit the Link Child Fields and Link Master Fields properties so that both include only the PA ID field, as shown in figure 9.30.

Open

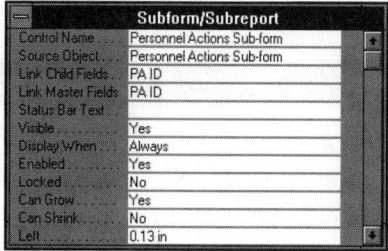

FIG. 9.30

The Properties dialog box for the Personnel Actions history subform.

Failure to edit the linkage between the main form and the subform to remove the PA Type and PA Scheduled fields may lead to an error message stating that an object in the subform cannot be linked to an object in the main form. You may find that you cannot edit the missing (Null-value) field that creates this error. In this case, you must close the form and reopen it before you can edit it.

Using Transaction Forms

When you display your form in Run mode (Form view), four new buttons for selecting records appear on the toolbar. Table 9.3 lists all the buttons that appear on the toolbar in Form Run mode, with their functions and equivalent menu choices.

Table 9.3. Standard Toolbar Buttons in Form Run Mode

Button	Function	Menu Choice
	Selects Form Design mode.	View Form **Design**
	Displays the form in Run mode.	View **Form**
	Displays the table or query that is the source of data for the main form.	View Data**s**heet
	Selects Print Preview to display how your form will appear if printed. You can print the form from the Print Preview window.	**F**ile Print Preview

continues

Table 9.3. Continued		
Button	**Function**	**Menu Choice**
	Finds (searches for) a value in the selected field or all fields. Displays the Find dialog box.	Edit Find
	Create or edit filter/sort criteria to display only selected records in an order other than that in which they appear in the data source.	Records Edit Filter/Sort
	Applies the current filter/sort criteria to the records of the source of the data for the main form.	Records Apply Filter/Sort
	Removes the filter/sort criteria and displays all records.	Records Show All Records
	Returns the form to its state before the last modification.	Edit Undo
	Displays the Help menu for forms.	F1 key

 The Find button serves the same purpose in Form Run mode as it does for tables and queries. You enter characters in the Find dialog box, using wild cards if needed, and the first record that matches your entry displays.

 The Create/Edit Filter Sort button displays a query form (a subquery) in which you can select a field(s) on which to sort or enter record-selection criteria. You make the entries in the same manner as for conventional queries. Sorting specified in the subquery overrides the sort criteria of the primary query used as the source of the data. The filter or sort criteria you have specified doesn't take effect until you click the Apply Filter/Sort button or make the equivalent menu choice.

Using the Personnel Actions Form

Forms you create with the FormWizard use the standard record-selection buttons located at the bottom of the form. The record-selection buttons perform the same functions with forms as with tables and queries. You can select the first or last records in the table or query that is the source of data for your main form, or you can select the next or preceding record. Subforms employing Datasheet view always include their own set of record-selection buttons that operate independently of the set for the main form.

Navigation between the text boxes used for entering or editing data in the form is similar to that for queries and tables in Datasheet view, except that the up-arrow and down-arrow keys cause the caret (insertion point) to move between fields, rather than between records. You accept the values you enter by pressing Enter or the Tab key.

To edit or append new records to a table in Form view, the Allow Editing property must be set to Yes, the default. You can toggle this property by choosing Editing Allowed from the **R**ecords menu. A check mark next to Editing Allowed indicates that you can edit the records in the table. Make sure that the check mark is present before attempting to append new records or edit existing ones.

Appending New Records to the Personnel Actions Table

In Datasheet view of a table or query, the last record in the datasheet is provided as a *tentative append* record (indicated by an asterisk on the record-selection button). If you enter data in this record, the data automatically is appended to the table, and Access adds a new tentative append record. Because a form doesn't provide a tentative append record automatically, you must create one by using the record-selection buttons.

To append a new record to the Personnel Actions table and enter the required data, follow these steps:

1. Open the Personnel Actions form if it is not already open, and click the Form Run Mode button if you are in Design mode. Data for the first record of the query appears in the text-box controls of your form.

2. Click the Last Record button to select the last record in the Personnel Actions query.

3. Click the Next Record button to advance the record pointer beyond the end of the query. This action creates a tentative append record and places the record pointer on this new record.

4. All the text-box controls of your form become empty, except for the Type and Scheduled fields, which have default values supplied by the properties that are assigned to these fields. When you add new data, your form appears as shown in figure 9.31. The subform datasheet is empty because you haven't entered the employee ID number that is required to link the subform data.

FIG. 9.31

The blank Personnel Actions form when appending a new record.

5. Access places the caret in the first text box of the form, the ID text box. Enter a valid Employee ID number (1 to 9, because Northwind has only 9 employees) in the ID field. This example uses B. L. Buchanan, whose employee ID is 5. Use the Tab or Enter key to accept the ID number and move the caret to the next data-entry text box, Type.

   The pencil symbol, which indicates that you are editing a record, replaces the triangle at the top left of the Detail section of the form. The Description property you entered for the field in the table underlying the query appears in the status bar and changes as you move the caret to the next field. (To change a previous entry, use Shift+Tab or the up-arrow and down-arrow keys to maneuver to the text box whose value you want to change.)

6. Because data from the Employees table is included in the query, the name and title of the employee appear in the text boxes below the ID text box after you enter the ID number. You cannot edit Last Name, First Name, or Title data, because these fields are incorporated in the one table (Employees) of a many-to-one relationship. The editing capability of a form is the same as that for the underlying table or query that serves as its source of data.

If you added an entry for the chosen employee ID when you created the Personnel Actions table in Chapter 4, the entry appears in the subform datasheet because you now have created the required link to the Personnel Actions table.

7. Mr. Buchanan was hired on September 15, 1989, and you want to bring his personnel records up-to-date by adding data from previous quarterly and yearly performance reviews. You can accept the default *Q* for quarterly reviews, or override the default by typing **Y** for yearly reviews in the Type text box. Press Tab or Enter to move to the Initiated By field.

8. Mr. Buchanan reports to the Vice President of Sales, Andrew Fuller, whose employee ID is 2. Enter **2** in the Initiated By text box, and press Enter.

9. Your first entry should be dated about three months after Mr. Buchanan was hired, so a date near 1/15/90 is appropriate for the Scheduled text box. Today's date is the default for the scheduled date. Edit the date, or press F2 to select the default date and replace the default value with a new date.

10. Because Mr. Fuller is a Vice President, he has the authority to approve salary increases. Enter Mr. Fuller's employee ID, **2**, in the Approved By text box.

11. The effective date for salary adjustments for Northwind Traders is the first or fifteenth of the month in which the performance review is scheduled. Enter the appropriate date in the Effective text box.

12. You can enter any number from 0 (terminated) to 9 (excellent) in the Rating text box that reflects the employee's performance.

13. You can be as generous as you want with the salary increases that you enter in the New Amount text box. The value of the New Amount is a new monthly salary (or a new commission percentage), not an incremental value.

14. Add any comments you care to make concerning how generous or stingy you were with the salary increases in the Comments multiline text box below the Title text box. Multiline text boxes include a scroll bar that appears when the caret is within them.

15. When you complete your entries, Access stores them in a memory buffer but does not add the new record to the Personnel Actions table. You can add the record to the table by choosing Save Record from the File menu or by changing the position of the record pointer with the Prior or Next button. If you want to cancel the addition of a record, press the Esc key. In this case, click the Next button to append another record.

16. Repeat steps 7 through 14 to add a few additional records. If you click the Next button and don't make any entries, you can click the Prior button and no record is added to the table.

After you have added several records, your form appears like the one in figure 9.32. Each record for an employee appears in the subform datasheet in the order in which you entered it.

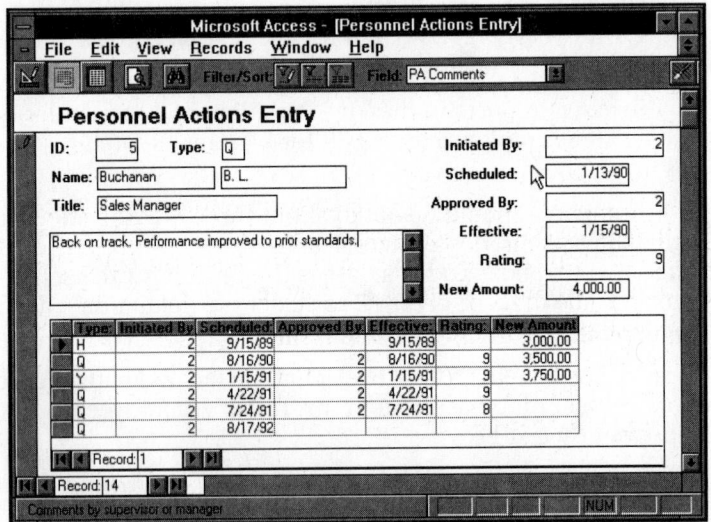

FIG. 9.32

The form after appending several Personnel Actions records for a single employee.

If you don't enter an ID number (or delete the ID number value), but other values have been entered, the new record has no link to the Employees table that is a member of the Personnel Actions query. In this case, you receive the message box shown in figure 9.33. If you receive this message, add the appropriate ID number.

FIG. 9.33

The message box that indicates a value is missing in the PA ID field.

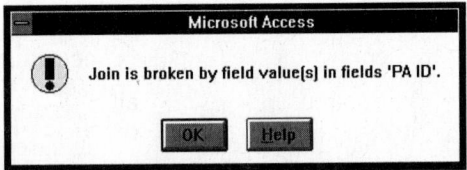

The key fields of the Personnel Actions table are PA ID, PA Type, and PA Scheduled Date, and duplicate values of the combination of the three fields aren't allowed. If you try to enter a duplicate of another record, the message box shown in figure 9.34 appears. In this case, change the Type or Scheduled Date entries so that they do not duplicate another record.

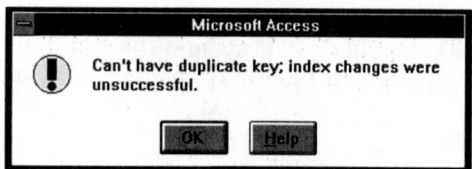

FIG. 9.34

The message box that results from a duplicated entry.

Editing Existing Data

You can edit existing records in the same way you add new records. Use the Next button to find the record you want to edit and then make your changes. You can use the toolbar's Find button to locate records by employee number or by one of the dates in the record. If you prefer that the records be ordered by Effective date to find records for which an effective date hasn't been entered, use the Create/Edit Filter Sort button and specify an Ascending Sort to the Effective field. Click the Apply Filter Sort button to apply the sort to the records.

You cannot edit the First Name, Last Name, or Title, as mentioned earlier in this section, because of their one-to-many relationship. If you attempt to edit these fields, a `Control Bound to Read-Only Column` message appears in the status bar.

Committing and Rolling Back Changes to Tables

As with tentative append records, Access does not apply record edits to the underlying table until you move the record pointer with the record-selection buttons or choose Save Record from the File menu. Either action is the equivalent of the Commit instruction in transaction-processing terminology.

Rollback reverses a Commit instruction. You can accomplish the equivalent of rolling back a single Commit transaction by clicking the Undo button on the toolbar immediately after you save the record to the table or by choosing Undo Saved Record from the Edit menu if Undo Saved Record is offered as a choice.

Deleting a Record in Form View

In Datasheet view, no direct method exists (such as a "delete record" button) for deleting a record from the Personnel Actions table. To delete the current record underlying the form, choose Select Record from the **Edit** menu. The vertical bar to the left of the Detail section of the form becomes a darker shade of gray, and the triangle used to identify a selected record appears at the top of the dark gray bar. Press the Delete key, and the message box shown in figure 9.35 appears. Choose OK to delete the record.

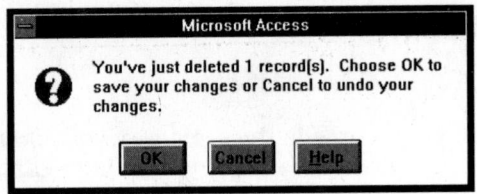

Modifying the Properties of a Form or Control After Testing

The entries you added and edited gave you an opportunity to test your form. Testing a form to ensure that it accomplishes the objectives you establish usually takes much longer than creating the form and the query that underlies it. During the testing process, you may notice that the order of the fields isn't what you want or that records in the subform aren't displayed in an appropriate sequence. The following two sections deal with modifying the properties of the form and the subform control.

Changing the Order of Fields for Data Entry

The order in which the editing caret moves from one field to the next is determined by the Tab Order property of each control. The FormWizard established the tab order of the controls when you created the original version of the form. The default Tab Order property of each field is assigned, beginning with the value 0, in the sequence in which you add the fields. Because the FormWizard created a single-column form, the order of the controls in Personnel Actions is top to bottom. The order originally assigned doesn't change when you relocate a control.

To change the sequence of entries—to match the pattern of entries on a paper form, for example—follow these steps:

1. Click the Form Design Mode button on the toolbar.

2. Choose Ta**b** Order from the **E**dit menu to display the Tab Order dialog box shown in figure 9.36. The order of entry is shown by the sequence of field names in the Custom Order list box. (In this example, changing the sequence of the entries is unnecessary because the sequence is logical, even after moving the controls to their present location on the Personnel Actions form.)

FIG. 9.36

The Tab Order dialog box used to change the sequence of data-entry fields.

3. Click the Auto Order button to reorder the entry sequence to left to right by rows, then top to bottom.

4. Drag a control by clicking the button to the left of its name and dropping it at the new location that represents the desired sequence.

5. Choose OK if you decide the changes you made should be implemented; click Cancel to retain the original entry sequence.

The Tab Order dialog box is a major improvement over the technique used by Visual Basic 1.0 in which you must select each control and manually edit the value of its Tab Order property.

Changing the Source of Data for the Subform and Sorting the Subform Data

The Personnel Actions table is indexed by PA Type and PA Scheduled Date, but the sequence of the records appears in the order of the primary key—PA ID, PA Type, and PA Scheduled date. Because only PA ID is used to link the records, records for a particular employee appear in the order in which you entered them. Eventually, the number of records for an employee can become quite large, so having the records appear in date order is convenient. Because only a few records can be displayed in the subform datasheet, the latest entries should appear by default. This result requires a reverse (descending) sort on the Personnel Actions table. You can establish a descending sort only by substituting a sorted query containing all the records of the Personnel Actions table, as described in the following two procedures.

To create a new sorted query, follow these steps:

1. Close the Personnel Actions form.

2. Click the Query button in the Database window and then click the New button to create a new query.

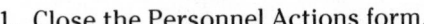

3. Select Personnel Actions as the table on which to base the query, click Add, and then click Close.

4. Drag the * field to the Query grid and drop it in the first column.

5. Drag the PA Scheduled Date field to the Query grid and drop it in the second column.

6. Click the Show box in the new PA Schedule Date column to remove the diagonal cross so that you don't duplicate a field name in the query.

7. Click the Query Run Mode button to check that the records are sorted in reverse date order.

8. Close your query and name it **Personnel Actions Subquery**.

To change the data source for the subform to the new sorted query, complete the following steps:

1. Click the Form button in the Database window and open the Personnel Actions subform.

2. Click the Form Design Mode button.

3. Click the Properties button to display the Properties dialog box.

4. Click the Record Source box, open the list box, and select Personnel Actions Sub-query as the new data source for the subform, as shown in figure 9.37.

5. Close the Properties box and click the Form Run Mode button on the toolbar to verify that the datasheet display is correct.

6. Close the Personnel Actions Subform.

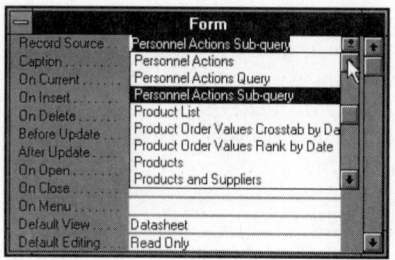

FIG. 9.37

The Form Properties dialog box entry to change the Record Source property.

7. Reopen the Personnel Actions form. If you didn't use B. L. Buchanan, the first Northwind employee in alphabetical order, enter the number of the employee for whom you added additional records. The history now appears sorted in reverse date sequence.

Open

If an error message appears in the Scheduled column of the subform datasheet, you didn't click the Show box in step 6 of the preceding series of steps. When a field is duplicated in a query, Access doesn't know which of the two fields to use if the Show property of both fields is Yes.

8. To verify that the sort is active when you add new entries, add a new record with today's date and then click the Prior button to save the new entry. Click Next to display the new entry and verify that the sorting operation is functional.

You can use the same method described in the preceding steps to change the data source of a main form.

Choosing Save Record from the File menu doesn't update the subform, and the new entry isn't displayed. You must choose Refresh from the Records menu to update the subform's display. The Refresh command doesn't requery the database, but it does cause any updates that may have occurred before the last automatic refreshing operation to appear. The best approach, therefore, is to use the record position buttons to commit the new or edited record. The Refresh command is discussed in Chapter 21, "Using Access in a Network Environment."

Chapter Summary

This chapter demonstrated the capabilities of relatively simple Access forms, created by the FormWizard, to add and edit data. You learned to relocate, resize, and edit control objects that the FormWizard added to the form for you. The chapter also explained the basic steps involved in using a form to add, edit, and delete records. After testing your form, you made changes to the form's design to make it more effective. Database application developers use this process to create the forms that ultimately comprise a full-scale database application.

When you specify a Single-column or Main/Subform type, the FormWizard uses only text-box control with associated labels to create the basic form. The Access toolbox provides many other types of controls you can add to a basic or a blank form that you create without the FormWizard's help.

In the next chapter, you use the toolbox to add new controls that make using your form easier. A form that is easier to use increases the productivity of data-entry operators and occasional users. The next chapter also describes the other capabilities of forms, such as establishing a set of validation rules that apply only to the form, rather than to the tables themselves, and displaying calculated values.

Designing Custom Forms

The controls that the FormWizard adds to the forms it creates are only a sampling of the 16 control functions offered by Access. Until now, you used labels, text boxes, and subform controls to display and edit data in the Personnel Actions table. These three kinds of controls are sufficient to create a conventional transaction form; you can duplicate a dBASE or Paradox 3+ DOS data entry screen by using only Access labels and text boxes.

The remaining 13 controls described in this chapter enable you to take full advantage of the Windows graphical user environment. List boxes and combo boxes increase data entry productivity by enabling you to choose from a list of predefined values rather than requiring that you type the value. Option buttons, toggle buttons, and check boxes supply values to Yes/No fields. If you place option buttons, toggle buttons, and check boxes in an option frame, these controls can supply the numeric values you specify. Page breaks control how forms print. Command buttons enable you to execute Access macros or Access Basic procedures. You add controls to the form by using the Access toolbox.

Understanding the Access Toolbox

The Access toolbox is based on the toolbox created for Microsoft Visual Basic. Several Access buttons are the same as the buttons employed by Visual Basic 1.0, and the method of adding controls to the form also is similar, but not identical, to the method used in Visual Basic 1.0. You choose one of the 16 tools to add a control, represented by the tool's symbol, to the form. When you create a report, the toolbox serves the same purpose—although the tools that require user input, such as a combo box, are seldom used in reports.

Control Categories

Three control object categories exist in Access forms and reports:

- *Bound controls* are associated with a field in the data source for the form or subform. The data source can be a table or a query. Bound controls display and update values of the cell in the associated field of the currently selected record. Text boxes are the most common bound control. You can display the content of graphic objects or play a waveform audio file with a bound OLE object. You can bind toggles, check boxes, and option buttons to Yes/No fields. All bound controls have associated labels that display the caption property of the field; you can edit or delete these labels without affecting the bound control.

- *Unbound controls* display data you provide that is independent of the data source of the form or subform. The label used as the title for the Personnel Actions form is an example of an unbound control. You use the unbound OLE object to add a drawing or bit-mapped image to a form. You can use Lines and rectangles to divide a form into logical groups or to simulate the boxes used on the paper form. Unbound text boxes are used to enter data not intended to update a field in the data source but are used for other purposes, such as establishing a value used in an expression. Some unbound controls, such as unbound text boxes, include labels and others, such as unbound OLE objects, don't include labels.

- *Calculated controls* use expressions as their source of data. Usually, the expression includes the value of a field, but you also can use values created by unbound text in calculated control expressions.

The Toolbox

You use the Access toolbox to add control objects to forms and reports. The toolbox appears only in Design mode for forms and reports and appears only if you toggle **Toolbox** from the **View** menu. When the toolbox is visible, the **Toolbox** menu choice is checked. You can choose from the 16 controls whose names and functions are listed in table 10.1.

Table 10.1. Control Objects of the Access Toolbox		
Tool	**Name**	**Function**
▶	Pointer	Deselects a previously selected tool and returns the mouse pointer to normal function. Pointer is the default tool when you display the toolbox.
A	Label	Creates a frame in which you can enter descriptive or instructional text.
ab|	Text Box	Creates a frame to display and edit data. The data may be text or a graphic object.
⌐xyz⌐	Option Group	Creates a frame of adjustable size in which you can place toggle buttons, option buttons, or check boxes. Only one of the objects within an object group frame may be selected. When you select an object within an option group, the previously selected object is deselected.
☰	Toggle Button	Creates a button that changes from on to off when clicked with the mouse. The On state corresponds to Yes (-1) and the Off state to No (0). When used within an option group, toggling one button on toggles a previously selected button off. You can use toggle buttons to select a value from a set of values.

continues

Table 10.1. Continued

Tool	Name	Function
⊙	Option Button	Creates a round button (originally called a *radio button*) that behaves identically to a toggle button. Option buttons are most commonly used within option groups to select between values in a set.
⊠	Check Box	Creates a check box that toggles on and off. The behavior of check boxes is identical to toggle and option buttons. Multiple check boxes are most often used outside of option groups so that you can select more than one check box at a time.
▤	Combo Box	Creates a drop-down combo box with a list from which you can select an item or enter a value in a text box.
▤	List Box	Creates a drop-down list box from which you may make a choice. A list box is a combo box without the editable text box.
▥	Graph	Launches the GraphWizard to create a graph object based on a query or table.
▦	Subform	Adds a subform or subreport to a main form or report. The subform or subreport you intend to add must exist before you use this control.
▦	Unbound Object	Adds an OLE object, created by an OLE server application, such as Microsoft Graph or Microsoft Draw, to a form or report.
▦	Bound Object	Displays the content of an OLE field of a record if the field contains a graphic object. If the field contains no graphic object, the

Tool	Name	Function
		icon that represents the object appears, such as the Sound Recorder's icon for a linked or embedded .WAV file type.
	Line	Creates a straight line that you can size and relocate. The color and width of the line can be changed by using the Palette.
	Rectangle	Creates a rectangle that you can size and relocate. The border color and width and the fill color of the rectangle are determined by selections from the palette.
	Page Break	Causes the printer to start a new page at the location of the page break on the form or report. Page breaks don't appear in Form or Report Run mode.
	Command Button	Creates a command button that, when clicked, executes an Access macro.
Lock	Tool Lock	Maintains the currently selected tool as the active tool until you select another tool, click Lock again, or click the pointer. Without the lock, Access reselects the pointer after you use a tool.

Using controls in the design of reports is discussed in the following chapter, which is entirely devoted to the subject of Access reports. The use of bound objects is described in Chapter 13, "Using the OLE Field Data Type for Graphics." Applications for unbound objects, lines, and rectangles are shown in Chapter 14, "Adding Graphics and Color to Forms and Reports." Using command buttons to execute macros is covered in Part IV of this book, which deals with Access macros. Writing Access Basic code for command buttons is included in Part VI. You learn how to use the remaining 13 controls on your forms in the following sections.

The Appearance of Controls in Design and Run Modes

The appearance in Form Design mode of the 16 different controls you can create with the toolbox, before you assign values to create their content, is shown in figure 10.1. Labels were added to the graph, unbound object, bound object, line, and rectangle controls to identify them in the illustration; the labels aren't actually components of the controls.

FIG. 10.1

The 16 controls of the toolbox in Design mode.

When you choose Run mode with the form of figure 10.1, the controls appear as shown in figure 10.2. The text box displays a #Name? error message because no value is assigned to the content of the text box. The list and combo boxes are empty, as are the unbound and bound objects, because no values for their content is assigned to them. A value, Personnel Actions Subform, is assigned to the subform control, because a subform control isn't created unless you enter the name of an existing form as the value.

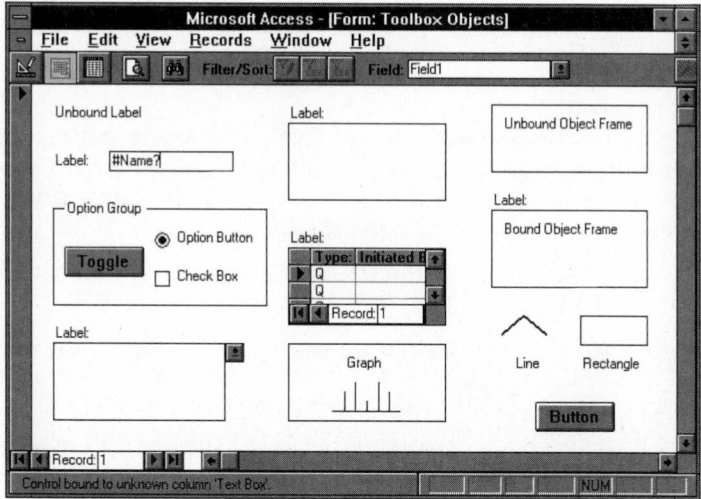

FIG. 10.2

The toolbox controls without assigned values, displayed in Form Run mode.

Using the Toolbox To Add Controls

Experimenting is the best way of learning how to use a new computer application. No matter how well the product's documentation or a book, such as this one, describes a process, no substitute exists for trying the methods. This axiom holds true whether you are designing a form or writing programming code. The Microsoft programmers who created Access cleverly designed the user interface for creating custom forms so that the interface is intuitive and flexible. When you complete the examples in this chapter, you probably will agree with this statement.

The examples in this chapter use the Personnel Actions table that you created in Chapter 4 and the Personnel Actions query and subquery that formed the basis of the Personnel Actions form and subform of Chapter 9. The data dictionary needed to create the Personnel Actions table appears in Appendix E.

For Related Information:

◄◄ "Creating the Personnel Actions Table," p. 151.

◄◄ "Creating the Query on which To Base the Form," p. 378.

FROM HERE...

Creating a Blank Form with a Header and Footer

When you create a form without using the FormWizard, Access provides a default blank form to which you add controls that you choose from the toolbox. To create a blank form with which to experiment with Access controls, perform the following steps:

1. Click the Form button in the Database window, and then click New.

2. Even an experimental form requires a data source, so choose Personnel Actions Query from the drop-down list, and then click Blank Form.

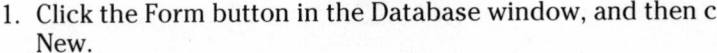

3. Access creates a new blank form with the default title Form1. Click the Maximize button to expand the form to fill the document window.

4. If the toolbox isn't visible, choose Toolbox from the View menu to display the toolbox. Move the toolbar to the right of the window by clicking and dragging the toolbar's top bar. In this position, the toolbox stays accessible but is no longer in the way while you build the new form.

5. From the Layout menu, choose Form Hdr/Ftr. The blank form appears as shown in figure 10.3. If the grid doesn't appear on the form, choose Grid from the View menu.

FIG. 10.3

Access's default blank form.

6. To adjust the depth of the Detail section of the form, place the mouse pointer on the top line of the Form Footer bar. The mouse pointer becomes a double-headed arrow with a line between the heads. Hold down the left mouse button and drag the bar to about one-half inch from the bottom of the window. The active surface of the form, which is white with the default 0.1-inch grid dots, expands vertically as you move the Form Footer bar, as shown in figure 10.4.

FIG. 10.4

Expanding the Detail section of the blank form.

You use the blank form to create a form similar to the Personnel Actions form that you created in Chapter 9.

Adding a Label to the Form Header

The label is the simplest control in the toolbox to use. Labels are un-bound and static, and they display only text you enter. *Static* means that the label retains the value you assigned for as long as the form is displayed. To add a label to the Form Header section, complete the following steps:

1. Click the Label button in the toolbox. When you move the mouse pointer to the active area of the form, the pointer becomes the symbol for the Label button, combined with a position indication cross-hair at its upper left. The center point of the cross-hair defines the position of the upper left corner of the control.

2. Locate the cross-hair pointer at the upper left of the Form Header section, and then press and hold down the left mouse button. Drag the cross-hair pointer to the position for the lower-right corner of the label, as shown in figure 10.5.

FIG. 10.5

Adding a label control to the Form Header section.

As you drag the cross-hair pointer, the outline of the container for the label follows your movement. The number of lines and characters that the text box can display in the currently selected font is shown in the status bar.

3. If you move the cross-hair pointer beyond the bottom of the Form Header section, the Form Header bar expands to accommodate the size of the label. When the label is the size you want, release the mouse button.

4. The mouse pointer becomes the text editing caret inside the outline of the label. Enter **Personnel Actions Entry** as the text for the label. If you don't type at least one text character in the label after creating the label, the box disappears the next time you click the mouse.

You use the basic process described in the preceding steps to add any of the other types of controls to a form. After you add the control, you use the anchor and sizing handles described in Chapter 9 to move the control to the desired position and to size the control to accommodate the content. The location of the anchor handle determines the Left (horizontal) and Top (vertical) properties of the control. The sizing handles establish the control's Width and Height properties.

Formatting Text and Adjusting Text Control Sizes

When a control is selected that accepts text as the value, the typeface and font size combo boxes appear on the toolbar. To format the text that appears in a label or text box, complete the following steps:

1. Click the Personnel Actions Entry label you created in the previous section to select the label.

2. Double-click the label or click the Properties button on the toolbar to display the Properties window.

3. Open the Typeface list box on the toolbar and select Times New Roman or a similar font if you aren't using Windows 3.1.

4. Open the Font Size list box and select 14 points.

5. Click the Bold attribute button on the toolbar. The label now appears as shown in figure 10.6.

FIG. 10.6

The form title label and its Properties window.

6. The size of the label you created isn't large enough to display the larger font. To adjust the size of the label to accommodate the content of the label, choose Size to Fit from the **L**ayout menu. If one or more control is selected, one of the two sizing commands (Size to **G**rid or Size to Fit) of the **L**ayout menu is applied to the selected control(s). If no controls are selected, the chosen sizing

command applies as the default to all objects you subsequently create, move, or resize.

When you change the properties of a control, the new values are reflected in the Properties window for the control, as shown in figure 10.6. If you move or resize the label, you see the label's Left, Top, Width, and Height values change in the properties box. You usually use the Properties window to change the characteristics of a control for which a toolbar button or a menu choice isn't available.

You can choose different fonts and the Bold, Italic, and Underline attributes (or a combination) for any label or caption for a control. You can assign the text content of list boxes and combo boxes to a typeface or size other than the default, but this practice is uncommon in Windows applications.

Creating Bound, Multiline, and Calculated Text Boxes

Access uses the following four basic kinds of text boxes:

- *Single-line* text boxes usually are bound to controls.

- *Multiline* text boxes usually are bound to Memo field types and include a vertical scroll bar to allow access to text that doesn't fit within the dimensions of the box.

- *Calculated* text boxes obtain values from expressions that begin with the = (equal) sign and usually are a single-line. If you include a field value, such as [PA Scheduled Date], in the expression for a calculated text box, the text box is bound to the PA Scheduled Date field. Otherwise, calculated text boxes are unbound. You cannot edit the value of a calculated text box.

- *Unbound* text boxes that aren't calculated text boxes can be used to supply values, such as limiting dates, to macros or Access Basic procedures. Using unbound text boxes is described in Chapter 18, "Creating Macros for Forms, Reports, and Custom Menus."

The following sections show you how to create the first three of these basic kinds of text boxes.

Adding a Text Box Bound to a Field

The most common text box used in Access forms is the single-line bound text box that comprised the majority of the controls of the

Personnel Actions form you created in Chapter 9. To add a text box that is bound to a field of the form's data source with the Field List window, complete the following steps:

1. Click the Field List button on the toolbar. The Field List window appears.

2. Click the PA ID field in the Field List window. Hold down the left mouse button and drag the field to the upper left of the Detail section of the form. When you move the mouse pointer to the active area of the form, the pointer becomes a field symbol, but no cross-hairs appear. The position of the field symbol indicates the upper-left corner of the text box, not the label, so drop the symbol in the approximate position of the text box anchor handle, as shown in figure 10.7.

FIG. 10.7

Adding a text box control, bound to the PA ID field.

3. Drag the text box by the anchor handle closer to the ID label and decrease the box's width.

4. Small type sizes are more readable when you set the Bold attribute on. Choose the ID label, then click the Bold button, and do the same for the PA ID text box.

B

Steps 3 and 4 in the preceding example are included to show how to make minor design adjustments to controls that improve the appearance of forms.

Adding a Multiline Text Box with Scroll Bars

Although you can use a conventional text box to display comments or other text fields with lengthy content, you must scroll the caret through the text box to read the content. Multiline text boxes enable you to display long strings of text as a series of lines whose width is determined by the width of the multiline text box. To create a multiline text box, perform the following steps:

1. Choose PA Comments from the Field List window. Drag the Field List pointer to about the middle of the Detail section and drop the pointer.

2. Relocate the Comments label and size the text box as shown in figure 10.8.

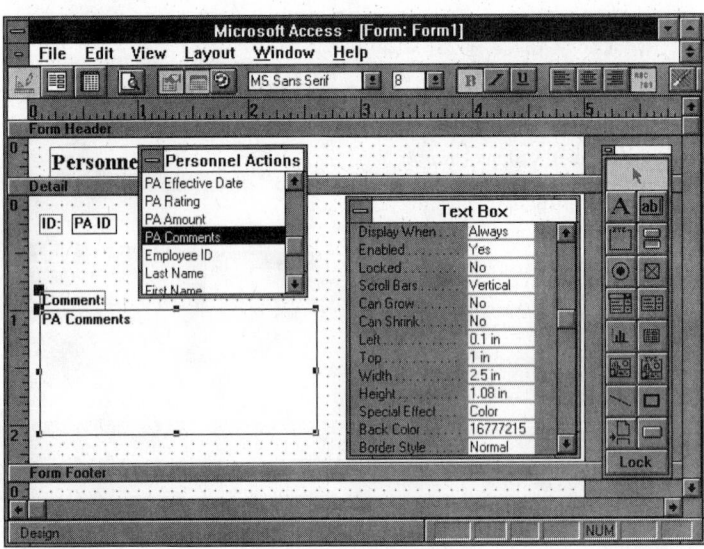

FIG. 10.8

Adding the multiline Comments text box.

3. Scroll the Properties list for the text box until the Scroll Bars property appears.

4. Open the Scroll Bars list box and choose Vertical to add a vertical scroll bar to the Comments text box.

5. If you plan to print the form, change the Can Grow and Can Shrink properties from No to Yes, for the height of the printed version of the form to vary with the number of lines of text in the box. The Can Grow and Can Shrink properties don't affect the appearance of the form in Run mode.

The vertical scroll bar of a multiline text box is visible only in form Run mode, and then only when the multiline text box has the focus (when the caret is within the text box).

Creating a Calculated Text Box

You can display the result of all valid Access expressions in a calculated text box. An expression must begin with an = (equal) sign and may use Access functions to return values. As mentioned in the introduction to this section, you can use calculated text boxes to display calculations based on the values of fields. To create a calculated text box that displays the current date and time, complete the following steps:

1. Click the Text Box symbol in the toolbox to add an unbound text box at the upper right of the Detail section of the form.

2. Edit the label of the new text box to read Date/Time: and relocate the label so that it is adjacent to the text box.

3. Enter **=Now( )** in the text box to display the current date and time from your computer's clock.

4. Adjust the length of the text box to accommodate the number of characters in the default DD/MM/YY HH:MM:SS PM format used for dates and times. The entry appears as shown in the Date/Time text box of figure 10.9. You add the other two text boxes in the following section.

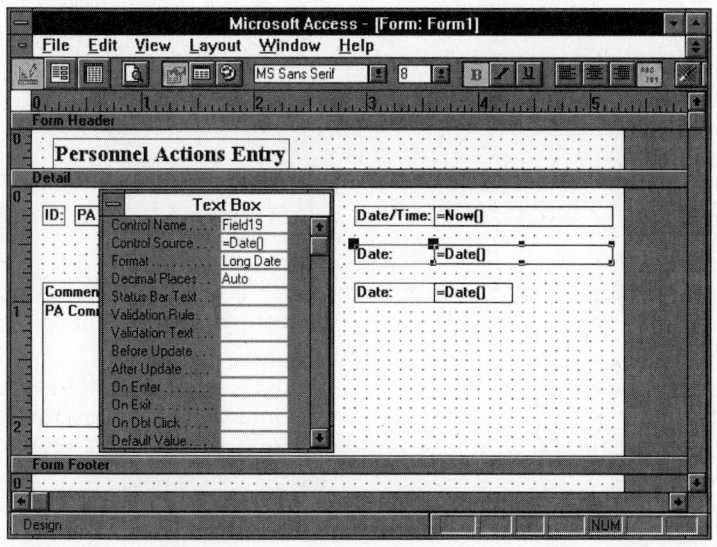

FIG. 10.9

Creating a calculated text box to display the date and time.

Formatting Values

You can use the Format property you learned about in Chapter 4 to determine how dates, times, and numbers are displayed in a text box. To format a date entry, perform the following steps:

1. Using the Text Box tool, add a second unbound text box under the first, and adjust the new box's dimensions to correspond to the other text box.

2. Edit the label to read Date: and enter **=Date()** in the text box.

3. Choose the text box and double-click it, or click the Properties button if the Properties dialog box isn't visible.

4. Click the Format property and open the list box. Choose Long Date from the list.

A Format property applied to a bound text box overrides the format assigned to the field in the table design that supplies the value to the text box.

When you display a form in Run mode, the value displayed in the Date/Time text box is the time that you open the form. To update the time, choose **R**efresh from the **R**ecords menu. The refreshing process that occurs at an interval determined by the Refresh Interval property of the Multiuser Options (the default value is 15 seconds) doesn't update unbound text boxes.

FROM HERE...

For Related Information:

◀◀ "Selecting a Display Format," p. 139.

Using the Clipboard with Controls

You can use the Windows Clipboard to easily make copies of controls and their properties. As an example, create a copy of one of the Date/Time controls by using the Clipboard, by performing the following steps:

1. Select the label and the text box by holding down the Shift key and clicking the label associated with the second date text box you added in the preceding section.

2. Press Ctrl+C, or choose **C**opy from the **E**dit menu to copy the control to the Clipboard.

3. Press Ctrl+V, or choose **P**aste from the **E**dit menu to paste the copy of the control below the original version.

4. Click the Format property in the Properties window for the copied control, and choose Short Date from the drop-down list.

5. To display the controls you created, click the Run Mode button on the toolbar. The form appears as shown in figure 10.10.

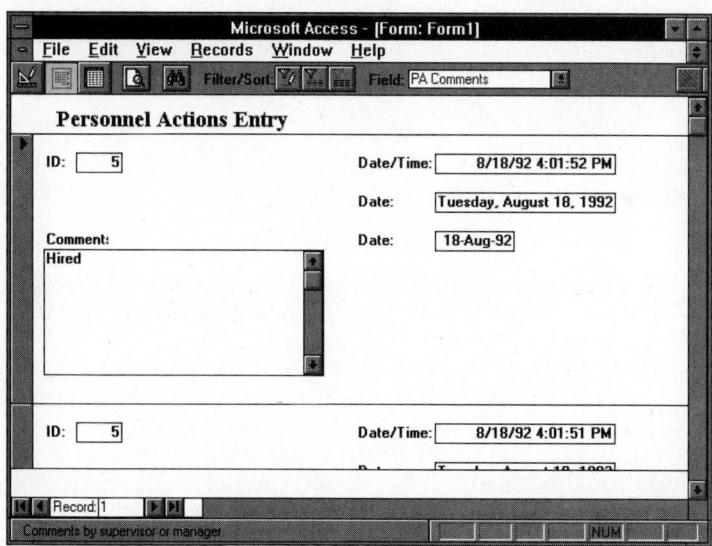

FIG. 10.10

The form title and text boxes displayed in Form Run mode.

6. Delete the two Date text boxes and labels by enclosing both with a selection boundary, created by dragging the mouse pointer from the upper left to the lower right of the text boxes and then pressing the Delete key.

Text boxes (and the associated labels) are the most commonly used control objects on Access forms.

Changing the Default View and Obtaining Help for Properties

A form that fills Access's Design window may not necessarily fill the window in Form Run mode. Run mode may allow the beginning of a second copy of the form to appear, as shown at the bottom of figure 10.10. The second copy is created because the Default View property has a default value of Continuous Forms. Forms have the following three Default View properties (in the Forms Properties window) from which you can choose:

- *Single Form* displays one record at a time in one form.

- *Continuous Forms* displays multiple records, each record having a copy of the Detail section of the form. You can use the vertical scroll bar or the record selection buttons to select the record to display. Continuous view is the default value.

- *Datasheet* displays the form fields arranged like a spreadsheet (in rows and columns).

To change the Default View property of the form to Single Form, complete the following steps:

1. Click the Design Mode button on the toolbar.

2. Choose Select Form from the Edit menu.

3. Click the Properties button on the toolbar if the Properties dialog box isn't visible. The Properties dialog box appears.

4. Click the Default View property to open the list box.

5. Choose Single Form from the list.

6. While the Default View property is selected, press F1. The help window for the Default View property appears. This help window also explains how the Default View and Allow View properties relate to one another.

You can verify that the Default View property has changed to Single Form by clicking the Run Mode button to review the form's appearance. Only a single copy of the form appears, as shown in figure 10.11.

Adding Option Groups, Binding Controls, and Using the Lock Tool

Option buttons, toggle buttons, and check boxes can return only Yes/No (-1/0) values when used by themselves on a form. Here, their use as bound controls is limited to providing values to Yes/No fields in a table. When you place any of these controls within an option group, the buttons or check boxes can return a number you specify for the Option Value of the control.

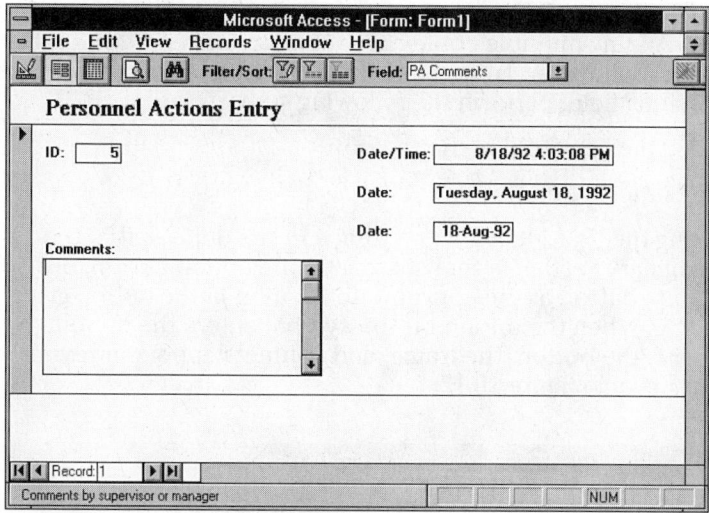

FIG. 10.11

The appearance of the Personnel Actions Entry form, with the Default View property set to Single Form.

The capability of assigning numbers to the Option Value enables you to use one of these three controls inside an option group frame to assign values to the PA Ratings field of the Personnel Actions table. Option buttons are most commonly employed in Windows applications to select one value from a limited number of values.

By default, all the tools you add with the toolbox are unbound controls. You can bind a control to a field by choosing the control you want to use and then clicking the field name in the Field List window to which you want the control bound. To bind an option group frame to the PA Rating field of the Personnel Actions query, complete the following steps:

1. Click the Option Frame tool in the toolbox.

2. Click the Field List button on the toolbar to display the Field List window.

3. Choose the PA Rating field from the list.

4. Hold down the left button of the mouse and drag the Field pointer to a position under the Date/Time text box.

5. Resize the option group frame so that it can accommodate several option buttons and their associated labels.

Option buttons, toggle buttons, and check boxes within bound frames inherit many of their properties, such as Control Source, from the frame. The option frame provides the binding of these tools when they are inside a frame. Therefore, you don't use the Field List with these controls. Adding multiple copies of controls is easier if you set the Lock tool in the toolbox on. To add five option buttons to assign values to the PA Rating field, perform the following steps:

1. Click the Lock tool in the toolbox.

2. Click the Option Button tool.

3. Using the cross-hair as a reference to the upper-left corner of an imaginary rectangle that surrounds the option button, drop the option button at the appropriate location in the option group frame. When the option button symbol enters the option group frame, the button, the frame, and contents appear in reverse video as shown in figure 10.12.

FIG. 10.12

Adding an option button to an option frame.

4. Repeat step 3 four more times to include a total of five Rating option buttons inside the Rating option group frame. The labels of the buttons are assigned numbers in the sequence of addition.

   If you need to increase the size of the option group frame, drag the corner handle.

5. Click the Lock button in the toolbox again to unlock the Option Button tool and click the Pointer.

6. Edit the labels to read, from top to bottom: Excellent, Good, Acceptable, Fair, and Poor, corresponding to values of 9, 7, 5, 3, and 1, respectively.

7. Double-click the option button at the top and replace 1 with 9 as the Option Value in the Properties list. Default Option Values are assigned in sequence from 1 to the number of buttons in the frame.

8. Repeat step 7 for the four remaining buttons, replacing the default values 2, 3, 4, and 5 with 7, 5, 3, and 1, respectively.

9. Click the field list and drag the PA Rating field to create a text box under the option frame to verify the values assigned, as shown in figure 10.12.

10. To test the entries, click the Run Mode button on the toolbar. The form appears as shown in figure 10.13.

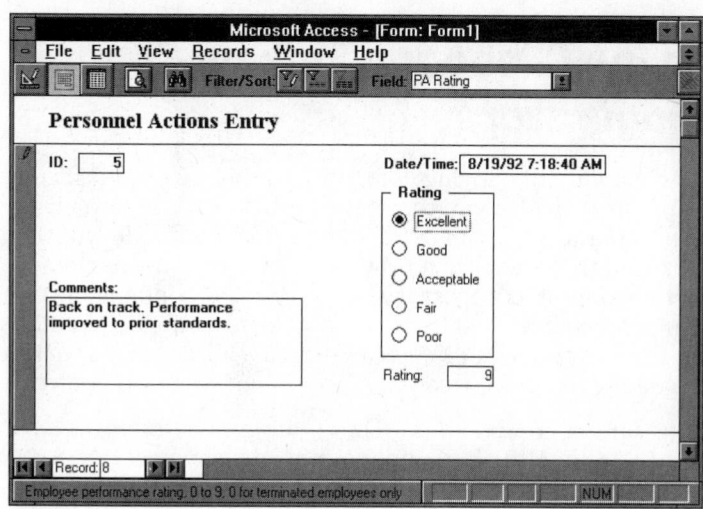

FIG. 10.13

The option group frame and option buttons, displayed in Run mode.

11. Using the record selection buttons, choose a record to edit. If you previously assigned ratings with odd-numbered values, the option button that corresponds to the value is selected.

12. Click the option buttons in sequence to verify that the proper numeric values appear in the Rating text box.

If you have a Yes/No field in the table, you can use a single option button bound to a field (not inside an option frame) to create the Yes/No values, -1/0, for the user.

If you add a button or a check box within a frame with the Field List drag-and-drop method, the button is independently bound to the selected field, rather than to the field through the option frame. In this case, the button's Properties dialog box doesn't include the Option Value property, and the button assigns Yes/No values to the field.

An independently bound button inside an option frame doesn't follow the rules of the option frame; you can choose this button and another button simultaneously.

Adding independently bound buttons within option frames results in assignment of inconsistent values to fields.

Using the Clipboard To Copy Controls to Another Form

Access's capability of copying controls and their properties to the Windows Clipboard enables you to create controls on one form and copy them to another form. If you use a standard header style, you can copy the controls in the header of a previously designed form to a new form and edit the content as necessary. The form that contains the controls to be copied need not be in the same database as the destination form in which the copy is pasted. You can create a library of standard controls in a dedicated form used only for holding standard controls.

The Rating option group and the Time/Date calculated text box are candidates to add to the Personnel Actions form you created in Chapter 9. You may want to add a Time/Date text box to the header of all your transaction forms. To add the Rating option group and Time/Date controls to the Personnel Actions form, perform the following steps:

1. Choose the Ratings option frame and all the controls within it by dragging a selection frame around it with the mouse.

2. Press Ctrl+C, or choose **C**opy from the **E**dit menu to copy the group of controls to the Clipboard.

3. Minimize the example form (Form1), and open the Personnel Actions form from the Database window.

4. Click the Design Mode button on the toolbar.

5. Make room for the Ratings option group by decreasing the width of the First Name and Comments text boxes.

6. Press Ctrl+V, or choose **P**aste from the **E**dit menu. A copy of the control appears on the form.

7. Position the mouse pointer over the copied option group so that the pointer becomes a hand symbol.

8. Click the left mouse button and drag the option group to the position shown in figure 10.14, and then release the mouse button.

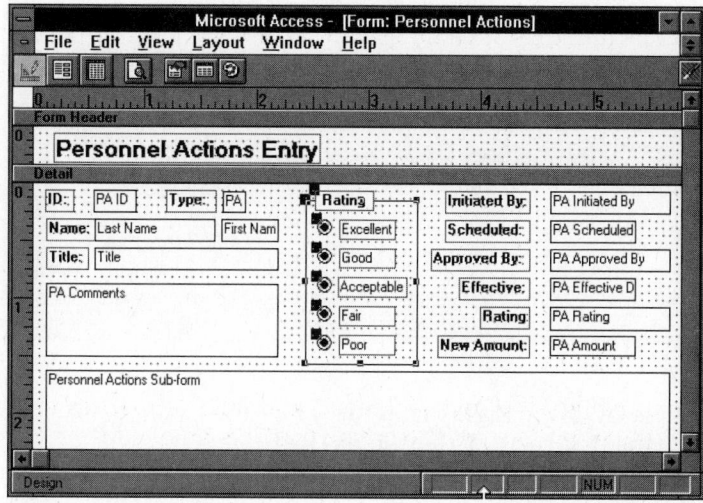

FIG. 10.14

Copying the option group to the Personnel Actions form by using the Clipboard.

9. Minimize the Personnel Actions form, and double-click the Form1 icon to restore Form1.

10. Select the label and the text box of the Date/Time calculated text box and copy the controls to the Clipboard.

11. Minimize Form1, and double-click the Personnel Actions icon to restore it.

12. Paste the Date/Time control and relocate it to the right in the Form Header section.

13. You cannot edit the value in the Date/Time calculated text box, so do not add a border. Usually, only text boxes that display data from a table or query that you can edit should have a border. Double-click the Date/Time text box to open the Properties dialog box and change the Border Style to Clear.

14. Click the Run Mode button on the toolbar. The Personnel Actions form appears as shown in figure 10.15.

15. Close the Personnel Actions form and save the changes.

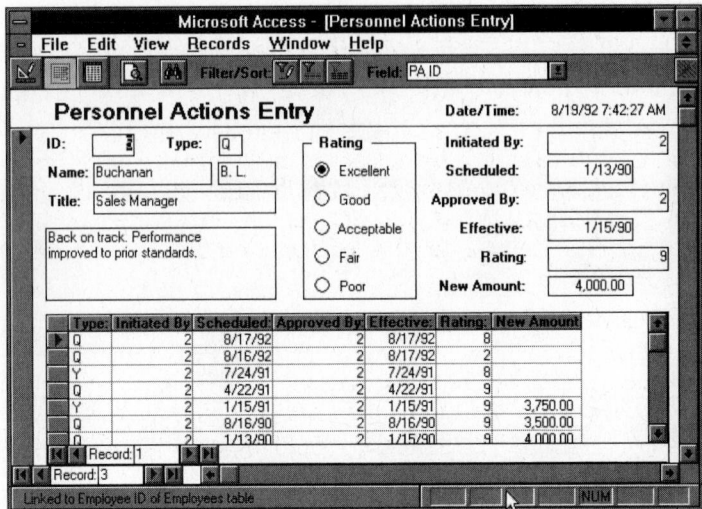

FIG. 10.15

The Rating option
group displayed
in Run mode.

16. Double-click the Form1 icon to restore the example form, and
    click the Design Mode button on the toolbar.

If you copy a control to a form that uses a data source different
from the one used to create the original control, you need to
change the Control Source property to correspond with the field
to which the control is to be bound. Changing the Control Source
property doesn't change the Status Bar Text, Validation Rule, or
Validation Text properties for the new Control Source; you must
enter the appropriate values manually.

Using List Boxes and Combo Boxes

List boxes and combo boxes both serve the same basic purpose by
enabling you to pick a value from a list, rather than type the value in a
text box. These two kinds of list boxes are especially useful when you
need to enter a code that represents the name of a person, firm, or
product. You don't need to refer to a paper list of the codes and names
to make the entry. The differences between list boxes and combo boxes
are shown in the following list:

■ *List boxes* don't need to be opened to display their content; the
portion of the list that fits within the size of the list box you assign
is visible at all times. Your choice is limited to values included in
the list.

■ *Combo boxes* consume less space than list boxes in the form, but you must open these boxes to select a value. Combo boxes in Access are drop-down list boxes with a text box, not traditional combo boxes that display the list at all times. You can allow the user to enter a value in the text box element of the combo box or limit the selection to the members in the combo box's list. If you limit the choice to members of the list, the user can type the beginning of the list value, and Access searches for a matching entry. This feature reduces the time needed to locate a choice in a long list.

List and combo boxes are two of the most powerful controls that the Microsoft programmers developed for Access. The data source for these boxes may be a table, a query, a list of values you supply, or the names of Access Basic functions. The boxes may have as many columns as you need to display the data needed to make the correct choice.

Adding a Combo Box with a Table or Query As the Data Source

In the majority of cases, you bind the list box or combo box to a field so that the choice updates the value of this field. Two-column boxes are the most commonly used. The first column contains the code that updates the value of the field to which the box is bound, and the second column contains the name associated with the code. An example of where a limit-to-list, multiple-column combo box is most useful is the assignment of supervisor and manager employee ID numbers to the PA Initiated By and PA Approved By fields in the Personnel Actions form.

To substitute two-column combo boxes for the text boxes of the Initiated By and Approved By text boxes in the Personnel Actions form, complete the following steps:

1. Minimize Form1 and open the Personnel Actions form from the Database window.

2. Click the Design Mode button on the toolbar.

3. Choose the Initiated By text box, and press the Delete key to remove this text box from the form.

4. Click the Field List button on the toolbar to open the Field List window.

5. Click the Combo Box tool in the toolbox. Then click PA Approved By, and drag and drop the field symbol at the preceding location of the Approved By text box. Size the combo box to the approximate dimensions of the text box it replaces.

6. Double-click, or select, the combo box, and then click the Properties button on the toolbar to display the Properties dialog box.

7. The source of the data for the combo box is the Employees table, so the default value of the Row Source Type, Table/Query, is correct. Open the Row Source combo box and select Employees.

8. The first two columns of the Employees table need to provide the Employee ID to be assigned as the value of the PA Initiated By field and Last Name to identify the supervisor. Enter **2** as the Column count to create a two-column combo box.

9. The default width of each column of the combo box is 1 inch. The Employee ID column can be less than 1 inch wide, because it consists of only 1 digit. Enter **0.25** as the width of the first column, followed by a semicolon separator (or a comma), and enter **0.75** as the width of the second column. Access adds together both inches units.

10. The first column of the Employees table, Employee ID, contains the value to assign to the PA Initiated By field, so the default value, column 1, is correct. You can choose any column by its number (in left-to-right sequence) as the value to be assigned to the field to which the combo box is bound.

11. Only an employee included in the Employees table can initiate or approve a Personnel Action, so open the Limit to List list box and choose Yes. If you want to allow the user to add a value not included in the list, accept the default No value. The Personnel Actions form appears as shown in figure 10.16.

12. Delete the Approved By text box and repeat steps 5 through 11 to replace the Approved by text box with a combo box, substituting the PA Approved By field for PA Initiated By in step 5.

13. Click the Run Mode button on the toolbar to test the combo boxes. When you open the Initiated By combo box, the display appears as in figure 10.17.

14. To display only the name of the supervisor or manager in the list and text boxes, change the Column width of the first column from 0.25 to 0 inches. This action causes only the second column to appear in the text box and list.

    As an example, if the fourth column of the table or query is the column you want to display in the combo box, type three zero-width columns preceding the width you want for the column that you want to display (**0,0,0,1**).

List and combo boxes are a boon to developers because Access does all the work. Users who, in early versions of Clipper or later versions of dBASE, wrote the code necessary to create a pop-up window that contains a pick list will appreciate the ease of creating a combo box in Access.

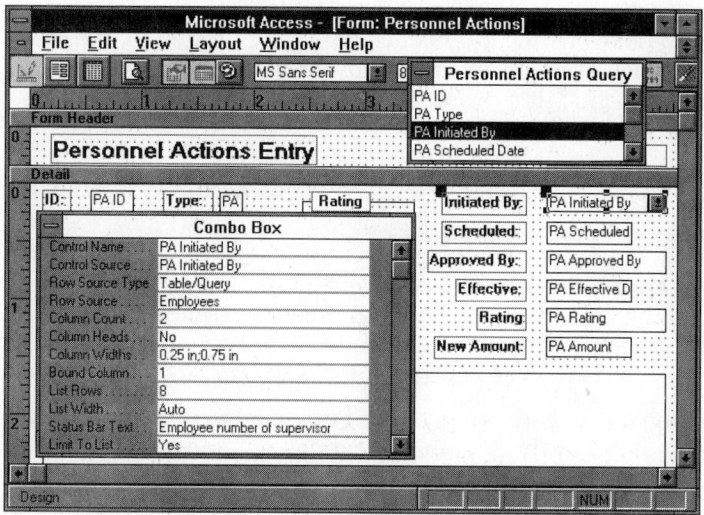

FIG. 10.16

The Properties dialog box for the Initiated By multiple-column combo box.

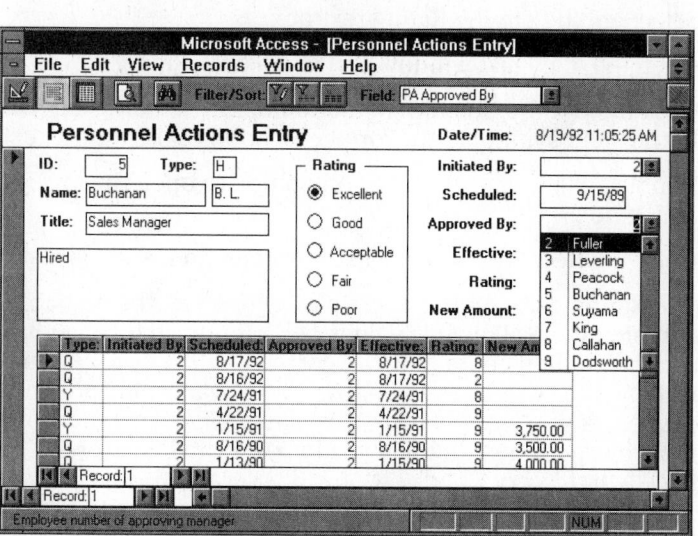

FIG. 10.17

The Approved By multiple-column combo box in Form Run mode.

If the Row Source for a combo box is a query, you can substitute an SQL statement for a named query. The advantage of the substitution is that this process prevents the list of queries in the Database window from becoming cluttered with named queries used to create a multitude of combo boxes. Using SQL statements to fill combo boxes with values is discussed in Chapter 20, "Working with Structured Query Language."

Creating a Combo Box with a List of Static Values

Another application for list boxes and combo boxes is picking values from a static list of options that you create. A combo box pick list to choose a Rating value saves space in a form compared with the equivalent control created with option buttons within an option frame.

The option frame you added to the Personnel Actions form provides a choice of only 5 of the possible 10 ratings. To add a static combo box to allow entry of all the possible values, perform the following steps:

1. Click the Design Mode button on the toolbar.

2. Select and delete the Rating text box.

3. Open the Field List window and choose PA Rating.

4. Click the Combo Box tool in the toolbox. Then drag and the PA Rating field symbol at the former location of the Rating text box.

5. Double-click the new Rating combo box to open the Properties dialog box.

6. Open the Row Source Type list box and choose Value List.

7. The Rating combo box requires two columns, the first column containing the allowable values of PA Rating, 0 through 9, and the second column containing the corresponding description of the rating code. Access assigns Row Source values in column-row sequence; you enter each of the values for the columns of the first row, and then do the same for the remaining rows. Enter **9**, Excellent; **8**, Very Good; **7**, Good; **6**, Average; **5**, Acceptable; **4**, Marginal; **3**, Fair; **2**, Sub-par; **1**, Poor; **0**, Terminated. Press Shift+F2 to use the zoom box to make the entry easier.

8. Enter **2** for the Column Count property.

9. Enter **0;0.75** for the Column Width property so that only the rating names are displayed.

10. The default Bound Column value of 1 assigns the numeric value to the PA Rating field, so the default is correct.

11. You have room on the form to display all 10 values of the Rating list, so enter **10** for the List Rows property.

12. Choose Limit to List and choose Yes from the combo box. The Personnel Actions form in Design mode appears as shown in figure 10.18.

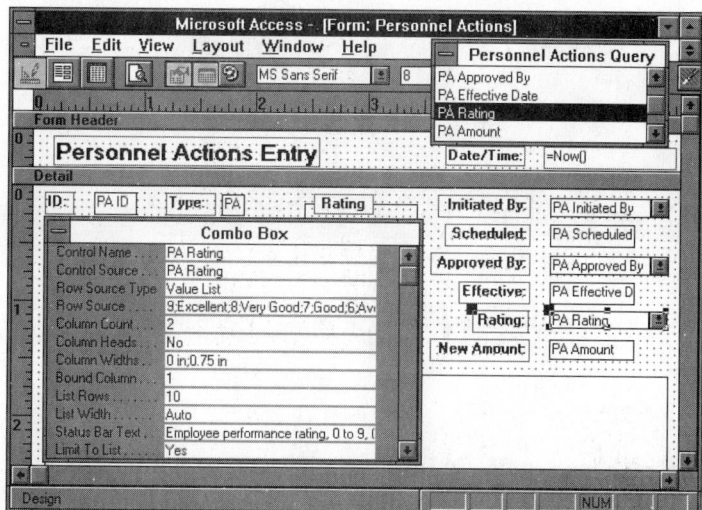

FIG. 10.18

Entering the Control Source values for a static-value combo box.

13. Click the Run Mode button on the toolbar to display the form. The open Rating static-value combo box appears as shown in figure 10.19.

Another opportunity to use a static-value combo box is as a substitute for the Type text box. Several kinds of performance reviews exist: Quarterly, Yearly, Bonus, Salary, Commission, and so on, each represented by an initial letter code. This combo box is added in the example of the next section.

You can improve the appearance of columns of labels and associated text boxes, list boxes, and combo boxes in Form Run mode by right-aligning the text of the labels and left-aligning the text of the boxes. Select all the labels in a column with the mouse, and click the Right Justify button on the toolbar. Then select all the boxes, and click the Left Justify button. Figure 10.19 shows the result of this alignment procedure.

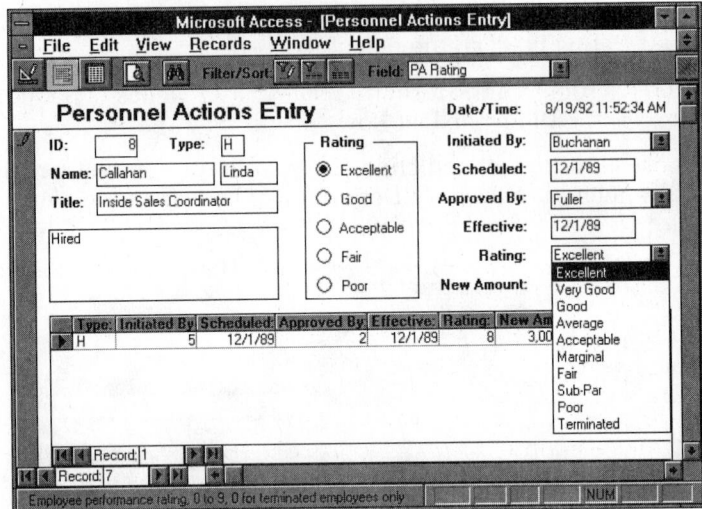

FIG. 10.19

The Rating static-value combo box, opened in Run mode.

Creating and Using Continuous Forms

Continuous forms are useful for displaying data contained in multiple records of a table or query in a format other than Datasheet view. The Personnel Actions subform, for example, is designed only to display the most recent Personnel Action records for an employee. Editing isn't allowed in the subform, so you don't need the field headers, record selection buttons, and scroll bars associated with Datasheet view. These graphic elements focus more attention on the subform than deserved. You need a *plain vanilla* display of the history for the employee; this plain display requires a continuous form.

The FormWizard offers the choice of creating a continuous tabular form, so using the FormWizard is the quickest method of creating a plain vanilla subform. To create a continuous tabular form with the FormWizard, complete the following series of steps:

1. Close the Personnel Actions table and save the changes you made in the preceding section.

2. Click the New button in the Database window to create a new form.

New

3. Use the Personnel Actions subquery as the source of data for the new form.

4. Click the FormWizard button. The FormWizard Selection dialog box appears.

5. Choose Tabular as the type of FormWizard to use and choose OK. The field selection FormWizard window appears.

6. Add all the fields to the form with the >> button. Then remove the PA ID and the PA Comments fields with the Back button, and click the Next button. The FormWizard displays the Style window.

7. Choose Standard as the style for the form and click the Next button.

8. Type **Test** as the name of the form. Click the Design button to modify the design of the form.

The FormWizard created the Standard tabular form by using the Personnel Actions subquery the data source. To customize the form to make the size and appearance compatible with the Personnel Actions form, follow these steps:

1. Click the Form Header bar, and delete the Test title label in the header, leaving the labels for the field names, as shown in figure 10.20.

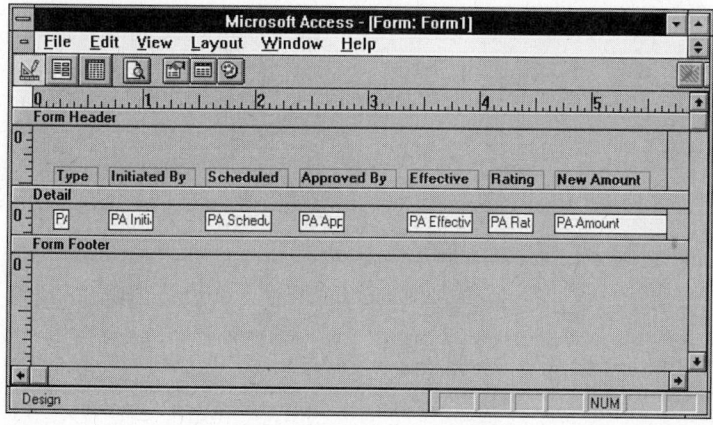

The Rating static-value combo box opened in Run mode.

2. Click the Palette button on the toolbar, and change the Fill color to white.

3. Click the Detail header on the toolbar, and change the Fill color to white.

4. Choose Select For**m** from the **E**dit menu, and then click the Properties button on the toolbar.

5. Set the Default Editing property to Read Only, Allow Editing to Unavailable, Scroll Bars to Neither, and Record Selectors to No. These settings disable all editing capability. Set the Grid X and Grid Y properties to 16 to make easier aligning the labels in the Form Header with the text boxes in the Detail section.

6. Choose **S**nap to Grid from the **L**ayout menu. Relocate and resize the labels in the Form Header and the text boxes in the Detail section, as shown in figure 10.21.

7. After you finish modifying the labels and text boxes, Choose **S**nap to Grid from the **L**ayout menu again to turn off this command. Adjust the depth of the Form Header and the Detail section as shown in figure 10.21.

FIG. 10.21

Modifying a continuous form created by the FormWizard.

8. Click the Run Mode button on the toolbar. The continuous form displays all the records in the Personnel Actions subquery, as shown in figure 10.22.

9. Close the new subform and assign the new name, **Personnel Actions Tabular Subform**.

Now, you need to replace the Personnel Actions subform with the new Personnel Actions Tabular subform that you created in the preceding steps. To perform this procedure, take the following steps:

1. Open the Personnel Actions form, and click the Design Mode button on the toolbar.

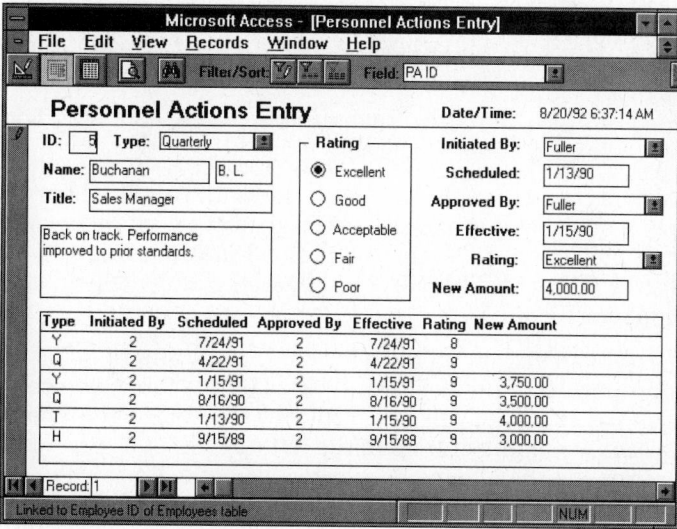

Microsoft Access - [Form: Personnel Actions Tabular Sub-form]

File _Edit_ _View_ _Records_ _Window_ _Help_

Filter/Sort: | Field: PA Type

Type	Initiated By	Scheduled	Approved By	Effective	Rating	New Amount
H	5	10/15/91	2	10/15/91		3,000.00
Y	2	7/24/91	2	7/24/91	8	
Q	2	4/22/91	2	4/22/91	9	
Y	2	1/15/91	2	1/15/91	9	3,750.00
Q	2	8/16/90	2	8/16/90	9	3,500.00
Q	2	1/13/90	2	1/15/90	9	4,000.00
H	5	12/1/89	2	12/1/89	9	3,000.00
H	2	9/15/89	2	9/15/89	9	3,000.00
H	5	9/15/89	2	9/15/89		4,000.00
H	2	9/14/89	2	9/14/89	8	2,000.00
H	2	4/1/88	2	4/1/88		2,250.00
H	2	3/1/88	2	3/1/88		2,250.00
H		7/15/87		7/15/87		3,500.00
H		4/1/87		4/1/87	0	2,000.00

H = hired, S = salary adjustment, Q = quarterly review, Y = yearly review   NUM

FIG. 10.22

The appearance of the continuous form of figure 10.20 in Run mode.

2. Double-click the subform control to select it and open the related Properties dialog box.

3. Change the Control Source property to **Personnel Actions Tabular Subform**.

4. From the **E**dit menu, choose Select For**m** and change the Scroll Bars property to Neither.

5. On the toolbar, click the Run Mode button. The form appears as shown in figure 10.23. If the subform has scroll bars or a record selector, close the Personnel Actions form and reopen it from the Database window.

Form

Open

Microsoft Access - [Personnel Actions Entry]

File _Edit_ _View_ _Records_ _Window_ _Help_

Filter/Sort: | Field: PA ID

Personnel Actions Entry   Date/Time: 8/20/92 6:37:14 AM

ID: 5 Type: Quarterly   ┌ Rating ┐   Initiated By: Fuller
Name: Buchanan   B. L.   ● Excellent   Scheduled: 1/13/90
Title: Sales Manager   ○ Good   Approved By: Fuller
                                ○ Acceptable Effective: 1/15/90
Back on track. Performance   ○ Fair   Rating: Excellent
improved to prior standards.   ○ Poor   New Amount: 4,000.00

Type	Initiated By	Scheduled	Approved By	Effective	Rating	New Amount
Y	2	7/24/91	2	7/24/91	8	
Q	2	4/22/91	2	4/22/91	9	
Y	2	1/15/91	2	1/15/91	9	3,750.00
Q	2	8/16/90	2	8/16/90	9	3,500.00
T	2	1/13/90	2	1/15/90	9	4,000.00
H	2	9/15/89	2	9/15/89	9	3,000.00

Record: 1

Linked to Employee ID of Employees table   NUM

FIG. 10.23

The Personnel Actions form with a continuous subform substituted for the Datasheet subform.

Delete the vertical scroll bar when all the control objects of the noncontinuous form fit in a maximized form window. The horizontal scroll bar must be present when record selectors are used. You can eliminate both the horizontal scroll bar and the record selection buttons when you substitute command buttons for the record selection buttons in Part IV of this book. Unnecessary graphic elements are distracting and have a negative influence on the overall appearance of the form.

Overriding the Field Properties of Tables

Access uses the table's property values assigned to the fields as defaults. The form or subform *inherits* these properties from the table or query on which the form is based. You can override the inherited properties by assigning a different set of values in the Properties dialog box for the control. Properties of controls bound to fields of tables or queries that are inherited from the table's field properties are shown in the following list:

- Format
- Decimal Places
- Status Bar Text
- Validation Rule
- Validation Text
- Default Value
- Typeface characteristics, such as Font Name, Font Size, Font Bold, Font Italic, and Font Underline

GET,
PICTURE,
VALID

Values of field properties that you override with properties in a form apply only when the data is displayed and edited with the form. Here, the Format, Decimal Places, and Validation Rules you apply in forms are similar to xBase PICTURE and VALID instructions appended to the GET command.

You can establish validation rules for controls bound to fields that differ from properties of the field established by the table; you can narrow or broaden the rule. The validation rule for the content of the PA Type field, for example, limits entries to the letters H, S, Q, Y, B, and C. The form can broaden the allowable entries if you add T as a valid choice

by editing the validation rule for the PA Type field to
InStr("HSQYBCT",[PA Type])>0. Similarly, you can narrow the entries
by substituting **InStr("SQYB",[PA Type])>0**.

Validation rules applied in forms that broaden the validation rules
of the underlying table violate a fundamental rule of database
design: table validation rules shall limit all field data entry, regardless of the source. Version 1.0 of Access doesn't comply with this
rule. If you change the validation rule in a form, make sure that
you *narrow*, not *broaden*, the range of choices. Limiting choices by
creating static-value combo boxes, where possible, is a better
practice than changing the validation rule.

Adding Page Headers and Footers for Printing Forms

Access enables you to add a separate pair of sections, Page Header and
Page Footer, that appear only when the form prints. You add these
sections to the form in pairs, by choosing **P**age Hdr/Ftr from the **L**ayout
menu. The following list shows the purposes of Page Headers and
Footers:

■ *Page Header* sections enable you to use a different title for the
printed version. The depth of the Page Header can be adjusted to
control the location where the Detail section of the form is printed
on the page.

■ *Page Footer* sections enable you to add dates and page numbers to
the printed form.

Page Header and Page Footer sections appear only in the printed form,
not when you display the form in Run mode. The Personnel Actions
form with Page Header and Page Footer sections added is shown in
figure 10.24. The subform control was deleted so that the Form Footer
and Page Footer sections appear in the window. Usually, you need to
use the vertical scroll bar to display these sections in Design mode.

You can control whether the Form Header and Form Footer appear in
the printed form with the Display When property of the Properties dialog box for each section. In figure 10.24, the Form Header duplicates the
Page Header (except for the Date/Time label and text box), so you don't
want to print both. To control when a section of the form prints or is
displayed, perform the following steps:

1. Double-click the title bar of the section of the form that you want to change to open the related Properties dialog box.

2. Open the Display When list box.

3. To display, and not print, the section only in Run mode, select Screen Only.

4. To print, and not display, the section only on the form, select Print Only.

Using the Print Only property, you can add a Page Footer, such as the example shown in figure 10.24, that appears only when you print and not when you display the form.

FIG. 10.24

The Personnel Actions form with Page Header and Page Footer Sections added.

Chapter Summary

The examples presented in this chapter demonstrate the ease with which you can add productivity features to an Access form created by the FormWizard or build a custom form from ground zero. The toolbox and the related methodology suffice to create forms that satisfy the majority of your database transaction and decision support applications.

If you previously worked with other windows database front ends, such as Borland's ObjectVision, you probably noticed something missing from this form—the OK and Cancel command buttons and perhaps a New command button to add a record to the table. To add usable command buttons to a form, you need to employ Access macros, the subject of Part IV of this book.

The forms you created up to now are plain black and white: black type on a white background. If colored backgrounds made reading easier or less fatiguing, this book would be printed on colored paper. Intelligently decorating forms with color and adding static graphics is the subject of Chapter 14, "Adding Graphics and Color to Forms and Reports."

Conventional database front-ends provide three basic functions: query entry, forms development, and report generation. The last chapter of Part II shows you how to create Access reports. Report generation often is the weakest element of commercial database front-ends; the following chapter demonstrates that report generation is among the most powerful features of Access.

Printing Formatted Reports

The final product of most database applications is a report. In Access, a *report* is a special kind of continuous form designed specifically for printing. Access combines data in tables, queries, and even forms to produce a report that you can print and distribute to people who need or request it. A printed version of a form may serve as a report, which often occurs with reports designed for decision support, one of the topics of Chapter 14, "Adding Graphics and Color to Forms and Reports." Printing a continuous form can create a report that displays some or all of the values of fields in a table or query.

Most methods of creating transaction-oriented forms, which you learned in Chapters 9 and 10, also apply to reports. The principal differences and similarities between reports and forms are detailed in the following list:

- Reports are intended for printing only and, unlike forms, aren't designed for display in a window. When an 8 1/2-by-11-inch report is viewed in Print Preview, its content is not legible. In the zoomed (full-page) view, only a portion of the report is visible in the Print Preview window.

■ You cannot change the value of the underlying data for a report with a control object from the toolbox, as you can with forms. With reports, Access disregards user input from option buttons, check boxes, and the like. You can use these controls, however, to indicate the status of Yes/No option buttons and check boxes and of fields with values derived from multiple-choice lists.

■ No Datasheet view of a report is available. Only Print Preview and Design mode views are available.

■ You can create an *unbound* report that isn't linked to a source of data. You cannot create an unbound form. Unbound reports are used as "containers" for individual subreports that use unrelated data sources.

■ In a report, minimum left, right, top, and bottom printing margins are controlled by the Printer Setup dialog box. If a report is less than the printable page width, the report's design determines the right margin. You can increase the left margin over the default setting by positioning the print fields to the right of the left margin of the display.

■ In multicolumn reports, the number of columns, column width, and column spacing are controlled by settings in the Printer Setup dialog box, not by controls you add or properties you set in Design mode.

Access reports share many characteristics of forms, as shown in the following list:

■ *ReportWizards* can create the three basic kinds of reports: single-column, groups/totals, and mailing labels. You can modify the reports the ReportWizard creates as necessary. The ReportWizard is similar in function to the FormWizard discussed in Chapter 9.

■ *Sections* include report headers and footers that appear once at the beginning and at the end of the report, and page headers and footers that print at the top and bottom of each page. The report footer often is used to print grand totals. Report sections correspond to similarly named form sections.

■ *Group sections* of reports as a whole comprise the equivalent of the Detail section of forms. Groups often are referred to as *bands*, and the process of grouping records is known as *banding*. You can add Group Headers that include a title for each group, and Group Footers to print group subtotals. You can place static (unbound) graphics in header and footer sections and bound graphics within group sections.

■ *Controls* are added to reports from the Access toolbox, and then moved and sized with their handles.

■ *Subreports* can be incorporated in reports the same way you add subform controls within main forms.

To fully understand the process of designing Access reports, you should be familiar with Access functions, one subject of Chapter 7. You also need to understand the methods used to create and design forms, which are covered in Chapters 9 and 10. Access functions, such as Sum(), and expressions like ="Subtotal of " & [*Field Name*] & ":" are used extensively in reports. The toolbox used to add controls to forms also adds controls when you create or modify reports. You assign properties of controls, such as labels and text boxes, with the methods you use with forms. If you skipped over Chapter 7 or Chapters 9 and 10, you may want to refer to the sections of these chapters that cover unfamiliar subjects or terminology in this chapter.

Types of Access Reports

Reports created by Access fall into five basic classifications, which are detailed in the following list:

■ *Single-column reports* list in one long column of text boxes the values of each field in each record of a table or query. A label indicates the name of a field, and a text box to the right of the label provides the values. Single-column reports seldom are used because this format wastes paper.

■ *Multicolumn reports* are created from single-column reports by using the "newspaper" or "snaking" column approach of desktop publishing and word processing applications. The format of multicolumn tables wastes less paper, but has limited uses because the alignment of the columns is unlikely to correspond to how you want them aligned.

■ *Groups/totals reports* are the most common kind of report. Access groups/totals reports are similar to reports created by other database managers, such as dBASE and Paradox. You summarize data for groups of records, and then add grand totals at the end of the report. Groups/totals reports are the most commonly used in Access.

- *Mailing labels* are a special kind of multicolumn report designed to print names and addresses (or other multifield data) in groups. Each group of fields constitutes a cell in a grid with a number of rows and columns on a page determined by the design of the stock adhesive label on which you are printing.

- *Unbound reports* contain subreports based on unrelated data sources, either tables or queries.

The first four types of reports use a table or query as the data source, as forms do; these kinds of reports are said to be *bound* to the data source. The main report of an unbound report is not linked to a table or a query as a data source. The subreports contained by an unbound report, however, must be bound to a data source. Unbound reports enable you to incorporate subreports that are bound to independent tables or queries.

Creating a Groups/Totals Report with the ReportWizard

This section uses an example query, Products and Suppliers, from the Northwind Traders sample database to create a groups/totals report. This report displays the quantity of each specialty food product in inventory, grouped by product category.

You modify the basic report created by the Wizard to create an inventory report. The process of creating a basic report with the ReportWizard is similar to the process you used to create a form in Chapter 9. An advantage of using the Groups/Totals ReportWizard to introduce the topic of Access reports is that the steps for this process parallel the steps you take when you start with a default blank report.

To create a Product on Hand by Category report, follow these steps:

1. Click the Report button in the Database window, and then click the New button.

2. Similar to forms, reports require a data source that can be a table or a query. Select the Products and Suppliers query from the choices offered in the New Report dialog box's list box (see fig. 11.1). Then click the ReportWizards button. The Products and Suppliers query includes most of the fields from both the Products table and the Suppliers tables.

FIG. 11.1

The New Report dialog box used to select the source of data for a report.

3. You want a report that groups individual products by category and then totals the product on hand for the group comprising each product category. Click the Groups/Totals Wizard entry in the list box, as shown in figure 11.2, and then choose OK. The Field Selection dialog box appears.

4. The fields you choose to display represent rows of the report. You need the report to print the product name and supplier so that users do not have to refer to another report to associate codes with names. The fields that you need for this report are Category ID, Product ID, English Name, Supplier ID, Company Name, and Units in Stock. With the > button, select these fields in sequence from the Available Fields list box (see fig. 11.3). The fields appear from left to right in the report, based on the top-to-bottom sequence in which the fields appear in the Field Order on Report list box. Then click the Next button.

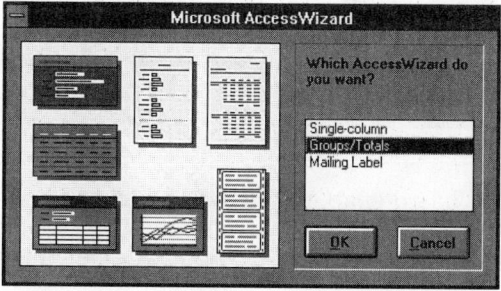

FIG. 11.2

The dialog box from which you choose the ReportWizard to create.

You can retrace your steps to correct an error by clicking the Back button any time this button is activated or by clicking the Rewind button to start over again. The Fast Forward button accepts all defaults and jumps to step 9, so using this button is not recommended.

5. The groups of products are based on the product category, so
   choose Category ID as the field to group by (see fig. 11.4). Then
   click the Next button. Access enables you to group fields in an
   outline format with up to three levels of nesting of groups: group,
   subgroup, and sub-subgroup.

6. The ReportWizard enables you to group data by a coded field, as
   shown in the Records Will Be Grouped By list box (see fig. 11.5).
   Select Normal—the default—and click the Next button.

 If Northwind uses a coding scheme, such as BEVA for alco-
   holic beverages and BEVN for non-alcoholic beverages, you
   can combine all beverages in a single group by selecting
   1st 3 Characters from the list box.

7. You can sort the records within groups by any field you choose
   (see fig. 11.6). Category ID is not offered as a choice because this
   field is where the records are grouped. Choose Product ID with
   the > button and click the Next button.

FIG. 11.5

The ReportWizard dialog box that enables you to group records by coded categories.

8. You can choose from three different styles for the report: Executive, Presentation, and Ledger (see fig. 11.7). An inventory report deserves the *plain vanilla* ledger presentation favored by accountants. Click the Ledger option button and then click the Next button. (Creating decorative forms and reports is the subject of Chapter 14, "Adding Graphics and Color to Forms and Reports.")

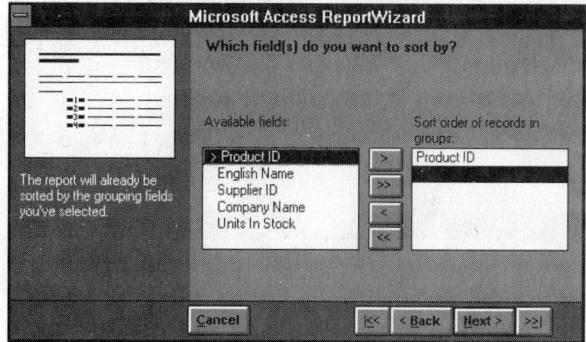

FIG. 11.6

The Product ID field selected as the sort field.

FIG. 11.7

The styles available for a Product on Hand by Category report.

9. In the Report title text box, type **Product on Hand by Category** as the name for the report (see fig. 11.8). You want all the fields to fit across a single 8 1/2-inch wide page, so mark the check box Fit All Fields on One Page.

10. Click the Print Preview button to display how the report appears in print. (If you click the Design button rather than the Print Preview button, the report appears in Design mode.)

The basic report created by the ReportWizard appears in figure 11.9. Use the vertical and horizontal scroll bars to position the preview as illustrated. (Leave the report in Print Preview mode for now because you use this report as the basis for examples in subsequent sections of this chapter.)

FIG. 11.8

Assigning a title to your report.

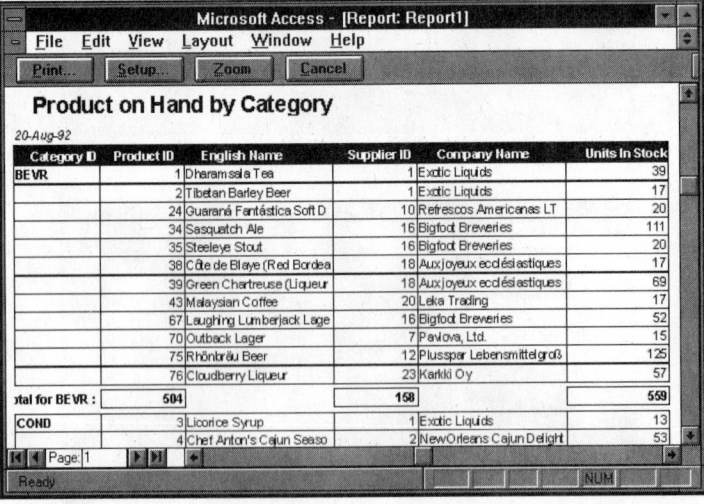

FIG. 11.9

The basic report created by the ReportWizard.

The Access ReportWizard is not omniscient. The Wizard has mistakenly assumed that, because both columns have numeric values, you wanted to sum the Product ID and Supplier ID columns. With a few simple modifications, you can obtain a finished report with the information necessary to analyze Northwind's current inventory (see "Modifying a Basic ReportWizard Report" later in this chapter).

Using Access's Report Windows

The windows you use to design and run Access reports are easier to use than those windows you use for the other basic functions of Access. To open an existing Access report, click the Report button in the Database window, and then select a report name from the Database window. If you click the Design button, or click the New button to create a new report, the Design mode toolbar appears with the buttons listed in table 11.1.

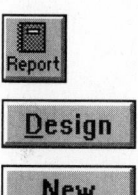

Table 11.1. Standard Toolbar Buttons in Report Design Mode		
Button	**Function**	**Menu Choice**
	Chooses Print Preview to show the way the report appears if printed. You can print the report from the Print Preview window.	File Print Preview
	Displays the Sorting and Grouping dialog box used to establish the structure of reports and the order in which the data is presented.	View Sorting and Grouping
	Displays the Properties dialog box for the entire report, the sections of the report when you click the section divider bars, or the properties of a control when a control is selected.	View Properties

continues

Table 11.1. Continued

Button	Function	Menu Choice
	Displays a list of fields in the query or table that is the data source for the main report.	View Field List
	Displays a palette from which you can select the color of the text, background (fill), and border of a control.	View Palette
	Returns the report to the state prior to the last modification.	Edit Undo
	Displays the Help menu for reports.	F1

 If you double-click the name of an existing report, or click the Open button, the report is displayed in Print Preview mode, which is the Run mode for reports. The buttons on the toolbar in Print Preview mode are listed in table 11.2.

Table 11.2. Standard Toolbar Buttons in Report Print Preview Mode

Button	Function	Menu Choice
Print...	Displays the standard Windows Print dialog box that enables you to choose the number of pages and copies to print, and other basic printing parameters.	File Print
Setup...	Displays the Print Setup dialog box. You set printing margins and other printing parameters in this dialog box.	File Print Setup
Zoom	Toggles between full-page and full-size views of the report. Clicking the mouse when its pointer appears as the magnifying glass symbol produces the same effect.	None

Button	Function	Menu Choice
Cancel	Returns to Design mode if you are creating a new report or if you opened the report by clicking the Design button. Otherwise, the report is closed and you are returned to the Database window.	None
?	Displays the Help menu for reports.	F1

Modifying a Basic ReportWizard Report

The ReportWizard creates the best possible final report in the first pass. Usually, the Wizard comes close enough to a finished product that you spend far less time modifying a Wizard-created basic report than you spend creating a report from the default blank template.

In the following sections, you use Access's report design features to make the report easier to read and more attractive.

Deleting, Relocating, and Editing Existing Controls

The first step in the process of modifying the Wizard report is to modify the existing controls on the report. You don't need to align the labels and text boxes precisely during the initial modification; control alignment is covered in "Aligning Controls Horizontally and Vertically," later in this chapter. To modify the Wizard's report in order to create space to add additional controls, follow these steps:

1. Click Cancel on the Print Preview toolbar to enter report Design mode. The Wizard's report design appears in figure 11.10.

FIG. 11.10

The basic report in Design mode.

2. You first need to eliminate the unnecessary subtotals of fields with numeric field data types that the Wizard mistakenly totaled. Click the =Sum([Product ID]) text box in the Category ID Footer section, and press the Delete key to remove the subtotal. Select the =Sum([Supplier ID]) text box and also delete this subtotal.

3. Repeat step 2 for the same text boxes in the Report Footer section of the report, but do not delete the Grand Total label. The report now creates category totals and grand totals only for Units in Stock.

4. This report is more useful if you include the value of both the inventory and the number of units on hand. To accommodate one or two additional columns, you must compress the widths of the fields. Category ID occupies a column, but you can display this column's content in the Category ID footer. Select and delete the Category ID label from the Page Header section and the Category ID text box from the Detail section. Your report appears as shown in figure 11.11.

5. All the Page Header labels, Detail text boxes, and the Totals text boxes in the Category ID Footer and Report Footer sections must be moved to the left as a group. Click the Product ID label to select it, and then press and hold the Shift key. Click the remaining Page Header labels, each of the Detail text boxes, and the two Totals text boxes in the Category ID Footer and Report Footer sections, and then release the Shift key.

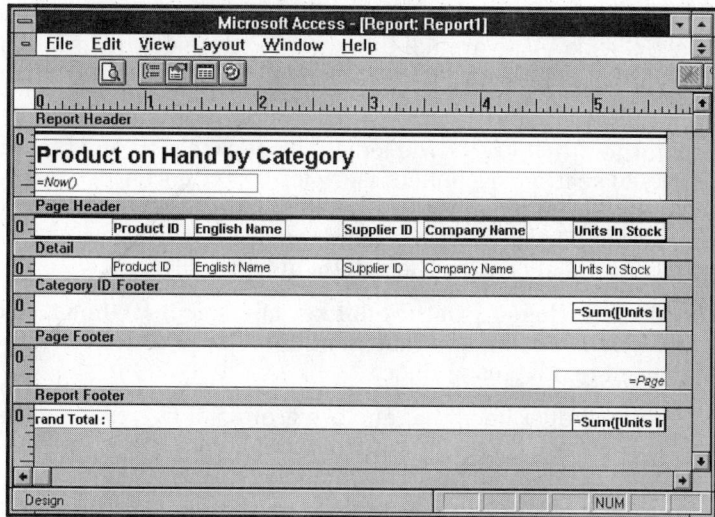

FIG. 11.11

The basic report, after deleting the Category ID label and text box.

6. Position the mouse pointer over the Product ID label at a location where the pointer turns into the symbol of the palm of a hand. Hold down the left mouse button and drag the selected fields to the left margin. Your report appears as shown in figure 11.12.

FIG. 11.12

Selected labels and text boxes, moved to the left margin of the report.

7. Editing and positioning the labels is easier if you left-justify the labels. Click a blank area of the report to deselect the group, select all the Page Header labels, and click the Left Justify button on the toolbar. Do the same for the Grand Total label.

8. The borders that create the ledger lines around the text boxes in the Detail section are unnecessary for this report. Click the Palette button on the toolbar to display the palette. Select each text box and set the border color to Clear by marking the Clear Border check box, as shown on the palette in figure 11.13.

   You also can hold down the Shift key and select all the text boxes in the Detail section, and then mark the Clear Border check box to change all text boxes at once.

9. The heavy ledger lines that enclose groups of five product lines are created by a rectangle control hidden under the text boxes in the Detail section. Temporarily increase the depth of the detail section by dragging the Category ID Footer bar down 1/2-inch. Move the Product ID text box down to expose the rectangle control, as shown in figure 11.14. Select and delete the rectangle. Return the Product ID text box and the Category ID Footer bar to their original positions.

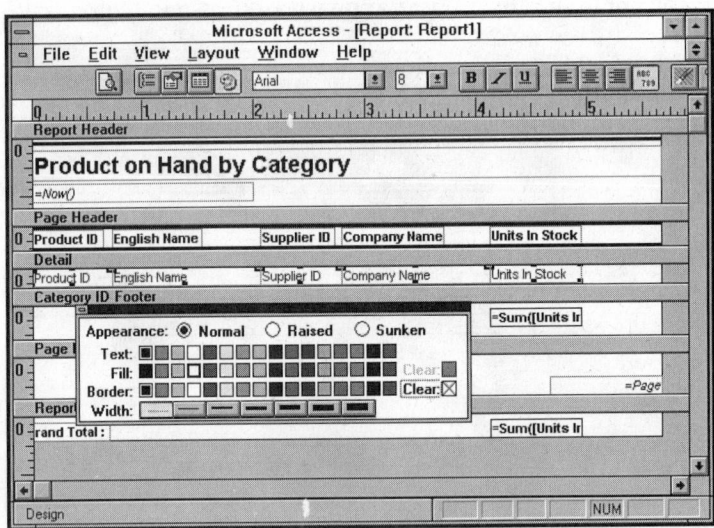

FIG. 11.13

Changing the borders of the Detail section fields that you want to clear.

FIG. 11.14

Exposing and
selecting the
rectangle control
under the Product
ID field for
deletion.

10. Edit the Product ID and Supplier ID labels to remove "ID," and
    decrease the width of each label. Edit the Units in Stock label to
    read only "Units." Reduce the width of the Product ID, Supplier ID,
    and Units in Stock text boxes to match the width of the labels.
    Relocate the labels to provide more space on the right side of the
    report, as shown in figure 11.15.

FIG. 11.15

The Product
on Hand by
Category report
after editing,
resizing, and
relocating
existing controls.

If the width of a report becomes greater than the net printable width (the paper width, minus the sum of the left and right margins), the number of report pages doubles. Columns of fields that do not fit the width of a page print on a second page, similar to the printing method used by spreadsheet applications.

11. You now need to add a bound text box to identify the subtotal in the Category ID Footer section. Click the Field List button on the toolbar. Choose Category ID from the list box in the Field List window.

Click and drag the field symbol to the left margin of the Category ID footer. Click the Bold button on the toolbar to add the bold attribute to the Category ID text box.

You don't need to precisely align the labels and text boxes at this point; these boxes were deliberately misaligned in figure 11.15.

To check the progress of your work, periodically click the Print Preview button on the toolbar to display the report prior to printing.

Adding Calculated Controls to the Report

Calculated controls are useful in reports, especially to determine extended values, such as quantity times unit price or cost. Now you have enough space at the right of the report to add a column for the Unit Cost field and a column for the extended inventory value, which is Unit Price multiplied by Units on Hand. To add these controls, follow these steps:

1. Choose **T**oolbox from the **V**iew menu to display the Access toolbox if it isn't already displayed.

2. Click the Label tool in the toolbox and place the label to the right of the Units label in the Page Header section. Type **Price** as the label.

3. Add another label to the right of Price, and type **Value**.

4. Click the Field List button on the toolbar to display the Field List dialog box. Select Unit Price, and drag the field symbol to a position under the Price label in the Detail section. Drop the text box.

5. Select the Unit Price text box and the Price and Value labels. Change their border color to Clear by marking the Clear Border check box on the palette. The new column appears as in figure 11.16.

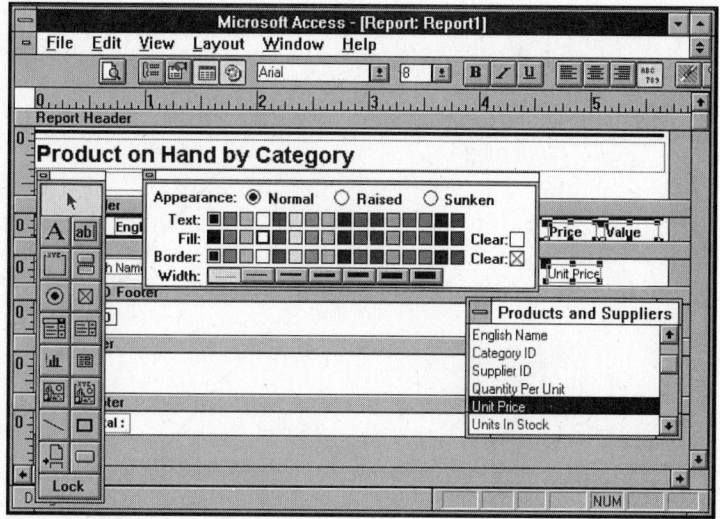

FIG. 11.16

Adding the Price column to the report.

6. To create the calculated Value text box, click the Text Box button in the toolbox and place the text box to the right of the Unit Price text box.

7. Type =[Units in Stock]∗[Unit Price] as the expression for the Value text box. Set the Border color of the text box to Clear.

   Entering expressions is easier if you double-click the text box to display the Properties dialog box and enter the expression as the Control Source property.

8. Repeat steps 6 and 7 to create the Value subtotal text box in the Category ID Footer section, but type =Sum([Units in Stock]∗[Unit Price]) as the subtotal expression. Click the Bold button on the toolbar to set the Font Bold property to Yes.

9. Repeat step 8 to create the Value grand total box in the Report Footer section. The report design appears, as shown in figure 11.17.

10. Click the Print Preview button on the toolbar to check the result of your additions. If the Enter Parameter Value dialog box appears, you misspelled one or more field names in the expressions; click Cancel and review the Control Source properties of the expressions you added in steps 7 through 9. The report appears as in figure 11.18; use the vertical scroll bar, if necessary, to display the category subtotal. You correct the misaligned values and the spacing of the rows of the Detail section in the next section.

FIG. 11.17

Controls added to calculate the value of products, plus value subtotals and grand totals.

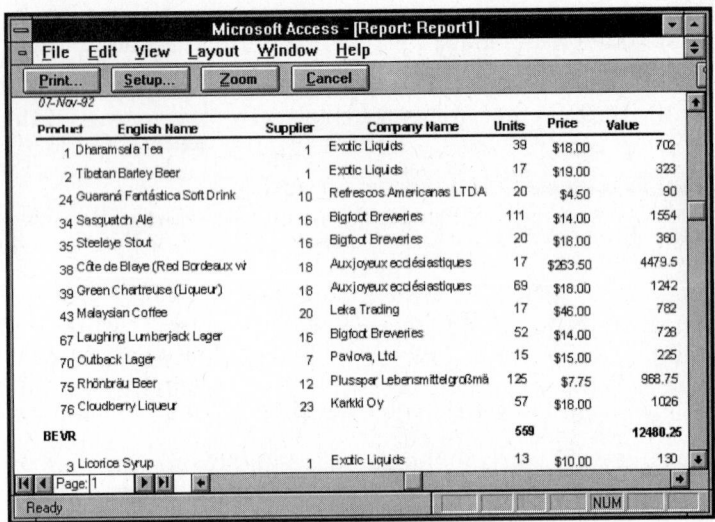

FIG. 11.18

Page 1 of the report, with calculated product values and value subtotals.

 11. Click the Bottom of Report page selector button to display the grand totals for the report (see fig. 11.19). The record selector buttons become page selector buttons when you display reports in Run mode.

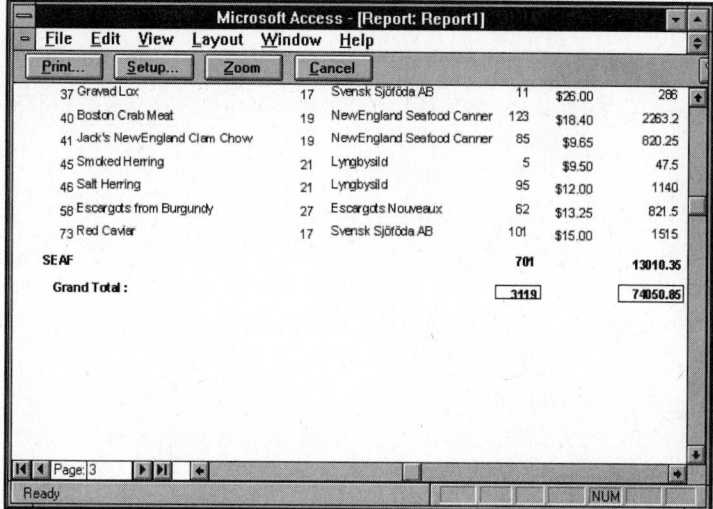

Aligning and Formatting Controls; Adjusting Line Spacing

On reports, the exact alignment of label and text box controls is more important than alignment on forms because in the printed report, any misalignment is obvious. Formatting the controls further improves the appearance and readability of the report.

The spacing of rows of the report in the Detail section is controlled by the depth of the section. White space above and below headers and footers is controlled by the depth of their sections and the vertical position of the controls within the sections. You need to adjust the alignment and formatting of controls and line spacing of sections to create a professional-looking report.

Aligning Controls Horizontally and Vertically

Alignment of controls is accomplished by first selecting rows to align, and then aligning the columns. To align the controls you created, follow these steps:

1. Click Cancel on the toolbar to return to Design mode.

2. You can adjust the height of all the text boxes simultaneously to fit the font used for their contents. Choose Select **A**ll from the **E**dit menu to select all the controls in the report.

3. Choose Size to Fit from the **L**ayout menu to adjust the height of the selected controls. All the controls are adjusted to the proper height. To deselect all the controls, click a blank area of the report.

The title of the report in Design mode may have one or more characters missing as a result of the size-to-fit operation (see fig. 11.20). The missing characters reappear when you change to Print Preview mode.

4. Select all the labels in the Page Header sections. Choose **A**lign from the **L**ayout menu, and then click Top in the fly-out submenu. This process aligns the tops of each selected label with the upper-most selected label. Click a blank area of the report to deselect the labels.

5. Select all the text boxes in the Detail section, and repeat step 4 for the text boxes.

6. Select the labels and text boxes in the Category ID Footer and Report Footer sections, and repeat step 4.

7. Select all the controls in the Units column. Choose **A**lign from the **L**ayout menu, and then click Right so that the column is aligned to the right edge of the text farthest to the right of the column.

8. Select all controls in the Values column (except the Page Footer text box) and repeat step 7. The report in Design mode now appears (see fig. 11.20).

9. Click the Print Preview button on the toolbar to display the report with the improved alignment of rows and columns (see fig. 11.21).

Formatting Controls

Figure 11.18 shows that you need to revise the formatting of several controls. Product ID and Supplier ID values are right-aligned. Center or left justification is more appropriate for values used as codes rather than as numbers to total. The repeated dollar signs in the Unit Price field detract from readability, and the format of the Value column is inappropriate here.

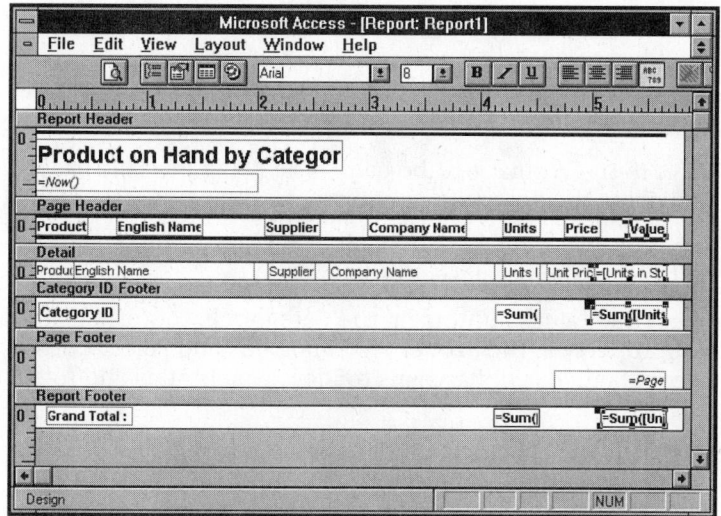

FIG. 11.20

The Product on Hand by Category report, with labels and text boxes aligned in rows and columns.

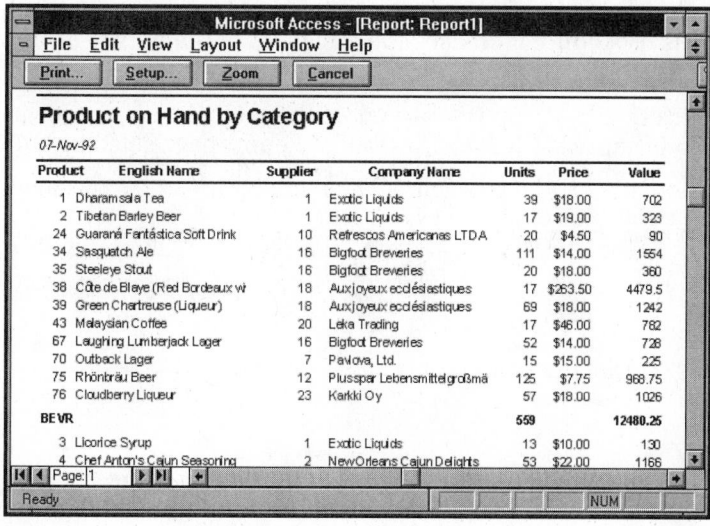

FIG. 11.21

The report in Run mode, with aligned rows and columns.

To change the Format properties of these fields, follow these steps:

1. Click the Cancel button on the toolbar to return to Design mode.

2. Select the Product ID text box in the Detail section and click the Center Justify button on the toolbar.

3. Select and then center-justify the Supplier ID text box in the detail section.

4. Double-click the Unit Price text box to open its Properties dialog box.

5. Move to the Format text box and type **#,###.00**. This procedure eliminates the dollar sign but preserves the monetary formatting.

6. Repeat steps 4 and 5 for the Values text box. Dollar signs aren't required in the Detail section.

7. Select the Values subtotal in the Category ID footer. Click the Format property in the Properties dialog box and select Currency. Accountants use dollar signs to identify subtotals and totals in ledgers.

8. Select the Values grand total in the report footer and set the Values grand total's Format property to Currency.

9. The Values grand total in the report footer is the most important element of the report, so click the Palette button on the toolbar and change the border thickness to the third sample from the left. This procedure increases the thickness of the border around the grand total.

10. Click the Print Preview button on the toolbar to check formatting modifications. Click the Bottom of Report page selector button to display the last page of the report (see fig. 11.22).

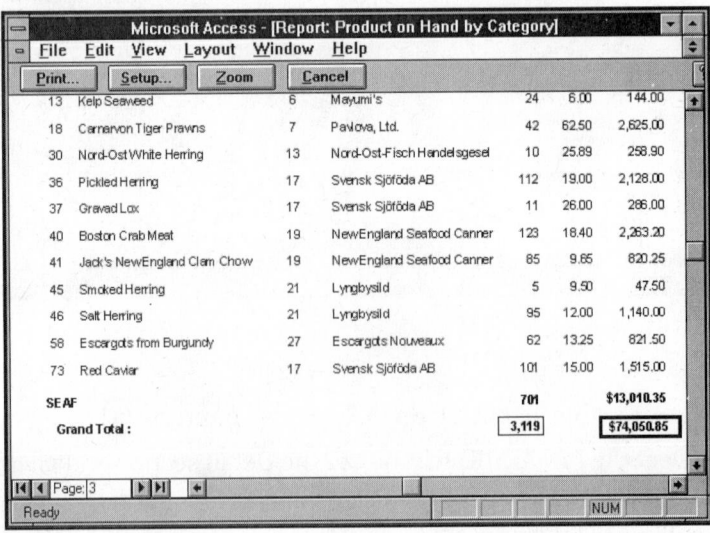

FIG. 11.22

The last page of the report, with the correct format properties assigned to the values.

You may need to return to Design mode and adjust the width or position of the Subtotals and Grand Totals text boxes to align these values with the values for the individual products.

Adjusting Line Spacing

The line spacing of the Detail section, shown in figure 11.22, is greater than necessary, and the depth of the page header is out of proportion to the size of the text. The line spacing of the remainder of the report's sections is satisfactory, but you can change this spacing, too. Minimizing line spacing enables you to print a report on fewer sheets of paper.

To change the spacing of the Page Header and Detail sections of the report, follow these steps:

1. Click the Cancel button on the toolbar to return to Design mode.

2. Select all the labels in the Page Header and move the group as close to the top of the section as possible.

3. Click a blank area of the report and then move the Detail section header to the bottom of the labels. You cannot reduce the depth of a section to less than the Height property of the label with the maximum height in the section.

4. Select all the text boxes in the Detail section and move those boxes as a group to the top of the section. Move the Category ID footer up to the bottom of the labels. The report in Design mode now appears (see fig. 11.23).

5. Click the Print Preview button on the toolbar to check the Page Header depth and Detail line spacing. The spacing shown in figure 11.24 is the minimum you can achieve. You cannot reduce the line spacing of a section to less than the spacing required by the tallest text box or label by reducing the section's Height property in the Properties box, because Access rejects the entry and substitutes the prior value.

6. Click the Zoom button on the toolbar to display the report in full-page view (see fig. 11.25). Clicking the mouse when the pointer is the magnifying glass symbol accomplishes the same results as the Zoom button. Alternate clicks toggle between full-size and full-page views.

7. Choose **S**ave from the **F**ile menu to save your changes.

Cancel

Zoom

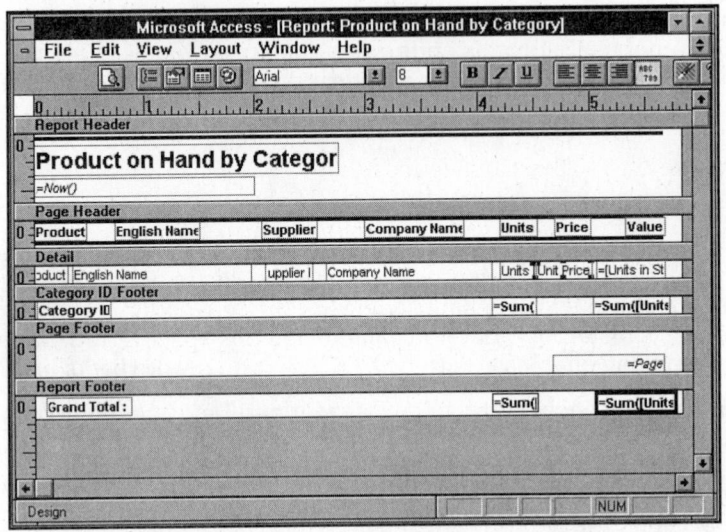

FIG. 11.23

The report in Design mode after the depth of the Page Header and Detail sections is adjusted.

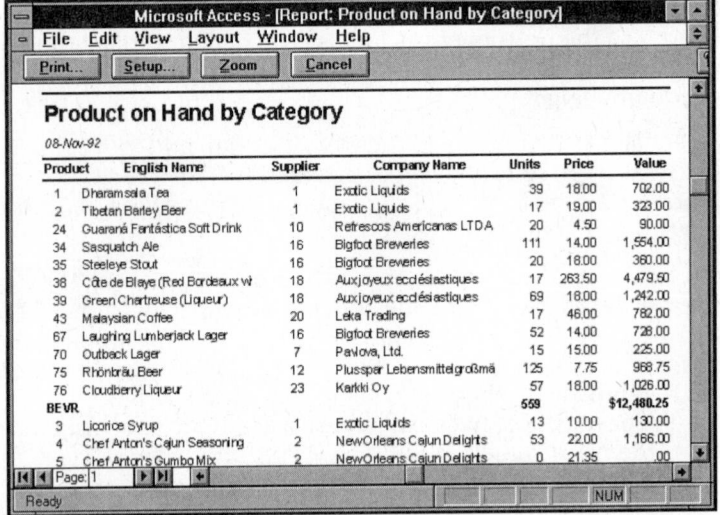

FIG. 11.24

The final version of the report in full-size view.

Adjusting Margins and Printing Conventional Reports

The full-page view of the report shows the report as it would print, using Access's default printing margins of one inch on the top, bottom, and sides of the report (see fig. 11.25). To change the default printing margins, choose **O**ptions from the **V**iew menu, and then select Printing from the list box. The rest of the adjustments to the printed version of the report are made in the Print Setup dialog box. The procedure for printing a report also applies to printing the data contained in tables and queries, as well as single-record or continuous forms.

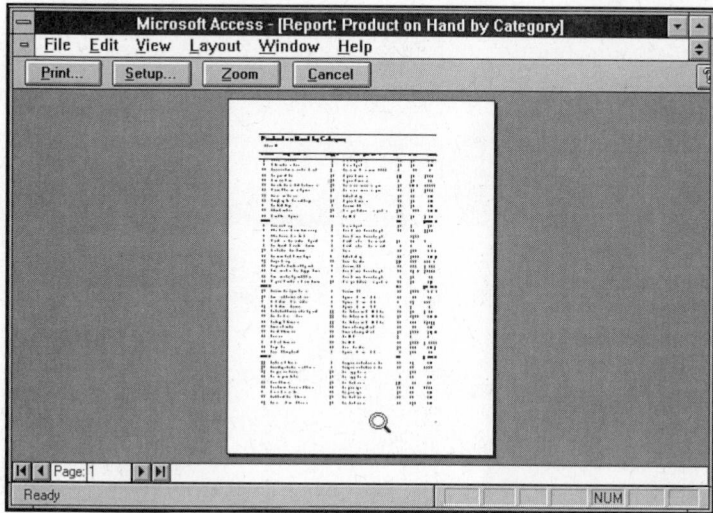

To change the printing margins for a report, follow these steps:

1. To open the Print Setup dialog box of figure 11.26, click the Setup button on the toolbar in report Run mode. You also can display the Print Setup dialog box at any time by choosing P**r**int Setup from the **F**ile menu.

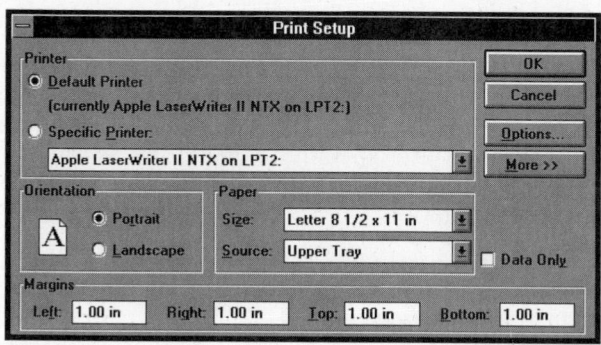

2. The Print Setup dialog box is similar to the Print Setup dialog box of other Windows applications, but an additional section for printing margins is included. To increase the amount of information on a page, decrease the top and bottom margins. Mark the Data Only check box; you can print only the data in the report. Report and page headers and footers do not print when Data Only is specified.

3. Enter **1.5** inches for the left margin and substitute **0.75** inches for the top and bottom margins. Choose OK. The full-page view of the report with the revised margins appears (see fig. 11.27).

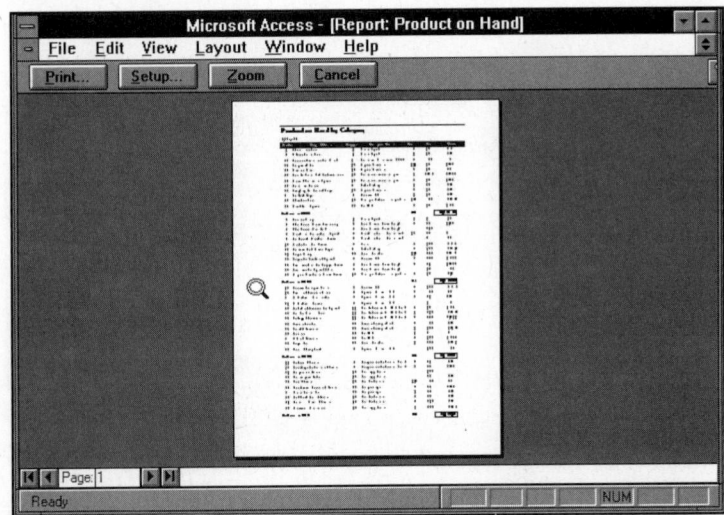

FIG. 11.27

The full-page view of the report with new printing margins applied.

The printing margins you establish in the Print Setup dialog box for a report apply to the active report only; each report has a unique set of margins. The margin settings are saved when you save the report.

<kbd>Print...</kbd>

4. To print the report, click the Print button on the toolbar, or choose **P**rint from the **F**ile menu. The standard Print dialog box appears for the printer specified in Windows as the default printer. Figure 11.28 shows the Print dialog box for a PostScript printer, as an example.

5. You can choose to print all or part of a report, print the report to a file for later printing, and choose the number of copies to print. Clicking Options enables you to change the parameters applicable to the printer you are using. Choose OK to print the report.

FIG. 11.28

The Print dialog
box controls
printing of data
sheets, forms,
and reports.

The Print Setup dialog box includes a More >> button that expands the
basic Report Setup dialog box to establish specifications for printing
mailing labels and other multiple column reports. These specifications,
and the way these specifications are set, are described in the "Printing
Multicolumn Reports" section at the end of this chapter.

Grouping and Sorting Report Data

Most reports you create require that the data in the reports are organized in groups and subgroups, in a style similar to the outline of a
book. The ReportWizard helps you establish the grouping and sorting
properties for your data.

You can modify these report properties in Design mode with the Sorting and Grouping dialog box (see fig. 11.29). To display the dialog box,
click the Cancel button to return to Design mode and click the Sorting
and Grouping button on the toolbar.

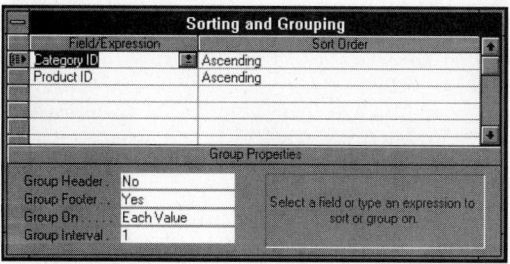

FIG. 11.29

The Sorting and
Grouping dialog
box for the
report.

The Sorting and Grouping dialog box enables you to determine the field(s) or expression(s) on which the products are grouped, for a maximum of three levels. You can sort the grouped data in ascending or descending order, but you must select one or the other; "unsorted" is not an option. The Sorting and Grouping symbol in the selection button at the left of the dialog box indicates that the field or expression in the adjacent column is used to group the records.

Grouping Data

The method you use to group data depends on the data in the field by which you group. You can group by categories, in which case each category must be represented by a unique value. You can group data by a range of values, which usually are numeric, but you also can group by an alphabetical range. You can use the data in a field to group the data, or you can substitute an expression as the basis for the grouping.

 You cannot limit the number of rows of detail data in a report by the properties or the controls of reports. All the rows of a table or query appear somewhere in the Detail section of the report, provided the report includes a Detail section with at least one control. To include only a selected range of dates in a report, for example, you need to base the report on a query with the criteria necessary to select the Detail records. If the user is to choose the range of records to include in the report, use a parameter query as the data source for the report.

Grouping by Category

You elected to group by category when you told the ReportWizard to use Product Category as the field by which to group. You can alter the grouping sequence easily with the Sort and Group dialog box. To group by Supplier ID, for example, choose Supplier ID as the first group field. Change the title label in the Report Header to **Product on Hand by Supplier**, and the expression for the label in the Supplier ID Footer to =**"Subtotal for " & [Company Name] & ":"**. The report appears as shown in figure 11.30.

If you use a systematic code for grouping, you can group by the first five or fewer characters of the code. With an expression, you can group by any set of characters within a field. To group by the second and third digits of a code, for example, use the expression =Mid([*Field Name*],2,2).

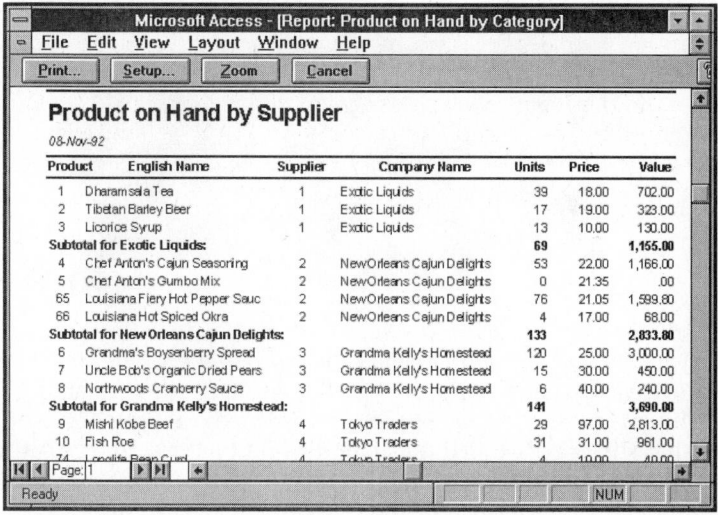

FIG. 11.30

The effect of changing the report grouping so that it displays records by Supplier ID.

If your table or query contains appropriate data, you can group reports by more than one level by creating subgroups. The Employee Sales by Country report (one of the Northwind Traders sample reports), for example, uses groups (Country) and subgroups (Employee) to organize orders received within a range of dates. Open the Employee Sales by Country report in Design mode to view the additional section created by a subgroup.

For Related Information:

◄◄ "Text Manipulation Functions," p. 283.

FROM HERE...

Grouping by Range

You often need to sort reports by ranges of values. (If you opened the Employee Sales by Country report, close this report and reopen the Product on Hand by Category report in Design mode.) If you want to divide the Product on Hand by Category report into a maximum of six sections, each beginning with a five-letter group of the alphabet (A through E, F through J, and so on) based on the English Name field, the entries in the Sorting and Grouping dialog box should look like the entries in figure 11.31.

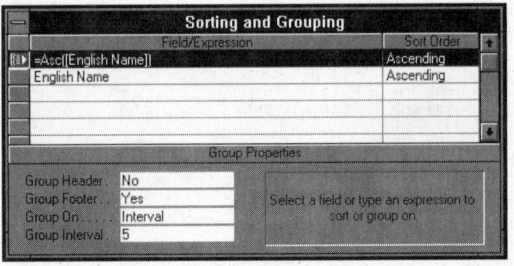

FIG. 11.31

The Sorting and
Grouping criteria
to group records
in alphabetical
intervals.

The =Asc([English Name]) function of Access Basic returns the ASCII
(numeric) value of the first character of its string argument, the English
Name field. You set the Group On specification to Interval, and then set
the Group Interval to 5. This setup groups the data into names beginning with A through E, F through J, and so on (see fig. 11.32). Although
of limited value in this report, a grouping of this kind often is useful for
grouping long, alphabetized lists to speed entry location.

```
┌─────────────────────────────────────────────────────────────────────┐
│              Microsoft Access - [Report: Product on Hand by Category] │
│  File   Edit   View   Layout   Window   Help                          │
├─────────────────────────────────────────────────────────────────────┤
│  Print...    Setup...    Zoom    Cancel                               │
├─────────────────────────────────────────────────────────────────────┤
│  Product on Hand Alphabetically                                       │
│  08-Nov-92                                                            │
└─────────────────────────────────────────────────────────────────────┘
```

Product	English Name	Supplier	Company Name	Units	Price	Value
17	Alice Springs Lamb	7	Pavlova, Ltd.	0	39.00	.00
57	Angelo Ravioli	26	Pasta Buttini s.r.l.	36	19.50	702.00
14	Bean Curd	6	Mayumi's	35	23.25	813.75
40	Boston Crab Meat	19	New England Seafood Canner	123	18.40	2,263.20
11	Cabrales Cheese	5	Cooperativa de Quesos 'Las	22	21.00	462.00
18	Carnarvon Tiger Prawns	7	Pavlova, Ltd.	42	62.50	2,625.00
4	Chef Anton's Cajun Seasoning	2	New Orleans Cajun Delights	53	22.00	1,166.00
5	Chef Anton's Gumbo Mix	2	New Orleans Cajun Delights	0	21.35	.00
76	Cloudberry Liqueur	23	Karkki Oy	57	18.00	1,026.00
38	Côte de Blaye (Red Bordeaux wl	18	Aux joyeux ecclésiastiques	17	263.50	4,479.50
59	Courdavault Raclette Cheese	28	Gai pâturage	79	55.00	4,345.00
1	Dharamsala Tea	1	Exotic Liquids	39	18.00	702.00
48	Dutch Chocolate	22	Zaanse Snoepfabriek	15	12.75	191.25
58	Escargots from Burgundy	27	Escargots Nouveaux	62	13.25	821.50
				580		19,597.20
10	Fish Roe	4	Tokyo Traders	34	31.00	961.00

```
┌─────────────────────────────────────────────────────────────────────┐
│ |◀ ◀ Page: 1  ▶ ▶|  ◀                                                │
│ Ready                                                         NUM     │
└─────────────────────────────────────────────────────────────────────┘
```

FIG. 11.32

A report in which
products are
categorized
by five-letter
alphabetical
intervals.

If you group data on a field with a Date/Time data type, Access enables
you to set the Group On property in the Sorting and Grouping dialog
box to Year, Qtr (quarter), Month, Week, Day, Hour, or Minute. To
group records so that values of the same quarter for several years print
in sequence, type **=DatePart("q",[*Field Name*])** in the Field/Expression
column of the Sorting and Grouping dialog box.

For Related Information:

◀◀ "Text Manipulation Functions," p. 283.

FROM HERE...

Sorting Data Groups

Although most data sorting within groups is based on the values contained in a field, you also can sort by expressions. When compiling an inventory valuation list, the products with the highest inventory value are the most important, and users of the report may want these products listed first in a group. This decision requires a sort of the records within groups on the expression =[Units in Stock]*[Unit Price], the same expression used to calculate the Value column of the report. The required entries are shown in the Sorting and Grouping dialog box of figure 11.33.

The descending sort on the inventory value expression results in the report shown in figure 11.34. As expected, the products with the highest inventory value appear first in each field.

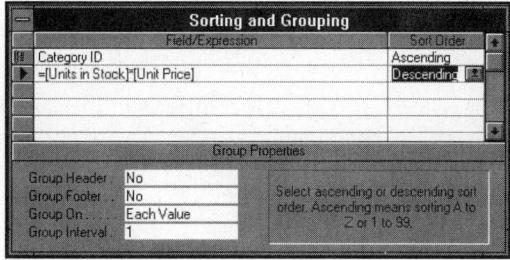

FIG. 11.33

Sorting grouped data on an expression.

Working from a Blank Report

Usually, the fastest way to set up a report is to use the ReportWizard to create a basic report and then modify the basic report as described in the previous sections of this chapter. If you create a simple report, however, the time needed to modify a standard report style created by the ReportWizard may be more than you need to create a report by using the default blank report provided by Access.

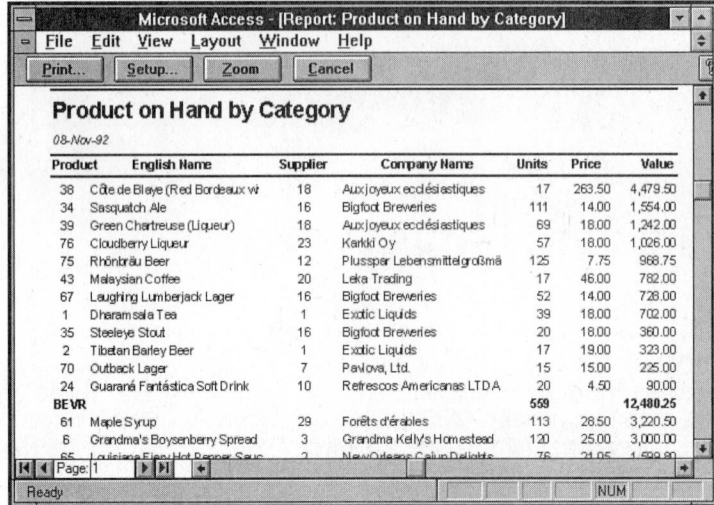

FIG. 11.34

The Product on Hand by Category report, with groups sorted by inventory value.

The Basis for a Report

To create a report to use as the Year-to-Date Sales by Product subreport in the following section of this chapter, follow these steps:

1. Close the Product on Hand by Category report, and click the Query button in the Database window.

2. Select the Year-to-Date Sales by Product query that you created in Chapter 8 and click the Design button. A slightly modified version of this crosstab query serves as data source for the report of the same name.

3. Change the field name of the first column from Category Name to Category ID by opening the Field list box and double-clicking the Category ID field name. You need the Category ID field to link with the Category ID field in the Products on Hand query that is used as the data source for the Products on Hand by Category report.

4. Change the range of dates in the Criteria row of the Order Date column to **Between #1/1/91# and #12/31/91#** to provide data for each month. The modified query appears as shown in figure 11.35.

5. From the File menu, Choose Save **As** and name the modified query **Monthly Sales for 1991**. Then close the Query window.

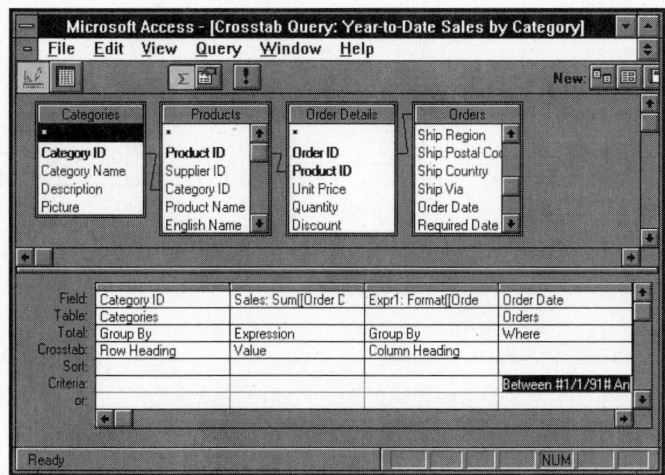

FIG. 11.35

The modified crosstab query for the Year-to-Date Sales by Category report.

6. In the Database window, click the Report button and then click the New button. The New dialog box appears.

7. Choose Monthly Sales for 1991 as the query on which to base the report, and then click Blank Report. Access creates the default blank report shown in figure 11.36.

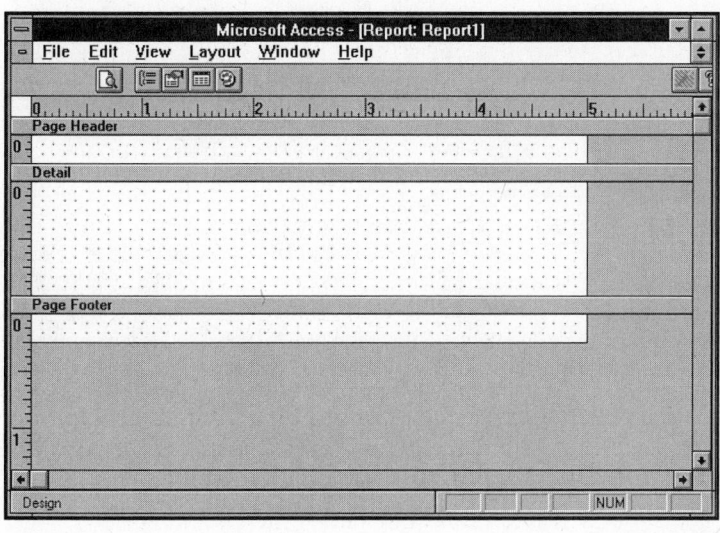

FIG. 11.36

The starting report presented by Access after you click Blank Report in the New dialog box.

Adding and Deleting Sections of Your Report

When you create a report from a blank template or modify a report created by the ReportWizard, you may want to add a new section to the report by using the following guidelines:

- To add Report Headers and Footers as a pair, choose Report **H**dr/Ftr from the **L**ayout menu.

- To add Page Headers and Footers as a pair, choose **P**age Hdr/Ftr from the **L**ayout menu.

- To add a group Header or Footer, click the Sorting and Grouping button on the toolbar and set the Group Header or Group Footer property to Yes.

A blank report, with the headers and footers for each section that you can include in a report, appears in figure 11.37.

FIG. 11.37

A blank report with all sections added.

If you group the data in more than one level (group, subgroup, sub-subgroup), you can add a group header and/or footer for each level of grouping. This action adds another pair of sections for each subgroup level to your report.

You delete sections from reports by using methods similar to those used to create the sections. To delete unwanted sections, use the following guidelines:

■ To delete the Detail section or an individual Report Header, Report Footer, Page Header, or Page Footer section, delete all the controls from the section, and then drag the divider bar below up, so that the section has no depth. To delete a report footer, drag the bottom margin of the report to the Report Footer border. These sections aren't deleted; sections with no depth do not print or affect the report's layout.

■ To delete report headers and footers as a pair, choose Report Hdr/Ftr from the **L**ayout menu. If the report header or footer includes a control, a message box warns you that you will lose the deleted sections.

■ To delete page headers and footers as a pair, choose **P**age Hdr/Ftr from the **L**ayout menu. A warning message box appears if either section contains controls.

■ To delete a group header or footer, click the Sorting and Grouping button on the toolbar and set the Group Header or Group Footer property to No.

Page and report headers and footers that incorporate thin lines at the upper border of the header or footer can be difficult to delete individually. Executive-style reports created by the FormWizard use thin lines difficult to distinguish from the edges of borders. To make these lines visible, choose Select All from the **E**dit menu to add sizing anchors to the lines. Hold down the Shift key and click the controls you want to save to deselect these controls, and then press the Delete key to delete the remaining selected lines.

Controlling Page Breaks and the Printing of Page Headers and Footers

Manual page breaks are controlled by the Force New Page and Keep Together properties of the group Header, Detail section, and group Footer sections of the report. To set these properties, double-click the section border of the group to display the Properties dialog box for the section. Force New Page causes an unconditional page break immediately before printing the section. If you set the Keep Together property to Yes, and insufficient room is available on the current page to print the entire section, a page break occurs and the section prints on the next page.

To control whether page headers or footers print on the first or last page of a report, choose Select Form from the Edit menu, and then click the Properties button on the toolbar. You then select a Page Headers and Page Footers printing option in the Properties dialog box (see fig. 11.38).

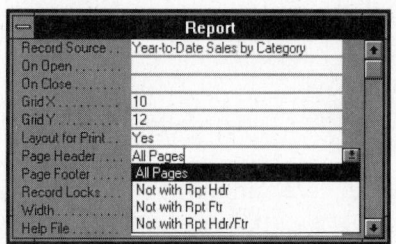

FIG. 11.38

The Properties dialog box for a report, displaying page-section printing options.

Creating the Monthly Sales for 1991 by Category Report

The Monthly Sales for 1991 by Category report is an example of a report that lends itself to starting with a blank report. This report includes information about total monthly sales of products by category. Comparing the monthly sales to the inventory level of a category enables the report's user to estimate inventory turnover rates. This report serves two purposes—as a report and as a subreport within another report. You add the Monthly Sales for 1991 by Category report as a subreport in the Incorporating Subreports section.

The crosstab query that acts as the report's data source is closely related to a report, but the crosstab query doesn't include detail records (see Chapter 8). Each row of the query consists of subtotals of the sales for a category for each month of the year. One row appears below the inventory value subtotal when the subreport is linked to the main report, so this report needs only a Detail section. Each detail row, however, requires a *header* label to print the month. The Category ID field is included so you can verify that the data is linked correctly.

To create the Monthly Sales for 1991 by Category report (and subreport), follow these steps:

1. Delete all sections of your blank report except the Detail section. Snap to Grid is selected and 0.1-inch grid dots appear by default in blank reports.

2. Drag the bottom margin of the detail section down so that you have an inch or two of depth in the section. You need maneuvering room to relocate the text boxes and associated labels that you add in the following steps.

3. Click the Sorting and Grouping button on the toolbar to display the dialog box and select Category ID as the field to use to sort the data with a standard ascending sort. Close the Sorting and Grouping dialog box.

4. Click the Field List button on the toolbar, select Category ID, and drag the field symbol to the Detail section.

5. Click the Categories ID label, and relocate the label to the upper left of the detail section and the Category ID test box to the lower left. Adjust the depth of the label and the text box to 0.2 inches (two grid dots) and the width to 0.5 inches (five dots). Edit the text of the label to read ID.

6. Click and drag the January field in the field list to the right of the Category ID field. Move the label to the top of the section, adjacent to the right border of the field to its left. Adjust the label's depth to 2 dots and width to 8 dots. Edit the text to delete the colon.

7. Repeat this process for the text box, locating the text box below the box's label.

8. Repeat steps 6 and 7 for the months of February through June. The report design now appears as shown in figure 11.39.

9. Select each label while holding down the Shift key so that all the labels (and labels only) are selected.

10. Click the Bold button on the toolbar to add the bold attribute to the labels. Then click the Center Text button to center the labels above the text boxes.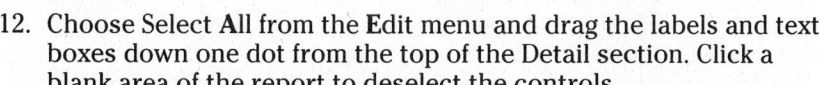

11. Select the Category ID text box and click the Bold button on the toolbar.

12. Choose Select All from the Edit menu and drag the labels and text boxes down one dot from the top of the Detail section. Click a blank area of the report to deselect the controls.

13. If the toolbox is invisible, choose Toolbox from the View menu. Click the Line tool and add a line at the top edge of the labels. Drag the line's right end handle to the right edge of the June text box.

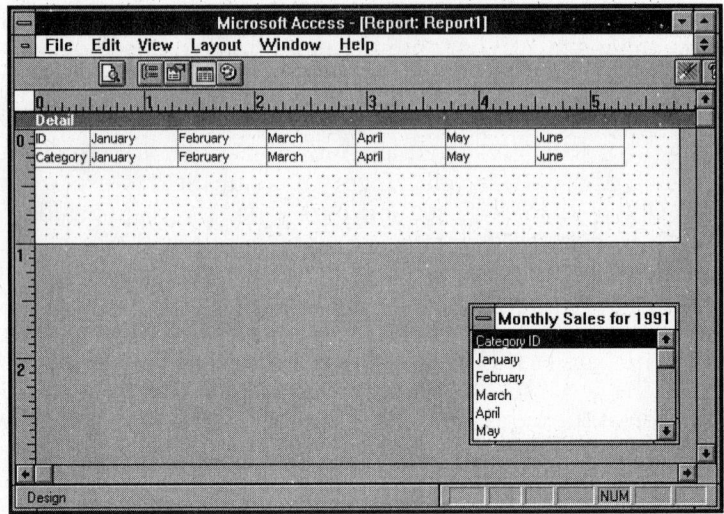

FIG. 11.39

The report with labels and text boxes added for the first six months of 1991.

14. Click the Palette button and click the third line-thickness box from the left.

15. Repeat steps 13 and 14 for another identical line, but add the new line under the labels.

16. Drag the margins of the Detail section to within one dot of the bottom and right edge of the controls. The report appears as shown in figure 11.40.

17. Click the Print Preview button on the toolbar to verify the design. The full-size view of the report appears (see fig. 11.41).

18. Choose Save **As** from the **File** menu and type **Monthly Sales for 1991 by Category** as the name of the report.

To add the remaining months of the year to your report, follow these steps:

1. To accommodate another row of labels and text boxes, increase the depth of the Detail section by dragging the bottom margin down (about one inch).

2. Choose Select **A**ll from the **E**dit menu.

3. Press Ctrl+C to copy the labels and text boxes to the Clipboard.

4. Press Ctrl+V to paste a copy of the labels and text boxes to the Detail section.

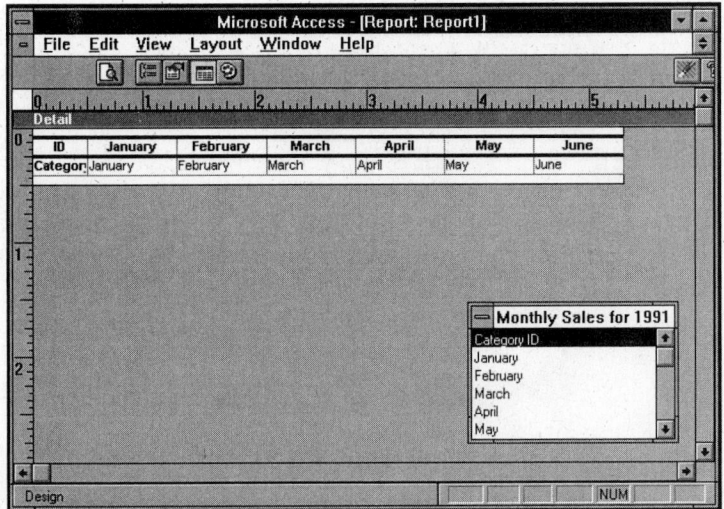

FIG. 11.40

The layout of the detail section of the report.

FIG. 11.41

The report in Print Preview mode.

5. Move this copy under the original labels and text boxes, spaced one grid dot below the originals, as shown in figure 11.42.

6. Click a blank area of the report to deselect the controls, and then select the new Category ID text box. Delete the Category ID text box. Deleting this text box also deletes the associated label.

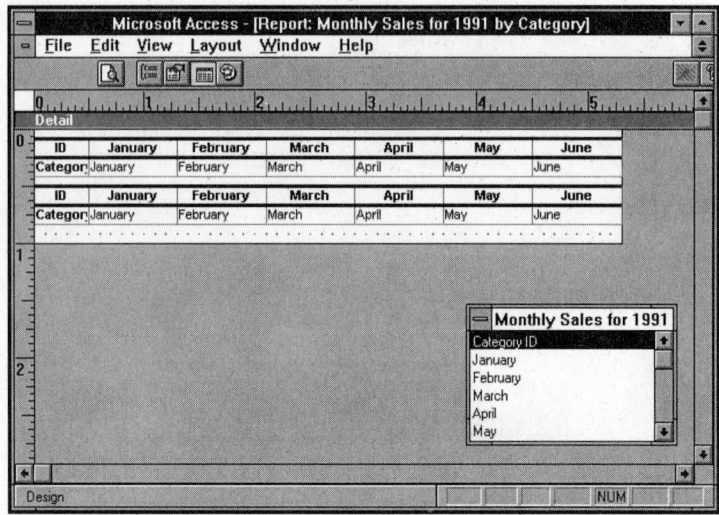

FIG. 11.42

The report
design, with a
copy of the
labels and text
boxes added.

7. Edit the labels and text boxes to read July through December.

8. Delete the ID label in the first row and drag the Category ID text box up to the label's former place. This replacement improves the report's appearance.

9. Drag the bottom margin up to within one dot of the bottom of the text boxes in the second row. The final design appears in figure 11.43.

10. Click the Print Preview button on the toolbar to display the double-row report (see fig. 11.44).

11. Close the Monthly Sales for 1991 by Category report and save the changes.

Copying controls to the Clipboard, pasting copies to reports, and then editing the copies is often faster than creating duplicate controls that differ from one another only by the text of labels and text boxes.

Incorporating Subreports

Reports, like forms, can include subreports. Unlike the FormWizard, however, the ReportWizard offers no option of automatically creating reports that include subreports. You can add subreports to reports that you create with the FormWizard, or you can create subreports from blank reports, as shown in the preceding section.

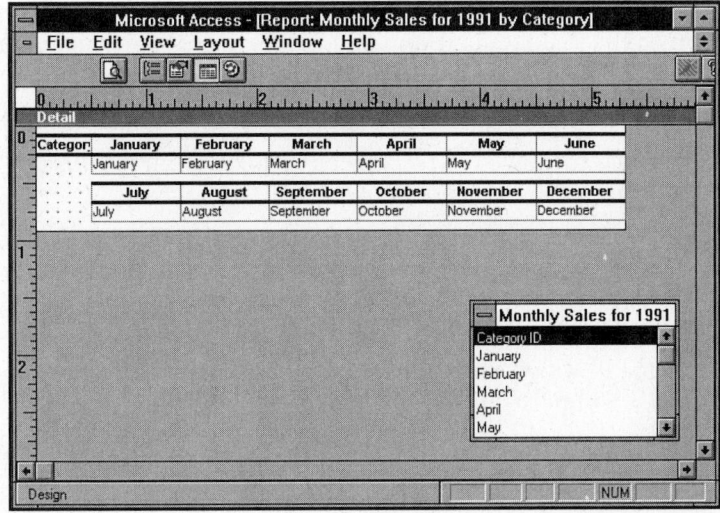

FIG. 11.43

The final design of the Monthly Sales for 1991 by Category report.

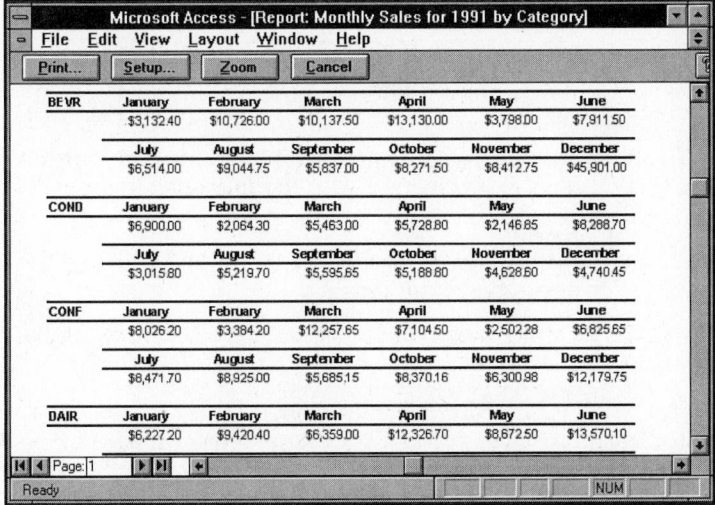

FIG. 11.44

The Monthly Sales for 1991 by Category report with data for 12 months.

Adding a Linked Subreport to a Bound Report

If a main report is bound to a table or a query as a data source and the data source for the subreport can be related to the data source of the main report, you can link the data in the subreport to the data in the main report.

To add and link the Monthly Sales for 1991 by Category report as a subreport to the Product on Hand by Category report, for example, follow these steps:

1. Open the Product on Hand by Category report in Design mode.

2. Drag down the Page Footer border to make room for the subreport in the Category Footer section.

3. From the **Windows** menu, choose Database: NWIND to open the Database window. If the Database window is maximized, click the Document Control button and choose **R**estore.

4. Click and drag the small Report icon from the left of the Monthly Sales for 1991 by Category report to a location inside the Category Footer section. Drop the icon below the Category ID text box.

5. A subreport box similar to a text box, with an associated label, is created at the point where you drop the icon (see fig. 11.45).

FIG. 11.45

Dragging and dropping a report as a subreport within another report.

6. Click the Data Maximize button to restore the Report Design window.

7. Click the Palette button on the toolbar to display the Palette dialog box.

8. Choose Clear for the Border color of the label. You cannot change the color properties of the subreport with the Palette dialog box; all Palette choices are inactive for subreports.

9. Adjust the depth of the Category ID Footer to provide about 0.1-inch margins above and below the controls in the section. The report appears in Design mode (see fig. 11.46).

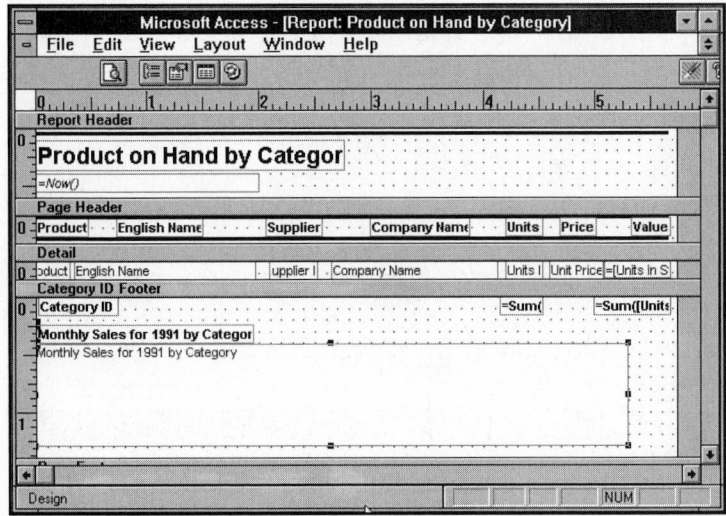

FIG. 11.46

Adding the Monthly Sales for 1991 by Category subreport to the Product on Hand report.

10. You need to link the data in the subreport to the data of the main report so that only the sales data that corresponds to the Category ID value of a specific group appears on-screen. Select the subreport box and click the Properties button to display the Properties dialog box for the subreport. Enter Category ID as the Link Master Fields property and Category ID as the Link Child Fields property.

Access attempts to create the link, if possible. If the main report and subreports are based on tables, and a relationship is set between the tables, Access creates the link to the related fields. If the main report is grouped to a key field and the subreport's table or query contains a field of the same name and data type, Access creates the link.

11. Click the Print Preview button on the toolbar to display the report in the full-size view. The subreport appears as shown at the bottom of figure 11.47. Click the page selector buttons to view other parts of the subreport to confirm that the linkage is correct.

12. Choose **S**ave from the **F**ile menu to save the changes.

You can add and link several subreports to the main report if each subreport has a field in common with the data source of the main report.

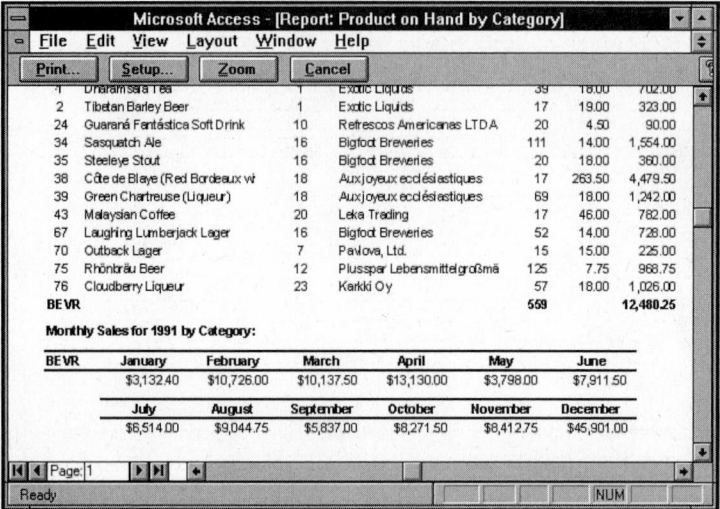

FIG. 11.47

The Monthly Sales for 1991 by Category subreport, linked to the Product on Hand report.

You can use calculated values to link main reports and subreports. Calculated values often are based on time: months, quarters, or years. To link main reports and subreports by calculated values, you must create queries for both the main and subreport that include the calculated value in a field, such as Month or Year. You create the calculated field in each query by using the corresponding Access date function, Month( ) or Year( ). To group by quarters, select Interval for the Group On property and set the Group Interval property to 3. You cannot use Qtr as the Group On property because the calculated value lacks the Date/Time data type.

Using Unlinked Subreports and Unbound Reports

Most reports you create use subreports linked to the data source of the main report. You can, however, insert independent subreports within main reports. Here, you don't enter values for the Link Child Fields and Link Master Fields properties—or, if Access added values, you delete these values. The data source of the subreport can be related to or completely independent of the main report's source of data. Figure 11.48 shows how a portion of page 2 of the Monthly Sales for 1991 by Category subreport appears within the Product on Hand report when you delete the Category ID values of the Link Child Fields and Link Master Fields properties.

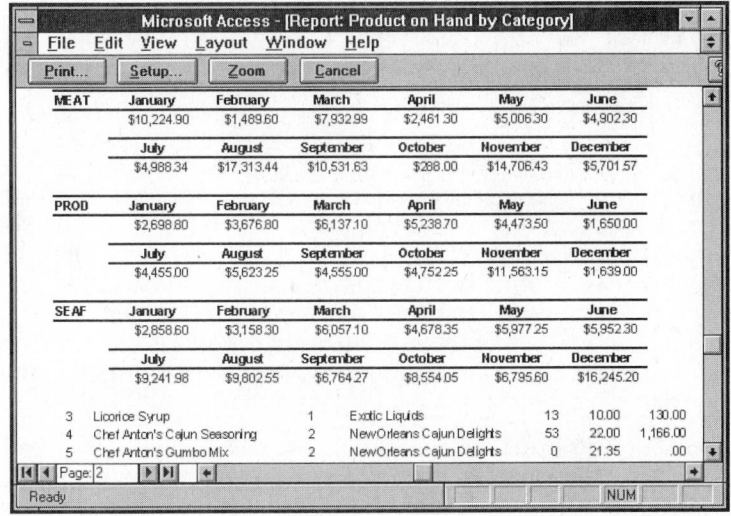

MEAT	January	February	March	April	May	June
	$10,224.90	$1,489.60	$7,932.99	$2,461.30	$5,006.30	$4,902.30
	July	August	September	October	November	December
	$4,988.34	$17,313.44	$10,531.63	$288.00	$14,706.43	$5,701.57
PROD	January	February	March	April	May	June
	$2,698.80	$3,676.80	$6,137.10	$5,238.70	$4,473.50	$1,650.00
	July	August	September	October	November	December
	$4,455.00	$5,623.25	$4,555.00	$4,752.25	$11,563.15	$1,639.00
SEAF	January	February	March	April	May	June
	$2,858.60	$3,158.30	$6,057.10	$4,678.35	$5,977.25	$5,952.30
	July	August	September	October	November	December
	$9,241.98	$9,802.55	$6,764.27	$8,554.05	$6,795.60	$16,245.20

3	Licorice Syrup	1	Exotic Liquids	13	10.00	130.00
4	Chef Anton's Cajun Seasoning	2	New Orleans Cajun Delights	53	22.00	1,166.00
5	Chef Anton's Gumbo Mix	2	New Orleans Cajun Delights	0	21.35	.00

FIG. 11.48

The complete Monthly Sales for 1991 by Category subreport, inserted in the Product on Hand report.

You can add multiple subreports to an unbound report, if all the subreports fit on one page of the report or if all the subreports fit across the page. In the latter case, you can use landscape mode to increase the available page width. To create an unbound report with multiple subreports, follow these steps:

1. Click Report in the Database window, and then click the New button.

2. Keep the text box of the New Report dialog box blank and click Blank Report. This action creates an unbound report.

3. Choose Database: NWIND from the **W**indow menu to display the Database window and drag the Report icon for the first subreport to the Detail section of the blank form.

4. Drag the Report icon for the second subreport to the Detail section of the blank form. If the two subreports fit vertically on one page, place the second subreport below the first subreport. If either of the two subreports requires more than a page, place the second subreport to the right of the first. In this case, you need to add column labels for the subreports in the Page Header section of the main report so that the columns are identified on each page.

Adding Other Controls to Reports

Access places no limit on the toolbox controls that you add to reports. Up to this point, the controls you have modified or added have been limited to labels, text boxes, and lines. These three kinds of controls are likely to comprise more than 90 percent of the controls used in the reports you create. Controls that require user interaction, such as list boxes and combo boxes, can be used in a nonprinting section of the report, but practical use of these controls in reports is limited. The other controls you may want to add to reports are described in the following list:

- *Bound objects* print the contents of the OLE Object field data type. An OLE object can be a still or animated graphic, a video clip, waveform or CD audio, or even MIDI music. Reports are designed only to be printed, so animated graphics and sound are inappropriate for reports.

- *Unbound objects* display OLE objects created by OLE server applications, such as Microsoft Chart (included with Access), Windows Paintbrush, Excel, or the Microsoft WordArt or Equation OLE applets included with Word for Windows. Usually, unbound objects are placed in the Form Header or Form Footer section of the report, but you can add a logo to the top of each page by placing the image object in the Page Header section. A graph or chart created by the ChartWizard is a special kind of unbound OLE object.

- *Lines* and *rectangles* create decorative elements on reports. Lines of varying width can separate the sections of the report or lend emphasis to a particular section.

- *Check boxes* and *option buttons* can be used to indicate the values of Yes/No fields or within group frames to indicate multiple-choice selections. Group frames, option buttons, and check boxes used in reports indicate only the value of data cells, and do not change the values. Toggle buttons seldom are used in reports.

- *Command buttons* execute Access macros and Access Basic procedures.

Bound objects are the subject of Chapter 13, "Using the OLE Field Data Type for Graphics." Using unbound graphic object, line, and rectangle controls is described in Chapter 14, "Adding Graphics and Color to Forms and Reports." Using Access Basic macros is covered in Part IV of this book, and Access Basic programming is the topic of Part VI.

Printing Multicolumn Reports

Access provides the capability of printing multicolumn reports. You can create a single-column report with the ReportWizard, for example, and then arrange the report to print values from the Detail section in a specified number of columns across the page. The most common application of multicolumn reports is the creation of mailing labels.

You can create mailing lists with the ReportWizard, or you can start with a blank form. The ReportWizard's advantage is that it includes the dimensions of virtually every kind of adhesive label for dot matrix or laser printers made by the Avery Commercial Products division. You select the product number of the label you plan to use, and Access determines the number of columns and rows per page, and the margins for the Detail section of the report.

The Northwind Traders database includes a Customer Mailing Labels report, which you can modify to suit the design of any mailing label. Figure 11.49 shows the detail section of the Customer Mailing Labels report with the typeface changed to Courier New in a 10-point font.

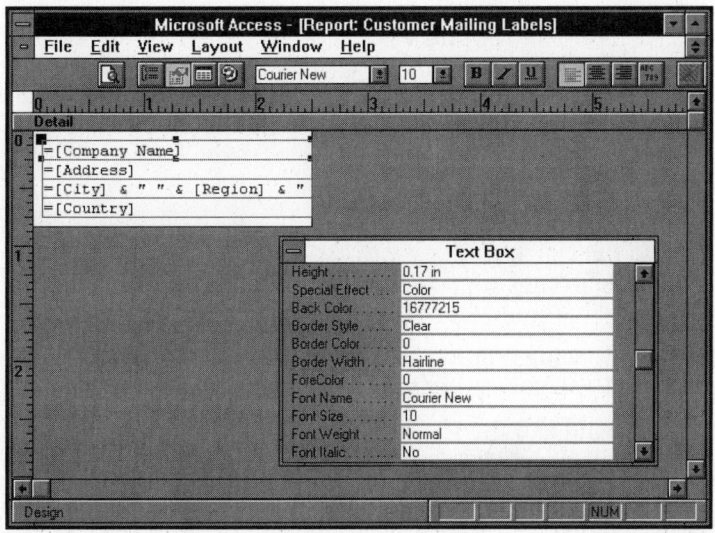

FIG. 11.49

The modified Customer Mailing Labels report in Design mode.

The number of columns in a row and the number of rows on a page are determined by settings you choose in the lower sections of the expanded Print Setup dialog box, shown in figure 11.50. This dialog box appears when you click the Setup button on the toolbar in Print Preview mode. Then click the More >> button.

Setup...

FIG. 11.50

The expanded
version of the
Print Setup
dialog box,
displayed when
you click the
More >> button.

The text boxes, check boxes, and option buttons enable you to perform the following procedures:

- The Items Across property sets the number of labels across the page; in this example, this property changed from 2 to 3.

- The Left and Top margin properties determine the position at which the upper left corner of the first label on the page is printed. These values cannot be less than about 0.2 inch for most laser printers. Labels designed for laser printers are die-cut so that the marginal areas remain on the backing sheet when you remove the individual labels.

- The Width property in the Item Size group overrides the left margin and the Height property overrides the bottom margin you establish in report Design view, if you don't select Same as Detail to use the margins you set in the Detail section.

- Column Spacing determines the position of the left edge of columns to the right of the first column.

- Row Spacing and the Height property determine the number of labels that fit vertically on a page and the vertical distance between successive labels. If you set Row Spacing to 0, the vertical spacing of the labels is determined by the depth of your Detail section.

- Horizontal Item Layout causes the labels to print in columns from left to right, and then in rows from the top to the bottom of the page.

■ Vertical Item Layout causes the labels to print in *snaking* column style, in the first column, top to bottom, and then the next column, top to bottom, and so on.

The values of these properties are set for three columns of 11 labels per page and appear in the expanded Print Setup dialog box.

After you set the dimensions of the mailing labels and choose OK, the full-size view of the labels appears as shown in figure 11.51.

Three-across mailing labels shown in Print Preview's full-size view.

Click the Zoom button on the toolbar to display the full-page layout (see fig. 11.52). To test the label layout properties you set, print only the first page of the labels on standard paper or a xerographic duplicate of the label template supplied with labels designed for laser printing.

You may need to make minor alignment adjustments because the position of the upper left corner of the printer's image and the upper left corner of the paper may not correspond exactly.

If you select Vertical Item Layout, the technique used to print successive Detail rows is identical to the technique used by word-processing applications and page layout applications, such as Aldus PageMaker, to create newspaper (*snaking*) columns. When the first column fills to the specified Height property, Detail rows fill the next column to the right.

FIG. 11.52

A page of
mailing labels,
set up in a 3-by-
11-label grid
shown in full-
page view.

Newspaper columns are suitable for mailing labels, but are difficult to format correctly when you convert other kinds of single-
column reports to multiple-column. For newspaper columns to
operate at all, you need to set the Keep Together property of the
Detail section of the report to No and then set the Height property
so that the field data for a single record appears in a single set of
rows. If the Detail data includes Memo fields with variable
amounts of text in a text box with the Can Grow property set to
Yes, formatting newspaper columns properly becomes almost
impossible. The easier approach is to lay out the Detail
section with multiple columns in Design mode, rather than having
Access attempt to create newspaper columns.

Chapter Summary

This chapter completes Part II of this book, which includes all the
basic functions of Access that duplicate the capabilities of database
front ends. In Part II, you learned the basic steps to create queries,
forms, and reports. Although the Northwind Traders sample database
was used in all examples, the queries, forms, and reports you created

can be applied to tables attached to Access, rather than within the .MDB structure. If the Access or attached tables are on a network server rather than on the computer's fixed disk, the same procedures you learned in the preceding five chapters apply.

Access queries, forms, and reports deal with databases *transparently*; you can create a local .MDB database, duplicate this database as an SQL Server database, and use the same queries, forms, and reports that you created for the Access database. These capabilities make Access an ideal development tool for creating the client-server database systems described in Chapter 21, "Using Access in a Network Environment."

The following part of this book is devoted to Object Linking and Embedding, the method with which you can most easily create or share data with other applications. You use OLE to add, edit, and present the data contained in fields that use Access's OLE Object data type. OLE also is the method by which you add static, unbound graphic images to forms and reports. OLE is a powerful extension to the early concept of Dynamic Data Exchange (DDE), and has been a component of Windows since Version 2.1. Using DDE requires Access Basic programming, so DDE is among the subjects of Part VI of this book, which is devoted to elementary programming methods in Access.

Integrating Access with Other Applications

PART

III

OUTLINE

Introducing OLE: A Quick Start

Windows 3.1 formally introduced Object Linking and Embedding (OLE, pronounced as the Spanish *olé*) to the PC. OLE is a method of transferring information, known as *objects*, between different Windows applications. This method is similar in concept to, although more sophisticated than, copying text or graphics to the Clipboard and pasting the copied text or graphic to other applications. This quick start chapter explains how OLE works and how you use OLE with Access.

Earlier implementations of OLE, such as in Microsoft Excel 3.0 and PowerPoint 2.0, existed before the release of Windows 3.1. OLE was implemented from within the application, however, not by the Windows operating environment. Windows 3.1 made OLE a function of Windows by providing two new files, OLECLI.DLL and OLESVR.DLL, that orchestrate OLE. If you purchased Word for Windows 2.0 before you installed Windows 3.1, advance copies of OLECLI.DLL and OLESVR.DLL were included so that you could use the Microsoft Draw, Chart, WordArt, and Equation applets bundled with Word 2.0. Windows *applets* are special applications designed for use within other Windows applications. Applets, as a rule, cannot be used as conventional, stand-alone applications that you launch from an application group. Publishers of Windows applications are releasing OLE-compliant versions of existing products at a rapid pace; soon, all mainstream Windows applications will incorporate OLE capabilities.

According to industry reports, OLE is understood by fewer users than all other new features of Windows 3.1. This lack of understanding is due in part to the few pages in the *Windows 3.1 User's Guide* devoted to explaining the principles of OLE, compared to the many pages that describe how to perform simple OLE operations. Windows 3.1 added two applets, Object Packager and the Registration Database Editor (RegEdit), that assist in implementing OLE. Surveys indicate that less than five percent of Windows 3.1 users have attempted to use these accessories. This quick start chapter explains the basic principles of OLE from the perspective of the user, not the programmer, of Windows applications.

The Importance of OLE

Understanding OLE principles is important because OLE is the sole method by which you may add graphic images to your forms and reports and add or edit data in OLE Object fields of Access. Using OLE as the method of applying and storing nontext information holds the following advantages over database managers with built-in graphics processing:

- You can use any image processing application that functions as an OLE server to create and edit graphics: from the simple Windows 3.1 Paintbrush applet to photographic-quality editors, such as Micrografx Picture Publisher 3.1.

- You can embed or link vector-based images from applets, such as Microsoft Draw, or from full-fledged illustration packages, such as CorelDRAW! 3.0 or Micrografx Designer 3.1. Microsoft Chart is included with Access.

- The added overhead associated with bit-map editors incorporated in the application is eliminated. Self-contained bit-map editors and drawing functions are seldom as capable as stand-alone, shrink-wrapped applications.

- You don't need to install a collection of import and export filters for different kinds of files. The OLE server applications provide file import from and export to a variety of different file types.

- You can export objects stored in OLE Object fields in Access tables or within bound or unbound object frames to other applications via the Clipboard. Bound object frames display the presentation of OLE objects stored in OLE Object fields of Access tables. Unbound object frames display the presentation of static OLE objects, such as company logos used to embellish forms and reports.

■ You can store a variety of OLE objects in one OLE Object field. You can link or embed in one OLE Object field waveform audio (.WAV), MIDI music (.MID), animation (.FLI and .MMM), and audio video interleaved (.AVI) files. You need a large-capacity fixed disk to embed .AVI and long-duration .WAV files, however.

■ You can choose between embedding the data within a table, form, or report or linking the OLE object to a file that contains the data.

The most common kinds of OLE objects used in Access applications are 16-color and 256-color embedded bit-map graphic images. Figure 12.1 shows a portion of a page from the Northwind Traders' Catalog report that includes an embedded bit-map image. The image is a Windows 3.1 Paintbrush bit map embedded by OLE in the Picture field of the Categories table.

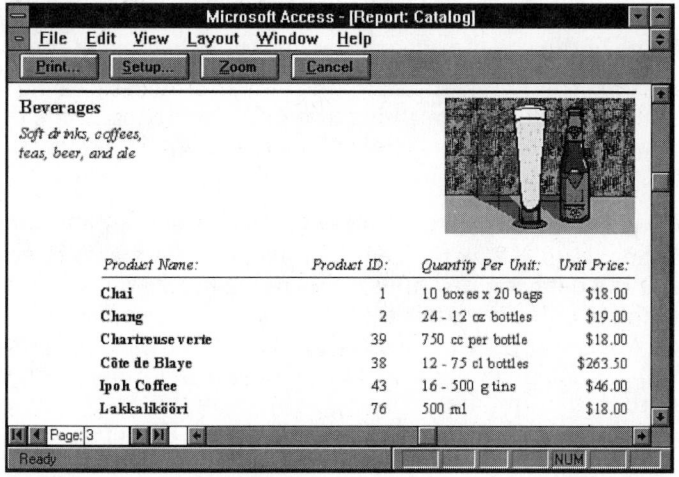

FIG. 12.1

One page of the Northwind Trader's Catalog report in Print Preview mode.

What Is OLE?

OLE is a member of a class of computer operations known as Inter-Process Communication (IPC). *IPC* operations enable different applications to send data to and receive data from other applications by an agreed-on procedure. The Clipboard is the current IPC path for Windows; all present-day communication of data between running applications (other than by reading or writing to disk files) involves using the Windows Clipboard. Windows 3.1 defines a set of standard data types that you can copy to or paste from the Clipboard. OLE uses these standard Windows data types: bit-mapped and vector-based graphic images, plain and formatted text, digital audio sound, and so on. You may have used (or tried to use) Dynamic Data Exchange (DDE) as an IPC to transfer data between Windows applications. OLE is a major improvement over DDE, because OLE is easier to implement than DDE.

OLE operations differ from conventional Windows copy-and-paste operations—performed with Ctrl+C and Ctrl+V or by way of DDE— because OLE includes a substantial amount of information about the source of the data along with the actual data. An OLE object copied to the Clipboard by Excel 4.0, for example, includes the following information:

- The name of the application from which the data originated (Excel, for example).

- The kind of data file, such as worksheet, macro sheet, or chart.

- The full path to the file, beginning with the drive letter and the file name, if the data is derived from a file or was saved to a file.

- A name of the sheet or chart that contains the data, if the data isn't derived from or saved to a file. The name usually is a long combination of numbers and letters.

- The name or coordinates of the range of the data, if only a portion of a sheet is included.

When you paste the data in the spreadsheet cells in another application and then double-click the cells' surface, Excel pops up to enable you to edit the data and disappears when you finish. With OLE, you paste complete objects, rather than just data, in an element of the application. When you copy an Access control object to the Clipboard and then paste the object to another location on a form and report, the object's properties and methods are included in the pasted copy. Properties and methods are the two principal sets of characteristics that define an OLE object.

A Brief Introduction to Objects

When the term *object* is used in conjunction with a computer application or programming language, the term doesn't refer to a tangible object, such as a rock, a saxophone, or a book. Objects in computer programming and applications are intangible representations of real-world objects. A computer object combines *properties*, such as the properties you assign to an Access control object in a form or report, and *methods* that define the behavior of the object. Text box properties—such as text the box contains, the size, typeface, and font the text uses, and the colors and borders employed—vary widely. The way text box controls behave when you type new text or edit existing text are the methods associated with text box objects of forms and reports. All text boxes in Windows applications share similar, but not identical, methods.

Properties and Methods Encapsulated in Objects

A musical instrument, such as a saxophone, can serve as an example of a tangible object that has an intangible representation: sound. Some *properties* of a saxophone are size (soprano, alto, tenor, bass, and baritone), kind of fingering, materials of construction, and the name of the instrument's manufacturer.

The *methods* applicable to saxophones are the techniques used to play these instruments: blowing into the mouthpiece, biting the reed, and fingering the pads that determine the note that you play. Figure 12.2, a vector-based drawing created with CorelDRAW! 3.0, illustrates the properties and methods of a tenor saxophone object.

Properties   Methods

FIG. 12.2

A graphic representation of the properties and methods of a tenor saxophone object.

If you create a programming object that simulates all the properties and all the methods of a particular kind of saxophone, and have the proper audio hardware for a computer, you can create an object that imitates the sound of Charlie Parker's, Art Pepper's, or Stan Getz's style. Stanford University's new WaveGuide acoustic synthesis computer programs create objects capable of this kind of imitation. The properties of, and the methods of the artist playing, a particular saxophone are said to be *encapsulated* in a particular kind of saxophone object. The object acts as a container for the properties and methods that comprise the object.

One more item is found in the container of an OLE object: *presentation*. Presentation is how the user perceives the object—how the object looks or sounds. The presentation of a WaveGuide saxophone is a musical sound. If the saxophone object is used in a Windows 3.1 application, the sound probably is reproduced through digital audio techniques by an audio adapter card. The presentation of a large graphic image may be a miniature copy, or *thumbnail*. At first glance, presentation may appear to be a property. Presentation isn't a property in the true sense, however, because the presentation of an object is dependent on factors *outside* the object, such as the kind of hardware available, the computer operating system used, and the application in which the object is employed. The presentation of a 256-color bit map on a 16-color VGA display, for example, is quite different from the presentation on a 256-color display driver.

Object-Oriented Applications

Applications and the programming languages—which also are applications—that programmers used to create these applications are *object-oriented* if the applications can encapsulate properties and methods within an object container. Before object-oriented programming was developed, programmers considered properties and methods as two separate entities. Programmers wrote code that defined the methods of an application. Separate data files contained the properties that the programmer's application manipulated. A classic example of this separation is xBase; a set of .DBF files contains properties (data), and a separate collection of .PRG files contains the methods (programs) applicable to the set of .DBF files.

In contrast to conventional programming technique, Access takes a thoroughly object-oriented approach to database management. Access combines the data (tables) and the methods (queries, forms, reports, macros, and Access Basic code) in a single, often massive .MDB container, known as the *database object*. Form and report objects act as containers for control objects. Query objects consist of Structured Query Language (SQL) methods applied to table objects. Although lacking some characteristics of a truly object-oriented programming language, Access Basic, however, comes close enough to the mark that you can consider this programming application *Object Basic*.

The Advantages of Objects

Combining properties and methods into an object and then adding a standard presentation provides the following advantages to users of—and the programmers who create—applications:

- Objects combine data (properties) and the program code that deals with the data (methods) into one object that you can treat as a *black box*. You need not understand the internal elements of the box to use a box in an application. This characteristic of objects aids in the programming of large-scale applications in which many programmers participate. You can modify an object without affecting how the object is used by other programmers.

- Objects can be reused when needed. You can create and use a library of objects in many programs or applications. If you create a library of vector-based images created by CorelDRAW! in an Access table, for example, you can edit these images from within Access and then save a copy of the edited drawing in a separate file.

- Objects can be used with any Windows application that supports OLE. You can use the same graphic or sound object with Access, Excel, or Word for Windows. If you copy an embedded drawing in an Excel spreadsheet to the Clipboard, you can paste the drawing as an unbound object in an Access form or report or in a data cell of an OLE Object field in a table. Windows for Workgroups enables you to share the content of Clipboard with other users on the network.

- Objects are easy to create with OLE. If you copy all or a portion of the data you create in an OLE-compliant application, you create a temporary OLE object in the Clipboard.

When you copy an object, such as a graphic, to the Windows 3.1 Clipboard, you can save the object in the form of a .CLP file with the Clipboard Viewer apple. A .CLP file contains a *persistent* object, which is an object that exists independently of the Windows application that creates or uses the object. Persistent objects are stored in files. You can load a persistent object into the Clipboard and then paste the object in an application.

To save an object in the form of a .CLP file, perform the following steps:

1. Click the Form button in the Database window.

2. Double-click the Categories form to open this form in Run mode.

3. Select the picture by clicking the picture's surface.

4. Press Ctrl+C or choose Copy from the Edit menu to paste the selected picture object to the Clipboard.

5. Launch Clipboard Viewer (CLIPBRD.EXE) from the Main program group. The current content of the Clipboard appears in the Clipboard Viewer's window when this window opens. Figure 12.3 shows Clipboard Viewer's display of the picture.

6. Choose Save As from Clipboard Viewer's File menu and give the object a file name, such as BEVR.CLP.

7. Choose OK to save the object; then close Clipboard Viewer.

You now have a persistent image in the form of a .CLP file. When you need the object in an application, perform the following steps:

1. Launch Clipboard Viewer.

2. Choose Open from the File menu and type the path and file name that you previously used to save the .CLP file. This action copies the content of the Persistent Object file to the Clipboard.

3. Minimize or close Clipboard Viewer.

4. Launch an OLE client application, such as Excel 4+ or Word for Windows 2+, with a blank document.

5. Choose Paste Special from the Edit menu.

6. Select the kind of object, Paintbrush Picture Object, from the list in the dialog box and choose OK. A copy of the object appears at the current insertion point.

7. To edit the object, double-click the object's surface. This action launches the OLE server application, Paintbrush, that was used to create the object.

You can build a complete library of various kinds of persistent objects in the form of .CLP files, but this process is tedious at best; ultimately, you may forget the association of the file names with the file content. Access streamlines this process by minimizing the steps involved to create persistent objects. Access stores the equivalent of a .CLP file in a data cell of an OLE Object field of a table or within an unbound object frame. You create tables to organize and classify the objects in OLE Object fields by coding schemes and descriptive text. Rather than cluttering the disk with a variety of .CLP files, the objects you create are stored as subobjects in the table objects of the database.

Object Classes, Types, Hierarchies, and Inheritance

Computer objects, like real-world objects, are organized in hierarchies of classes and subclasses and in types that have no subclasses. The hierarchy of classes of musical instrument synthesis objects is shown in figure 12.4. (The subclasses are shown for woodwinds only.) At the top of the hierarchical structure, you see the master class, Simulated Musical Instruments, for example, that defines the presentation of all the subclasses as digital audio sound.

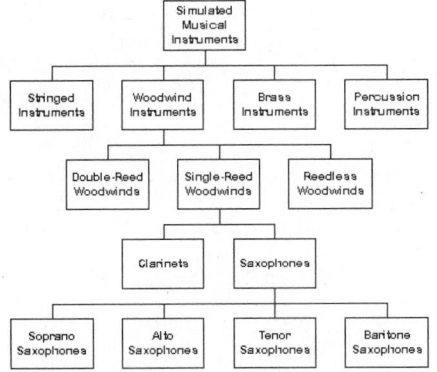

FIG. 12.4

A hierarchy diagram of objects that represents the sound of simulated musical instruments.

Musical instruments are classified by the method used to create the sounds. Saxophones are members of the general woodwind class, which you can further subclass as single-reed woodwinds (see fig. 12.4). Single-reed woodwinds include clarinets and saxophones and share many playing methods. Saxophones can be subclassed further by size and the musical key in which these instruments play. At the bottom of the hierarchy are types that have no further subclasses.

A B-flat (tenor) saxophone has a unique set of property values (data), but the kinds of properties are common to all saxophones. Similarly, the tenor saxophone's playing methods are common to all saxophones. The Tenor Saxophone type *inherits* both the methods and the list of properties from the Saxophone subclass, which in turn inherits properties from the Single-Reed Woodwind class. *Parent* classes are a level above *child* classes in the genealogy of classes, and *siblings* are members of the same class or type. Access uses the term *Master* to indicate a parent class object, as in the Link Master Fields and Link Child Fields properties of subforms and subreports.

Figure 12.5 illustrates the hierarchy of the objects within Access that are described up to this point in the book. Tables, forms, and reports are objects that have distinctive properties and methods. Forms and reports share the same group of control objects. Queries aren't true objects; queries comprise a set of methods applied to table objects. Control objects can be classified further into bound and unbound control objects. Only object frames can incorporate OLE objects and only a bound object frame can display or provide access to editing capability for OLE data in tables or queries.

FIG. 12.5

The hierarchy of database objects in Access.

The control objects in Access inherit some methods from the object that contains the control objects. Subform and subreport controls inherit all related methods and many properties from form and report objects, respectively. OLE child objects inherit a large number of their properties and methods from the parent OLE class that defines how OLE objects behave (or *should* behave). Each OLE child, however, has a complement of properties and methods that apply only to that child. OLE object subclasses at the bottom of figure 12.5 aren't types, because each subclass may have different OLE object types. The Bit-mapped Graphic Class, for example, may include Paintbrush Picture, CorelPhotoPAINT! Picture, and PicturePublisher Picture OLE object types.

The Concept of Compound Documents

OLE is designed to allow a single *destination document* to be built with contributions, known as *source documents*, from foreign applications. The destination document may be created by most applications that are OLE compliant; Access forms and reports, proposals created in Word for Windows, Excel spreadsheets, and PowerPoint presentation visuals are common destination documents. More than one application that contributes to the content of a document is referred to as *compound*. The application that creates the compound document is the OLE *client*, and the foreign applications that contribute source documents to the compound document are OLE *servers*. Access is an OLE client and creates the compound destination documents; Access forms, reports, and tables that incorporate OLE objects are compound documents.

Each source document created with OLE servers and contributed to a destination document is an individual, identifiable object that possesses properties, behavior and has its own presentation. You can choose to *embed* the source document within an Access destination document that acts as a *container* for one or more source document objects. Embedding includes the object's data in the source document. You also can *link* the source document; in this case, the data resides in a separate file. The difference between embedding and linking objects is the subject of the next section.

Whether you embed or link the source document, the code to perform the server's methods isn't incorporated in the compound document. Consider the size an Access table that contains several copies of EXCEL.EXE would become. Instead, the server's methods are incorporated by a reference to the application's name, known as the OLE type, in the source document. On a fixed disk, you need a copy of the server application that created the source document to edit an embedded source document or to display most linked source documents. Include in the DOS path statement the directory in which the OLE server application's executable (.EXE) file is located. The reason for including the path is explained in "The Registration Database" section at the end of this chapter.

Understanding Differences between OLE and DDE

If you previously used dynamic data exchange between Windows applications, OLE gives you the opportunity to add a new dimension to DDE operations. The difference between OLE and DDE techniques to transfer data is illustrated by figure 12.6. DDE transfers data (properties) from the server to Access text boxes, labels, or other controls that can accommodate text and numbers; OLE transfers data and methods from the server only to unbound or bound object frames.

FIG. 12.6

A diagrammatic representation of the differences between DDE and OLE data transfer in Access.

Access includes a function, DDE( ), that you can use to create a DDE link to data in any Windows application with DDE server capability. Using Access's DDE( ) function is described in the "Using DDE Links with Excel" section in Chapter 15. To fully explore the capabilities of DDE with Access, you need to write an Access Basic function that includes a series of DDE functions, beginning with DDEInitiate(). You then execute the Access Basic function with an Access macro. Writing code to make full use of DDE with Access, the subject of Chapter 26, or any other Windows application, is and always was a difficult process. In specific cases discussed in the following chapter, Access will create a DDE link to an element in the source application and embed the data transferred through the link in an OLE Object field.

OLE requires no programming. All OLE operations in Access use the Paste **S**pecial or Paste **L**ink choices of the **E**dit menu. You can copy OLE objects in Access to the Clipboard from the **E**dit menu so that other OLE client applications can use the objects. Only one Access Basic statement relates exclusively to OLE, the OLE Class property that returns the class of an OLE object as a text description. Microsoft deliberately designed OLE for use by nonprogrammers.

Embedding versus Linking Source Documents

When you embed a source document, Windows creates a copy of the source document data and embeds the copy permanently in the destination document. The client application retains no connection to the embedded data. Subsequent editing or deletion of the file or data from which the source document was created has no effect on the embedded copy in the table or displayed on the forms and reports.

Embedding is the only option if you do not or cannot save the source document as a file. The Microsoft Draw, Graph, WordArt, and Equation Editor applets allow you only to embed a file. These applets have no **S**ave or Save **A**s choices in their **F**ile menus. When you choose Exit from an applet **F**ile menu, a dialog box appears, asking whether you want to update the destination document with the edited source document.

Windows 3.1 Paintbrush is the source application for all graphics displayed in bound or unbound objects of the Northwind Traders sample database. Paintbrush enables you to import and save images in .BMP or .PCX files, so you can use Paintbrush to embed or link all bit-mapped graphics you possess or create in either of these file formats.

Open the Categories form in Run mode, if necessary, then double-click the picture. Paintbrush appears so that you can edit the image, as shown in figure 12.7. All bit maps in the Northwind Traders sample database are Paintbrush Picture Objects, embedded in OLE Object fields of tables and in unbound object frames on forms and reports. The title bar of Paintbrush's window in figure 12.7 indicates that the data is embedded in an Access object.

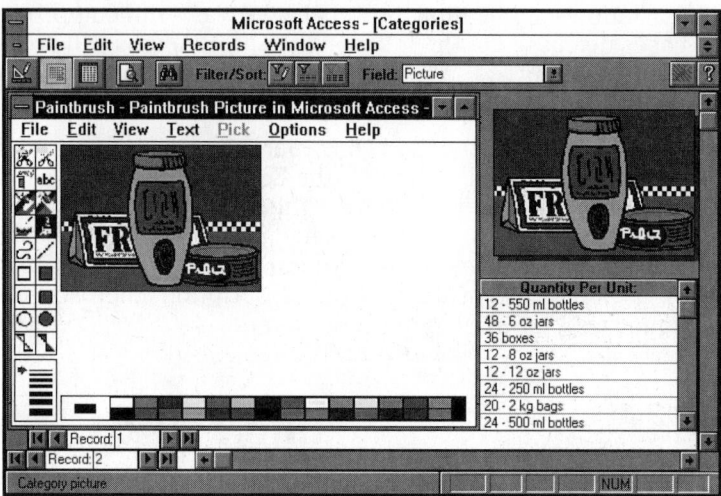

FIG. 12.7

Windows
Paintbrush
editing an
embedded bit
map, displayed
in a bound
object frame.

If you link an object, you create a reference to the data of the source document, the name of a file. When you or others change the data in a file linked to the object, the data in the source document permanently changes. The next time you display the data, if you use the Auto Update feature of Access, the presentation of the object incorporates all changes made to the file. In Version 1.0 of Access, Auto Update is applicable only to OLE objects in unbound object frames. The capability of updating everyone's linked objects at once is useful in a networked Access application that displays data that periodically is updated by others who share these files on the network.

To link rather than embed an object created by an OLE server, perform the following steps:

1. Open the OLE server (Paintbrush, for example).

2. Load the file that contains the data you want to link.

3. Select the data to copy to the Clipboard. Most image editors use a selection tool to select a section of the graphic.

4. Press Ctrl+C to copy the data to the Clipboard.

5. Activate the client application (Access, for example).

6. Choose Paste **L**ink—not Paste **S**pecial—from the **E**dit menu of the client application.

7. Choose the OLE type to link from the Paste Link dialog box and choose OK.

Before creating the OLE link in the destination application, you need to open the source application and load the file because opening a file in many OLE servers breaks the existing OLE connection.

When you double-click to edit a linked Paintbrush Picture Object, the title bar of Paintbrush's window displays the name of the file that created the image, as shown in figure 12.8. This method is the only way that you can determine if an OLE object is linked, rather than embedded in most OLE client applications (including Access).

FIG. 12.8

Paintbrush, editing a graphic object linked to the file BEVR.BMP.

Another advantage of linking some objects whose data resides in files is that you don't waste disk space with duplicate copies of the files in the database. Access creates a copy of the source document's presentation in the table, so you don't save disk space when you link graphic images, spreadsheets, or other source documents whose presentation consists of the data. The presentation of animation, waveform audio, and digital video files is either an icon or the first image of a sequence, so the presentation is small in size. Here, the disk space saved by linking, rather than embedding, is substantial.

The disadvantage of linking is that the linked files must be available to all users of the application. The files must reside in the same directory for their lifetime, unless you edit the linkage to reflect a new location. A fully specified path, including the drive designator, is included with the file name in the linking information. The presentation of the source document appears in the form or report, but when you double-click the bound object frame to edit the linked object, you see an error message that the linked file is not found.

Viewing the Presentation of Source Documents

The presentation of an OLE object when displayed in a compound document is determined by the object's class and type. The presentation of three OLE objects in a continuous Access form is illustrated in figure 12.9. You cannot display some object classes, such as sound files, because these classes lack a graphic presentation. If an object cannot be displayed, Access substitutes the application's icon in the object frame.

FIG. 12.9

A continuous form that displays the presentation of OLE objects of different classes.

Each source document for the three OLE objects shown in figure 12.9 comes from a different OLE object class. These objects are described in the following list:

- Bourbon Street is a packaged object created with Windows 3.1's Object Packager applet. Twelve Tone Systems' Cakewalk Professional for Windows is packaged with a Prosonus' MusicBytes MIDI file converted to Cakewalk's native .WRK file format. The presentation of packaged objects is the icon of the source document's application, regardless of whether the object can be displayed. Using Object Packager is the subject of the following section.

- Confections is a bit-mapped image created by Windows' Paintbrush applet. You can embed bit-mapped graphics created by other image editors that have OLE server capability, such as Micrografx Picture Publisher 3.1 and CorelPhotoPAINT! The presentation is a Windows device-independent bit map (DIB), one of the standard Clipboard formats.

- Saxophone Player is a vector graphic from a clip-art image supplied with CorelDRAW! 3.0. Vector graphics usually have smaller file sizes than bit-mapped graphics of equivalent dimensions. The presentation is a bit-mapped image created from a Windows meta file (WMF) vector graphic by the graphic device interface (GDI), one of Windows' primary components.

Access determines the size of the source document's presentation and how the presentation fits within the object frame, but the content of the presentation usually is controlled by the server application that created the source document. The exceptions are OLE servers with proprietary formats, such as Word for Windows. If you embed all or part of a Word for Windows document, Word's icon appears. Word uses a native (proprietary) Clipboard format not recognized by Access. You can store and edit a Word for Windows document, but you cannot view the document in an Access frame.

When you double-click the presentation of source documents, the OLE server becomes the active application and creates a new presentation in the native format. Although graphics probably will constitute the majority of OLE objects, a wide range of other classes and kinds of OLE objects exist that you can embed or link through object frames. When you double-click the BOURBON3.WRK object in the form shown in figure 12.9, Cakewalk Professional for Windows appears so that you can play or edit the embedded musical data, as shown in figure 12.10.

FIG. 12.10

The presentation
of Cakewalk
Professional for
Windows,
playing or
editing embed-
ded MIDI data.

Packaging an Object for Embedding or Linking

The Object Packager applet included with Windows 3.1 enables you to create OLE source documents with applications that are not OLE servers. Packages created with Object Packager may contain linked or embedded data, but the packages always are embedded—not linked—in the destination document.

Creating an OLE package with embedded data involves the following steps:

1. Launch Object Packager from the Accessories group.

2. From Object Packager's File menu, choose Import to display the Import File dialog box.

3. Select the file whose data you want to embed or to which you want to link the object. The file you choose needs an association with an application. .TXT and .WRI files associated with Windows Notepad or Write, respectively, are good choices because neither of these applications are OLE servers (although Write can be an OLE client). Choose OK. Object Packager's window appears as shown in figure 12.11.

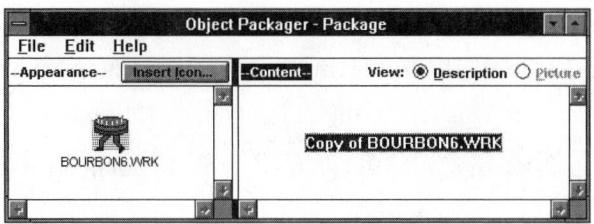

FIG. 12.11

Creating an OLE package that embeds a Cakewalk.WRK song object.

The application whose icon appears in the Appearance window is determined by the application's association with the extension of the file in the Content window. Associations are discussed in the following section of this chapter. The package shown in figure 12.11 created the Bourbon Street object from figure 12.10.

4. From the **E**dit menu, choose Copy Pac**k**age to place the object on the Clipboard.

5. Choose Paste **S**pecial from the **E**dit menu of Access to embed the object's data in a bound or unbound object frame.

Object Packager, not the client application, determines whether a packaged source document is embedded or linked. Creating a package with a link to a file by completing the following steps is a more complex task:

1. Launch File Manager and select the file name for the source document. The file you choose needs an association with an application. The MIDI music file, CANYON.MID, which normally is installed in the \WINDOWS directory, is associated with Media Player, which isn't an OLE server in Version 1.0, so CANYON.MID is a logical choice for linking.

2. From File Manager's **F**ile menu, choose **C**opy.

3. Click the Copy to Clipboard option button in the Copy dialog box shown in figure 12.12; then choose OK to copy the file name and path to the Clipboard.

FIG. 12.12

File Manager's Copy dialog box, used to copy the file name and path to the Clipboard.

4. Launch Object Packager.

5. Select the Content window by clicking the window's surface.

6. Choose Paste **L**ink from Object Packager's **E**dit menu. Object Packager's window appears as shown in figure 12.13. Link to rather than Copy of precedes the file name in the Content window.

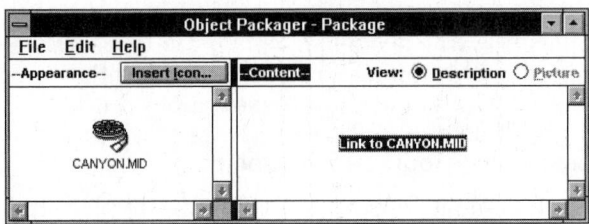

An OLE package
that creates a
linked MIDI music
object.

7. Choose Copy Pac**k**age from the **E**dit menu to place the linked package on the Clipboard.

8. Choose Paste **S**pecial from the **E**dit menu of the client application to embed the linked package.

You usually don't package a file that has an association with an OLE server, such as a .WAV file associated with Sound Recorder, because you can use the actual server to embed the data or link the file. Sound Recorder is a special case. To make Sound Recorder's window appear rather than playing the sound when you double-click a sound object, use Object Packager for the .WAV file in the same manner as for a .MID file.

An embedded package behaves much like a source document created by an OLE server. If you use a package to create a bit-mapped or vector image, however, you must double-click the iconic presentation of the package to display the image. Access plays .WAV files embedded with Sound Recorder when you double-click Sound Recorder's iconic pre-sentation. If you create a package of a .WAV or .MID file and Media Player, Media Player's window appears, and you click the Play button to hear the sound. Packages are identified by the characters ~PKG fol-lowed by four digits and the file extension. This naming convention allows including several packages that consist of portions of a common file in a single compound document.

Microsoft developed an OLE server version of Media Player for use with the audio-video interleaved (AVI) enhancement to Windows. If you want to create a database that contains embedded or linked MIDI files, animated graphics, or video clips from AVI, DVI (Intel's Digital Video Interactive system), or videocassette sources, purchase Media Player 2.0 from Microsoft. Media Player 2.0 is included with Microsoft's Video for Windows application and has several enhancements, discussed in the following chapter, that aid in creating multimedia databases.

The Registration Database

The WIN.INI file of Windows 3+ has the section [Extensions] that includes a series of entries like bmp=pbrush.exe ^.bmp and wri=write.exe ^.wri. This section of WIN.INI creates the associations between applications and file extensions used by File Manager to launch an application when you double-click a file name. If you double-click a file with a .BMP extension, File Manager launches Windows Paintbrush (PBRUSH.EXE) and opens the chosen file.

The addition of OLE to Windows 3.1 and the improvements made to File Manager required more information about applications than the simple associations of file name extensions with applications in WIN.INI. Rather than expand WIN.INI beyond an already considerable size, Microsoft added a new file, REG.DAT, the registration database, to provide file extension association and other details about applications needed by File Manager and OLE-compliant applications.

When you install Windows 3.1, REG.DAT is added to the \WINDOWS directory. When you install new applications or upgrades designed for use with Windows 3.1, the application appends records to REG.DAT. Most of these applications add a file extension association to REG.DAT during the installation process, usually at the beginning of the REG.DAT file. If the application is an OLE server, the application adds information about its OLE capabilities and presentations to REG.DAT.

The Registration Database Editor

A new applet, RegEdit, is included with Windows so that users can display and edit the registration database. The *Windows 3.1 User's Guide* refers you to a Windows help file that provides some help, and the *Windows 3.1 Resource Kit* includes only a cursory explanation of the contents of REG.DAT and the use of RegEdit. If you plan to make extensive use of the OLE Object field data type or add sophisticated graphic images to your forms and reports, you need to know more about REG.DAT and RegEdit than appears in the Windows 3.1 documentation.

 When you launch RegEdit from the Accessories group, using the Program Item properties that Windows 3.1 assigned, a Registration Info Editor window similar to figure 12.14 appears. If RegEdit isn't installed in the Windows Accessories group, choose **R**un from Program Manager's **F**ile menu, and type **regedit.exe** in the Command Line text box and press Enter.

FIG. 12.14

RegEdit's editing window for the registration database file.

Each Windows 3.1 applet and each application designed for Windows 3.1 that you added since you installed Windows 3.1 appears in the window. Entries also exist for some applications that you may not have installed; entries for popular pre-Windows 3.1 applications were included in REG.DAT by Microsoft. Installing new applications updated to Windows 3.1 standards adds new entries to REG.DAT. When you double-click an entry, such as Word for Windows document, the Modify File Type dialog box shown in figure 12.15 appears.

The entries in the Modify File Type dialog box are used by File Manager when you double-click a file name with an extension associated with the application whose executable file name appears in the Command textbox. Word for Windows uses DDE to open the file; when you double-click a file with a .DOC extension, the entry in RegEdit causes DDE to send a FileOpen (FileName) instruction to WinWord. Most applications use a command with the file name appended as a replaceable command line parameter to open a file. An example of this kind of command is WRITE.EXE %1, where %1 is replaced by the file name you double-click in File Manager. This syntax is identical to the syntax used in DOS batch files.

Modify File Type

Identifier: WordforWindows

File Type: Word for Windows docume

Action
- ⦿ Open   ○ Print

Command: winword.exe

☒ Uses DDE

DDE
DDE Message:
[[fileopen("%1")]]

Application:
Winword

(optional)
DDE Application Not Running:

Topic:
System

OK | Cancel | Browse... | Help

FIG. 12.15

The Modify File Type dialog box of RegEdit for editing REG.DAT commands used by File Manager.

RegEdit hides the information pertinent to OLE. To view the entire content of REG.DAT, you need to add a parameter to the command line that Windows 3.1 uses to launch REG.DAT by completing the following steps:

1. If open, close RegEdit.

2. Click the appropriate icon in Program Manager's Accessories group to select RegEdit.

3. From the **F**ile menu, choose **P**roperties.

4. Edit the Command Line entry of the Program Item Properties dialog box to read d:\windows\regedit.exe -v, where *d:* is the drive in which Windows is installed. The *-v* parameter stands for *verbose*. Choose OK to close the dialog box.

5. Double-click the RegEdit button to relaunch RegEdit. RegEdit's display now appears in a format similar to the format shown in figure 12.16.

Registration Info Editor

File   Edit   Search   Help

Full Path: \SoundRec

Value: Sound

```
SoundRec = Sound
├ protocol
│ ├ StdFileEditing
│ │ ├ PackageObjects
│ │ ├ verb
│ │ │ ├ 0 = &Play
│ │ │ └ 1 = &Edit
│ │ └ server = SoundRec.exe
│ └ StdExecute
│   └ server = SoundRec.exe
└ shell
  ├ print
  └ open
    └ command = SoundRec.exe %1
.wav = SoundRec
```

FIG. 12.16

The verbose display of RegEdit that includes OLE server expressions.

6. Use the vertical scroll bar or the down-arrow key to locate the entry for Sound Recorder, SoundRec = Sound, shown in figure 12.16.

The entries for Sound Recorder are treated as though they are file names preceded by a path. Levels in REG.DAT's hierarchy of expressions are separated by backslashes. The first level of expressions from the left of RegEdit's window is the *root*. The level at which the selected expression is located is shown by the entry in the Full Path text box. Values follow an equal (=) sign; values appear or are entered in the Value text box. The registration expressions for Sound Recorder have the following meanings:

- The \.wav = SoundRec entry associates waveform audio files with the .WAV extension with REG.DAT's code for the Sound Recorder, SoundRec.

- File Manager uses the \SoundRec\shell expressions of REG.DAT. Double-clicking a .WAV file in File Manager launches Sound Recorder and opens the specified file by executing the SoundRec.exe %1 instruction that follows the \SoundRec\shell\open\command = expression. The %1 is the replaceable file name parameter discussed previously.

- You cannot print a .WAV file, so the \SoundRec\shell\print expression is empty (no = sign and value). Applications that can print files, such as Paintbrush, include an expression similar to ...\print = pbrush.exe /p %1 to open and print a file from File Manager.

- Sound Recorder is an OLE server; you can identify OLE server applications by a \SoundRec\protocol entry in the hierarchy of the related REG.DAT expressions.

- The type name of the OLE object is the value of the \SoundRec = Sound expression. Sound Recorder methods and properties (data) from .WAV files comprise the Sound OLE object type. Similarly, \PBrush = Paintbrush Picture establishes the Paintbrush Picture OLE object type.

- An OLE server must have at least one protocol, usually the default OLE protocol, StdFileEditing. OLE protocols determine what action the server takes when it opens the linked file or embedded data. Standard file editing usually displays the chosen file in the server's standard presentation.

- Some OLE servers enable you to make a choice of standard file editing presentations chosen by a verb. Sound Recorder enables you to choose between playing or editing the sound file as the standard file editing presentation by using the following expressions:

```
\...\StdFileEditing\verb\0 = &Play
\...\StdFileEditing\verb\1 = &Edit
```

■ OLE servers capable of performing actions, such as playing a waveform audio file with Sound Recorder, may include a second protocol, StdExecute, that executes the application with embedded or linked data. With Sound Recorder, StdExecute is equal to StdFileEditing with the &Play verb added.

■ The location of the PackageObjects expression determines the presentation of the packaged object. If the expression is attached to \SoundRec\protocol\StdFileEditing, the Sound Recorder window appears. If you move the expression below \SoundRec\protocol\StdExecute, as shown in figure 12.17, the copy or linked sound file plays when you double-click the package's icon.

■ Some OLE servers use a proprietary Clipboard format. In this case, the servers add the following expressions:

```
\...\protocol\SetDataFormat = native
\...\protocol\RequestDataFormats = FormatTypes
```

Most OLE clients don't display servers that use a native format in lists of objects that you can insert, unless they can use alternate Clipboard formats, provided by the server, to display the data.

FIG. 12.17

Changing the location of the PackageObjects expression to execute Sound Recorder when packaged.

How Access and Other OLE Applications Use REG.DAT

When you choose Insert **O**bject from the **E**dit menu of Access, or similar menu commands in other OLE client applications, a dialog box displays a list of the object types available from OLE servers that are located on the computer. The Insert Object dialog box of Access is shown in figure 12.18.

FIG. 12.18

Access's Insert Object dialog box that enables you to select an available object type, based on REG.DAT.

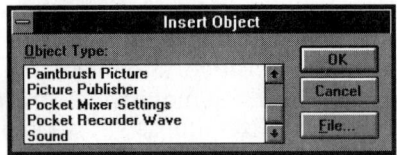

Each Object Type in the Object Type list box is a specific type of the OLE object. The entries in the list box are derived from REG.DAT's value of each registered OLE server. The Sound type, for example, is entered from the SoundRec = Sound expression in REG.DAT. If the REG.DAT file becomes corrupted, some or all of the OLE data types provided by the OLE server applications will be missing from the list.

Make periodic disk backups of the REG.DAT file with backups of WIN.INI and SYSTEM.INI. If the REG.DAT file becomes corrupted and you don't have a backup, you must reinstall all the OLE server applications so that the REG.DAT entries are added to the list, which is a major task because you need to start with the REG.DAT file supplied with Windows 3.1 and expand the file from compressed form on the Windows 3.1 distribution disk. Restoring a backup REG.DAT file is much easier than re-creating REG.DAT from scratch.

When you create a packaged object and select a file for the content, the file extension association expression, .ext = RegDatName, determines the application that provides the methods appropriate to the properties in the file. If you choose an .MID MIDI music file as the content for Object Packager, for example, the following process occurs:

1. Object Packager searches REG.DAT for .MID in the root, \.MID.

2. The expression \.MID = MPlayer tells Object Packager to search for \MPlayer in the root.

3. Object Packager finds \MPlayer = Media Player.

4. The \MPlayer path leads to the following expression:

```
\MPlayer\shell\command\open = mplayer.exe %1
```

Media Player isn't an OLE server, so the following expression is used to specify the packaged application:

```
...\shell\command\open = AppName FileParameter
```

5. Object Packager opens MPLAYER.EXE and places the icon in the Appearance section.

6. If Object Packager cannot find the extension in REG.DAT, the [Extensions] section of WIN.INI is searched for a matching file extension entry and the application whose executable file name follows the .ext = entry is used.

If the executable file of the OLE server isn't on the DOS path, the fully specified path to the file is required. One purpose of REG.DAT is to eliminate the necessity of including the drive and directory data for all the OLE servers in the DOS path statement. If you delete the server's executable file or move the executable file to a directory different from that specified in REG.DAT, you see an error message when a destination application tries to launch the OLE server.

When you move or delete an OLE server application, edit or delete the related entry in REG.DAT. If you move the application to a new directory, edit the pathname value(s) for the server = d:\pathname\filename expression. If no path name precedes the file name, the client applications expect to find the executable file on the DOS path. Otherwise, you see a Not Found message when you try to use the server in an OLE operation.

Chapter Summary

In this quick start chapter, you learned the principles of OLE, designed to aid in the use of the OLE Object field data type and provide the background you need when you decorate forms and reports with static graphics, such as logos. A basic understanding of how OLE works is useful when you see an Access message box that requests that you use RegEdit to check the content of REG.DAT. Although this chapter is directed to using OLE with Access, these principles are the same with all OLE-compliant applications.

In the following two chapters, you use the techniques you learned here about OLE to add, edit, replace, and delete OLE objects in tables, forms, and reports. Chapter 13, "Using the OLE Field Data Type for Graphics," deals with OLE fields in tables, and Chapter 14, "Adding Graphics and Color to Forms and Reports," explains how to add graphs, OLE objects created by the GraphWizard, and other decorative bit-map or vector images to forms and reports.

Using the OLE Field Data Type for Graphics

One of the principle incentives for using a Windows database manager is the ability to display graphic images contained in or linked to database tables. Early Windows DBMs could display images stored in individual bit-mapped graphic files with common formats such as .BMP, .PCX, and .TIF, but could not store the bit-map data within the database file. A few publishers enhanced some of these early products with BLOB (binary large object) field data types. A BLOB field is of variable length and can hold any type of data, regardless of its format. Other Windows DBMs use auxiliary files, similar to dBASE's .DBT memo files, to store graphic images and other types of nontext data. When an auxiliary file is used, a field in a database table provides a reference, called a *pointer*, to the location of the data in the auxiliary file.

This chapter describes the use of Access's OLE Object field for storing graphic images and the bound object frame to display and edit graphics. The OLE Object field in Access is a BLOB field whose values are limited to OLE objects and pictures. Pictures consist of data without a connection to an OLE server; a *picture* is a permanent presentation of the data. Access is an OLE client application, so it can import OLE objects from other OLE server applications and store the objects as values in OLE Object fields of tables or within unbound object frames.

Access does not have OLE server capability, but you can export OLE objects contained in OLE Object fields and unbound object frames to other OLE-compliant applications. Using unbound object frames in forms and reports is the subject of Chapter 14.

Object-oriented databases, mentioned in Chapter 1, enable you to store complex objects such as engineering and architectural drawings and then retrieve all or selected portions by creating queries based on the objects' properties. Although Access is a relational database, its OLE Object field provides many of the capabilities of an object-oriented database without the complexities of object-oriented DBMs. This chapter also explains how you can embed or link other types of OLE objects commonly employed in multimedia applications, including waveform audio (.WAV), MIDI music (.MID), and even digital video (.AUI) files in Access's OLE Object fields.

Making full use of the Access OLE Object field requires Windows 3.1. If you have not yet upgraded from Windows 3.0, your ability to use the OLE Object field is limited. Although Access adds some of the OLE capabilities of Windows 3.1 with the OLECLI.DLL and OLESVR.DLL files it installs in your \WINDOWS\SYSTEM directory, you need the OLE version of Windows Paintbrush, plus Object Packager, Sound Recorder, and Media Player to explore the full capability of Access's OLE Object field.

Adding a Bound Object Control to a Form or Report

Graphic images and other OLE objects stored in OLE Object fields require a bound object control to display their presentation. The *bound object control* is a frame within which a bit-mapped image can be displayed; therefore, bound object controls are called *bound object frames* in this book. In the case of still graphic images, the presentation within the bound object frame is a copy of the object's data property. The presentation of animated images and video objects may be the icon of the application that created or supplies the image, or the first image in the sequence. Sound objects substitute the icon of the OLE server with which their file type is associated in REG.DAT. Double-clicking the bound object frame launches the OLE server that was used to add the object to a data cell in an OLE Object field of your table.

In the following sections, you are introduced to one example of adding a bound object frame to a database form. You learn how to display a photograph in the Personnel Actions form of the sample PERS3ACT.MDB database. You also learn how to scale the photograph within the bound object frame so that you get exactly the look you want.

Including Photos in the Personnel Actions Query

The majority of Access applications use the OLE Object field data type to store graphic images. One such type of graphic image included in the Northwind Traders Employees table is a photograph for each employee. You can use the OLE Object field data type to add the photograph to your Personnel Actions form. The first step is to incorporate the Photo field of the Employees table in your Personnel Actions query by following these steps:

1. Click the Query button in the Database window and choose the Personnel Actions query.

2. Click the Design button on the toolbar to open the query in Design mode.

3. Use the horizontal scroll bar button to position the Query Design grid so that the blank column after the Title column is visible.

4. Select the Photo field of the Employees table.

5. Click and drag the field symbol to the Field row of the column to the right of the Title column. Your query appears as shown in figure 13.1.

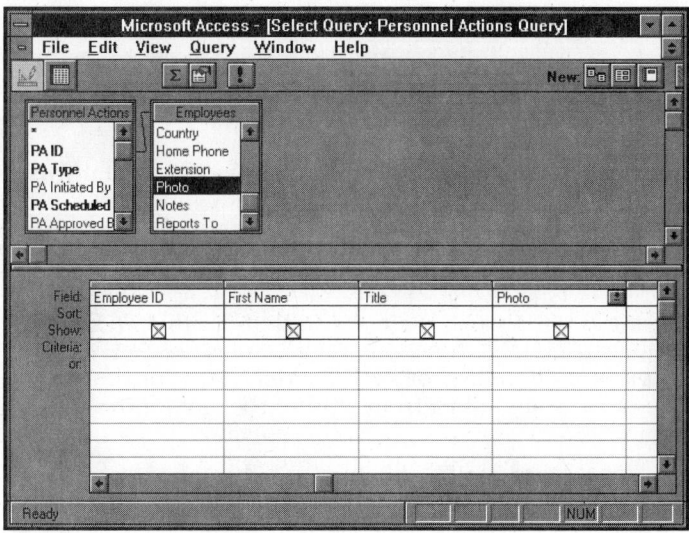

FIG. 13.1

Adding the Photo field to the Personnel Actions query.

Next, run the query so that you can view one of the photographs in the
Paintbrush window by following these steps:

1. Click the Datasheet button on the toolbar to run the query.

2. Drag the horizontal scroll bar button to the right to display the
   Photo field in the resulting table.

3. Double-click one of the Paintbrush Picture data cells to display
   the image in Windows Paintbrush. The chosen image appears in
   the Paintbrush window (see fig. 13.2).

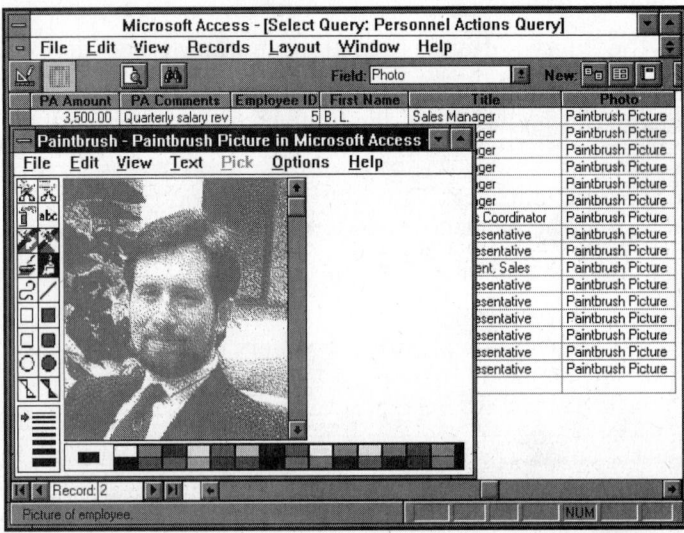

FIG. 13.2

Displaying a bit-
mapped image
from the Photo
field.

4. Choose Exit & Return to Microsoft Access from Paintbrush's **F**ile
   Menu to close the editing window.

Microsoft

Access

5. Chose **C**lose from Access's **F**ile menu and save your changes to
   the query.

The behavior of Paintbrush is similar to that of other OLE server applications used to add or edit the values (contents) of data cells in OLE
Object fields.

Displaying the Employee's Picture
in the Personnel Actions Form

You can edit OLE objects in Access tables and queries only through the
window of the OLE server (Paintbrush, in this example) you used to

add the objects to the table. The presentation of OLE objects, however, is stored in the OLE field and is automatically displayed in a bound or an unbound object frame. You double-click the object frame to edit the object.

To add a bound object frame to the Personnel Actions form so that you can display the Photo field of your Personnel Actions query, follow these steps:

1. Click the Form button in the Database window and choose the Personnel Actions form. If the Personnel Actions form is open, you must close it and then reopen it; the reason for this action is explained in the tip at the end of this section.

2. Click the Design button on the toolbar to open the form in Design mode.

3. Position the mouse pointer near the upper left corner of the Rating group frame.

4. Hold down the left mouse button and drag the mouse pointer to the lower right of the frame so that the entire frame is enclosed within the gray rectangle.

5. Release the mouse pointer. The frame and all the objects within it are selected.

6. Press the Delete key to remove the frame and its contents from your form to make room for the image.

7. Click the Field List button and select Photo from the Field List window.

8. Click Photo and drag the Field symbol to the approximate position of the upper left corner of the deleted Rating object frame. Access creates a bound object frame rather than a text box when you create a control directly from the Field List dialog box.

9. Select the Photo label and press the Delete key. A caption is not required for the employee photograph.

10. Position and size the new bound object frame as shown in figure 13.3.

11. Click the Form Run Mode button to display your form with the photograph. The form appears as in figure 13.4. Note that only a portion of the photograph appears within the frame. You still need to scale the image, which is the subject of the next section.

12. Click the Design button on the toolbar to return to Design mode.

FIG. 13.3

Adding a bound
object frame to
the Personnel
Actions form.

FIG. 13.4

The Personnel
Actions form in
Run mode with a
clipped image.

13. Click the Photo bound object frame; then click the Properties but-
    ton on the toolbar to display the frame's Properties window. You
    use entries in the Properties window described in the next section
    to modify your bound object frame.

An alternate method for creating a bound object frame is to click the
Bound Object Frame tool of the toolbox, and then click the Photo field

and drag the Field symbol to the form. The extra step involved in this process serves no purpose because Access chooses a bound object frame for you when you choose a field in the Field list that is of the OLE Object data type.

If you add the Photo field to your query and follow the procedure for adding a bound object frame while the Personnel Actions form is open, your frame may appear empty when you display the form in Run mode. In this case, the Photo field is added to the Datasheet view of your form, but the field's cells have null values. Pressing the Shift+F9 does not replace the null values with Paint-brush Picture. If this problem occurs, you must close the form and then reopen it from the Database window. Access runs the modi-fied query when you open the form, and the pictures appear.

Scaling Graphic Objects

Access provides three methods for scaling graphic objects within the confines of a bound object frame. You select one of these methods by choosing the value of the Scaling property in the Bound Object Frame Properties dialog box displayed in figure 13.5.

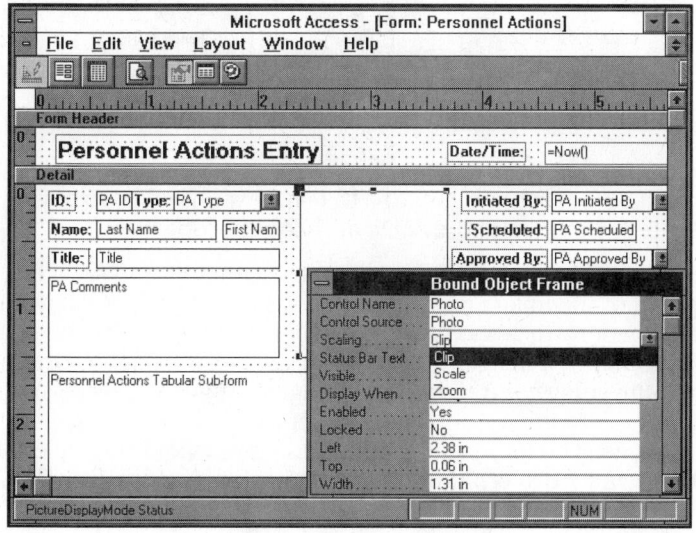

FIG. 13.5

Setting the Scaling property for a bound object frame.

The three options offered for the value of the Scaling property display the image in the following ways:

■ *Clip*, the default, displays the image in its original aspect ratio. The *aspect ratio* is the ratio of the width to the height of an image, measured in pixels or inches. A *pixel* is the smallest element of a bit map that your computer can display, a single dot. The aspect ratio of the standard VGA display is 640/480 pixels, which is 1.33:1, for example. If the entire image does not fit within the frame, the bottom and/or right of the image is cropped. *Cropping* an image is a graphic arts term that means cutting off the portions of an image so that it fits within a window of a specified size, as shown in the left-hand picture of figure 13.6.

■ *Scale* independently enlarges or shrinks the horizontal and vertical dimensions of the image to fill the frame. If the aspect ratio of the frame is not identical to that of the image, the image is distorted, as illustrated by the center image of figure 13.6.

■ *Zoom* enlarges or shrinks the horizontal or the vertical dimension of the image so that the image fits within the frame and the original aspect ratio is maintained. If your frame has a different aspect ratio than the image, a portion of the frame is empty, as shown in the right-hand image of figure 13.6.

FIG. 13.6

Examples of the Clip, Scale, and Zoom properties applied to a bit-mapped image.

Clip	Scale	Zoom

The bound object frames in figure 13.6 are expanded horizontally to accentuate the effects of the Scale and Zoom properties.

Version 1.0 of Access does not include the capability to specify a particular area of the image to be clipped, so zooming to maintain the original aspect ratio is the best choice in this case. When you scale or zoom a bit-mapped image, the apparent contrast is likely to increase, as shown in the center and right-hand images of figure 13.6. This increase results from deleting a sufficient number of pixels in the image to make it fit the frame. The increase in contrast is less evident if you choose a 256-color display driver, but doing so may slow the operation of Access significantly.

To apply the Zoom property to your bound object frame in Design mode, follow these steps:

1. Select the Photo bound object frame.

2. Click the Properties button on the toolbar to open the Bound Object Frame Properties dialog box.

3. Click the Scaling text box and open its list box.

4. Choose Zoom.

To display the form so that you can view the photograph with its new property, follow these steps:

1. Click the Form Run button on the toolbar to display your form, which now appears as shown in figure 13.7.

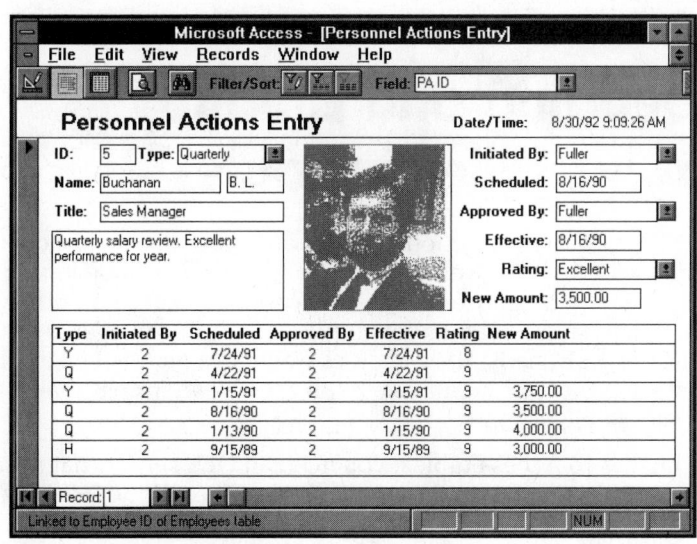

FIG. 13.7

The Personnel Actions form with a zoomed image.

2. If your frame includes an empty area, as illustrated in figure 13.7, return to Design mode, adjust the size of the frame, and rerun the form to verify that the frame has the correct dimensions (Width = 1.25 inches and Height = 1.44 inches in the Bound Object Frame Properties dialog box).

3. Choose **C**lose from the **F**ile menu and save your changes to the Personnel Actions form.

Adding a bound object frame that contains a vector image created with a drawing application, a sound clip from a .WAV or .MID file, or any other OLE object type involves the same technique described in this section.

To add a bound object frame to the Detail section of a report, you also use the same method outlined here. The quality of the printed image depends on the type of image and the laser or inkjet printer you use. Vector-based images, such as drawings created in CorelDRAW!, Micrografx Designer, or Windows DRAW!, result in more attractive printed reports than do bit-mapped images, especially when the bit map is scaled. The contrast problem discussed previously may be accentuated when color images are printed. If your use of images is intended primarily for printing, as in desktop publishing, and you do not have a color printer, use shades of gray for vector-based images. The 256-gray-scale palette is preferred for printing bit-mapped images; change color images to gray scale if your image-editing application supports this conversion.

Embedding and Linking Graphics Files in Tables

The modified Personnel Actions query you created in the preceding section provided the images for your form. In the example in this section, you create a database designed to catalog images and other OLE objects. If you have a substantial number of graphic images, such as clip art, or of multimedia files, such as waveform audio clips or MIDI music, storing them in a database (with their description) makes them readily accessible.

To add images to Access tables, you need an OLE server that is capable of importing bit-mapped and/or vector-based files. Windows 3.1's Paintbrush can serve this purpose for bit-mapped images, and the Microsoft Draw applet supplied with Word for Windows can import vector-based images in a variety of formats. Bit-mapped images are the most common form of graphic image, and bit maps are used exclusively in the Northwind Traders database.

Working with bit-mapped and other images when Access is running consumes a substantial proportion of Windows' *system* and *graphic resources*. Resources are areas of memory that Windows reserves for use by Windows itself (system resources) and screen images (graphic resources). Each application, whether in a window or minimized to an icon, consumes both system and graphic resources. You should close all applications except Access when you are embedding and linking graphic images.

If you need to open an application to copy an object to the Clipboard or create an image file, close the application when you are finished. If you receive `Insufficient Memory` or similar messages from Access or your OLE server application, press Ctrl+Esc to display the Windows Task Manager. Then select applications that are not required, and choose End Task to close them. If you continue to receive `Insufficient Memory` messages, close Windows and restart it from the DOS prompt. If the problem continues, you probably need to increase the amount of RAM memory in your computer; 4M of RAM is required for many of the examples that follow.

Examining Bit-Map Image File Formats

Graphics files are identified by generally accepted file extensions that serve to define most or all of the basic characteristics of the format. The following file extensions identify bit-map image files that have achieved the status of "industry standards" for the PC. The majority of commercial bit-map image editing applications support these formats, although some do not import .GIF files. The "standard" extensions follow:

■ *.BMP* for Windows bit-map files in 1-, 2-, 4-, 8-, and 24-bit color depths. .BMP files contain a bit-map information *header* defining the size of the image, the number of color planes, the type of compression used (if any), and information on the palette used. A header is a block of data in the file that precedes the image data.

■ *.DIB* for device-independent bit-map files. .DIB files are a variant of the .BMP format that include a color table in the header defining the .RGB values of the colors used.

■ *.PCX* for files that are compatible with ZSoft Paint applications. The .PCX file format is the common denominator for most bit-map file format conversions; almost every graphics application created in the past five years can handle .PCX files, including Windows Paintbrush. .PCX files are compressed by a method called *run-length encoding* (RLE) that can decrease the size of bit-map files by a factor of 3 or more, depending on their contents.

■ *.TIF* (an abbreviated form of TIFF) for tagged image format files. The TIFF format was originally developed by Aldus Corporation and now is managed by Microsoft Corporation. TIFF files originally were used primarily for storing scanned images but now are used as the preferred bit-map format by a substantial number of applications, including those for Windows. A special version of TIFF that uses file compression is used for fax transmission. TIFF files for conventional bit maps are found in both uncompressed and compressed formats. A tag in the header of the file defines information similar to that found in the information header of .BMP files.

■ *.JPG* for files created by applications that offer *JPEG* graphics compression and decompression options, such as Micrografx Picture Publisher 3.1. JPEG is an acronym for the Joint Photographic Experts Group, which has developed a standard methodology to compress and decompress still color images. Special JPEG adapter cards are available to speed the compression and decompression processes. JPEG compression often is used for video images, but MPEG (Moving Pictures Experts Group) compression is expected to predominate in the video field because it provides better compression ratios for video images than does the JPEG method. MPEG compression requires special adapter cards to display live-motion video images at the standard 30 frame-per-second rate.

■ *.PCD* (an abbreviation for Photo CD, Kodak's trademark) for photographic images that are digitized and stored on CD-ROMs by photofinishers. .PCD files use a special compression system devised by the Eastman Kodak Co., and you need Kodak's Photo CD Access application for Windows or an image editor, such as Picture Publisher 3.1, to display the images and save them to .PCD files.

■ *.GIF* for the graphics interchange file format used to archive bit-mapped images on CompuServe. Shareware and freeware .GIF file conversion applications for all popular types of personal computers are available for downloading from CompuServe's Graphic Support forum (GO GRAPHSUP). Graphic Workshop for Windows, GWSWIN.ZIP in Library x of the Zenith forum (GO ZENITH), is a shareware Windows graphics application that enables you to edit and convert compressed .GIF files to .BMP format. .GIF is the standard bit-map format for background images used by Autodesk Animator.

■ *.TGA* for files in the TARGA file format developed by True Vision for its TARGA product line of graphics adapter cards. TARGA cards were the first to offer relatively high-resolution, wide-spectrum color images with PCs by employing a separate video monitor. TARGA cards were the unchallenged standard for professional graphic artists until the advent of large-screen super-VGA displays.

■ *.IMG* for files created by applications that use Digital Research's GEM application, a graphical interface used by many applications that predate Windows 3.0, such as early versions of Ventura Publisher.

If you do not have a Windows image-editing application with OLE file server capability, you need to convert bit-map files in .TIF, .GIF, .TGA, or .IMG format to .BMP or .PCX format and use Windows 3.1's Paintbrush applet to import images and copy them to the Clipboard as OLE objects. You can use Word for Windows 2.0's bit-map file-conversion capability to insert a .TIF file in a new document and then copy the image to the Clipboard as a picture. You cannot edit the Word for Windows image that you paste into an Access table with Paste **S**pecial because the image is not an OLE object; it is a bit-map picture created from a DDE link to Word. Using Word for Windows to convert file formats is the subject of a section later in this chapter.

Store individual bit-map images in .PCX, not .BMP, files for use with Windows Paintbrush. Using .PCX files saves disk space compared with the .BMP format because .PCX uses RLE file compression. Line art (black on a white background) files compress the most, and 24-bit full-color photographic images the least. The JPEG (Joint Photographic Experts Group) compression offered by Micrografx Picture Publisher 3.1 works best for color images, especially images with more than 256 colors (16-bit, 18-bit, or 24-bit color).

Obtaining Graphics Files To Embed or Link

You need a few graphic images to paste into the OLE Objects table you create. If you are involved in desktop publishing or have an interest in the graphic arts, you probably have accumulated a collection of clip-art images in a variety of file formats. Convert a few of these images, if necessary, to .BMP or .PCX format with your image-editing application if it is not an OLE server.

You can download a wide range of clip-art and other graphics files in .GIF format from CompuServe's extensive collection. To search for graphics files, use the Graphics File Finder (GO GRAPHFF) and enter a keyword, such as **nouveau** for art nouveau, that describes the content of the image in which you are interested.

You also can create .BMP or .PCX files from the bit maps contained in the Categories table of NWIND.MDB. To export the bit-mapped images from the Categories table, follow these steps:

1. Click the Table button of the Database window and choose the Categories table.

2. Click the Open button to display the table in Datasheet view.

3. Double-click the Paintbrush Picture cell in the OLE Object field for the Beverages category. Paintbrush's window appears.

4. Choose **I**mage Attributes from the **O**ptions menu. The image size is approximately 1.79 by 1.25 inches or 172 x 120 pixels (pels). The image is a 16-color bit map, so the default file type, 16-color Bitmap (.BMP), is satisfactory. Make a note of the image size so that you can add the dimensions to the table later. Choose Cancel (choosing OK will cause you to lose the image).

5. Choose Save **A**s from the Paintbrush's **E**dit menu and name the file **bevr.bmp**. Choose OK to save the file. You can choose to save the file in .PCX format by choosing .PCX Files (.PCX) from the Save File as Type combo box. As mentioned previously, .PCX format is the better choice with large 256-color bit maps because the image is compressed and consumes less disk space.

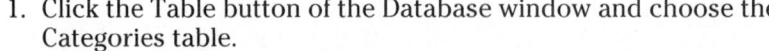

6. Choose E**x**it from Paintbrush's **F**ile menu to close the instance of Paintbrush.

7. Repeat steps 3 through 6 for the remaining categories, using the value of the Category ID field for the file name.

Access

You now have a collection of .BMP or .PCX files that you can import into the OLE Object field of the tables in your new database.

Creating a New OLE Objects Database

The OLE objects that serve as examples in the remainder of this chapter aren't related to Northwind Traders' operations. A good database design practice is not to include tables that contain unrelated data in an existing database. Creating a new database adds a margin of safety; if one of your OLE servers misbehaves and corrupts the database, you don't destroy the existing database (NWIND.MDB, in this case). In this section, you learn how to create a new OLE Objects database to serve as a catalog of the OLE objects you embed and link.

To create your new database, follow these steps:

1. Open the Database window and choose New Database from the File menu.

2. Assign the file name **ole_objs.mdb** to your new database in the File Name text box and choose OK. Access creates the new database.

3. Click the Table button; then click the New button to create a new table.

4. Add the fields listed in table 13.1 to the new table.

Table 13.1. Field Specifications for the OLE Objects Table			
Field Name	**Data Type**	**Size/Format**	**Description**
Name of Object	Text	30	Short description of object
Copyright	Text	20	Owner, if copyrighted, Public (domain), if not
Filename	Text	12	Name of source file
Date	Date/Time	Short Date	Date object was acquired
Linked	Yes/No	N/A	Yes if linked, No if embedded
Type	Text	20	Type of OLE object: Bitmap, Drawing, MIDI file, WAVE file, or Video
Format	Text	20	Source application
Size 1	Number	Single	Original size of image, in inches or pixels (horizontal) or bytes (other files)
Size 2	Number	Single	Original size of image, in inches or pixels (vertical)
OLE Object	OLE Object	N/A	Linked or embedded OLE object
Description	Memo	N/A	Description of object

5. Click the Properties button on the toolbar and type **OLE Objects Catalog** in the Description text box of the Table Properties dialog box.

6. Set the index (in the Index1 text box) to **Type;Date**. This table does not need a primary key because the table is not related to any other table. Your table in Design mode appears as shown in figure 13.8.

7. Click the Datasheet button on the toolbar to display the table in Run mode. Save the changes and give your new table the name **OLE Objects** in the Save As dialog box. Click No when asked whether you want to add a primary key.

Additional fields are required to indicate the beginning and ending positions of multimedia sound files, such as waveform audio, MIDI, animation, and video files. Adding multimedia-related OLE objects is the subject of the section "Adding Multimedia Objects to Your Tables," later in this chapter.

For Related Information:

◄◄ "Creating a New Database," p. 127.

Incorporating Bit-Mapped Images in Tables

The common denominator for bit-mapped images in Access databases is Windows 3.1's Paintbrush application. Although you may have an OLE-compatible image editor, such as Micrografx Picture Publisher 3.1 or Corel PhotoPaint!, Paintbrush is quick to load and easy to use. The techniques you use with most OLE-compliant image editors are similar to those presented here for Paintbrush.

In the following sections, you learn various methods for adding bit-mapped images to your tables, including embedding images from other files, linking other bit-map files, pasting non-OLE objects, and creating OLE objects from objects in non-OLE applications.

Embedding Images from Files

Access includes a feature that is not commonly found in other OLE clients. It gives you the ability to specify a file to be loaded into the server application, instead of requiring that the server be able to paste from a previously opened file. This action saves several steps in the embedding process.

To embed an image in your OLE Objects table, follow these steps:

1. Click the Datasheet View button, if necessary, to return to Run mode. Type **NWIND Beverages** in the Object Name field of the append record of the OLE Objects table, and type **bevr.bmp** in the File Name field.

2. Move to the OLE Object field and choose Insert Object from the **E**dit menu. The Insert Object dialog box shown in figure 13.9 appears.

3. Choose Paintbrush Picture from the Object Type list box and click the File button to display the Insert Object from File dialog box shown in figure 13.10.

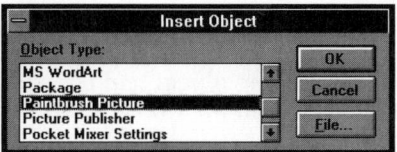

FIG. 13.9

Choosing an OLE object from available object types.

FIG. 13.10

Viewing the list of files compatible with the chosen object type.

4. Double-click BEVR.BMP (or select BEVR.BMP and choose OK). Paintbrush Picture appears in the OLE Object data cell of the first record.

5. Double-check that the correct image has been pasted by double-clicking the Paintbrush Picture cell. Paintbrush's window appears as shown in figure 13.11.

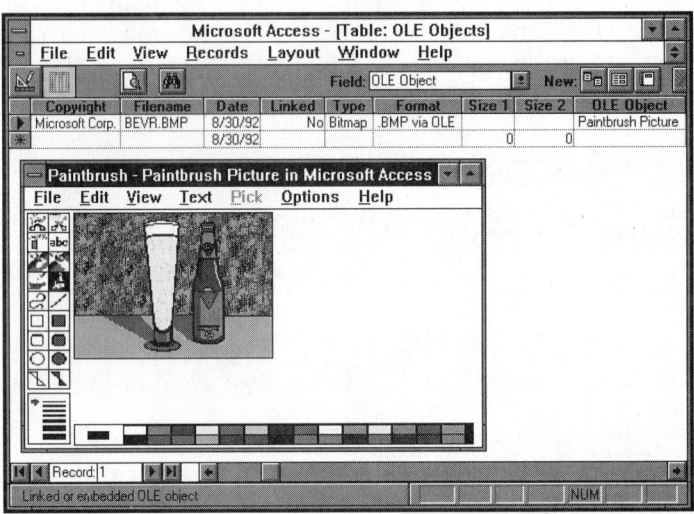

FIG. 13.11

Viewing the picture you added to the OLE Object field.

The text in the title bar, Paintbrush Picture in Microsoft Access, indicates that the image has been embedded in, not linked to, the OLE Object data cell. (If the object had been linked, the file name BEVR.BMP would appear in the title bar.)

Access

6. Choose **E**xit & Return to Microsoft Access from the **F**ile menu to close Paintbrush.

If you choose a file extension in the List Files of Type combo box that is associated by an entry in REG.DAT with an OLE server different from the OLE object type you chose in the Insert Object dialog box, the server changes. Your original OLE object type selection is overridden by the OLE server specified for the extension in REG.DAT. Some image editors appropriate all bit-map file types in REG.DAT by changing the .bmp = PBrush and .pcx = PBrush entries, plus other bit-map extensions, to their own server alias. Picture Publisher 3.1, for example, changes the value of both .bmp and .pcx entries to =BitmapImage, its server alias.

If you have installed Picture Publisher or another OLE-compliant image editor and want to use Paintbrush in the examples, change the values of .bmp and .pcx to PBrush in the Value text box. Choose **S**ave Changes from the **F**ile menu to revise the file extension associations. This situation is one of the reasons an entire section of Chapter 12 is devoted to RegEdit and the registration database.

You cannot use the Insert Object from File process under any of the following five conditions:

- An error message states that the OLE server is not responding or that it cannot establish a link to the file.

- An error message states that the OLE data you are attempting to paste is corrupted.

- The file type you want to paste to your table field has been assigned to one OLE server, and you want to use another, such as Corel Photo-Paint!, that does not add its own file association entries to REG.DAT.

- The file extensions associated with the server in REG.DAT do not include the extension of the file type you want to use.

- You want to link, not embed, the file. Linking image files is the subject of the next subsection.

To embed a file when one of the first four of these conditions prevails, follow these steps:

1. Move to the OLE Object field and select the OLE Object data cell in the append record.

2. Choose Insert Object from the **F**ile menu.

3. Choose Paintbrush Picture or the OLE object type you want from the Insert Object list box and choose OK. Paintbrush is used in this example.

4. Paintbrush appears with a blank window. Choose Paste **F**rom from the **E**dit menu and choose your Access directory in the Paste From dialog box that appears.

5. Double-click BEVR.BMP to paste it into Paintbrush's window. Make sure that you do not click the mouse anywhere inside the image-editing window; if you do, you delete the selection (cutout) rectangle that outlines the image.

6. If you do not want to embed the entire image, use the rectangular selection tool to create the dashed selection rectangle that outlines the portion of the image you want to embed. Choose **C**opy from the **E**dit menu to paste the selection to the Clipboard.

Access

7. Choose Exit & Return to Microsoft Access from the **F**ile menu. The message box shown in figure 13.12 appears.

8. Click No because you paste the copy from the Clipboard to your OLE Object field.

9. Choose Paste **S**pecial from Access's **E**dit menu. In the Paste Special dialog box that appears, choose Paintbrush Picture Object, if necessary, and click the Paste button (see fig. 13.13).

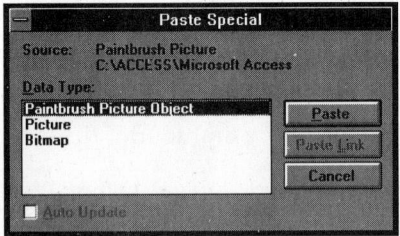

10. If you receive a message that the server is not responding, click No to avoid further retries. The server does not need to respond after the object has been copied to the Clipboard.

Make sure that you choose Paste From from the Edit menu, not Open from the File menu, in step 4. If you make the latter choice, you are informed by a message box that you will break the link between Paintbrush and your Access table. Choose Copy from the Edit menu in step 6, not Exit & Return to Microsoft Access from the File menu (the normal procedure for exiting an OLE server application). Exit & Return to Microsoft Access embeds the 640-by-480-pixel bit map, not the selected portion of the image, in your OLE Object data cell.

Linking Bit-Mapped Image Files

Linking files requires that you *open* rather than *paste* the file in the OLE server application. To link COND.BMP to a new record in your OLE Object field, for example, follow these steps:

1. Move to the OLE Object field and select the OLE Object data cell of the append record. Choose Insert Object from the Edit menu.

2. Choose Paintbrush Picture from the Object Type list box of the Insert Object dialog box; then choose OK.

3. Choose Open from Paintbrush's File menu and double-click COND.BMP in your Access directory.

4. When the message box shown in figure 13.14 appears, indicating that the link to Access will be broken, click No so that you do not update the data in the cell.

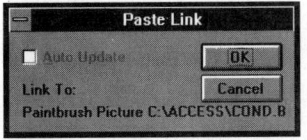

FIG. 13.14

The Paste Link dialog box for a Paintbrush picture.

5. Using the rectangular selection (cutout) tool, select the portion of the image you want to copy.

6. Choose Copy from the Edit menu to paste the selected portion of the image to the Clipboard.

7. Choose Exit from the File menu. (Exit & Return to Microsoft Access does not appear as a File menu command, because the link to Access was broken in step 5.)

Access

8. Choose Paste **L**ink from Access's **E**dit menu. The Paste Link dialog box that appears verifies that you are linking, not embedding, the image data (see fig. 13.14). The **A**uto Update check box is disabled (dimmed) because the Auto Update feature that automatically updates the linked image when it is edited in another application is not available for Bound Objects.

9. Confirm that the data is linked rather than embedded by double-clicking the OLE Object data cell and verifying that the file name appears in the Paintbrush title bar, as shown in figure 13.15.

10. Close Paintbrush by choosing E**x**it from the **F**ile menu.

Access

If the server cannot open a linked file, you receive the message shown in figure 13.16. The image continues to appear in the bound object frame, because Access maintains a persistent image of the linked object in the form of a picture. Pictures of linked graphics files are a copy of the last presentation of an object.

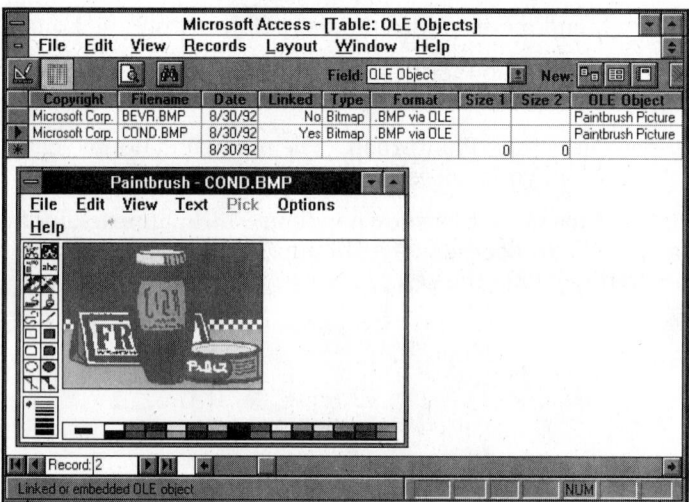

FIG. 13.15

Confirming a link to a graphics file by viewing the title bar of the OLE server's window.

FIG. 13.16

The message box indicating that the OLE server cannot find the linked file.

If you change the location of a linked file on your local fixed disk or on a network server and then try to edit the file, you receive a message similar to the one shown in figure 13.16. The fully qualified path to the linked file is included in the linking data. If you are creating an application with linked files for others to use, the linked files must be located on a drive with the same designator and in a directory with the same path as when the link was stored in your table. If the linked files are located on a network server, the user's logical drive designator must be the same as yours when you created the link. Similarly, the directory tree structure must be identical. Changing a link to reflect a new file name or path is the subject of a section later in this chapter called "Changing the Link to an Object."

Pasting Images That Are Not OLE Objects

OLE Object fields are capable of displaying images incorporated in applications that do not support OLE or that use an OLE Clipboard format not recognized by Access. Word for Windows was mentioned earlier in the chapter as an example of an application that can import graphic images in a variety of formats and display them as bit maps in a document. You can copy Word for Windows pictures to the Clipboard and paste them into Access OLE Object fields. To do so, you create a dynamic data exchange (DDE) link rather than an OLE process. After the image is pasted into the OLE Object data cell, the DDE link is broken, and a connection to the server that created the image no longer exists.

To paste a picture from a Word for Windows document into a data cell of an OLE Object field, follow these steps:

1. Select the picture in the Word for Windows document; then press Ctrl+C to copy the picture to the Clipboard.

2. Open Access; open the OLE_OBJS database; then open the OLE Object data cell into which you want to paste the picture.

3. Choose Paste **S**pecial from the **E**dit menu. The Paste Special dialog box offers three choices for graphics data type—Picture, Device Independent Bitmap, and Bitmap—as shown in figure 13.17. Note that the Paste **L**ink button is disabled because you cannot link to an OLE Object field an object that is not created by an OLE server.

4. Choose the Picture data type, if it is not selected by default; then click the Paste button. The image is pasted to the selected data cell, which displays Picture as its content.

FIG. 13.17

Preparing to
paste a non-OLE
object.

Importing Encapsulated PostScript (EPS) images into Word for Windows 2+ does not result in an image you can edit, nor is Word's bit-mapped presentation of EPS images satisfactory for most applications. Incorporating EPS images in Access tables is discussed in the section "Adding Vector Images," later in this chapter.

The Picture data type appears in the Paste Special dialog box even if you copy an image from a Windows application that does not support DDE. In this case, however, the source is indicated as Unknown. Images pasted from these applications appear to copy to the Clipboard, but other applications do not recognize the copy as a valid Clipboard object. Use the method outlined in the following section to paste images from these applications to Access OLE Object fields.

Creating OLE Objects from Images Created in Non-OLE Applications

A better, but indirect, approach than that of the preceding section is to paste the image into Windows Paintbrush or any other OLE-compliant image-editing application and then link or embed the image to or in your Access OLE Object field. This method creates an editable image that you can link to or embed in your table. The method is especially useful when you scan images with a Windows scanning application that does support OLE or a DOS scanning application that cannot save files in .PCX or .BMP format.

To create an OLE object with Paintbrush and link or embed the object to or in your Access table, follow these steps:

1. Select and copy the image to the Clipboard if the image was created by a Windows application.

 2. Launch Paintbrush.

3. If the image has been copied to the Clipboard, choose **P**aste from the **E**dit menu; otherwise choose **O**pen from the **F**ile menu and open the file. If you open a file, use the rectangular selection tool to enclose the portion of the image you want to use. Only selected images can be copied to the Clipboard.

4. If you want to link the image, choose Save **A**s from the **F**ile menu, give the image an appropriate file name, and save the image as a .BMP or .PCX file. If you want to embed the image, skip this step. You choose the file type from the Save File as Type drop-down list box.

5. Press Ctrl+C or choose **C**opy from the **E**dit menu to copy the image to the Clipboard as an OLE object.

Access

6. Open Access and the OLE Objects table, if it is not open. Select the OLE Object data cell into which you want to paste the image.

Table

7. Choose Paste **S**pecial (to embed) or Paste **L**ink (to link) from Access's **E**dit menu.

8. Choose OK to paste or link the Paintbrush Picture object.

You can use Paintbrush or any other OLE-compliant image editor to create an OLE object of any bit-mapped picture that you can select and copy to the Clipboard or that you can save as a .BMP or .PCX file.

The default image attributes of Paintbrush determine the maximum size of the image that you can display and edit. The default value for the image size is determined by the VGA mode in use—640 x 480 pixels for standard VGA mode. If the default image size is less than the dimensions of your image, Paintbrush compresses the image to fit.

If an image you paste into Paintbrush is compressed, choose **I**mage Attributes from the **O**ptions menu and set the dimensions in pixels (pels) to values equal to or greater than those of the image you want to paste. After changing the image attributes, click No when asked whether you want to save the compressed image. Choose **P**aste from the **E**dit menu again to import an uncompressed version of the image.

Considering Database File Size

The size of the .MDB file containing one or more tables that include graphic images embedded in or linked to values in OLE Object fields grows rapidly. The data component of bit-mapped graphic images is stored in .DIB format. Device-independent bit maps are not compressed; your file, therefore, may grow by much more than the increment of the size of a .PCX file whose data you embed. The number of bytes per pixel of the four different types of .DIBs that can be stored in OLE fields and the size of the data of a full-screen standard VGA image using each type of .DIB is shown in table 13.2.

Table 13.2. Comparing File Sizes of Bit-Map Images in Access Tables		
Type of Bit Map	**Bytes per Pixel**	**Size of 640-by-480 Image**
Black and white	1/8	38.4K
16-color	1/2	153.6K
256-color	1	307,200K
24-bit color	3	921,600K

You can approximate the file-size increment of smaller images from table 13.2 by dividing by 4 for a 320-by-240-pixel image and by 16 for a 160-by-120-pixel image. You can see from the table that your file can become large quite quickly as you add new images. File sizes can become astronomical when you embed or link large, 24-bit color images from sources such as Kodak's Photo CD. Fortunately, Photo CDs contain small *contact sheet* images, also called *thumbnails*, about the size of the image in a 35-mm slide, that you can embed or link with Picture Publisher 3.1.

Your .MDB file grows larger by the file size of your image whether you link or embed the images. If you link a .PCX file, your .MDB file may grow by more than the size of the .PCX file because .PCX files are compressed, and the data stored in .DIB format in your OLE Object field is not compressed.

As briefly mentioned earlier in the chapter, Version 1.0 of Access maintains a copy of the presentation of linked OLE objects so that the image displays whether the link to the file is intact or broken. You don't, therefore, save file space by linking images or other OLE objects whose presentations consist of their data. All graphic objects and spreadsheets created with Excel fall into this category, but most multimedia objects do not.

Chapter 15, "Using Access with Microsoft Excel," describes methods of creating links to worksheets without embedding the entire worksheet in your Access table. You can use Object Packager with a file linked to the package to embed or link to OLE graphic objects without a graphic presentation. This technique is discussed in the section on "Linking or Embedding MIDI Files with Media Player 1.0 and Object Packager," located near the end of this chapter.

Designing a Form To Add, Display, and Edit Images

Adding images to your OLE objects catalog by making entries in Table Datasheet view is tedious, at best. With only a few minutes of work, however, you can create a simple form to display and edit images in your table and to add images when necessary.

To create the basic OLE Objects Catalog form, follow these steps:

1. Click the Form button in the Database window; then click the New button.

2. Choose OLE Objects as the table to act as the data source for your form.

3. Click the Blank Form button in the New Form dialog box.

4. Drag the right and bottom margin lines to expand the size of the default blank form to the full width of the Design window and about three-fourths the depth.

5. Click the Field List button on the toolbar. From the Field List dialog box that appears, add each of the fields of the OLE Objects table by clicking and dragging the field symbol to your form. Figure 13.18 shows a suggested design. You may want to edit the labels to correspond with those shown in the figure and set their text attributes to bold by selecting each label and clicking the Bold button on the toolbar.

6. Click the OLE Object field in the Field List box and drag the Field symbol to add a second, smaller bound object frame (shown selected in fig. 13.18) in the lower-right corner of the large bound object frame. The purpose of the smaller frame is to display a zoomed "thumbnail" image.

7. With the small bound object frame selected, click the Properties button on the toolbar, and choose Zoom for the frame's Scale property in the Properties window. You then can display a miniature version of the entire image. The larger bound object frame displays the image with the default Clip setting for the Scale property so that image's size is evident when displayed.

FIG. 13.18

The design of the OLE Objects form.

8. Choose the Describe text box and set its Scrollbars property in the Properties window to Vertical.

9. Click the Form Run Mode button on the toolbar. The first image you added to the OLE Objects table and a portion of the second image appears, as shown in figure 13.19.

FIG. 13.19

Viewing the OLE Objects form in Run mode.

10. Choose Save **As** from the **File** menu, and save Form1 as **OLE Objects**.

You can use your OLE Objects form with any type of OLE object, including sound and video clips. Adding multimedia objects to your database is discussed in the last section of this chapter, "Adding Multimedia Objects to Your Tables."

For Related Information:

◄◄ "Selecting, Editing, and Moving Form Elements and Controls," p. 392.

FROM HERE...

Adding Vector Images

Vector images define lines and surfaces by the numeric values of their positions (coordinates) within a rectangular window. Each element of a vector image, including text, is independently scalable and may be assigned colors and attributes. The properties of an OLE vector-image object consist of a list of each element in the image and the element's characteristics, such as position relative to the window, color, line style (solid, dotted, dashed, and so on), text character, typeface name, and font size. OLE vector-image objects are created by drawing applications and computer-aided design (CAD) applications. Vector images are used to display maps created by geographic information systems (GIS), a new and growing market for Windows applications. Clip-art images for desktop publishing usually are supplied in vector rather than bit-mapped format.

Vector images have the following advantages compared with bit-mapped images:

■ *Scaling* the image is accomplished without distortion. When you change the scale of a bit-mapped image by other than powers of 2 (2, 4, 8, 1/2, 1/4, 1/8, and so on), the image appears distorted, and its contrast changes, as discussed earlier in the chapter.

■ *Colors* of individual elements of vector drawings may be altered to your preferences. You can create a colorful version of an image for on-screen display of forms and a similar image with gray-scale tones or patterns for the printing of reports.

- *Printing* takes advantage of the full 300-dpi (dots per inch) or higher resolution of your laser printer. When you print a bit-mapped image with a laser printer, the resolution of the image is limited to that of the original; 96 pixels per inch is typical resolution. The lower resolution gives bit-mapped images a property called "the jaggies" that is evident when you examine a printed bit-map image containing curved lines.

- *Size* of the data used to create vector images is usually much smaller than a bit map of equal dimensions.

The Microsoft Graph application supplied with Access creates vector images, as do the Microsoft Draw and WordArt applets included with Word for Windows 2+. Each of these applications is an OLE server only; none of them can save files that you can link to an Access OLE Object field. Full-scale OLE-compliant drawing applications, such as Micrografx Windows Draw! 3.0 with OLE, Micrografx Designer 3.1, and CorelDRAW! 3.0, can save files in a variety of formats, including Windows meta files (.WMF), which is the native Clipboard format for vector images. If you have a pre-OLE version of a drawing application that can create .WMF, .DRW, or .DXF files, you can embed them in an OLE Object field with Microsoft Draw.

Examining Vector Image File Formats

Just as many vector file formats as bit-map formats are in common use. The "standard" file formats for vector-based images on the PC are similar to each other but store the vector data by different methods, as described in the following paragraphs:

- *.WMF* indicates a Windows meta file, the standard vector-based file structure of Windows. You can embed or link .WMF files by importing them into the Microsoft Draw applet.

- *.PPT* files are created by Microsoft PowerPoint. These files contain single or multiple Windows meta files.

- *.CGM* stands for computer graphics meta file, the original vector image file format for PCs. .CGM files are uncommon today, but the majority of full-scale drawing packages support the format.

- *.DRW* files are Micrografx Designer files. Windows Draw! also uses .DRW files as its native format. These files contain mathematic representations of *Bézier curves*. The shape of a Bézier curve is determined by positioning control points at each end of the curve. Microsoft Draw embeds and links .DRW files.

- *.CDR*, CorelDRAW! format, uses Bézier curves and is similar to Micrografx's .DRW format.

- *.EPS* is an abbreviation for Encapsulated PostScript files whose structure was developed by Adobe Systems, Inc., for compatibility with its PostScript page-description language for printers. .EPS is the most popular format for commercial clip-art packages that are not provided by a drawing application publisher. .EPS files can include bit maps, and a low-resolution bit-map header is usually added to the basic .EPS vector data to provide a rough illustration of the vector image contained in the file. .EPS also is referred to as .AI (Adobe Illustrator) format.

- *.DXF* files are drawing exchange files created by Autodesk's AutoCAD product and are used primarily for architectural and engineering drawings. Most advanced drawing applications include .DXF file conversion. Most other CAD applications can import and export .DXF files. The Microsoft Draw applet includes limited .DXF file embedding and linking capability.

- *.WPG* files are WordPerfect graphic files created by WordPerfect Corporation's DOS and Windows word processing and DOS WordPerfect Presentations graphics applications. Microsoft Draw imports .WPG files.

- *.FLI* and *.FLC* files, created by Autodesk Animator, are the file types most often supported by presentation and animation applications that include animation capabilities.

With the exception of .FLI and .FLC files, most drawing applications include the capability to import any of these vector file formats and convert them, by an application component called an *import filter*, to the format native to the application. Export filters usually mirror the import filter set.

In addition, you can use Word for Windows graphic import capability to insert CGM, EPS, HGL (Hewlett-Packard Graphic Language), and PLT (AutoCAD plotter files) and import them via DDE as pictures, using the process described in a previous section, "Pasting Images That Are Not OLE Objects." The images lose their capability to scale without distortion because Word converts them to bit maps, not vector images.

Using Microsoft Draw To Embed Vector Images

The techniques used to embed and link bit-mapped images discussed in the previous sections apply in most instances to vector images. If you substitute Microsoft Draw for Windows Paintbrush in many of the preceding examples, you achieve the same result, although some of the menu choices differ. The following example uses Microsoft Draw to embed a portion of a .CGM vector drawing of a U.S. Geological Survey 7.5-minute map of the Oshkosh quadrangle. The file was created by American Digital Cartography of Appleton, Wisconsin, and can be downloaded from CompuServe as CGMMAP.ZIP (.CGM format) or DRWMAP.ZIP (Windows Draw! format) from the Micrografx library of the IBM Applications A forum (GO WINAPA). You can use any vector image you have in a compatible file format if you don't want to download one of these maps.

Creating a zoomed bound object, especially from a vector image, takes longer than displaying a clipped image. Access must scale each component of the image to fit the zoomed object's frame. To speed movement between records, change to Design mode and delete the bound object frame you created for the thumbnail image in the examples.

To embed a vector image in the OLE Objects table from a .CGM, .DRW, .DXF, .WMF, or .WPG file, follow these steps:

1. Append a new record to the table by using the Record Selection buttons.

2. Click the surface of the bound object frame to select the OLE Object field.

3. Choose Insert Object from Access's **E**dit menu.

4. Double-click Microsoft Drawing in the Object Type list box of the Insert Object dialog box. Microsoft Draw's window opens.

5. Choose **I**mport Picture from Draw's **F**ile menu. The Import Picture dialog box appears, as shown in figure 13.20. 44088a5.CGM is the file name for the map of Oshkosh, Wisconsin, to be imported in this example.

6. Choose the directory in which your vector-image file is located, choose the file name, and choose OK.

7. If you are importing from a file type other than .WMF, choose only the Emulate Line Styles and Use Scalable Fonts check boxes in the next dialog box that appears. Emulate Line Styles chooses the closest approximation of the original file's line style (such as dashed, dotted, and so on) that is available in Microsoft Draw. Use Scalable Fonts causes the size of typefaces to change in proportion to any scale changes you make to the drawing in Microsoft Draw.

FIG. 13.20

Using Microsoft Draw to select an image to import.

8. Microsoft Draw converts the file to its native .WMF format and displays the image. You can select specific elements of the file to include in your imported image. Refer to the documentation or on-line help for Microsoft Draw for instructions on editing the image.

9. After editing the image, choose **E**xit & Return to Microsoft Access from Draw's **F**ile menu. Your image and its thumbnail (if you did not delete the thumbnail object frame) appear as shown in figure 13.21.

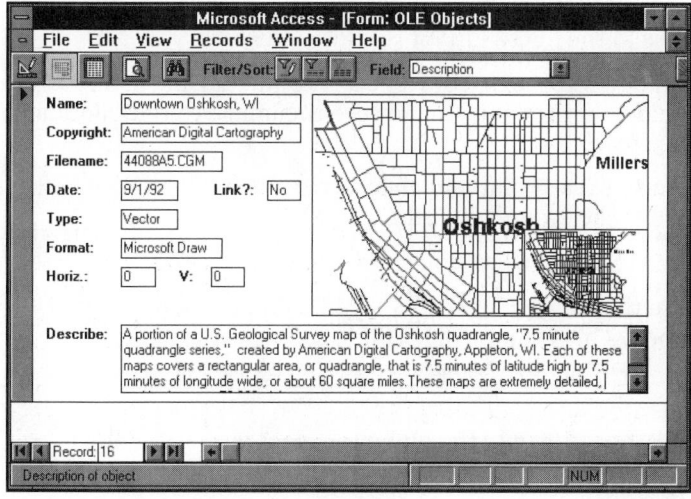

FIG. 13.21

A presentation of the vector image in the OLE Objects form.

After you have pasted the vector image to a record, you can double-click the bound object frame to edit the image. The process described in the preceding nine steps is applicable to any vector file that you can import into Microsoft Draw. If you use a commercial OLE-compliant drawing application, the process is identical, but the menu choices for importing a file may differ slightly.

 WordPerfect 5+ for DOS, WordPerfect for Windows, and WordPerfect Presentations each include a graphic-conversion utility that you can use to convert .CGM, .HGL,, .EPS, and .IMG files to .WPG files. The WordPerfect for DOS application is GRAPHCNV.EXE. You can import the WPG files into Microsoft Draw if you included the DrawPerfect graphics filter for use with Microsoft Draw when you installed Word for Windows. If you did not install the WPG filter, run the SETUP application from your Word for Windows distribution disks, choose Custom Installation, and then choose only Text Conversions and Graphics Filters. You can choose the filters to install from the list box.

Embedding Nonstandard OLE Vector Images in Tables

Some Windows applications published by Microsoft that predate Windows 3.1, such as Excel 3.0 and PowerPoint 2.0, incorporate OLE capabilities but are not fully compatible with the version of OLE in Windows 3.1. PowerPoint 2.0, a component of Microsoft Office, is a rich source of vector images in Windows meta-file format. The images are contained in PPT files in the \POWERPNT\CLIPART directory.

To embed a .WMF image from a PowerPoint .PPT file in an Access OLE Object field, you first need to capture the image to the Clipboard. Follow these steps:

1. Launch PowerPoint and choose **O**pen from the **F**ile menu.

2. Choose the \POWERPNT\CLIPART directory and open a file, such as MAPS.PPT.

3. From the list of images displayed, choose the image you want to embed. This example uses Slide 3, Side View of Globe. You can use the **C**olor menu commands if you want to change the colors of the globe.

4. Click the surface of the globe to select only the globe image, shown framed (selected) in figure 13.22.

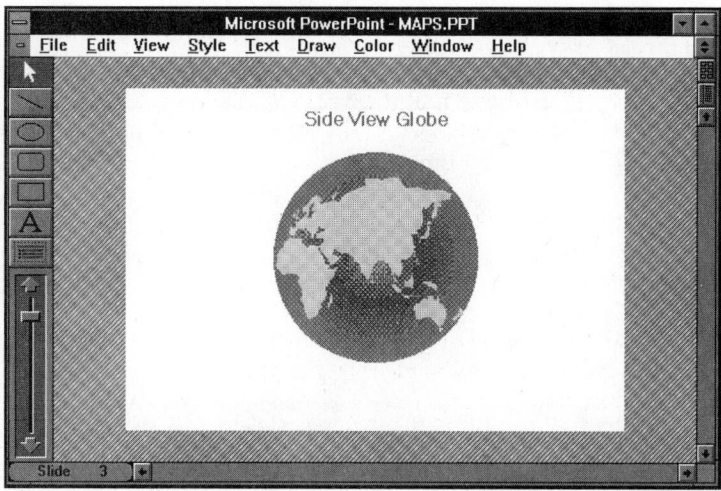

FIG. 13.22

A clip-art image of a world map displayed in PowerPoint.

5. Press Ctrl+C, or choose **C**opy from PowerPoint's **E**dit menu to copy the selected image to the Clipboard.

6. Choose E**x**it from the **F**ile menu to close PowerPoint.

Now you are ready to embed the object in your Access table by following these steps:

1. Append a new record to the OLE Objects table in Access by using the record selection buttons.

2. Click the bound object frame to select it and then choose Insert Ob**j**ect from Access's **E**dit menu.

3. Choose Microsoft Drawing from the Object Type list box of the Insert Object dialog box and choose OK.

4. When Microsoft Draw's window appears, choose **P**aste from Draw's **E**dit menu.

5. For this example, click the upper-right selection handle of the image and drag it diagonally down and to the left to reduce the size of the image to that shown in figure 13.23. This process requires two or three steps; relocate the image to the upper-left corner of Draw's window each time you reduce the globe's size.

6. Choose E**x**it & Return to Microsoft Access from Draw's **F**ile menu. The image appears in your Access form as illustrated in figure 13.24.

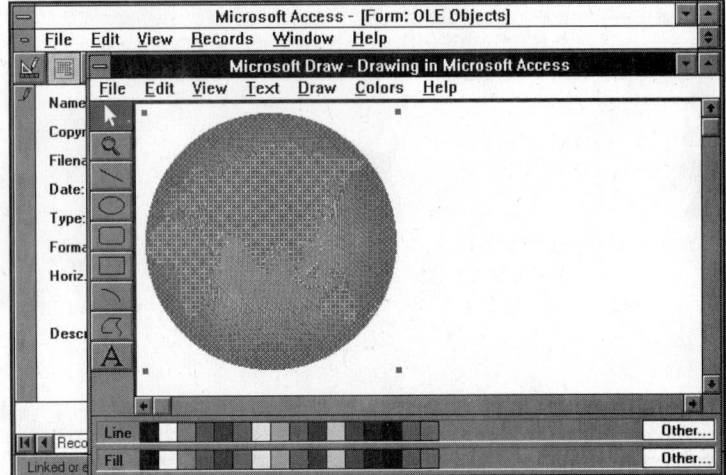

FIG. 13.23

A PowerPoint image imported into Microsoft Draw.

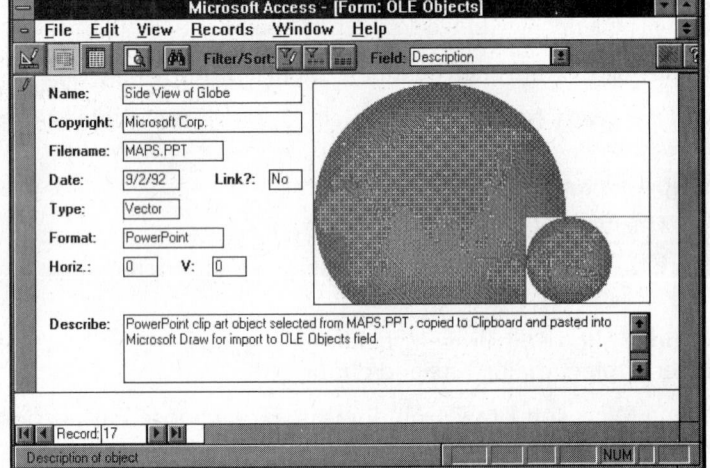

FIG. 13.24

The presentation of the world globe image in the OLE Objects form.

If you have created a large number of slides in PowerPoint or any other OLE-compliant presentation graphics application, you can catalog them by subject in the OLE Objects table. Just add another field or two to categorize the slides. If you use keywords to describe the slides, you can apply filters to display only the specific slides you want for a new presentation.

The process just described is applicable to any vector image that you cannot import as an editable OLE object into an OLE Object field of an Access table. Non-OLE objects are indicated by an Unknown data source and a single choice, Picture, in the Data Type list box of the Paste Special dialog box. For example, if you copy a PowerPoint image to the Clipboard and then choose Paste **S**pecial from Access's **E**dit menu, the Paste Special dialog box appears as shown in figure 13.25.

FIG. 13.25

The Paste Special dialog box when an uneditable image is in the Clipboard.

If you paste an image with the Picture data type directly into the OLE Object field of an Access table, you cannot edit the image or change its size. If you do not know whether the application you are using is OLE compliant, copy a test image to the Clipboard and then use Access's Paste Special dialog box to display the available data formats. If Object appears in the Data Type list box, the application is a Windows 3.1 OLE server.

Do not choose **P**aste as a substitute for Paste **S**pecial when importing OLE or other objects to OLE Object fields. If you choose **P**aste, the image is imported with the default data type, whatever that may be for the item copied to the Clipboard. With **P**aste, you do not get the opportunity to verify that the Clipboard item is the one you want or to choose the data type.

Controlling Links to the Original Object

The links that bind OLE objects to fields in Access tables can be changed when necessary or abandoned if you prefer. Links are controlled by a pop-up menu of the *Object Name* Ob**j**ect command on the **E**dit menu, shown in figure 13.26. (The name of the object, such as Paintbrush Picture in fig. 13.26, appears in place of *Object Name* on the **E**dit menu.) This command does not appear for images that have been added as or changed to the Picture data type.

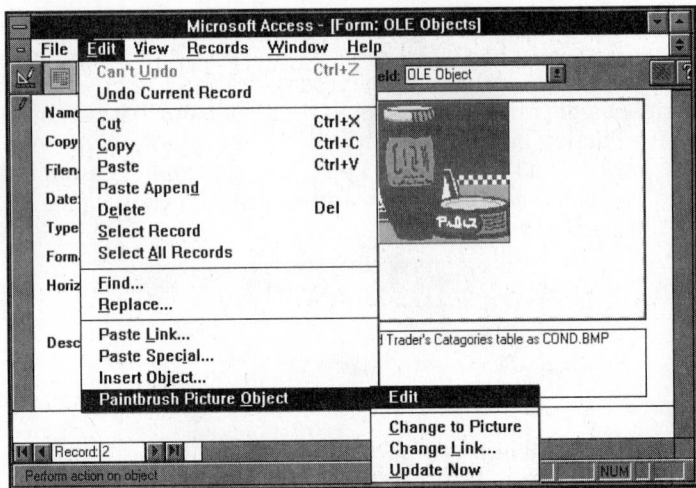

FIG. 13.26

The *Object Name* Object menu.

The four commands on the *Object Name* Object menu have the following effects:

- *Edit* launches the OLE server application that enables you to modify the image.

- *Change to Picture* breaks the link with the file (when linked) and the OLE server and changes the data type to Picture. After you make the change permanent, the object is no longer editable.

- *Change Link* is enabled only for linked objects. You can change the file to which the OLE object is linked.

- *Update Now* updates the image to the current version of the linked file. Update Now redraws the image if it is embedded.

The Change Link and Change to Picture commands are discussed in the following sections.

Changing the Link to an Object

If you change the name or location of a file to which your object is linked, you receive an error message when you attempt to edit the object. To reestablish the link to a file, follow these steps:

1. Select the bound object frame by clicking its surface.

2. Choose *Object Name* Object from the Edit menu.

3. Choose Change Link from the pop-up menu. The Change Link dialog box shown in figure 13.27 appears.

FIG. 13.27

Using the Change Link dialog box to modify or restore an OLE link to a file.

4. If the server supports more than one file type, choose the appropriate file type from the List Files of Type combo box. (See the tip that follows regarding changing OLE servers at this point.)

5. Choose the drive and directory where the file is located, choose the file name, and choose OK.

The link is reestablished, and you can edit the object as necessary.

If you install a new image editor or drawing server application that is an OLE server, it may change the association of the file extension in REG.DAT. If this situation occurs, you must either change the REG.DAT value for the file extension to its original server alias or create a new OLE object with the new server, copy it to the Clipboard, and replace the current image by using Paste Special to replace the data in the OLE Object data cell of your table. Refer to the tip in an earlier section in this chapter, "Embedding Images from Files," that discusses changing REG.DAT associations of file extensions with server applications.

Cutting the Link to an Object or Server

Changing the OLE Object field's data type for an image or other object type is a drastic step. After you have cut the link, the image is no longer an OLE object, and it is not editable in Access or in any other application into which you paste the object. When you double-click the bound object frame to edit the object, you receive the no-can-do message box in figure 13.28.

If a linked file is no longer accessible to your Access application or if you remove the OLE server that you used to embed or link the file, you may want to break the OLE link to prevent the message box of figure 13.28 from appearing. To break the link of an embedded OLE object with the server, or to break the link with the file and the server, and change the OLE object's data type to Picture, follow these steps:

1. Select the bound object box by clicking its surface.

2. Choose *Object Name* **O**bject from the **E**dit menu.

3. Choose **C**hange to Picture from the pop-up menu.

FIG. 13.28

The message box that appears when the link to an OLE object has been severed.

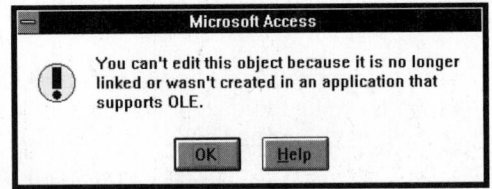

If you change your mind immediately after having made the change, choose U**n**do Current Field from the **E**dit menu, or press Ctrl+Z. If you have saved the record, choose U**n**do Saved Record from the **E**dit menu instead.

Using Access with OLE Client Applications

The commercial success of Windows 3.1 and the growing number of OLE client applications compatible with Windows 3.1's implementation of OLE has resulted in a tidal wave of product updates by publishers of Windows applications. The wave will ebb, but OLE is the chosen IPC method for Windows; the first or second generation of almost all applications introduced subsequently to Windows 3.1 are or will be OLE servers, clients, or both.

You can use any OLE server application to import OLE objects into bound or unbound object frames in Access forms and reports or directly to OLE Object fields in tables and queries. You can copy OLE objects from Access tables, queries, forms, and reports and then paste the objects into any client application. The OLE object you paste into the client is associated with the same server you assigned in Access.

The purpose of the OLE objects catalog you created in this chapter is to provide a central source for images and other OLE objects that you can use with OLE client applications, such as Microsoft Word for

Windows, Aldus PageMaker, CorelDRAW! 3.0, and many others. Access is not an OLE server, so you must use the server with which you embedded or linked the object into Access to act as a surrogate server for Access. For example, you can embed in a Word for Windows document the map of Oshkosh created in "Using Microsoft Draw To Embed Vector Images" by following these steps:

1. Double-click the bound object frame for the Oshkosh map in your OLE Objects form. The editing window of the server used to import the object appears. In this case, an expanded map of downtown Oshkosh was imported into OLE Objects from Windows Draw! 3.0 with OLE; Draw's editing window is shown in figure 13.29.

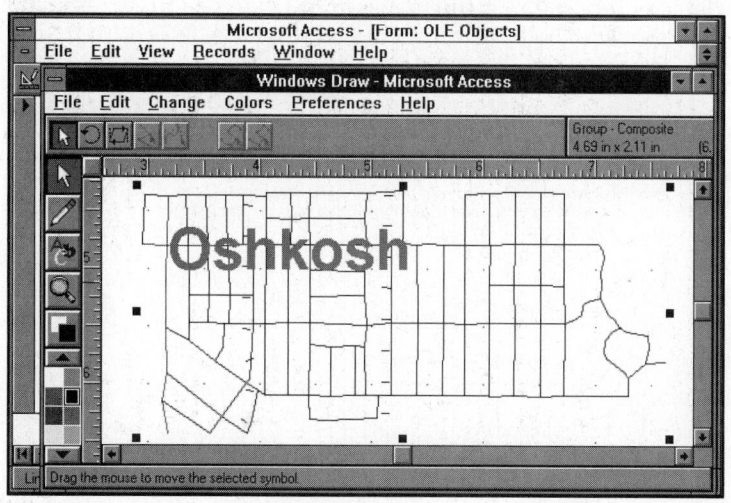

FIG. 13.29

The map of Oshkosh displayed in the editing window of Micrografx Windows Draw!.

2. Select the object or elements of the object that you want to paste into your Word for Windows document.

3. Choose Copy from the Edit menu of the server; then choose Exit from the server's File menu. (The wording of the Exit command varies with the server you use.)

4. Launch Word for Windows and open the document into which you want to insert the object.

5. Locate the caret (insertion point) where you want the object and choose Paste Special from Word's Edit menu. The Paste Special dialog box appears as shown in figure 13.30. If the object you selected was linked rather than embedded, the Paste Link button is enabled, and you can choose between embedding or linking the object in Word.

FIG. 13.30

Using the Paste
Special dialog
box of Word for
Windows to
insert a Windows
Draw! object.

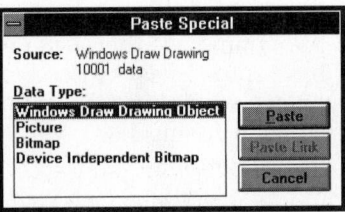

6. Click the Paste button to *embed* the object in your Word for Windows document, or click Paste Link (if the button is enabled) to *link* the object to the OLE Objects data cell in your Access file. If you link the object, the image in the Word document will be updated when you edit the image in the data cell in Access with an OLE server. The object appears as shown in figure 13.31.

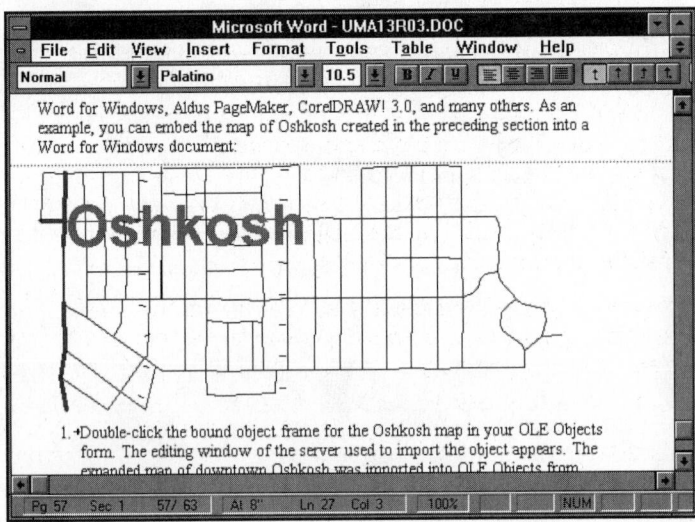

FIG. 13.31

The map of
Oshkosh inserted
as a drawing in
a Word for
Windows
document.

The process described applies to OLE objects imported into Access OLE Object fields by the most popular image-editing and image-drawing applications for Windows 3.1 and also applies to exporting them to mainstream Windows OLE clients updated to Windows 3.1 standards. When a "future version of Access" incorporates OLE server capability, the process will be automated. During the interim, you have to settle for the manual method just described.

Adding Multimedia Objects to Your Tables

Creating multimedia productions, whether for distribution on CD-ROMs or videotapes, involves many individual elements, ranging from graphics used as backgrounds or titles to music and narration files. Keeping track of the objects used to create multimedia productions is a common application for Windows DBMs. Several commercial database applications, such as Lenel International's MediaOrganizer and MPCOrganizer, are designed specifically for this purpose. Both of the Lenel applications are OLE servers. With a simple process, however, you can create your own custom multimedia database with Access to meet your specific requirements for classification and cataloging.

The examples that follow merely touch on the wide variety of data types used in multimedia applications. An increasing number of applications for authoring multimedia productions incorporate OLE client capabilities. Sound Recorder, supplied with Windows 3.1, is an OLE server. Version 1.0 of Media Player is not OLE-compliant, but Microsoft's Media Player 2.0 has been upgraded to OLE server status. You can incorporate animated graphics created by Macromedia's Director application on Apple Macintosh computers and converted to DOS MMM format by using the Movie Player driver supplied with the Multimedia Development Kit (.MDK).

If you have an audio adapter card, you can link or embed waveform audio sound, including music and narration, in your OLE Objects table or any other table that includes an OLE Object field. Embedding sound data in your table maintains a copy of the sound, independent of the .WAV file in which it was stored, at the expense of disk space. Linking .WAV files is the preferred method in most cases because the data in the file is available to other applications without the use of Access as an intermediary. You can link to Access tables waveform audio files located on your fixed disk, a network server, or a CD-ROM.

Embedding Waveform Audio Data with Sound Recorder

Embedding a sound file is the simplest method of adding a multimedia object to an Access table. To embed a .WAV file in your OLE Objects table, follow these steps:

1. Append a new record to the OLE Objects table by using the record selection buttons.

2. Select the bound object frame and choose Insert Object from the Edit menu.

3. In the Insert Object dialog box, choose Sound from the Object Type list box and click the File button. The Insert Object from File dialog box shown in figure 13.32 appears.

The Insert Object from File dialog box for Sound Recorder objects.

4. From the Drives and Directories list boxes, choose the drive and directory in which your .WAV files are located. You can use the system sounds, such as TADA.WAV, in your \WINDOWS directory if you do not have a collection of .WAV files to use in this example.

5. From the File Name list, choose the .WAV file to embed; then click OK. The data from the .WAV file is embedded in the OLE Object field of the new record. Sound Recorder's presentation appears in the bound object frame as shown in figure 13.33.

 To play the embedded waveform audio data, just double-click Sound Recorder's icon.

 Instead of inserting a file, you can use Sound Recorder's controls to record sounds that you embed directly into Access without creating a .WAV file. To do so, choose OK rather than the File button in the Insert Object dialog box; then use the controls in Sound Recorder's window to record your waveform audio data. Choose Exit from Sound Recorder's File menu when your recording is complete. Embedding long-duration .WAV files, especially at sampling rates of 22.05 KHz or 44.1 KHz, can create very large Access tables.

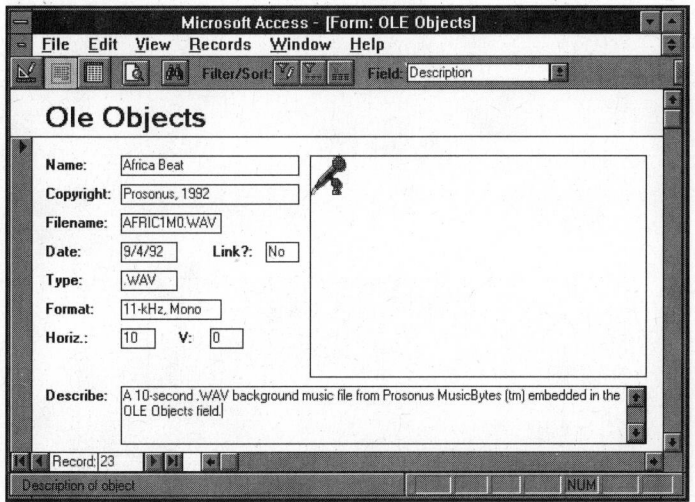

FIG. 13.33

Sound Recorder's
icon used as the
presentation for
embedded and
linked .WAV
files.

Linking .WAV Files with Sound Recorder

Linking sound files to OLE Object fields of your tables requires that you use Sound Recorder to open rather than insert the .WAV file. The file name must appear in Sound Recorder's title bar in order for a link to be created. To use Sound Recorder to link a .WAV file to the OLE Objects table, follow these steps:

1. Append another new record to the OLE Objects table by using the record selection buttons.

2. Select the bound object frame and choose Insert Object from the Edit menu.

3. In the Insert Object dialog box, choose Sound from the Object Type list box and choose OK. Sound Recorder's window appears.

4. Choose Open from Sound Recorder's File menu. In the Open dialog box that appears, double-click the name of the file you want to link (see fig. 13.34).

5. Press Ctrl+C or choose Copy from Sound Recorder's Edit menu to copy the link to the Clipboard.

6. Choose Exit from Sound Recorder's File menu to return to Access.

FIG. 13.34

Using Sound Recorder's Open dialog box to choose a .WAV file to link.

Access

7. With the bound object frame selected, choose Paste **L**ink from Access's **E**dit menu.

8. Choose OK from the Paste Link dialog box. The presentation of sounds is Sound Recorder's icon, not the data in the file, so Auto Update is not applicable to sound files.

The presentation of a linked file is no different from that of an embedded sound file. As with embedded .WAV files, you simply double-click Sound Recorder's icon to play the linked file.

You can verify that a link to the file was created by choosing Sound Ob**j**ect from the **E**dit menu and observing that the **C**hange Link command in the pop-up menu is enabled. If you want to display Sound Recorder's window and play the sound manually, choose Sound Ob**j**ect from the **E**dit menu and then choose **E**dit from the pop-up menu.

Linking or Embedding MIDI Files with Media Player 1.0 and Object Packager

Media Player 1.0 is not an OLE server, so you need to use Windows 3.1's Object Packager to create an OLE package that contains the methods of Media Player and properties of your sound file. This procedure is applicable to the creation of any OLE object of a data type for which you do not have an OLE server application.

You can use Object Packager to link large graphic files without increasing the size of your database by the size of the DIB required to create the presentation. Use the linking process described for Object Packager in the following steps, using .PCX files linked to Windows Paintbrush or .JPG files linked to Picture Publisher 3.1. This method results in a substantial saving in the disk space required by your database file. With either of these graphics applications, you can create a small image to embed in an additional OLE Object field if you want a thumbnail image. If you are using 24-bit color, you can reduce the number of colors in your thumbnail image to 256 to decrease the file size by one-third.

To create a package of Media Player and a linked or an embedded MIDI file, follow these steps:

1. Append another new record to the OLE Objects table by using the record selection buttons.

2. Select the bound object frame and choose Insert Object from the Edit menu.

3. In the Insert Object dialog box, choose Package from the Object Type list box and choose OK. Object Packager's window appears.

4. If you want to *embed* the .MID file, skip to step 8. If you want to *link* the .MID file, press Ctrl+Esc to display the Windows Task list. Launch File Manager, if it is open, or open it from Program Manager.

5. Choose the .MID file you want to link, choose Copy from File Manager's File menu, click the Copy to Clipboard button, and choose OK.

6. Close or minimize File Manager and click the content area of Object Packager's window to select it.

7. Choose Paste Link from Object Packager's Edit menu. The file name appears in the Content window; Media Player's icon and the filename appear in the Appearance (presentation) window, as shown in figure 13.35.

   To embed rather than link the data in the file, choose Import from Object Packager's File menu. From the Import dialog box that appears, choose the file to embed in the package; then choose OK.

8. Choose Exit from Object Packager's File menu to return to Access. Click the Yes button when the Update Object message box appears.

Access

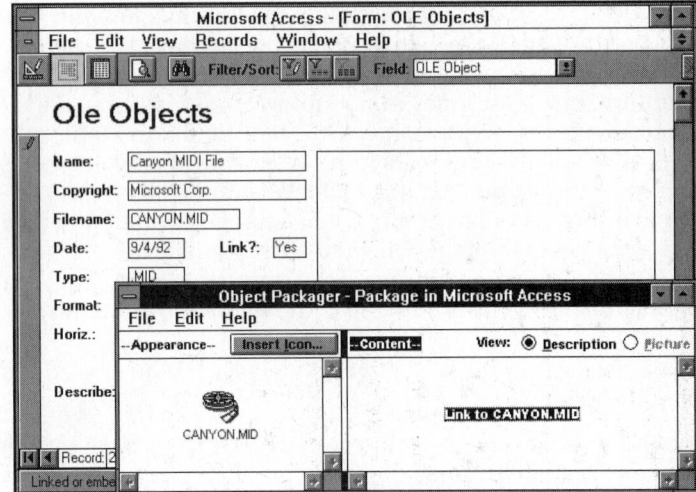

FIG. 13.35

Object
Packager's
window contain-
ing a linked MIDI
file package.

 The presentation of a packaged object includes the filename of the
source, whether the file is linked to or embedded in the package.
Double-click the presentation to play the file or the embedded data.
Media Player's window appears as shown in figure 13.36. You can determine whether the file is linked to or embedded in the package by looking at Media Player's title bar. The file name is displayed if the file is
linked to the package; the prefix ~PKG, followed by a random assortment of characters, identifies embedded data.

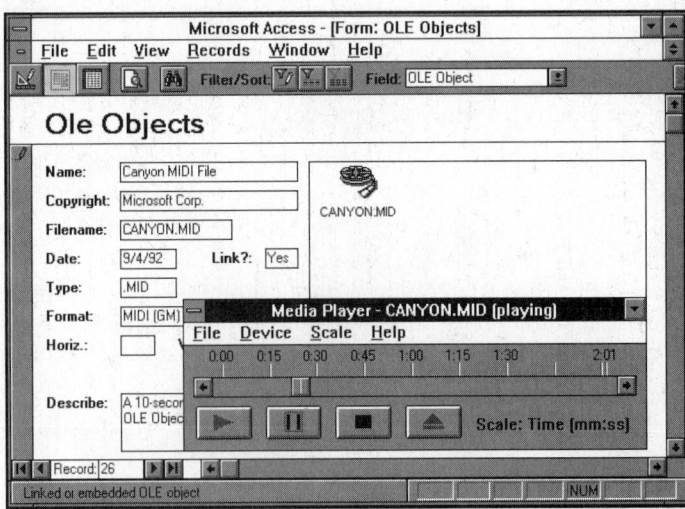

FIG. 13.36

Media Player 1.0
playing a
packaged object
with a linked
MIDI file.

MIDI files are quite small compared to .WAV files of the same duration, so you can embed MIDI files without unduly increasing the size of your tables. Embedding an MIDI file in a package, however, prevents other applications from using the file's data; the data is bound to Media Player and, once embedded, cannot be extracted to a file. As a rule, you always should link files to objects created with Object Packager so that the data the files contain can be used by other applications.

Packaged objects are embedded in OLE Object fields, as mentioned in the preceding chapter. Object Packager's presentation does occupy a significant amount of file space.

The File button of the Insert Object dialog box, which you use to embed other types of objects directly from files, does not work with packaged objects. Packaged objects have no file extension associations in REG.DAT, so Access does not know what type of object should be embedded in Object Packager. No matter what choice you make from the List Files of Type combo box, it will not be correct, because Access cannot test it for conformity with REG.DAT entries.

Using Media Player 2.0 To Link Multimedia Files

Media Player 2.0 is an OLE server version of the Media Player 1.0 applet included with Windows 3.1. In addition to adding OLE server capabilities, Media Player 2.0 enables you to control the starting and ending points of the play function as well as the presentation of the object in the client application. Media Player 2.0 is included in Microsoft's new Video for Windows application and is likely to be incorporated in future versions of Windows.

The default OLE server process of Media Player 2.0 is linking. This preference makes sense when you consider that multimedia files, especially AVI (Audio Video Interleaved) files, usually are very large. Media Player 2.0 as an OLE server behaves similarly to Object Packager; files are linked with Media Player 2.0, but Media Player 2.0 objects always are embedded in client applications. The object type for Media Player 2.0 is Media Clip. If you intend to create a multimedia database, your investment in a Microsoft application that includes Media Player 2.0 will be repaid quickly.

If you have Media Player 2.0 and the required drivers, you can link OLE objects such as Multimedia Movies (MMM files), video clips (AVI files), and audio CD tracks to your OLE Objects table. Media Player 2.0 also accommodates .WAV and .MID files, so you can provide a common interface for all your multimedia files. To link a multimedia object with Media Player 2.0 to an Access OLE Object field, follow these steps:

1. Select a data cell of the OLE object type; then choose Insert Object from the Edit menu.

2. Select Media Clip from the Object Type list box of the Insert Object dialog box and choose OK. Media Player 2.0's window appears.

3. Select the type of multimedia device from the list of installed drivers that appears when you choose the Device menu, as shown in figure 13.37.

FIG. 13.37

Selecting a device type for linking with Media Player 2.0.

4. Choose Open from the File menu and choose a file corresponding to the Device type you selected in step 3. The default file type that appears in the List Files of Type list box of the Open dialog box is determined by the device you selected (see fig. 13.38). Choose OK.

5. Play the file by clicking the Play button (with a right arrow) to verify that it is the file you want.

FIG. 13.38

Choosing a multimedia file corresponding to the device type.

6. Choose **O**ptions from the **E**dit menu to display the Options dialog box shown in figure 13.39. The Auto Rewind, Caption, Border around object, Play in client document, and Control Bar on playback are the appropriate options for use as an Access OLE object.

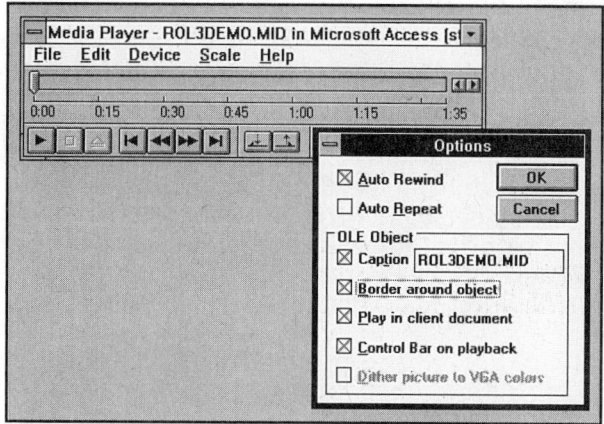

FIG. 13.39

Picking options for playback of a multimedia file as an Access OLE object.

7. Choose **E**xit & Return to Microsoft Access from the **F**ile menu. Choose OK when asked if you want to update your Access table.

Figure 13.40 shows Media Player 2.0's full window, displayed by choosing Media Clip Ob**j**ect from Access's **E**dit menu and choosing **E**dit from the pop-up menu.

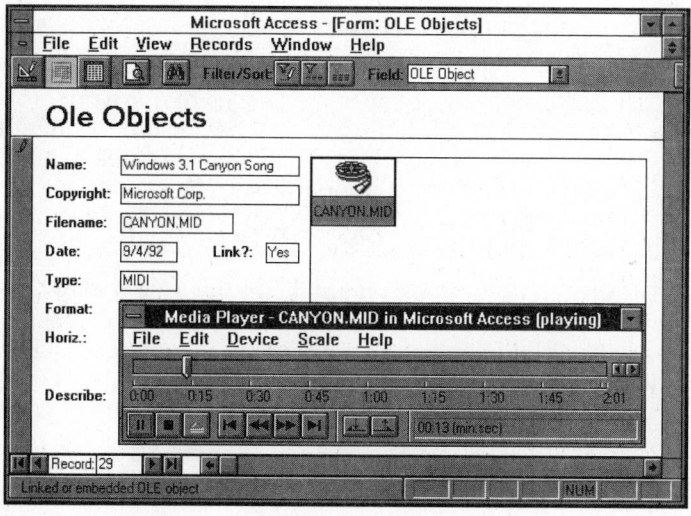

FIG. 13.40

Media Player 2.0 playing a linked MIDI file in Edit mode.

Third-party drivers that use the media command interface (MCI) common to all multimedia data types in Windows 3.1 add their data types to the **D**evice menu of Media Player 2.0. Therefore, if you have a Sony VDeck video cassette recorder and its Windows MCI driver, you can play Hi8 video clips through your Video Blaster or Bravado adapter card with a Media Player 2.0 Sony VISCA object embedded in an OLE Object field.

 Compact your OLE_OBJS.MDB database file when you have completed the examples in this chapter. If you have embedded or linked large graphic images or waveform audio files and then deleted the objects, the file space they occupied is not released until you compact the database. Periodic compaction of your database is especially important when you are experimenting with graphic images, because the database file size easily can become two or three times larger than what is required to store its active content.

Chapter Summary

The examples presented in this chapter demonstrate the versatility of the OLE Object field type in Access tables. You can embed or link still and animated graphics, waveform audio sound and MIDI music, and even video clips in Access tables. Embedding or linking large graphics files in Access tables results in large database file sizes, but the techniques described for packaging linked files by using Windows 3.1's Object Packager can circumvent this problem.

You can consider the OLE Object field to be the equivalent of a BLOB field in other DBMs because it can store images that are not created by OLE servers as Access Picture, Bitmap, and Device Independent Bitmap object types. You can export these non-OLE object types to most Windows applications through the Clipboard, but you cannot edit the objects unless you independently import them into an image-editing application.

Chapter 14 introduces the unbound object frame that you can use to add graphic images to embellish your forms and reports. Most of the OLE techniques and tips in this chapter apply to unbound OLE objects, but you need not be concerned with file space. Only a single copy of the image, usually located in the header or footer section of your form or report, is stored.

Chapter 15 extends the coverage of OLE use to servers that are not specifically related to graphics or multimedia objects. Microsoft Excel is used for the examples because it is one of the most popular Windows applications. The techniques described for using Excel with Access are applicable to most other applications that deal primarily with numeric data.

Adding Graphics and Color to Forms and Reports

With the judicious use of graphic images, such as company logos, you can enhance the appearance of forms and reports. With colors, you can emphasize fields, or provide attractive backgrounds for forms. You can add graphs and charts to your forms and reports to summarize the data contained in tables or queries. You can substitute bit maps for the text captions of command buttons and assign design styles with a background color that makes controls appear raised or recessed. The windows of the AccessWizards you have used in preceding chapters are Access forms. The Wizard forms are examples of the stylistic possibilities in Access.

Whether created from bit-mapped images or vector drawings, or generated by Microsoft Graph, graphic images that are not stored in OLE Object fields of tables are held in unbound object frames contained in forms and reports. The form or report with OLE source documents becomes a compound destination document. Most of the graphics-manipulation techniques that you applied to bound objects in Chapter

13 can be used with unbound object frames, because bound and un-bound object frames are subclasses of the object frame class. Both subclasses inherit from the object frame class most of their properties and methods that are independent of an associated OLE server.

For Related Information:

◄◄ "A Brief Introduction to Objects," p. 512.

◄◄ "The Concept of Compound Documents," p. 519.

◄◄ "Adding a Bound Object Control to a Form or Report," p. 538.

FROM HERE...

Understanding Unbound Object Frames

Instead of using OLE Object fields, images in unbound object frames store their properties as data in the area of your .MDB file devoted to forms and reports. Like the methods you use with bound object frames, the methods you use to create or edit unbound objects are contributed temporarily by the OLE server. After you embed or link the unbound object, the Access application contains the methods used to display the images.

The use of unbound object frames differs from that of bound object frames in the following ways:

■ You set the Enabled property of most unbound object frames to No so that the OLE server that supplied those unbound objects does not appear if you double-click the object in Run mode. The Enabled property does not affect your ability to edit the object in Design mode. A bound object's Enabled property is usually set to Yes (the default value).

■ Unbound object frames have properties like Row Source, Link Child Fields, Link Master Fields, and Column Count that are not applicable to bound object frames. Graphs and other unbound objects use these properties to obtain or present data in an un-bound object field.

■ You can create a master-child linkage between the content of an unbound object frame and the value of a field in the underlying table or query or the value entered in a text box on your form.

■ Multimedia objects, such as sound or animated graphics, are seldom useful in unbound object frames.

This chapter provides examples that utilize the important additional
properties available when you use unbound object frames.

For Related Information:

◄◄ "Modifying Linkages between Main Forms and Subforms,"
p. 404.

◄◄ "Adding a Linked Subreport to a Bound Report," p. 495.

FROM HERE...

Creating a New Logo for Your Personnel Actions Form

Logotypes and symbols that identify an organization are among the
most common graphic objects on forms and in reports. The bit map
example in this section uses the image of a lighthouse from the
Northwind Traders database, but you can substitute your organization's logo if you have a bit-map file or a scanner to create an image of
suitable dimensions.

To create the image used in the example of a vector-based logo, you
need the Microsoft Draw and WordArt applets that are supplied with
Word for Windows 2+ and Microsoft Publisher. Although you import
the basis of a world globe image from PowerPoint, you can simulate the
image with a circle added in Microsoft Draw if you don't have a vector-
based image to use.

Using the Bit-Mapped Logo from the Forms Switchboard

To add an image to a new form the easiest way, you copy to the Clipboard an existing unbound object frame of a form or report that contains the image. You then duplicate the image by pasting it into another
form. This process is similar to the process for copying OLE objects
that are to be used by other applications. You can edit the image as
necessary with Windows Paintbrush or another OLE-compliant image
editor.

For Related Information:

◀◀ "Embedding and Linking Graphics Files in Tables," p. 546.

FROM HERE...

Copying the Contents of an Unbound Object Frame

Northwind Traders' Forms Switchboard form contains an image that almost fits the space that now contains the employee photograph on your Personnel Actions form. To copy the Northwind Traders logo to your Personnel Actions form, follow these steps:

1. Click the Forms button in the Database window. Choose Forms Switchboard from list, and then click the Design button.

2. Select the Northwind logo by clicking the lighthouse in the logo.

3. Choose Copy from the Edit menu to copy the logo to the Clipboard. Close the Forms Switchboard form.

4. Select the Personnel Actions form in the Database window, and click Design.

5. Select the Photo bound object frame (that you added in Chapter 13) and delete it to make room for the new logo. Select the caption for the photograph and delete it.

6. Choose Paste from the Edit menu to create a copy of the logo on your form. Position the logo within the unbound object frame (see fig. 14.1).

7. Open the Properties window for the unbound object frame, choose the Scaling property text box, and select Clip from the list box. Access applies the Scaling property to the presentation of the image; Scaling does not modify the image itself.

The copied image extends into the area occupied by the subform; this problem is corrected after you edit the image in the next section.

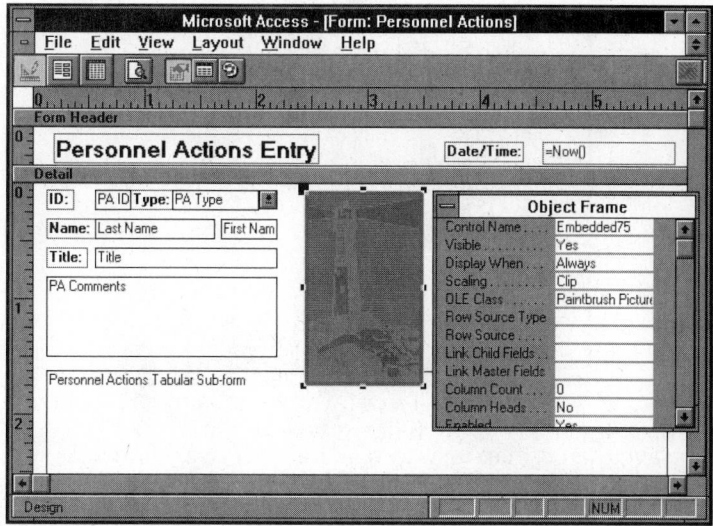

FIG. 14.1

An unbound object frame containing a copied bit map.

For Related Information:

◄◄ "Scaling Graphic Objects," p. 543.

FROM HERE...

Editing the Logo with Windows Paintbrush

The dark cyan background of the copied image is inappropriate for your form because the form's background is white. So you need to change the image's background color to white. Fortunately, Windows Paintbrush includes a Color Eraser tool that can change occurrences of one color to another.

To change the background color of the logo to white and create a .BMP file for the logo, follow these steps:

1. With the logo selected, choose Paintbrush Picture Object from the Edit menu, and then choose Edit from the fly-out menu. (Double-clicking an unbound object frame to activate its OLE server is difficult.)

2. Click the dark blue-green color (under the bright cyan color) on the palette at the bottom of Paintbrush's window, and then double-click the Color Eraser tool (in the left column) to change the background color to white. Your logo appears (see fig. 14.2).

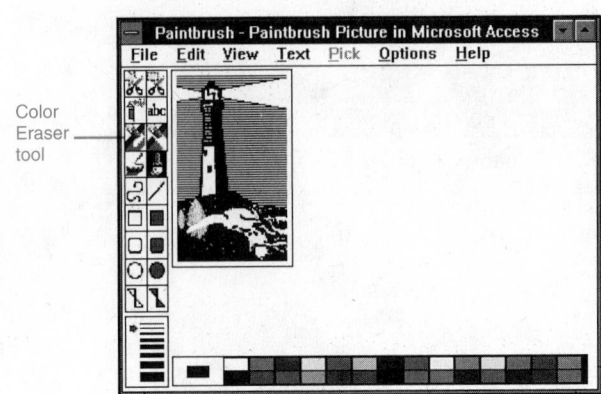

Color
Eraser
tool

FIG. 14.2

The bit-mapped image from the copied unbound object frame in Windows Paintbrush.

3. To save the bit-map logo to disk for later use, choose Save **As** from Paintbrush's **F**ile menu. Click Yes to save the changes in your Access form before you create the file. Give the bit map a filename, such as **NWIND1.BMP**, in the Save As dialog box, and choose OK.

Access

4. Click E**x**it from the **F**ile menu to return to Access. (The link to Access has been broken, so E**x**it and Return to Microsoft Access does not appear in the **F**ile menu.)

5. Drag the bottom of the object frame up, and align it with the bottom of the Comments text box.

6. Click the Form Run Mode button on the toolbar to display your new logo in the form (see fig. 14.3).

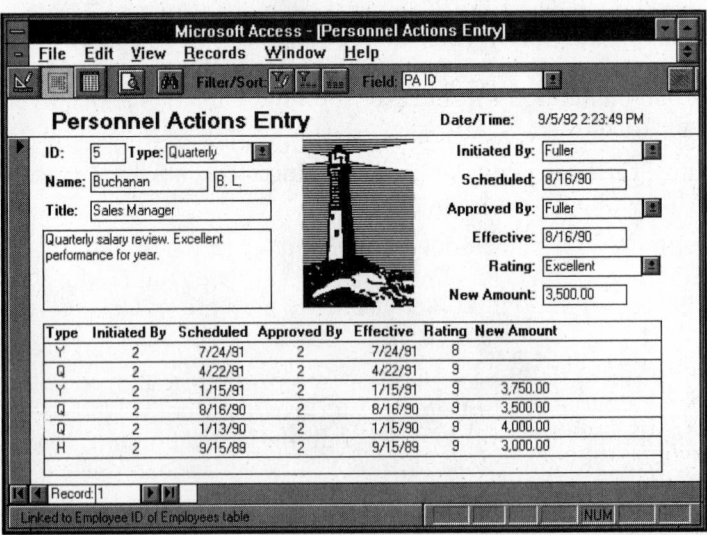

FIG. 14.3

The clipped bit-mapped image in Form Run mode.

7. If you want to save your form with the new logo, choose Save **As** from Access's **F**ile menu, and give the form a name such as **PA with Bit Map**.

8. Close the form. If you did save the form with a new name, do not save changes so that your original version of Personnel Actions is preserved.

Importing a Bit Map File into an Unbound Object Box

You can import a bit-mapped image from a file as a new unbound object with the Import Object choice from the **E**dit menu. This technique is a quick way to add a graphic image to your form if the image is contained in a .BMP or .PCX file and has dimensions appropriate to your form's design. Most Windows applications for scanners can create files in both .BMP and .PCX formats.

To add an unbound object that contains a bit-mapped image derived from a file to a form in Design mode, follow these steps:

1. Choose Insert Object from the **F**ile menu.

2. Choose Paintbrush Picture from the Object Types list box and click File.

3. Open the file you want to use in the Insert Object from File dialog box. Choose NWIND1.BMP, the file you created in step 3 of the preceding example, to use the black-and-white Northwind logo.

4. Choose OK. Access creates an unbound object box the size of the image on your form.

5. Position the image, and in the Properties window, set the Scaling property to Clip for the image.

6. Set the Enabled property of the unbound object frame to No so that Paintbrush does not appear when you double-click the image in Run mode.

Creating a Composite Vector Logo

Few bit-mapped images have a satisfactory appearance when you reduce or enlarge their size with the Zoom or Scale values for the Scaling property. Doubling the pixels when you expand the image or losing pixels when you contract it causes distortion of the resulting graphic.

You can scale vector images, however, without a substantial change in image quality. Vector images print with improved resolution. For these reasons, the majority of logos and symbols used on forms and reports are created with vector images.

The example of a vector-based logo that you create in subsequent sections uses the world globe image created from the PowerPoint MAPS.PPT clip-art file, but you can use any image in .WMF, .DRW, .WPG or .DXF format for the example. The drawing is combined with stylized text to create a composite logo. As mentioned in this chapter's introduction, you need the Microsoft Draw and WordArt applets for this example, or you need a commercial drawing application, such as Windows Draw! 3 with OLE, Designer 3.1+, or CorelDRAW! 3+.

Importing a Vector-Based Logo from the OLE_OBJS Database

If you added the world globe image from MAPS.PPT when you tried the vector-based image example in Chapter 13, import the image as an unbound object frame in Personnel Actions. To import the object, perform the following steps:

1. Choose **O**pen Database from the **F**ile menu, and open OLE_OBJS.

2. Click Form in the Database window, and double-click OLE Objects to display the form.

3. Find the record that contains the drawing object that you created from the PowerPoint globe clip-art image in Chapter 13.

4. Select the image and press Ctrl+C to copy it to the Clipboard.

5. Close the OLE Objects form and choose **O**pen Database from the **F**ile menu. Then reopen NWIND.MDB.

6. Open the Personnel Actions form in Design mode and press Ctrl+V to paste the image to the form.

7. Delete the Photo bound object frame and the caption. Then relocate and resize the new unbound object box (see fig. 14.4).

Although originally contained in a bound object frame in OLE_OBJS, the world globe image is pasted into Personnel Actions as an unbound object frame. This change in object type occurs because the OLE Objects field to which the image was bound in OLE_OBJS.MDB does not exist in the Personnel Actions table that serves as the data source for the current form.

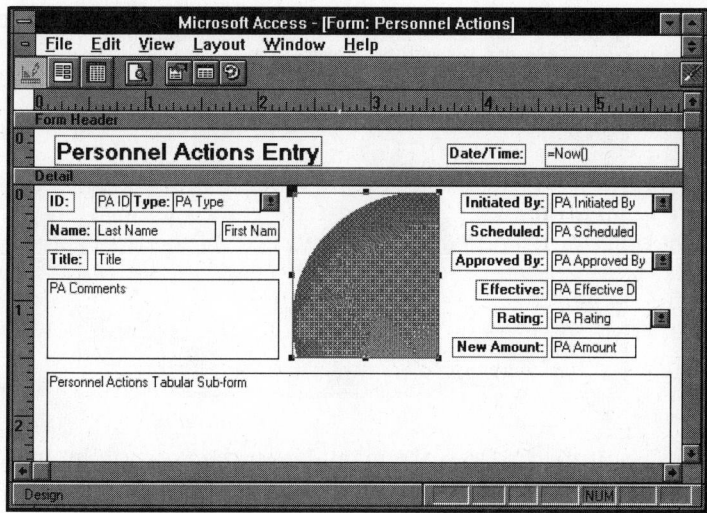

FIG. 14.4

The initial clipped image of the world globe drawing in Design mode.

If you do not have PowerPoint or did not paste the world globe image into the OLE Objects table in Chapter 13, you can use Microsoft Draw to simulate the globe by following these steps:

1. With the Personnel Actions form open in Design mode, select the unbound Lighthouse logo and delete it.

2. Choose Insert Object from the Edit menu. The Insert Object dialog box appears.

3. Select Microsoft Drawing from the Object Type list box and choose OK.

4. In the Microsoft Draw window, create a circle with about a 1 1/2-inch diameter (on a 640 x 480-pixel VGA display) by choosing the Ellipse tool, holding down the Shift key, and dragging the mouse to expand the circle to the proper diameter.

   If you are familiar with Microsoft Draw, you can add ellipses to simulate latitudinal and longitudinal lines, as shown in figure 14.5.

5. Choose Exit and Return to Microsoft Access from the File menu. Click OK when you are asked whether you want to update Access.

6. Select the Globe unbound object frame and position it in the former location of the lighthouse logo. Adjust the size of the object frame by dragging the handles so that the frame occupies the same area as the lighthouse logo did.

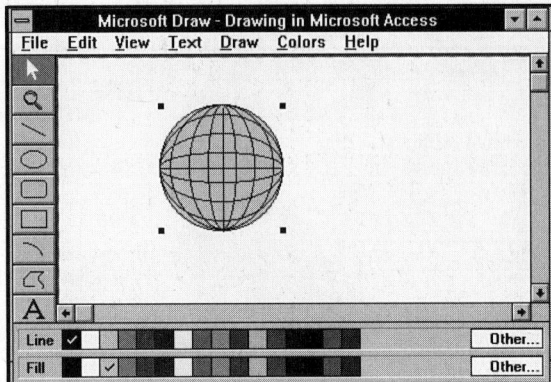

FIG. 14.5

Creating a world globe image in Microsoft Draw.

You can substitute the Draw globe image for the PowerPoint image in the following section.

Adding Stylized Type with Microsoft WordArt

You can use the Microsoft WordArt OLE server applet supplied with Word for Windows 2+ and Microsoft Publisher to create and add a stylized version of Northwind Traders' name to the logo. This example also illustrates how you can use multiple OLE servers to create a single image in Microsoft Draw that you import to an unbound object frame. You can create a similar image with a sophisticated drawing application, such as CorelDRAW! 3.0 or Micrografx Designer, but Microsoft Draw and WordArt are much easier to use.

To create the type for the logo with WordArt, follow these steps:

1. Choose Insert Object from the **E**dit menu to create a temporary unbound object frame in which to hold the object you create in WordArt.

2. Select MS WordArt from the Object Types list in the Insert Object dialog box, and choose OK. WordArt's window appears in the form of a dialog box.

3. Type **northwind**, press Ctrl+Enter to create a new line, and then type **traders** in the multiline text box.

4. Open the Font combo box and choose Langley.

5. Open the Style combo box and choose Button. Your type appears as shown in the Preview window of figure 14.6.

6. The default values of the remaining properties are correct for this example. Choose OK to return to Access.

You remove the extra "traders" in the center of the image in the next series of steps.

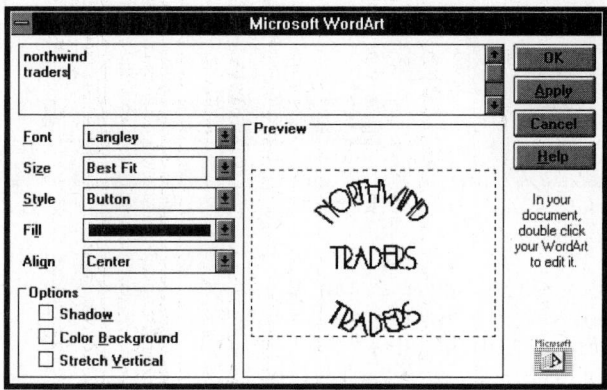

FIG. 14.6

Stylized type in Microsoft WordArt's dialog box.

Combining the World Globe and WordArt Type with Microsoft Draw

To create composites, you can combine images, including bit maps, with Microsoft Draw. Temporary unbound object frames store any elements you want to add to your image.

To create the new Northwind Traders logo by combining the WordArt text and the PowerPoint (or Draw) image, follow these steps:

1. Select the unbound object frame containing the type. Press Ctrl+C to copy the type image to the Clipboard.

2. Double-click the World Globe image to launch the Microsoft Draw OLE server.

3. When Draw's window appears, press Ctrl+V to paste the type to the Draw image.

4. Position the mouse pointer on a black area of the type, and while holding down the left mouse button, drag the type to the right of the globe (see fig. 14.7).

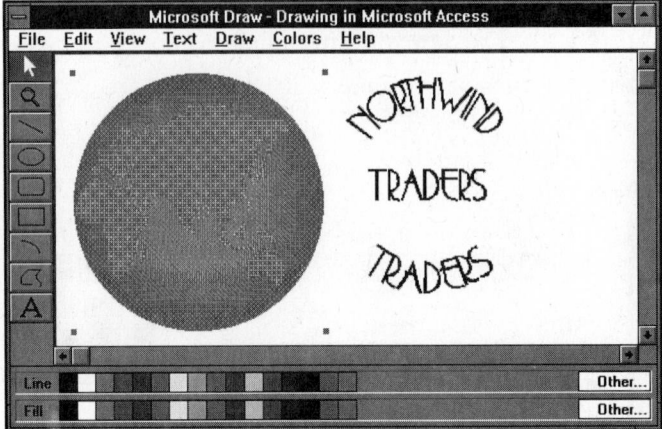

FIG. 14.7

The world globe
drawing and
stylized type
imported to
Microsoft Draw.

5. Select the word *traders* in the center of the type image by dragging an enclosing rectangle around the word. Be sure to include every element (line) from which the word is made. Press Delete to remove the extra *traders*.

6. Drag a selection rectangle around the type, and then choose **G**roup from the **D**raw menu to make the type a single group of elements.

7. Select the globe element and scale that element to fit between *northwind* and *traders* by holding down the Ctrl key and dragging one of the image's corner-selection handles. The Ctrl key maintains the aspect ratio of the image so that the globe remains a circle.

8. Position the globe between the two lines of type. Rescale and reposition the globe to align it with the type.

9. When the two groups of elements are aligned, drag an enclosing element around the entire image. Choose **G**roup from the **D**raw menu to create a single object (see fig. 14.8).

Access

10. Choose E**x**it & Return to Microsoft Access from Draw's **F**ile menu. Click Yes when you are asked whether you want to update Access.

    Your form in Design mode appears (see fig. 14.9).

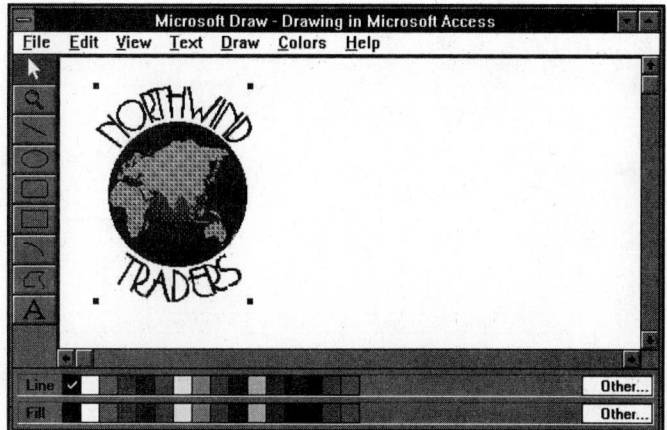

FIG. 14.8

The new Northwind Traders logo grouped as a single object.

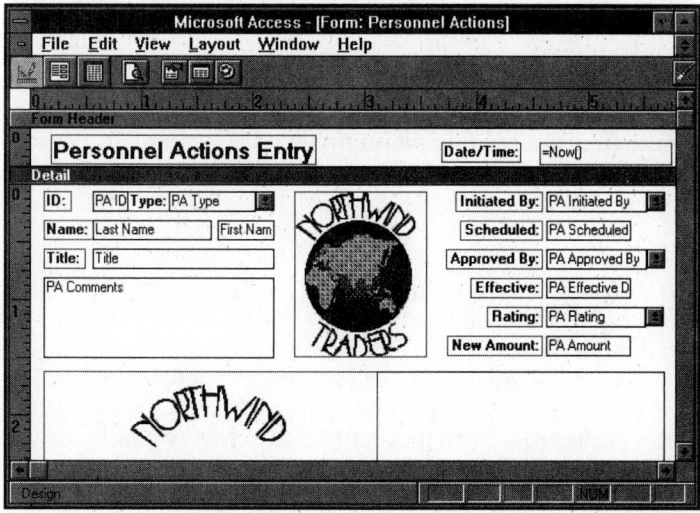

FIG. 14.9

The vector drawing of the new logo imported into an unbound object box.

11. Select the logo and set its Scaling property to Zoom.

12. Set the Enabled property of the logo to No.

13. Select the unbound object frame that contains the WordArt type and delete it. Figure 14.9 displays this frame in the lower-left corner of the form.

14. Click the Form Run Mode button on the toolbar to display the form with the new logo (see fig. 14.10).

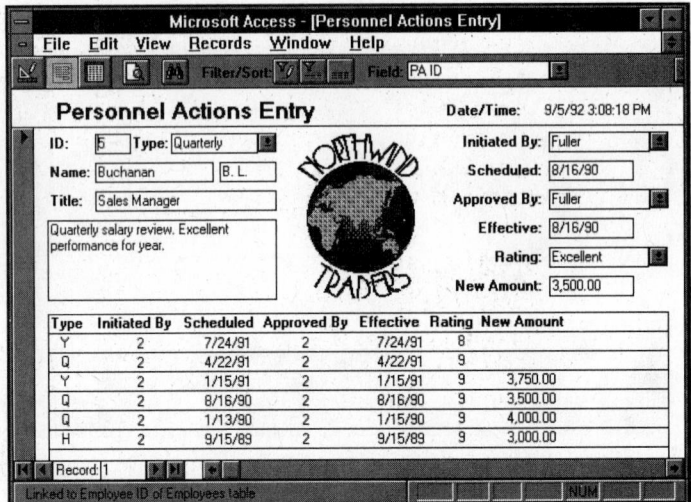

FIG. 14.10

The Personnel
Actions form in
Run mode with
the new
Northwind
Traders logo.

If you want to save a copy of the new logo in your OLE_OBJS database, select its unbound object frame and copy the logo to the Clipboard. Choose Save **As** from the **F**ile menu to save your modified Personnel Actions form with a new name. Then open OLE_OBJS, append a new record to the OLE Objects table, and paste the image to the OLE Object field.

The procedures described in this section also apply to forms and reports. Logos and other static images are usually incorporated in the headers or footers of forms and reports. In the preceding examples, the only available space on the form in 640 x 480 VGA mode is the location of the photograph. Adding a logo to the header or footer of a form can reduce the area available for bound text boxes used for data entry. Whether the image is in the header, footer, or detail section, the form's behavior does not change. Unbound object boxes in reports are almost always incorporated in page or report headers or footers.

Adding a Background Color to Your Form

A background color in a form can improve the form's appearance and emphasize text boxes that require entries from the user. Northwind

Traders favors dark cyan as a background color, but light gray provides better contrast with black type. As a general rule, use light gray as the background color when you don't want white. Bright colors distract, and dark colors make text difficult to read, especially small text.

To add a light gray background color to your Personnel Actions form, follow these steps:

1. Click the Palette button on the toolbar to open the palette.

2. Click the Form Header bar to select the header, and then click the light gray box in the fill section of the palette to change the header's background color.

3. Repeat step 2 for the Detail section and the Footer section if your form includes a footer.

   If you added the vector graphic logo and its background color is white, select the logo and repeat step 2. In most cases, vector graphic images have transparent background colors. Alternatively, you can choose Clear as the Fill color for the unbound object frame to allow the background color to appear behind the logo.

4. Choose Save from the File menu to save your changes.

Your form in design view appears as in figure 14.11.

FIG. 14.11

Adding a light gray background color to your Personnel Actions form.

The Personnel Actions tabular subform is used to display data, not to edit data. You need to set subform's background color to gray so that only controls requiring data entry have a white background. To set the background color to gray, follow these steps:

1. Open the Personnel Actions tabular subform in Design mode.

2. Click the Form Header bar and use the palette to set the background color to light gray.

3. Repeat step 2 for the Detail and Form Footer sections.

4. Select the text boxes in the form's Detail section by holding down the Shift key and clicking each text box in succession. Set the fill color of the text boxes to light gray. Your form appears as shown in figure 14.12.

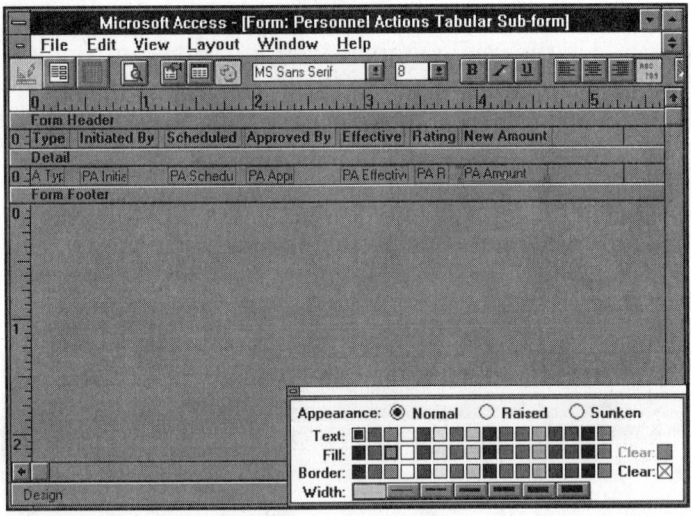

FIG. 14.12

Adding the background color to the subform used with the Personnel Actions form.

5. Choose **S**ave from the **F**ile menu to save your modified subform. Then close the subform window.

6. With the main Personnel Actions window active, click the Form Run Mode button on the toolbar. Your main form and subform appear with the new *executive* look (see fig. 14.13).

Unless you have a color printer, do not add background colors to reports. If you have a dye-sublimation or thermal-transfer color printer, the cost of printing a report in color usually exceeds $2.00 per page. Large areas of solid or half-tone color consume substantial amounts of toner in conventional laser printers or ink in inkjet printers, as do areas of reverse (white-on-black) type. If you decide to add a background color to elements of a report, choose light gray. Your laser printer prints a half-tone screen to duplicate the color.

FIG. 14.13

The Personnel
Actions form in
Run mode with
the light gray
background
applied.

Enhancing Your Forms and Reports with Lines and Rectangles

To create forms and reports with the appearance of conventional business forms, you can draw lines and boxes with the two graphic tools provided in Access toolbox—the Line and Rectangle tools. Figure 14.14 shows the design of a form intended to duplicate a printed form previously completed by hand. This form is linked to a query that lists orders that have not been received more than 30 days after they were placed.

You can draw boxes with the Rectangle tool or the Line tool. You have seven choices for the Width property of lines and rectangle borders, and you select those choices by clicking one of the samples on the palette. The samples range in width from a hairline to about 6 points (1/12 inch). You use the palette's Border color row to choose the color of both lines and rectangle borders. When you use lines and rectangles in the design of a form, you ordinarily set the borders of text boxes to Clear.

Figure 14.15 shows the appearance of the Request for Shipping Information form in Run mode.

FIG. 14.14

Using the Line tool to create a simulation of a standard business form.

FIG. 14.15

The appearance of the simulated business form in Run mode.

You also can use lines and rectangles as graphic design elements of forms and reports. You can use filled rectangles to create shadow boxes for labels that appear to be raised or sunken, and an example of this technique is provided in a subsequent section, "Adding a Graph that Displays Individual Records."

Converting a Form to a Report

A continuous form prints one form for each row of the query, whereas a single-screen form can print forms from selected records. If you change the form to a report, however, you can gain more control over how the form prints.

> You can print the Request for Shipping information form, one to a page, by adding a Page Break from the toolbox to the bottom of your form.

If you choose Save as Report from the File menu in Design mode, Access copies your form to a report with the same name as your form; however, you can choose a different name. Using a report enables you to adjust the printing margins and print two forms per A-size (8 1/2-by-11-inch) sheet.

To save a form as a report, follow these steps:

1. With the form in Design mode, choose Save as Report from the File menu.

   A dialog box appears with the name of your form as the default name for the report. You can rename the report if necessary.

2. Close your form and click Reports in the Database window.

3. Select the report name (the new name if you renamed the report), and click the Design button.

4. Select the Detail section header bar and click the Properties button on the toolbar.

5. Set the Keep Together property of the Detail section to Yes. This action prevents the printing of partial forms on a page.

6. Click the Print Preview button on the toolbar to view the report. The Request for Shipping Information form, converted to the Shipping Status report, is shown in Print Preview mode in figure 14.16.

When a form is zoomed to page view (with a standard 640 x 480-pixel VGA display), *hairlines*, the thinnest on the palette, are accentuated so that they are visible, even though they are only one pixel in width (thickness). In other display modes (800 x 600 or 1024 x 768 pixels), hairlines may not be visible. To confirm that the lines have the thickness you assigned, click the Zoom button on the toolbar to display the form in full-size view.

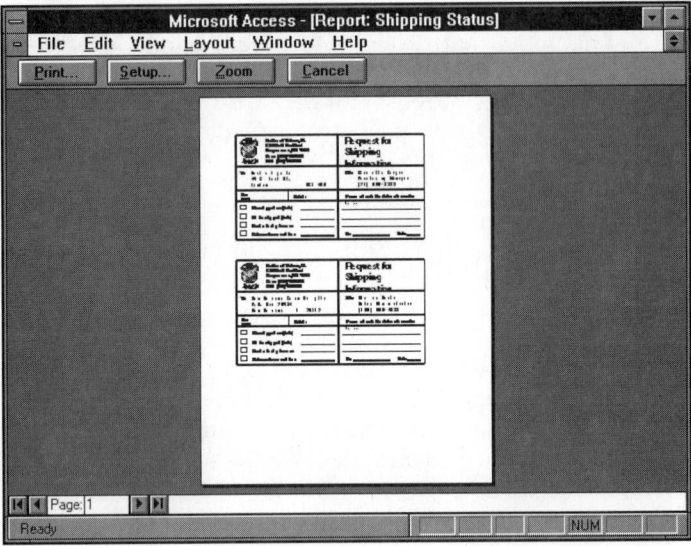

FIG. 14.16

The simulated
business form
saved as a
report.

 Logos and other static information are usually placed in the Report Header or Page Header (or Footer) of reports. In the case of the Shipping Status report, the logo, address, and form title appear in the detail section because these elements must print two to the page, along with the detail. This circumstance is one of few in which static graphics occur in the detail section of a report.

Adding Graphs to Forms and Reports

Graphs and charts that summarize information contained in many individual records are the basis of forms and reports for decision support. Time-series graphs or bar charts provide a quick view of trends in sales or costs. Pie charts are useful for making comparisons of summarized data.

You have four ways to add graphs and charts to Access forms and reports. The following list describes those ways:

■ *Use the GraphWizard when you create a new form:* The Wizard graphs or charts all the data in the query or table that acts as the source of data for your form. This method is applicable only to forms, not reports.

- *Use the Graph tool in the toolbox:* In this case, the FormWizard creates a custom graph linked to the form's query or table, or to another table or query you select. You have additional options when you create the graph or chart.

- *Use Microsoft Graph directly as an OLE server to import data from another application, such as Excel:* To create a fully-customized graph, choose Insert Object from the Edit menu, and then select Microsoft Chart from the Object Types list. This method is explained in the next chapter, which describes techniques specific to using Microsoft Excel with Access.

- *Use a third-party OLE graph server application such as CorelChart! to create a chart using data imported from applications other than Access:* CorelDRAW! and CorelChart! are closely integrated, so you can use sophisticated illustration techniques to modify the chart and then import the chart as a CorelDRAW! object.

Very few, if any, situations arise in which you need to use a separate graphing and charting application. When creating a new form or adding a graph to an existing form with the toolbox's Graph tool, using the GraphWizard is a simpler process than using Microsoft Graph directly or employing a third-party OLE graph server. After you have created the graph with the Wizard, you can edit the graph as necessary in Microsoft Graph, or change one or more of its properties in the Properties list box for the unbound object.

Modifying the Year-to-Date Sales by Category Query

The Year-to-Date Sales by Category crosstab query, which serves as the source of data for the forms that contain the graph, needs to be modified from the original version you created in Chapter 8.

To modify the query, follow these steps:

1. Click Query in the Database window, select the Year-to-Date Sales by Category query, and click Design.

2. Choose Query Properties from the View menu, and change the names of the months in the Fixed Column Headings text box to standard three-letter abbreviations, as shown in figure 14.17. Then choose OK.

   The use of abbreviations minimizes the width of the chart required to display all 12 months of the year. The spelling of each month's abbreviation must be correct, or data is omitted for that month.

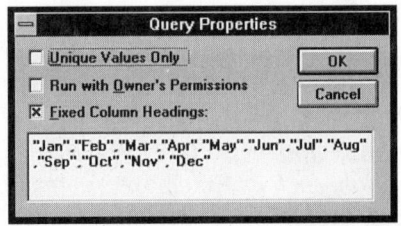

FIG. 14.17

The query modifications required for the graph examples.

3. Click the Field row of the Expr1 column and press Shift+F2 to display the Field1 expression in the Zoom dialog box. Change the mmmm format to mmm to correspond with the abbreviated month names entered in step 2. Press Enter to close the Zoom dialog box.

4. If you did not change the range of dates in the Criteria Row of the Order Date field, click the cell and press Shift+F2 to zoom the expression. Change Between #1/1/92# and #3/31/92# to **Between #1/1/91# and #12/31/91#** to obtain a full year's data (see fig. 14.18).

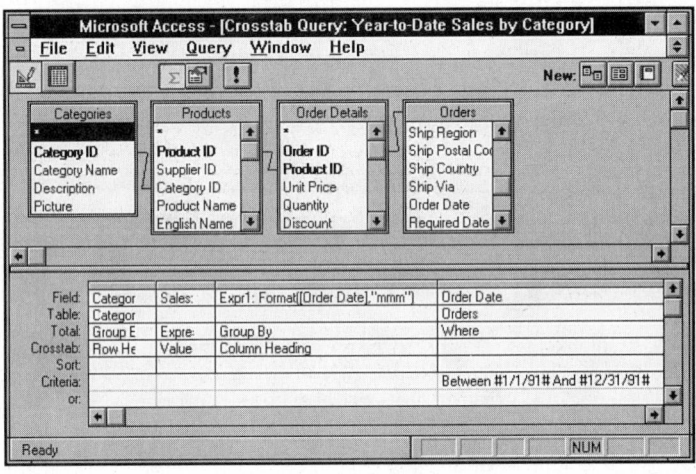

FIG. 14.18

The modified Year-to-Date Sales by Category query.

5. Click the Datasheet button on the toolbar to run the query. Review each month's data to check for spelling errors in your Fixed Column Headings text box.

6. Close the query and save the changes you made.

Both examples in this section use the modified Year-to-Date Sales by Category query.

Adding a Graph That Displays Individual Records

Tables or queries with many categories of data often create graphs that are difficult to interpret, especially if the data falls in the same range of values. The lines and symbols overlap, and the colors used to differentiate elements of the chart may disappear into colored backgrounds. An example of a difficult-to-interpret graph with eight different categories occurs toward the end of this section. Most graphs are much easier to read when you display one category of data at a time. This section describes how to create a time-series graph for the sales of a specific category of Northwind's product line for 1991.

Using the Graph Tool To Create a Wizard Graph

When you use the GraphWizard as you create a form, the Wizard creates a graph of all the data in your table or query. In conjunction with the GraphWizard, the Graph tool of the toolbox is used to create custom graphs. You have several additional options available when you add a graph from the toolbox. As an example, you can display a graph based on a table or query other than that to which your form or report is linked. In this example, the graph is linked to the form through child and master fields.

To create a graph that displays the data from a single record of your query instead of all the records, follow these steps:

1. Click Form in the Database window, and then click the New button to create a new form.

2. Choose Year-to-Date Sales by Category as the query that serves as the source of data for the form, and then click **B**lank Form.

3. Expand the margins of your blank Form1 until it almost fills the maximized document window by dragging the vertical and horizontal margin lines with the mouse.

4. Click the Graph tool in the toolbox; put the mouse pointer, which has the symbol of the graph attached, at the upper left corner of your form; and click the left mouse button. Access creates a default-size unbound object frame and launches the ChartWizard.

5. Choose Year-to-Date Sales by Category from the drop-down list as the source of data for your graph, and click the line graph symbol (first row, fourth symbol left to right), as shown in figure 14.19. In this case, you need to choose a data source for the graph because you can link a graph created with the Graph tool to a table or query other than the one to which the form is linked. Click Next >.

6. The Wizard needs to know which fields to include in your graph. In this case, you want only the months of the year to be included, because the Category Name field's value is determined by the record of the query that you select with the Record Selection buttons. Click >> to add all the fields, and then select the Category Name field from the Fields for graph list and click < to remove it from the list. Your field selection dialog box appears, as shown in figure 14.20. Click Next >.

FIG. 14.19

The opening dialog box of the GraphWizard when launched from the Graph tool.

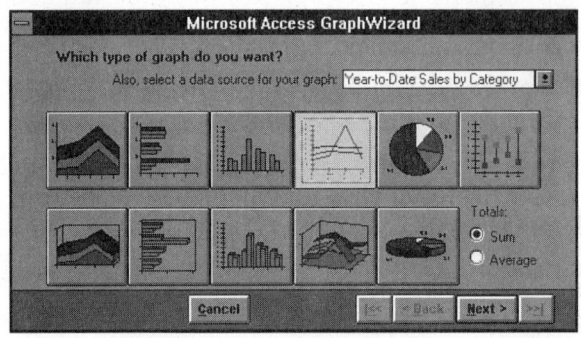

FIG. 14.20

The GraphWizard's dialog box in which you select the fields to include in the graph.

7. For each month of the year, you need labels for the abscissa (X or horizontal axis) of your graph. Click >> to add all the Available fields to the Labels for graph box. Click Next >.

8. Click the Display legend check box to remove the default mark. When you display only one category in a graph, you do not need a legend to identify the category.

9. The message box shown in figure 14.21 enables you to link the graph to the form. Your form is linked to the Year-to-Date Sales by Category query. You want a graph that displays the data in each of the query's records as you bring up a new record with the Record Selection buttons; so you need to link the graph to the form. Click Yes.

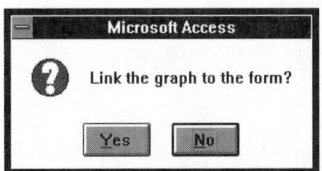

FIG. 14.21

The message box that enables you to link your graph to the data source for your form.

10. When you choose to link the graph to the form, the ChartWizard needs to know which field in the graph is linked to a field in the form. In most cases, the two field names are the same. You want to display a chart of sales for each category of products, so select Category Name in both the Form fields and Graph fields lists, and then click <=> between the two lists to create the link (see fig. 14.22). This action establishes the child-to-master field linkage, similar to that used when a subform is included in and linked to a main form. Click Next >.

11. The final GraphWizard dialog box requests a title for your graph. The Wizard supplies the name of your query as the default. Use the Delete or Backspace key to delete the title (see fig. 14.23). You add a more appropriate title in a later step. Do not press Esc in an attempt to restore your title. Pressing Esc terminates the ChartWizard's operation. Click the Design icon to return to your form in Design mode.

FIG. 14.22

The dialog box that establishes the master-child field linkage from the form to the graph.

FIG. 14.23

The last Wizard dialog box assigns a title to your graph.

Creating and Editing Your Graph

When you return to your form in Design mode, your unbound object frame is empty. If you double-click the frame, Microsoft Graph appears with a blank graph window, which might lead you to believe that you made an error in one of the above steps. The blank graph window appears because the GraphWizard has supplied all the information necessary for creating the graph to your form, but Microsoft Graph has not yet received the information.

To create your first graph and edit the graph to conform with the style of your form, follow these steps:

1. Click the form Run Mode button on the toolbar. Access first runs the Year-to-Date Sales by Category query, and then runs an additional query to create the data for the graph. The query's record number determines the Category Name; the default record is record 1, the Beverages category. The OLE server, Microsoft Graph, is loaded; it calculates the values necessary to create the graph. Finally, your graph appears (see fig. 14.24).

   The default title Graph appears because you deleted the graph's title in step 11 of the preceding series of steps. You add a title label and a label to identify the category in a subsequent step.

2. The default size of the unbound object frame determines the initial size of the graph created by Microsoft Graph. You need to modify the design of the graph to increase its size, and you need to make other changes so that the data is presented uniformly when different records are selected. Double-click the surface of the graph to display the Microsoft Graph editing window.

3. Click the ordinate (Y or vertical axis) of the graph, and then choose Font from the Format menu. Select the MS Sans Serif from the Font list so that the typeface matches the default face used by Access, and select 10 points in the Size list. Click the Bold check box to turn off the boldface attribute.

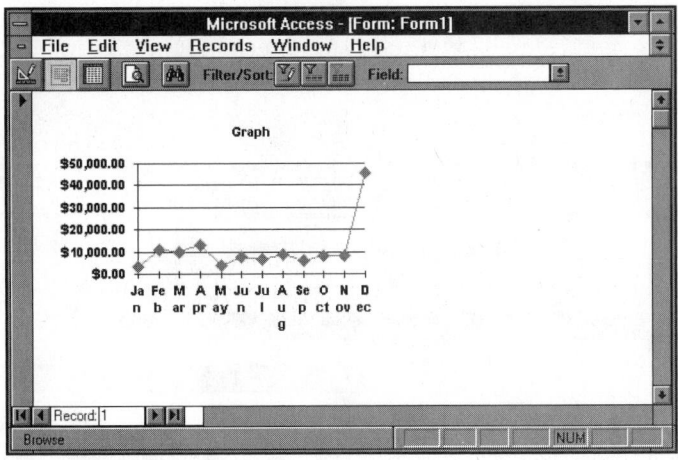

FIG. 14.24

The default format of the graph created by the GraphWizard.

4. Click the graph's abscissa (X or horizontal axis), and then repeat step 3 for this axis to make the font of both sets of labels the same.

5. By default, Microsoft Graph adjusts the scale of the ordinate so that its maximum value corresponds to the maximum value in the data series for the graph. When you compare values in a series of graphs, you want all graphs to have the same scale for both the ordinate and the abscissa. So you need to set the minimum and maximum values for the ordinate and specify the scale of the units labels.

Click the ordinate of the graph, and then choose Scale from the Format menu. Set the Minimum value to 0 and the Maximum to 25000, and enter 5000 in the Major Unit and Minor Unit text boxes. Click any check boxes that remain checked so that all check boxes are empty (see fig. 14.25). Then click OK.

If you select and delete the default title, Graph, it disappears when you return to Access but reappears the next time Access runs Microsoft Graph. If you edit the title in Microsoft Graph, the default title still eventually reappears. The reason for the default's reappearance is discussed in the section on SQL that follows. You cover the default graph title with a label in your form in a later step.

6. Adjust the vertical and horizontal size of the graph by dragging the borders of the graph unbound object frame until the graph is approximately the size you want on the form. Although you can

use the Zoom property to adjust the size of the graph in your form, the preferred method is to determine the size in Microsoft Graph and use Clip as the Scaling property for the unbound object frame.

7. Choose Exit & Return to Microsoft Access from Graph's File menu. Click Yes when asked whether you want to update Microsoft Access.

8. Chose Save Form As from the File menu and give your form the title **1991 Sales by Category**.

9. Click the Design button on the toolbar to return to Design mode. Select the unbound object frame and choose Size to Fit from the Layout menu so that you can adjust the dimensions of the frame to fit the modified graph.

10. Click the Properties button on the toolbar, and set the Enabled property of the graph object to No (see fig. 14.26). This setting prevents Microsoft Graph from appearing when you double-click the graph in Run mode. You can edit the graph in Design mode when an unbound object frame is not enabled.

    The linkage that you set in step 10 in the section "Using the Graph Tool To Create a Wizard Graph" appears as the values of the Link Child Fields and Link Master Fields properties of the unbound object frame (refer to fig. 14.26).

11. Relocate the frame so that it is approximately centered on the form.

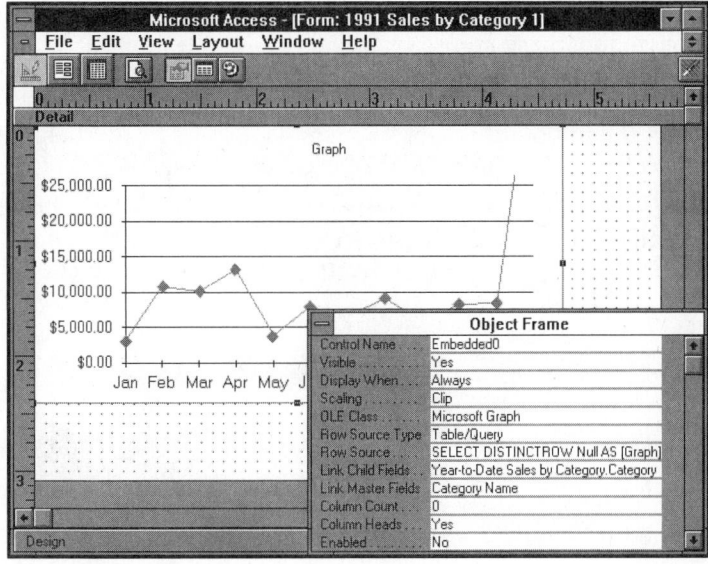

FIG. 14.26

The formatted
graph and its
properties shown
in Design mode.

12. Click the Form Run Mode button on the toolbar, and then display
your graph for several different categories with the Record Selection buttons.

Unbound object frames containing graphs require the Default
View property to be set to Single Form. You cannot include unbound object frames containing OLE objects in Continuous Forms
mode. If you attempt to set the Default View property to Continuous Forms, you receive a nocando error message.

Using SQL Statements To Create Data
and Change the Titles of Graphs

SQL is the subject of Chapter 20, "Working with Structured Query Language." However, a brief description of the way in which Access creates
SQL statements to generate queries for graphs is useful at this point, as
this description shows the behind-the-scene activity that occurs in
Access when you use the GraphWizard to create a graph or chart. You
need to edit the SQL statement if you want to change the name of your
graph from the name that you specified in the last ChartWizard dialog
box, or from the default title added by Access.

To display the SQL statement that creates the data for the graph in the Zoom box, follow these steps:

1. Click the Design button on the toolbar to return to Design mode.

2. Select the unbound object frame and click the Properties button on the toolbar to open the Properties window.

3. Select the Row Source property, and then press Shift+F2 to display the value of the Row Source property in the Zoom box. The SQL statement that creates the graph is shown in the Zoom box (see fig. 14.27).

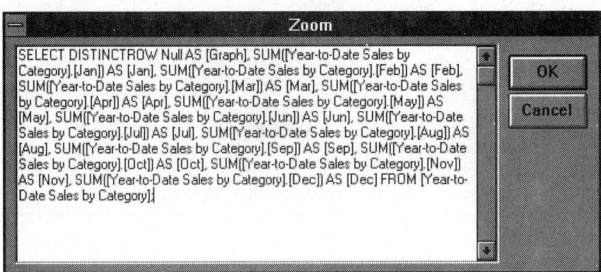

FIG. 14.27

The SQL statement that supplies the data required by Microsoft Graph.

The following is a version of the SQL statement, formatted here for clarity, that creates the data for one 1991 Sales by Category graph. The statement consists of 14 lines, 7 of which are replaced by the ellipsis in the sixth line:

```
SELECT DISTINCTROW Null AS [Graph],

        SUM([Year-to-Date Sales by Category].[Jan]) AS [Jan],

        SUM([Year-to-Date Sales by Category].[Feb]) AS [Feb],

        SUM([Year-to-Date Sales by Category].[Mar]) AS [Mar],

        SUM([Year-to-Date Sales by Category].[Apr]) AS [Apr],

    ...

        SUM([Year-to-Date Sales by Category].[Dec]) AS [Dec],

    FROM [Year-to-Date Sales by Category];
```

The individual parts of the SQL statement serve the following purposes:

■ Null specifies that there is no conventional *select-list*, because the *select-list* is created by the SUM statements. *Select-list* normally contains a list of the fields from the tables employed in the query.

■ AS [Graph] specifies the *correlation-name* (alias) of the object that receives the query result, which is the title (caption) of your graph. *Correlation-names* are ordinarily the values of the Caption properties of fields in the *select-list*.

■ SUM([Year-to-Date Sales by Category].[*Mon*]) specifies that the fields Jan ... Dec are each to be summed if more than one record is in the query. This example has only one record to sum because the query is linked to one record for each category. The GraphWizard offers grouping options when crosstab queries are not used.

■ AS [*Mon*] assigns the *correlation-name* for each of the values to be displayed on the graph. The *correlation-names* serve as labels for the graph.

■ FROM [Year-to-Date Sales by Category] specifies the name of the data source, in this case the query.

To change the title of your graph, edit the *correlation-name* following the AS reserved word to the title you want.

SQL expressions used in the creation of graphs can become much more complex than this example. Before integrated applications like Access were available, you had to enter SQL statements manually, and then write programming code to pass the query result to another application that created a graph. Access, the GraphWizard, and Microsoft Graph act together to create most graphs in less than five minutes. A year or two ago, creating the graph displayed in figure 14.28 might have taken hours or days to program, test, and debug.

Using Labels and Rectangles To Give Your Form the "Executive" Look

Combinations of labels and filled rectangles can give your graph a polished "executive" appearance (see fig. 14.28). Enhancing decision support forms with recessed rectangles and other *objets d'art* available from the toolbox and palette does not increase the form's information content; however, such embellishments can add to the attractiveness of your forms.

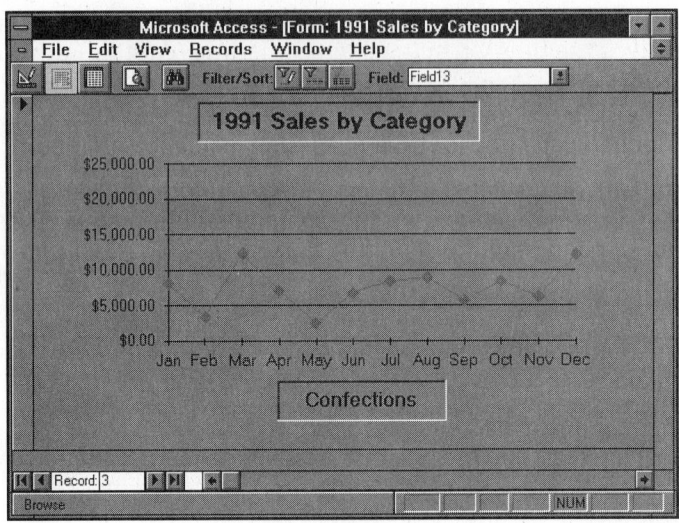

FIG. 14.28

Labels sur-
rounded by
sunken rectangles
can enhance the
appearance of
your form.

To add titles and shaded rectangles to your 1991 Sales by Category
form, follow these steps:

1. Click the Palette button on the toolbar to display the palette.

2. Click a blank area of the form to select the Design section, and
   choose light gray for the fill color.

3. Select the graph unbound object frame and change its fill to light
   gray.

4. Use the Label tool in the toolbox to add a label with the caption
   1991 Sales by Category. Set the label's Border property to Clear
   and its Fill property to light gray. Position the label so that it fully
   covers the default title of the graph.

5. Set the Size of the font to 14 points and click the Bold button on
   the toolbar.

6. Click the Rectangle tool in the toolbox and add a rectangle surrounding the label. Set the rectangle's Border and Fill properties
   to Clear, and click the Sunken Appearance option button. The
   advantage of adding a separate sunken rectangle is that you can
   position the rectangle independently of the text box content's
   position.

7. Click the Field List button on the toolbar, select the Category
   Name field, and drag the field symbol to the bottom center of your
   form. You need only the text box, so select the label and press the
   Delete key to remove the label from the form.

8. Set the text box's Fill property to Clear, and click Sunken Appearance to create a sunken border around the Category Name text box. Set the size of the font to 12 points.

   Your form appears as illustrated in figure 14.29.

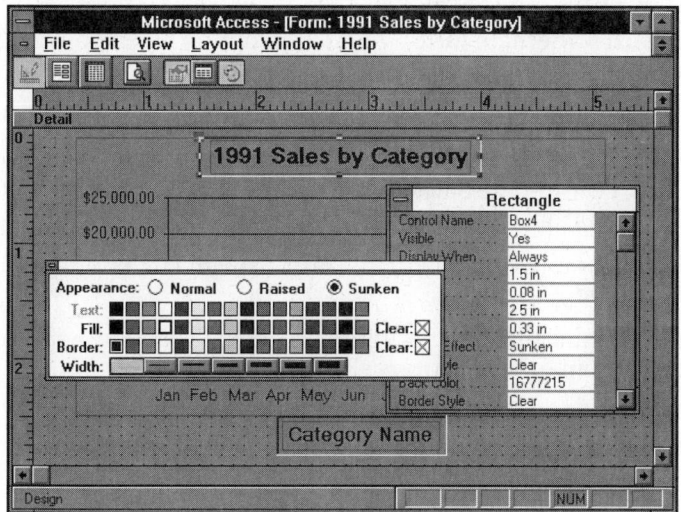

FIG. 14.29

Adding a sunken rectangle enclosing a label.

9. Click the Form Run Mode button on the toolbar to display your form, which appears as illustrated in figure 14.28.

   You can further embellish the form with Northwind's new logo in an unbound object frame, but you cannot display a picture in a crosstab query within a bound object frame. Access ignores the Categories table's Picture field if you add it to the query.

Adding a Summary Graph at the Top of Your Form

It is useful to add a summary graph created in a temporary form to display all the data for the categories. If you place the summary graph above the area where the graphs for the individual categories appear, the user can use the Pg Up and Pg Down keys to alternate between the two views.

Creating the Summary Graph in a Temporary Form

Unbound object boxes in a temporary form are handy places to store individual objects that you intend to add to your form and combine to create a composite object. To create a summary graph with the GraphWizard's alternate form, which is an option when you create a new form, follow these steps:

1. Choose New from the File menu, and click Form in the fly-out menu.

2. Select Year-to-Date Sales by Category in the list box and click the Wizard button.

3. Choose GraphWizard in the Wizard Type dialog box, and then choose OK.

4. Choose the line graph, as in the preceding example, and leave the default Sum option button selected. Click Next >.

5. All the fields are required by this chart because Category Names are used for the legend. Click >> to add all the fields, and then click Next >.

6. As in the previous example, only the months are used as labels for the abscissa of your graph. Add all the fields with >>, and then remove the Category Names field with <. In this case, leave the Display legend check box marked. Click Next >.

7. Delete the title, or change the title to **1991 Sales - All Categories**, and then click Open. Your graph appears as shown in figure 14.30.

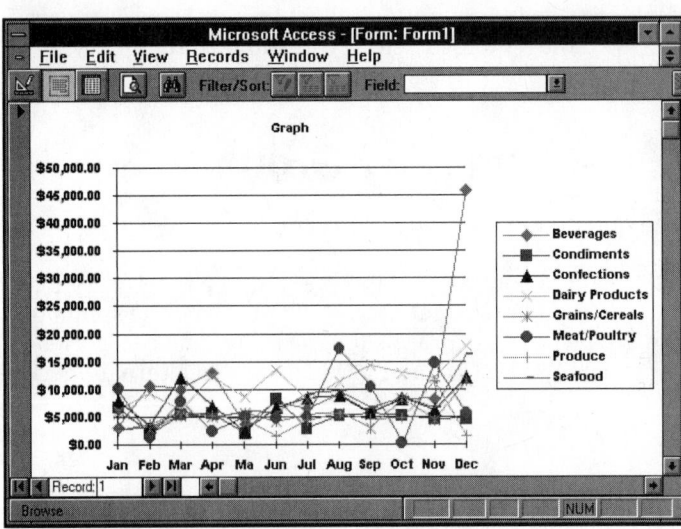

FIG. 14.30

The summary graph that results when the GraphWizard is used to create a new form.

8. Double-click the graph to display the Microsoft Graphs window. Change the fonts of both axes, plus the fonts in the legend box, to 9-point MS Sans Serif Roman (not bold). Change the scale for the ordinate to display **$0.00** to **$25,000**, with **$5,000** intervals as in the previous example.

9. Adjust the size of the graph to make it about 1/2-inch wider than the 1991 Sales By Category graph, compensating for the legend at the right of the graph.

10. Choose Exit to Access from Graph's **F**ile menu. Click Yes when asked whether you want to update Access.

11. Click the Design button on the toolbar to display the graph in Design mode. Your edited graph appears as illustrated in figure 14.31.

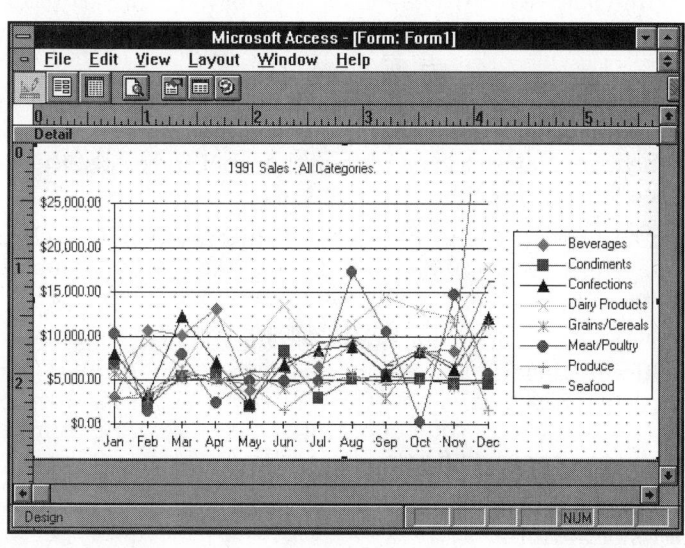

FIG. 14.31

The reformatted summary graph stored in a temporary form.

12. With the bound object frame selected, press Ctrl+C to copy the control object to the Clipboard. Then choose **C**lose from the **F**ile menu and do not save your changes.

Closing the form to which the bound object frame you copied to the Clipboard is related is important. If you do not break the relationship between the Microsoft Graph OLE server and your OLE client form by closing the temporary Form1, the graph does not display in Run mode in your destination form.

Adding the Summary Graph to a Form

Next, to paste the copy of the graph to your 1991 Sales by Category form, follow these steps:

1. Make 1991 Sales by Category the active form if necessary, and click the Design button on the toolbar to return to Design mode.

2. Choose Select **A**ll from the **E**dit menu. Drag all the objects down the form to make room for the new graph at the top of the form.

3. To paste the copy of the summary graph in the Clipboard to your form, press Ctrl+V.

4. Adjust the positions of the other objects in your form so that the other objects are centered under the summary graph.

5. Use the palette to change the fill color of the summary graph to light gray.

6. Select the rectangle and the label of the original graph, and press Ctrl+C to copy the controls to the Clipboard. Press Ctrl+V to paste the copy, and then move the copied controls near the top center of the form. Revise the caption of the label and adjust the widths of the label and rectangle to suit the new text.

7. Add a label with the text **Use Page Down to Display by Category** under the legend box. Set the label's background color to Clear on the palette.

8. Click the Form Run Mode button on the toolbar to display your multipurpose form. It takes longer for the form to appear initially because the OLE server, Microsoft Graph, must run twice to create the two graphs. After some intense disk activity, your form appears as shown in figure 14.32.

9. Use the Pg Up and Pg Down keys to alternate between the two views of the form.

You can use more elegant methods of displaying different forms by employing command buttons and macros, but the subject of the next part of this book is macros. Even without macros, you can create a usable form for decision support by management.

4. Choose E**x**it & Return to Microsoft Access from Graph's **F**ile menu.

Access

5. With the graph selected, press Delete to remove it from the form.

6. Choose Insert Ob**j**ect from Access's **F**ile menu, choose Microsoft Drawing from the Object Types list box, and choose OK.

7. When the empty window of Microsoft Draw appears, choose **P**aste from Draw's **E**dit menu. An image of the graph appears.

8. Click a blank area of the window to deselect all the elements of the drawing.

9. Edit individual elements of the drawing as necessary. If you want, delete the title of the chart, which changes the height of the chart.

10. Choose Select **A**ll from Draw's **E**dit menu. The drawing with all objects selected appears, as shown in figure 14.33.

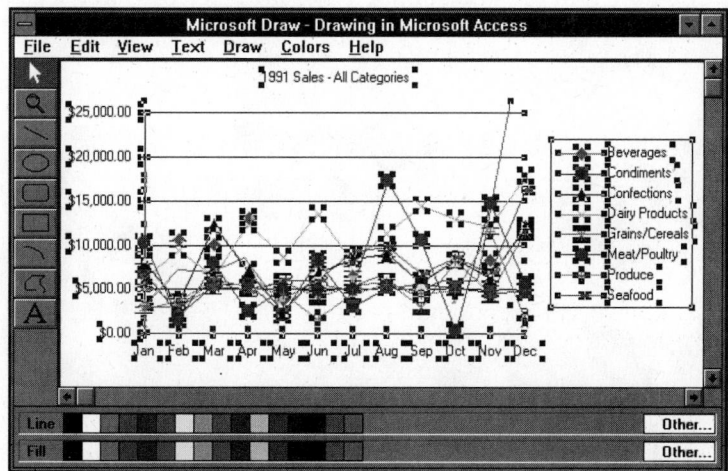

FIG. 14.33

A graph object copied and pasted into Microsoft Draw with all elements selected.

11. Choose **G**roup from the **D**raw menu to group all the elements into one object.

12. Choose E**x**it & Return to Microsoft Access from Draw's **F**ile menu. Click Yes when asked whether you want to update Access.

Access

13. With the new unbound object frame selected, choose Size to Fit from Access's **L**ayout menu. Adjust the position of the drawing so that the drawing occupies the area of the graph it replaces.

14. Set the background color to Clear, and your form appears as it did before you changed the object type.

15. Click the Form Run Mode button on the toolbar. The form displays much faster because only one instance of Microsoft Graph needs to run to create the 1991 Sales Category now that the All Categories graph is static.

Although the data that underlies the individual categories for 1991 is static, the 1991 Sales by Category graph is not static. So you cannot convert this graph to a drawing.

Adding Graphs to Reports

Although the examples of creating graphs in this section exclusively use forms as containers for the Microsoft Graph and Draw objects, the techniques employed are identical for the creation of graphs to be included in reports. You can save your form as a report and then review the design of the new report. The 1991 Sales by Category form saved as a report by the same name is shown in Print Preview mode (see fig. 14.34).

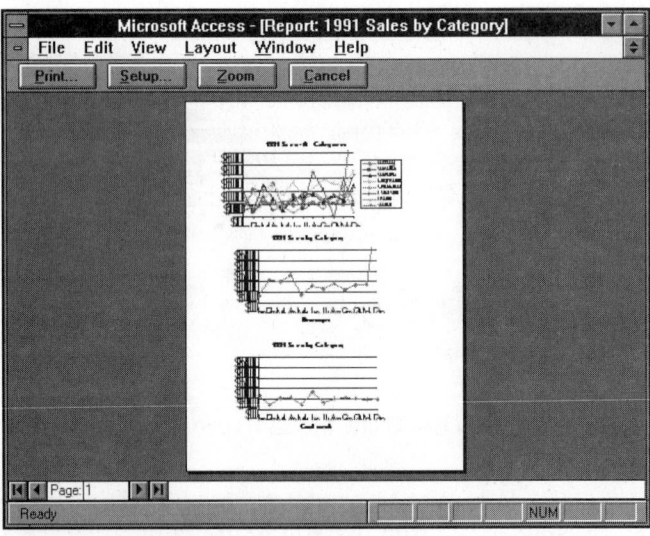

FIG. 14.34

The 1991 Sales by Category form saved as a report and displayed in Print Preview mode.

In this case, the drawing of the summary graph is moved to the Report Header section so that the graph prints only once. The balance of the form is included in the detail section of the report. You can print three graphs per page so that the summary graph and the eight-category graphs fit nicely on three pages. The strange appearance of the graphs' ordinate labels occurs because of the inability of the Print Preview function to scale the font to an appropriately small size.

Use forms to create corresponding reports whenever possible, especially if you include graphs on the form that are to be printed in the report. Reports are much slower to test than forms because of the page formatting required when you switch to Print Preview mode, the report's equivalent of Form Run mode. When your form is complete and tested, copy the form as a report and make the necessary modifications, such as removing fill colors from the sections and control objects of the report.

Chapter Summary

In this chapter, you were introduced to examples of the most common use of unbound object frames. In this chapter and the preceding chapter, you gained experience manipulating OLE servers and the objects those servers create, which helps you develop an understanding of the full capabilities of Microsoft's object linking and embedding technology incorporated into Windows 3.1.

The majority of Access users are experienced with Microsoft Excel. Many Access users and developers approach Access as an extension of Excel and intend to use Access where Excel macros and its other advanced features cannot achieve a particular goal. The next chapter almost exclusively deals with ways to use Access to enhance or supplant applications created with Microsoft Excel. If you are not an Excel user, skip the next chapter and proceed to Part IV of this book, which introduces you to the power of Access macros.

Using Access with Microsoft Excel

Spreadsheet and word processing applications dominate the Windows software market. According to industry reports, more than 70 percent of all Windows installations in the business environment include a spreadsheet application. Spreadsheets include the capability to emulate some of the features of database managers, such as sorting ranges of cells defined as a worksheet "database."

One of the principal uses of Access is expected to be the conversion of worksheet data to tables in a relational database structure. Some of the primary justifications for converting from the familiar worksheet model to an Access database include the following:

- Access queries provide much greater flexibility in selecting and sorting data than is offered by the limited sort and selection criteria of spreadsheet applications.

- You can create Access forms to simulate common business forms, which is difficult or impossible to do with present-day Windows spreadsheet applications. Data-entry validation is much easier in Access than in worksheets.

- Access offers many more options for printing formatted reports from your data than are available with worksheets.

- Access macros are easier to implement than macros written in the application languages of spreadsheet programs.

■ Access Basic enables you to write programs in a full-featured language and does not restrict you to using a set of predetermined worksheet functions.

■ Properly designed Access relational databases minimize the duplication of information and reduce disk file storage requirements for large aggregations of data.

In many situations, however, changing a worksheet to a database is impractical. You may need to be able to view, import, or edit data contained in a worksheet within an Access application. In this case, linking the spreadsheet as an OLE object is the best method because you cannot attach a worksheet file to an Access database. The reason you cannot attach worksheet files is demonstrated in the first section of this chapter by the conversion process necessary to restructure the data. The second section of this chapter, "Using Excel as an OLE Server," describes how to link or embed worksheet data as OLE objects in bound or unbound object frames.

This chapter also includes a brief example of the use of Access's DDE( ) function to paste the values of individual cells of a Microsoft Excel worksheet into unbound text boxes on an Access form. This technique is useful when you want to obtain the value of a specified data cell or range of cells to display or update values in Access tables. You can use the DDE( ) function with any Windows spreadsheet application that has DDE server capability. To exploit fully the DDE capabilities of Access, you need to write Access Basic functions that you execute with macros. Parts IV and VI of this book describe these techniques.

 Microsoft Excel is used in the following examples, but you can use any Windows spreadsheet application that has OLE server capability. The first series of examples—which show you how to reorganize spreadsheet data into Access tables—don't require a spreadsheet application; you only need a suitable file in Excel .XLS or Lotus .WKS, .WK1, or .WK3 format to import.

Importing and Reorganizing Worksheet Data

Worksheets created by Excel and other spreadsheet applications often contain data suitable for processing with relational database techniques. The worksheet usually is organized for viewing the data quickly; however, this organization seldom is appropriate for manipulation of the data by a DBM.

STK_21_1.XLS (described in the next section) is an example of a worksheet formatted for viewing data. Four rows of 22 columns each contain the equivalent of a database record—all available data for a single stock. This type of structure, where a group of individual rows constitute a database record, is common in worksheet design. This structure differs from the design of a true worksheet database in which all the data for a single entity (in this case a stock) is contained in a single row. The examples that follow in this section illustrate how to import a spreadsheet of this type and convert the data it contains to related Access tables. Make-table and update queries assist in the reorganization of the data into relational form.

Obtaining and Converting the Example Worksheet

The file used to create many of the examples in this chapter contains the high and low prices and the trading volume of more than 300 individual stocks for a 21-day period beginning on April 10, 1992. This file was created as a Lotus 1-2-3 worksheet file (STK_21.WK1) by Ideas Unlimited and is available for downloading as STOCK.ZIP (146K in size) from the Excel for the PC Library 3 of the Microsoft Excel forum on CompuServe (GO MSEXCEL). If you do not want to download STOCK.ZIP, the data for the first 201 rows (records for 50 stocks) of STK_21.WK1 are listed in Appendix D, "Data to Create the STK_21.XLS Worksheet."

If you download the worksheet file to use in the following examples, you can import it directly into Access as a Lotus-1-2-3 WK1 file. If you have Excel, convert the file to Excel worksheets of three different sizes by using the following steps:

1. Expand the file to STK_21.WK1 with PKUNZIP.EXE. (Type **PKUNZIP STOCK** at the DOS prompt.) If you don't have PKUNZIP.EXE, download PKZ110.EXE from the IBM New User Library 2, Library Tools (GO IBMNEW).

   After downloading PKZ110.EXE, execute the file (type **PKZ110** at the DOS prompt) to obtain PKUNZIP.EXE and several other accompanying files, including user documentation.

2. Launch Excel, choose **O**pen from the **F**ile menu, and open STK_21.WK1 as a Lotus 1-2-3 file (*.WK*) in Excel. The worksheet appears as shown in figure 15.1.

FIG. 15.1

The 21-day
stock price and
trading volume
worksheet,
displayed in
Excel.

3. Make A1 the selected cell, and press Shift+Ctrl+End to select the entire worksheet. Choose **C**opy from the **E**dit menu, or press Ctrl+C to copy its contents to the Clipboard. Close the worksheet, and click Yes when Excel asks whether you want to save the contents of the large Clipboard. Closing the worksheet requires a little time so that Excel can copy the worksheet to a temporary file.

4. Choose New from the **F**ile menu to open a new worksheet window. Choose **P**aste from the **E**dit menu, or press Ctrl+V to copy the Clipboard contents to the new worksheet. Click OK when Excel asks whether you want to continue without Undo.

5. Press Shift+Ctrl+End to select the entire worksheet, and choose **N**umber from the **F**ormat menu to open the Number Format dialog box. Enter **#,###.000** as the format expression in the code text box. (Three decimal digits are adequate to display fractional prices.)

6. With the entire worksheet selected, choose **C**olumn Width from the **F**ormat menu. Choose Best Fit and choose OK.

7. The first row of the worksheet is used to provide field names for the table. Enter **Day** in cell A1, replace the dates (now in numeric format) in the first row of the worksheet with the numbers **1** through **21**. Following the procedure of step 5, format this row with no decimal digits (format **0**).

8. Select row 2 by clicking the row number button, and choose **De-lete** from the **Edit** menu to remove the row of hyphens. The worksheet appears as shown in figure 15.2.

	A	B	C	D	E	F
		Day				
1	Day	1	2	3	4	5
2	AAL-S	18.500	18.250	18.750	19.125	19.000
3	High	19.250	18.500	18.875	19.250	19.125
4	Low	18.500	18.125	18.500	18.875	18.875
5	Volume	59,200	52,800	84,000	63,400	16,700
6	AAQ-S	55.500	56.500	58.750	60.500	59.000
7	High	57.500	56.750	59.250	60.875	60.750
8	Low	55.000	55.250	57.250	57.500	58.500
9	Volume	2,447,000	1,078,200	1,289,300	1,940,700	2,309,700
10	AA-S	68.000	73.750	71.750	74.500	76.625
11	High	68.750	73.875	73.750	74.875	76.750
12	Low	68.000	67.000	71.250	72.000	74.375
13	Volume	381,900	270,800	1,162,900	723,900	1,079,600
14	ABT-S	65.250	65.625	67.250	66.375	64.875
15	High	66.125	65.750	67.875	67.750	66.000

FIG. 15.2

The edited version of the stock price and trading volume worksheet.

9. Choose Save **As** from the **File** menu and save the worksheet (in Excel .XLS format) as **STK_21_1.XLS** in your Access directory.

Now you need to make some smaller versions of the worksheet to use in the examples that follow. To create STK_21_2.XLS (201 rows and 50 stocks) and STK_21_3.XLS (17 rows and 4 stocks), follow these steps:

1. Use the mouse, or the Shift key with the arrow keys to select the first 201 rows of STK_21_1.XLS. Choose **Copy** from the **Edit** menu, or press Ctrl+C to copy the selection to the Clipboard.

2. Create a new worksheet window. Choose **Paste** from the **Edit** menu, or press Ctrl+V to paste the 201 rows to the new worksheet.

3. Choose **Column Width** from the **Format** menu and click Best Fit in the Column Width dialog box.

4. Save the new worksheet as **STK_21_2.XLS**.

5. Copy the first 17 rows of STK_21_2.XLS to the Clipboard; then open a new window and paste the cells. Set Best Fit for this worksheet, and save the file as **STK_21_3.XLS**. Exit Excel.

If you are using another spreadsheet application, the procedure is likely to be quite similar. The two smaller files, STK_21_2.XLS and STK_21_3.XLS, demonstrate the effect of worksheet size on Access performance in sections related to OLE later in this chapter. (You don't need to create the smaller files if you don't have a spreadsheet application that can act as an OLE server.)

The organization of these worksheets is especially well suited to the first example in the next section, which shows you how to reorganize a worksheet to create a properly designed table. Alternatively, you can use for the examples any Excel or .WK* file you have that contains multiple series of numbers.

Importing the Example Worksheet

The first step in the importing process is to create a new database in which to import the worksheet data. Follow these steps:

Access

1. Launch Access if it is not open, or select the Database window if Access is open. Choose New Database from the File menu. The New Database dialog box appears.

2. In the New Database dialog box, enter **STOCKS.MDB** as the name of your new database; then choose OK.

3. Choose Import from the File menu. The Import dialog box opens (see fig. 15.3).

The Import dialog box.

4. Select Microsoft Excel from the Data Source list box; then choose OK. The Select File dialog box appears.

5. Select STK_21_1.XLS in the Select File dialog box. (Use STK_21_2.XLS if you want to conserve disk space.) Click the Import button to display the Import Spreadsheet Options dialog box (see fig. 15.4).

6. Choose the First Row Contains Field Names option in the Import Spreadsheet Options dialog box; then choose OK. Access imports your worksheet as a table and reports the number of records imported in the message box shown in figure 15.5.

Import Spreadsheet Options - STK_21_1.XLS

☒ First Row Contains Field Names   [OK]

Table Options   [Cancel]
  ⦿ Create New Table

  ◯ Append to Existing Table: [▾]

  Spreadsheet Range: [   ]

Import Results - STK_21_1.XLS

ⓘ Import to STK_21_1 finished – 1220 records
   processed. No errors were detected.

   [OK]   [Help]

7. Choose OK, and then click the Close button in the Select File dialog box.

   Access assigns the imported worksheet's file name to the imported table.

8. Make sure the imported table is selected, and click the Open button to display the table in Run mode.

9. Select all 22 fields by clicking the Day column header button, holding down the mouse button, and dragging the mouse to the right. Choose **C**olumn Width from the **L**ayout menu to display the Column Width dialog box (see fig. 15.6).

10. Set the column width to **10**. Choose OK, and then click anywhere in the table window to deselect the fields. The table appears as shown in figure 15.7.

Table

Column Width

Column Width: [10]   [OK]

☐ Standard Width   [Cancel]

You can approximately halve the disk-space requirement for the stock tables you create by setting the field-size property of the numeric fields with the Numbers data type to Single. Access assigns the Double field size to numeric data imported from worksheets by default. Single-precision numbers can accommodate all of the numeric values in the table. The comparative sizes of the worksheet file and the resulting Access file are listed in table 15.1.

FIG. 15.7

STK_21_1.XLS
imported to an
Access table.

The field names of the columns that contain numeric data and
that you numbered 1 through 21 in your Excel worksheet appear
as 2 through 22 in your imported table (see fig. 15.7). Access mis-
interpreted the numeric values in the worksheet as column numbers, not numbers representing days. Because a 1 was in column 2
of the worksheet, Access incremented the column numbers by 1
to create field names that correspond to the column numbers,
starting with 1 as the leftmost (Day) column. The field names are
arbitrary, so you do not need to change them; in the examples
that follow, the field names have been changed to 1 through 21.

Table 15.1. Comparative Sizes of Worksheet and Access Database Files

File and Status	Size, Bytes
STK_21_1.XLS worksheet file (Excel 4.0a)	403,543
STOCKS.MDB with Double Field Size	327,680
STOCKS.MDB fields changed to Single Field Size	425,984
STOCKS.MDB with Single Field Size after compacting	196,608

The file-size data of table 15.1 demonstrates the necessity for compacting Access databases when you change the Data Type or Field Size properties of Access tables. In this and most other cases, table size increases when you change the Field Size property. To gain the benefit of reducing the Field Size property, you need to compact the database as described in the procedure that follows. Table 15.1 also demonstrates the efficiency with which Access stores data imported from worksheets. Despite the 64K of database overhead, Access stores the worksheet data in a file that is smaller than the original worksheet file. If you used STK_21_2.XLS to create the table, the file-size savings are less pronounced than those shown in the table.

To change the Field Size property of the numeric fields of the STK_21_1 table, follow these steps:

1. If you want to verify the sizes of the worksheet and Access database files shown in table 15.1, open File Manager, choose the drive and directory in which the files are located, and note the file sizes. Close File Manager and return to Access.

2. Click the Design button to change to Design mode.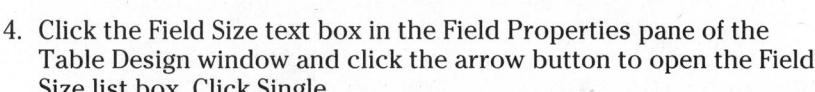

3. Select the first numeric field—the field named 2. Change the Field Name value to 1 and the Field Size value from 255 to 20.

4. Click the Field Size text box in the Field Properties pane of the Table Design window and click the arrow button to open the Field Size list box. Click Single.

5. Repeat step 4 for the remaining 20 numeric fields, changing the Field Name value to one less than the original number.

6. Click the Datasheet button to return to Table Run mode. Click Yes when asked whether you want to save your changes. Access converts the field sizes in the STK_21_1 table from Double to Single at this point.

7. Choose **C**lose Database from the **F**ile menu in preparation to compact STOCKS.MDB.

8. Reopen File Manager and note the increased size of STOCKS.MDB caused by the change of the Field Size property. Close File Manager.

9. Choose **C**ompact Database from Access's **F**ile menu and double-click STOCKS.MDB in the File Name list box of the Database to Compact From dialog box. The Database to Compact Into dialog box appears.

Access

10. Type **STOCKS.MDB** in the File Name text box of the Database to Compact Into dialog box and click OK. Answer Yes when Access asks whether you want to replace the existing version of STOCKS.MDB. Access compacts STOCKS.MDB to a temporary file and replaces the original when the compaction is completed.

11. Reopen File Manager and observe the decreased size of STOCKS.MDB resulting from the compaction—about 60 percent of the original size. Close File Manager.

12. Choose **O**pen Database from Access's **F**ile menu and double-click STOCKS.MDB to reopen your compacted table.

The savings in database file size increases with the number of records in the tables whose Field Size properties are made smaller. As an example, if you were to add many more records to the STK_21_1 table, the savings in disk space would approach the theoretical 50 percent savings when replacing double-precision with single-precision values.

For Related Information:

◄◄ "Compacting Databases," p. 117.

◄◄ "Creating a New Database," p. 127.

◄◄ "Importing Spreadsheet Files," p. 203.

Developing a Conversion Strategy

The second step in the conversion process is to define the tables to be created. Very few worksheets can be converted to a single table that meets relational database standards. Designing the tables to contain the data and establishing the relationships of these tables to each other is the most important element of the conversion process. Following are the two objectives of your design strategy:

■ *A design optimized for data display, entry, and editing:* This objective is primary if you plan to use Access for data entry. In the stock prices example, data entry and editing aren't a consideration because the data is supplied in worksheet format by Ideas Unlimited and other purveyors of stock price data.

■ *A design that enables you to extract the imported data with the few-est steps:* If you obtain periodic updates to your stock price data in worksheet format, for example, ease of importing the data is the principal consideration.

The initial design usually is a compromise between these two objec-tives. The stock price example does not involve a compromise because data entry and editing are unnecessary.

When planning the initial design of the tables to contain the stock price and volume data, use this strategy:

■ *The data for each element of the group—Close, High, Low, and Vol-ume—is incorporated in an individual table.* A table with the 84 fields required to hold all the data for a stock is unwieldy at best. Reconstructing a worksheet from a table with such a design re-sults in a cumbersome worksheet. One of the principles of rela-tional database design is that you should be able to reconstruct your database with the data (see Chapter 19, "Exploring Relational Database Design and Implementation").

■ *The key field of each table, Symbol, is the ticker symbol of the stock.* (Ticker symbol is the abbreviation for the name of the stock as-signed by the New York Stock Exchange.) This key field enables the tables to be linked in a one-to-one relationship based on the unique values of the ticker symbols. One-to-one relationships are uncommon in relational databases, but in this example a one-to-one relationship is quite useful.

■ *Queries organize the data in the tables as required for Access forms and reports.* Because each field in the query is prefaced by the table name, the names of the tables should be short to save keystrokes.

■ *When multiple tables are combined in a query, the records in each table must be identified by type.* The second field, Type, is a single-letter abbreviation of the type of data: C(lose), H(igh), L(ow), and V(olume).

■ *The tables must be designed so that the data can be viewed in tabu-lar or graphical form.*

Now you need to develop the tactics to create the required tables in accordance with your strategy. The conversion plan involves these elements:

■ The records to be included in the individual tables are extracted from the STK_21_1 table by make-table queries with criteria based on the values in the Day field.

■ The Symbol field from the Close table must be added to the High, Low, and Volume tables.

■ In the query used to create the final table, adding the Symbol field to a table requires a unique key to link the Close table and the tables that don't have symbol values. A Counter field added to the Close, High, Low, and Volume tables can serve as a temporary key field.

■ Creating the new tables is a two-step process. First, the data is extracted to a temporary set of tables (Hi, Lo, and Vol. Hi). The second step combines these three tables with the Symbol field of another temporary table, Close, to create the final High, Low, and Volume tables. You need temporary tables in this case because make-table queries cannot alter tables on which they are based.

■ Because the Close table lacks a type identifier field, a Type field must be added to this table. The remaining tables have a type identifier word that can be replaced by the corresponding code letter.

Now that you have a conversion strategy and have decided the tactics to carry it out, you are ready to test merits of both, as described in the next section.

FROM HERE...

For Related Information:

▶▶ "Normalizing Data to the Relational Model," p. 793.

Extracting Data

Make-table queries are designed specifically for creating new tables from data in existing tables that meets a specified set of criteria. For STK_21_1, you use make-table queries to create one final table (Close) and three temporary tables (Hi, Low, and Vol). To create these four tables with make-table queries, follow these steps:

New

1. Click the Query button of the Database window; then click the New button to create a new Query1. The Add Query dialog box appears.

2. Add the STK_21_1 table to the query in the Add Query dialog box.

3. Click the Day field and drag the field symbol to the first column of the query.

4. Click the asterisk (*, all fields) and drag the field symbol to the second column of the query.

5. Click the Show check box in the Day field. (Day is included in the fields in the second column of the query. You cannot include two fields of the same name in a make-table query.)

6. In the Criteria row of the Day field, enter ="**High**" to include only records for the high price of the stock in the temporary Hi table. Your query appears as shown in figure 15.8.

7. Choose **M**ake Table from the **Q**uery menu.

8. Enter **Hi** in the Table Name text box and then choose OK (see fig. 15.9). The default values for the remaining elements in the Query Properties dialog box are satisfactory.

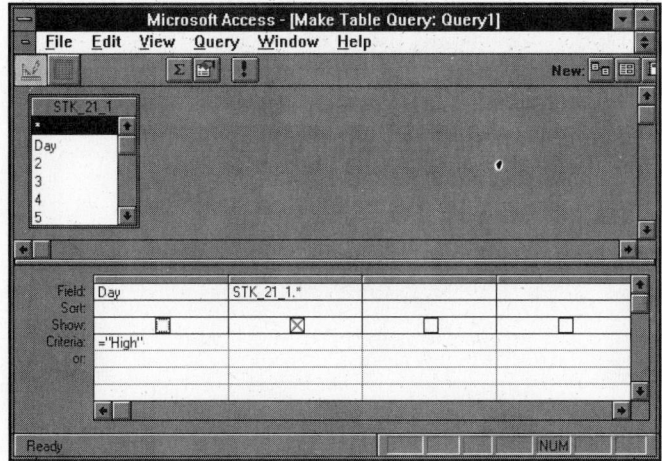

FIG. 15.8

The make-table query that creates the temporary Hi table.

FIG. 15.9

The Query Properties dialog box for a make-table query.

9. Click the Run Query button on the toolbar to create the tempo-rary Hi table. Access displays a message box that indicates the number of records to be added to the new table (see fig. 15.10). Choose OK.

10. Open the Database window, click the Table button, and double-click the Hi entry in the list to view the table (see fig. 15.11).

FIG. 15.10

The message box indicating the number of records that comprise the new table.

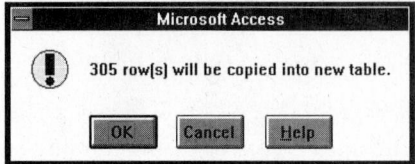

FIG. 15.11

The temporary Hi table created by the make-table query.

Day	1	2	3	4	5	6	7	8	9	10
High	19.25	18.5	18.875	19.25	19.125	19.125	19	19.125	19.125	19.125
High	57.5	56.75	59.25	60.875	60.75	60.75	59	57.25	58	58.25
High	68.75	73.875	73.75	74.875	76.75	76.75	78.25	77.375	76.375	75.625
High	66.125	65.75	67.875	67.75	66	66	64.5	64	63.375	63.875
High	12.5	12.375	12.5	12.375	12.25	12.25	12.375	23.125	12.125	12.125
High	62.625	62.75	64.375	64.75	64.75	64.75	62.375	61.75	61.625	61.375
High	25.125	25.5	26	25.875	24.5	24.5	24.125	23.5	24.375	24.25
High	31.375	31.25	31.875	32	32.25	32.25	32.25	32.25	32.125	31.875
High	43.75	44.5	44.25	43.75	43.25	43.25	43.25	43.75	44.125	43.875
High	42	42	42.25	42.375	42.625	42.625	42.375	42.5	43.25	45
High	40.5	40.125	41.5	42.375	42.625	42.625	42.375	41.875	41.375	39.875
High	16.625	16.625	16.75	16.875	17	17	16.875	17	17.375	17.25
High	77.75	77.75	82	81.875	80	80	77.875	77.25	76.875	77.5
High	86	85.625	87.75	87.5	87.5	87.5	86.375	86.375	85.125	85.375
High	58.875	59.375	59.5	59.625	60.75	60.75	61.125	61.5	62.75	63.75
High	54.125	54.375	55.75	55.5	57.125	57.125	56.5	57.125	56.75	59
High	18.125	18	17.75	17.875	18.25	18.25	18.25	18	18	18.125
High	19.625	20.625	20.375	20.25	21.125	21.125	21.375	21	21.125	21.25

11. Change the Criteria value to ="**Low**" and repeat steps 6 through 10, substituting **Lo** for the table name in steps 6 and 10.

12. Change the Criteria value to ="**Volume**" and repeat steps 6 through 10, using **Vol** for the table name.

13. The closing prices are in the row with the ticker symbol. Each of the symbols has a hyphen followed by a character that identifies the type of security; -S represents a common stock. Change the Criteria value to **Like "*-*"** to select these rows and repeat steps 6 through 10, using **Close** for the table name. The expression *-* selects all records containing a hyphen. You don't need to create a temporary table in this case because the Close table includes the ticker symbols, as illustrated by figure 15.12.

FIG. 15.12

The Close table that contains the ticker symbols and closing price of the stocks.

For Related Information:

◄◄ "Creating New Tables with Action Queries," p. 351.

FROM HERE...

Modifying the Table Structure

Each table you created in the preceding section requires additional fields. A Counter field is used as a temporary key field in each of the four tables. The Close table needs a Type field added, and the Day field of each temporary table needs the name changed to Type. Follow these steps to make the changes:

1. Click the Table button in the Database window, select the Hi table, and click the Design button.

2. Change the name of the first field from Day to **Type** and set the Field Size property to 1, as shown in figure 15.13. This action truncates the Type field value, High, to the required single-letter code H.

3. Click the Datasheet button on the toolbar. Save the changes to the table. Another message box advises you that some data may be lost due to truncating the length of the Type field. Click Yes to approve the change.

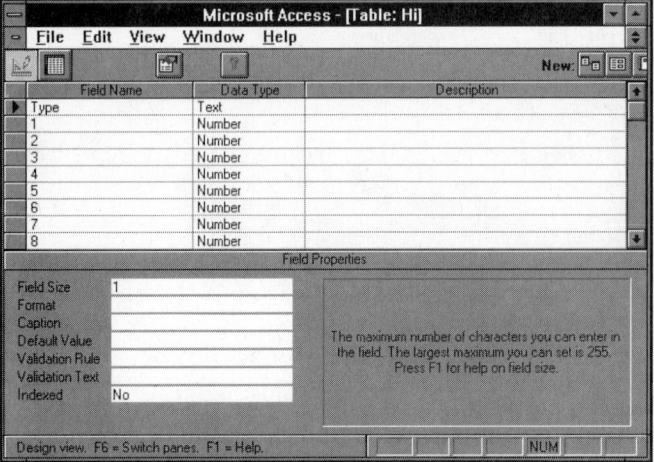

The modifications
to the temporary
Hi table, shown
in Query Design
mode.

4. No key field has been selected. To add a key field, click Yes in the
dialog box shown in figure 15.14.

The table appears as shown in figure 15.15. The primary key that
Access creates is a Counter field with the default name ID.

FIG. 15.14

The message box
that enables you
to add a key
field to a table.

FIG. 15.15

The temporary Hi
table with the key
field ID added.

5. Repeat steps 1 through 4 for the Lo and Vol tables.

6. Open the Close table in Design mode. Change the Day field name to **Symbol** and change its Field Size property to **10** to accommodate longer ticker symbols.

7. Click the Selection button for the first of the Number fields and then press Ins to add a new field.

8. Enter **Type** as the Field Name of the new field (added fields default to the Text data type) and set its Field Size property to **1**. Figure 15.16 shows the design of the Close table.

9. Click the Datasheet button on the toolbar, save your changes, accept the truncated field, and add a key field to the table. Figure 15.17 shows the resulting Close table.

FIG. 15.16

Modifications made to the Close table, prior to adding the ID key field.

The extraction of data from STK_21_1 to the required tables is a relatively simple process because the labels used to identify the data are consistent throughout the worksheet. You may need to write a worksheet macro that creates consistent labels for rows to be included in a specific table, if the labels don't exist or aren't consistent in the original version of the worksheet.

			Microsoft Access - [Table: Close]						

Table:

ID	Symbol	Type	1	2	3	4	5	6	7	8
1	AAL-S		18.5	18.25	18.75	19.125	19	19	18.75	19.125
2	AAQ-S		55.5	56.5	58.75	60.5	59	59	56.75	56.25
3	AA-S		68	73.75	71.75	74.5	76.625	76.625	77.75	76.25
4	ABT-S		65.25	65.625	67.25	66.375	64.875	64.875	63.25	62.875
5	ABY-S		12.375	12.375	12.5	12.125	12.25	12.25	12.375	23.125
6	ACY-S		61.875	62.375	64.375	64.5	62.625	62.625	60.25	61.5
7	ADM-S		25	25.375	25.625	24.375	23.875	23.875	23.375	23.375
8	AEP-S		31.25	31.125	31.625	32	32.25	32.25	32.25	32.25
9	AET-S		43.5	44	43.625	43.125	43.25	43.25	43.125	43.75
10	AGC-S		41.875	41.375	42.125	42.375	42.625	42.625	42.25	42.5
11	AHC-S		39.375	40	41.375	42.375	42.375	42.375	41.875	41.5
12	AHM-S		16.375	16.625	16.625	16.625	16.75	16.75	16.75	16.875
13	AHP-S		76.875	77.75	81.625	80	78.25	78.25	76.125	77.125
14	AIG-S		85.375	85.5	86.75	87.25	86.75	86.75	86	85.25
15	AIT-S		58.75	58.875	59.375	59.625	60.75	60.75	61.125	61.125
16	ALD-S		53.75	53.75	54.625	55.5	57	57	56.5	56.75
17	ALK-S		18.125	17.75	17.5	17.875	18.125	18.125	18	17.875
18	AL-S		19.625	20.625	20.125	20.25	20.875	20.875	21.125	20.875
19	ALS-S		32	32.25	32.125	31.875	32.25	32.25	32.375	32.375

FIG. 15.17

The Close table with the ID and Type fields added.

Adding the Type Value to the Close Table

When you need to replace data in a field containing values, the **R**eplace command on the **E**dit menu is usually a faster process than creating an update query. Because the Replace What text box in the Replace in Field dialog box doesn't accept a Null value, however, you cannot use the **R**eplace command on the **E**dit menu to add the C code (for "Close") to the Type field of the Close table. Instead, you must use an update query to change the Type field value. Follow these steps:

1. Choose **N**ew from the **F**ile menu, and then choose **Q**uery.

2. Choose **A**dd Table from the **Q**uery menu to access the Add Table dialog box. Double-click the Close item in the list box, and then click the Close button.

3. Choose **U**pdate from the **Q**uery menu.

4. Select the Type field and drag the field symbol to the first column of the query.

5. Enter **C** in the Update To row. This action changes the Type field value in all records from the default Null to C. Figure 15.18 shows the update query design at this point.

6. Click the Run Query button on the toolbar to update the Type field of the Close table. When the message box shown in figure 15.19 appears, choose OK.

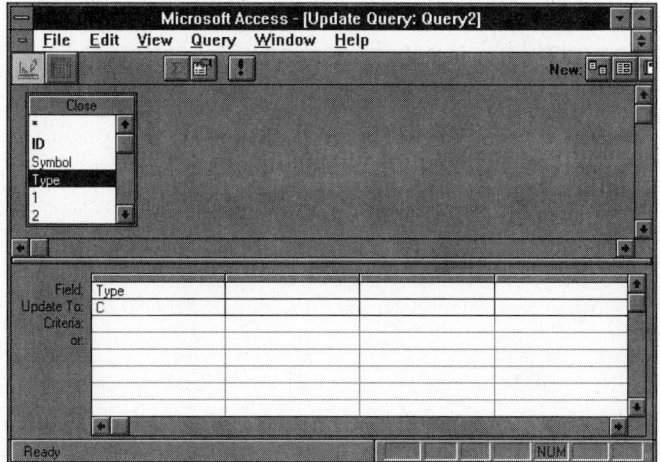

FIG. 15.18

The update query used to add C to the Type field of each record in the Close table.

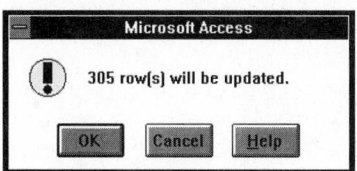

FIG. 15.19

The message box that indicates the number of records to be updated.

For Related Information:

◄◄ "Updating Values of Multiple Records in a Table," p. 361.

FROM HERE...

Creating the Final Tables

Now you need to combine the Symbol field of the Close table with the data in the Hi, Lo, and Vol tables to create the final High, Low, and Volume tables. In this example, you use the same query each time, changing the temporary table name to create the three final tables.

> If you are creating an application that uses macros to automate the conversion process, save each query with a unique name so that the query can be run by a macro. (Using Access macros is the subject of the next part of this book.)

To create your final High, Low, and Volume tables with make-table queries, follow these steps:

1. Choose **M**ake Table from the **Q**uery menu. The Query Properties dialog box appears.

2. Enter **High** in the Table Name text box as the name of the final table to create.

3. Delete the Type entry in the field column of the query.

4. Select the Symbol field and drag it to the first column of the update query.

5. Choose **A**dd Table from the **Q**uery menu. Select Hi from the Table/Query list box and choose OK. Then choose the Close button.

6. Create a relationship between the ID fields of the Close and Hi tables by selecting the ID field of the Close table and dragging the field symbol to the ID field of the Hi table.

This is a very important step. If you fail to establish this relationship, you create a *semi-Cartesian product* instead of the result you want. The *Cartesian product* is all possible combinations of all the field values contained in the two tables. In this case, the Cartesian product contains about 95,000 (305 × 305) rows.

7. Click the asterisk (*, all fields) of the Hi table and drag the field symbol to the second column of the query. The make-table query appears as shown in figure 15.20.

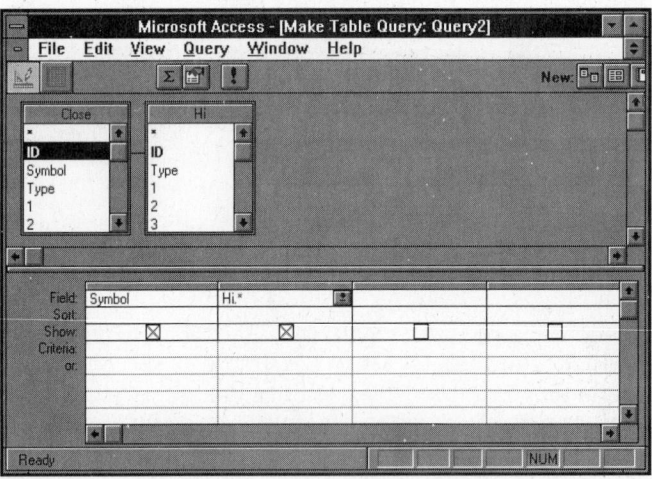

FIG. 15.20

The make-table query that creates the final High table.

8. Click the Run Query button on the toolbar to create the final High table. Choose OK from the message box that appears.

9. Select the Hi table field list and press Del to remove the field list from the query. Repeat steps 5 through 8 for the Lo table, substituting **Low** as the name for the new final table.

10. Repeat step 9 for the Vol table, entering **Volume** as the name of the final table.

11. Close the query and don't save the changes.

You must remove the temporary key field, ID, from each of the final tables so that you can make Symbol the key field. Follow these steps:

1. Open the Database window, click the Table button, and select the Close table. Click the Design button.

Table

2. Click the Properties button on the toolbar to display the Properties dialog box.

3. Delete the ID entry in the Primary Key field of the Properties dialog box. You must delete this entry before you can delete a primary key field.

4. Click the field select button of the ID field; then press Del. When Access displays message boxes asking you to confirm deletion of the field and deletion of the key field, choose OK.

5. Select the Symbol field; then click the Key Field button on the toolbar to make the Symbol field the primary key field. Figure 15.21 shows the Design mode view of the Close table.

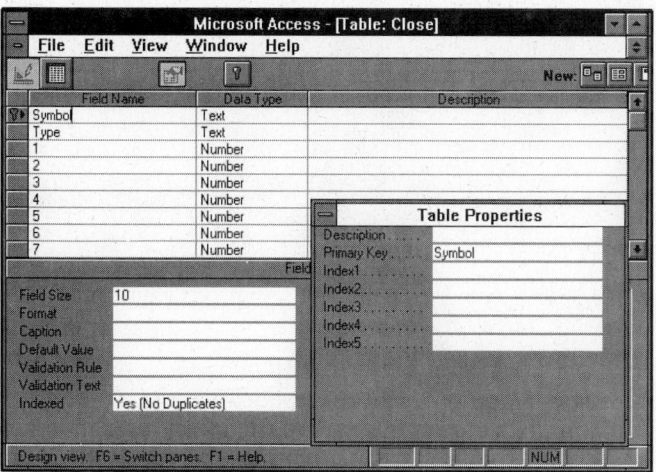

FIG. 15.21

The Close table, with the key field changed to Symbol.

6. Click the Datasheet button on the toolbar to display the contents of the table. Choose OK when asked to confirm your changes.

7. Select all columns of the table by dragging the mouse pointer over the column's field name buttons.

8. Choose **C**olumn Width from the **L**ayout menu; the Column Width dialog box appears. Enter **9** in the Column Width text box (see fig. 15.22); then choose OK. (The column width value has no effect on the Field Size property of the underlying table.)

Figure 15.23 shows the resulting Close table.

FIG. 15.22

The Column Width dialog box.

FIG. 15.23

The final version of the Close table.

Symbol	Type	1	2	3	4	5	6	7	8	9
AA-S	C	68	73.75	71.75	74.5	76.625	76.625	77.75	76.25	75
AAL-S	C	18.5	18.25	18.75	19.125	19	19	18.75	19.125	19
AAQ-S	C	55.5	56.5	58.75	60.5	59	59	56.75	56.25	57.625
ABT-S	C	65.25	65.625	67.25	66.375	64.875	64.875	63.25	62.875	63.375
ABY-S	C	12.375	12.375	12.5	12.125	12.25	12.25	12.375	23.125	12.125
ACY-S	C	61.875	62.375	64.375	64.5	62.625	62.625	60.25	61.5	61
ADM-S	C	25	25.375	25.625	24.375	23.875	23.875	23.375	23.375	24.125
AEP-S	C	31.25	31.125	31.625	32	32.25	32.25	32.25	32.25	31.875
AET-S	C	43.5	44	43.625	43.125	43.25	43.25	43.125	43.75	43.875
AGC-S	C	41.875	41.375	42.125	42.375	42.625	42.625	42.25	42.5	43
AHC-S	C	39.375	40	41.375	42.375	42.375	42.375	41.875	41.5	40
AHM-S	C	16.375	16.625	16.625	16.625	16.75	16.75	16.75	16.875	17.125
AHP-S	C	76.875	77.75	81.625	80	78.25	78.25	76.125	77.125	76.125
AIG-S	C	85.375	85.5	86.75	87.25	86.75	86.75	86	85.25	84.875
AIT-S	C	58.75	58.875	59.375	59.625	60.75	60.75	61.125	61.125	62.625
AL-S	C	19.625	20.625	20.125	20.25	20.875	20.875	21.125	20.875	21
ALD-S	C	53.75	53.75	54.625	55.5	57	57	56.5	56.75	56.25
ALK-S	C	18.125	17.75	17.5	17.875	18.125	18.125	18	17.875	17.875
ALS-S	C	32	32.25	32.125	31.875	32.25	32.25	32.375	32.375	31.875

9. Choose **S**ave Layout from the **F**ile menu to save the column width change.

10. Repeat steps 1 through 9 for the High, Low, and Volume tables. As you verify that each of the final tables is correct, choose the corresponding temporary table (Hi, Lo, or Vol) in the Database window and press Del to delete the table. If the table is open, you must close the table before you can delete it.

Deleting temporary tables conserves disk space, but only after you compact the database.

Verifying the Tables by Recreating the Worksheet

An important step when creating tables from external data sources is to verify that the tables contain the correct information. In most cases, the best method of testing is to use the tables to recreate the data in its original format—or as close to the original format as possible. This strategy enables you to make a direct comparison of the source data and the data contained in the tables.

To create a replica of the original STK_21_1 worksheet, follow these steps:

1. Open the Database window, click the Table button, and select the Close table.

2. Press Ctrl+C to copy the table to the Clipboard; then press Ctrl+V to create a copy of the table. The Paste Table As dialog box appears.

3. Enter **Stock Data** as the name of the new table in the Paste Table As dialog box (see fig. 15.24). Make sure that the default Structure and Data options button is selected, and then choose OK.

   Access creates a new Stock Data table.

FIG. 15.24

The Paste Table As dialog box.

4. Select the Stock Data table in the Tables list of the Database window and then click the Design button on the toolbar.

5. Click the Properties button on the toolbar to display the Properties dialog box.

6. Add **; Type** to the Symbol field name in the Primary Key text box to create the compound primary key Symbol; Type on the two fields.

   Alternatively, select both the Symbol and Type fields by holding down the Shift key and clicking the two field selection buttons. Then click the Key Field button on the toolbar.

7. Select the Symbol field and click the Indexed text box in the Field Properties section of the Design window. Choose Yes (Duplicates OK) from the Indexed drop-down list. If you choose Yes (No Duplicates), you cannot append records. Indexing the Symbol field can speed up queries based on a specific symbol or set of symbols. Figure 15.25 shows the design for the Stock Data table.

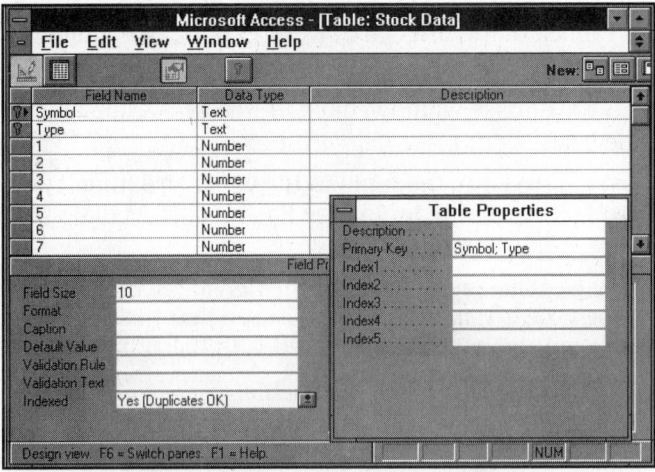

FIG. 15.25

Modifying the key field and indexing properties of the Stock Data table.

8. Click the Datasheet button on the toolbar and choose OK when asked whether you want to save your changes. Review the data in the table, and then close the Stock Data window.

To add the data in the High, Low, and Volume tables to the Stock Data table, follow these steps:

1. Choose **New** from the **File** menu; then choose **Query**, or click the New Query button on the toolbar.

2. Select the Stock Data field list and press Del to remove the field list.

3. Choose Append from the Query menu to display the Query Properties dialog box. Open the Table Names list box and choose Stock Data (see fig. 15.26). Stock Data is the table to which you want to append the records. Choose OK.

The Query Properties dialog box for an append query.

4. Choose Add Table from the Query menu and double-click High to add the High table to the query. Choose the Close button.

5. Select the asterisk field of the High table field list and drag the field list symbol to the first column of the query. Figure 15.27 shows the append query design.

6. Click the Run Query button on the toolbar to append the High records to Stock Data. The message box shown in figure 15.28 indicates the number of records to be appended. Choose OK.

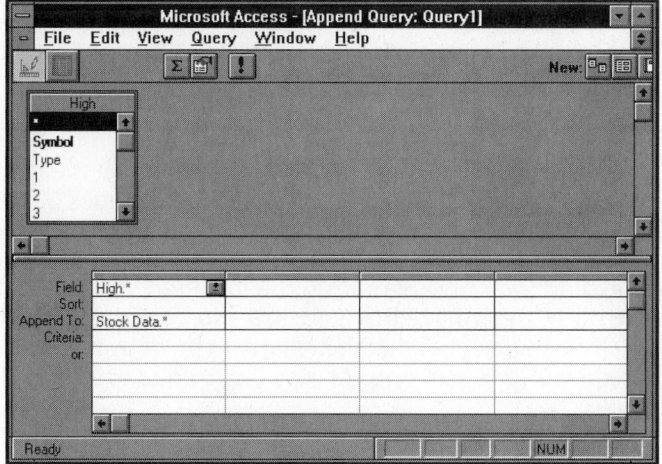

The append query design to add the records from the High table.

FIG. 15.28

The message
box confirming
the append
operation.

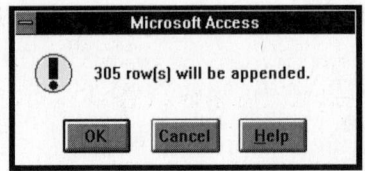

7. Click the New Query button on the toolbar and repeat steps 3 through 6 to append the Low and Volume table data to Stock Data. Add the table whose data you want to append to the query.

8. After you have appended the data from the High, Low, and Volume tables to Stock Data, open the Stock Data table from the Database window. The table appears as shown in figure 15.29. The data for Close, High, Low, and trading Volume appears in the same sequence as in the worksheet because the table is indexed on the combination of the Symbol and the Type fields. Access creates a no-duplicates index on the key field(s).

   If you did not close the Stock Data table in step 7 of the preceding series of steps, the High, Low, and Volume data does not appear. You need to close and then reopen the table for the added records to appear in the correct order. Choosing **R**efresh from the **R**ecords menu is not a substitute for closing and reopening the table.

9. Click the Document Control Menu box in the Stock Data window and choose Restore from the Document Control menu. Open the STK_21_1 table; then click the exposed surface of the Stock Data window to compare it with the original version (see fig. 15.30).

   Indexing Stock Data has changed the order of some of the entries. Confirm that the data for a few stocks in both tables are the same.

You can add stock price data for later dates by consecutively numbering the fields in successive Excel tables. As an example, the next 21 days of prices and trading volumes would use field names 22 through 42 for the numeric values. You could name the tables you create Close2, High2, Low2, and Volume2, and then add these tables to your queries to extend the range of dates to be included. Alternatively, you could create tables that have the high, low, close, and volume data for a given stock on a specific date. Making this type of transformation, however, requires that you write Access Basic code to restructure the tables.

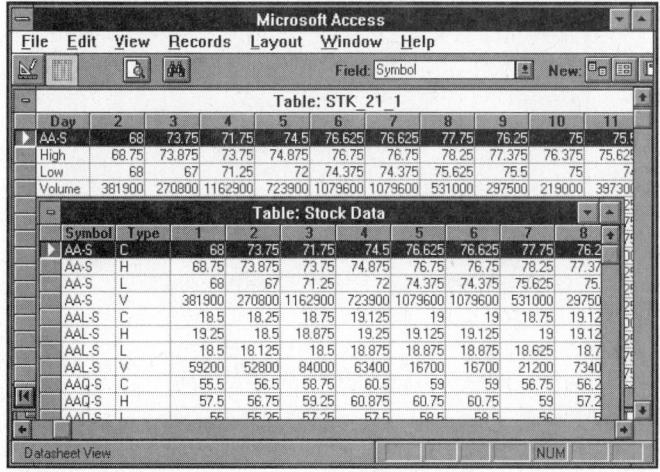

FIG. 15.29

The final version of the Stock Data table with all records appended.

FIG. 15.30

Comparing the Stock Data table with the original version in the STK_21_1 table.

For Related Information:

◄◄ "Copying and Pasting Fields, Records, and Tables," p. 178.

FROM HERE...

Using the Tables You Created

In this section, queries combine the data in the tables to create forms and reports that display the data in tabular or graph form. The relationships between the tables should be established automatically for the queries you create. In addition, you need to maintain referential integrity; that is, you shouldn't be able to delete a closing price for a stock for which you have high, low, and volume data. This obligation requires that you include relationships as properties of the tables.

To establish the relationships between the tables, follow these steps:

1. Open the Database window, click the Table button, and choose **R**elationships from the **E**dit menu. The Relationships dialog box opens (see fig. 15.31).

FIG. 15.31

Adding default relationships between stock data tables.

2. Choose Close from the Primary Table list box.

3. Choose High from the Related Table list box. Access chooses Symbol as the most likely field to relate.

4. Choose the One option to establish a one-to-one relationship between the tables.

5. Choose the Enforce Referential Integrity option (if it isn't selected) to prevent deletion of fields related to other fields. Then click the Add button.

6. Repeat steps 3 through 5 for the Low and Volume tables.

7. Choose High as the Primary Table and repeat steps 3 through 5 for the Close, Low, and Volume tables.

8. Choose Low as the Primary Table and repeat steps 3 through 5 for the Close, High, and Volume tables.

9. Choose Volume as the Primary Table and repeat steps 3 through 5 again for the Close, High, and Low tables.

10. Click Close to close the Relationships dialog box.

Always establish default relationships between the tables of your database so that these relationships are added automatically to the queries you create. If you don't establish default relationships and then you forget to add relationships to your query, you may obtain the Cartesian product (described earlier in this section) instead of the result you want. The Cartesian product of large tables can be large and take several minutes to create. Pressing Esc may not halt the process, and Windows may exhaust its resources in creating the Cartesian product, creating an out-of-memory error.

To create a test query that includes all the data in your tables, follow these steps:

1. Click the Query button in the Database window; then click New. The Add Table dialog box appears.

2. Select the High table and click the Add button.

3. Repeat step 2 for the Low, Close, and Volume tables. Then click the Close button.

4. Click the asterisk field in the High table and drag it to the first column of the query.

5. Repeat step 4 for the Low, Close, and Volume tables. The joins between the tables are established automatically (by the relationships you established in the preceding series of steps) as you add the each table, as shown by the lines connecting the Symbols fields in figure 15.32.

6. Click the Datasheet button on the toolbar to display the query, as shown in figure 15.33.

You can use this query to display or edit any data in the four tables by using a form, or to print part or all of the stock data with an Access report. You might design other queries that display only stocks that meet a specific criterion, such as minimum trading volume or a range of stock closing prices.

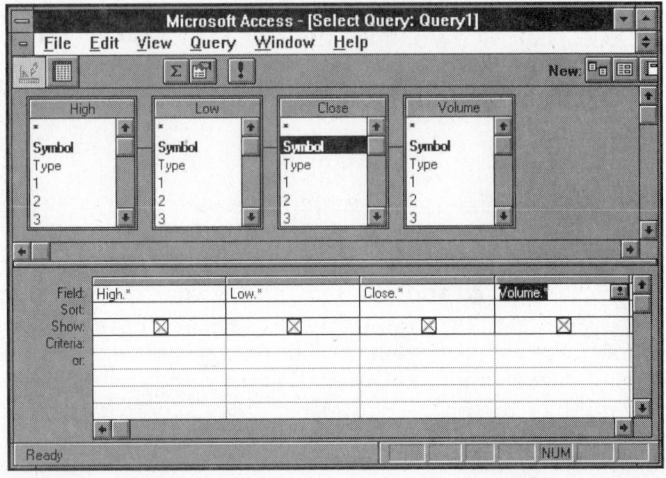

FIG. 15.32

Creating a select query that includes all fields of the four tables.

FIG. 15.33

The all-fields select query in Query Run mode.

FROM HERE...

For Related Information:

◄◄ "Establishing Relationships between Tables," p. 161.

◄◄ "Maintaining Referential Integrity," p. 164.

Exporting Stock Data as a Worksheet

When you are collecting data on the same set of common stocks, you can simplify the conversion process by modifying the design of the Excel worksheet to correspond to the design of the tables. You can avoid making a large number of changes to the worksheet in Excel by exporting the Access Stock Data table in Excel format.

To export the Stock Data table to an .XLS worksheet file, follow these steps:

1. Activate the Database window and choose **E**xport from the **F**ile menu to display the Export dialog box.

2. Select Microsoft Excel in the Data Destination list of the Export dialog box and then choose OK. The Select Microsoft Access Object dialog box appears.

3. Select Stock Data in the Tables in EXCEL list box and choose OK. The Export to File dialog box appears. The database name, with an .WLS extension, is the default file name.

4. Enter **STK_DATA.XLS** in the File Name text box of the Export to File dialog box; then choose OK. Access exports the data in Excel's .XLS format.

5. Launch Excel and open the STK_DATA worksheet. The rows in the worksheet display in the order in which they were added to the Stock Data table (see fig. 15.34). Access doesn't export data from a table in the order in which the table is indexed. (The primary key's index is based on the Symbol and Type fields.)

6. Select cell A2 and then press Shift+Ctrl+End to select all but the first row of the worksheet.

7. Choose **S**ort from Excel's **D**ata menu to open the Sort dialog box. Then enter or select **A2** as the 1st Key and **B2** as the 2nd Key on which to sort (see fig. 15.35).

8. Choose OK; the sorted worksheet appears as shown in figure 15.36.

9. Choose **S**ave from the **F**ile menu to save the sorted worksheet.

   If you are using Excel 3.0 or 4.0, the dialog box in figure 15.37 appears because Access exports Excel worksheet data in Excel 2.1 format. Click Yes to save the data in Excel 3.0 or 4.0 format.

FIG. 15.34

The Stock Data table, exported to an Excel worksheet.

FIG. 15.35

Excel's Sort dialog box for STK_DATA.XLS.

You can export the worksheet data in the order in which it is indexed by creating a make-table query that includes the Symbol and Type fields (with the Show property off) and the asterisk field. Sort the Symbol and Type fields in ascending order. Run the query and export the sorted table you create to Excel.

	Microsoft Excel - STK_DATA.XLS										
File	Edit	Formula	Format	Data	Options	Macro	Window	Help			

	Normal			Σ	B	I	A	A							

A1 — Symbol

	A	B	C	D	E	F	G	H	I	J	K
1	Symbol	Type	1	2	3	4	5	6	7	8	9
2	AA-S	C	68	73.75	71.75	74.5	76.625	76.625	77.75	76.25	75
3	AA-S	H	68.75	73.875	73.75	74.875	76.75	76.75	78.25	77.375	76.375
4	AA-S	L	68	67	71.25	72	74.375	74.375	75.625	75.5	75
5	AA-S	V	381900	270800	1162900	723900	1079600	1079600	531000	297500	219000
6	AAL-S	C	18.5	18.25	18.75	19.125	19	19	18.75	19.125	19
7	AAL-S	H	19.25	18.5	18.875	19.25	19.125	19.125	19	19.125	19.125
8	AAL-S	L	18.5	18.125	18.5	18.875	18.875	18.875	18.625	18.75	19
9	AAL-S	V	59200	52800	84000	63400	16700	16700	21200	73400	44100
10	AAQ-S	C	55.5	56.5	58.75	60.5	59	59	56.75	56.25	57.625
11	AAQ-S	H	57.5	56.75	59.25	60.875	60.75	60.75	59	57.25	58
12	AAQ-S	L	55	55.25	57.25	57.5	58.5	58.5	56	56	56.25
13	AAQ-S	V	2447000	1078200	1289300	1940700	2309700	2309700	1839700	1610400	1531500
14	ABT-S	C	65.25	65.625	67.25	66.375	64.875	64.875	63.25	62.875	63.375
15	ABT-S	H	66.125	65.75	67.875	67.75	66	66	64.5	64	63.375

Ready   NUM

FIG. 15.36

The sorted version of the STK_DATA.XLS worksheet.

Microsoft Excel

? 'STK_DATA.XLS' was created in a previous version. Do you want to update it to Microsoft Excel 4.0 format?

[Yes]   [No]   [Cancel]   [Help]

FIG. 15.37

Converting STK_DATA.XLS to Excel 4.0 format.

You can use the new worksheet as a template for entry or import of stock price and trading volume data for other ranges of dates. Using the new format eliminates the necessity of creating temporary tables during the conversion process.

Using Excel as an OLE Server

This section describes methods of creating links between data cells in OLE Object fields and worksheets created with Excel 4.0. You can duplicate some examples with Excel 3.0, but version 4.0—designed for use under Windows 3.1—has several added features that simplify the process. The step-by-step examples in this section are based on the assumption that you are familiar with Excel.

You can embed or link an Excel worksheet, macrosheet, or graph as a bound or unbound OLE object. You can copy data from the OLE worksheet object to the Clipboard and then paste the data into a bound or unbound text box. If you embed or link an Excel chart, you have access to the underlying worksheet that created it. This section provides examples of each of these techniques.

Embedding an Excel Worksheet

You can embed an entire Excel worksheet in the OLE Object field, of the OLE_OBJS database, with the simple, four-step process that follows. In this case, the presentation of an Excel worksheet (or what you can display in a bound object frame) is the entire content of the worksheet. Large embedded worksheets may require a substantial period of time to display their presentation; a small worksheet (5K or less file size—such as STK_21_3.XLS) is recommended for use in this example.

To embed an Excel worksheet in a data cell of your OLE Object field, follow these steps:

1. Close the Stocks database and choose **O**pen from the **F**ile menu to open the OLE_OBJS database you created in Chapter 13.

2. Click the Form button in the Database window and double-click OLE Objects in the Forms list box.

3. Append a new record to the OLE Objects table, using the record selection buttons. (Click the Bottom of File button and then the Next Record button.)

4. Select the bound object frame. Choose Insert Ob**j**ect from the **E**dit menu to display the Insert Object dialog box.

5. Choose Microsoft Excel Worksheet from the Object Type list box; then click the File button.

6. Select the file whose data you want to embed (in this case, STK_21_3.XLS); then choose OK. The Excel presentation appears in the bound object box, as shown in figure 15.38.

If a message box appears, indicating that the Excel worksheet is corrupted or that your computer is Out of Memory, when you attempt to embed a worksheet with the preceding procedure (using the File button), use the following procedure to embed an Excel worksheet in a field of the OLE Object data type:

1. Select the data cell in a field of the OLE Object data type or the bound object frame into which you want to embed the worksheet.

2. Choose Insert Ob**j**ect from the **E**dit menu to open the Insert Object dialog box.

3. Double-click Microsoft Excel Worksheet in the Object Type list box, or select Microsoft Excel Worksheet and choose OK. Excel's window appears with an empty worksheet entitled "Worksheet in Microsoft Access."

Microsoft Access - [Form: OLE Objects]

File   Edit   View   Records   Window   Help

Filter/Sort: Field: Description

Ole Objects

Name:

Copyright:

Filename:

Date: Link?:

Type:

Format:

Horiz.:   0   V: 0

Describe:

	A	B	C	D
1		1	2	3
2	AAL-S	15.500	18.250	18.750
3	High	19.250	18.500	18.875
4	Low	18.500	18.125	18.500
5	Volume	59,200	52,800	84,000
6	AAQ-S	55.500	56.500	58.750
7	High	57.500	56.750	59.250
8	Low	55.000	55.250	57.250
9	Volume	2,447,000	1,078,200	1,289,300
10	AA-S	68.000	73.750	71.750

Record: 19

Description of object   NUM

FIG. 15.38

The OLE Objects form with an embedded Excel worksheet.

4. Choose **O**pen from Excel's **F**ile menu. The Open dialog box appears.

5. Double-click the file name in the File Name list box, or enter the name of the file you want to embed in the File Name text box and choose OK.

6. Select cell A1; then press Ctrl+Shift+End to select the entire worksheet. Choose **C**opy from the **E**dit menu, or press Ctrl+C to copy the worksheet to the Clipboard.

7. Activate the Worksheet in Microsoft Access window and select cell A1. Choose **P**aste from the **E**dit menu, or press Ctrl+V to paste the worksheet data from the Clipboard to the blank worksheet.

8. Choose E**x**it from the **F**ile menu to return to Access. Click Yes when asked whether you want to update Microsoft Access, and click No when Excel asks whether you want to save the content of the large Clipboard.

Access

The worksheet is now embedded in the OLE Object field of your Access table. You can double-click the data cell or the bound object frame to confirm that the data you want has been embedded.

Extracting Values from an OLE Object

You can copy individual numeric or text values from a linked or embedded Excel OLE object and place the values in a text box. To add the close, high, and low values of the AAL-S stock to a multiline text box, follow these steps:

Access

1. Double-click the bound object box to display Excel's window.

2. In Excel, select the cell or range of cells you want to import to a text control object. In this case, select A2:F4.

3. Choose **C**opy from Excel's **E**dit menu, or press Ctrl+C to copy the A2:F4 range to the Clipboard.

4. Choose E**x**it from Excel's **F**ile menu to return to your Access form. If you receive the Save the Large Clipboard message box, click Yes. If you have edited the data in the Excel worksheet, click Yes when asked whether you want to update Access.

5. Position the caret in the text control object at the position where you want to paste the copied data—in this case, the Describe text box; then choose **P**aste from the Access **E**dit menu.

   Your OLE Objects form appears as shown in figure 15.39. The vertical bars between the values in the Describe text box represent the tab characters that Excel uses to separate data columns in a row.

FIG. 15.39

The OLE Objects form with the data pasted from the worksheet to the Describe text box.

If you create one or more bound text boxes with a numeric data type, you can paste a number from a selected single cell to each text box and then use the values to update the fields of the table to which the text box is bound. A more efficient method, however, uses DDE to update values in tables with data from another application. (Using DDE is described later in this chapter.)

Linking to an Excel Worksheet

Embedding Excel objects is useful if you want to create an archive of successive revisions to a worksheet. In most cases, however, creating an OLE link to all or a range of cells in a worksheet is a more common practice. Linking enables you to display or edit the most recent version of the worksheet's data from its source file. The conventional process of linking a file in Excel is similar to that for linking graphics files. To create a link with an Excel file, perform the following steps:

1. Choose Append or Paste **A**ppend to add a new record to the OLE Objects table.

2. Launch or open Excel independently of Access.

3. Choose **O**pen from Excel's **F**ile menu and, in Excel's Open dialog box, select the file you want to link.

4. Select the cells of the worksheet to be included in your Access table; then copy the selected cells to the Clipboard with Ctrl+C.

5. Close or minimize Excel and select the bound object frame or the data cell in a field of the OLE Object type in Access. If you receive an `Insufficient Memory` message, you need to close Excel to free system resources.

6. Choose Paste Link from the Access **E**dit menu.

You can verify that your Excel worksheet object is linked by choosing Microsoft Excel Worksheet Object from the **E**dit menu and confirming that the Change Link option is enabled.

Linking or Embedding a Range of Cells from an Excel Worksheet

Access uses a feature of Windows called the *multiple document interface* (*MDI*) to display tables, queries, forms, and other database objects in separate windows within the Access main, or parent window. The windows in which you display database objects are called *MDI child windows*. Each MDI child window has its own Document Control menu, and you can size or move MDI child windows independently within the confines of the parent window. Excel, Word for Windows, and many other Windows applications employ MDI child windows.

You can use Excel's MDI windows to open a worksheet file in a new window, copy a range of cells from the new window to the Clipboard, and then paste the range to the window embedded in your Access table. Follow these steps:

1. Open the OLE_OBJS database (if necessary); click the Form button and open the OLE Objects form. Choose **G**o To from the **R**ecords menu; then click Ne**w** in the fly-out menu (or use the record selection buttons) to append a new record.

2. Select the bound object frame and then choose Insert Ob**j**ect from the **E**dit menu. The Insert Object dialog box appears.

3. Select Microsoft Excel Worksheet in the Data Type list box and click OK.

4. Excel's window appears with the blank MDI child window representing the object to be embedded—Worksheet in Microsoft Access. Choose **O**pen from Excel's **F**ile menu. The Open dialog box appears.

5. From the File Name list box, select the file containing the data to be linked or embedded; then choose OK.

6. Select the desired range of cells in the newly opened window. Then press Ctrl+C to copy the data in the selected cells to the Clipboard. For this example, select the range R1C1:R5C6 of STK_21_1.XLS. If the worksheet has named ranges, you can choose **G**oto from Excel's **F**ormula menu and specify the named range.

7. Choose Worksheet in Microsoft Access from Excel's **W**indow menu. If you want to be able to edit the underlying worksheet (STK_21_1.XLS) through an Excel link between the two worksheets, choose Paste **L**ink from Excel's **E**dit menu. Otherwise, press Ctrl+V to paste the selected data from the Clipboard. The Worksheet window appears as shown in figure 15.40.

Access

8. Choose E**x**it from Excel's **F**ile menu to return to Access. If you created a link to STK_21_1.XLS, click Yes in response to the message that asks whether you want to save your changes. Excel displays the message shown in figure 15.41. Click Yes.

The form displays only the range of data you pasted or linked to the worksheet in Access (see fig. 15.42).

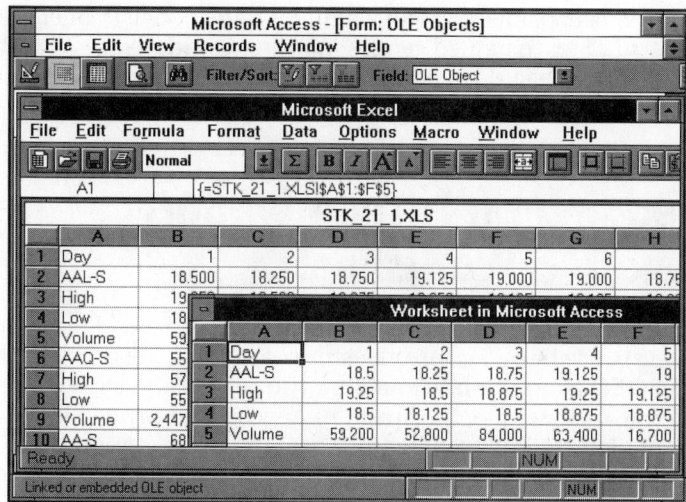

FIG. 15.40

Linking an embedded or linked portion of a worksheet to a larger worksheet.

FIG. 15.41

The message box that verifies that you want to update the worksheet.

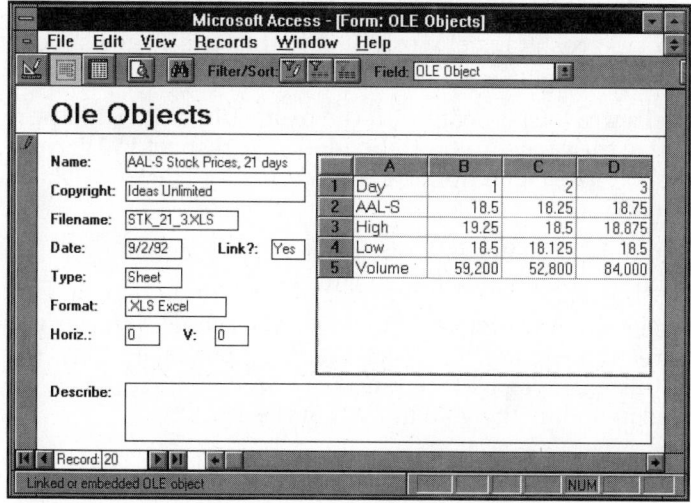

FIG. 15.42

The linked worksheet fragment in a bound object box.

This method is especially useful when the table consists of embedded worksheets linked to named ranges in a single underlying worksheet. You save file space and speed the operation of the form by not incorporating a large worksheet as an OLE object in the Access table.

Embedding an Excel 4.0 Chart to Link to a Worksheet

You can use the link that Excel creates between an Excel chart and the underlying worksheet that provides the data to create a link to that worksheet file. In addition to enabling you to edit and save changes to the linked worksheet file, the speed of Access is improved when large worksheet files are involved. In this case, the presentation is the chart, in .WMF format, not the spreadsheet. The simpler your chart, the faster Access moves between records.

To link or embed an Excel chart object in the OLE Objects field of your table, follow these steps:

1. Open the OLE_OBJS database (if necessary); click the Form button and open the OLE Objects form. Choose **G**o To from the **R**ecords menu; then click Ne**w** in the fly-out menu (or use the record selection buttons) to append a new record.

2. Select the bound object frame and then choose Insert Ob**j**ect from the **E**dit menu. The Insert Object dialog box appears.

3. Select Microsoft Excel Worksheet in the Data Type list box and choose OK.

4. Excel's window appears with the blank MDI child window representing the object to be embedded—Worksheet in Microsoft Access. Choose **O**pen from Excel's **F**ile menu. The Open dialog box appears.

5. From the File Name list box, select the file containing the data to be linked or embedded; then choose OK.

6. In the newly opened window, select the range of cells from which to create the chart; then click the Chart button on Excel's toolbar. For this example, use the range R1C1:R4C6 of STK_21_3.XLS to avoid including the volume data in the graph.

7. Drag the crosshair pointer to create a chart approximately equal to the size of the bound object frame in Access. Then use Excel's ChartWizard to complete the chart.

8. Select the chart in the worksheet and then press Ctrl+C to copy the chart to the Clipboard.

9. Choose E**x**it from Excel's **F**ile menu to return to Access. Answer No when asked whether you want to update Access. A fragment of an Excel worksheet appears in the bound object frame.

Access

10. Choose Paste **S**pecial from the Access **E**dit menu. The Paste Special dialog box opens (see fig. 15.43).

11. Click the Paste button. The Excel chart appears in the bound object frame (see fig. 15.44).

FIG. 15.43

The Paste Special dialog box for Excel chart objects.

FIG. 15.44

The Excel chart, embedded in an OLE Object field.

12. Double-click the bound object frame to edit the chart as desired.

You can create graphs for other ranges in STK_21_3.XLS by selecting the record with the graph, copying it to the Clipboard, and paste-appending a duplicate record. Double-click the graph of the appended record; then edit the SERIES( ) expression of each line of the graph in Excel's chart-editing window. You need to alter the scale of the Y-axis of the graph to suit the range of values for each new entry.

Embedding the graph—rather than linking it—provides a degree of independence from the underlying worksheet and any modifications other users may make to your graph while editing the worksheet. You can format the embedded graph object to fit the bound object frame without affecting the dimensions of the graph stored in the worksheet.

Editing a Worksheet Linked to an OLE Object

You can edit the underlying worksheet (from which you created the OLE worksheet and graph objects in the preceding two sections) when Excel is launched as an OLE server. To edit STK_21_3.XLS with the examples shown in figures 15.37 and 15.39, follow these steps:

1. Double-click the bound object frame containing the Excel graph to launch Excel as an OLE server.

2. Choose **Links** from Excel's **File** menu. The Links dialog box opens (see fig. 15.45).

FIG. 15.45

Excel's Links dialog box, used to open an internally-linked worksheet for editing.

3. Double-click the link to STK_21_3.XLS (selected in fig. 15.45). An MDI child window appears, displaying the file.

4. In STK_21_3.XLS, edit one of the values used in the worksheet or chart OLE object.

5. Choose Worksheet in Microsoft Access from Excel's **W**indow menu. If you selected the record with the Excel chart for this example, your screen should resemble figure 15.46. The value of cell B2—the closing price for AAL on the first day of the series—was changed from 18.500 to 15.500 for this example.

6. Choose E**x**it from Excel's **F**ile menu to close the worksheet and chart.

7. Click Yes when Excel asks whether you want to save changes to STK_21_3.XLS; then click Yes again in response to the message that asks whether you want to update Access. The revised version of the Excel chart in the bound object frame appears as shown in figure 15.47.

Access

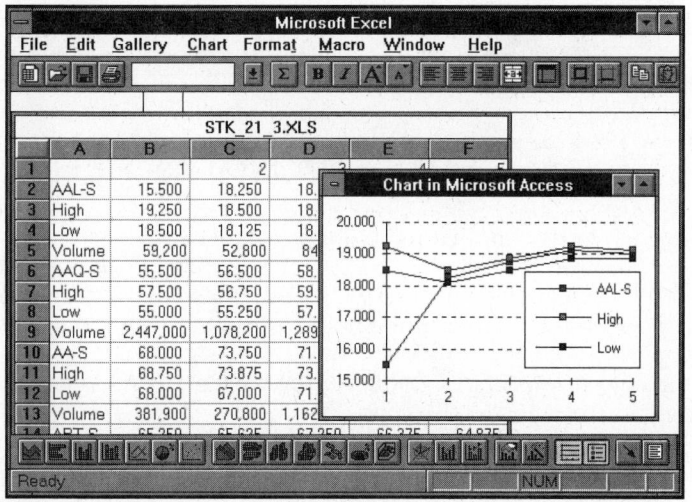

FIG. 15.46

Editing the internal link by changing a value of a cell in STK_21_3.XLS.

The techniques described in this example also apply to worksheet objects displayed in unbound object frames. You may want to include a link to a worksheet to provide the user with the ability to view the worksheet while entering or editing related data in a table. Waiting for the server to load and display the worksheet when you double-click the object frame may tax your patience, however. A faster way to display data in worksheets is to use Dynamic Data Exchange (DDE) to display the data, as described in the next section.

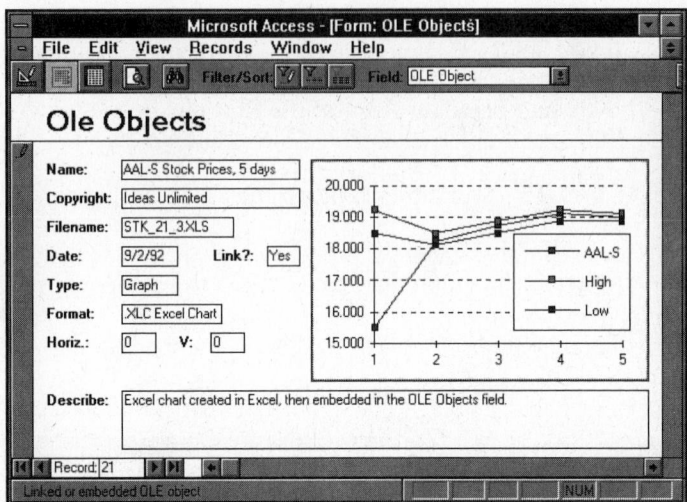

FIG. 15.47

The effect of
changing the
value of a cell
linked to an
embedded Excel
chart.

Using DDE Links with Excel

If you need to extract individual numeric or text values from a
worksheet to update values in your database, *dynamic data exchange*
(DDE) is a better method than OLE. DDE enables you to transfer data
from a specific cell within a worksheet to a bound or unbound text box
on a form or report. Figure 15.48 shows the design of a form that displays the data from the STK_21_3.XLS worksheet, using Access's DDE( )
function.

The syntax of the DDE( ) function follows:

    DDE(*AppName, TopicName, ItemName*)

AppName, *TopicName*, and *ItemName* are enclosed within quotation
marks when you use *string literals* (the actual names). The following list
describes these arguments:

- *AppName* is the Windows task name of the DDE server application, assigned by its publisher. *AppName* consists of a single word
  (no spaces allowed) and is often a contraction of the full name of
  the product, such as *WinWord* for Word for Windows. You usually
  can find the DDE *AppName* for an application in documentation
  for that application.

- *TopicName* is, in the majority of cases, the full path and file name
  of the file that contains the data to be sent to Access.

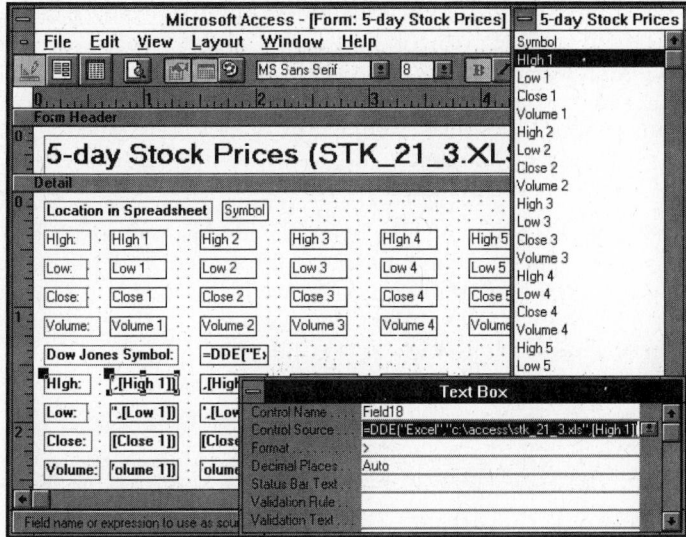

FIG. 15.48

The 5-day Stock
Prices DDE form
in Design mode.

■ *ItemName* is the name of the location of the data to be sent within *TopicName*. For a worksheet, *ItemName* can be a range of cells in Excel's row-column format (R1C1) or the name of a range of cells (except Database in Excel 3+). In Word for Windows, *ItemName* is usually a bookmark.

If the worksheet file is located in the C:\ACCESS directory, for example, and you want to extract the data from cells A2:F5, the function is as follows:

```
DDE("Excel","c:\access\stk_21_3.XLS","R2C1:R5C6")
```

Cell A2 corresponds to column 1 of row 2 and cell F5 is located in column 6 of row 5. You can substitute a named range from the worksheet for the R#C# coordinates as the DDE topic.

The 5-day Stock Price table underlying the form has a Symbol field and five sets of text fields for the high, low, and close prices of the stock, plus the trading volume, one set for each of the five days of data in the table. Figure 15.48 shows the fields in the Field List dialog box. The value of each field is the coordinates of the cell containing the corresponding value in the worksheet, expressed in R#C# (row number, column number) format that Excel documentation refers to as R1C1. Bound text boxes display the field coordinates and enable you to enter new coordinate values as you append records to the table.

The lower group of text boxes obtain the data in the spreadsheet cell corresponding to the coordinates supplied by the field in the table. Following is the Control Source expression shown in reverse type in the figure:

```
=DDE("Excel","c:\excel\stk_21_3.XLS",[High 1])
```

This expression sends the topic corresponding to the value of the High 1 field of the current record (R3C2) via DDE to the worksheet. When you use a field name as a topic, don't add the enclosing quotation marks. The remainder of the lower group of text boxes contain =DDE() expressions that are identical except for the field name used to supply the value of the topic. The field names used in the expressions appear in the text boxes visible in figure 15.48.

Figure 15.49 shows the form from figure 15.48 in Run mode. When you enter the appropriate R#C# values in the upper set of text boxes, the data in the worksheet corresponding to the cell coordinates appears in the lower text boxes. Until valid entries are made for the cell coordinates, #Error appears in the lower text boxes.

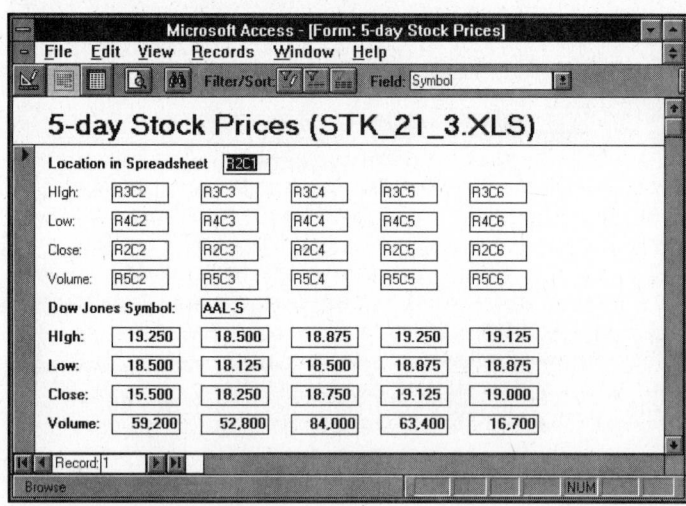

FIG. 15.49

The 5-day Stock Prices form, showing worksheet cell values sent by DDE.

You can use the Access DDE() function to obtain and display specific data items from worksheets more quickly and easily than by copying them from an OLE server that supplies worksheet objects in bound or unbound object frames. You only need to open Excel or another DDE-compliant spreadsheet application once; the server runs minimized to an icon. After loading the spreadsheet application, data transfer to the form or report is rapid, and DDE consumes much less memory than OLE during the process.

You cannot edit data in a text box supplied by the =DDE() expression. To use the full capabilities of DDE, you need to create an Access Basic function and then call the function with an Access macro.

Access provides a second DDE function, DDESend( ), that enables you to transfer data, usually from a text box, from an Access form to an Excel worksheet or any other document in a Windows application that supports DDE. The syntax of the DDESend( ) function is as follows:

```
DDESend(AppName, TopicName, ItemName, Data)
```

AppName, *TopicName*, and *ItemName* are the same as the arguments for the DDE( ) function. *Data* is a string that can be a literal value enclosed within quotation marks, a function that returns a string, or the value of a text box control. As an example, if you want to change "Day" in cell A1 of the STK_21_3.XLS worksheet in your C:\ACCESS directory to "Date", you add a text box control to your form and enter **=DDESend("Excel", "c:\access\stk_21_3.xls", "R1C1", "Date")** as the Control Source property of the text box.

You can send the value of another text box on your form by substituting the control name of the other text box for the literal string in the preceding example. If you have a text box with the control name Close 1, whose data you want to send to cell B2, the syntax of the DDESend( ) statement for the Control Source property of the DDESend( ) text box is **=DDESend("Excel", "c:\access\stk_21_3.xls", "R2C2", [Close 1])**. The Control Source property of a DDESend( ) text box must be that of another text box, because text boxes with DDESend( ) as their Control Source property are read-only in Run mode. The text box that contains the DDESend( ) function appears blank in Form Run mode; thus you set the visible property of DDESend( ) text boxes to No. You can specify the DDESend( ) function as the Control Source property of an Option Group, Check Box, or Combo Box control, but these controls are also read-only and are disabled (dimmed) in Run mode.

Both the DDE( ) and DDESend( ) functions execute immediately upon the opening of the form in which they are used. If your Access application includes multiple *TopicNames*, an instance (copy) of the application specified by *AppName* is opened for each TopicName you add to your forms. Thus you can rapidly deplete the resources available to Access with multiple copies of Excel (or other DDE servers), resulting in Out of Memory messages from Access. You must close each instance of the DDE server application manually by choosing the instance in Task Manager's list box and clicking End Task, or by clicking the DDE server's icon and choosing Close from the Application Control menu. Like the DDE( ) function, using the Access Basic DDE commands, explained in Chapter 23, is the preferred method of implementing the equivalent of the DDESend( ) function.

Chapter Summary

This chapter provided typical examples of the ability of Access to interact with data in worksheets. Importing and reorganizing data formerly contained in worksheets is one of the most common tasks you encounter if you are using Access for business applications. If conversion isn't practical or desirable, you can use OLE to display and edit worksheet data in Access. If you only need to display values of a few specific data cells in a worksheet, DDE is the quickest and easiest approach.

You have completed your introduction to the capabilities of Access that are available without programming. As you have seen from the examples to this point, you can create useful and even complex forms and reports without learning programming methods. Streamlining the operation of forms and reports and automating applications requires that you use programming techniques.

Macros, the subject of Part IV of this book, are simple programs disguised as sequences of macro "actions." With macros, you can create Access applications that fulfill the majority of your database management needs by combining tables, queries, forms, and reports.

Powering Access with Macros

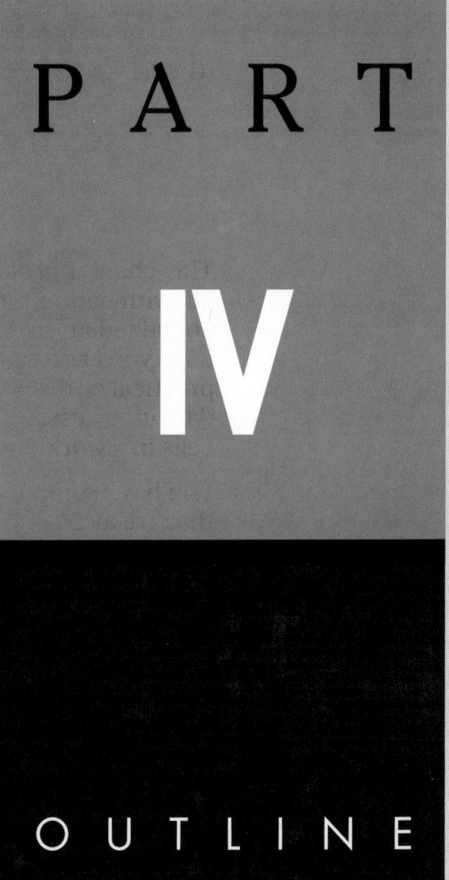

PART

IV

OUTLINE

Automating Applications with Macros: A Quick Start

Macros can help you become more productive. A few simple macros can automate mundane, repetitive procedures. In Access, you can use complex macros to do work that otherwise requires extensive programming with a database other than Access.

Macros are lists of actions. These actions are listed in the order you want the action to occur. Nearly all the commands in the menu bars, and also other features, are available through actions.

Most of these actions use easily-recognized names, such as OpenForm or Beep. Most actions require arguments. *Arguments* specify how an action works. Two arguments for the OpenForm action, for example, are Form Name and View. You set these arguments to specify the name of the form being opened and the view in which the form appears.

You enter macros in *Macro windows*, which are database objects. You open a new or existing Macro window from the Database window.

The following quick start guides you through the steps of creating a macro that runs when you click a button in the Customers form. This macro runs a query that displays a dynaset, showing all the products purchased by the customer shown in the Customers form. Figure 16.1 shows the Customers form on which you create a button that runs the macro. Figure 16.2 shows the result of clicking the button.

FIG. 16.1

The Customer form on which you create a button that runs the macro.

The complete list of all actions and arguments for the completed macro is in table 16.1, in the section "Seeing the Complete Macro Listing."

Creating a Macro To Query by Clicking a Button

This macro runs a query based on the Customer ID in the Customers form. You assign the macro to a button on the Customers form so that when you click the button, the macro displays all the products purchased by the customer.

You build this macro in three stages. First, you learn how to open or activate a form and turn off the screen display to prevent screen flashing. In the process, you learn how to enter macro actions and arguments. These first steps ensure that the Customers form is active when the remainder of the macro runs. In the second stage of building this macro, you learn how to add to the existing macro so that the macro opens and refreshes a query that shows all products purchased by the customer. In the third stage, you learn how to assign the macro to a button on a form.

FIG. 16.2

The completed macro opening a query onto the current customer's purchase history.

Creating a New Macro

Before you begin the macro, open the NWIND.MDB database, which comes with Access. To open the NWIND.MDB database, choose the File Open command, select NWIND.MDB from the Open dialog box, and choose OK.

You create the macro in a new Macro window. Although you can put more than one macro in a Macro window, in this example, the window will contain this macro only. To open a new Macro window, follow these steps:

1. Activate the Database window and then click the Macro button, or choose the View Macro command. Either action displays macros in the Database window.

2. Choose the New button in the Database window. A new Macro window appears (see fig. 16.3).

FIG. 16.3

The Macro window in which you create the macro.

A Macro window can have four columns: Names, Conditions, Action, and Comments. In the example, Access defaults are set so that only the Action and Comments are displayed. Your Macro window title bar number may differ from the number shown in figure 16.3.

Opening a Form

The next step to creating a macro is to enter the actions you want the macro to perform. Place actions in the Action column in the order in which you want the actions to occur. You can enter actions in three ways. You can type an action, select an action from a combo-list box in the cell, or, in some cases, drag and drop a database object into the action cell. Because the macro sheet is similar to a Microsoft Excel worksheet, you later can edit, insert, delete, or rearrange macro actions on the sheet.

To enter the OpenForm action by selecting actions and arguments, follow these steps:

1. The Macro window still should be active. If the Macro window is not active, press Ctrl+F6 until the window is activated.

2. Use arrow keys to move the insertion point to the uppermost cell of the Active column.

3. Click the pull-down list or press Alt+Down arrow to pull down the combo list and select the OpenForm action. To select the OpenForm action, click OpenForm or press the arrow keys to highlight OpenForm, and then press Enter.

4. Press F6 to move to the Form Name argument in the lower portion of the Macro window.

5. Press Alt+Down arrow to pull down the combo list and select Customers. Press Enter.

To enter the action that opens the Customers form by using the drag-and-drop method, follow these steps:

1. Click the Database window to make this window active.

2. Click the Form button in the Database window.

3. Select the Customers form name from the Database window, drag the form name to the first cell in the Action column, and release the mouse button. As you drag the Customers form name, the mouse pointer changes to the Form icon.

Releasing the Form icon over the uppermost cell in the action column inserts the OpenForm action and enters the appropriate arguments that open the Customers form. Figure 16.4 shows how the Macro window appears. Notice that the arguments were entered by Access. Dragging and dropping from the Database window to the Macro window works for the OpenTable, OpenQuery, OpenForm, OpenReport, and RunMacro actions.

FIG. 16.4

The OpenForm action in the Action column of the Macro window opening the form specified by the Form Name argument.

Leave the remaining arguments with the default settings. The Macro window should look like the one shown in figure 16.4; however, the Database window will show Forms.

Running the Macro

Before you can run a macro you just created or edited, you must save the Macro window. To save the Macro window, follow these steps:

1. Choose the **File Save As** command.

2. Type the name **Customer Purchases** in the Macro Name edit box.

3. Choose OK.

You can run a macro in several ways. To run a macro, you can select it from the Database window, use the **File Run** Macro command, click a button to which the macro is assigned, run the macro from one or more of many kinds of *events* (changes to a Database object, record, or field), or run the macro from another macro.

To run the new macro from the Database window, follow these steps:

1. Click the Database window to activate it, or choose the **Window** Database: NWIND command.

2. Click the Macro button in the Database window or choose the View **M**acros command.

3. Select the Customer Purchases macro name from the list.

4. Click the **R**un button from the Database window.

The macro opens the Customers form. If the macro doesn't open the form, activate the Macro window and make sure that the arguments for the OpenForm command specify the Customers form to open in the Edit view.

Polishing the Process of Opening a Form

The one-line macro demonstrates how easily you can create a simple macro. This section tells you how to open the form and give the form a more professional appearance by performing the following actions:

■ Reducing screen flicker while the form opens

■ Ensuring that the form opens and sizes correctly

■ Displaying an hourglass as the pointer until the form is completely opened and sized

During the process, you learn more ways to enter actions and arguments and ways to insert rows for new actions.

The first two actions you add to the macro you created need to come before the OpenForm action. To insert two blank rows before the OpenForm action in the Macro window, follow these steps:

1. Activate the Customer Purchases Macro window.

2. Select the cell that contains OpenForm.

3. If you use a mouse, click the arrow to the left of OpenForm to select the row and then press the Insert key twice.

   If you use the keyboard, move the insertion point into the cell that contains OpenForm and then choose the **E**dit **I**nsert Row command twice.

The Customer Purchases Macro window now should look like figure 16.5.

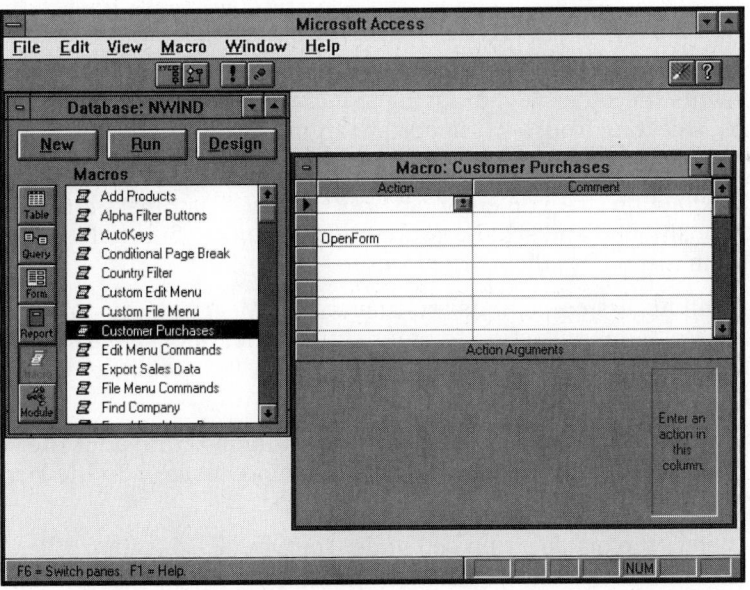

FIG. 16.5

The Customer Purchases Macro window, with two blank rows inserted above OpenForm.

In the two blank Action cells above the OpenForm action, you enter an Echo action that turns off the screen display until the macro is complete, and then enter an Hourglass action that changes the mouse pointer to an hourglass so that the operator knows to wait. To enter these two actions and the related arguments, follow these steps:

1. Select the uppermost cell in the Action column.

2. Choose the Echo action from the combo-list box in the first cell. (Click the down arrow to the right of the cell or press Alt+Down arrow to display the list.)

3. Click the Echo On argument cell in the lower portion of the Macro window, or press F6 to move the insertion point to the lower portion.

4. Choose the No argument from the combo-list box in the Echo On argument. This argument turns off screen refresh until the macro finishes or until the macro reaches an Echo On that uses the Yes argument.

5. Select the blank cell under the Echo action by clicking the cell, or by pressing F6 and using the arrow keys to move to the cell.

6. Type **Hourglass** in this cell and press Enter. You do not need to change the Hourglass On argument.

Now you know three ways to enter actions: by dragging and dropping, by selecting the action from a combo list, or by typing the action. If you incorrectly type the action, Access displays an alert box. You can enter arguments the same way: dragging and dropping for Database object names, selecting from a list in certain arguments, or typing an argument name.

The next action that you enter ensures that the Customers form is correctly positioned and sized on-screen. The **W**indow Size to Fit Form on the Form menu bar adjusts the form.

Nearly all Access commands are available as Macro actions. You can use the DoMenuItem action to enter actions that duplicate a menu command. The arguments for DoMenuItem specify the menu bar, menu, and command the action performs.

In the following steps, you enter the DoMenuItem action after the form has opened. To enter the equivalent DoMenuItem action to the **W**indow Size to Fit Form command, follow these steps:

1. Select the blank action cell under the OpenForm action. Click the cell with a mouse or press the arrow keys to move the insertion point.

2. Choose the DoMenuItem action from the action cell's combo list.

3. Move to the Action Arguments half of the window by clicking Action Arguments or pressing F6.

   The Menu Bar argument already shows that Form will be active and the Form menu bar will be displayed.

4. Select or type **Window** in the Menu Name argument.

5. Select or type **Size to Fit Form** in the Command argument.

Save this macro by choosing the **F**ile **S**ave command. Run the macro from the Database window by using the procedure described in the section, "Running the Macro," earlier in this chapter. The screen may have less flicker, and the hourglass rather than the mouse pointer is displayed on-screen. Before you start the following section, you may want to minimize the Macro window to an icon in order to reduce the clutter on-screen.

Creating a Query Object

The second stage of this macro requires a query that creates a dynaset, which shows the purchase history of the customer displayed in the Customers form. In this section of the quick start, you create a query object you run with macro actions you add later. This query joins three tables to find the following information: Shipped Date, English Name (of the product), and Quantity. To restrict the query to only shipments that involve the customer name shown in the Customers form, the Customer ID field is included in the query. See Chapters 6, 7, and 8 for more information on queries.

The query that you build will look like the query in figure 16.6.

Creating the Query

To create this query, follow these steps:

1. Make the Database window the active window and then click the Query button, or choose the **V**iew **Q**ueries command.

2. Choose the New button to open a new query window.

3. Choose the Orders table from the Table/Query scrolling list and choose the Add button. The screen should look like figure 16.7.

4. Select the Order Details table and then click the Add button; select the Products table and click the Add button.

5. Click the Close button to close the Add Table dialog box.

FIG. 16.6

The complete query to create a dynaset of the customer's purchase history.

FIG. 16.7

Selecting the tables you need to query.

The query window with joined tables should look like the window in figure 16.8. Notice that Access has recognized fields that have previously defined relationships. These fields enable Access to join the information between tables as though all the information resides in a single large database.

FIG. 16.8

Joining tables to access the information for the customer purchase histories.

Enter the field names across the top of the query window for the fields you want to include in the query. The fields to be included and the order of those fields from left to right across the Field row of the query are shown in the following list and in figure 16.6:

Order in Field	RowTable	Field of Query
1	Orders	Shipped Date
2	Products	English Name
3	Order Details	Quantity
4	Orders	Customer ID

To enter a field name by using the mouse, follow these steps:

1. Drag the field name from the scrolling list of the appropriate table.

2. Drop the field name onto the Field cell in the query.

To enter a field name from the keyboard, follow these steps:

1. Move to the Field cell in which you want to enter a field.

   Press Tab or Shift+Tab, or press the arrow keys to move between cells.

2. Press Alt+Down arrow to display the list of tables and fields. If you have not previously selected a field in this cell, fields appear as *table.fieldname*: Orders.Shipped Date, for example.

3. Select the *table.fieldname* for each Field cell.

To sort the query results so that reading the purchase history is easy, follow these steps:

1. Select the Sort cell under the Shipped Date field and choose Ascending from the combo-list box.

2. Select the Sort cell under the English Name field and choose Ascending from the combo-list box.

To enter the criteria for the query, select only the history for the current customer displayed in the Customers form, and enter a criterion under the Customer ID field that specifies that the match will occur for records that have the same customer ID as the customer ID in the form. To enter this criteria, follow these steps:

1. Select the Criteria cell under the Customer ID field.

2. Type the following control name:

[Forms]![Customers]![Customer ID]

This entry makes the query compare the Customer ID field of the query with the contents of the Customer ID control on the Customers form.

The query you created now should look like figure 16.6. Save this query by choosing **File** Save **As**, and typing **Customer Purchases**.

Testing the Query

Before testing the query, you may want to minimize the Query window in order to reduce screen clutter.

To test the query before you run it from a macro, follow these steps:

1. Open the Customers form and select a customer name. Note the Customer ID, such as AROUT.

2. Activate the Database window and click the Query button, or choose the **View** **Queries** command.

3. Select the Customer Purchases query from the list.

4. Click the Open button.

A window opens, displaying a sorted list of all purchases made by the same company as the company displayed in the form. Check the Customer ID field in the query to make sure that the ID matches the same company as the company in the form. Close the query and the form after testing.

Running the Query from a Macro

The Customer Purchases macro now opens the Customers form. The following final additions to the macro open the query on top of the form:

1. The dynaset from the query shows the purchase history of the company.

2. After the query is complete, the MoveSize command is used to correctly size the query window.

3. The screen is refreshed.

The current Customer Purchases macro opens the Customers form. The changes you make to the macro open a query after the form opens. Usually, this macro runs when the Customers form already is open. In this case, the OpenForm command doesn't reopen the Customers form; it makes the Customers form the active window. Placing the OpenForm action before the OpenQuery is a good way to ensure that the correct form is active and the correct menu bar is displayed. This placement also ensures that the macro will run correctly, even if the macro is not run from the button.

To modify the Customer Purchase macro, follow these steps:

1. Open or activate the Customer Purchase macro to make it appear in a window.

2. Move to the blank action cell under DoMenuItem by clicking the cell, or press F6 and move to the cell by using the arrow keys.

3. Select the Echo action from the combo list. Change the Echo On argument to Yes.

4. Select the next blank action cell and enter an Echo action, but use an Echo On argument of No.

These two Echo actions are used to refresh the screen at the correct time so that you can see the opened Customers form before you start the query. The first Echo action refreshes the screen so that you can see the Customers form after the form opens. The second Echo action turns off the screen refresh again while the query works. After you complete this macro, try running the macro without using Echo actions so that you can see the difference in appearance.

The following steps add the OpenQuery, Requery, MoveSize, and Beep actions. The OpenQuery action opens the Customer Purchases query you created in the previous section. This query's Data Mode argument is specified as read only so that the operator cannot change the purchase history. The Requery action ensures that the query is up to date.

If the operator doesn't close the past query window, but moves to a new customer record and then runs the macro, the Requery action repeats the query to make sure that the query window is current. MoveSize positions the query window, and Beep notifies the operator.

To make the final additions to the macro, follow these steps:

1. Select the blank action cell under the last Echo action.

2. Select the OpenQuery action from the combo list. Switch to the Action Arguments, and select the Customer Purchases as the Query Name (the query you built). Change the Data Mode argument to read only.

3. Select the next action cell.

4. Select the Requery action, but do not enter a Control action, which causes the entire query to rerun if necessary.

5. Select the next blank action cell.

6. Select the MoveSize action and enter the following measurements. (Your measurements may need to be different, depending on the screen's resolution.) The result is shown in figure 16.9.

Right	1.6 in
Down	1.1 in
Width	3.75 in
Height	1.5 in

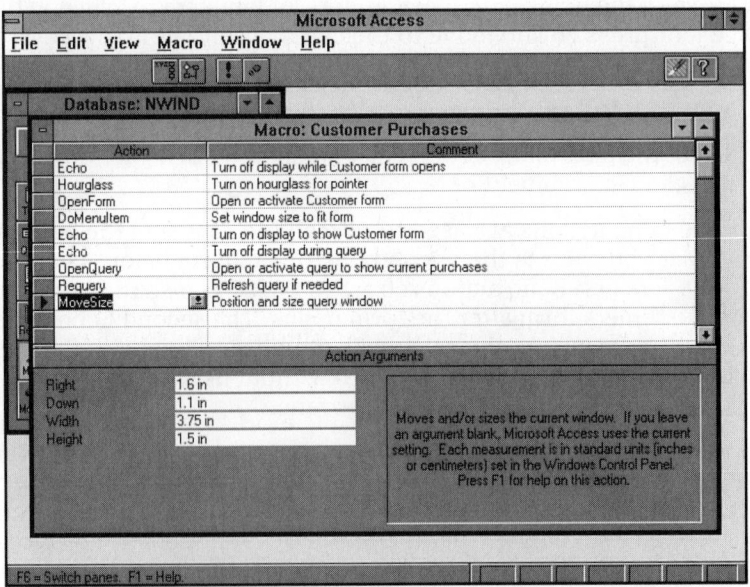

7. Select the next blank action cell and type **Beep** as the action.

8. Choose the **F**ile **S**ave command, or press F12 and save the macro with the same name.

The Customer Products Macro window now looks like figure 16.10.

FIG. 16.10

The complete macro activating the Customers form and then running a customer purchase history query.

Test the macro. If the macro window is active and you use a mouse, click the Run button on the Macro toolbar. If you use a keyboard, choose the **F**ile **Ru**n Macro command when any window is active. Type the name of the macro, **Customer Purchases**, and press Enter.

Attaching a Macro Button to a Form

You can make the macro convenient to run by adding a button to the Customers form. You then can click the button to run the macro.

To use the mouse to add a button to the Customers form, follow these steps:

1. Open the Customers form in Design view, and activate the Database window.

2. Click the Macro button in the Database window or choose the **V**iew **M**acros command to display the list of macros in the

Database window. Figure 16.11 shows the two windows in preparation to create a button.

Creating a macro button by dragging the macro name onto the form while in Design view.

3. Drag the name of the Customer Purchases macro onto the form where you want the button to appear. Release the button. Figure 16.12 shows the Customer Purchases button in the top right corner of the form.

4. Select and delete the button's text label.

5. Click the button.

6. Display the Form Properties window and change the Control Name property for the button to Button Customer Purchases. The caption is the name of the macro. You can change the button's caption by editing the Caption property. Figure 16.12 shows the completed button on the form.

7. Click the Form button on the toolbar, or choose the **View Form** command to display the form as the operator sees it during normal operation.

8. Choose the **File Save** command to save the form with the button.

To run the macro from the button, display the Customers form in Form view and click the button. The macro reactivates the Customers form, changes the pointer to an hourglass, and beeps when the completed query appears. After the macro is complete, the screen resembles figure 16.2.

FIG. 16.12

The completed button with the related properties list.

If you don't have a mouse, refer to Chapters 17 and 18 to learn how to assign a macro to a shortcut key or menu command so that you can quickly run the macro from the keyboard.

Seeing the Complete Macro Listing

Table 16.1 shows the complete listing of all actions and the related arguments. Abbreviated comments also are listed for each action. You may want to enter these comments in the macro to make the lines of the macro easier to understand.

Table 16.1. Complete Macro Actions and Arguments

Action	Argument	Argument Entry	Comment
Echo	Echo On	No	Turn off display while Customers form opens.
	Status Bar Text	(none)	
Hourglass	Hourglass On	Yes	Turn on hourglass as pointer.
OpenForm	Form Name	Customers	Open Customers form if closed; activate if form is open.
	View	Form	
	Filter Name	(none)	
	Where Condition	(none)	
	Data Mode	Edit	
	Window Mode	Normal	
DoMenuItem	Menu Bar	Form	Fit window to the form size.
	Menu Name	Window	
	Command	Size to Fit Form	
Echo	Echo On	Yes	Refresh the display to show the Customers form.
	Status Bar Text		
Echo	Echo On	No	Turn off the display during query.
	Status Bar Text		
OpenQuery	QueryName	Customer Purchases	Open or activate the query to show current Customer ID's purchases.
	View	Datasheet	
	Data Mode	Read Only	

Action	Argument	Argument Entry	Comment
Requery	Control Name	(none)	Redo the query to make it current in case query was activated and not opened.
MoveSize	Right	1.6 in	Move and size the query window.
	Down	1.1 in	
	Width	3.75 in	
	Height	1.5 in	
Beep			Notify operator query is complete.

Chapter Summary

Macros can make mundane tasks disappear with the click of a mouse or the press of a key. Many people find macros fun to create. If you create a database system for others to use, you may want to use macros to make Access operation easier for other users who may not know all the Access commands.

You can learn much more about making macros. You can learn just the basics, or you can develop macros that make decisions based on some condition. You can create custom shortcut keys and even create custom menus. Chapter 17 describes how to create simple or more complex macros, using step-by-step procedures. If, after reviewing the fundamentals, you have a specific kind of macro you need to make, look at Chapter 18, which contains examples of many of the most frequently used macros.

Understanding Access Macros

Macros give you the power to automate your work and to create systems that others can use without your assistance. Macros are well worth taking the time to learn.

Macros help you with repetitive tasks such as opening a collection of forms together and arranging them on-screen. They also help you automate your forms and reports. You may need new records, for example, that appear with default values already entered or you may want forms to open and display information from the same records.

Most of the database tasks you do manually can be duplicated by a macro action. A *macro action* is a single task being performed within a larger procedure. Even the commands you choose from the menu can be used as actions within a macro.

In addition to completing tasks or procedures for you, macros can make decisions. Macros or a sequence of actions within a macro can "decide" to work depending on some condition you specify. If a user enters an incorrect value, for example, your macro can display a unique alert message for each type of error.

Macros also enable you to customize Access. Your macros can be assigned to custom shortcut keys for frequently used actions. Novice users may want to add buttons to forms or reports so that the click of a mouse runs the macro. For a professional look, systems you create with Access can even have their own custom menus and commands.

The following list may give you some ideas about how you can effectively use macros in your system:

- Open and arrange forms and screens used on start-up. Display custom menus by creating a macro that runs automatically when a database opens.

- Open forms and reports. Opening one form can automatically open related forms and reports and arrange them on-screen.

- Synchronize forms so that updating one form displays the appropriate record in another form.

- Automate queries and finds.

- Print forms and reports by clicking a button that runs a print macro.

- Ensure data accuracy with macros that perform greater error checking than is possible with the error checking done with a control's properties.

- Transfer data between Access and other Windows applications by clicking a button that runs an import or export macro.

- Close the system gracefully when the user clicks a button or closes a main form.

Understanding the Macro Window and Toolbar

Whenever you are creating, testing, or editing macros, you work with the Macro window and the Macro Window toolbar. You need to understand how to use the buttons on the toolbar and parts of the window before you learn how to create macros.

The Macro Window

You create macros within a Macro window. Open a new Macro window from the Database window by clicking the Macro button or by choosing the **View M**acros command. The new Macro window opens in Design view. It looks like the grid in a worksheet, similar to a Microsoft Excel worksheet (see fig. 17.1).

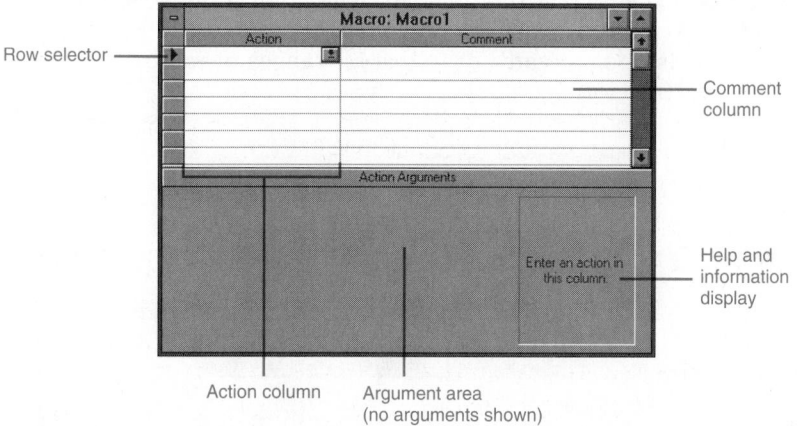

Row selector
Comment column
Action column
Argument area (no arguments shown)
Help and information display

FIG. 17.1

A new Macro window showing only the Action and Comment columns.

You can open a Macro window to read, edit, or copy existing macros. To open an existing macro, click the Macro button in the Database window or choose the **View M**acros command. Select a macro from the list in the Database window. Click the Design button in the Database window or press Alt+D. Figure 17.2 shows a simple macro, the Review Employee Orders macro from the NWIND database. The actions in the Action column define the action the macro performs. Each action has one or more associated arguments that define the way the action works. An OpenTable action, for example, has to know the name of the table to open. Comments are optional and require you to manually type them, but they are worth completing. They can help you or others understand how the macro works.

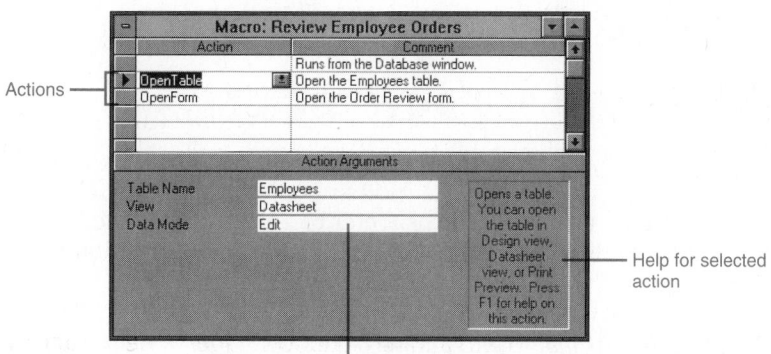

Actions
Arguments for selected action
Help for selected action

FIG. 17.2

Using arguments to define the way an action works.

Figure 17.3 shows a more complex macro in a Macro window. The Macro Name column identifies the start of each macro when the Macro window contains more than one macro. This capability enables you to group related macros in the same Macro window. The Condition column specifies a condition that controls when a portion of the macro runs. This capability is useful when you want to run a macro only if a specific form is open already, or to test for ranges of values the operator has typed into form controls.

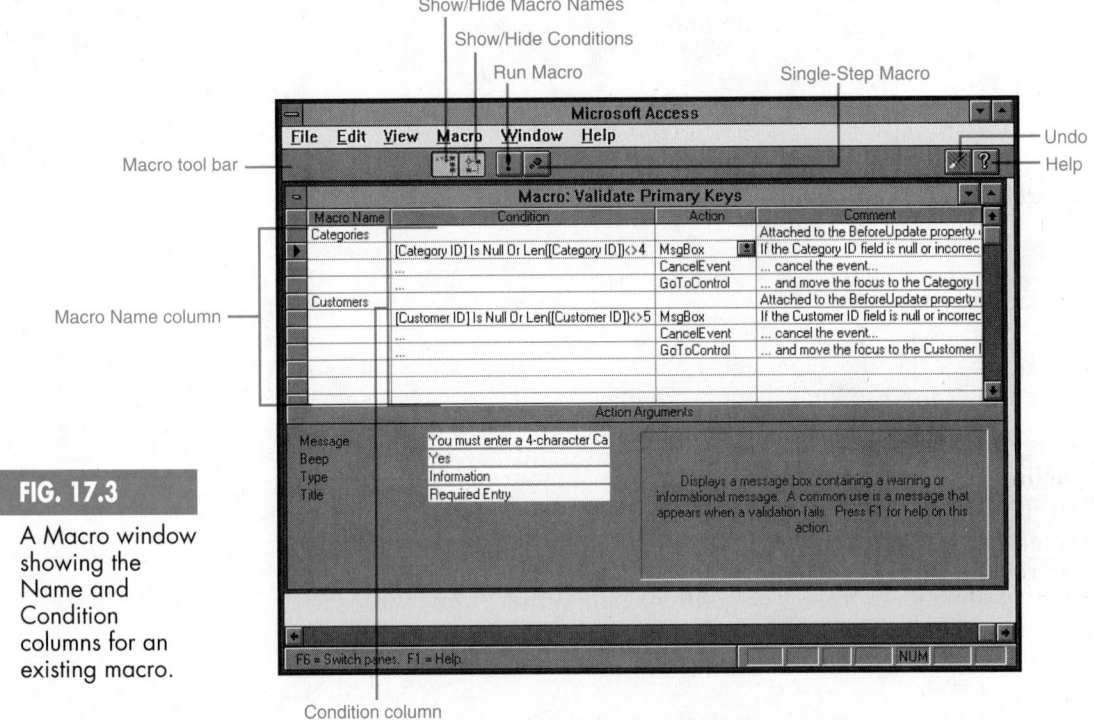

FIG. 17.3

A Macro window showing the Name and Condition columns for an existing macro.

The Macro Window Toolbar

The Macro toolbar is displayed under the menu bar whenever the Macro window is active. This toolbar contains six tools to help you program, run, and test macros (refer to fig. 7.3). The Macro Names and Condition tools toggle on and off the Names and Condition columns in the Macro window. The Run tool runs the active macro, and the Single Step tool is used to troubleshoot macros that aren't operating correctly. These tools are described in later sections of this chapter.

Creating a Macro

You create macros by starting with a blank Macro window (see fig. 17.1) and adding the actions and arguments that make your macro do work. Creating a macro consists of four steps:

1. Opening a new or existing Macro window.

2. Entering an action for each command or task you want the macro to accomplish. (The term *action* is referred to as "macro code" or "program code" in other applications or macro languages.) For most actions, you also must enter arguments that specify what or how an action works.

3. Saving the Macro window. A Macro window must be saved before the new or edited macro can be run.

4. Running the macro to test it.

Inserting Actions and Arguments

To create a new macro, you open a Macro window and then enter the actions you want to occur in the order you want each action to occur. You can enter actions in the Action column by choosing them from a combo list in each action cell or by typing them in the action cell. As you enter each action, you should enter the arguments for the action in the Arguments window in the lower half of the Macro window.

To create a macro, follow these steps:

1. Click the Macro button in the Database window or with the Database window active, choose the **View Macros** command. This action displays in the Database window a list of existing macros.

2. Click the New button or press Alt+N. A new Macro window appears (see fig. 17.1).

3. Click the first cell of the Action column if it isn't selected already. Notice the pull-down arrow in the active cell of the Action column. Figure 17.4 shows the pull-down arrow that will display the combo list.

4. Click the down arrow to the right of the action cell (or press Alt+Down arrow), and then select the action you want from the combo list that appears. When you select an action, notice that action arguments for the action you have chosen in the lower part of the window change. Figure 17.5 shows the arguments for opening a form.

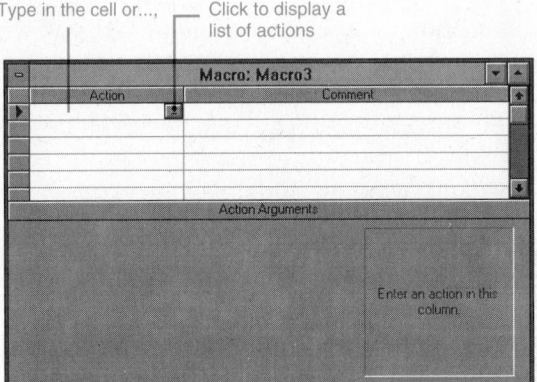

FIG. 17.4

The combo box arrow enables you to type or select actions from a list.

FIG. 17.5

Arguments specifying how an action works.

5. Click the first argument edit box or press F6 to move to the Action Arguments portion of the window.

6. Type or select the arguments for the current action.

   Enter arguments down the column starting from the topmost edit box. Arguments you select in upper boxes may change the alternatives for lower boxes. You can select many arguments from combo lists. If you select an argument's edit box and a combo list arrow appears to the right, you can select an argument from the combo list; otherwise, you must type the argument.

7. If you have to enter additional actions, click the next blank cell of the Active column or press F6 and press the arrow keys to select the next blank active cell. Return to step 4 to enter the action and its argument.

   If you don't need to enter additional actions, continue with step 8.

8. Choose the **F**ile Save **A**s command or press F12. In the Save As dialog box, type a descriptive name for the macro. Because the macro isn't saved as a separate file, the name can have spaces and doesn't need a file extension. Choose OK.

If you are entering a long macro action or argument and have difficulty seeing all the material you are typing, use the Zoom box shown in figure 17.6. The Zoom box expands the action cell or argument to display multiple lines. In the figure, the Zoom box displays the complete IsLoaded condition in the second condition cell.

To display the Zoom box, move the caret into the action cell or argument in which you want to type or edit. Press Shift+F2, and the Zoom box appears, showing the action cell or argument contents. When you are finished editing, choose OK or Cancel.

FIG. 17.6

Displaying the Zoom box for easier editing.

Entering Actions

You can enter actions in the Action column in three ways: Type the action, select the action from a combo list, or drag a database object into the cell. Each of these methods has advantages and disadvantages.

If you want to enter an action quickly, type it into the Action column. When you press Enter or an arrow key, the action is entered if you spelled it correctly. If you misspelled the action, a warning message notifies you. The list of available actions is displayed, making it easy for you to select the action you want.

If you want to browse through a list or are unfamiliar with how to spell an action, select the cell in the Action column and click the down arrow (or press Alt+Down arrow) to display the combo list. Scroll to the action and click it or press Enter.

You can find actions quickly in the action combo list by typing the first letter of the action in the cell, and then clicking the down-arrow for the combo list (or pressing Alt+Down arrow or Enter). When the list is displayed, it scrolls to the section of the list that starts with the letter you typed.

Two different actions can be inserted by dragging and dropping. Dragging and dropping a table, query, form, or report object from the Database window to an action cell inserts the Open action for that object—OpenTable, for example. Dragging and dropping a macro object from the Database window to an action cell inserts a RunMacro action. Figure 17.7 illustrates how windows can be arranged to drag and drop.

To insert an action using drag and drop, follow these steps:

1. Display both the Database window and the Macro window.

2. Click a button in the Database window to display the name of the object you want the action to open.

3. Drag the name of the object from the Database window to the cell in the Action column in which you want the action inserted. As you drag the name, the mouse pointer becomes an icon representing that type of object.

4. Release the mouse button with the mouse pointer (an object icon) over the cell in which you want the action.

If you drag a table, form, query, or report, an OpenTable, OpenForm, OpenQuery, or OpenReport action, respectively, appears in the cell over which you released the object icon. If you dragged a macro, the RunMacro action appears. Examine the arguments for the Open or RunMacro action created to make sure that the appropriate arguments also were entered by the drag-and-drop operation.

FIG. 17.7

Dragging the object from the Database window to the Action cell in which you want the action inserted.

Entering Arguments

Arguments define the way an action works. The MsgBox action, for example, has the arguments Message, Beep, Type, and Title. These arguments define how the MsgBox action works. Some arguments must be typed into an edit box in the lower half of the Macro window. Other arguments have a combo list from which you can select valid arguments. A Help message and description of the selected argument appear in the lower right corner of the Macro window. Examples of these arguments and their meanings are shown in table 17.1.

Table 17.1. MsgBox Arguments

Argument Name	Entry Method	Defines
Message Name	Manually typed	The message you type appears in the message dialog box that is displayed
Beep	Combo list: Yes No	The box either beeps or not when it is displayed

continues

Table 17.1. Continued		
Argument Name	**Entry Method**	**Defines**
Type	Combo list: None Critical Warning? Warning! Information	The type of icon appears in the message box
Title	Manually typed	The title for the title bar of the dialog box

When you enter arguments, either manually or from a combo list, begin with the first argument and work downward. Selections for some arguments are affected by the settings of earlier arguments.

Most arguments can be set with an expression beginning with an equal sign. Examples of arguments set by expressions are shown in the examples in Chapter 18, "Creating Macros for Forms, Reports, and Custom Menus." The arguments that cannot be set by expression are the ObjectType for the Close, GoToRecord, RepaintObject, SelectObject, or TransferDatabase actions. No item from the DoMenuItem action can use an expression as an argument.

You can enter arguments that call for the name of a database object, such as a table or form name, by dragging the database object from the Database window and dropping its icon on the argument's edit box.

Entering Comments

Don't ignore comments in your macros. They can save you or someone else time when your macro must be reviewed or modified. Enter comments in the Comment column to identify the macro and what it does, identify the event or other macro that runs this macro, and identify what the individual macro actions do. In addition, you can insert blank rows as spaces to separate macros visually when you have more than one macro in a Macro window. Figure 17.8 shows a Macro window that contains macros and their documenting comments. Notice how comments are used on lines with blank action cells as the title of the macro and to document how the macro is run or called.

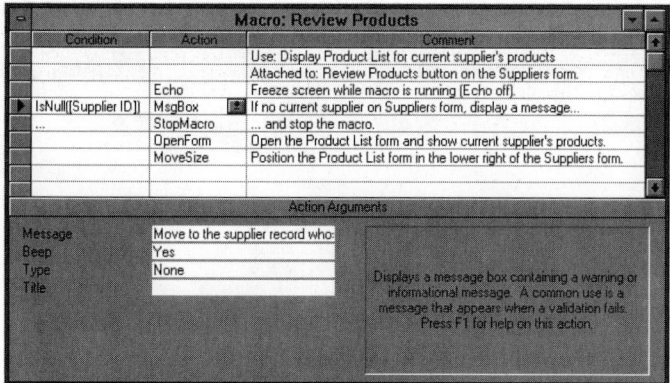

FIG. 17.8

Using comments and blank rows to document macros and make them easier to read.

Understanding the Available Macro Actions

Access macro actions can duplicate the commands you choose from menus as well as control many processes such as synchronizing the records that forms display. The following list, shown in table 17.2, shows you the macro actions available—both those that duplicate menu commands and those that are different from menu commands.

Getting On-line Help and Examples for Actions

Use Help for in-depth information about macro actions. To see the entire list of macro actions for which help is available, choose the **Help Contents** command. Then, at the bottom of the Contents window, click the underlined word, Actions. With the keyboard, press Tab until Actions is selected, and then press Enter. Figure 17.9 shows the Actions Reference window that appears.

To learn more about a macro action shown in the window in figure 17.9, click the action or press Tab to select the action and then press Enter.

If you already know for which action you want information, choose the **Help Search** command. Type in the top edit box the name of the action. As you type, the list scrolls to match as many characters as you have typed. Choose the Show Topics button to display subtopics in the lower list. Select one of the subtopics and then choose the Go To button. Figure 17.10 shows OpenTable typed in the top edit box.

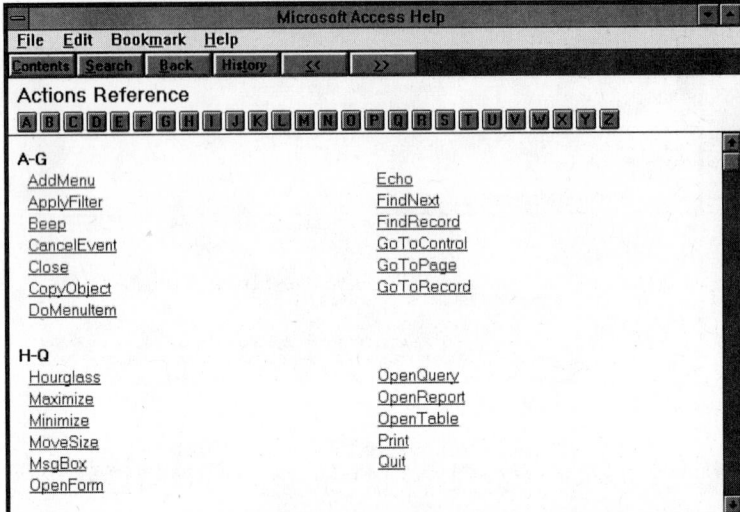

FIG. 17.9

Selecting an action from the Help window to learn about the action and see an example.

FIG. 17.10

Using the Help system to search for macro commands.

Figure 17.11 shows an example of the help for OpenTable. In the Help window, underlined words are linked to additional help. You can jump to this related help by clicking an underlined word or pressing the Tab key until the underlined word is selected and then pressing Enter. Return to the Help document from which you started by clicking the Back button or pressing Alt+B. Choose the underlined word Example at the top of the window to see an example of the action or how its arguments are completed.

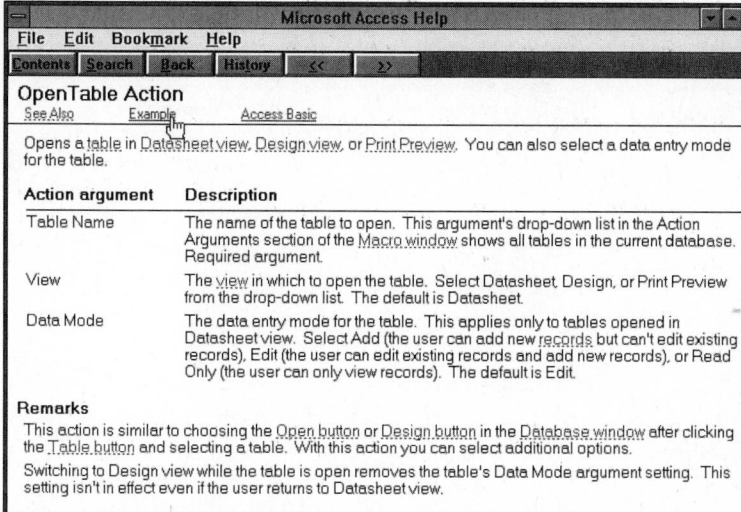

FIG. 17.11

Using Help to
learn about
actions and to
see examples.

Access Help is a separate Windows application that runs in a separate
window. To close the window when you are finished, press Alt+F4, the
shortcut key for closing a Windows application, or choose Close from
the Control menu.

Finding the Appropriate Action

Macro actions can duplicate most of the actions needed in an automated database. Before you begin to automate your work, you should
read table 17.2 to understand the actions available. Macro actions will
satisfy most of your needs. If you need a feature or expression that isn't
available, you can create it with Access Basic.

For more explicit information about these actions, their syntax, and
arguments, use the Help command in Access as described earlier to
display information about an action. Chapter 18 shows the use of many
actions in actual macros. Table 17.2 is a complete list of macro actions,
their arguments, and their functions.

Table 17.2. Macro Actions

Action	Argument	Function
AddMenu	Menu Name Menu Macro Name Status Bar Text	Creates a menu bar containing drop-down menus. The menu bar appears when the form to which AddMenu has been assigned is active.
ApplyFilter	Filter Name Where Condition	Filters the data available to a form or report using a filter, query, or SQL WHERE clause.
Beep	(no arguments)	Produces a beep tone for use in warnings or alerts.
CancelEvent	BeforeUpdate OnClose OnDelete OnInsert OnOpen	Cancels an event. This action is useful if a user enters invalid data in a record; then the macro can cancel the update of the database.
Close	Object Type Object Name	Closes the active (default) or a specified window.
CopyObject	Destination Database New Name	Duplicates the specified database object in another database or in the original database using a different name.
DoMenuItem	Menu Bar Menu Name Command Subcommand	Runs any command on the standard Access menu bars.
Echo	Echo On Status Bar Text	Turns on or off the screen refresh during macro operation. Hides results until they are complete and speeds macro operation.
FindNext	(no arguments)	Finds the next record specified by the FindRecord action or the Find command.

Action	Argument	Function
FindRecord	Find What Where Match Case Direction Search As Formatted Search In Find First	Finds the next record after the current record meeting the specified criteria. Searches through a table, form, or dynaset.
GoToControl	Control Name	Selects the control named in the argument. Used to select a control or field when a form opens.
GoToPage	Page Number Right Down	Selects the first field on the designated page in a multi-page form. The first field is the first field as designated by Tab order.
GoToRecord	Object Type Object Name Record Offset	Displays the specified record in a table, form, or dynaset.
Hourglass	Hourglass On	Displays an hourglass in place of the mouse pointer while the macro runs. Use it while long macros run.
Maximize	(no arguments)	Maximizes the active window.
Minimize	(no arguments)	Minimizes the active window to an icon within the Access window.
MoveSize	Right Down Width Height	Moves or changes the size of the active window.
MsgBox	Message Beep Type Title	Displays a warning or informational message box.
OpenForm	Form Name View Filter Name Where Condition Data Mode Window Mode	Opens or activates a form in one of its views. Form can be restricted to data-matching criteria, different modes of editing, and whether the form acts as a modal or pop-up dialog box.

continues

Table 17.2. Continued

Action	Argument	Function
OpenQuery	Query Name View Data Mode	Opens or activates a dynaset or crosstab query. You can specify the view and data entry mode.
OpenReport	Report Name View Filter Name Where Condition	Opens a report in the view you specify and filters the records before printing.
OpenTable	Table Name View Data Mode	Opens or activates a table in the view you specify. You can specify the data entry or edit mode for tables in Datasheet view.
Print	Print Range Page From Page To Print Quality Copies Collate Copies	Prints the active datasheet, report, or form.
Quit	Options	Exits from Access and saves unsaved objects according to the command you specify.
Rename	New Name	Renames the object selected in the Database window.
RepaintObject	Object Type Object Name	Completes recalculations for controls and updates the specified or active database object.
Requery	Control Name	Updates the specified control by repeating the query of the control's source.
Restore	(no arguments)	Restores a maximized or minimized window to its previous window.
RunApp	Command Line	Runs a Windows application.
RunCode	Function Name	Runs a user-defined function written in Access Basic.

Action	Argument	Function
RunMacro	Macro Name Repeat Count Repeat Expression	Runs the specified macro.
RunSQL	SQL Statement	Runs an action query as specified by the SQL statement.
SelectObject	Object Type Object Name In Database Window	Selects a specified database object.
SendKeys	Keystrokes Wait	Sends keystrokes to any active Windows application.
SetValue	Item Expression	Changes the value of a field, control, or property.
SetWarnings	Warnings On	Turns warning messages on or off.
ShowAllRecords	(no arguments)	Removes any filters or queries and displays all records in the current table or query.
StopAllMacros	(no arguments)	Stops all macros.
StopMacro	(no arguments)	Stops the current macro.
TransferDatabase	Transfer Type Database Type Database Name Object Type Source Destination Structure Only	Imports, exports, or attaches non-Access databases.
Transfer-Spreadsheet	Transfer Type Spreadsheet Type Table Name File Name Has Field Names Range	Imports or exports Access data to a worksheet or spreadsheet file.
TransferText	Transfer Type Specification Name Table Name File Name Has Field Names	Imports or exports Access data to a text file.

Duplicating a Menu Command with an Action

After you work with Access, you will know how to manually do many of the jobs you want to automate. These manual tasks usually use commands from the Access menus. To enter macro actions or create an entire macro that duplicates a series of menu commands, you use the DoMenuItem macro action. Keystrokes you enter in dialog boxes displayed by a command can be entered by the macro using the SendKeys macro action.

The DoMenuItem action duplicates commands on the standard Access menu bars. The arguments for a DoMenuItem action are shown in table 17.3.

Table 17.3. DoMenuItem Arguments

Argument	Description
Menu Bar	Each menu bar corresponds to a view. Select from the combo list the view that will be in use when this command runs. If you use DoMenuItem when a form is active, for example, choose Form.
Menu Name	Select from the combo list the menu heading that contains the command you want.
Command	Select from the combo list the command you want.
Subcommand	If a subcommand is required, select the subcommand. On a form, for example, the **R**ecords **G**oTo commands requires a subcommand such as **F**irst.

Macros halt if an action attempts to run and the incorrect object or view is displayed. If you are unsure of the view or object that is active when an action runs, use the single-step method of running the macro. By running a macro in single-step mode, you can step through the macro's actions one at a time. When you run single-step, note which menu bar (Database object) is active when the DoMenuItem action attempts to run. Use the **M**acro **S**ingle Step command or the Step button on the Macro toolbar to single-step a macro. This process is described later in this chapter, in the section "Troubleshooting Macros."

You can enter predefined information in a dialog box displayed by the DoMenuItem action. To do this, use the SendKeys action. SendKeys sends characters to an open Access dialog box or the active Windows application just as though you had typed the characters. The arguments for SendKeys are shown in table 17.4.

Table 17.4. SendKeys Arguments	
Argument	**Description**
Keystrokes	As many as 255 characters can be sent through this argument. Some keyboard characters are replaced by symbols, as described in the next table.
Wait	Enter Yes to make the macro pause until the keystrokes are executed. The default is No.

Send keystrokes to a dialog box displayed by DoMenuItem by putting the SendKeys action before the DoMenuItem and specifying No for the Wait argument of the SendKeys action. If the string of characters you want to send is more than the 255-character limit, use multiple SendKeys actions. Chapter 18 shows examples of how to use DoMenuItem and SendKeys to enter information in a dialog box.

To send alphanumeric characters used as text, such as *a, A, b, B* or 1, 2, or 3, enclose in quotation marks the characters you want to send—"Denver", for example. Text characters sent to some arguments don't require quotation marks.

Use Echo No and StopMacro to see interim results from SendKeys.

If a long macro is running and you are sending text and keystrokes to a dialog box, in the middle of the macro you will want to see whether the characters are accepted correctly, whether the correct options are chosen, and whether quotation marks around text are needed. To see the SendKeys work, change the Echo On argument to Yes for any preceding Echo actions. This step lets you see what is happening. Insert a StopMacro after the DoMenuItem that opens the dialog box that will receive the keystrokes. When you run the macro, you can see the characters as they are entered in the dialog box.

Keystrokes that have no symbol, such as Enter or Esc, are described with a code. The following list shows the codes you should use to send keystrokes such as Tab, Delete, and arrow movements.

Key to Send	Use in Keystroke Argument
Command Keys	
Backspace	{BACKSPACE} or {BS} or {BKSP}
Break	{BREAK}
Caps Lock	{CAPSLOCK}
Clear	{CLEAR}
Del	{DELETE} or {DEL}
End	{END}
Enter	{ENTER} or ~
Esc	{ESCAPE} or {ESC}
Help	{HELP}
Home	{HOME}
Ins	{INSERT}
Num Lock	{NUMLOCK}
Print Screen	{PRTSC}
Function Keys	
F1	{F1}
F2	{F2}
F3	{F3}
F4	{F4}
F5	{F5}
F6	{F6}
F7	{F7}
F8	{F8}
F9	{F9}
F10	{F10}
F11	{F11}
F12	{F12}
F13	{F13}
F14	{F14}
F15	{F15}
F16	{F16}

Key to Send	Use in Keystroke Argument
Movement Keys	
Down Arrow	{DOWN}
Left Arrow	{LEFT}
Page Down	{PGDN}
Page Up	{PGUP}
Right Arrow	{RIGHT}
Scroll Lock	{SCROLLLOCK}
Tab	{TAB}
Up Arrow	{UP}

Many actions in Access require the use of keystroke combinations—keys used in combination with Shift, Ctrl, or Alt keys. These keys are represented by the following:

To Use	Use in the Keystroke Argument
Shift	+
Control	^
Alt	%

When you press two keys in combination, such as Alt+S, specify this action as:

    %S

To press Alt+S, followed by R (without the Alt), use

    %SR

If a key is held down while two or more keys are pressed, enclose the group of following keys in parentheses:

    %(DV)

When you want to send the same keystroke many times, add to the keystroke a number specifying how many times to repeat. To move down three times, for example, use the following:

    {DOWN 3}

Some characters are used as symbols for keys or are reserved for use in programming features such as dynamic data exchange. To use these characters, enclose them in braces ({ }). These characters are shown in the following list:

To Use	Use in the Keystroke Argument
+ (plus)	{+}
^ (caret)	{^}
% (percent)	{%}
~ (tilde)	{~}
[or] (brackets)	{[} or {]}
{ or } (braces)	{{} or {}}

Beware of using movement keys such as {Down} or {Tab} as arguments of the SendKeys action to select commands or dialog box items. Future versions of Access may include additional menu commands that will change the order of menu items, or may involve dialog boxes with a different structure. There is less chance that you will have to modify your SendKeys argument for future versions if you use an Alt+*Letter* combination to choose commands or dialog box items.

Editing and Copying Macro Actions and Arguments

You may need to edit a macro to change its actions or to correct an error. You also may want to copy all or part of a macro from one Macro window to another to eliminate having to repeat work you already have done. You can even copy macros between databases.

Editing Macros

Using a mouse to edit a macro requires fewer steps than editing from the keyboard. To edit an action or argument, click the mouse pointer in an edit box in which you want to edit and then use normal Windows editing actions.

If you are using a keyboard, press Tab or Enter to move right and then down through the Macro window. Press Shift+Tab or Shift+Enter to move left and then up. You can move in any direction with the four directional arrows.

As you move between cells, the entire cell contents are selected. You can type or select an item from a combo list to replace all of the selected entry. To edit, press F2 and then press the left- or right-arrow keys or Delete or Backspace to edit. If the contents you are editing are too long to edit conveniently in the active column cell or the argument cell, press Shift+F2 to display the Zoom box. This box displays the entire cell contents in an edit window. Table 17.5 shows some other useful keys.

Table 17.5. Editing Keys

Key	Movement
Esc	Cancel edit before moving caret out of cell
Home	Move to far left cell in the same row
End	Move to far right cell in the same row
Ctrl+Home	Move to far left cell in the top row
Ctrl+End	Move to far left cell in the last row
Shift+← Shift+→	Select characters as caret moves
Ctrl+← Ctrl+→	Move one word at a time
Shift+Ctrl+← Shift+Ctrl+→	Select one word at a time

Deleting, Inserting, or Moving Rows

You should delete rows in a macro when you no longer need the action or condition in that row. To delete a row, move the caret into the row and then choose the **E**dit **D**elete Row command. When you are using the mouse, you can delete one or more rows by first selecting the rows by clicking the row selector arrow to the left of the Macro window. To select multiple rows, click the top row selector and drag down as many rows as you want selected. After the rows are selected, press Del.

To undo an insertion or deletion that has just occurred, choose the **E**dit **U**ndo command or press Ctrl+Z.

Insert rows in a macro when you want to insert an action between existing actions or when you want a blank space between macros to make them more readable. To insert a row, move the caret into a row. (The inserted row appears above the row containing the caret.) Choose the **E**dit **I**nsert Row command. If you are using a mouse, click the row selector or drag across multiple row selectors and then press Ins.

To move one or more rows with the mouse, click the row selector or drag across multiple row selectors so that the rows you want to move are selected. Release the mouse button. Then move the mouse pointer over one of the selected row selectors and hold down the mouse button. As you hold down the button, the pointer becomes a pointer overlying a shaded square box.

Drag the mouse pointer to the row in which you want to move the selected rows. Notice that a horizontal line appears where the moved rows will appear. Release the mouse pointer at the location in which you want the moved rows.

Copying Macros

You can copy all or a portion of a macro from one Macro window to another. This capability can help you reuse macros or use portions of a macro more than once.

To copy a single cell, such as an action, select all the characters in the cell, choose the **E**dit **C**opy command, or press Ctrl+C. Move the caret to the location where you want to paste and then choose the **E**dit **P**aste command or press Ctrl+V.

To copy entire rows or an entire macro, click the row selector arrows to select the rows you want to copy. Choose the **E**dit **C**opy command or press Ctrl+C. Open a new or existing macro. Select the cell in which you want to paste the copied data and choose the **E**dit **P**aste command or press Ctrl+V.

To copy a macro from one database to another, copy the macro rows you want to move using the methods described. Choose the **F**ile **O**pen command while the Database window is active and open the database in which you want to move the macro. Open an existing or new Macro window in this database. Select the cell in which you want to paste the first macro cell. Choose the **E**dit **P**aste command or press Ctrl+V. Save the new macro.

Copying rows from a macro and pasting them into another macro doesn't change the arguments for the actions. Make sure that you check arguments after pasting to ensure that they reflect what you want them to do in the new location.

Referring to Form or Report Controls

You must know how to refer to a control name from within a macro for many reasons. You must know how to refer to control names if you want to perform such tasks as the following:

- Synchronizing records in two forms by matching values of controls.

- Setting a control to a specific value.

- Changing a macro's action based on the value of a control.

- Checking data entries values using complex checks and responding with a message.

- Moving the focus to a control on a form when the form opens or a record changes.

- Entering SQL statements in macro actions that filter or query.

Chapter 18 has numerous examples of how controls are referenced from within macros.

The syntax for referring to controls follows:

For a form:

    Forms!*formname*!*controlname*

For a report:

    Reports!*reportname*!*controlname*

Examples for these controls follows:

For a form:

    Forms!Orders!Quantity

For a report:

    Reports!MonthEnd!Item

This syntax has two variations. First, when the macro containing the reference is run from the form or report containing the control, you don't have to specify the full control name. Consider a form named Orders, for example, which contains a button that runs a macro. In the macro run by the button on the form, you don't have to use the full syntax:

```
Forms!Orders!Quantity
```

You have to refer only to the following:

```
Quantity
```

 If you are in doubt as to which syntax to use, use the full syntax. If you use the short syntax in an inappropriate situation, the macro will not run.

Second, if a form, report, or control name contains spaces, you must enclose the name in square brackets. If you want to reference the control named Amount Shipped on the Product Shipments form, for example, you must use this syntax:

```
Forms![Product Shipments]![Amount Shipped]
```

If a macro run from the Product Shipments form had to reference the Amount Shipped control, it would use the following syntax:

```
[Amount Shipped]
```

The macro contains this syntax because of the first rule that the full syntax doesn't have to be used when the macro is run from the form or report containing the control that is referenced.

Using Conditional Tests To Change Macro Actions

Your macros can have the capability to make decisions about how they operate. Macros can test whether a condition is true and, when that condition is true, they run actions you specify.

So far, you have seen a Macro window containing two columns: Action and Comment. You can add to this window a third column on the left in which you can put a conditional test (see fig. 17.12). You enter in this Condition column expressions that can be evaluated as True or False. If the expression is True, the macro action on the right runs. If the expression is False, the macro action doesn't run.

Macro: Validate Primary Keys			
Macro Name	Condition	Action	Comment
Categories			Attached to the BeforeUpdate prope
	[Category ID] Is Null Or Len([Category ID])<>4	MsgBox	If the Category ID field is null or inco
	...	CancelEvent	... cancel the event...
	...	GoToControl	... and move the focus to the Catego
Customers			Attached to the BeforeUpdate prope
	[Customer ID] Is Null Or Len([Customer ID])<>5	MsgBox	If the Customer ID field is null or inco
	...	CancelEvent	... cancel the event...
	...	GoToControl	... and move the focus to the Custor

Action Arguments	
Message	You must enter a 4-character Ca
Beep	Yes
Type	Information
Title	Required Entry

Displays a message box containing a warning or informational message. A common use is a message that appears when a validation fails. Press F1 for help on this action.

FIG. 17.12

Using tests in the Condition column to determine whether the adjacent macro action runs.

Create conditions in the Condition column with the use of expressions and control names. The following list shows some examples:

Condition Being Tested	Description
[Last Name]="Smith"	True when the Last Name control contains the text *Smith*
Forms!Orders!Quantity<10	True when the control named Quantity on the Orders form is less than 10
[Quantity]>5 AND [Quantity]<20	True when the control named Quantity on the current form is between 5 and 20

If you want macro actions to run when a condition is True, display the Condition column in the Macro window and enter the condition. Display the Condition column by choosing the **View Conditions** command, or by clicking the Show/Hide Condition button on the toolbar. Put in the adjacent Action column the macro action you want to run when the condition is True. If you want multiple actions to run when a condition is True, type an ellipsis (...) in the Condition column next to each action that also should be run. Figure 17.13 shows a Macro window with a condition and multiple actions that run when the condition is True. Conditions can control whether one action runs, an entire macro runs, or a portion of a macro runs.

Condition column   Action column

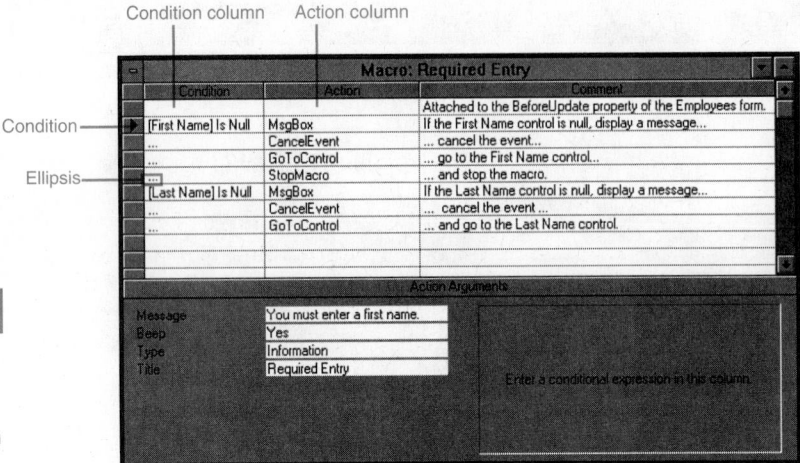

Condition ——

Ellipsis ——

FIG. 17.13

Indicating
additional
actions that run
when a condition
is True.

To create macro actions that run when the condition evaluates as True,
follow these steps:

1. Click the Show/Hide Condition button on the Macro toolbar or
   choose the **View Conditions** command to display the Condition
   column in the Macro window.

2. Enter the condition in the Condition column.

3. Enter in the Action column the action you want to run when the
   condition is true.

4. If you want to run additional actions when the condition is true,
   enter them down the Action column below the action in step 3.

5. If you entered additional actions in step 4, put an ellipsis (...) in
   the Condition column next to each action. All these actions will
   run when the condition is True.

If you save a Macro window with the Condition column displayed, the
next time you open the window in Design view, the Condition column is
visible. If you want the Condition column for all Macro windows to be
displayed, choose the **View Options** command and then select Macro
Design from the Category list. Enter **Yes** in the Show Condition Column
edit box.

The conditional IF test in Access macros is different from the test
in most macro and programming languages. Access macros run
actions if a test is True, but there is no False portion of the test.
Access Macros use an IF *test* THEN *action* syntax. If the *test* is True,
the *action* runs. If the *test* is False, the *action* is skipped and Access
jumps to the next action that doesn't have an ellipsis.

Grouping Multiple Macros in a Macro Window

When you have many related macros, you probably will find it most convenient to put all the related macros in a single Macro window. Each macro in the Macro window must have its own unique name. You enter these names by displaying the Macro Name column and then typing in the names. Display the Macro Name column by choosing the **D**isplay **N**ames command or by clicking the Show/Hide Macro Names button on the toolbar. Like the Condition column, this column is displayed to the left of the Action column (see fig. 17.14).

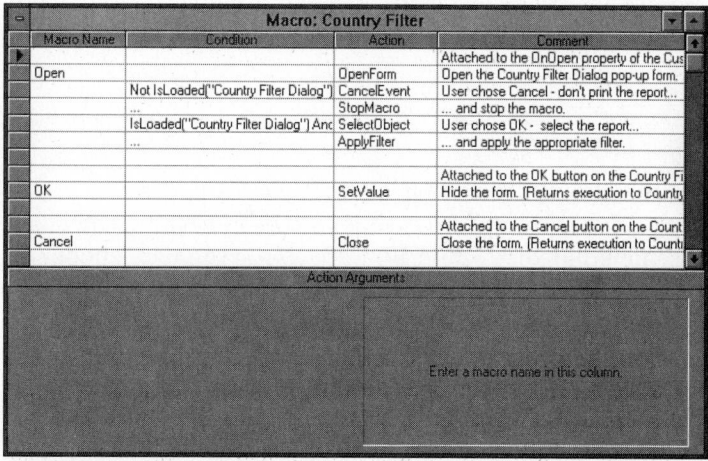

FIG. 17.14

Using the Macro Name column to name individual macros in a Macro window.

Each unique macro in a Macro window begins with the Action to the right of the name. The macro ends when it reaches the beginning of the next macro or runs out of actions. You don't have to end a macro with a particular "end" action, as you might in many macro or programming languages.

Each Macro window is a database group. If the Macro window contains one macro, you can reference that macro or run the macro by using just the name of the Macro window. In the NWIND database that comes with Access, for example, the Export Sales Data Macro window contains a single macro. You can run this macro by referring to Export Sales Data.

When a Macro window contains multiple macros (refer to fig. 17.14), you must reference a specific macro using the following syntax:

    macrogroupname.macroname

where a period separates the *macrogroupname* from the *macroname*. The third macro in the figure, for example, can be run using the following syntax:

    Country Filter.Cancel

To run this third macro, for example, by choosing the **File Run** Macro command, you type **Country Filter.Cancel** in the Run Macro dialog box. To reference this macro from an event, you use the same syntax to reference one macro from the entire group.

 If you run or reference a macro group, but identify only the group and not a name within it, the first macro within the group runs.

Running Macros

You can run macros in many ways. If you are creating quick macros for your own immediate use, you may want to run them by choosing them from the Macro window or the Database window. To create a system that is more automated or one that is easier to use, you can run a macro as shown in table 17.6.

Table 17.6. Ways To Run a Macro	
Macros Can Run When	**Sample Use**
Operator clicks a button	Buttons on form to open other forms or print reports
A specified event occurs	Operator moves between fields, records change, form or table opens or closes
Operator presses shortcut key	Shortcut key for frequently used operations
Operator chooses a custom command from a custom menu	A database system needs its own custom menus

Running Macros from the Macro Window

You can run macros from the Macro window of the macro you want to run. This capability is useful when you want to test a macro. Figure 17.15 shows the mouse pointer poised over the Run button on the toolbar. Clicking the Run button runs the first macro in the active macro window, Country Filter.

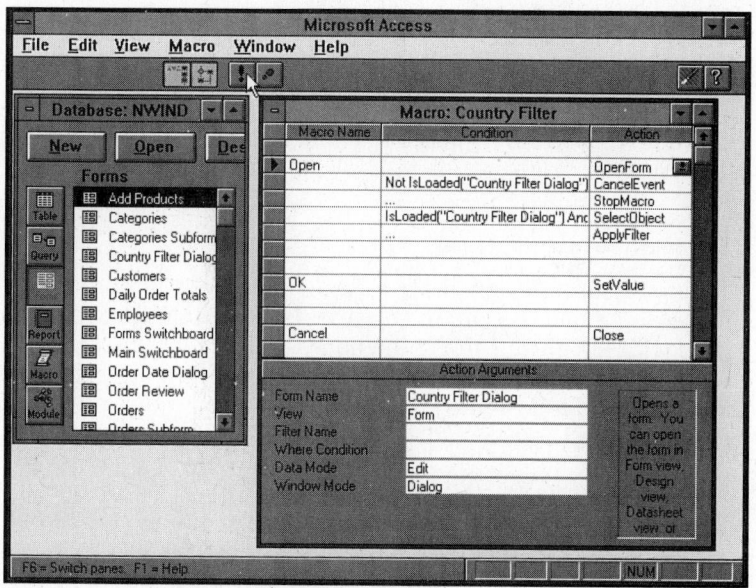

FIG. 17.15

Clicking the Run button on the toolbar to run the first macro in the active Macro window.

To run a macro when the macro's window is active, click the Run button on the toolbar. You can choose the **M**acro **R**un command also. If the macro doesn't run as expected or if an Action Failed dialog box appears (see fig. 17.16), you may not have had the correct forms, reports, or windows open for the macro to work correctly. Some macros may require a specific form to be active when they run. In this case, open or activate the necessary objects and run the macro using the **F**ile **R**un Macro technique described in the following section.

If the active Macro window contains a group of macros, only the first macro in a Macro window runs when you click the Run button on the toolbar. Choosing the **M**acro **R**un command and specifying only the name of the Macro window is another way of running the first macro in a Macro window. To run a specific macro within a group, use the **F**ile **R**un Macro command described in the following section.

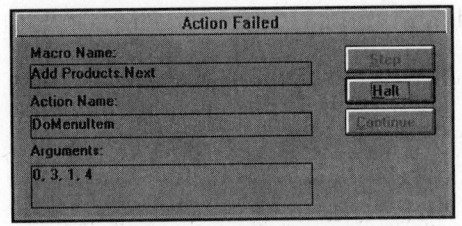

FIG. 17.16

The Action Failed
dialog box.

Running Macros with Any Window Active

Use the File Run Macro command to run macros when the Macro window isn't active or to run a macro in a macro group. To run a macro using the File Run Macro command, follow these steps:

1. Choose the File Run Macro command. The Run Macro dialog box appears (see fig. 17.17).

2. To run the first or only macro within a Macro window, select the name of the macro from the combo list. To run a specific macro from within a group, select the name of the macro group from the combo list, move the insertion point to the end of the name, and type a period followed by the name of the macro within the group: PrepareForm.PrepDate, for example.

3. Choose OK or press Enter.

FIG. 17.17

Using the Run
Macro dialog
box to run a
macro when any
window is active.

Running Macros from the Database Window

Another convenient method of running the first or only macro within a Macro window is to run it from the Database window. To run a macro from the Database window, follow these steps:

1. Open any database objects expected by the macro, such as forms or reports.

2. Click the Macro button to display the list of macros.

3. Double-click the macro name or select the macro name and choose the **R**un button at the top of the Database window.

Running Macros from Another Macro

You can run a macro from within another macro by calling the macro you want to run with the RunMacro action. After the called macro runs, Access returns control to the next action in the first macro. To run a macro from within another macro, enter macro actions within a Macro window to the point where you want the other macro to run. At that point, enter the RunMacro action in the Action column. In the Macro Name argument, select the name of the macro from the combo list. If you want one macro from within a group to run, select the name of the macro group, type a period, and type the name of the macro within the group. In figure 17.18, the RunMacro action runs one macro that loads all the forms, tables, and queries needed during initial start-up. Another RunMacro sets the default values used when the forms initially are displayed.

Action	Comment
	Prepares system for operation
Echo	Turn off screen display
Hourglass	Display hourglass during startup
OpenForm	Open startup screen graphic
MoveSize	Arrange startup form
OpenForm	Display startup message form over startup screen graphic
Echo	Turn screen on to show startup screen and message
Echo	Turn screen off to freeze startup message
RunMacro	Load working forms, tables and queries used during startup
RunMacro	Set default values
Close	Close startup message form

Action Arguments

Macro Name	Startup Default Values
Repeat Count	
Repeat Expression	

Enter or select the macro you want to run. The list shows all macros in the current database. You can also enter macrogroupname.macroname to run a macro in a macro group. Required argument. Press F1 for help on this argument.

FIG. 17.18

Running a macro from within a macro.

Table 17.7 shows the arguments used with the RunMacro action.

Table 17.7. RunMacro Arguments

Argument	Description
Macro Name	Select the name of the macro to run from the combo list. If you are using one macro from a macro group, select the macro group name from the combo list, and type a period and then the name of the macro as described earlier in this chapter.
Repeat Count	Type the number of times you want the macro to repeat. If you don't enter a number, the macro runs once. If you are familiar with programming constructs, this process is similar to a FOR-NEXT loop.
Repeat Expression	Create an expression that can be evaluated as True or False. The macro repeats until the Repeat Expression evaluates as False. If you are familiar with programming constructs, this process is similar to a WHILE loop.

Running Macros from an Event

Macros can be "triggered" when specific events in forms and reports occur. For example, you may want a macro to run when a form is opened, when the user selects or exits from a field, or when a field is double-clicked. Macro events can make your system easier to use and make it use the same operating procedures as commercially developed applications. Event-driven macros also are useful for opening multiple forms together, printing reports using specific queries, or creating error checks that are more extensive than those available through control properties.

Both forms and reports have events to which you can assign a macro. These events are specified within an object's properties. The events in a form or a record are shown in table 17.8.

Table 17.8. Events in a Form or Record

Form Property	Event Description	Use
OnOpen	Runs the macro when the form opens but before displaying a record	Opens or closes other forms when a form is opened
OnCurrent	Runs the macro before a record becomes current or is displayed in the form	Moves the focus to a specific control every time the record is updated
OnInsert	Runs the macro when you begin entering data in a new record	Displays needed data or a warning when the user begins to enter data
BeforeUpdate	Runs the macro after you leave a record but before the record is updated in the database; *see also* BeforeUpdate for control-level events	Asks the operator for confirmation that the record should be updated
AfterUpdate	Runs the macro after you leave a record and after changes in the record have been recorded in the database; *see also* AfterUpdate for control-level events	Transmits changed records to other applications or updates other forms using the new data
OnDelete	Runs the macro when you attempt to delete a record but before the record is deleted	Asks the operator to confirm that the record should be deleted before deleting it
OnClose	Runs the macro before the form disappears	Asks the operator to confirm that the form should be closed or transmits data to another application when the form is closed

The events associated with controls in a form are shown in table 17.9.

Table 17.9. Events in a Form Control

Form Control Property	Event Description	Use
OnEnter	Runs the macro when you move the focus to a control but before focus is on the control	Asks the operator for a password for that field or displays information about how to enter in the field
OnPush	Runs the macro when you click a command button in a form; *see also* OnDoubleClick in this table	Runs any type of macro associated with button operations, such as opening other forms, printing a form, or updating records
BeforeUpdate	Runs the macro after you leave a control but before the control is changed; *see also* BeforeUpdate for form events	Validates the entry for this control using more extensive validation than is available with control properties
AfterUpdate	Runs the macro after you leave a control and after the control changes; *see also* AfterUpdate for form-level events	Updates other controls depending on the entry in the control that has just changed
OnDoubleClick	Runs the macro when you double-click a control or control label	Displays help information or forms that help the user with data entry
OnExit	Runs when you attempt to move to another control but before the focus moves away	Uses the GoToControl action to move the focus to a specific control; uses conditions to define different controls to go to depending on the values entered

The events that occur in a report are shown in table 17.10.

Table 17.10. Events That Occur in a Report

Report Event	Event Description	Use
OnOpen	Runs a macro when the report opens but before printing	Asks the user to enter the criteria for a query
OnClose	Runs a macro when the report closes	Writes the data and time of the report to a logging file

Within a report, events are controlled by what happens to a report section. The events that control macros are shown in table 17.11.

Table 17.11. Events That Occur in a Report Section

Section Events	Event Description	Use
OnFormat	Runs a macro after Access has accumulated or calculated the data for the section but before printing the section	Changes the appearance or layout of a section depending on data in one of the controls
OnPrint	Runs a macro after the data in a section is laid out but before printing	Changes the headers, footers, or page numbers in a section

To assign an existing macro to a specific event associated with a form, report, or control, follow these steps:

1. Open the form or report and switch to Design view.

2. Select the form, report, section, or control to which you want to assign a macro using one of these procedures:

   Select a form or report by clicking in the gray background or in a report, by clicking outside a report section, or by choosing the Edit Select Form or Edit Select Report command.

   Select a report section by clicking the section header.

   Select a control by clicking the control.

3. Display the property sheet by clicking the Properties button on the toolbar or by choosing the View Properties command.

4. Select the event in the property sheet that you want to run the macro. These events are listed in the preceding tables: OnOpen and OnEnter, for example. Different events are available for forms, reports, and controls.

5. Select from the event's combo list the macro you want to run. If the macro is part of a group, select the group's name from the list, move the insertion point to the end of the name, and then type a period and the macro name: **NewRecord.GotoName**, for example.

Running Macros from a Button

Your forms can be easier to use and can have a professional appearance with the addition of command buttons that run macros. Also, command buttons are extremely easy to add to a form.

Before you add a button to a form, create and save the macro you want the button to run, and then follow these steps:

1. Open the form on which you want to add the button.

2. Switch to Form Design view by clicking the Design button on the toolbar or by choosing the **View Form Design** command.

3. Scroll the form so that you can see where you want to put the button.

4. Open the Database window and click the Macro button to display available macros.

5. Drag the macro's icon from the Database window and drop it on the location where you want the button to appear.

Figure 17.19 shows the mouse pointer ready to drag the PA Next Record macro from the database window. After dropping the PA Next Record icon at the bottom of the form, the macro icon changes to the button as shown in figure 17.20.

Test whether the macro works by activating the form and switching to Form view, by clicking the Form button on the toolbar, or by choosing the **View Form** command. Click the button to make the macro run.

While the form is in Design view, you can change the name on the button by selecting the button, dragging across the text in the button, and typing new text.

FIG. 17.19

Creating a button by dragging a macro from the Database window to the form.

FIG. 17.20

Dropping the macro on a form to produce a button.

You can create an activating (underlined) letter in your button's name: **O**pen, for example. With an activating letter, you can press Alt+*Letter* to run the macro as though you had clicked the button. To create an activating letter in the button name, follow these steps:

1. Create the button on the form. (Remember that the form must be in Design view.)

2. Select the text in the button and type the button name. Type an ampersand (&) before the character you want to be the activating letter.

3. Press Enter when you finish typing the new caption, and the button name appears with the activating letter underlined.

You can create an activating letter also by typing an ampersand before a letter in the Caption property for the button. Display the Caption property by switching the form to Design view, select the button, and then display the property sheet by clicking the Properties button on the toolbar or by choosing the View Properties command. In the Caption edit box, type the button name with the activating letter preceded by an ampersand (&).

Using the drag-and-drop method of creating buttons automatically sets the button's OnPush property to the name of the macro. In Form Design view, you can change other button properties such as whether the button prints, its text color, and its font.

Buttons have more events than just OnPush. You can run other macros from a toggle or command button by using the OnDoubleClick, OnEnter, and OnExit properties.

Create your own custom buttons that have picture faces by drawing toggle buttons on your form. Assign a macro to the button by entering the macro name in the OnEnter, OnExit, or OnDoubleClick property. Lay a bit-map drawing from Windows PaintBrush over the button by typing in the Picture property the path and file name for the bit map.

Running Macros from a Custom Menu Command

Your database system should be easy and convenient to use. Although the buttons described in the preceding section are convenient for frequent procedures, they are inappropriate when many commands or options are available in a form. In that case, you probably will want to build a custom menu system containing commands that run your macros.

Every form you design can have its own custom menu bar. When the form opens, the custom menu bar is displayed. As figure 17.21 illustrates, the menu bar can have multiple menus, and each menu can contain multiple commands.

FIG. 17.21

Accessing your
custom menu
bar.

Follow these fundamental steps for creating a menu bar and attaching it
to a form:

1. Create a macro group for each menu. Each macro within a group
   corresponds to a command on the menu.

2. Create the macro that displays menu headings using the AddMenu
   action.

3. Attach to a form the menu macro created in step 2. The menu
   appears when the form is open.

Remember to give yourself and your users a custom command or
button that closes the form and thereby reverts the menu back to
an Access menu. If you fail to give your users a way to close the
form and revert to other menus, they may be forced to exit and
restart Access to regain control.

Creating Custom Commands

A macro group composes the custom commands on a custom menu.
Each macro relates to a command on the menu. The name of each
macro in the group becomes the command name in the pull-down
menu. Figure 17.22 shows each macro name that will become a command on a pull-down menu.

Each macro name becomes a
command name on a menu

Macro Name	Action	Comment
		Called by an AddMenu action in the Form View Menu Bar macro.
Form &Design	DoMenuItem	Add the Form Design command.
&Form	DoMenuItem	Add the Form command.
Data&sheet	DoMenuItem	Add the Datasheet command.
S&ubform Datasheet	DoMenuItem	Add the Subform Datasheet command.
&Options...	DoMenuItem	Add the Options command.

Macro: View Menu Commands

Action Arguments

Menu Bar	Form
Menu Name	View
Command	Form Design
Subcommand	

Runs a Access menu command. You must select a command that is appropriate for the Access view you are in when the command is called by the macro. Press F1 for help on this action.

FIG. 17.22

Viewing the
macro names.

To create the macro groups that will become commands for the pull-down menus used by a form, follow these steps:

1. Create macros that produce the action you want for each custom command. All macros that appear on one pull-down menu must be in the same macro group (Macro window).

2. Display the Macro Name column, and name each macro using the name as you want it to appear in the pull-down menu. Type an ampersand (&) in front of a letter you want to be the activating letter for a command.

3. Organize the macros within the Macro window in the same order you want the commands to appear in the pull-down menu.

4. Save this macro group and remember its name for reference in the next procedure.

5. Create an additional macro group for each custom pull-down menu for the form you are developing.

 You don't have to copy each individual macro into the workgroup that creates the custom commands. A macro can be kept in another Macro window and run from within the command's macro group using the RunMacro action.

Creating a Custom Menu Bar

A custom menu bar is composed of one or more pull-down menu headings. To create a custom menu bar, you have to specify only which headings go on a bar. Use a macro containing only AddMenu actions to add menu headings and create the bar. Each AddMenu action adds one menu heading. The AddMenu arguments specify which macro group contains the commands that go on the pull-down menu. Figure 17.23 shows the AddMenu actions that become menus on a custom menu bar.

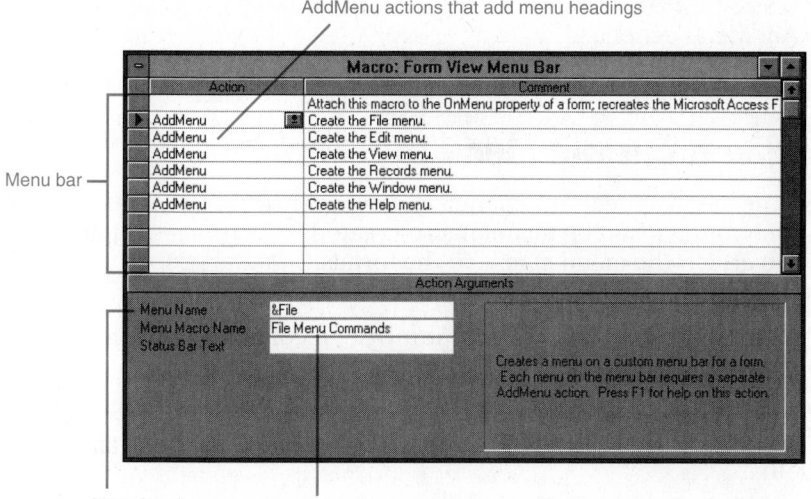

FIG. 17.23

An AddMenu action adding each custom menu on the menu bar.

To create the menu bar that displays a menu heading and the custom commands created in the preceding procedure, follow these steps:

1. Open a new Macro window.

2. Select AddMenu in the Action column.

3. Name the AddMenu arguments:

Argument	Description
Menu Name	Type the name you want to appear as the menu heading. Type an ampersand (&) before the letter you want to be the activating letter for the menu.
Menu Macro Name	Type or select the name of the macro group containing the commands.
Status Bar Text	Type the message that will appear in the status bar when this menu heading is selected.

4. Type a description in the Comment column to remind yourself which menu this action adds to the bar.

5. Return to step 2 if there are additional menu headings. Insert the AddMenu action and arguments down the column in the order in which you want the menu headings to appear across the menu bar.

6. Save this macro, run it to test the menu and commands, and re-member its name.

The macro that adds custom menus to the menu bar can contain only AddMenu actions.

Attaching a Custom Menu to a Form

To make the menu appear automatically whenever the form opens, you must attach to the form the menu macro created in the preceding pro-cedure. To attach the menu macro to the form's OnMenu property, follow these steps:

1. Open the form and choose the **View Design** command or click the Design button in the Form toolbar.

2. Display the properties sheet for the form by choosing the **View Properties** command or by clicking the Properties button on the toolbar.

3. Select the name of the menu macro in the OnMenu property.

4. Save the form.

5. Open the form in Form view and make sure that the custom menus and commands are displayed.

Running Macros from a Shortcut Key

You may want to assign macros you use frequently to a shortcut key-stroke. This capability enables you to press a shortcut key such as Ctrl+N to see the next record or Ctrl+P to print.

Macros are assigned to keystrokes using a three-step process:

1. Create the macros you want assigned to keys in one macro group.

2. In the Macro window's Name column adjacent to the first macro action for each macro, type the shortcut key code for that macro.

3. Enter the name of the macro group into the Key Assignment Macro field of the Keyboard Category of the View Options command.

Figure 17.24 shows a macro group containing shortcut key codes in the Macro Name column and the macros those codes run. Figure 17.25 shows the Options dialog box and the Key Assignment Macro property into which you must type the name of the macro group containing shortcut key assignments.

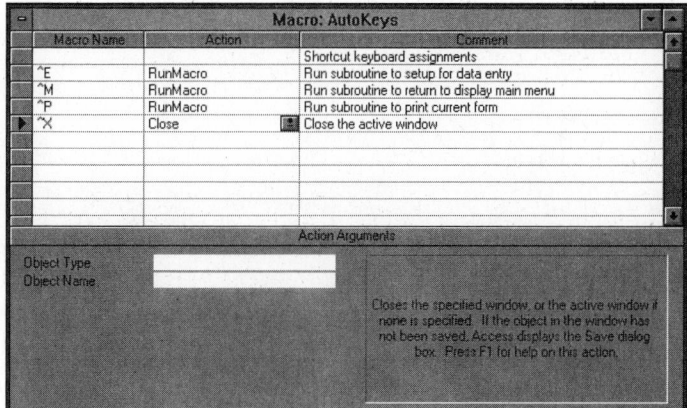

Codes in the Macro Name column specifying which key combination runs a macro.

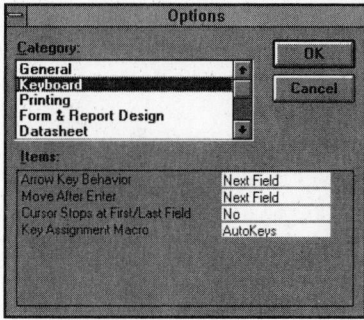

The Key Assignment Macro property specifying which macro group identifies shortcut keys.

Access uses the name AutoKey by default in the Key Assignment Macro property of the Options dialog box. You can save the macro group containing shortcut keys with the name AutoKey or you can change AutoKey in the Key Assignment macro to name any macro group.

The list of shortcut key codes is a subset of the key codes described for the SendKeys action. These codes also use a caret (^) to indicate the Ctrl key and a plus sign (+) to indicate the Shift key. The keys and keycodes to which you can assign macros are shown in table 17.12.

Table 17.12. Keys and Keycodes to Which You Can Assign Macros

Shortcut Key or Combination	Key Code for the Macro Name Column
Ctrl+*Letter*	^*letter*
Ctrl+*Number*	^*number*
Function key	{F1} and so on
Ctrl+*Function key*	^{F1} and so on
Shift+*Function key*	+{F1} and so on
Insert or Ins	{Insert}
Ctrl+Insert or Ctrl+Ins	^{Insert}
Shift+Insert or Shift+Ins	+{Insert}
Delete or Del	{Delete} or {Del}
Ctrl+Delete or Ctrl+Del	^{Delete} or ^{Del}
Shift+Delete or Shift+Del	+{Delete} or +{Del}

Shortcut key combinations involving letters that are predefined in Access, such as Ctrl+C and Ctrl+X, can be assigned to your own macros. Your macro takes precedence, however, over the pre-defined meaning of the shortcut combination. Beware of using Ctrl+C, Ctrl+V, Ctrl+X, and Ctrl+Z for this reason.

Changing Shortcut Keys During Operation

If your Access system always will use the same shortcut keys for all forms, reports, and operators, you can put all your shortcut keys in a single macro group. As described, you can use the default name AutoKey to name that macro group or give the macro group any name and change the Key Assignment Macro property in the View Options dialog box. The name of the macro in the Key Assignment Macro property is read by Access when you first open the database.

To use different sets of shortcut keys for different forms, reports, or operators, you have to create a macro that changes the macro name in the Key Assignment Macro property of the View Options dialog box.

The macro uses SendKeys and DoMenuItem to do this. The macro necessary for changing shortcut key assignments during database operation is shown in table 17.13.

The macro in table 17.13 works as follows. The SendKeys action sends the keystrokes to the computer's keyboard buffer before the View Options dialog box opens. Those keystrokes wait for the dialog box to open, and then they stream into the dialog box as though you just typed them.

The keystrokes listed in the Keystrokes argument select the Categories list in the View Options dialog box and move down to the second item, Keyboard. The keystrokes then select the Items list and move down three cells to the Key Assignment Macro property. In this property edit box, the keystrokes type *newkeymacro*. The name of your macro, *newkeymacro,* contains the new shortcut keys. Using the tilde (~) is the same as pressing Enter to close the View Options dialog box. The DoMenuItem action displays the View Options dialog box, and the keystrokes from the buffer stream into the dialog box as though you typed them, changing the Key Assignment Macro property and closing the box. From that point, Access looks at the macro named in the Key Assignment Macro property whenever it has to find the macro that matches a shortcut key.

This macro renames shortcut keys to the new set specified in the macro, *newkeymacro*—where *newkeymacro* is the name of the macro you have written that contains a new set of shortcut keys.

Table 17.13. A Macro To Change Shortcut Keys

Action	Argument	Argument entry
SendKeys	Keystrokes Wait	%C{Down}%I{Down 3} *newkeymacro~* No
DoMenuItem	Menu Bar Menu Name Command	Form View Options

Remember that the *newkeymacro* name shown in the table should be replaced with the name of the macro you have created that specifies new shortcut keys.

When you create this macro, you will see the keystrokes typed in the Options dialog box. If you want the macro to run faster and not display the dialog box, insert an Echo action with a No Argument at the beginning of the list of actions.

Be careful about frequently changing numerous shortcut keys. It can make your programs difficult to learn. One way to help users learn shortcut keys is to type the shortcut key combination into the command name if there is a custom menu. Another way is to display an abbreviated list of shortcut keys at the bottom of the form.

Running Macros at Start-up

Polished systems use a start-up macro to prepare the database before the user sees the first screen. Some of the things you may want to happen automatically during start-up are changing display settings, arranging forms, setting defaults, and importing data from files or servers. After you write a macro that performs these tasks, you can make it run at start-up by saving it with the name AutoExec. The next time you open your database, the macro with the name AutoExec runs immediately.

To prevent an AutoExec macro from running at start-up, hold down the Shift key when you choose OK or press Enter in the Open Database dialog box.

Troubleshooting Macros

Like other forms of programming, building macros is a continuous process of testing and refining. Building a macro usually begins with creating a simple macro, checking to ensure that it works, and then adding more actions to it. You repeat this process until the macro is complete. The process continues from simple to complex functionality. At each stage, the macro operation is checked so that problems can be resolved while they are small. This section describes some of the troubleshooting aids available in Access and gives you tips about how to resolve problems.

Handling Failed Macros

When a macro reaches an error that causes it to halt operation, Access displays an Action Failed dialog box (refer to fig. 17.16). This dialog box shows you the name of the macro that failed, the action on which it failed, and the arguments for that action. Note the macro name and action that caused the problem. Note also which form or report is displayed and what action was occurring on-screen; you may find a clue to why the action failed. Choose the Halt button.

Switch to the Macro window of the macro that failed. Examine the action that failed. Some things to check are whether the action matched the displayed view and object at the time of failure, whether the logic was correct for the procedure the macro was attempting, and whether the data in the arguments is correct.

Single-Stepping through Macro Operation

When a macro fails, its cause may not be readily apparent. Then, it often helps to operate the macro one step at a time. This process enables you to see clearly, for example, what is happening on-screen, which view is present, and what characters are sent with SendKeys. To run a macro using the single-step method, follow this procedure:

1. Open the Macro window.

2. Choose the **Macro Single Step** command or click the Single Step button (a footprint) on the Macro toolbar.

3. Arrange the screen and database system as it would appear when the macro runs.

4. Run the macro.

In single-step mode, the macro displays a Macro Single Step dialog box before each action. Once a Single-Step mode is turned on, it stays on until you turn it off. Figure 17.26 shows a Macro Single Step dialog box. This dialog box is similar to the Action Failed dialog box, but the Step and Continue buttons are available.

```
                  Macro Single Step
Macro Name:
Add Products                          Step
Action Name:
OpenForm                              Halt
Arguments:                            Continue
Add Products, Form. . . Add, Normal
```

FIG. 17.26

The Macro Single Step dialog box.

Choosing the Step button runs the action displayed in the dialog box and then stops at the next action and displays that action in the dialog box. If one of the arguments involves an expression, the Macro Single Step dialog box displays the result of that expression.

When the macro reaches a point at which you want it to continue without stepping through each action, choose the Continue button. Then, the macro will run at normal speed.

Troubleshooting Common Macro Issues

The troubleshooting tips in this section may help you troubleshoot your macros more quickly.

Run with the Incorrect Object Active

When a macro runs and then halts with the warning that a database object or control isn't available, the macro probably hasn't activated the correct database object.

This commonly happens when the macro needs to run with a specific form active. The macro may be looking for a control that doesn't exist on the active object, for example. To prevent this situation, get in the habit of inserting an Open*object* action to open or activate the proper form, query, table, or report before the macro runs. Misspelled control names also may cause this problem.

Display All Actions During Single-Step Operation

Remove or remark out Echo actions so that you can see screen changes while running with single step.

Echo with the Echo On argument of No hides screen changes. This action prevents you from seeing what is happening during single-step operation. Change the No argument to Yes to see what the macro is doing. After you have found and resolved the problem, change the Yes argument back to No. Another technique for tricking an Echo action into not running is to type **FALSE** in the Condition column next to the Echo you want to not run.

Alert Yourself to Critical Points in Operation

Insert message boxes at critical points in a macro to tell yourself what the macro is doing at that point.

A message box, using MsgBox, can display which portion of the macro is ready to run or what should happen on-screen. This capability enables you to run the macro at normal operating speed and receive notices about which operations are taking place.

Insert Brakes To Check Intermediary Results

Insert a StopMacro action so that you can run a macro at normal speed and stop at a specific point.

If a long macro takes a while to run, you may not want to single-step through its actions to the point where you suspect a problem. Rather, insert a StopMacro action after the action you suspect is causing the problem. You then can run the macro at normal speed. When it stops, you can check results to see whether the macro worked correctly to that point. Move the StopMacro action forward or backward in the macro to pinpoint the area causing a problem. You also can use a condition in the Conditional column to stop the macro for a specific condition. A condition can check the value of a control, for example, and stop the macro if the value is incorrect.

Use Segments of Reusable Macros

Learn to write reusable macros or to write large macros as collections of smaller macros. Run the reusable or small segments with the RunMacro action.

Troubleshooting a small macro is much easier than troubleshooting a large one. If you build small subroutine macros that work correctly, you can join them into a larger macro by running them in the order you want with the RunMacro action. Use the comment lines at the beginning of subroutine macros to document which larger macros or events call the subroutine. This practice helps you if you have to change the subroutine. The comments help you determine how changes to the macro may affect other parts of the database.

Monitor How the Macro Is Related to Other Macros and Objects

Take care in changing macros that may be used in numerous locations.

After changing a macro that seems to work correctly, other parts of your database may not work correctly. The macro you changed may have been used by other parts of the database. Changing the macro to meet the requirements for one part of the program may have changed it so that it doesn't work correctly in another part of the program.

Watch That SendKeys Sends Characters to the Correct Location

If you see menus pull down by themselves or data is entered as though it is being typed by a ghost, you have an errant SendKeys action.

SendKeys sends keystrokes to Access just as though you were typing the keys. If you have the Wait argument set incorrectly or if there is no dialog box that opens to receive the sent keys, the keystrokes may be sent directly to the menu bar or into a form, just as though you had typed them.

Be Careful About the Full Macro Name

If only one macro from a macro group runs, check the macro name.

If you specify only the name of a Macro window, only the first macro in the macro group runs. To run a specific macro in a group, you must specify the macro group name, and then a period and the name of the specific macro in the group. The syntax is

```
macrogroupname.macroname
```

When you copy a macro to a new database or Macro window, the action arguments don't change. In its new database or new environment, arguments such as form, query, or control names may be different. Check the arguments. Even though the actions may be in the correct order, the arguments may be wrong.

Chapter Summary

Whether you are a beginning or advanced Access user, you will find that macros are helpful. For practice and a guided tour in creating a few simple macros, refer to Chapter 16, "Automating Applications with Macros: A Quick Start." It guides you through creating and editing a few simple but useful macros.

After you have created the macros described in Chapter 16, you probably will want to use this chapter as a reference for creating your own macros. Don't forget to look through all the examples in Chapter 18, "Creating Macros for Forms, Reports, and Custom Menus." Examining useful examples and duplicating them in your own databases is one of the best ways you can learn more about the power of macros.

Once you understand how macros operate, you will want to learn about Access Basic. Access Basic is a robust programming language that enables you to control all aspects of Access. To learn about Access Basic, refer to Part VI, Chapters 22 through 25.

Creating Macros for Forms, Reports, and Custom Menus

Whether you use macros as simple productivity aids or to create a complete system that includes menus, buttons, and event-driven actions, the ability to use macros makes a valuable addition to your skills. In Chapter 17 you saw the fundamentals involved in creating different kinds of macros. In this chapter you see examples of frequently used macros. Reading and experimenting with the macros in this chapter help you better understand how macros work and how to create new macros by synthesizing and recombining what you learn in these examples.

Make a copy of the Northwind Traders database in a separate directory where you can experiment safely without altering the original database. Use the File Manager to create a \DBPRACTC or \DBEXPER directory. Copy the NWIND.MDB file from the \ACCESS directory into this new directory.

In this chapter, many of the macros are designed to augment the Personnel Actions Entry form used in other chapters of the book (most recently in Chapter 14). If you have built the Personnel Actions Entry form, you can add many of these macros to make the form easier to use. The Personnel Actions Entry form, with buttons that run some of the macros, is shown in figure 18.1.

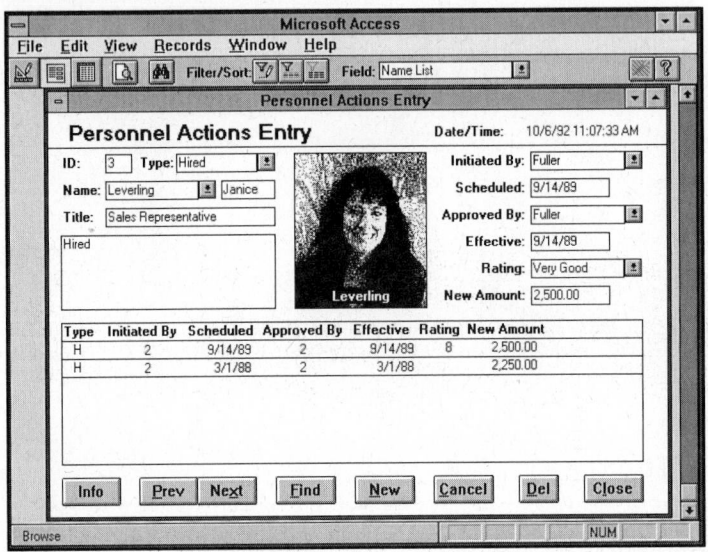

FIG. 18.1

The Personnel Actions Entry form.

Controlling Forms with Macros

Forms lend themselves to the use of macros. Database operators spend a high percentage of their time working in forms—entering and editing data or choosing options from pop-up forms that look like dialog boxes.

Opening and Sizing a Form

One of the more frequently needed and easiest to create macros is a macro that opens and sizes a form. You created just such a macro in Chapter 16, "Automating Applications with Macros: A Quick Start." Figure 18.2 shows a macro that opens a form. The OpenForm action is selected so that you can see the related arguments in the Action Arguments part of the window macro. The OpenForm arguments specify the name of the form to open, whether the form can be edited or read only, and in which view the form appears. The Where Condition specifies the record on which the form opens. The Zoom window is shown in the lower part of the screen so that you can see the full Where Condition argument.

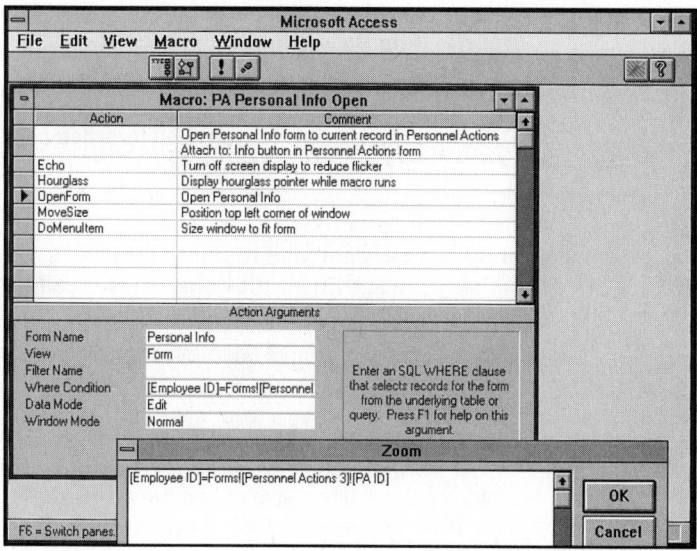

FIG. 18.2

Macros that open a form.

You enter the OpenForm action in the cell of the Macro window by selecting OpenForm from the Action list or by dragging the form's name from the Database window into the action cell of the Macro window. Dragging the form's name enters the appropriate arguments. Chapters 16 and 17 describe how to do these two procedures.

Opening a form with a macro gives you greater control than when you open a form manually. With the addition of the actions described in the following tables, the macros can open a form and reduce the screen flicker, change the pointer to an hourglass, size the form, and position the focus on a specific control. Examples that show how to use most of these actions are shown in Chapter 16's quick start and are not duplicated here.

The following list shows the Echo and Hourglass actions you can use to reduce screen flicker and to let the operator know to pause during operation.

Action	Function
Echo	Reduces screen flicker during opening. Set Echo On argument to No before OpenForm to freeze the screen. After form is opened and sized, and the focus is positioned on a control, set the Echo On argument to Yes to display the completed form. Echo turns on automatically at the end of a macro.
Hourglass	Set the Hourglass On argument to Yes to indicate that the user needs to wait. Helpful when running long macros or opening large files.

Use MoveSize, OnMenuItem, and Maximize to control the size of the form when it opens. Put the Echo action with Echo On to Yes after the form has resized. The following list describes these actions.

Action	Function
MoveSize	Positions and sizes a form using inches measured from the top left corner of the form display area. Use Form Design view with **View Ruler** turned on to see the relative size of inch measurements on-screen.
DoMenuItem	Uses the equivalent of the **Window Size to Fit Form** command to exactly fit the window around the form. Set the following arguments: Menu Bar to Form, the Menu Name to Window, and Command to Size to Fit Form.

You have a number of ways to open a form and display the results of a query or filter that limits the records shown in the form. You can use the Filter Name and Where Condition arguments of the OpenForm action to specify the filter or statement that limits records. You also can use the ApplyFilter and ShowAllRecords actions to filter the records in the current form. Following sections of this chapter describe some of these methods.

Selecting a Control in a Form

One action that macros frequently need is the capability of moving to a specific control, page, or record. You often may use the GoToControl action after performing another action to move the focus to a specific control on the form—the control where the user expects to enter data.

The following simple macro opens a form and then uses the GoToControl action to move the focus to the Last Name control. Use only the control name in the Control argument. The control must be on the active form when the GoToControl action runs. You also can use GoToControl to move to a control in a form datasheet, table datasheet, or query dynaset.

Action	Argument	Argument Entry	Explanation
OpenForm	Form Name	Personal Info	Opens the Personal Info form
	View (other arguments)	Form	
GoToControl	Control	Last Name	Moves to the control on which the FindRecord action searches

If you are working in a report, the GoToPage enables you to move to the first control on a specific page. The GoToRecord action enables you to move to the first, last, next, previous, or new record. You also can move to a specific record number. The record number is the number indicated in the horizontal scroll bar when you scroll through a table or form.

Selecting a Record in a Form

The macros described in this section use the GoToRecord action to change the current record in a form. You will probably want to attach these record selecting macros to buttons, menu commands, or short-cut keys to make it easy to move between records. You can use the GoToRecord action to select a record in a table, form, or query dynaset.

The following macro shows how to make the first record current in a form, table, or query dynaset. You generally want a macro like this to run whenever you open the form. The directions for attaching a macro so that the macro runs whenever the form opens are given at the end of this section.

Action	Argument	Argument Entry	Explanation
GoToRecord	Object Type	Form	Moves to first record (Attach to On Open in form so that the form displays the first record when the form opens)
	Object Name	Personnel Actions	
	Record	First	
	Offset	(none)	

The following macro moves the current record to the next record by using the GotoRecord action, with the Record argument specified as Next. This macro is attached to the Next button on the Personnel Actions Entry form (see fig. 18.1). The Personnel Action form is assumed to be active because the macro runs only when you choose the Next button. The GoToRecord action is straightforward and moves the current record to the next record in the form.

One potential problem with this macro, however, is that the operator may click the Next button while in a new (blank) record. This situation can occur if you click the New button to move to the last record and then click the Next button. Attempting to move to the next record beyond the last causes a macro error. The following macro shows one method of checking for the blank record and avoiding a macro error.

Condition	Action	Argument	Argument Entry	Explanation
IsNull(Forms! [Personnel Actions]![PA ID])	MsgBox	Message	This is the last record	Checks whether already on a blank record
		Beep	Yes	
		Type	None	
		Title	Add Record	
...	StopMacro			Stops macro if IsNull is true
	GoToRecord	Object Type	Form	Goes to next record
		Object Name	Personnel Actions	
		Record	Next	
		Offset	(none)	

This macro needs the IsNull condition and the MsgBox and StopMacro actions to resolve the problem that occurs when you attempt to select the next record while you are on the last record. The Personnel Actions Entry form is built so that the PA ID control always contains a value. The only record in which PA ID is blank is the last (blank) record. The condition, IsNull(Forms![Personnel Actions]![PA ID]), is true only when the current record is the last record. When the condition is true, the MsgBox action displays a warning to the operator and the StopMacro action stops the macro. Notice that the ellipsis (...) in the cell under the IsNull condition indicates that the StopMacro action should also run when the condition is true.

To attach a macro to a form's On Open property so that the macro runs whenever the form opens, perform the following steps:

1. Create and save the macro.

2. Open the form in the Design view. Display the Properties window.

3. Scroll to the On Open property.

4. Select from the On Open property list the name of the macro that you want to run when the form opens. If the macro is one of a macro group, type a period after the name selected and then type the name of the macro.

5. Save the form.

Adding a New Record

Adding a new record uses a macro very similar to the macro that moves to the next record. In the following example, the macro runs when you click the New button on the Personnel Actions Entry form. Clicking the button opens the Add Personnel Actions form shown in figure 18.3 so that you can add a new personnel action for the employee you were viewing in the Personnel Actions Entry form. Notice that the ID on both forms is the same.

This macro is attached to the On Push property of the New button on the Personnel Actions Entry form. The macro begins with an IsNull function that checks to see whether the current record contains a PA ID (Employee ID) or is blank. If the record is blank, the macro stops. If the current record in the Personnel Actions Entry form does contain an employee, then the rest of the macro runs.

The Echo action turns off the screen display so that the opening process runs faster and with less flicker. The display is turned back on when the macro finishes running. The OpenForm action opens the Add Personnel Actions form. The DoMenuItem action then moves the form to a new record (see fig. 18.3).

Condition	Action	Argument	Argument Entry	Explanation
IsNull([PAID])	MsgBox	Message	Move to a record that has an employee to add an action	Checks whether on a blank record
		Beep	Yes	
		Type	None	
		Title	Add Record	
...	StopMacro			Stops macro if IsNull is true
	Echo	Echo On	No	Stops screen flicker by not refreshing display until done
	OpenForm	Form Name	Add Personnel Actions	
		View	Form	
		Filter Name	(none)	
		Where Condition	(none)	
		Data Mode	Edit	
		Window Mode	Normal	
	DoMenuItem	Menu Bar	Form	
		Menu Name	Records	
		Command	Go To	
		Subcommand	New	
	SetValue	Item	Forms![Add Personnel Actions]![PA ID]	
		Expression	[PA ID]	
	GoToControl	Control Name	[PA Type]	

The SetValue action transfers the PA ID value from the Personnel Actions Entry form, which contained the button, to the Add Personnel Actions form that just opened. Notice that because the macro was run from the Personnel Actions Entry form, the PA ID on the Personnel

Actions Entry form can be referred to as [PA ID] instead of Forms![Personnel Actions]![PA ID]. The GoToControl action moves the focus to the PA Type where you will make your first entry.

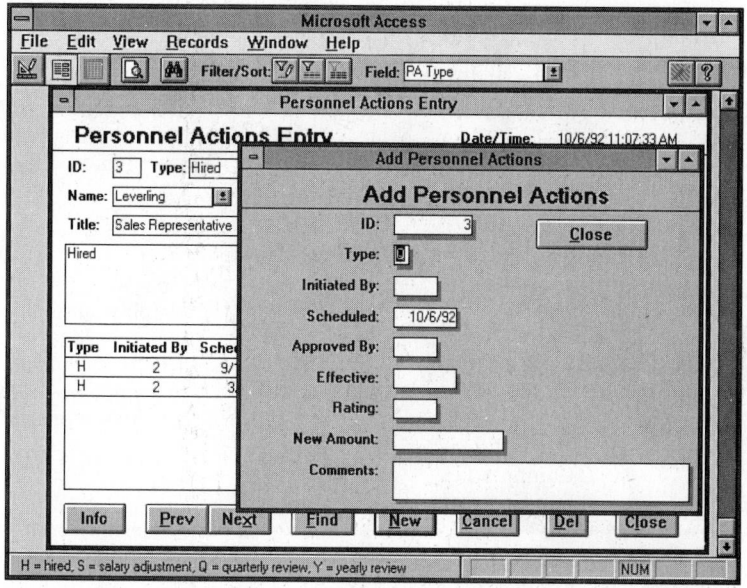

FIG. 18.3

The Add Personnel Actions form.

When entering a new record from a data entry form, you get an error when the values in key field(s) are the same as values in existing records.

Deleting a Record

You need to be able to delete records that are no longer valid. The Del button on the Personnel Actions Entry form is attached to a Delete macro that deletes the current record. The form shows more than one personnel action record in the subform. The macro deletes the record containing the information shown at the top right corner of the Personnel Actions Entry form.

In the macro shown in the following table, the first DoMenuItem action selects the current record and then the second DoMenuItem deletes the selected record. An Access warning box displays when you attempt to delete a record and asks whether you are sure you want to delete the record. Choose OK in this warning box. The final DoMenuItem runs the **R**ecords **R**efresh command to update the display. Use Records Refresh to update the display for deleted or edited records. (Records Refresh does not work to update the display for added record.)

Action	Argument	Argument Entry	Explanation
DoMenuItem	Menu Bar	Form	Selects the current record using menu commands
	Menu Name	Edit	
	Command	Select Record	
	Sub-Command	(none)	
DoMenuItem	Menu Bar	Form	Deletes the current record using menu commands
	Menu Name	Edit	
	Command	Delete	
	Sub-Command	(none)	
DoMenuItem	Menu Bar	Form	Refreshes the display after deleting record (Records Refresh does not work when adding records.)
	Menu Name	Records	
	Command	Refresh	
	Sub-Command	(none)	

Canceling Changes

You can undo the most recent edits to the Personnel Actions Entry form by clicking the Cancel button. The On Push event for the button runs the Cancel macro shown in the following table. This macro runs a DoMenuItem action that replicates the Edit Undo Current Record command. A final action, RepaintObject, ensures that the entire Personnel Actions Entry form is updated on-screen.

Action	Argument	Argument Entry	Explanation
DoMenuItem	Menu Bar	Form	Undoes the last change to the current record
	Menu Name	Edit	
	Command	Undo Current Record	
	Sub-Command	(none)	

Action	Argument	Argument Entry	Explanation
RepaintObject	Object Type	Form	Refreshes the screen without redoing any queries
	Object Name	Personnel Actions	

If you need the equivalent of pressing the Esc key, use the SendKeys action to send the keystrokes {Esc}.

Setting Values in a Form

You can set values in a form or a property, just as though you typed them, through the SetValue action. A few of the ways you can use SetValue include the following:

- Set control values in a form

- Set default values in custom dialog boxes

- Change the appearance of a control or form by changing its properties

The SetValue action transfers the result of an expression into the control you specify. The expression can be text, a number, or a reference to another control. If the control used in the expression is on the form from which the macro ran, then you do not have to use the full syntax for the control.

The following table shows the SetValue action as it was used in the "Adding a New Record" section of this chapter. Clicking a button on the Personnel Actions Entry form runs the macro. In that example, SetValue transferred the PA ID out of the current Personnel Actions Entry form into another form called Add Personal Actions. That transfer ensured that the new record entered in the Add Personal Actions form used the same employee you were viewing when you clicked the New button.

Action	Argument	Argument Entry
SetValue	Item	Forms![Add Personnel Actions]![PA ID]
	Expression	[PA ID]

Item is the control being set to a new value. Because Item is not on the form containing the button that started the macro, you must specify the argument using the full syntax as follows:

```
Forms![Add Personnel Actions]![PA ID]
```

Expression is the value being placed into the control. Because the control containing the Expression, PA ID, is on the form containing the button from which the macro ran, you can specify PA ID as **[PA ID]**, instead of using the full control syntax.

You also can use the SetValue action to change the property of a control. When the Add Personnel Actions form opens, for example, you may want the normally visible PA ID control to turn invisible. To change a control's property, enter as the Item argument the name of the control, followed by a period and then followed by the property value. In the following macro, the PA ID control has been turned invisible. You must use the full syntax for PA ID because the macro starts from a form other than the one containing the PA ID that you want to turn invisible.

Action	Argument	Argument Entry	Explanation
SetValue	Item	Forms![Add Personnel Actions]![PA ID].Visible	Specifies the control property
	Expression	No	Specifies the value for the control property

In some cases you may need to change a property for an entire form. For example, you may want a form that is normally visible to become invisible. This change can be useful so that the form does not show on-screen, but its controls are still available for their contents.

To reference a control for an entire form from which the macro runs, you can use the property name in the Item argument—for example, **Visible**.

Synchronizing Forms to the Same Record

In earlier chapters of this book, you learned how a main form can display information and also a subform of related information. The lower portion of figure 18.4 shows a subform displaying the personnel actions for the person listed in the main Personnel Actions Entry form. Although this subform gives you an information-packed view into your database, it does restrict some of the flexibility of seeing related data. You are limited to seeing what fits in the subform.

FIG. 18.4

The Personnel
Actions Entry
form with a
subform dis-
played.

Another, more flexible method of viewing, adding, and editing information related to the current form is to open a second form. This second
form displays only data related to the first form. The following macro
demonstrates how to keep the record in the second form synchronized
with the record displayed in the first form. You need to use macros
that use the values from the first form to specify which record should
be opened in the second form.

Action	Argument	Argument Entry	Explanation
OpenForm	Form Name	Personal Info	Opens the Per-sonal Info form
	View	Form	
	Filter	(none)	
	Where Condition	[Employee ID]=Forms![Personnel Actions]![PA ID]	
	Data Mode	Read Only	
	Window Mode	Normal	

This example runs from the Personnel Actions Entry form shown in figure 18.4. Clicking the Info button in the lower left corner runs the Personal Info Open macro shown in the preceding table. This macro opens the Personal Info form shown in figure 18.5.

The macro is attached to the On Push event for the Info button. The OpenForm action opens the Personal Info form, which was created by the FormWizard from the Employee table to show personal information such as address and phone number. The form opens with the Data Mode argument in Read Only. This mode limits the user to reading, but not changing personal information.

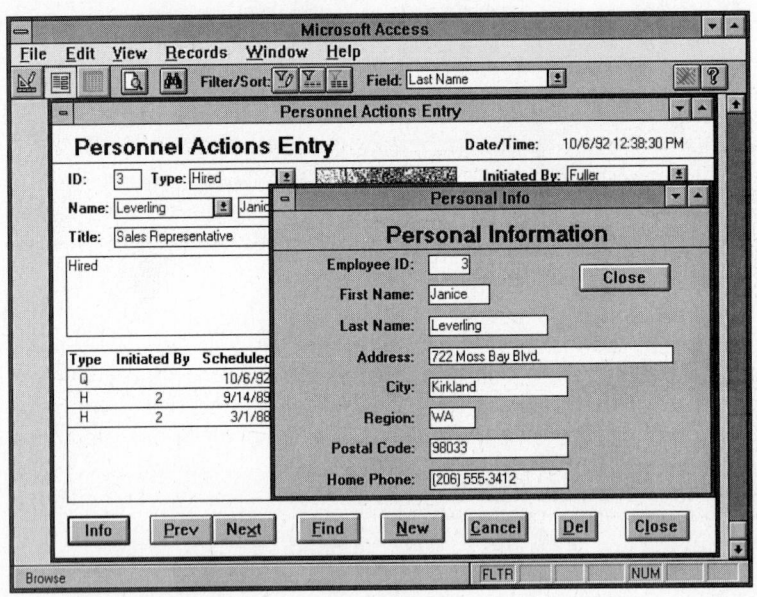

FIG. 18.5

The Personal Info form synchronized with another form to show related data.

The Where Condition argument makes the Personal Info form open and display information about the person shown in the current Personnel Actions Entry form. The Where Condition argument uses the following condition:

```
[Employee ID]=Forms![Personnel Actions]![PA ID]
```

This condition sets the Employee ID control in the Personal Info form to the same value as the PA ID in the Personnel Actions Entry form. Employee ID and PA ID are the same for each individual.

 If you need a control such as Employee ID on a form, but do not want the control to display, set its Visible property to No. Although the control becomes invisible, you can still use the value it contains.

As you can see in figure 18.5, a Close button on the Personal Info form enables you to close the form. The Close macro runs from this button and uses the Close action to close the Personal Info form.

Printing a Form

You have to print copies of forms whenever you need filing copies, invoices for mailing, or data for distribution. Printing forms is easy. Use the OpenForm or Print actions to print your forms.

The OpenForm action in the following table enables you to open or activate a form and immediately display that form in the Print Preview screen.

Action	Argument	Argument Entry	Explanation
OpenForm	Form Name	Personnel Actions	Displays print preview onto the current form
	View	Print Preview	

From the Print Preview screen, you can manually change the page setup options or options in the Print dialog box. Clicking the Print or Setup button shown in figure 18.6 displays the Print or Setup dialog boxes. When you do not specify a Filter or Where Condition, all the current records print.

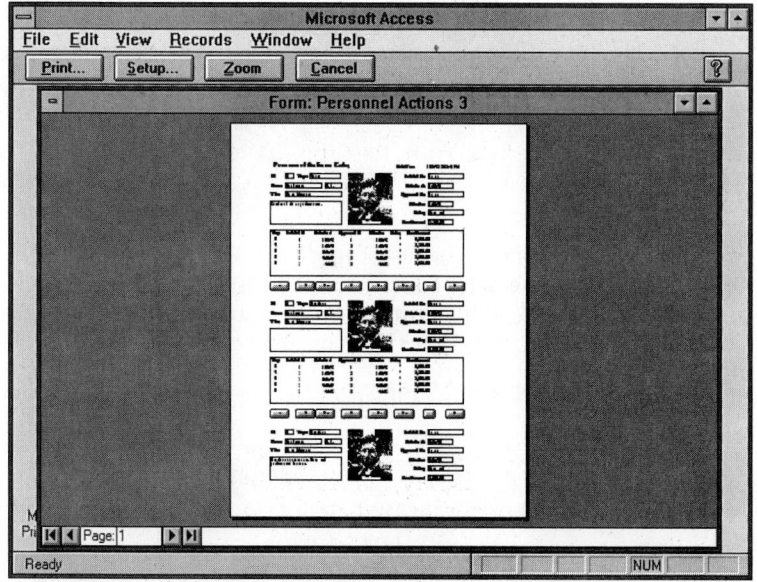

FIG. 18.6

The Print Preview screen.

Another method of printing is to use the SelectObject action to select the object you want to print, and then use the Print action to do the actual printing. The Print action gives you the capability of specifying printing details, such as the page numbers and number of copies. The following table shows the SelectObject-Print macro.

Action	Argument	Argument Entry	Explanation
SelectObject	Object Type	Form	Specifies the opened or closed object to be printed
	Object Name	Personnel Actions	
	In Database Window	No	
Print	Print Range	(All records, the current selection, or the specified)	Specifies printing parameters and then prints pages without showing the Print Preview or dialog box
	Page From	(starting page)	
	Page To	(ending page)	
	Print Quality	(High, Medium, Low)	
	Copies	(default 1)	
	Collate Copies	(Yes/No)	

Chapter Summary

This chapter has shown you some simple, yet timesaving macros. You learned how some of the easy-to-use actions—such as OpenForm, Echo, and DoMenuItem—can reduce your repetitive work load. With the DoMenuItem action, you can replicate frequently used menu commands.

From here you should learn more about Access Basic, which is covered in Chapters 22 through 24. Access Basic gives you unlimited control over features in Access, using the Basic programming language to control Access operations. You can build totally customized applications. With the Access professional developers kit, you can then compile your database and Access Basic program so that any computer with Windows can run your database program.

Using Advanced Access Techniques

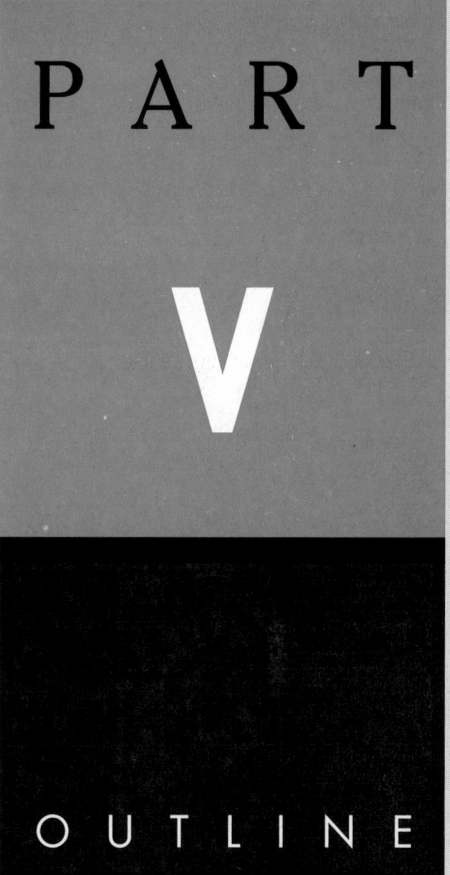

PART

V

OUTLINE

Exploring Relational Database
  Design and Implementation

Working with Structured Query
  Language

Using Access in a Network
  Environment

Exploring Relational Database Design and Implementation

You were introduced to a few of the elements of relational database design when you created the Personnel Actions table and joined it with the Employees table of the Northwind Database. Chapter 15 gave you a bit more insight into how to create a relational database from information contained in a worksheet. When you are presented with the challenge of designing a database from ground zero, however, especially a complex or potentially complex database, you need to understand the theory of relational database design and its terminology.

This chapter takes a step back and starts with the definition of data objects and how you identify them. Because Access is object-oriented, the concepts of database design presented in this chapter have an object-oriented bent. The reason for this approach is twofold:

■ Access's relational tables incorporate many of the features of object-oriented databases. Properties, such as validation rules and indexes, and methods that include preventing duplicate primary key entries, are combined in the table object.

■ Access Basic treats the database itself and each of Access's database elements—tables, queries, forms and reports—as programming objects.

After you have identified the data objects that are to be included in the tables of your database, you need to design the tables to contain the data objects. You use a process called data *normalization* to create tables that conform to the relational database model. Normalization is the process of eliminating duplicate information in tables by extracting the duplicate data to new tables that contain records with unique data values. You then join the tables you create by fields with common data values to create a relational database structure. Normalizing data is the subject of the second section of this chapter.

The role of indexes in maintaining unique values in primary-key fields and organizing data tables was described briefly in preceding chapters. This chapter provides an explanation of how indexes are constructed and maintained with Access. Properly designed indexes improve the performance of your applications without consuming excessive amounts of disk space or slowing appending of near records to a crawl.

This chapter also deals with the rules that establish and maintain referential integrity, one of the most important considerations in designing a database. Referential integrity enforces uniqueness in primary keys and prevents the occurrence of orphaned records, such as records of invoices whose customer data records have been deleted.

This chapter covers the following subjects:

■ *Database systems.* Designing a database system, including the objectives, terminology, and structure of databases.

■ *Normalizing data.* Creating tables that comply with the basic rules of relational database design.

■ *Data dictionaries.* Documenting your Access database application, including using the ANALYZER.MDB library supplied with Access, to do much of the documentation for you.

■ *Access indexes.* Understanding Access indexes and using them to speed queries.

■ *Enforcing database integrity.* Preventing deletion of records in tables on which records contained in other tables depend and precluding addition of new dependent records without corresponding records in a master or primary table.

Understanding Database Systems

Prior to this chapter, you have used the Northwind Traders demonstration database, created a few simple databases, and perhaps imported your own data in another database format into an Access table. No formal theories were presented to aid or hinder your understanding of the underlying design of the database examples. Now that you have gained some experience using Access, the more theoretical concepts of database design should be easier to understand.

This section takes a systems approach to database design, starting with a generalized set of objectives, outlining the steps necessary to accomplish the objectives, and then explaining the theory and practice behind each step.

The Objectives of Database Design

The strategy of database design is to accomplish the following objectives:

■ Fulfilling your own needs or the needs of the organization for information in a timely, consistent, and economic manner.

■ Eliminating or minimizing the duplication of database content across the organization. In a large organization, eliminating duplication may require a distributed database. Distributed databases use multiple servers to store individual databases. The individual databases are attached to one another, to use Access terminology, through a local-area network (LAN) or wide-area network (WAN) so that they appear as a single database to the user.

■ Providing rapid access to the specific elements of information in the database required by each user category. Operating speed is a function of the database manager (DBM) itself, the design of the applications you create, the capabilities of the server and client computers, and network characteristics.

■ Accommodating expansion of databases to adapt to the needs of a growing organization, such as the addition of new products and processes, complying with governmental reporting requirements, and incorporating new transaction and decision-support applications.

- Maintaining the integrity of the database so that it contains only validated, auditable information. Some client-server databases, such as Microsoft SQL Server, provide built-in *triggers* to maintain database integrity. Triggers are a set of rules that are included in the database. If you violate a rule, the trigger sends an error message instead of performing the transaction. The Enforce Referential Integrity checkbox in Access's Relationships dialog box creates the equivalent of a trigger.

- Preventing access to the database by unauthorized persons. Access provides a security system that requires users to enter a password to use a particular database.

- Permitting access only to those elements of the database information that individual users or categories of users need in the course of their work. You can permit or deny users the right to view the data in specific tables of the database.

- Allowing only authorized persons to add or edit information in the database. Permissions in Access are multilevel; you can selectively allow users to edit tables or alter their structure, as well as edit or create their own applications.

- Easing the creation of data entry, editing, display, and reporting applications that efficiently serve the needs of the users of the database. The design of the DBM's front-end features determines the ease with which new applications are created or existing ones can be modified. You have seen in the preceding chapters that Access is especially adept as a front-end application generator.

The first two objectives are independent of the database manager you choose. The DBM influences or determines the other objectives. Operating speed, data validation, data security, and application creation are limited by the capabilities built into the DBM and the computer environment under which it operates. If your database is shared on a network, you need to consider the security features of the network operating system and the client-server database system (if one is used) in the security strategy.

The Process of Database Design

The process of designing a relational database system consists of 10 basic steps:

1. Identifying the objects (data sources) that the database system is to represent

2. Discovering associations between the objects (when you have more than one object)

3. Determining the significant properties and behaviors of the objects

4. Ascertaining how the properties of the objects relate to one another

5. Creating a preliminary data dictionary to define the tables that comprise the database

6. Designating the relationships between database tables based on the associations between the data objects contained in the tables, and incorporating this information in the data dictionary

7. Establishing the types of updates and transactions that create and modify the data in the tables, including any necessary data integrity requirements

8. Determining how to use indexes to speed up query operations without excessively slowing down the addition of data to tables or consuming excessive amounts of disk space

9. Deciding who can access and who can modify data in each table (data security), and altering the structure of the tables if necessary to assure data security

10. Documenting the design of the database as a whole, completing data dictionaries for the database as a whole and each table it contains, and writing procedures for database maintenance, including file backup and restoration

Each step in the design process depends on preceding steps. The sections in this chapter follow steps 1 through 8 in sequence. Database security is the subject of Chapter 21, "Using Access in a Network Environment."

The Object-Oriented Approach to Database Design

Databases contain information about objects that exist in the real world. These objects may be people, books in a library, paper invoices or sales orders, maps, money in bank accounts, or printed circuit boards. Such objects are *tangible*. Whatever the object, it must have a physical representation, even if only an image on a computer display that never finds its way to the printer, as in the mythical "paperless office." References to objects in this book, not preceded by a word describing the type of object such as "table object" or "OLE object," indicate real-world, tangible objects.

Tangible objects possess *properties* and *behavior*. This combination might appear to be applicable only to databases of persons, not books or bank balances; however, all database objects other than those in archival databases have both properties and behavior. Archival databases are used to store information that never changes—new data is simply added to such databases. An example of an archival database is one containing the text of previously published newspapers.

Considering Static and Dynamic Properties of Objects

An object's properties determine the content of a database or table that contains object representations of the same type. Books are assigned subject codes, derived from the Dewey decimal system. Modern books have an identifying ISBN code, and most now have a Library of Congress catalog number. These numbers are properties of a book, as are the title, author, number of pages, and binding type. Such properties are *static*: they are the same whether the book is in the stacks of a library or checked out by a cardholder. Customer information for a bank account, such as account number, name, and address, also is considered static, even though customers occasionally change addresses. Book check-out status and bank account balances are *dynamic* properties: they change from day to day or hour to hour.

Describing Data Entities and Their Attributes

A single object, including all of its static properties, is called a *data entity*. Each individual data entity must be unique so that you can distinguish it from others. A bank's checking account customer is a data entity, for example, but money in the customer's account is not, because the money cannot be uniquely identified. Because a customer may have more than one account, a social security number or federal employer identification number doesn't suffice as a unique identifier; an account number must be assigned to ensure the uniqueness of each customer data entity.

Deposit slips and checks are objects that are represented in the database as other data entities that *relate* to the customer entity. Check numbers aren't unique enough to distinguish them as entities; many different customers might have checks numbered 1001. Combining the customer number and the check number doesn't suffice as a unique identifier because different banking firms might use the same customer number to identify different people. The bank identification number, customer number, and the check number together uniquely identify a debit entity. Each check contains this information printed in magnetic ink. The amount property of each debit (check) or credit (deposit) entity is used to adjust the balance in the customer's account by simple subtraction and addition, a process called a *transaction*.

You wouldn't want to wait while an Automated Transaction Machine (ATM) calculated your balance by processing every transaction since you opened your account. Therefore, a *derived* static property, the last statement balance, can be included in the customer data entity and updated once per month. Only last-statement-to-date transactions need be processed to determine the current balance—a dynamic, *calculated* property. In figure 19.1, lines connect static properties of bank account objects to the data entities derived from them. Properties of objects included in data entities, such as account number and customer name, are called *attributes*.

FIG. 19.1

Relationships between objects, entities, events, and methods in a banking database.

Accounting for the Behavior of Objects with Methods

The behaviors of related database objects determine the characteristics of transactions in which their data entities participate. Books in a library may be acquired, checked out, returned, and lost. Bank account behavior is very easy to describe: a customer opens the account; deposit transactions and interest accumulations (credits) increase the account balance; and writing checks, withdrawing cash from an ATM, and incurring bank charges (debits) reduce the balance. Crediting or debiting a bank account is an example of a transaction. Transactions occur in response to *events*, such as making a deposit or withdrawal at an ATM. Access implements transactions by using *methods* in response to events initiated by the user, such as opening a form or clicking a command button.

In conventional relational databases, you can represent tangible objects and object properties as data entities, but not object's real-world behavior. The OLE Object field data type, described in Chapter 13, is an exception to this rule. The behavior of an OLE data object is determined by the methods available in the OLE server that was used to create it or add it to the OLE Object field. With conventional data entities, you emulate the behavior of tangible objects by using the methods that you incorporate into your applications.

Programs that you write using the DBM's native language implement database methods. In the case of Access, macros consisting of one or more *actions* implement the methods. A macro action is a prepackaged set of methods designed for a specific purpose. If one of the standard actions doesn't fit your requirements, you can use the RunCode( ) macro action to use Access Basic functions that include the methods you need. As you learned in Part IV of this book, the events that you can use to initiate macro action methods are listed in the Properties dialog boxes of forms, reports, and control objects.

Access is unique among today's PC database managers because it saves the macros and programs that you create for a database within the database file itself, not in separate *.SC, *.PRG, or *.EXE files as do other PC DBMs. Access tables have self-contained properties and methods; other PC DBMs require separate programs to validate data, display status text, and create indexes. Therefore, Access database files and the tables they contain conform to the object "paradigm"—a synonym for the word "model" that has become an object-oriented cliché.

Combining Different Entities in a Single Table

You can include representations of different types of objects in a single table as long as you can represent their properties and behavior in the same manner and yet distinguish the different object types. For example, checks and debits are shown as a single data-object type in figure 19.1, although one originates from a paper check and the other from an Electronic Funds Transfer debit. A Debit Type field can indicate the different sources. You can combine cash deposits and transfers from a savings account into a single data-entity type in a Credits table. You might want to combine both Debits and Credits in a single table, which you can do by using different codes for Debit Types and Credit Types. To identify a debit or credit uniquely, you need to include fields for bank ID, customer number, debit/credit type, and a transaction number. Although a check number can serve as the transaction number, the system must assign transaction numbers to other types of transactions, such those conducted at ATMs. Access can use a counter field to add a unique transaction number to each data entity, including checks. The check number becomes another attribute.

Database Terminology

The terms used to describe formally a database and the elements that comprise it derive from four different sources. The data-description language, of which *entity* and *attribute* are members, derives from the terminology of statistics. Another set of terms, which describe the same set of elements, is based on computer terminology and relates to how the elements are stored within disk files. Query By Example introduced new terms to the language of databases—row, column, and cell are examples—and Structured Query Language adopted these terms. Table 19.1 compares words that are used for data description, in QBE and SQL, and for describing data-storage methodologies employed by Access, xBase, and Paradox. The Access Basic language takes an object-oriented approach to programming, so table 19.1 also includes terms applicable to object-oriented programming (OOP).

Table 19.1. A Comparison of Data-Description and Data-Storage Terminologies

Data Description	QBE and SQL	Object-Oriented	Access Storage	xBase/Paradox
Heterogeneous Universe	Database	Base Object Class	File	Directory
Universe (homogeneous)	Table	Object Class	Table (Sub-File)	Data File
Entity (object, instance)	Row	Data Object	Record	Record
Attribute	Cell	Object Property	Field	Field
Attribute Data Type	Datatype	Data Type	Field Data Type	Field Type
Attribute Domain	Validation Rule	Enumeration	Validation Rule	Valid Statement
Attribute Value	Cell Value	Property Value	Field Value	Field Value
Identifier	Primary Key	Property Value	Key, Index	Index File

The real-world object is the basic source of information that is represented in a database as an entity. In explaining the terms included in table 19.1, therefore, the following definition list begins with an entity, breaks it down into its component parts, and then establishes its position in the hierarchy of databases and tables.

- *Entity:* A unique representation of a single real-world object, created using the values of its attributes in computer-readable form. To ensure uniqueness, one or more of an entity's attributes must have values unlike the corresponding values of any other entity of the same class. An entity corresponds to a *row* in QBE and SQL, or a *record* in data-storage terminology. Entities are also called *data entities*, *data objects*, *data instances*, or *instances.*

- *Attribute:* A significant property of a real-world object. Every attribute carries a value that assists in identifying the entity of which it is a part and distinguishing the entity from other members of the same entity class. Attributes are contained in *fields* (data-storage terminology) or *columns* (QBE and SQL). An attribute also is called a *cell* or *data cell*, a term that describes the intersection of a row and a column or a field and a record.

- *Attribute data type:* Basic attribute data types consist of all numeric (integer, floating point, and so forth) and string (text or alphanumeric) data types without embedded spaces or separating punctuation. The string data type can contain letters, numbers, and special characters (such as those used in languages other than English). An attribute with a basic attribute data type is indivisible and is called an *atomic* type. Text data types with spaces or other separating punctuation characters are called *composite attribute data types*. You can divide most composite types into basic data types by *parsing*. Parsing means to separate a composite attribute into basic attributes. For example, you can parse "Smith, Dr. John D., Jr." to Last Name (Smith), Title (Dr), First Name (John), Middle Initial (D), and Suffix (Jr) basic attribute types. Special field types, such as Memo, Binary Large Object (BLOB), and OLE, are composite attribute data types that cannot be parsed to basic data types by conventional methods. You cannot, therefore, create Access indexes that include Memo and OLE attribute data types; only attributes with basic attribute data types can be indexed.

- *Attribute domain:* The allowable range of values for an attribute of a given attribute data type. The attribute data type determines the domain unless the domain is limited by a process external to the data in the table. As an example of attribute domain limitation, the domain of an employee age attribute that has an integer data type might be limited by a data validation method to any integer greater than 13 and less than 90. In object-oriented terms, the domain consists of an *enumeration* of acceptable values. A days-of-the-week enumeration (the domain of days) consists of a list of its members: Monday, Tuesday, Wednesday, and so forth. Access validation rules, stored in tables, maintain *domain integrity*, limiting data entry to limits set by the data validation expression.

■ *Attribute value:* The smallest indivisible unit of data in an entity. Attribute values are limited to those within the attribute domain. *Cell value* and *data value* are synonyms for attribute value.

■ *Identifier:* An attribute or combination of attributes required to uniquely identify a specific entity (and no others). Identifiers are called *primary-key field(s)* in Access and are used to create the primary index of the entities. When an entity's attribute values are duplicated in other entities' corresponding attributes, you need to combine various attributes to ensure a unique identifier for the entity. When more than one attribute is used as an identifier, the key fields are called a *composite* or *compound* primary key.

■ *Homogeneous universe:* The collection (set) of all data entities of a single data entity type. The data entities must have an identical set of attributes, attribute data types, and attribute domains. This set corresponds to an Access or Paradox *table*, or a *data file* in xBase. The set also is called an *entity class* or *entity type*, and its members are sometimes called *entity instances*, or just *instances*.

■ *Heterogeneous universe:* The collection (set) of related entity classes comprising related homogeneous universes—the *database*. A database is stored as a single file in Access and most client-server databases. Paradox and xBase store databases as collections of related files, usually in a single directory. A dBASE catalog is a file that includes records to identify the individual files that comprise the entire database. Access databases include a special table that catalogs the objects that the databases contain. You can reveal the content of the catalog by using the techniques described in the "Access's Integrated Data Dictionary System" section, near the end of this chapter.

Much of the formal terminology used to describe data objects in relational databases is quite technical and rather abstract. You need to understand the meaning of these terms, however, when you create the data models that form the basis of the design of your database.

Types of Tables and Keys in Relational Databases

Specific to relational databases are certain types of tables and keys that enable relationships between tables. Understanding these tables and keys is essential to comprehending relational databases and the rules of data normalization, which are discussed in the "Normalizing Data to the Relational Model" section. The following list defines the various relational keys and tables:

■ *Primary key:* A primary key consists of a set of values that uniquely specifies a row of a base table, which in Access is the *primary table.* For any primary-key value, one and only one row in the table matches this value. You can base the primary key on a single field if each data cell's value is unique at all times.

■ *Candidate keys:* Any column or group of columns that meets the requirements for a primary key is a candidate to become the primary key for the table. Name and social security number are candidate keys to identify a person in the U.S.; however, social security number is the more appropriate choice because two people can have the same name but not the same valid social security number.

■ *Composite keys:* If you need data from more than one column of the table to meet the uniqueness requirement of a primary key, the key is said to be a composite or a *concatenated key.*

■ *Foreign keys:* A foreign key is a column whose values correspond to those contained in a primary key, or the far left portion of a composite primary key, in another related table. A foreign key can consist of one column or a group of columns (a *composite foreign key*). If the length of a foreign key is less than the corresponding primary key, the key is called a *partial* or *truncated foreign key.*

■ *Base table:* In a relational database, a base table is the table that incorporates one or more columns of an object's properties and contains the primary key that uniquely identifies that object as a data entity. A base table must have a primary key. Base tables are often called *primary tables* because of the requirement for a primary key.

■ *Relation table:* A table that is used to provide linkages between other tables and isn't a base table (because it doesn't incorporate properties of an object or because it doesn't have a primary key field) is called a *relation table.* Key fields in relation tables each must be foreign keys, related to a primary key field in a base table.

Technically, a true relation table is comprised wholly of foreign keys and contains no independent data entities. The Order Details table of the Northwind Traders database is an example of a relation table that contains data values that aren't foreign keys (the Unit Price and Quantity fields, for example). Its Order ID field is related to the field of the same name in the Orders table. Likewise, the Product ID field is related to the Product ID field of the Products table. Although Order Details has a composite key, it isn't a true primary key; its purpose is to prevent duplication of a product entry in a specific order.

Examples of the preceding keys and tables occur in the discussions of normal forms in the "Normalizing Data to the Relational Model" section, later in this chapter. But first, the following sections examine the process of data modeling.

Data Modeling

The first step in designing a database is to determine which objects to represent within the database and which of the objects' properties to include. This process is called *data modeling*. The purpose of a data model is to create a logical representation of the data structure that is used to create a database. Data modeling can encompass an entire organization, a division or department, or a single type of object. Models that deal with objects, rather than the tables that you later create from the objects, are called *conceptual data models*.

Figure 19.2 illustrates two different approaches (conceptual data models) to database design: the bottom-up approach to create an application database and the top-down method used to develop subject databases. These two approaches, discussed in the following sections, result in databases with quite different structures.

Application Databases

You can base data models on specific needs for data presented in a particular manner. For such a needs-based model, you can use the *bottom-up* approach and start with a view of the data on a display, a printed report, or both, as shown in the left-hand example of figure 19.2. This approach results in an *application database*. If you are creating a simple database for your own use or dealing with a single type of data object, the *bottom-up* approach may suffice because the presentation requirements and the properties of the objects involved are usually well defined. The problem with the bottom-up approach is that it leads to multiple individual databases that may duplicate each other's information. Several persons or groups within an organization might have a requirement for an application database that includes, for example, a customers table. When a new customer is added or data for an existing customer is changed in one application database, you need to update each of the other application databases. The updating process is time-consuming and subject to error.

FIG. 19.2

A comparison of bottom-up and top-down database designs.

Conceptual data models, such as those shown in figure 19.2, are independent of the database manager you use and the type of database files it accesses. Therefore, the same data model accommodates databases in Access's native format, as well as the others with which Access is compatible. Data models aren't connected with any programming language or tools used to create applications. The applications box in figure 19.2 isn't a component of conventional data models, but is added to show where application design fits into the overall picture.

Subject Databases

A better approach is to base the design of the database on groups of objects that are related by subject matter. For a manufacturing firm, tables are usually grouped into databases devoted to a single department or function. The following lists some database examples:

■ *Sales* database consisting of customer, sales order, sales quota, product discount, and invoice tables

■ *Production* database including product, price, parts, vendor, and cost accounting tables

■ *Personnel* database with employee, payroll, and benefits tables (large firms may include tables relating to health care providers and employment applicants)

■ *Accounting* database incorporating general ledger and various journal tables

Databases that consist of tables relating to a single class of subjects or functions are called *subject databases*. Even if you are creating the first database application for a small organization, starting with an overall plan for the organization's total information requirements in subject databases pays long-term dividends. If you decide or are assigned to create an invoicing application, for instance, you can establish sales, production, and personnel databases from the beginning, rather than have to split up a single invoice database at a later time and rewrite all your applications to access tables within multiple databases.

Subject databases require *top-down* design, depicted in the right-hand diagram of figure 19.2. In this case, the properties of the data objects, not the applications used with them, determine the design. Designing subject databases involves creating a diagram of the relevant objects and the associations between them, and then creating models for each database involved. You distribute the model diagrams to users and then interview them to determine their information needs based on the content of the model databases.

Diagrammatic Data Models

Large, complex data models resemble the work-flow and paper-flow diagrams commonly used in analyzing organizations' administrative procedures. If you have such diagrams or descriptions, they make the data-modeling process much easier. Generating an organization-wide data model may involve a substantial amount of research to determine the needs of the organization as a whole and of individuals using specialized applications. In many cases, users and potential users aren't able to define what information they need or how they want to see it presented.

Many methods exist of creating diagrams to represent data models. One of the more useful methods is the Entity-Relationship (E-R) diagram, developed by Peter Chen in 1976 and expanded on by David R. McClanahan in a series of articles entitled "Database Foundations: Conceptual Designs" in *DBMS* magazine (see fig. 19.3). You can use E-R diagrams to represent relationships between objects and depict their behavior.

FIG. 19.3

An Entity-
Relationship
diagram of two
data entities from
figure 19.1.

Data entities are enclosed within rectangles, data attributes within ovals, and relations between entities within diamonds. Relations between database objects, at the conceptual stage, can be defined by their behavior; therefore, E-R diagrams include at least one verb whose object, unless otherwise indicated, is to the right of the diamond relation symbol. You add symbols to the diagram as the model's detail increases. One of the advantages of the E-R diagram is that you can use it to represent the conceptual design of very large systems with multiple databases in a relatively small amount of space.

Database Schema

A graphic description of the layout of tables in the form of bars that contain their field names and show a simplified version of relationships between them can be employed to aid users to grasp the concept of the database. A diagram that shows the logical representation of data is called a *schema*. A schema, such as the one shown in figure 19.4 for an ocean shipping line, is independent of the DBM used to implement the database.

In figure 19.4, the primary keys are shaded, and the relations between the table keys are indicated by lines that connect the keys. Foreign keys are unshaded, except when they correspond to a component of a composite primary key. The descriptions shown between the bars are optional; they are useful in describing the relationships to users. You can expand a schema of this type to include the source documents involved, the reports to be generated, and the applications that pertain to all or a portion of the tables.

External Determinants of Database Design

Finding the data objects that provide the information to meet all of an organization's requirements may require extensive detective work. Many objects may not be available within the organization itself. For instance, if you are developing a database application that involves geographic positioning (called *geocoding*), you may need map tables such as the U.S. Census Bureau's TIGER/Line files or tables derived from them by others. Images to be incorporated as OLE objects may not be available in file formats that are compatible with your OLE server applications and require file-type conversion. If the accounting department is using packaged accounting software, you need to incorporate representations of the structure of its database into your model. In this case, you also need to plan how to exchange information with the accounting data, but you need not include the access methodology in your conceptual data model.

FIG. 19.4

The schema for the operations database of a shipping line.

Normalizing Data to the Relational Model

Up to this point, most of the subject matter in this chapter has been applicable to any type of database—hierarchical, relational, or even the new class of object database systems. However, because Access is a relational database management system (often abbreviated RDBMS), the balance of the chapter is devoted to relational databases. Because Access fully implements the relational model in its native database structure, and you can attach tables from other relational DBMs to Access databases, the discussion that follows is general in nature and applies to any database system with which Access is compatible.

The theory of relational database design is founded in a branch of mathematics called *set theory*, with a great deal of combinatorial analysis and some statistical methodology added. The set of rules and symbols by which relational databases are defined is called *relational algebra*. This chapter doesn't delve into the symbolic representation of relational algebra, nor does it require you to comprehend advanced mathematics. The chapter does, however, introduce you to many of the terms used in relational algebra for the sake of consistency with advanced texts that you may want to consult on the subject of database design.

Normalization Rules

Normalization is a formalized procedure by which data attributes are grouped into tables and tables are grouped into databases. The purposes of normalization include the following:

■ Eliminate duplicated information in tables

■ Accommodate future changes in the structure of tables

■ Minimize the impact of change on user applications that access the data

Normalization is done in steps, the first three and most common steps Dr. E.F. Codd described in his 1972 paper, "Further Normalization of the Data Base Relational Model." These steps are depicted in figure 19.5. The following sections describe each of the five steps that comprise the normalizing process.

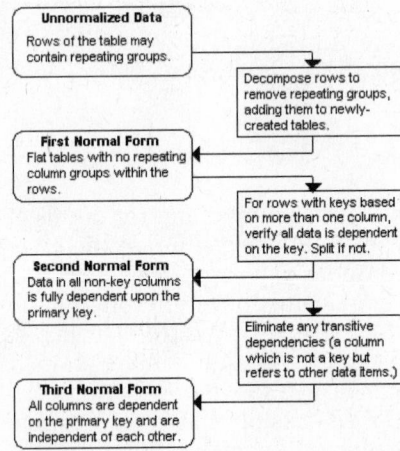

FIG. 19.5

A graphic representation of relational database normalization to the third normal form.

First Normal Form

First normal form requires that tables be flat and contain no repeating groups. A flat table has only two dimensions—length (number of records or rows) and width (number of fields or columns)—and cannot contain data cells with more than one value. For a single cell to contain more than one data value, the representation of the cell's contents requires a third dimension, depth, to display the multiple data values. Flat tables and the flat-file databases referred to in prior chapters are similar in that both have two dimensions. Flat-file databases, however, consist of only one table and have no restrictions on the content of the data cells within the table.

An example of unnormalized data for a shipping line appears in figure 19.6. This presentation often is seen in the schedules published by transportation firms where the stops are displayed across the page. This example is representative of a schedule created by importing the worksheet file that was used to create the printed version of the schedule. In the various examples of tables that follow, missing borders are the equivalent of ellipsis; that is, a missing right border indicates that additional columns (fields) exist beyond the far right column, and a missing bottom border means that more rows (records) follow. (Those readers who are mariners will recognize the example as a mythical schedule for the vessels of the former Pacific Far East Lines.)

Vessel	Name	Voyage	Embarks	From	Arrives	Port	Departs	Arrives	Port	Departs
528	Japan Bear	9203W	5/31/92	SFO	6/6/92	HNL	6/8/92	7/15/92	OSA	7/18/92
603	Korea Bear	9203W	6/05/92	OAK	6/19/92	OSA	6/21/92	6/25/92	INC	6/28/92
531	China Bear	9204W	6/20/92	LAX	7/10/92	PAP	7/11/92	8/28/92	SYD	9/2/92
528	Japan Bear	9204W	8/20/92	SFO	8/27/92	HNL	8/29/92	9/30/92	OSA	10/2/92

FIG. 19.6

A partial schedule of voyages for a ocean shipping line.

Because the vessels stop at a number of ports, the Arrives, Port, and Departs columns are duplicated for each stop in the voyage. This type of data structure is allowed in COBOL, where the repeating group (Arrives, Port, and Departs) OCCURS any number of TIMES, but not in relational databases. The data in the preceding schedule isn't in first normal form because it contains repeating groups. The table must be *decomposed* (divided) into two tables, therefore, with the repeating groups (shown in shaded type in figure 19.6) removed from the Schedule table and placed in two new tables, Ports and Vessel Voyages, as shown in figure 19.7.

FIG. 19.7

The Vessel
Voyages and
Ports tables
created from the
Schedule table.

Vessel	Name	Voyage	Embarks	From
528	Japan Bear	9203W	5/31/92	SFO
603	Korea Bear	9203W	6/5/92	OAK
531	China Bear	9204W	6/20/92	LAX
528	Japan Bear	9204W	8/20/92	SFO

Arrives	Port	Departs
6/6/92	HNL	6/8/92
6/19/92	OSA	6/21/92
7/10/92	PAP	7/11/92
8/27/92	HNL	8/29/92
7/15/92	OSA	7/18/92
6/25/92	INC	6/28/92
8/28/92	SYD	9/2/92
9/30/92	OSA	10/2/92

Now you need to provide for a link between the Ports and Vessel Voyages tables to retain the relationship between the data. Because this shipping line numbers voyages for each vessel with the year and voyage for the year, as well as the general direction of travel (9204W is the fourth voyage of 1992, westbound), both Vessel and Voyage need to be used to relate the two tables. Neither Vessel nor Voyage is sufficient in itself, because a vessel has multiple voyages during the year, and the voyage numbers used here recur for other vessels. Because you must create a new Ports table to meet the requirements of the first normal form, you have the chance to order the columns in the order of their significance. Columns used to establish relations are usually listed first, in the sequence in which they appear in the composite primary key, when more than one column is included in the key (see fig. 19.8).

Vessel	Voyage	Port	Arrives	Departs
528	9203W	HNL	6/6/92	6/8/92
603	9203W	OSA	6/19/92	6/21/92
531	9204W	PAP	7/10/92	7/11/92
528	9204W	HNL	8/27/92	8/29/92
528	9203W	OSA	7/15/92	7/18/92
603	9203W	INC	6/25/92	6/28/92
531	9204W	SYD	8/28/92	9/2/92
528	9204W	OSA	9/30/92	10/2/92

FIG. 19.8

Linking fields
added to the
Ports relation
table.

Next, you establish the key field(s) for the Ports table that uniquely identify a record in the table. Clearly, Vessel and Voyage must be included, because these columns constitute the relation to the Vessel Voyages table. You need to add the Port field to create a unique key (Vessel + Voyage can have duplicate values). Vessel + Voyage + Port creates a unique composite primary key because the combination takes into account stopping at a port twice—when returning eastbound, the voyage carries an "E" suffix. You need a primary key for the Ports table because other tables may be dependent on this table.

A spreadsheet application, such as Microsoft Excel, can speed up the process of normalizing existing data, especially when the data contains repeating groups. Import the data into a worksheet; then cut and paste the data in the repeating groups into a new worksheet. When the data for both of the tables is normalized, save the worksheets and then import the files to Access tables. This process is usually faster than creating make-table queries to generate normalized tables.

Second Normal Form

Second normal form requires that data in all nonkey columns be fully dependent on the primary key and on each element (column) of the primary key when it is a composite primary key. *Fully dependent* means that the data value in each nonkey column of a record is determined uniquely by the value of the primary key. If a composite primary key is required to establish the uniqueness of a record, the same rule applies to each value of the fields that comprise the composite key of the record. Your table must be in first normal form before examining it for conformity to the second normal form. The second normal form removes much of the data redundancy that is likely to occur in a first-normal table.

Returning to the Vessel Voyages table, you can see that it requires a composite key, Vessel + Voyage, to create a unique key because the vessel number (and vessel name) recurs. However, when you create such a key, you observe that the Vessel and Name aren't dependent on the entire primary key, because neither is determined by Voyage. You also find that the vessel name occurs for each of a vessel's voyages; for example, the Japan Bear appears twice. This lack of depending violates the rules of the second normal form and requires Vessel Voyages to be split into two tables, Vessels and Voyages. One row is required in the Vessels table for each ship and one row in the Voyages table for each voyage made by each ship (eastbound and westbound directions are considered separate voyages for database purposes). As was the case for Ports, a unique key is required to relate voyages to the vessel, so the vessel number column is added to the Voyages table, as shown in figure 19.9.

FIG. 19.9

The Vessels and Voyages tables created from the Vessel Voyages table.

Vessel	Vessel Name
528	Japan Bear
603	Korea Bear
531	China Bear

Vessel	Voyage	Embarks	From
528	9203W	5/31/92	SFO
603	9203W	6/5/92	OAK
531	9204W	6/20/92	LAX
528	9204W	8/20/92	SFO

Third Normal Form

The third normal form requires that all nonkey columns of a table be dependent on the table's primary key and independent of one another. Tables must conform to the first and second normal forms to qualify for third-normal-form status.

Your Vessels and Voyages tables are now in third normal form, because there are no repeating groups of columns and the data in nonkey columns is dependent on the primary key field. The nonkey columns of Ports, Arrives and Departs, are dependent on the composite key (Vessel + Voyage + Port) and independent of one another. Ports, therefore, meets the requirements of first, second, and third normal forms. The departure date is independent of the arrival date, because the difference between the two is based on the vessel's lading into and out of the port, the availability of berths and container cranes, and the weather.

To demonstrate normalization to the third normal form, suppose that you want to identify the officers of the vessel, including the master, chief engineer, and first mate, in the database. Your first impulse might be to add their employee numbers, the primary key of an Employee table, to the Vessels table (see fig. 19.10).

FIG. 19.10

A table with a transitive dependency between vessels and crew members.

Vessel	Vessel Name	Master	Chief	1st Mate
528	Japan Bear	01023	01155	01367
603	Korea Bear	00955	01203	00823
531	China Bear	00721	00912	01251

This table violates the third normal rule because none of the officers assigned to a vessel is dependent on the vessel itself. This type of dependency is called *transitive*. The master's, chief's, and first mate's maritime licenses allow them to act in their respective capacities on any vessel for which the license is valid. Any officer may be assigned to other vessels as the need arises, or remain on board for only a portion of the voyage.

One method of removing the transitive dependency might be to add the employee number columns to the Vessel Voyages table. This method doesn't provide a satisfactory solution, however, because the vessel may arrive at a port with one group of crew members and depart with another group. In addition, you need to specify the crew members who remain with the vessel while it is in port. A relation table, such as that shown for the Japan Bear in figure 19.11, solves the problem. Duplicate values in the Port and To (destination port) fields designate records for crew members responsible for the vessel while in port. The Crew table of figure 19.11 qualifies as a relation table because all of its fields correspond to primary keys or parts of primary keys in the base tables— Vessels, Voyages, Ports, and Employees.

Vessel	Voyage	Port	To	Master	Chief	1st Mate
528	9203W	SFO	HNL	01023	01156	01367
528	9203W	HNL	HNL	01023	01156	01367
528	9203W	HNL	OSA	01023	01156	01367
528	9203W	OSA	OSA	01023	01156	01367
528	9203W	OSA	INC	01023	01156	01367

FIG. 19.11

Removing transitive dependency with a relation table.

All of your tables are now flat, contain no duplicate information other than that in the columns used for keys, and conform to the first through third normal form.

Fourth Normal Form

Many database designers disregard the fourth and fifth normal forms; those designers consider the fourth and fifth forms too esoteric or applicable only in specialized cases. Disregarding the fourth normal form often results in poorly designed databases, but not necessarily malfunctioning ones.

The fourth normal form requires that independent data entities not be stored in the same table when many-to-many relationships exist between these entities. The table of figure 19.11 violates the fourth normal form because many-to-many relationships exist between the Vessel and the fields that identify crew members. The fourth normal form is discussed in the "Many-to-Many Relations and the Fourth Normal Form" section later in this chapter because it is the only normalization rule that is dependent on a specific type of relationship.

Fifth Normal Form and Combined Entities

The fifth normal form requires that you be able to reconstruct exactly the original table from those tables into which it was decomposed. Re-creating the Excel spreadsheet from the tables in the example in Chapter 15 demonstrates compliance with the fifth normal form. Fifth normal form requires that the tables comply with the rules for third normal form and, when many-to-many relationships are present, with the rule for the fourth normal form.

The Voyages table appears quite similar to that of Ports. The From column is equivalent to Port, and Embarks is the same as Departure. Therefore, you can move the data in the Voyages table to the Ports table and delete the Voyages table. Figure 19.12 shows the new Ports table. The rows from the Voyages table don't have values in the Arrives column because they represent points of departure.

FIG. 19.12

Records from the Voyages table appended to the Ports table.

Vessel	Voyage	Port	Arrives	Departs
528	9203W	HNL	6/6/92	6/8/92
603	9203W	OSA	6/19/92	6/21/92
531	9204W	PAP	7/10/92	7/11/92
528	9204W	HNL	8/27/92	8/29/92
528	9203W	OSA	7/15/92	7/18/92
603	9203W	INC	6/25/92	6/28/92
531	9204W	SYD	8/28/92	9/2/92
528	9204W	OSA	9/30/92	10/2/92
528	9203W	SFO		5/31/92
603	9203W	OAK		6/5/92
531	9204W	LAX		6/20/92
528	9204W	SFO		8/20/92

However, you cannot explicitly reconstruct the original table from the combined Voyages and Ports tables in all cases because you cannot distinguish an embarkation row from the other rows by a value in the table. A Null value in the Arrives field is a candidate to distinguish an embarkation, but most PC DBMs don't support null values. You eliminate any ambiguity that using a Null value might cause and bring the table into fifth normal form by adding a single-character field, Type, with single-letter codes to define the type of call. In figure 19.13, the codes E and S represent Embarkation and Scheduled call, respectively. Other codes might include M for Maintenance stop and R for Return voyage.

Figure 19.14 demonstrates that you can reconstruct the content of the original Schedule table from the Vessels and Ports tables. Query1 creates the first five columns of the Schedule table by adding the criterion E for the Type field, which isn't shown. You can re-create the remaining columns of the Schedule table from Query2 that uses the S criterion for the Type field.

Vessel	Voyage	Port	Type	Arrives	Departs
528	9203W	HNL	S	6/6/92	6/8/92
603	9203W	OSA	S	6/19/92	6/21/92
531	9204W	PAP	S	7/10/92	7/11/92
528	9204W	HNL	S	8/27/92	8/29/92
528	9203W	OSA	S	7/15/92	7/18/92
603	9203W	INC	S	6/25/92	6/28/92
531	9204W	SYD	S	8/28/92	9/2/92
528	9204W	OSA	S	9/30/92	10/2/92
528	9203W	SFO	E		5/31/92
603	9203W	OAK	E		6/5/92
531	9204W	LAX	E		6/20/92
528	9204W	SFO	E		8/20/92

FIG. 19.13

The Type field added to comply with the fifth normal form.

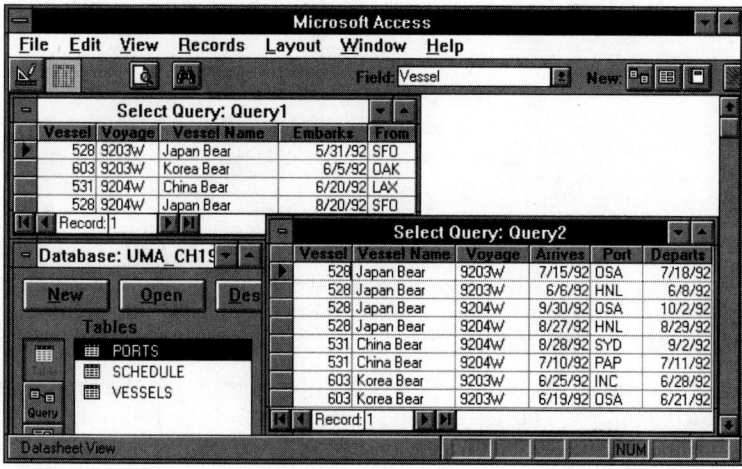

FIG. 19.14

The datasheets of the two queries required to reconstruct the Schedule table.

Types of Relationships

The subject of relationships between entities usually precedes discussions of normalization. Relationships are reserved for the second step in this book, however. You can only create valid relationships between tables that have been structured in accordance with at least the first three normalization rules of relational database design described in the preceding sections. This section describes the four basic types of relationships between tables and employs Entity-Relationship diagrams to depict the relationships graphically.

One-to-One Relations

The simplest relationship between tables is a one-to-one relationship. In such a relationship, the tables have exact one-to-one row correspondence; no row in one table has more than one corresponding row in the other table. You can combine one-to-one-related tables into a single table consisting of all the tables' columns.

One-to-one relations are often used to divide very wide base tables into narrower ones. You might want to divide a wide table to reduce the time needed to view fields containing specific sets of data, such as the stock prices table in the example of Chapter 15. Often you need to control access to the parts of tables that contain sensitive or confidential data. An example is an employee file; everyone might have read-only access to the employees' names, but only members of the personnel department are authorized to view salary and other payroll information (see fig. 19.15).

FIG. 19.15

Two tables with a one-to-one relationship.

Employee	Position	Last	First	MI
00668	Master	Johansson	Lars	F.
00721	Master	Karlsson	Bo	B.
00885	Chief	MacGregor	Paul	C.
00912	Chief	McDemott	John	R.
00955	Master	Olafson	Karl	T.
01023	Master	Kekkonen	Eino	K.
01156	Chief	McDougal	William	U.
01203	Chief	Kashihara	Matsuo	

Employee	Salary
00668	6500.00
00721	6250.00
00885	5100.00
00912	5000.00
00955	6100.00
01023	6050.00
01156	4900.00
01203	4850.00

If you are sharing tables on a network, dividing large tables can improve response time when many users are updating the tables' data. Chapter 21, "Using Access in a Network Environment," explains the reason for the speed improvement.

Figure 19.16 shows the Entity-Relationship diagram for the Employees and Salaries tables. The 1's added to each side of the relation diamond indicate the one-to-one relationship. The participation of entities in relations can be mandatory or optional. Optional relations are symbolized by a circle drawn on the line connecting the optional entity with the relation diamond. In the figure, the Paid-Salaries relation is optional because some employees can be paid on an hourly basis and linked to a Wages table. Tables with mandatory one-to-one relationships are base tables. A table with an optional one-to-one relation to a base table is a related table. Multiple tables with one-to-one relations where the corresponding records in the other tables are optional can reduce the database's disk space requirement.

FIG. 19.16

An E-R diagram for an optional one-to-one relationship.

Another example of a one-to-one relationship is that between an xBase memo field and a corresponding entry in a memo (DBT) file. Access treats free-text as the content of a data cell in the table, so no relationship is involved.

Memo Files

One-to-Many Relations

One-to-many relations link a single row in one table with two or more rows in another through a relation between the primary key of the base table and the corresponding foreign key in the related tables. Although the foreign key in the table containing the many relationships may be an component of a composite primary key, it is a foreign key for the purposes of the relationship. One-to-many relations are the most common type of relation.

The one-to-many relation shown in figure 19.17 links all records in the Ports table to one record in the Vessels table. The one-to-many relation enables you to display all records in the Ports table for scheduled ports of call of the Japan Bear.

Vessel	Vessel Name
528	Japan Bear

Vessel	Voyage	Port	Type	Arrives	Departs
528	9203W	HNL	S	6/6/92	6/8/92
528	9204W	HNL	S	8/27/92	8/29/92
528	9203W	OSA	S	7/15/92	7/18/92
528	9204W	OSA	S	9/30/92	10/2/92
528	9203W	SFO	E		5/31/92
528	9204W	SFO	E		8/20/92

FIG. 19.17

A one-to-many relationship between the Vessels and Ports tables.

The E-R diagram of figure 19.18 expresses this relationship, where the degree of the Vessel entity relations between the two tables are indicated by the "1" and "m" adjacent to their entities.

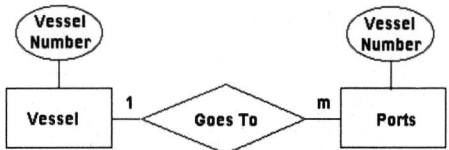

FIG. 19.18

The E-R diagram for the one-to-many relation of figure 19.17.

Many-to-One Relations

Many-to-one relations are the converse of the one-to-many type. The many-to-one relation enables you to display the vessel name for any record in the Ports table. If the roles of the participating entities are simply reversed to create the many-to-one relation, the relationship is said to be *reflexive*; that is, the many-to-one relation is the reflection of its one-to-many counterpart (see fig. 19.19). All many-to-one relations in Access are reflexive; you can specify only a one-to-one or one-to-many relation between the primary table and the related table with the two option buttons in Access's Relationship dialog box.

Vessel	Voyage	Port	Type	Arrives	Departs		Vessel	Vessel Name
528	9203W	HNL	S	6/6/92	6/8/92		528	Japan Bear
528	9204W	HNL	S	8/27/92	8/29/92			
528	9203W	OSA	S	7/15/92	7/18/92			
528	9204W	OSA	S	9/30/92	10/2/92			
528	9203W	SFO	E		5/31/92			
528	9204W	SFO	E		8/20/92			

If you select a record on the many side of the relationship, you can display the record corresponding to its foreign key on the one side. E-R diagrams for reflexive relationships are often drawn like the diagram in figure 19.20. Reflexive relationships are indicated by the appropriate form of the verb placed outside the diamond that defines the relation.

Many-to-Many Relations and the Fourth Normal Form

Many-to-many relationships cannot be expressed as simple relations between two participating entities. You create many-to-many relationships by making a table that has many-to-one relations with two base tables.

The Crews relation table created in the "Third Normal Form" section to assign crew members to legs of the voyage is shown again in figure 19.21. The Crews table creates a many-to-many relationship between the Vessels table, based on the Vessel entity, and the Employees table, based on the employee number entities in the Master, Chief, and 1st Mate fields.

Vessel	Voyage	Port	To	Master	Chief	1st Mate
528	9203W	SFO	HNL	01023	01156	01367
528	9203W	HNL	HNL	01023	01156	01367
528	9203W	HNL	OSA	01023	01156	01367
528	9203W	OSA	OSA	01023	01156	01367
528	9203W	OSA	INC	01023	01156	01367

FIG. 19.21

The first version of the Crews relation table.

The table in figure 19.21 has a many-to-one relation with the Vessels table and a many-to-one relation with the Employees table. This version of the Crews table creates a many-to-many relation between the Vessels and Employees tables. The employees who crew the vessel are independent of one another; any qualified employee can, in theory, be assigned to fill a crew position on any leg of a voyage. The table of figure 19.21 violates the fourth normal form, therefore, because it contains independent entities.

Figure 19.22 shows the restructured Crews relation table needed to assign employees to legs of voyages. The table has one record for each employee for each leg of the voyage.

Employee	Vessel	Voyage	Port	To
01023	528	9203W	SFO	HNL
01156	528	9203W	SFO	HNL
01367	528	9203W	SFO	HNL
01023	528	9203W	HNL	HNL
01156	528	9203W	HNL	HNL
01367	528	9203W	HNL	HNL
01023	528	9203W	HNL	OSA
01156	528	9203W	HNL	OSA
01367	528	9203W	HNL	OSA
01023	528	9203W	OSA	OSA
01156	528	9203W	OSA	OSA
01367	528	9203W	OSA	OSA
01023	528	9203W	OSA	INC
01156	528	9203W	OSA	INC
01367	528	9203W	OSA	INC

FIG. 19.22

The Crews table restructured to fourth normal form.

You can add new entities to this table, provided that the entities are wholly dependent on all the foreign-key fields. An example of a dependent entity is payroll data that might include data attributes such as regular hours worked, overtime hours, and chargeable expenses incurred by each employee on each leg of a voyage. Such entities are called *weak* or *associative* entities because they rely on other base tables for their relevance. The Crews table is no longer considered strictly a relation table when you add associative entities, because it no longer consists wholly of fields that constitute foreign keys.

The E-R diagram for the many-to-many relation table relating employees and the legs of a voyage to which the employees are assigned is shown in figure 19.23. The encircled Date connected to the Assigned Crew relation expresses *cardinality*: one employee can be assigned to only one voyage on a given date. The cardinality of the relation, therefore, is based on the departure and arrival dates for the leg. Automatically enforcing the condition that employees not be in more than one place at one time can be accomplished by creating a no-duplicates index consisting of all the Crews table's fields. Associative entities are shown in E-R diagrams as a relation diamond within an entity rectangle. If you add payroll data to the Crews table, an associative entity is created. Assignment of an employee to a voyage is optional, as indicated by the circled lines; employees may have shore leave, be indisposed, or be assigned to shoreside duties.

FIG. 19.23

An E-R diagram for a many-to-many relationship with an associative entity.

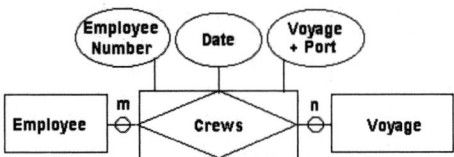

Using graphic schema and Entity-Relationship diagrams when you design an Access database helps ensure that the database meets your initial objectives. Schema also are useful in explaining the structure of your database to its users. E-R diagrams can uncover design errors, such as the failure to normalize tables at least to fourth normal form. Few experiences are more frustrating than having to restructure a large table when you realize its design wasn't fully normalized. Forethought, planning, and diagramming are the watchwords of success in database design.

Working with Data Dictionaries

After you have determined the individual data entities that comprise the tables of your database and established the relations between them, the next step is to prepare a preliminary written description of the database, called a *data dictionary*. Data dictionaries are indispensable to database systems; an undocumented database system is almost impossible to administer and maintain properly. Errors and omissions in database design often are uncovered when you prepare the preliminary data dictionary.

When you have completed and tested your database design, you prepare the final detailed version of the data dictionary. As you add new forms and reports to applications, or modify the existing ones, you update the data dictionary to keep it current. Even if you are making a database for your personal use, a simplified version of a data dictionary pays many dividends on your time investment.

Conventional Data Dictionaries

Data dictionaries contain a text description of the database as a whole, each table it contains, the fields that comprise the table, primary and foreign keys, and values that may be assigned to fields when they contain coded or enumerated information. The purpose and description of each application that uses the database is included. Data dictionaries shouldn't be dependent on the particular relational DBM used to create and manipulate the database. Because data dictionaries are hierarchical in nature, they lend themselves to the use of traditional outline formats that are implemented in Windows word processing applications. The following illustrates the structure of a conventional data dictionary using legal-style outline headings:

1. DATABASE - Proper name and filename

   A text description of the purpose and general content of the database and who may use it. A list of applications that operate on the database is useful, along with references to any other databases that use the information that the database contains. If a graphic schema of the database has been prepared, it appears in this section.

   1.1. DATA AREA - Name of the group of which tables are a member

   When tables are classified by group, such as the Payroll group within the Human Resources database, a description of the group

   1.1.1. TABLE - Individual tables that comprise the data area

      1.1.1.2. PERMISSIONS - User domains with access to the table

      1.1.1.2. RECORD - General definition of the data entities

         1.1.1.2.1. PRIMARY KEY - Field(s) in the primary key

            1.1.1.1.2.2 INDEX - Primary key index specification

         1.1.1.2.2. FOREIGN KEY(S) - Other key fields

            1.1.1.2.2.1 INDEX - Indexes on foreign keys

         1.1.1.2.3. FIELDS - Nonkey fields

            1.1.1.2.3.1 ENUMERATIONS - Valid codes for fields.

Text follows each heading and describes the purpose of the database element to which the heading refers. Subsequent headings include descriptions of the applications that use the database tables, with subheadings for queries, forms, and reports. Captured images of displays and copies of reports add to the usefulness of the data dictionary. Printouts of programming code usually are contained in appendixes. Complete data dictionaries are essential for database maintenance. An alternative format consists of content descriptions of each table in tabular form.

Access's Integrated Data Dictionary System

Access includes a library, called Database Analyzer, that was added to your \ACCESS directory as ANALYZER.MDA when you installed Access. *Libraries* are databases that include their own tables, queries, forms, macros, and modules, and that can even include reports. After you attach a library to Access, its content is available to any Access application you create. By convention, libraries have the extension MDA to distinguish them from conventional database files. Access Wizards are contained in the WIZARD.MDA library that is automatically attached when you launch Access.

Database Analyzer generates tables that you can use to create a data dictionary for your database. You can elect to store the tables created by Analyzer in the database you are analyzing or create a new database to hold them. Analyzer doesn't include forms to display the content of the tables it generates, but you can easily design a form to suit your specific purposes.

Attaching Database Analyzer to Access

You need to attach Database Analyzer to Access in the MSACCESS.INI file located in your \WINDOWS directory. To attach Database Analyzer, perform the following steps:

1. Close Access and open Windows Notepad.

2. Choose Open from Notepad's File menu, select your \WINDOWS directory if necessary, and type **MSACCESS.INI** in the File text box.

3. Locate the [Libraries] section of MSACCESS.INI and type **analyzer.mda=** after the Wizard.mda=ro entry (see fig. 19.24).

The =ro entry for the Wizard table means to attach the Wizard library as read-only, which prevents you from altering the design of the library's contents.

```
                  Notepad - MSACCESS.INI
 File   Edit   Search   Help
ParadoxNetPath=E:\ACCESS\
CollatingSequence=Ascii

[dBase ISAM]
CollatingSequence=Ascii
Century=Off
Date=American
Mark=47
Deleted=Off

[ISAM]
PageTimeout=300

[Libraries]
wizard.mda=ro
analyzer.mda=
```

FIG. 19.24

The entry in MSACCESS.INI to attach the Database Analyzer library.

4. Choose Save from Notepad's File menu, and then close Notepad.

5. Launch Access.

   The new MSACCESS.INI entry attaches Analyzer to Access.

Access

Adding the Macro To Run Analyzer

You need to add a macro that runs Database Analyzer to each database for which you want a data dictionary. To add the Database Analyzer macro, perform the following steps:

1. Open the Access database that you want to analyze.

2. Click the Macro button in the Database window, and then click the New button.

Macro

New

3. Open the Action list box in the first row and select RunCode as the action.

4. Type **StartAnalyzer( )** as the Function Name argument for RunCode action (see fig. 19.25).

5. Close the Macro window and save the macro as **Run Analyzer**.

   You can copy this macro to other databases by selecting it in the Database window, copying it to the Clipboard, and pasting it into the other database.

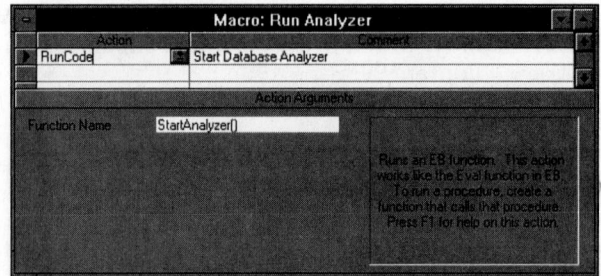

FIG. 19.25

Adding the
Run Analyzer
macro to your
database.

StartAnalyzer() is the name of a function, written in Access Basic, that
is included within a module in Analyzer. This function displays the form
that constitutes Database Analyzer's window.

Analyzing a Database

Database Analyzer's window, shown in figure 19.26, includes the familiar six buttons that select a class of Access database objects. You can
include all or selected objects of each class in the analysis by clicking
the double right-arrow and right-arrow buttons, respectively. By checking the box at the bottom of the window, you can include system objects in the analysis.

FIG. 19.26

Database
Analyzer's main
window.

To analyze all or a part of a database to which you have added the Run
Analyzer macro, perform the following steps:

1. If you want to create a database specifically for data dictionaries,
   instead of cluttering your database with extra tables, create a new
   database named ANALYZE.MDB.

2. Open the database you want to analyze: for this example,
   NWIND.MDB.

3. Click the Macro button in the Database window, and then double-
   click the Run Analyzer entry.

4. In the Database Analyzer, click the Table button.

   The tables in your database (and the tables in SYSTEM.MDA if you marked the Include System Objects checkbox) appear in the Items Available list box.

5. Double-click the Personnel Actions table to move its entry from the Items Available list to the Items Selected list; selecting the Personnel Actions table and clicking the right-arrow button produces the same result.

   You can use the double right-arrow button to move all the available items to the Items Selected list. The left-arrow button moves a selected item to the Items Available list. The double left-arrow button moves all items belonging to the specified object class from the Items Selected list to the Items Available list.

6. Repeat steps 4 and 5 for Queries, selecting the Personnel Actions query and subquery from the list.

7. Repeat steps 4 and 5 for Forms, adding the Personnel Actions form and Tabular Subform to the Items Selected list. In the case of forms, the Properties button is enabled. Click the Properties button to display the list of properties that are included by default and the list of additional properties you can add to the analysis (see fig. 19.27).

FIG. 19.27

Database Analyzer's properties selection window.

   Adding *reports* to your analysis also enables the Properties button.

8. Add the macros that you created for Personnel Actions to the Items Selected list.

9. Click the Analyze button. The Select an Output Database dialog box appears.

10. Select ANALYZE.MDB as the database to use if you created it; otherwise, select NWIND.MDB. Then choose OK.

    Database Analyzer indicates when it is finished with the analysis by displaying a Process Completed message box.

11. Choose OK, and then click the Close button in Analyzer's window to exit Analyzer.

Analyzer adds one or two tables for each class of database object in the current database or in ANALYZER.MDB if you created it in step 1. Each time you run Analyzer, it re-creates the tables and replaces any prior information they contained. To save the data in a set of Analyzer tables, close the open tables and rename them so that they aren't overwritten when you run Analyzer in another database, if you are using ANALYZER.MDB as the destination database.

If you accidentally add all the queries, forms, or reports of a database, you will find that clicking the Reset button and starting over is often faster than removing the spurious selections. Removing a large number of objects from the Selected list can be a very slow process.

Viewing the Result of the Analysis

Database Analyzer creates tables with standard names preceded by an "at" sign (@). This sign distinguishes Analyzer tables from conventional tables and places them at the end of the Tables list in the Database window. The content of the tables Analyzer can create is listed in table 19.2. The Analyzer tables that appear in the Tables list of the Database window depend on the database objects you select for analysis.

Table 19.2. Tables Containing Data Created by Analyzer

Object	Table Name	Fields in Record
Table	@TableDetails	Field names, data types, lengths, indexes
Query	@QuerySQL	The SQL statement for each query
Query	@QueryDetails	Source tables, field names, data types, and lengths
Form	@FormProperties	Properties of forms
Form	@FormControls	Controls and selected control properties
Report	@ReportProperties	Properties of reports

Object	Table Name	Fields in Record
Report	@ReportControls	Controls and selected control properties contained in reports
Macro	@MacroDetails	Macro actions and their arguments
Module	@ModuleProcedures	Access Basic procedures and their parameters, functions and their arguments
Module	@ModuleVariables	Access Basic variables declared with a Dim statement

When you display the @TableDetails table in Datasheet view, you see that Analyzer has added records for the Employees table to @TableDetails. You didn't select the Employees table for analysis, but Analyzer automatically adds the structure of each table that participates in the queries you select. You may find that Analyzer adds copies of table data as a result of this automatic addition process. Figure 19.28 illustrates a few of the tables that Analyzer created for the Personnel Actions objects.

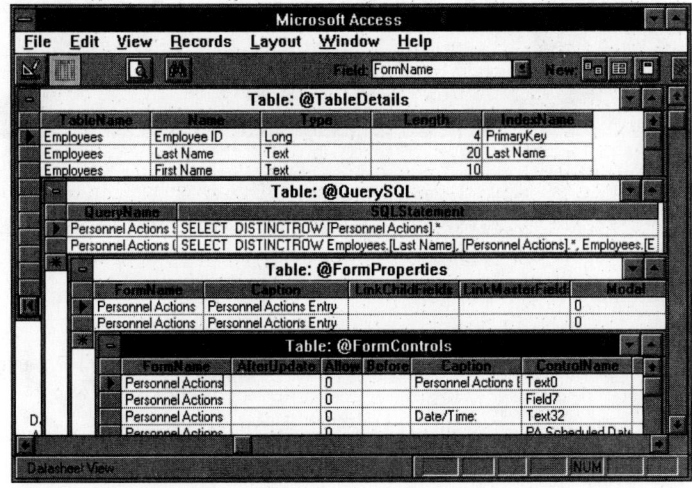

FIG. 19.28

Four of the tables created by Analyzer for Personnel Actions.

Creating a Data Dictionary from Database Analyzer Tables

Microsoft has left it up to you to create the forms and reports necessary for generating data dictionaries from the data included in the

Analyzer tables. One advantage of using ANALYZE.MDB as the destination database for Analyzer's tables is that you can create a standard set of forms and reports to display and print the data.

Expending the time and effort to create a data-dictionary application in Access is warranted only if you intend to create a very large database with many tables and other database objects that you need to document. Making a simple text table is much easier and faster. To create a text table, perform the following steps:

1. Select the records for a single table in the @TableDetails table.

2. Copy the selected records to the Clipboard.

3. Paste the records into Word for Windows.

4. Select the pasted lines in Word and convert the text to a table; delete the TableName column and change the table headings as necessary.

5. Use the IndexName field for key and index data, as well as a description of the field.

The table that results from the preceding procedure is similar to that in table 19.3.

Table 19.3. Table Created by Word for Windows from @TableDetails Records

Field Name	Data Type	Length	Comments
PA ID	Long	4	Primary Key, Index1, Employee ID
PA Type	Text	1	Index1, code for action, see footnote
PA Initiated By	Integer	2	Supervisor's employee number
PA Scheduled Date	Date/Time	8	Index1, date for performance review
PA Approved By	Integer	2	Manager's employee number
PA Effective Date	Date/Time	8	Date change to be implemented by Payroll Dept.
PA Rating	Integer	2	Performance, 1 to 9 (0 for terminated)

Field Name	Data Type	Length	Comments
PA Amount	Currency	8	Amount of change in monthly salary or commission accrual
PA Comments	Memo	N/A	Text summary of supervisor's performance review

You can make similar tables for queries, forms and reports to add to the application section of your data dictionary. The importing technique takes much of the drudgery out of documenting your database.

Using Access Indexes

Database managers use indexes to relate the values of key fields to the location of the data entity on the disk. The basic purpose of an index is to speed up access to specific rows or groups of rows within a database table. You also use indexes to enforce uniqueness of primary keys and establish upper and lower limits for queries. Using an index eliminates the necessity of resorting the table each time you need to create a sequenced list based on a foreign key.

Each PC database manager creates and uses indexes in a variety of ways. Paradox uses a mandatory primary index (*.PX) to speed up queries and to ensure nonduplicate keys. Secondary indexes on nonprimary-key fields are permitted by Paradox (*.X## and *.Y##), created either by the QuerySpeedUp menu choice or the PAL INDEX instruction. dBASE and some of its xBase dialects enable any number of indexes to be created in the form of individual *.NDX files, for a single file or table. The number of xBase indexes that you can have open at any one time, so as to keep them current, is determined by the xBase DBM you choose. You select the index you want to use with the SET ORDER TO IndexFileName instruction. Several xBase languages have their own index structures, such as Clipper's *.NTX and FoxPro's *.IDX. dBASE IV and FoxPro 2 go one step beyond, with their multiple index, *.MDX and *.CDX, structures that combine several indexes in a single file. You specify a TAG name to identify which index is to be used to find the records you want.

Indexed Sequential Access Method (ISAM)

If you watched carefully when you were installing Access or you looked at a directory of files in your \ACCESS directory, you saw file names, such as DBSISAM.DLL, BTRVISAM.DLL, and PDXISAM.DLL, that include the acronym, ISAM. ISAM stands for Indexed Sequential Access Method, a term that describes a file structure in which the records are logically located (sorted) in the sequence of the values of their primary key, with an index used to provide random access to individual records. The term *logically* is applied to record location because the records' physical location on the disk may not be sequential; their physical location is determined by the disk's file allocation table (FAT) and the degree of file fragmentation on the drive. ISAM is often used to describe any database structure that uses indexes for searching. This book adheres to the original definition in which the records must be in the order of their primary key.

Classic mainframe ISAM databases have file structures that use overflow sectors, space reserved on the disk to handle insertion of new records. The database administrator periodically sorts the file to insert the data from the overflow sectors into the body of the table structure at appropriate locations. The periodic sorting clears the overflow sectors for future additions. The process is called *file maintenance*. Improved insertion techniques have been applied to databases created by PC DBMs. These methods are described in the sections that follow.

DOS DBMs duplicate ISAM structures by using an insertion technique. For instance, many xBase dialects enable you to INSERT a record in the middle of a file (the ISAM method), rather than APPEND a BLANK to the end of a file (the *heap* technique). When you INSERT a record near the top of a large, indexed xBase file, you can catch up on your sleep while the DBM moves all the following records to make room for the new one, adjusting all of the index entries to refer to new locations. Figure 19.29 shows the difference between a record INSERT and APPEND. Paradox's native mode is ISAM, which explains why some of its operations, such as canceling an edit on a large table, take so long to complete.

Certain types of files created by DOS DBMs inherently fit the ISAM mold—sales order and invoice records with a numeric key incremented by one for each addition are the best examples; Access's Counter = field data type performs the numbering function automatically. Other types of tables, such as lists of customers, are often sorted alphabetically. You have to INSERT each record in the proper location or resort the file each time you add a new customer to maintain a true ISAM structure. The faster method with xBase is to APPEND BLANKS and REPLACE the blanks WITH data; this procedure adds the new records in a heap at the bottom of the file. Periodically, DOS adds another cluster to the file to accommodate the newly added data. Some xBase dialects, such as Clipper, don't include the INSERT command.

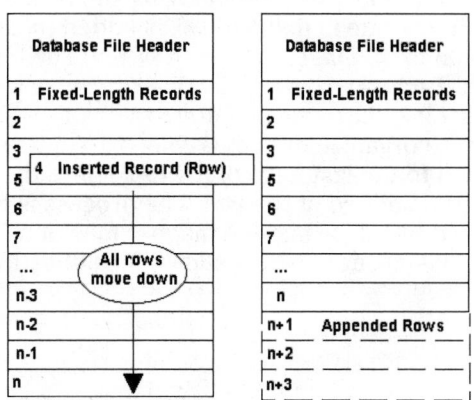

FIG. 19.29

Inserting versus appending new records in an xBase file.

The header of an xBase *.DBF file, such as the one in figure 19.29, includes the name of each field, its field data type, its length in bytes, and some additional data. All data records in the file are the same length, representing the sum of the field lengths plus one byte to indicate whether the record is marked for deletion. xBase files are called the *fixed-length record* type. Values that don't fill the length of a field are padded with spaces; character fields are padded with spaces to the right of the text, and numbers are right-justified by padding to the left. xBase files often incorporate much more padding than data.

The record numbers shown in figure 19.29 aren't present in the data, but are deduced by calculating the offset (the intervening number of bytes) of the record from the beginning of the file. If the header is 300 bytes long, record 1 begins at offset 300, corresponding to the 301st byte (the offset of the first byte is 0). Assuming the fields total 80 bytes in width, record 2 begins at offset 380, 3 at offset 460, and so forth. The location of a data item's value is determined by calculating the offset of the desired record, and then adding the offset to the beginning of the column (field) containing the data.

818

Access Data Pages and Variable Length Records

File and Record Structure

Access, like Microsoft SQL server and many other SQL databases, divides the data stored in its table structures into 2K *data pages*, corresponding to the size of a conventional DOS fixed-disk file cluster. A header, similar to the one in figure 19.30, is added to each page to create the foundation for a *linked list* of data pages. The header contains a reference, called a *pointer*, to the page that precedes it as well as to the one that follows. Linked lists use pointers to link the data pages to one another in order to organize the data table. If no indexes are in use, new data is added to the last page of the table until the page is full, and then another page is added at the end. The process is much like the heap method used by xBase and the manner in which DOS creates entries that link fixed-disk data clusters in its file allocation table (FAT).

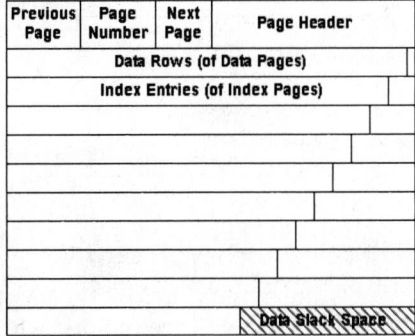

FIG. 19.30

The structure of a data page in an Access table.

Data pages contain only integral numbers of rows. The space that remains after the last row that fits in the page is called *slack*. You may be familiar with the concept of slack from the characteristic of current DOS versions that allocate fixed-disk file space in 2K clusters. A small batch file, for example, may be displayed as having a file size of 120 bytes, but the file actually occupies 2,048 bytes of disk space; the unused space is slack. Access uses variable-length records for its data rows instead of the fixed-length record structure of xBase. Variable-length records don't require padding for data that is shorter than the designated field size.

Data rows longer than 2K are contained in multiple pages. Avoid long rows if possible, as they may reduce storage efficiency by increasing the percentage of slack space in the data pages. Access files with relatively short rows store data, especially character-based data, more efficiently than xBase or Paradox. Special fields containing text and images are stored in separate data structures linked to the data item in the data page. The storage concept is similar to that for xBase memo files, but the implementation differs in Access.

The advantage of data pages with their own headers, over the single-header, record-based xBase structure of figure 19.29, is that you can keep a table's data pages in ISAM order by altering only the pointers in the page header and not the structure of the file itself. This process, which uses a *nonclustered index* (discussed in the "Nonclustered and Clustered Indexes" section), is much faster than the INSERT method for xBase files and usually matches the speed of the APPEND technique.

Balanced Binary Trees, Roots, and Leaves

Most database managers use an indexing method called a *binary tree* that is referenced by its abbreviated form, B-tree. In describing an index structure, the tree is inverted, with its root and trunk at the top, progressing downward to branches and leaves, the direction taken by the searching process. A binary tree is defined as a tree in which the trunk divides into two branches, with each branch dividing into two sub-branches and further two-fold divisions until reaching the leaves, which are indivisible. The points of the two-way divisions are called *nodes*. Binary trees for computer-based searching were first proposed by John Mauchly, one of the pioneers of electronic computers, in 1946.

When you make many insertions and deletions in a database, conventional B-tree structures can become very lopsided, with many sub-branches and leaves stemming from one branch and few from another. The reason for this is explained by mathematical theory that is beyond the scope of this book. Lopsided B-trees slow the searching process for records that are in an especially active area of the database. This situation causes undesirable effects in, for example, an airline reservation system where passenger reservations are being added to or deleted from a flight at a rapid rate immediately prior to its scheduled departure.

To solve the lopsided B-tree problem, two Russian mathematicians, G. M. Adelson-Velski and E. M. Landis proposed a balanced B-tree structure in 1963. In a balanced B-tree structure, the length of the search path to any leaf is never more than 45-percent longer than the optimum. Each time a new row is added to the index, a new node is inserted and the tree is rebalanced if necessary. A small balanced B-tree structure appears in figure 19.31. Its nodes are labeled + (plus) or − (minus), called the *balance factor*, according to whether the right subtree height minus the left subtree height is +1 or −1. If the subtrees are the same height, the node is empty. Balance factors are used to determine how a new node is added to maintain the tree in balance.

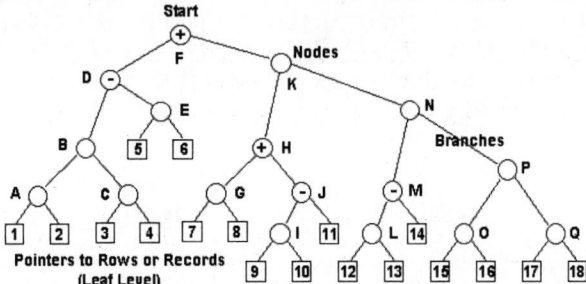

FIG. 19.31

A diagram of a simple balanced B-tree index.

Access and most other modern DBMs use the balanced B-tree structure to create indexes. Balanced B-trees improve search speed, at the expense of increasing the time necessary to add new records, especially when the table is indexed on several keys. In a multitasking or client-server environment, however, the server conducts the addition process independently. The user can then perform other client operations, such as entering the key to search for another record, while the server's insertion and index rebalancing operations are going on.

Nonclustered and Clustered Indexes

Most DBMs, including Access, use nonclustered indexes to locate records with specific key values. Nonclustered means that the DBM adds data by the heap or APPEND method, and the rows of the table aren't in the sequence of their primary key—that is, the table isn't structured as an ISAM table. Figure 19.32 shows the structure, compressed and truncated, of a nonclustered Access index. xBase indexes have a similar structure, substituting records for data pages.

Notice the more-or-less random association of the data pages to the location of the pointers at the leaf level of the index. This lack of order is typical for indexes on foreign keys in all types of databases and for indexes on primary keys in non-ISAM files. If organized into an ISAM structure with the index created on the primary key, the file would have the more organized appearance of the diagram in figure 19.33.

FIG. 19.32

A diagram of a conventional nonclustered index.

FIG. 19.33

A diagram of a clustered index.

Many client-server databases, such as Microsoft SQL server, can use a clustered index to create ISAM order out of heap-induced chaos. When you use a clustered index, its table converts from heap-based row-insertion structure to the balanced B-tree structure in figure 19.33. In this case, the leaf level of the index consists of the data pages themselves. This organization is accomplished by rewriting the pointers in each data page's header in the order of the key on which the clustered index is based. Because the header can have only one set of pointers, fore and aft, you can have only one clustered index per table. In almost all cases, you create the clustered index from the primary key.

To retain the balanced B-tree organization of data pages, a DBM needs a balancing technique for insertions. Instead of using overflow sectors, the DBM adds a new page, readjusts the header pointers to include the new page in the linked list, and then moves the last half of the rows in the original page to the new page. The DBM then updates the index to reflect the changes. This process speeds up data access, but slows updating; therefore, the process is practical only for a DBM running on a high-speed server computer under an advanced operating system, such as Windows NT or OS/2, and having large amounts of RAM.

Query Speed Versus Update Performance

Access, like Paradox, automatically creates an index on the primary-key field. Adding other indexes to Access tables, which is similar to using Paradox's QuerySpeedUp menu command, is a two-edged sword. You can speed up the performance of queries because the index assists the sort sequence; you don't need to sort the query's Dynaset on a primary key index, and sorts in the order of other indexes you specify are speeded. On the other hand, when you append a new record, Access must take the time to update all the table's indexes. When you edit a field of a record that is included in one or more indexes, Access has to update each of the indexes affected by the edit.

You can improve the performance of Access applications, especially when tables with large numbers of records or queries that join several tables are involved, by observing these guidelines:

■ Minimize the number of indexes used with transaction-based tables, especially in networked multiuser applications that share tables. Access locks pages so they aren't editable by other users while you are editing records, and for the time it takes Access to update the indexes when you are finished.

■ Minimize the number of indexes in tables that are used regularly with append and delete queries. The time required to update indexes is especially evident when making changes to the data in bulk.

■ Add indexes judiciously to tables that have large numbers of records and are used primarily in decision support applications.

Indexing becomes more important as the number of records in your tables increases. You may find that you need to experiment to determine whether an index is effective in significantly increasing the speed of a query. If you find the index is warranted by improved query performance, check the speed of transaction processes with the new index before committing to its use.

 If you are using a shared database on a peer-to-peer network, such as Windows for Workgroups, and the database is located on your computer, use another workgroup member's computer to test the effectiveness of indexes. Network characteristics may affect the performance of indexes significantly. Try to make the test during periods of maximum network traffic, not during off hours when no one is contributing to network congestion.

Enforcing Database Integrity

The integrity of a database is comprised of two elements: entity integrity and referential integrity. Entity integrity requires that all primary keys must be unique within a table, and referential integrity dictates that all foreign keys must have corresponding values within a base table's primary key. Although the normalization process creates entity and referential integrity, either the DBM itself or your application must maintain that integrity during the data-entry process. Failure to maintain database integrity can result in erroneous data values and ultimately in widespread corruption of the entire database.

Ensuring Entity Integrity and Auditability

Database managers differ widely in their capabilities to maintain entity integrity through unique primary-key values. Paradox, for instance, enforces unique primary keys within the DBM by flagging as a *key violation* any attempt to insert a row with an identical primary key and placing the offending record in the KeyViol table. Access uses a similar technique when you specify a no-duplicates index; if you paste or append records that have duplicate primary keys, Access appends those records to a Paste Errors or Append Errors table.

In xBase, you can add as many records with duplicate index keys as you want. Then if you use SET UNIQUE ON, a SEEK finds only the first record with the same key; however, any duplicate keys remain in the file and, for example, appear in an indexed LIST operation. Indexed DELETEs affect only the first undeleted record found for the SEEK parameter; you must perform a DELETE for each duplicate. You need to write xBase code, therefore, to test for data duplicates before you APPEND the record that adds the data to the file.

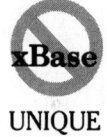

UNIQUE
Indexes ·

Enforcing entity integrity within the table itself, the process used by Access and Paradox, is more reliable than using application programming code to prevent duplication of primary-key values. Access provides two methods of ensuring entity integrity that are independent of the applications employing the tables:

- A key field that uses the Counter data type that creates unique values based on an automatically incremented long integer. You cannot create a duplicate primary key in this case because you cannot edit the values in fields of the Counter data type.

- An index on the primary-key field with the No Duplicates property. If you attempt to enter a duplicate value in the key field, Access displays an error message.

Either of these methods ensures unique key fields, but a Counter field is necessary so that documents, such as sales orders, invoices and checks, are sequentially numbered. Sequential numbering is necessary for internal control and auditing purposes. Counter fields normally begin with 1 as the first record in a table, but rarely does a real-world cash disbursements or invoice table need 1 as a starting number. You cannot create a table with a Long Integer Number field, enter the beginning number, and then change the field data type to Counter. Access issues a warning message if you attempt this procedure. You can use an append query, however, to establish a specific beginning Counter value.

To create a starting Counter value of 123456 in the Invoice field of an Invoice Data table's first record, perform the following steps:

1. Open the Database window, select the Orders table, and press Ctrl+C to copy the table to the Clipboard.

2. Press Ctrl+V and enter **Invoice Data** as the name of the table to create. Then click the Structure Only option button to create the new Invoice Data table with no records.

3. Open the Invoice Data table in Design mode, click the select button of the Order ID field, and then press Insert to add a new field.

4. Enter Invoice as the Field Name, and choose Counter as the Data Type.

5. Click the Properties button on the toolbar. Delete Order ID from the Key Field text box, and then set the Index property to No, which enables you to append a record that doesn't have a value for the key field (null values aren't allowed in key fields).

The Invoice Data table design appears (see fig. 19.34).

6. Close the Invoice Data table and save your changes. Don't create a primary-key field at this point.

7. Create a temporary table called First Invoice with one field called Invoice.

8. Set the Invoice fields Data Type property to Number and the Size property to Long Integer.

9. Change to Datasheet view and enter a value in Invoice 1 less than the starting number you want (for this example, use 123455).

10. Close the First Invoice table, save your changes, and don't create a primary-key field.

11. Create a new query and add the First Invoice table. Click and drag the Invoice field symbol to the first column of the query design grid.

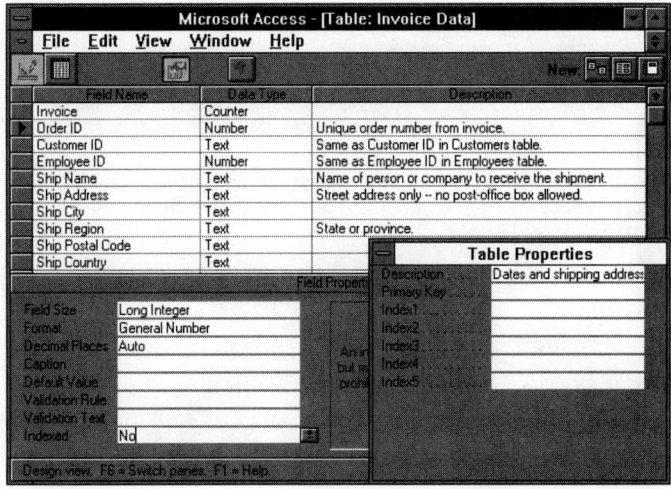

FIG. 19.34

A table designed
for adding a
Counter-type field
with an arbitrary
starting number.

12. Choose **A**ppend from the **Q**uery menu and enter Invoice Data as
    the table to which to append the record. Click the Run Query but-
    ton on the toolbar to add the single record in First Invoice to the
    Invoice Data table.

13. Close Query1 without saving your changes.

The next record you append to Invoice Data is assigned the value
123456 in the Invoice (Counter) field. To verify that this technique
works properly for appended records, perform the following steps:

1. Create a new query and add the Orders table. Click and drag the
   asterisk (all fields) symbol to the first column of the query grid.

2. Choose **A**ppend from the **Q**uery menu and enter Invoice Data as
   the table to which to append the records from the Orders table.
   Click the Run Query button on the toolbar to add the records
   from the Orders table.

3. Close Query1 and don't save the changes.

4. Open the Invoice Data table.

   Access has added numbers beginning with 123456 to the new Invoice field, corresponding to Order ID values of 10000 and higher,
   as shown in figure 19.35.

If you were adding a Counter-type field to real-world data, you would
delete the first blank record and then make the Invoice field the
primary-key field. Access creates a no-duplicates index when you
assign a Counter-type field as a primary-key field.

FIG. 19.35

The Invoice Data table with counter values starting with 123456.

Maintaining Referential Integrity

Maintaining referential integrity requires strict adherence to a single rule: *Each foreign-key field in a related table must correspond to a primary-key field in a base or primary table.* This rule requires that the following types of transactions be prevented:

■ Adding a record on the many side of a one-to-many relationship without the existence of a corresponding record on the one side of the relationship.

■ Deleting a record on the one side of a one-to-many relationship without first deleting all corresponding records on the many side of the relationship.

■ Deleting or adding a record to a table in a one-to-one relationship with another table without deleting or adding a corresponding record in the related table.

■ Changing the value of a primary-key field of a base table on which records in a relation table depend.

■ Changing the value of a foreign-key field in a relation table to a value that doesn't exist in the primary-key field of a base table.

A record in a relation table that has a foreign key with a value that doesn't correspond to the value of a primary key in a relation table is called an *orphan record*.

Whenever possible, maintain referential integrity at the database level and don't rely on applications to test for referential integrity violations when adding records to relation tables or deleting records from base tables. Access gives you the opportunity to maintain referential integrity automatically between tables in a database by marking the Enforce Referential Integrity checkbox in the Relationships dialog box.

Paradox Versions 3.0 and later automatically enforce referential integrity between master and detail table records. Paradox handles changes to the values of primary-key (link) fields with dependent records in relation (detail) tables in a different manner than Access. When you change a value in a Paradox link field, the corresponding fields of linked records in detail tables change automatically.

Changing Link Field Values in Master Tables

Access, on the other hand, prevents you from completing an edit of a base table's primary-key field that would result in orphan records. Access also prevents you from changing the foreign-key value in the relation table to a value that doesn't exist in the primary-key field of the base table. In this case, you have two choices if the base table's key field isn't a Counter-type field:

■ Delete the dependent records in the relation table, edit the primary-key value in the base table, and then reenter the dependent records with the new foreign-key values.

■ Temporarily change the foreign-key values of the dependent records to another valid value, edit the primary-key value in the base table, and then update the foreign key of dependent records to the new value.

Database designers often add *dummy records* to base tables to provide a key-field value for the temporary changes involved in the second choice.

Most xBase DBMs don't have the capability to enforce referential integrity automatically. You need to write xBase code that tests for the required records with SEEK commands on indexed files.

Referential Integrity

You cannot automatically enforce referential integrity between a primary table in one database and an attached related table in another database, or between two attached tables. Access's Relationships dialog box doesn't include tables from attached database tables in its primary or related tables lists. You must enforce referential integrity between native and attached tables with your applications that employ attached tables. You may be able to accomplish this with a combination of macros and validation rules. In the majority of cases, however, you need to write Access Basic code to enforce referential integrity between two databases.

Chapter Summary

This chapter covered the fundamental principles of relational database design and how to restructure tables so that they conform to these principles. Methods of documenting your database design, both in the preliminary and final stages, with text and graphical descriptions of data structures and relationships was emphasized. Many entire books have been written on each of these two subjects. Indexing techniques were covered in detail because of the differences between Access's approach to indexes and that of xBase. Indexes also play a critical role in maintaining entity integrity by preventing duplication of key-field values. Access's automatic enforcement of relational integrity at the database level provides protection against orphan records in your relation tables.

The next chapter covers Structured Query Language and its syntax. Although Access creates SQL statements for you, an understanding of Access's implementation of the language is useful if you have used other dialects of SQL and necessary if you plan to use Access Basic to create queries.

Working with Structured Query Language

This chapter describes Structured Query Language (SQL), the structure and syntax of the language, and how Access translates queries you design with Access's graphical query-by-example technique into SQL statements. A SQL background helps you understand the query process and design more efficient queries. A knowledge of SQL syntax is necessary for many of the applications you write in Access Basic. Examples of SQL have been presented in other chapters in this book. These examples, usually figures that illustrate a SQL statement created by Access, demonstrate what occurs *behind the scenes* when you create a query or a graph.

Access is a useful learning tool for gaining fluency in SQL. This chapter shows you how to create Access Query By Example (QBE) queries from SQL statements entered in the SQL dialog box. If you use SQL with another DBM, such as dBASE IV or Microsoft SQL Server, this chapter can help you make the transition from ANSI SQL or Transact-SQL, the extended version of SQL used by the Microsoft SQL Server, to Access's implementation of query-only SQL.

What Is Structured Query Language?

Structured Query Language, abbreviated SQL (pronounced "sequel" or "seekel") is the common language of database management. The principal advantage of SQL is that this language is standardized—you can use a common set of SQL statements with all SQL-compliant database management systems. The current U.S. SQL standard was established in 1986 as ANSI X3.135-1986.

ANSI, an acronym for the American National Standards Institute, is an organization devoted to establishing and maintaining scientific and engineering standards. ANSI-standard SQL was adopted for worldwide use by a 1987 standard, issued by the International Standards Organization (ISO), a branch of the United Nations. The ANSI and ISO standards were in the process of revision (ANSI X3H2 and ISO/TEC JTC1, SC21, WG3 Draft International Standard) while this book was being written.

SQL is an application language for relational databases, not a system or programming language. ANSI SQL doesn't include a provision for program flow control (branching and looping) nor keywords to create data entry forms and print reports. Programming functions usually are implemented in a system language such as xBase, PAL, C, or COBOL. Some implementations of SQL, such as Transact-SQL used by Microsoft SQL Server, add flow control statements (IF...ELSE and WHILE) to the language. Publishers of ANSI SQL-compliant DBMs are free to extend the language if the basic ANSI commands are supported. The ANSI/ISO implementation of SQL is independent of any system language with which it might be used.

ANSI SQL includes a set of standard commands that are broadly grouped into six categories: data definition, data query, data manipulation, cursor control, transaction processing, and administration or control. Provisions for SQL commands that maintain data integrity were added in a 1989 revision of the original standard as ANSI X3.135-1989, *Database Language - SQL with Integrity Enhancement*. Data integrity commands aren't implemented in Access SQL and aren't included in this chapter.

SQL has three different methods of implementation: Direct Invocation, Module Language, and Embedded SQL. Direct Invocation sends a series of SQL statements to the DBM. The DBM responds to the query by creating a table that contains the result and displays the table. Entering

SQL commands at the dBASE IV SQL prompt is an example of Direct Invocation. Embedded SQL is the most common implementation; the SQL statements are generated by the application or included as strings of text in a command of an application language. Access queries—whether created by graphical QBE, by an SQL property in Access Basic, or by the Row Source property of a graph—use Embedded SQL.

Looking at the Development of SQL

SQL was created because, early in the 1970s, IBM wanted a method with which nonprogrammers could extract and display the information they wanted from a database. Languages that can be used by nonprogrammers are called "fourth generation" or 4GL and sometimes are referred to as "structured English." The first commercial result of this effort was Query By Example (QBE), developed at IBM's laboratories in Yorktown Heights, New York. QBE was used, beginning in the late 1970s, on terminals connected to IBM System 370 mainframes. A user could obtain a result with less than an 80-character line of QBE code that required 100 or more lines to implement in COBOL or the other 3GL languages of the day.

Virtually any language developed by IBM, at least before the rise of Microsoft Corporation in the PC market, became the standard to which all other languages are compared. These languages often are adopted and improved on by others; Access, dBASE IV, and Paradox use QBE to display selected data from tables.

At the other end of the country, programmers at IBM's San Jose facility were developing System R, the progenitor of SQL/DS and IBM's DB2 relational database. In the mid-1970s IBM scientist Dr. E.F. Codd proposed SQL (then known as SEQUEL for *S*tructured *E*nglish *Q*uery *L*anguage) as a means of accessing information from the relational database model he had developed in 1970. Relational databases based on the Codd model that use the SQL language to retrieve and update data within them have become, like QBE, computer-industry standards.

SQL has achieved the status of being the exclusive language of client-server databases. A database server (the back end) application holds the data. Client applications (front ends) add to or edit the data. SQL statements are generated by the client application. If you deal regularly with databases of any type, the odds are great that you ultimately will need to learn SQL.

Comparing ANSI and Access SQL

Access SQL is designed for creating queries, not for creating or modifying tables. SQL, therefore, doesn't include many of the approximately 100 keywords incorporated in the ANSI standard for SQL. Few, if any, commercial SQL-compliant DBMs for the PC implement much more than half of the standard SQL keywords. The majority of the common SQL keywords missing from Access's implementation are provided by the expressions you create with operators, built-in Access functions, or user-defined functions you write in Access Basic. The effect of many unsupported ANSI SQL keywords related to tables is achieved by making selections from Access's Database window or from menus.

When you learn a new language, it is helpful to categorize the vocabulary of the language into categories by usage and then into the familiar parts of speech. SQL commands, therefore, first are divided into six usage categories:

- *Data Query Language* (DQL) commands, sometimes referred to as *data retrieval* commands, obtain data from tables and determine how the results of the retrieval are presented. The SELECT command is the principal instruction in this category. DQL commands often are considered members of the Data Manipulation Language.

- *Data Manipulation Language* (DML) commands provide INSERT and DELETE commands that add or delete entire rows, and the UPDATE command, which can change the values of data in specified columns within rows.

- *Transaction Processing Language* (TPL) commands include BEGIN TRANSACTION, COMMIT, and ROLLBACK.

- *Data Definition Language* (DDL) commands include CREATE TABLE and CREATE VIEW instructions that define the structure of tables and views. DDL commands are used also to modify tables and to create and delete indexes.

- *Cursor Control Language* (CCL) instructions that can select a single row of a query table for processing. Cursor control constructs, such as UPDATE WHERE CURRENT, are defined only for Embedded SQL, the subject of this chapter.

- *Data Control Language* (DCL) commands, such as GRANT and REVOKE, perform administrative functions that grant and revoke PRIVILEGES to use the database or a set of tables within the database, or to use specific SQL commands.

Keywords that comprise the vocabulary of SQL are identified further in the following categories:

- *Commands,* such as SELECT, cause an action to be performed.

- *Qualifiers,* such as WHERE, limit the range of values of the entities that comprise the query.

- *Clauses,* such as ORDER BY, modify the action of an instruction.

- *Operators*, such as =, <, or > compare values and are used to create joins.

- *Group aggregate functions*, such as MIN(), return a single result for a set of values.

- *Other* keywords modify the action of a clause or manipulate cursors that are used to select specific rows of queries.

As in dBASE and PAL programming, SQL keywords usually are capitalized, but the keywords aren't case-sensitive. The uppercase convention is used in this book, but SQL keywords aren't set in the monospace type reserved for Access Basic keywords, except in examples of SQL statements that you type. You use *Parameters*, such as *column_list*, to define or modify the action specified by keywords. Names of replaceable parameters are printed in lowercase italicized type.

SQL Reserved Words in Access

Access doesn't support all the ANSI SQL keywords with identical reserved words in the Access SQL language. In this chapter, *keywords* are defined as the commands and functions that comprise the ANSI SQL language. Access SQL commands and functions, however, are referred to here as *reserved words* to distinguish them from ANSI SQL.

The tables in the following section are intended to acquaint readers who are familiar with ANSI or similar implementations of SQL in other DBMs or database front-end applications, with the Access implementation of SQL. If you haven't used SQL, the tables demonstrate that SQL is a relatively sparse language, which has far fewer keywords than programming languages like Access Basic, and that Access SQL is even more sparse: Access SQL has few keywords you have to learn. You learned in earlier chapters to use the Access operators and functions in expressions that Access substitutes for ANSI SQL keywords.

Access SQL Reserved Words Corresponding to ANSI SQL Keywords

Access supports the ANSI SQL keywords listed in table 20.1 as identical reserved words in Access SQL. Don't use Access SQL reserved words that correspond to SQL reserved words as the names of tables, fields, or variables. The reserved words in table 20.1 are displayed in all capital letters in the Access SQL statements you create when you design a query or when you add a graph to a form or report.

Table 20.1. ANSI SQL Keywords Corresponding to Access SQL Reserved Words			
ALL	DISTINCT	INTO	SELECT
AND	FROM	JOIN	SET
AS	GROUP	ON	UPDATE
ASC	HAVING	OPTION	WHERE
BY	IN	OR	WITH
DELETE	INNER	ORDER	
DESC	INSERT	PROCEDURE	

The keywords that relate to data types—CHAR[ACTER], FLOAT, INT[EGER], and REAL—aren't included in table 20.1 because Access SQL uses a different reserved word to specify these SQL data types (refer to table 20.3 later in this chapter). The comparison operations— =, <, <=, >, and =>—are common to both ANSI SQL and Access SQL. Access substitutes the < > operator for ANSI SQL's not-equal (!=) operator.

As in ANSI SQL, the IN reserved word in Access SQL can be used as an operator to specify a list of values to match in a WHERE clause, but not to specify a list created by a subquery. Access SQL doesn't support subqueries. In Access SQL, IN is used also to identify a table in another database; this use is discussed near the end of this chapter, in the section "Adding IN To Use Tables in Another Database."

Access Functions and Operators Used in Place of ANSI SQL Keywords

Table 20.2 shows reserved words in Access that correspond to ANSI SQL keywords but that are operators or functions used in Access expressions. Access doesn't use ANSI SQL syntax for its aggregate functions; you cannot use the SUM(DISTINCT *fieldname*) syntax of ANSI SQL, for instance. Access therefore distinguishes between its use of the SUM() aggregate function and the SQL implementation, SUM(). Expressions that use operators such as And and Or are enclosed in parentheses in Access SQL statements; Access uses uppercase AND and OR (refer to table 20.1) when criteria are added to more than one column.

Table 20.2. Access Reserved Words that Substitute for ANSI SQL Keywords

Access	ANSI SQL	Access	ANSI SQL
And	AND	Max()	MAX()
Avg()	AVG()	Min()	MIN()
Between	BETWEEN	Not	NOT
Count()	COUNT()	Null	NULL
Is	IS	Or	OR
Like	LIKE	Sum()	SUM()

The Access IsNull() function that returns True (-1) or False (0), depending on whether IsNull()'s argument has a Null value, has no equivalent in ANSI SQL, and isn't a substitute for Is Null or Is Not Null qualifiers in WHERE clauses. Access SQL does not support distinct aggregate function references, such as AVG(DISTINCT *field_name*); the default DISTINCTROW qualifier added to the SELECT statement by Access serves this purpose.

Access SQL Reserved Words, Operators, and Functions Not in ANSI SQL

Access SQL contains a number of reserved words that aren't ANSI SQL keywords (see table 20.3). Most of these reserved words define Access data types; some reserved words have equivalents in ANSI SQL and others don't. You use Access DDL reserved words to modify the properties of tables Access Basic's SQL property. DISTINCTROW is described in the following section. PIVOT and TRANSFORM are used in creating cross-tab queries that are unique to Access. PARAMETERS allows you to enter a value in the Query Parameters text box to create a parameterized query.

Table 20.3. Access SQL Reserved Words Not in ANSI SQL

Access SQL	ANSI SQL	Category	Purpose
BINARY	No equivalent	DDL	Not an Access data type
BOOLEAN	No equivalent	DDL	Access Yes/No data type
BYTE	No equivalent	DDL	Byte data type, 1-byte integer
CURRENCY	No equivalent	DDL	Access Currency data type
DATETIME	No equivalent	DDL	Access Date/Time data type
DISTINCTROW	No equivalent	DQL	Updatable Access dynasets
DOUBLE	REAL	DDL	REAL in ANSI SQL
LONG	INT[EGER]	DDL	Long Integer data type
LONGBINARY	No equivalent	DDL	OLE Object data type
LONGTEXT	VARCHAR	DDL	Memo data type
OWNERACCESS	No equivalent	DQL	Run with owner's privileges
PARAMETERS	No equivalent	DQL	User-entered query parameters
PIVOT	No equivalent	DQL	Used in cross-tab queries
SHORT	SMALLINT	DDL	Integer data type, 2 bytes
SINGLE	No equivalent	DDL	Single-precision real number
TEXT	CHAR[ACTER]	DDL	Text data type
TRANSFORM	No equivalent	DQL	Creates cross-tab queries
? (LIKE wild card)	_ (wild card)	DQL	Single character with LIKE
* (LIKE wild card)	% (wild card)	DQL	Zero or more characters
# (LIKE wild card)	No equivalent	DQL	Single digit, 0 through 9
# (date specifier)	No equivalent	DQL	Encloses date/time values
<> (not equal)	!=	DQL	Access uses ! as a separator

Access provides four statistical aggregate functions that aren't incorporated in ANSI SQL. These functions are listed in table 20.4.

Table 20.4. Aggregate SQL Functions Added in Access SQL		
Access Function	**Category**	**Purpose**
StdDev( )	DQL	Standard deviation of a population sample
StdDevP( )	DQL	Standard deviation of a population
Var( )	DQL	Statistical variation of a population sample
VarP( )	DQL	Statistical variation of a population

Access's DISTINCTROW and SQL's DISTINCT Keywords

The DISTINCTROW keyword that follows the SQL SELECT keywords causes Access to eliminate duplicated rows from the query's result. The effect of DISTINCTROW is especially dramatic in queries used to display records in tables that have indirect relationships. To create an example of a query that you can use to demonstrate the effect of Access DISTINCTROW SQL keyword:

1. Open a new query in NWIND.MDB by clicking the Query button, and then click the New button.

2. Add the Customers, Orders, Order Details, Products, and Categories tables to the query, in sequence. Access creates the required joins.

3. Drag the Company Name field from the Customers field list to the Field row of the first column of the query design grid. Select the Sort cell, open the drop-down list with F4 and choose Ascending sort order.

4. Drag the Category Name from the Categories field list to the Field row of the second column of the grid. Add an ascending sort to this field.

5. Choose **S**QL from the **V**iew menu. The SQL statement that creates the query is shown in the SQL dialog box of Figure 20.1.

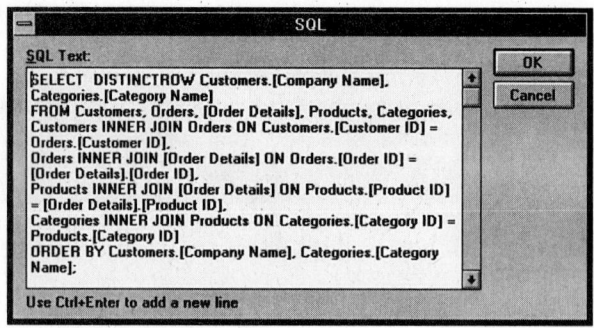

FIG. 20.1

The SQL statement that creates the query to determine customers purchasing categories of products.

6. Click the Cancel button to close the SQL dialog box, and then click the Run Query button on the toolbar.

7. Click the End of Table button to determine the number of rows in the query table. At the time of this writing, the number of row (Records) returned by the query is 641.

To demonstrate the effect of removing the DISTINCTROW keyword from the SQL statement and to verify, in this case, that the effect of ANSI SQL's DISTINCT and Access SQL's DISTINCTROW keywords is the same, follow these steps:

1. Click the query Design mode button on the toolbar, and then choose SQL from the View menu to edit the SQL statement.

2. Delete the DISTINCTROW keyword from the SQL statement and choose OK to close the SQL window.

3. Click the Run Query button. The new query result table contains many duplicated rows.

4. Click the End of Table button to check the number of rows in the result. The number of rows, 2,796, is more than four times the number of rows that results when the duplicate removal process of DISTINCTROW is applied to the query.

5. Click the query Design mode button, then choose SQL from the View menu to edit the SQL statement again. Add DISTINCT after the keyword SELECT.

6. Click the Run Query button again, and then click the End of Table button. You get the same result, 641 records, that you obtain when you use the DISTINCTROW keyword. (You may get 642 records because of a minor bug in Access that repeats the first entry in a query under certain conditions.)

7. Close, but do not save, the query.

DISTINCTROW is a special Access SQL keyword and is unavailable in standard (ANSI) SQL; DISTINCTROW is related to, but not the same as, the DISTINCT keyword in ANSI SQL. Both keywords eliminate duplicate rows of data in query result tables, but differ in execution, as shown in the following list:

■ DISTINCT in ANSI SQL eliminates duplicate rows based only on the values of the data contained in the rows of the query, from left to right. You cannot update values from multiple-table queries that include the keyword DISTINCT.

■ DISTINCTROW, available only in Access, eliminates duplicate rows based on the content of the underlying table, regardless of whether additional field(s) that distinguish records in the table are included. DISTINCTROW allows values in special kinds of multiple-table dynasets to be updated.

To distinguish between these two keywords, assume that you have a table with a Last Name and a First Name field and only 10 records, each with the Last Name value, Smith. Each record has a different First Name value. You create a query that includes the Last Name Field, but omit the First Name field.

■ DISTINCTROW returns all 10 Smith records because the First Name values differ in the table.

■ DISTINCT returns 1 record, because the First Name field that distinguishes the records in the table that contains the data is absent in the query result table.

All SQL statements created by Access include the default keyword DISTINCTROW, unless you purposely replace this keyword by the DISTINCT keyword, using the Query Properties dialog's Unique Values Only option. The only way of eliminating DISTINCTROW from queries is to delete it by editing the SQL statement. The circumstances that require you to delete DISTINCTROW are rare, possibly nonexistent.

For Related Information:

◄◄ "Creating Queries from Tables with Indirect Relationships, p." 311.

FROM HERE...

Common ANSI SQL Keywords and Features Not Supported by Access SQL Reserved Words

Access doesn't support the creation or modification of tables with SQL data-definition language statements entered in Query Design mode. Access substitutes choices in the Database window, entries in Table Properties text boxes, and menu choices for most of the DDL and DCL keywords in ANSI SQL. The record position buttons of Access queries and forms substitute for most cursor-control (CCL) statements in ANSI SQL that choose a particular row in a query. These substitutes are listed in table 20.5.

Table 20.5. Common ANSI SQL Keywords Not Supported in Access SQL

Reserved Word	Category	Substitute
ALTER TABLE	DDL	Alterations in Table Design mode
ANY	DQL	Query filter
AUTHORIZATION	DCL	Privileges dialog box
BEGIN	TPL	Access Basic BeginTrans method
CHECK	DQL	Table Validation Rule property
CLOSE	CCL	Document control menu of query
COMMIT	TPL	Access Basic CommitTrans method
CREATE INDEX	DDL	Add Index property to the table design
CREATE TABLE	DDL	Make-table query or Database window
CREATE VIEW	DDL	Query Design mode and filters
CURRENT	CCL	Query Run mode, record position buttons
CURSOR	CCL	Query Run mode
DECLARE	CCL	Query Run mode (cursors are automatic)

Reserved Word	Category	Substitute
DROP INDEX	DDL	Table Design mode
DROP TABLE	DDL	Delete the table in the Database window
DROP VIEW	DDL	Query Design mode
FETCH	DQL	Text boxes on a form
GRANT	DCL	Privileges dialog box
IN *subquery*	DQL	A nested query rather than a subquery
PRIVILEGES	DCL	Privileges dialog box
REVOKE	DCL	Privileges dialog box
ROLLBACK	TPL	Access Basic RollbackTrans method
UNION	DQL	Not supported by Access
VALUES	DML	Data values entered in tables or forms
WORK	TPL	Access Basic BeginTrans method
: (variable prefix)	DQL	Access Basic Dim statement
!= (not equal)	DQL	Access not-equal operator < >

You can substitute Access's IN clause to create a table in another database with the methods described near the end of this chapter in the section "Adding IN To Use Tables in Another Database."

Transaction processing (COMMIT and ROLLBACK [WORK]) can be implemented only by writing Access Basic functions that you call with a RunCode macro. Many other less commonly used SQL keywords, such as COBOL and PASCAL, don't have Access SQL reserved word equivalents.

Writing Select Queries in SQL

When you create a select query in Query Design mode, Access translates the QBE query design into an Access SQL statement. You can view the Access SQL equivalent of your design by selecting **S**QL from the **V**iew menu. Displaying and analyzing the SQL statements that correspond to queries you design or queries in the Northwind Traders sample database is useful when you are learning SQL.

The heart of SQL is the SELECT statement used to create a select query. Every select query begins with the SELECT statement. The following lines of syntax are used for a SQL SELECT statement that returns a query table (dynaset) of all or selected columns (fields) from all or qualifying rows (records) of a source table:

```
SELECT [ALL¦DISTINCT¦DISTINCTROW] select_list
    FROM table_names
[WHERE search_criteria]
[ORDER BY column_criteria[ASC¦DESC]]
```

The following list shows the purpose of the elements in this basic select query statement:

■ SELECT is the basic command that specifies a query. The *select_list* parameter determines the fields (columns) that will be included in the result table of the query. When you design an Access QBE query, the *select_list* parameter is determined by the fields you add to the Fields row in the Query grid. Only those fields with the Show check box marked are included in *select_list*. Multiple field names are separated by commas.

The optional ALL, DISTINCT, or DISTINCTROW qualifier determines how rows are handled. ALL specifies that all rows are to be included, subject to subsequent limitation. DISTINCT eliminates rows with duplicate data. DISTINCTROW is an Access SQL keyword, similar to DISTINCT, that eliminates duplicate rows, but also enables you to modify the query table.

■ FROM *table_name* specifies the name or names of the table or tables that form the basis for the query. The *table_names* parameter is created in Access QBE by the entries you make in the Add Table dialog box. If fields from more than one table are included in *select_list*, each table has to be specified in *table_names*. Commas are used to separate the names of multiple tables.

■ WHERE *search_criteria* determines which records from the selection list will be displayed. The *search_criteria* parameter is an expression with a text (string) operator, such as LIKE, for text fields or a numeric operator, such as >=, for fields with numeric values. The WHERE clause is optional; if you don't add a WHERE clause, all the rows that meet the SELECT criteria are returned.

■ ORDER BY *column_criteria* specifies the sorting order of the dynaset created by the query. Like the WHERE clause, ORDER BY is optional. You can specify an ascending or descending sort by the optional ASC or DESC keywords. If you don't specify a sort direction, ascending sequence is the default.

The following lines show an example of a simple SQL query statement:

```
SELECT [Company Name],[Customer ID],[Postal Code]
    FROM Customers
WHERE [Postal Code] LIKE "9*"
ORDER BY [Company Name];
```

You must terminate an SQL statement by adding a semicolon immediately after the last character on the last line.

Examples of SQL statements in this book are formatted to make the examples more readable. Access doesn't format the SQL statements. When you enter or edit SQL statements in the Access SQL Window, formatting these statements so that commands appear on individual lines makes the SQL statements more intelligible. Use Ctrl+Enter to insert newline pairs before SQL keywords. Spaces and newline pairs are ignored when Access processes the statement.

The preceding query results in an Access dynaset of three columns and as many rows as the number of records in the Customers table for companies located in ZIP codes with values that begin with the character 9, sorted alphabetically by the company name. You don't have to specify the table name with the field name in the *select_list* because only one table is used in this query. When Access creates a SQL statement, the table name always precedes the field name. Usually, Access processes queries you write in either ANSI SQL or Access SQL syntax. This example differs from ANSI SQL only in the substitution of the Access SQL asterisk for ANSI SQL's % wild card.

Programming Statements in xBase Equivalent to SQL

If you are accustomed to using the dot prompt—with xBase dialects that include interactive capability—or writing xBase programs, you can use much of your xBase experience in learning SQL. In xBase, you achieve a result identical to the preceding simple SQL query by the following set of statements, assuming that the CustName index exists:

```
USE Customers INDEX CustName
LIST FIELDS Company, CompanyID, PostalCode
FOR SUBSTR(PostalCode,1,1) = "9"
```

The CustName index is needed to provide the equivalent of the ORDER BY clause so that the list appears in customer name sequence, unless the Customer table was sorted previously by customer name, which is unlikely. The dot-prompt commands in xBase are closely related to SQL statements invoked directly. Many of the keywords differ between the two languages, but you can achieve similar results with either language. The advantage of SQL over xBase dialects is that SQL syntax is simpler and usually requires fewer keywords to obtain the same result.

Using SQL Punctuation and Symbols

SQL uses relatively few symbols, other than the comparison operators for expressions mentioned earlier. SQL uses commas, periods, semicolons, and colons as punctuation. The following list of symbols and punctuation is used in ANSI SQL and the Access SQL dialect; differences between the two forms of SQL are noted where appropriate:

- Commas are used to separate members of lists of parameters, such as multiple field names, as in Name, Address, City, Zip.

- Square brackets surrounding field names are required only when the field name includes spaces or other symbols, including punctuation, not allowed by SQL, as in [Company Name].

- A period is used to separate the table name from the field name, if fields of more than one table are involved in the query, as in Customers.[Company Name].

- ANSI SQL uses % and _ (underscore) symbols as the wild cards for the LIKE statement, rather than the * (asterisk) and ? used by Access SQL to specify zero or more and a single character, respectively. The Access wild cards correspond to the wild cards used in specifying DOS group file names.

- Access provides the # wild card for the LIKE statement to represent any single digit. Access also uses the # symbol to enclose date/time values in expressions. This symbol isn't available in ANSI SQL.

- The end of a SQL statement is indicated by a mandatory semicolon.

- Colons cannot be used in Access as a prefix to indicate user-declared variables you create in ANSI SQL. You cannot create variables with Access SQL; user-declared variables in Access are limited to the Access Basic functions and procedures you write.

- The exclamation mark is used by Access and ANSI SQL as a "not in" operator for character lists used with LIKE. ANSI SQL uses != for not equal; Access SQL uses < >.

As the preceding list demonstrates, relatively minor differences exist in the availability and use of punctuation and symbols between ANSI and Access SQL. Indentation often is used in writing multiple-line SQL statements. Indented lines indicate continuation of a preceding line or a clause that is dependent on a keyword in a preceding line.

Using SQL Statements To Create Access Queries

You can enter SQL statements in Query Design mode to create simple Access queries that are reflected in changes to the design of the Query grid. This method is another useful way to learn the syntax of SQL. If your entries contain errors in spelling or punctuation, Access displays a message box that describes the error and its approximate location in the statement. When you choose OK in the SQL dialog box, Access translates your SQL statement into a QBE query design.

To create an Access QBE select query with the SQL statement, break and repeat the previous query marked INSERT, as shown in the following lines:

```
SELECT [Company Name],[Customer ID],[Postal Code]
    FROM Customers
WHERE [Postal Code] LIKE "9*"
ORDER BY [Company Name];
```

To create the Access QBE select query, follow these steps:

1. Open the Northwind Traders database, and then open a new query in the Database window.

2. Close the Add Table dialog box without adding a table name.

3. Choose SQL from the View menu.

4. Delete any text, such as WITH OWNERACCESS OPTION, that may appear in the SQL Text box in the SQL dialog box. The WITH OWNERACCESS OPTION line is added if you check the Run with Owner's Permissions check box in the Relations dialog box.

5. Enter the SQL statement from the SQL Text box. Use Ctrl+Enter to create new lines. Your SQL statement appears as shown in figure 20.2.

6. Choose OK to close the SQL dialog box. Access creates the equivalent of your SQL statement in graphical QBE (see fig. 20.3).

7. Click the Run Query button on the toolbar. The result of your query in Datasheet view appears as shown in figure 20.4.

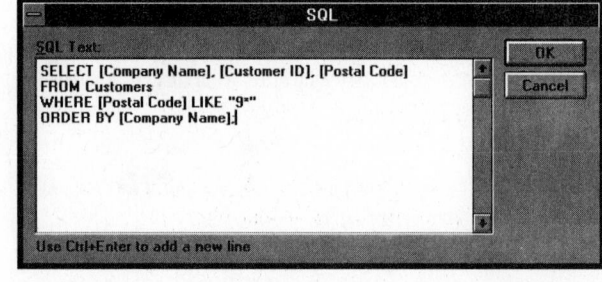

FIG. 20.2

An SQL statement for a simple select query.

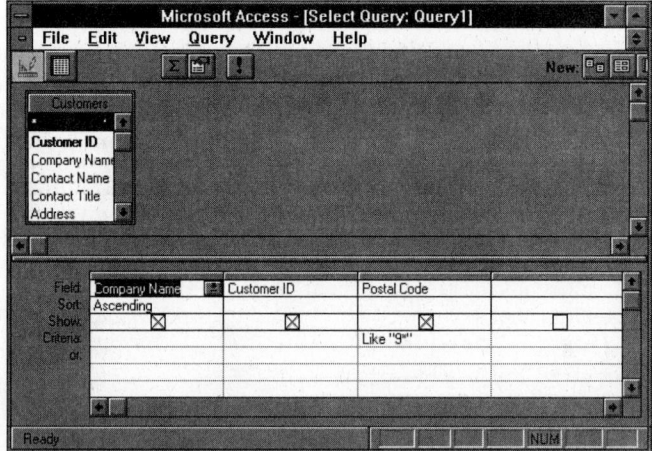

FIG. 20.3

The QBE design created by Access from the query in figure 20.2.

FIG. 20.4

The query in figure 20.3 in Datasheet view.

To change the order by which the query result is sorted, follow these steps:

1. Click the Design mode button on the toolbar, and then choose **SQL** again from the **View** menu.

2. Change **ORDER BY [Company Name]** to **ORDER BY [Postal Code],** and choose OK.

3. The query grid in Design mode displays Ascending in the Postal Code column rather than in the Company Name column, indicating that the dynaset is sorted by ZIP code.

4. Click the Run Query button on the toolbar to display the dynaset sorted in ZIP code sequence (see fig. 20.5).

Company Name	Customer ID	Postal Code
Village Food Boutique	VILLF	90071
La Tienda Granda	LATIE	91406
Rite-Buy Supermarket	RITEB	92701
Dollarwise Convenience Store	DOLLC	94103
Let's Stop N Shop	LETSS	94117
Gruenewald Delikatessen	GRUED	94701
Caesar's Mediterranean Imports	CAESM	94965
Oceanview Quickshop	OCEAQ	97006
The Big Cheese	THEBI	97201
Lonesome Pine Restaurant and Gift Shop	LONEP	97219
Lillegard's Old Country Deli	LILLO	97219
Lee's Oriental Food Mart	LEESO	97229
Live Oak Hotel Gift Shop	LIVEO	97229
Great Lakes Food Market	GREAL	97403
Frugal Feast Comestibles	FRUGF	97403
O'Connor's Town Store	OCONT	97435
Gorham Street Co-op	GORHS	97720
Hungry Coyote Import Store	HUNGC	97827

FIG. 20.5

The query in figure 20.4 in ZIP code order.

Using the SQL Aggregate Functions

If you want to use the aggregate functions to determine totals, averages, or statistical data for groups of records with a common attribute value, you add a GROUP BY clause to your SQL statement. You can further limit the result of the GROUP BY clause with the optional HAVING qualifier:

```
SELECT [ALL¦DISTINCT¦DISTINCTROW]
    aggregate_function(field_name) AS alias
    [,select_list]
    FROM table_names
[WHERE search_criteria]
GROUP BY group_criteria
    [HAVING aggregate_criteria]
[ORDER BY column_criteria]
```

The *select_list* includes the aggregate function with a field name as its argument. The field used as the argument of an aggregate function must have a numeric data type. The additional SQL keywords and parameters required to create a GROUP BY query are shown in the following list:

■ AS *alias* assigns a caption to the column. It is created in an Access QBE query by the *alias:aggregate_function(field name)* in the Field row of the Query grid.

■ GROUP BY *group_criteria* establishes the column on which the grouping is based. In this column, Group by appears in the Totals row of the Query grid.

■ HAVING *aggregate_criteria* is one or more criteria applied to the column that contains the *aggregate_function*. The *aggregate_criteria* of HAVING is applied after the grouping is completed. WHERE *search_criteria* operates before the grouping occurs; at this point, no aggregate values exist to test against *aggregate_criteria*. Access substitutes HAVING for WHERE when you add criteria to a column with the *aggregate_function*.

The following GROUP BY query is written in ANSI SQL, except for the # symbols that enclose date and time values:

```
SELECT [Ship Region], SUM([Order Amount]) AS Sales
   FROM Orders
WHERE [Ship Country]="USA"
   AND [Order Date] BETWEEN #01/1/91# AND #12/31/91#
GROUP BY [Ship Region]
   HAVING SUM([Order Amount]) >10000
ORDER BY SUM([Order Amount]) DESC;
```

The query results in a dynaset that consists of two columns: Ship Regions (states) and the totals of Order Amount for each Ship Region in the United States, for the year 1991. The dynaset is sorted in descending order.

To create an SQL GROUP BY query in Access, follow these steps:

1. Repeat steps 1 through 7 of the example in "Using SQL Statements To Create Access Queries" and enter the GROUP BY example code in the SQL dialog box (see fig. 20.6).

2. Choose OK to close the SQL dialog box. Your QBE GROUP BY query design appears as shown in figure 20.7.

3. Click the Run Query button on the toolbar. The states in which total orders exceeding $10,000 were received in 1991 are shown ranked by order volume and displayed in Datasheet view (see fig. 20.8).

FIG. 20.6

An SQL statement, using the SUM() aggregate function.

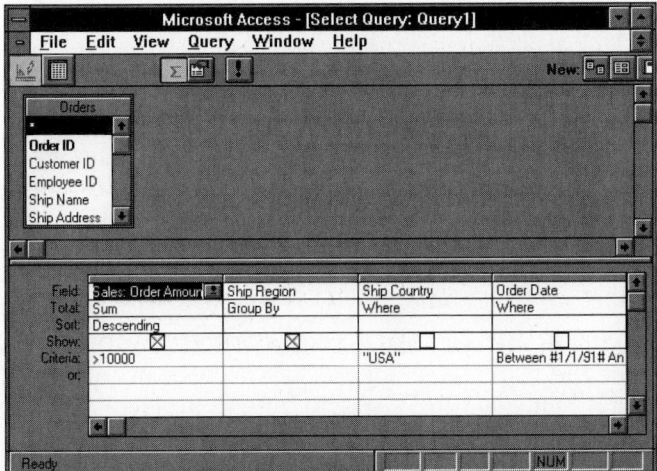

FIG. 20.7

Access's QBE design for the query in figure 20.6.

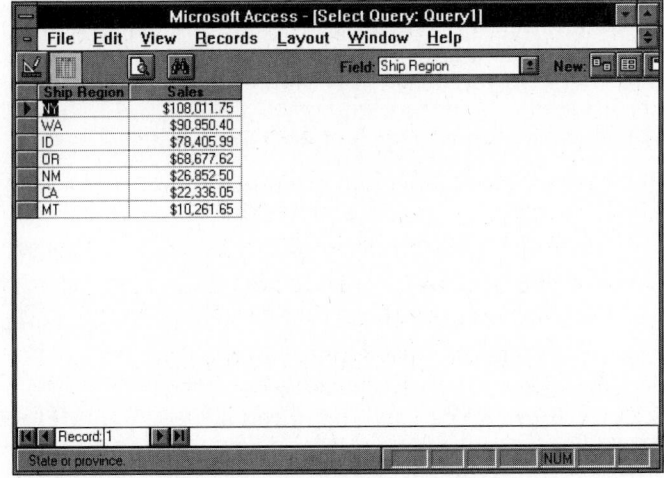

FIG. 20.8

The aggregate query design in figure 20.7 in Datasheet view.

Creating Joins with SQL

Joining two or more tables with Access QBE uses the JOIN ... ON structure that specifies the table to be joined and the relationship between the fields on which the JOIN is based:

```
SELECT [ALL|DISTINCT|DISTINCTROW]select_list
    FROM table_names
{INNER|LEFT|RIGHT} table_name JOIN join_table ON
    join_criteria
[{INNER|LEFT|RIGHT} table name JOIN join_table ON
    join_criteria]
[WHERE search_criteria]
[ORDER BY column_criteria]
```

The elements of the JOIN statement are shown in the following list:

■ *table_name* JOIN *join_table* specifies the name of the table that will be joined with other tables listed in *table_names*. Each of the tables participating in a join must be included in the *table_names* list and before and after JOIN. When you specify a self-join by including two copies of the field list for a single table, the second table is distinguished from the first by adding an underscore and a digit to the table name.

One of the three types of joins—INNER, LEFT, or RIGHT—must precede the JOIN statement. INNER specifies an equi-join; LEFT, a left outer join; and RIGHT, a right outer join. The type of join is determined in Access QBE by double-clicking the line connecting the joined fields in the table and clicking option button 1, 2, or 3 in the Join Properties dialog box.

■ ON *join_criteria* specifies the two fields to be joined and the relationship between the joined fields—one field in *join_table* and one in another field in a table in *table_names*. The *join_criteria* expression contains an equal sign (=) comparison operator and returns a True or False value. If the value of the expression is True, the record in the joined table is included in the query.

The number of JOIN statements you can add to a query usually is the total number of tables participating in the query minus one. You can create more than one JOIN between a pair of tables, but the result often is difficult to predict.

The Access SQL statement for the equi-join between the Personnel Actions and Employees tables based on ID values in each table is shown in figure 20.9 and Employees is repeated in the FROM clause. The copy of Employees is associated with the JOIN statement and is required in Access SQL joins. The JOIN reserved word in Access SQL creates the lines that connect the joined fields in Query Design View mode.

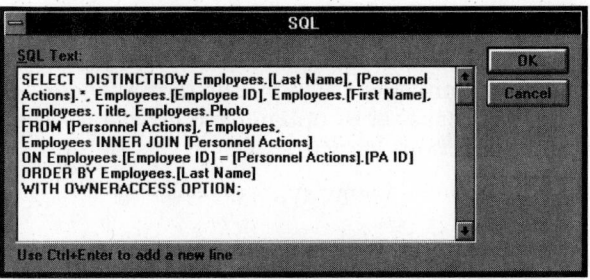

FIG. 20.9

The Access SQL implementation of an equi-join.

You create equi-joins in ANSI SQL with the WHERE clause, using the same expression to join the fields as that of the ON clause in the JOIN command. The WHERE clause is more flexible than the JOIN ... ON structure because you can use other operators such as BETWEEN...AND, LIKE, >, and <. These operators result in error messages when they are substituted for the equal sign (=) in the ON clause of the JOIN statement. You don't have to repeat the Employees field in this case. The ANSI SQL statement in figure 20.10, and in the following text, gives the same result as the Access SQL statement in figure 20.9:

```
SELECT DISTINCTROW Employees.[Last Name], [Personnel
Actions].*, Employees.[Employee ID], Employees.[First Name],
Employees.Title, Employees.Photo
FROM [Personnel Actions], Employees,
Employees INNER JOIN [Personnel Actions]
ON Employees.[Employee ID] = [Personnel Actions].[PA ID]
ORDER BY Employees.[Last Name]
WITH OWNERACCESS OPTION;
```

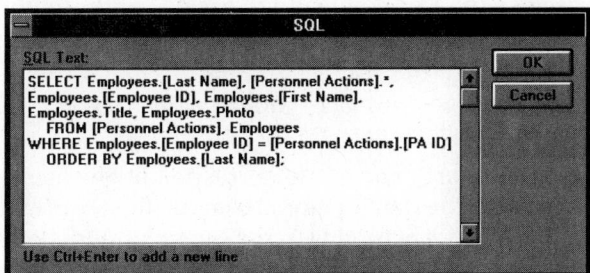

FIG. 20.10

The equi-join in figure 20.9, created by a WHERE clause.

You create multiple joins with WHERE clauses by separating each join expression with an AND operator. When you use the WHERE clause to create equi-joins in Access, the join lines don't appear between the fields in Query Design mode.

Specifying Action Query Syntax

Data-manipulation commands are implemented by Access's action queries: append, delete, make-table, update, and cross-tab. The syntax for each type of Access action query is shown in this section.

Append queries use the following syntax:

```
INSERT INTO dest_table
   SELECT [ALL¦DISTINCT¦DISTINCTROW] select_list
      FROM source_table
   [WHERE append_criteria]
```

If you omit the WHERE clause, all the records of *source_table* are appended to *dest_table*.

Delete queries take the following form:

```
DELETE FROM table_name
   [WHERE delete_criteria]
```

If you omit the optional WHERE clause in a delete query, you delete all data in *table_name*.

Make-table queries use the following syntax:

```
SELECT [ALL¦DISTINCT¦DISTINCTROW] select_list
   INTO new_table
   FROM source_table
      [WHERE append_criteria]
```

To copy the original table, substitute an asterisk (*) for *select_list* and omit the optional WHERE clause.

Update queries use the SET command to assign values to individual columns:

```
UPDATE table_name
   SET column_name = value [, column_name = value]
   [WHERE update_criteria]
```

Separate multiple *column_names* and corresponding values by commas if you want to update the data in more than one field. Access SQL doesn't support the ANSI SQL VALUES keyword for adding records to tables.

Cross-tab queries use the Access SQL keywords TRANSFORM and PIVOT:

```
TRANSFORM aggregate_function(field_name) AS alias
   SELECT [ALL¦DISTINCT¦DISTINCTROW] select_list
      FROM table_name
   PIVOT Format(field_name),"format_type") IN (column_list);
```

TRANSFORM defines a cross-tab query, and PIVOT specifies the GROUP BY characteristics plus the fixed column names. Cross-tab queries, like queries with multiple or nested JOINs, are better left to Access QBE to create the query. You can edit the query as necessary after Access has written the initial SQL statement.

Adding IN To Use Tables in Another Database

Access enables you to open only one database at a time, unless you write code to open another table with an Action Basic function or procedure. You can use Access SQL's IN clause, however, with a make-table, append, update, or delete query to create or modify tables in another database. Access provides only the capability to make a table or append records to a table in another Access database through graphical QBE. You click the Another Database option in the Query Properties dialog box for the make-table or append query and type the file name of the other database.

You have to write a SQL query or edit a query created by Access to update data or delete records in tables contained in another database of any type, or to perform any operation on a dBASE, Paradox, or Btrieve file that isn't attached to your database. The SQL query uses the IN clause to specify the external database or table file. The advantage of using the IN clause is simplicity: You don't have to attach the table before using it. The disadvantage of using the IN clause is that indexes associated with dBASE and Paradox tables aren't updated when the content of the table is modified.

Working with Another Access Database

You can create a table in another Access database, delete all the records and then append the records back to the table from which the records were deleted, using the IN clause to specify the name of the other database that contains the table. To try an example of using the IN clause, follow these steps:

1. Choose **S**QL from the **V**iew menu, delete any existing text, and type the following line in the SQL Text box (see fig. 20.11).

```
    SELECT * INTO Customers IN OLE_"OBJS.MDB"
FROM Customers;
```

   SELECT ... INTO creates a make-table query.

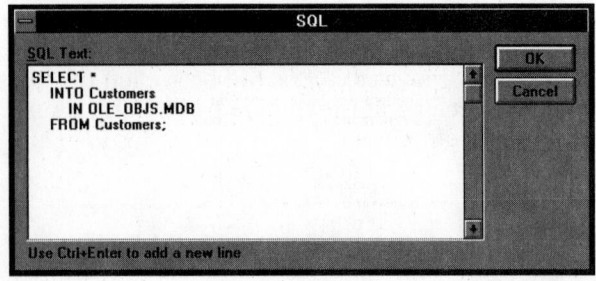

FIG. 20.11

A query that
creates a table
in another
database.

 2. Click the Run Query button on the toolbar to make the new Customers table in your OLE_OBJS database. Choose OK when the message box advises you of the number of records that are copied to the new Customers table created in OLE_OBJS.

3. Choose **S**QL from the **V**iew menu again, delete the existing text, and type the following line (see fig. 20.12):

   DELETE * FROM Customers IN "OLE_OBJS.MDB"

   DELETE ... FROM creates a delete query.

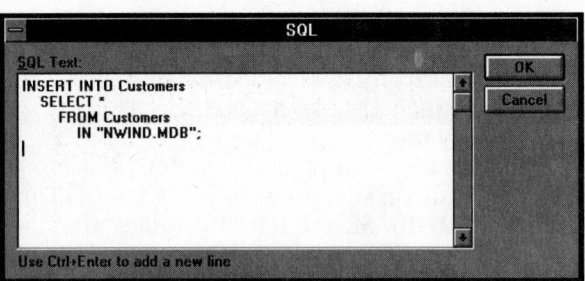

FIG. 20.12

Deleting all
records from a
table in another
database.

4. Choose OK to close the SQL dialog box. The message box that warns when you are operating on a table in a different database appears, as shown in figure 20.13.

 5. Click the Run Query button on the toolbar to delete the records in the OLE_OBJS Customers table. Choose OK to confirm the deletion of the records.

 6. Close Query1 and don't save the changes.

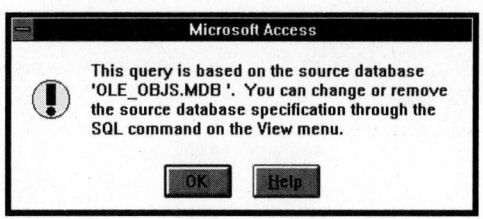

FIG. 20.13

The message box, warning that you are manipulating data in another database.

To append the records you deleted back into the Customers table of the OLE_OBJS database, follow these steps:

1. Choose **O**pen from the **F**ile menu, and choose your OLE_OBJS database, which contains the Customers table with no records.

2. Click the Query button on the Database window, and then click the New button. Close the Add Table dialog box without adding a table.

3. Type the following line in the SQL Text box (see fig. 20.14):

   INSERT INTO Customers SELECT * FROM Customers IN "NWIND.MDB"

   INSERT INTO creates an append query.

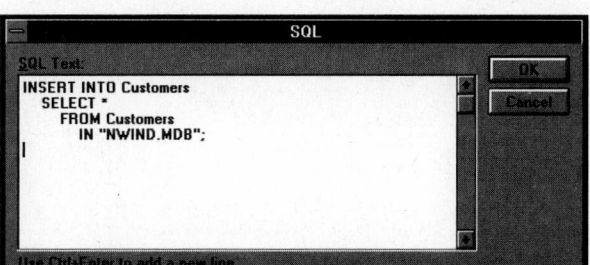

FIG. 20.14

A query to append records to a table in another database.

4. Choose OK and confirm operation with the NWIND.MDB database.

5. Click the Run Query button on the toolbar to add the records from NWIND's customers table. Confirm the append by choosing OK in the message box.

Although you accomplish the same objectives by attaching a table from another database or copying tables to the Clipboard and pasting the table into another database, using a SQL query for this purpose is a more straightforward process.

Using the IN Clause with Other Types of Databases

You can create or modify dBASE, Paradox, and Btrieve tables by specifying in an IN statement the path to the file and the file type, using the following special Access SQL syntax reserved for foreign database file types:

```
IN "[drive:\]path" "database_type"
```

The *path* to the file is required, even if the database is located in your \ACCESS directory; you receive an error if you omit the path entry. You can use"" to identify the current directory.

The *database_type* expression must be enclosed in quotation marks. It consists of one of the four foreign file types supported by ISAM DLLs supplied with Access, followed by a semicolon: dBASE III;, dBASE IV;, Paradox;, or Btrieve;. The semicolon after the file type name is required, but the database file type names are not case-sensitiv—dbase; is acceptable to Access. You can use the IN statement with files connected by way of ODBC; attaching client-server files by using the ODBC Administrator, however, is the preferred method.

You can create a dBASE III table from a query by using the syntax shown in figure 20.15.

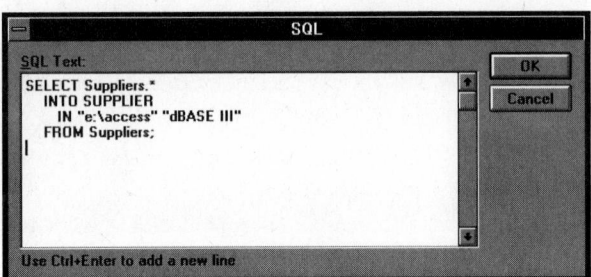

FIG. 20.15

Creating a dBASE III table from an SQL query.

You can append records to a dBASE III file with the syntax shown in figure 20.16. In deleting and updating records in foreign tables, use the syntax shown in the section "Action Query Syntax," with the IN clause added.

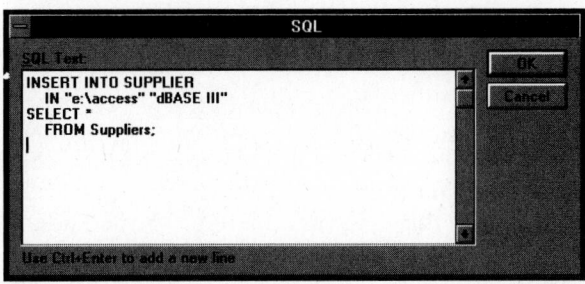

FIG. 20.16

Appending
records to a
dBASE III table
with a SQL
query.

Using SQL Statements in Forms, Reports, and Macros

If you create a large number of forms and reports based on queries or that use queries, or if you use macros to run select and action queries, the query list in your Database window can become cluttered. You can use SQL queries you write or copy from the SQL dialog box in place of the names of query objects and then delete the query from your database. SQL statements can be used for the purposes in the following list:

■ *Record Source property of forms and reports:* Substitute the SQL query text for the name of the query in the Record Source text box.

■ *Row Source property in list boxes and combo boxes on a form:* Using a SQL statement rather than a query object gives you greater control over the sequence of the columns in your list box.

■ *Argument of the RunSQL() macro action:* Only SQL statements that create action queries can be used with the RunSQL() macro action.

■ *Parameter of the SQL property of an Action Basic function that creates a select query or modifies an existing query:* You use the RunCode() macro action to create the query and then display it with the OpenQuery() macro action. Using this technique creates the equivalent of the RunSQL() macro action for select queries. The technique is described in Part IV, "Powering Access with Macros."

You can create and test your Access SQL statements in Query Design mode and then copy the statement to the Clipboard. Paste the text into the text box for the property or into your Access Basic module. Then close the test query design without saving it.

Chapter Summary

This chapter described the basic details of the use of Structured Query Language in Access. Important differences between the ANSI and Access implementations of SQL were outlined for readers who have used SQL in other database management applications. The syntax of the SQL example statements in this chapter adhere to ANSI standard syntax as much as possible. Using WHERE clauses rather than JOIN statements can save substantial amounts of typing when you write your own SQL statements. Writing your own SQL statements frees you from having to use some of the rigid conventions of the QBE methods implemented by Access.

Chapter 21, "Using Access in a Network Environment," introduces the use of Access in a network environment. Both client-server and peer-to-peer network applications are described. When you share database files with others on a network, data security becomes a major consideration. Database administration and Access's techniques for granting and revoking permissions to other users of your databases also are discussed in Chapter 21.

Using Access in a Network Environment

Personal computer networking is one of the fastest-growing areas in the PC marketplace. Many large organizations are engaged in downsizing database applications to personal computer networks. *Downsizing* means moving a database system that runs on a costly large-scale computer such as a mainframe, to smaller, lower-priced computers such as PCs. Small- to moderate-size organizations have discovered that installing a PC network can increase productivity and reduce the required investment in computing hardware. An organization need purchase only a single laser printer if all users can share it on a network. The cost of fixed disk drives is reduced when users share large files, rather than keep multiple independent copies on local disk drives.

Reducing operating costs is the principal incentive for installing PC networks. In many cases, savings in the investment for required PC components is the sole consideration in the decision to install a network. When you use a database application, however, productivity plays the most important role in the network decisionmaking process. The capability to share up-to-date information contained in a database system among many users is a strong incentive to install a PC network, because it increases productivity. Increasing productivity with a networked database system can, in turn, reduce operating costs by many times the savings offered by the reduction of the investment when you share computer peripheral equipment.

Another improvement in productivity when using a PC network is the capability of networked computers to send electronic messages (E-mail) to one another. E-mail applications such as Microsoft Mail and Lotus cc:Mail can improve productivity by reducing the never-ending flow of paper memoranda between members of larger organizations. You can attach files to e-mail messages and include graphic images or sounds in them. A new class of software, called *workgroup* or *scheduling* applications, enables users to schedule appointments and meetings jointly and contribute to jointly authored documents.

Access will be the first networked Windows application used by many readers of this book. The almost simultaneous release of Microsoft Access and Windows for Workgroups, a version of Windows 3.1 that provides highly simplified installation of very low-cost and easy-to-administer PC networks, should appeal to first-time network users. If you don't have a network now and you plan to create Access applications to be shared by other users, Windows for Workgroups is a logical choice as a "starter" network.

Microsoft Corporation designed Access specifically for use in a networked environment. Many of Access's features, especially the security system, were added primarily for network operation. If your network is already set up, you can choose to install Access on the network or install only the files you intend to share. If you don't have a network when you begin using Access, the process is simple to change your database files from single-user to shared status when you install a network. This chapter explains how to set up and use Access in a variety of network environments, use the ODBC Administrator to connect to network client-server databases, share database files, establish database security, and administer a multiuser database system.

Defining the Network Environment

A computer network consists of two or more computers that are connected, usually by electrical cabling. The purpose of a network is to enable computers to share *network resources*. The most common shared network resources are files on fixed disk drives and printers, but you can share CD-ROM drives, modems, fax cards, scanners, and a wide range of other devices by designating them as network resources. The method used to share network resources is determined by the type of network, server-based or peer-to-peer, you install.

Server-Based Networks

The majority of PCs that are connected to networks in North America are workstations connected to one or more server computers. *Workstations* are PCs that are equipped with a network adapter card and are connected by a cable to a computer, called the *server*, that is dedicated to providing resources to workstations. Diskless workstations that have no fixed or disk drives are sometimes used on networks for which data security is of paramount concern. The server has at least one network adapter card to which the workstations' cables connect. The method of installing cabling between multiple workstations and one or more servers depends on the type of network installed and the type of adapter cards used. Network adapter cards and cabling is the subject of a later section. Figure 21.1 is a diagram of a server-based network that shares files and a laser printer with four workstations.

Dedicated Server and
Shared Printer

Workstations

FIG. 21.1

A typical small network with a dedicated network file server.

The primary function of most servers is to supply resources and not to run applications, other than those applications necessary to administer the network. Client-server database applications, discussed in a section that follows, are exceptions, as are applications that are designed specifically for server use, such as Novell's NetWare Loadable Modules (NLMs). Modern PC servers use Intel 80486DX microprocessors and have very large disk drives, often with capacities exceeding 1 gigabyte (one billion bytes). More sophisticated servers use multiple microprocessors and disk drives for increased speed, storage capacity, and reliability. Other shared resources, such as printers and CD-ROM drives, are attached to adapter cards installed in the server. Servers usually include tape drives for backing up the shared files.

When all the workstations and the servers to which they are connected are located in the same area, such as single building or a floor of a building, the system is called a local area network (LAN). LANs can be connected by high-speed telephone lines or microwave radio links to create wide area networks (WANs). *Distributed* networks are created when any workstation can share at least the file resources of any server located on any LAN in the wide area network. An *enterprise-wide* network is defined as a distributed network in which *every* authorized employee of an organization can share server files, no matter where in the world the employee may be stationed.

Besides adapter cards and cables, you need network operating system (NOS) software so that the workstations and servers that comprise a LAN can communicate with their adapter cards and with each other via the cabling. Novell NetWare is the most common server-based network software used in the U.S.; Novell, Inc., reportedly has about 60 percent of the U.S. market for network software. Novell employs its own operating system and file structure for NetWare. Other popular server-based network operating systems include Microsoft LAN Manager and IBM's LAN Server (both of which use OS/2 as the operating system) 3-Com, and Banyan VINES. Windows NT will be used as the operating system for a future version of Microsoft LAN Manager, expected to be released in mid-1993.

Server-based networks require a network administrator who is thoroughly familiar with the workings of the NOS, server resources, and other hardware, and who performs other services such as ensuring that current and valid backup copies of all files exist. The network administrator installs new networked applications, and authorizes or denies access to applications and data files stored on the server. Depending on the size of the network, the duties of the network administrator comprise a full-time or part-time job.

Peer-to-Peer Networks

The first popular PC networks, such as IBM's PC-LAN, were *peer-to-peer* networks. A peer-to-peer network doesn't require a dedicated server computer; any computer attached to the network can be designated as a server and share its resources with other PCs. When a PC acts as a server in a peer-to-peer network, it must divide the processing time it devotes to running local applications and sharing resources with other peers. Designating every PC on a peer-to-peer network as a server is possible, but not common.

Peer-to-peer systems use DOS as the operating system and most add DOS drivers to perform network services. DOS drivers usually are specified in your CONFIG.SYS file and are loaded into your computer's memory during the boot process. These drivers make directories of disk drives on peer servers appear as new drive letters, such as an F or G on peer workstations. Similarly, workstations can designate a printer that is shared by a peer server as the workstation's own LPT1 or LPT2. Figure 21.2 is a diagram of a peer-to-peer network with five computers, any of which can act as a peer server. The computer in the lower center of figure 21.2 shares its local printer with other workstations.

Shared Printer — **Workstations and Peer Servers**

FIG. 21.2

A small peer-to-peer network.

Most peer-to-peer networks are administered by persons whose PCs are connected to the network, not by a skilled network administrator. Each user of a PC that acts as a server grants permission to other users to share files in specific directories of his or her fixed disk drive and is responsible for backing up locally stored files. Peer-to-peer networks are designed for easy installation and operation; network operating speed (the time it takes to read or write shared files) is often sacrificed for operational simplicity. In most peer-to-peer installations, users of applications such as Access install the application on their own fixed disks, rather than running the application from a master copy on a server peer, because of the reduced network operating performance when the server is running one of its own applications.

Artisoft Corporation's LANtastic is one of the most popular peer-to-peer network operating systems for PCs, and Novel offers NetWare Lite as an entry-level NOS. Both of these networks are designed primarily to run DOS applications, but can be used to share files used by Windows applications. AppleTalk for Apple Macintosh computers is a peer-to-peer LAN of moderate performance that is built into the computer itself. Windows for Workgroups is a peer-to-peer NOS that has been optimized for sharing files and resources used by Windows applications; the following section discusses Windows for Workgroups.

Windows for Workgroups

A *workgroup* is a collection of computer users that are connected by a network and share a common responsibility or interest. Creating workgroups isn't limited to peer-to-peer networks; the workgroup approach often is used in server-based LANs and WANs, where it is usually called a *domain*. For the purposes of the network, a workgroup consists of computers, identified by name, that share a set of files in a designated directory or several directories of one or more server computers. Sharing directories is discussed in the section, "Sharing Your Access Database Files with Other Users," later in the chapter. A workgroup can consist of a few users or all the members of a small organization.

Windows for Workgroups provides all the capabilities of Windows 3.1 and adds the following new features:

- *File Manager* is provided with a toolbar and several new functions that let you share directories with other members of a workgroup. You can share a directory so that some members of the group can only read the files, and others can read and modify files. You use File Manager to connect a directory shared by another user as a network drive, such as E, on your computer. File Manager enables you to see who in your workgroup is using the files you are sharing.

- *Print Manager* also is provided with a new toolbar that enables you to share your printer with others on the network and use printers shared with you by others. Print Manager's display has been changed to show you who is using your shared printer.

- *Microsoft Mail* is added to your Main group of Program Manager. Mail is a sophisticated e-mail processing system for creating and managing messages between users on your network or other networks. You need an application called a *gateway* to exchange mail in the formats used by other e-mail applications. Microsoft Mail's main window that lists your messages is shown in figure 21.3.

- *Schedule+* is another application that Windows for Workgroups adds to your Main group. Schedule+ lets you set up your own projects, tasks within projects, and appointments with others in your workgroup. You can share your schedule so that other workgroup members can add entries to it. The appointments entry window of Schedule+ is shown in figure 21.4. The numbers to the left of the calendar are week numbers; if you are dealing with European or Scandinavian organizations, you will find the week numbers feature very useful.

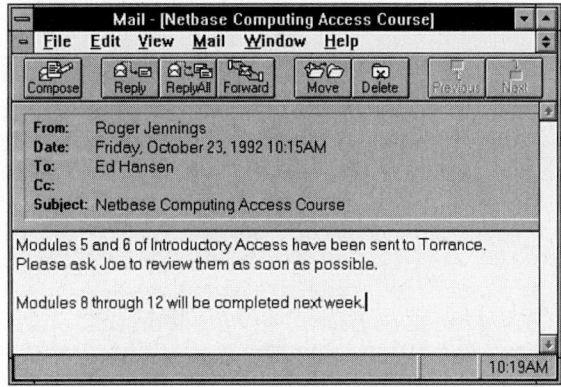

FIG. 21.3

The main
window of the
Microsoft Mail
application.

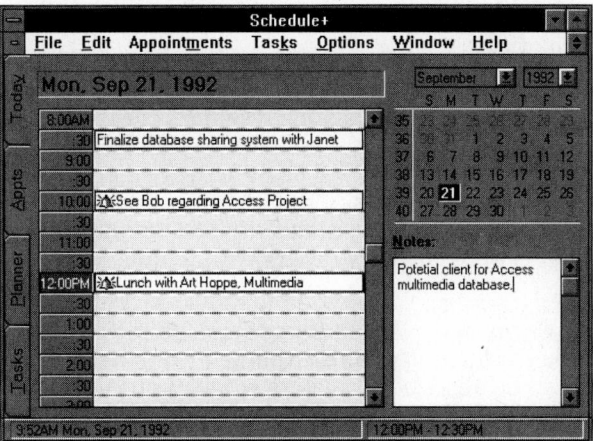

FIG. 21.4

Microsoft
Schedule+'s
appointments
window.

Schedule+ pops up reminders of the appointments you have set or others in your workgroup have set for you, as illustrated by figure 21.5. You can set the number of minutes before the appointment that the reminder will appear with the General Options command of the Options menu.

■ *Windows Clipbook* replaces the familiar Clipboard icon. Clipbook lets you share the content of your Clipboard with others. If you copy an OLE object in one of your compound documents to the Clipbook and designate it as shared, others in the workgroup can link to the object. Changes made to the shared object by any member of the workgroup are reflected in all the documents that contain the object.

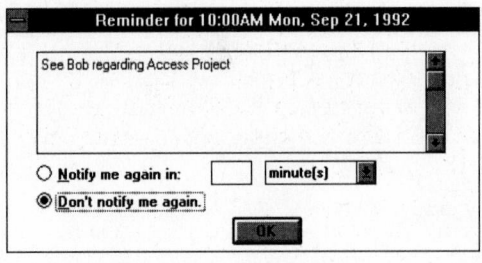

FIG. 21.5

The pop-up window of Schedule+ that reminds you of appointments.

Network

- *Control Panel* receives a new Network icon that enables you to change your computer name, the workgroup to which you belong, and your password. You use the Network function of Control Panel to allocate the percentage of your computer's resources that you devote to sharing files and printers with others. You also can change the setup of your network adapter card with the Network function.

- *Chat*, *Net Watcher*, and *WinMeter* are three applets that Workgroups for Windows adds to your Accessories group. Chat enables you to engage in typed conversations with other members of your workgroup. Net Watcher provides a history of the usage by other members of the resources you are sharing. Win-Meter monitors the percentage of your computer's processing time that is consumed by others with whom you are sharing your resources.

- *Hearts* is a game that up to four users can play interactively on the network. Productivity gains expected from installation of a network may be absorbed by users who become addicted to this game. Unlike Solitaire, Hearts consumes the formerly productive efforts of up to four network users at a time.

Windows for Workgroups includes features associated with conventional server-based networks, but it is lower in cost and easier to administer than a server-based NOS. Also, Windows for Workgroups does not require investment in a dedicated server. If you use Windows for Workgroups as a prototype of a larger scale network for sharing Access databases, you don't lose the investment you made in adapter cards, cabling, and the Windows for Workgroups software when you upgrade to a server-based NOS.

Using Windows for Workgroups with Other Networks

Windows for Workgroups also can connect workstations to Microsoft LAN Manager and Novell NetWare networks. The Control Panel's Network function includes only these two network operating systems as

Other Network options. When you add another network, you can share files and other resources provided by the network server and those shared by workgroup peer servers. Workgroup for Windows is said to "run on top of" the other network system; the features of Windows for Workgroups are added to the capabilities of the server-based network already installed.

Preparing To Install Windows for Workgroups

PCs that are to share their file and printer resources require at least an 80386SX microprocessor and 4M of RAM (640K of conventional memory and 3,072K of extended memory) and must run in 386 Enhanced mode. To use resources shared by other peer services, you need at least an 80286 processor and 1M of RAM to run in Standard mode, but 2M of RAM is the minimum recommended memory for running Windows 3.1.

The introduction to this book made the assumption that you have Windows 3+ (preferably Windows 3.1) installed on your computer. Installing Windows for Workgroups requires about 3.5M of additional disk space on the drive devoted to Windows. If you use Stac Electronics' Stacker, or a similar file compression application, the compression ratio of the added files is about the same as those for Windows 3.1, approximately 2.0:1. Installing Windows for Workgroups as a separate application requires about 9.5M of disk space.

Besides PCs with memory and free disk space meeting these requirements, you need network adapter cards and network cabling for each computer; this equipment is the subject of the next section. If you choose EtherNet or token-ring cards and cabling, the combination can be used with Windows for Workgroups and any other commonly used PC NOS.

Network Adapter Cards and Cabling

The network adapter cards you choose determine the type of cabling between the computers on the network. In most cases, the cost of installing cables exceeds by far the cost of the adapter cards. The majority of network operating systems can use a wide range of adapter cards and cabling systems, some of which are described in the following list:

■ *EtherNet* is presently the most popular method of cabling between networked computers. EtherNet adapter cards come in 8-bit (PC) and 16-bit (AT) versions and are designed for *thin EtherNet*, *thick EtherNet*, and *10BaseT* cabling. Cabling terminology is explained later in this section. The cost of EtherNet adapter cards declined sharply in mid-1992 due to intense competition between manufacturers; 16-bit cards for thin EtherNet cabling are advertised at prices of about $100. Intel is one the major suppliers of EtherNet cards using the integrated circuits it manufactures; Intel's EtherExpress 16 EtherNet card is one of their most popular models.

■ *Token-ring* adapter cards and cabling were developed by IBM Corporation. Token-ring systems offer high network operating speeds and are available for IBM mini- and mainframe computers. Token-ring networks are generally more costly than EtherNet to implement, but the cost differential has begun to decrease, even taking into account the declining cost of EtherNet cards. Token-ring systems are *redundant*, meaning that if the cable is cut or one system fails in a token-ring network, it continues to function (but at a slower speed).

■ *ARCnet* and *proprietary* network adapter cards, such as those manufactured by Artisoft for LANtastic, were originally offered as lower-cost substitutes for EtherNet and token-ring devices. Now that EtherNet card prices have declined, the cost incentive to use nonstandard network cards has disappeared. Windows for Workgroups doesn't support connection to Novell networks with ARCnet adapter cards.

EtherNet adapter cards that are configured for installation by software instead of on-board switches, such as those manufactured by Intel Corporation, aren't necessarily the least expensive but are the easiest to install, especially with Workgroups for Windows.

EtherNet and token-ring offer the following three choices of cabling:

■ *Thin EtherNet* (alias Thinnet) uses a coaxial cable about 1/4-inch in diameter that connects computers to one another and to the server in a server-based network. The cable is similar to that used to connect your television set to a community antenna or to a cable television service. The cable has a single inner connector with plastic insulation, a braided shield, and a plastic outer sheath. Connections are made with BNC connectors; a T-shaped connector is used to connect to the adapter cards. Terminating connectors are used at each end of the cable to prevent interference caused by reflections of signals traveling over the cable. You can purchase thin EtherNet cable and connectors at most Radio Shack stores.

■ *Thick EtherNet* (also called Thicknet) and standard token-ring uses a thicker coaxial cable that is more expensive than thin EtherNet cabling. However, you can install more computers on a thick EtherNet and token-ring cable. Both thick EtherNet and token-ring cables use special transceiver cables that connect the adapter card and the connection to the coaxial cable (called a transceiver on EtherNets and a Multi-Access Unit or MAU on token-rings). Two types of coaxial cables are used with token-ring installations, but Type 1 is the most common.

■ *10BaseT* cabling consists of twisted pairs of wires with plastic (RJ-45) connectors, similar to those used for telephone installations. Connections are made from each computer to a concentrator (also called a hub) using shielded (STP) or unshielded twisted-pair (UTP) cabling. STP provides increased immunity from outside interference (noise). The cost of the 10BaseT hubs (also called IEEE 802.3 multiport repeaters) is offset by the lower cost of the STP/UTP wiring. In many cases, you can attach computers and hubs to unused pairs in existing telephone wiring. Type 3 token-ring installations require two pairs for the connections; EtherNet requires only a single pair.

If you are installing 10 or fewer computers on a network and the distance between the computers isn't great, thin EtherNet is usually the most economical choice, because you don't need 10BaseT hubs. Some EtherNet adapter cards provide both thin EtherNet and 10BaseT connections, so you can start with thin EtherNet and convert to 10BaseT cabling when you add more computers to the network.

Installing Access on a Network

If you are using a server-based system, two ways exist to install Access in a network environment:

■ Install Access on the network server. All workstations run the server's copy of Access and don't require a copy of Access on their local disk drives. This approach saves disk space on the workstations but usually results in slower operation of Access. The degree of impairment of operating speed depends on your network's performance and the number of users who are accessing the network simultaneously. A full installation of Access requires about 15M of server disk space. This method is discussed in the following section, "Installing Access on a Network Server."

■ Install a copy of Access on each workstation that will use the application from an individual set of distribution disks or from the network server. Access requires between about 3M and 15M of disk space, depending on the features you include in the workstation installation. This is the only installation method recommended for computers connected in a peer-to-peer network. Two alternative methods of performing this installation are discussed in sections, "Installing Access on Individual Workstations" and "Installing Access on Workstations for Users of Applications," later in this section.

You need an individual copy of the Access software for each workstation that uses Access or a license for each workstation that uses the application. For additional details, refer to the license information that Microsoft supplies with Access.

The Microsoft Professional Toolkit for Access includes a run-time version of Access. Run-time Access consumes much less disk space than Access itself, because it enables users to run applications you create but not create or modify applications. Run-time Access enables multiple workstations to run Access applications without an individual license for each workstation. You can install run-time Access on the server or local workstations; installation of run-time Access on each workstation is recommended, because you gain operating speed with a much lower disk space penalty.

Do not attempt to share the complete or run-time version of Access on a peer-to-peer network. Peer-to-peer networks are designed for sharing data files, not the executable (.EXE) and help (.HLP) files of applications. The computer and network resources required to run Access from a peer server slow applications running on the server to a crawl and greatly increase network traffic.

Installing Access on a Network Server

Access is installed on a network server using a technique that is almost identical to installation on a local fixed disk drive. To install Access on a network server, complete the following steps:

1. Create the directory on the server drive where you plan to install Access. \DATABASE is a suggested name for this directory. Your network administrator usually will create the directory for you.

2. Close all open Windows applications.

3. Using a workstation, log on the network drive that corresponds to the directory that you or the system administrator created for Access in step 1. Depending on the NOS in use, adding the network drive may require changes in your CONFIG.SYS, AUTOEXEC.BAT, or other network-related files.

4. Insert Disk 1 of the Access distribution disk set into drive A or drive B.

5. Choose **R**un from Program Manager's **F**ile menu.

6. Type **d:\setup /a** in the Command Line text box, where *d* is the disk drive in which the distribution disk is located, and press Enter or choose OK. The /a command line switch is necessary to install Access correctly on a network server.

7. When the Access Setup application asks for the location in which to install Access, type **n:\access**, where *n* is the drive letter assigned to the server's DATABASE directory in step 3. This process creates an \ACCESS subdirectory. After you choose the drive and directory, the Installation Options dialog box appears.

8. Choose the Complete Installation option when Setup requests the type of installation desired in the Installation Options dialog box shown in figure 21.6.

FIG. 21.6

The Installation Options dialog box.

9. When you have completed the installation, create another subdirectory, \NWIND, from the root directory of the *n* drive.

10. Copy the files NWIND.MDB, NWIND.LDB, and SYSTEM.MDA from \ACCESS into \NWIND.

11. Make the \ACCESS subdirectory read-only for all users except the Access database administrator so other workstation users cannot modify the files that the subdirectory contains. Users can practice with the read-write copy of the Northwind Traders sample database you added to the \NWIND directory. The original version of the sample database you retained in \ACCESS can be used to restore the copy in \NWIND to its original state after users have modified it in practice sessions.

After you have installed Access on the server, you need to run the Setup application on each workstation that will use Access.

Installing Access on Individual Workstations

The procedure for installing Access on individual workstations depends on whether you have installed Access on a network server. If you have not installed Access on a network server, you can choose from two methods of installing Access on each workstation that is to create, modify, or run Access applications. Procedures for installing Access are described in the following sections.

Installing Access on Workstations from a Network Server

If you have installed Access on the network server, follow these steps to install the components of Access required on each workstation:

1. Close all open Windows applications.

2. Log on the network drive if necessary.

3. Choose **R**un from Program Manager's **F**ile menu.

4. Type **d:\access\setup /n** in the Command Line text box, where *d* is the network drive, and press Enter or choose OK. The /n parameter indicates that you are installing Access *from* a network.

5. When the Access Setup application asks for the location of the SYSTEM.MDA file, specify the D:\NWIND directory where the copy of the Northwind Traders sample database is located on the network server.

Access uses a special database file, SYSTEM.MDA, that contains security information and operating options for Access database files. Members of workgroups share a common SYSTEM.MDA file that usually is located in the same directory as the database file(s) to be shared by the workgroup.

Installing a Complete Copy of Access on a Workstation

If you don't install Access on a network server, set up Access in an \ACCESS directory of the local fixed disk of each workstation that will be used to create or run Access applications. In this case, you can follow the single-user installation procedure outlined in Appendix F. The procedures for sharing Access files are described in the section, "Sharing Your Access Database Files with Other Users," later in this chapter.

You can save the space occupied by the Northwind Traders sample database by sharing a copy of NWIND.MDB located on the server and not installing the drivers for dBASE, Paradox, and Btrieve files unless you need them. In this case, you choose the Custom Installation option during setup and click the drivers and Sample Files check boxes shown in figure 21.7 so that these files aren't installed. You can save additional disk space by installing the Minimum Installation of Access for users who will not create or modify applications.

FIG. 21.7

The Access Setup Options dialog box that appears when you choose Custom Setup.

The space required in your \WINDOWS directory is for Microsoft Chart and files that are used to add features of Windows 3.1, required to run Access, if you are using Windows 3.0. If you have installed Word for Windows 2.0 or another Microsoft application that installs Microsoft Graph and are running Windows 3.1, the additional disk space in your \WINDOWS directory is not required, because the files installed by Access will overwrite the previously installed versions.

Installing Access on Workstations for Users of Applications

Chances are small that all users of Access on workstations will need or want to create or modify Access applications. Many users will run only the applications you or others create. You can save a substantial amount of disk space by providing only the files required to run Access applications to these users. Choose the Minimum Installation option for these users when the Installation Options dialog box appears during setup.

If any of the applications you create include graphs created with the GraphWizard or the Graph tool, the workstation requires installation of the Microsoft Graph applet, because some OLE servers must be installed on the disk drive of the computer that uses them. To install Microsoft Graph or any other components of Access that a minimum-installation workstation indicates are missing, complete the following steps:

1. Close all open Windows applications.

2. Insert Disk 1 of the Access distribution disk set into drive A or drive B.

3. Choose **R**un from Program Manager's **F**ile menu.

4. Type **d:\setup** in the Command Line text box, where *d* is the disk drive in which the distribution disk is located, and press Enter or choose OK.

5. When the Access Setup asks for the location in which to install Access, type **c:\access**, or a different path if you installed the minimum version in a different directory. The Installation Options dialog box appears.

6. Choose the Custom Installation option when Setup requests the type of installation desired in the Installation Options dialog box shown in figure 21.6. The Access Setup Options dialog box appears (see fig. 21.7).

7. Click to unmark all the check boxes except Microsoft Graph and any missing item(s) so that only the missing items are installed.

8. Click the Continue button to install the missing items.

You can add the 3.4M MSACCESS.HLP file to a workstation using this method if your users require it. Substituting help files you write for specific applications, described in Chapter 24, "Adding On-Line Help for Users," can save a substantial amount of workstation disk space.

Deleting Unnecessary Components after Installation

If you installed Access on a workstation and included a library, such as WIZARD.MDA, that is not needed by users, you can delete WIZARD.MDA and save about 500K of disk space. When you delete WIZARD.MDA, you need to delete the corresponding entry, wizard.mda=ro, in the [Libraries] section of the MSACCESS.INI file in the \WINDOWS directory of the workstation.

You can delete unneeded import/export dynamic link libraries (DLLs) from the \ACCESS directory of workstations that use Access or client-server databases exclusively. The names of the files you can delete are listed in the [Installable ISAMs] sections of MSACCESS.INI. Make a backup copy of MSACCESS.INI before you make any changes. If you delete any of these files, you should delete the sections in MSACCESS.INI that correspond to the deleted files. If, for example, you erase PDXISAM.DLL, delete the entire [Paradox] section from MSACCESS.INI.

Using ODBC Drivers with Client-Server Database Systems

Client-server databases are designed specifically for use on server-based networks. Client-server databases have many advantages over conventional database systems, including increased database security, incorporation of all components of the database (and often all databases) in a single file, and faster access to data. The clients of a client-server database are workstations connected to the server. In these respects, Access databases and client-server databases are similar. The principal difference between Access and a typical client-server database manager, such as Microsoft SQL Server, is that the client-server application performs many operations on the server that traditionally are done by database applications running on the client workstation.

Client-server database managers (CSDBMs) accept SQL statements from client applications. The CSDBM interprets the SQL statement and executes the actions specified in the statement. If you send a select query SQL statement to the CSDBM, the CSDBM returns only the result table to the client; processing of the query occurs on the server computer. This action speeds query generation two ways: the amount of information traveling over the network is reduced, and server computers often have much more powerful and faster microprocessors than do the workstation clients.

Defining Open Database Connectivity

Access uses the Microsoft Open Data Base Connectivity (ODBC) application programming interface (API) to provide access to any database system for which ODBC *drivers* are available. An application programming interface is a standardized method by which an application communicates with elements of the computer's operating system or environment. For example, applications use the Windows API in GDI.EXE, a Windows DLL, to perform all display operations. The ODBC API enables a standard set of SQL statements in any application to be translated to commands recognized by the database. The role of ODBC drivers is explained in the following section.

The ODBC API is the first element of Microsoft's Windows Open Services Architecture (WOSA) that is intended to be used to create commercial Windows applications. Ultimately, WOSA will include a group of APIs that enable Windows applications to manipulate data residing in any format on any type of computer located anywhere in the world. Enterprise-wide sharing of data through local and wide area networks, using LAN cabling, dial-up and dedicated telephone lines, and microwave or satellite transmission now primarily employs large mainframe computers as centralized database servers.

One of today's trends in enterprise-wide computing is the use of distributed database systems. Distributed database systems enable elements of a large database to be stored on servers in different locations that act as if they were a single large server. As advanced Windows operating systems such as Windows NT are developed and WOSA becomes a reality, PCs will capture a larger share of the server market. Access is designed to play an important role in enterprise-wide, distributed database systems: creating the applications users need to view and update the myriad databases to which they can connect.

Understanding ODBC Drivers

The ODBC API consists of a driver manager and one or more ODBC drivers, as illustrated by the shaded boxes in figure 21.8. Windows uses drivers to adapt its standard API to specific combinations of hardware such as displays, keyboards, and printers. Likewise, the ODBC API uses drivers to translate instructions passed from the application through the driver manager to instructions compatible with various DBMs. When the ODBC driver manager receives instructions from Access intended for a data source, such as a SQL Server database, the driver manager opens the appropriate ODBC driver for the database. The relationship of the ODBC driver manager and drivers parallels Access's built-in JET (Joint Engine Technology) driver manager and the drivers used to connect to Access, dBASE, Paradox, and Btrieve files.

FIG. 21.8

A comparison of the ODBC and JET driver systems used with Access.

ODBC drivers are classified as one of the following two types:

- *Single-tier* drivers process ODBC actions, such as opening and closing a database or a table file, and SQL statements. Single-tier drivers are required for DBMs that don't process SQL statements directly. The widely used PC DBMs fall into this category; if SQL is offered, the application, rather than the database, processes the SQL statements. The drivers included with Access for connecting to dBASE, Paradox, and Btrieve databases are single-tier drivers (but they aren't ODBC drivers).

- *Multiple-tier* drivers process ODBC actions but pass SQL statements directly to the data source. All popular client-server DBMs that can run on PCs and most mini- and mainframe DBMs process SQL statements directly. The ODBC drivers shown in the list that follows are multiple-tier drivers, because the CSDBMs with which the drivers are used process SQL statements directly.

One ODBC driver is required for each type of client-server database whose tables you want to attach to an Access database, but a single driver can be used to connect to several databases of the same type. Each connection to a database is called an *instance* of a driver.

The ODBC API is based on a standard called the X/Open SQL Call Level Interface (CLI) developed by the SQL Access Group, an organization comprised of hardware manufacturers, software suppliers, and users of SQL databases. Microsoft has published the standards for creating ODBC drivers, so any DBM supplier can make its database product compatible with Access by writing the appropriate driver. Microsoft has stated that it intends to provide ODBC drivers for the following client-server databases:

- *Microsoft SQL Server* databases on LAN Manager, Novell, and Banyan networks and *Sybase SQL Server* databases on UNIX servers.

- *Oracle* databases on UNIX, OS/2, and other server platforms.

- *Rdb* databases on DEC VAX computers.

- *IBM DB2* (level 1 and level 2) databases on IBM mainframe and minicomputers.

When Version 1.0 of Access was released, only the ODBC driver for Microsoft SQL Server Versions 1.1 and higher was compatible with Access. Microsoft has stated its intention to supply other drivers in the preceding list, as each is certified, with interim releases of Access 1.0.

You can expect the publishers of major client-server database management systems to provide ODBC drivers for their products as Microsoft's ODBC API becomes more widely used. If the client-server DBM you are using is not one of the four included in the preceding list, check with the supplier to determine whether an ODBC-compliant driver is available for the DBM and whether the driver is compatible with Access.

Installing the Access ODBC Driver for SQL Server

Installing the Access ODBC driver for Microsoft SQL Server is a three- or four-stage process, depending on the version of SQL Server installed. Following are the basic steps in the process:

- Adding a special set of stored procedures to each SQL Server to which workstations running Access are connected if you are running a SQL Server version prior to 4.2.

- Granting permissions to the users of workstations that will access tables or columns of tables of SQL Server databases.

- Installing the Access ODBC driver on each workstation that needs to attach SQL Server tables to Access databases. If all workstations are to share the same SQL Server files, you can install the ODBC driver on the network server instead of on each workstation.

- Establishing connections to specific SQL Server databases with the Access ODBC Administrator application.

Each of these stages, except the second stage, is described in the sections that follow. SQL Server's documentation covers granting permissions to users of SQL Server databases. Granting permissions usually is performed by the database administrator or the database owner.

Configuring Microsoft SQL Server Versions Prior to 4.2

Versions of Microsoft SQL Server prior to Version 4.2 don't include the stored procedures necessary to provide information about the SQL Server system catalog that is required by the ODBC driver. If you are using a version prior to 4.2, use the batch file INSTCAT.SQL, included on the ODBC distribution disk, with SQL Server's isql command-line utility. INSTCAT.SQL installs the required catalog-stored procedures. Type the following statement at the DOS command line of a workstation connected to SQL Server:

```
isql -Usa -Ppass_word -Sserver_name < d:\instcat.sql
```

In this case, *d* is the drive in which the ODBC disk is located. This isql statement adds the stored procedures to SQL Server listed in table 21.1.

Table 21.1. SQL Server Stored Procedures Required for Use with the ODBC APIs

Procedure Name	Purpose of Stored Catalog Procedure
sp_column_privileges	Provides column privileges for the specified table(s)
sp_columns	Provides information about the columns in the table(s)
sp_databases	Supplies a list of databases
sp_fkeys	Provides information about foreign keys in tables(s)
sp_pkeys	Supplies data on primary keys of table(s)
sp_server_info	Provides attribute names and values for the server
sp_special_columns	Gives information on columns in a table that have special attribute types
sp_sproc_columns	Supplies data on columns for a stored procedure
sp_statistics	Lists the indexes for a table
sp_stored_procedure	Lists the stored procedures for the system
sp_table_privileges	Describes the privileges for the table(s)
sp_tables	Lists the table(s) that can be queried

The stored procedures listed in table 21.1 are included in Version 4.2+ of SQL Server.

Installing the ODBC Driver on Workstations

Each workstation that needs to attach SQL Server tables to Access databases must be connected to the SQL Server through the network operating system, Microsoft LAN Manager, or Novell NetWare. If you are running Windows 3+, the connection to Windows is made with the Networks option of the Windows Setup application. Windows for Workgroups connects to either of these two network operating systems by the method described in the prior section, "Using Windows for Workgroups with Other Networks."

To install the ODBC driver on a workstation, perform the following steps:

1. Close all open Windows applications.

2. Insert the ODBC disk of the Access distribution disk set into drive A or drive B.

3. Choose **R**un from Program Manager's **F**ile menu.

4. Type **d:\setup** in the Command Line text box, where *d* is the disk drive in which the ODBC disk is located, and press Enter or choose OK. The dialog box of figure 21.9 appears.

5. The ODBC Drivers and Administration check boxes are marked by default. Accept the default installation and click Continue.

6. When the ODBC Setup asks for the location in which to install the ODBC Administrator application, type **c:\ODBC** and press Enter. A different drive letter can be used if your workstation drive is partitioned. Setup displays the Driver Installation dialog box.

7. Click Microsoft SQL/Server in the Available Drivers list box; then click Install >. The entry for Microsoft SQL/Server moves to the Installed Drivers list, as shown in figure 21.10.

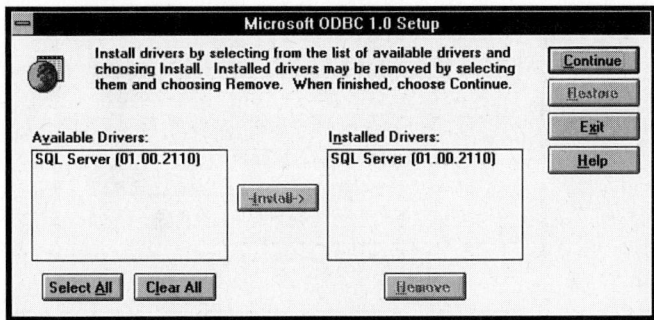

FIG. 21.10

The dialog box for selecting the ODBC driver you can use with Access.

8. Click Continue to display the Add Data Sources dialog box. You need not enter data sources at this point in the installation because you can use the ODBC Administrator Application to perform this step. Click Continue to bypass this step for now, or refer to the next section to add a new data source now.

9. Setup creates the ODBC Administrator icon in its own application group. You can move the icon to another application group, such as Windows Applications, and delete the ODBC application group.

Information about the ODBC drivers you have installed is included in the ODBCINST.INI file in the \WINDOWS directory of the workstation. After you have added the Microsoft SQL Server ODBC driver, you establish data sources with the ODBC Administrator application.

Adding and Removing SQL Server Data Sources

You use the ODBC Administrator application to add or remove SQL Server data sources. You need at least one SQL Server data source to enable Access to attach, export, or import SQL Server tables. To add a SQL Server data source, follow these steps:

1. If you completed the ODBC setup procedure described in the preceding section, double-click the ODBC Administrator's icon to launch the application. ODBC Administrator's main window appears, as shown in figure 21.11.

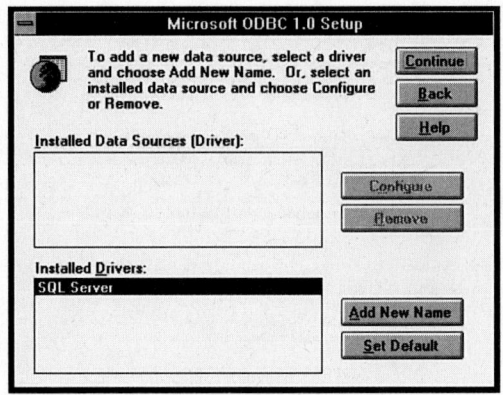

FIG. 21.11

Installing an SQL
Server data
source with the
ODBC Adminis-
trator.

2. Click the Microsoft SQL/Server entry in the Installed Drivers list box to select it, as shown in figure 21.11, and click Add New Name. If you are adding a new data source during the setup process, the title bar of the dialog box is Microsoft ODBC 1.0 Setup. The ODBC SQL Server Setup dialog box that you use to select a network host name appears, as shown in figure 21.12.

FIG. 21.12

Choosing the
server name from
the ODBC SQL
Server Setup
dialog box.

3. Choose the name of the server that stores the SQL Server database you want to use from the list in the Network Host box or type the name in the text box. Choose OK, and the Data Source dialog box appears, as shown in figure 12.13.

4. You can change the default entries that the ODBC Administrator assigns in the Data Source Name and Description text boxes, shown in figure 21.13, to entries that are more descriptive of the data contained in the data source.

   The Network Address entry depends on your network installation and the existing SQL Server database.

FIG. 21.13

Defining a new
ODBC data
source and
network address.

The Network Library entry, dbnmp3, is the named *pipes* library
required to run SQL Server under Windows.

The Convert OEM to ANSI checkbox changes special characters in
SQL Server database tables to their Windows (ANSI) equivalents,
when an ANSI equivalent is available.

Choose OK to add the new data source and close the Data Source
dialog box. Your new data source is added to the Installed Data
Sources list box of the ODBC Setup dialog box, as shown in
figure 21.14.

FIG. 21.14

The new SQL
Server data
source installed
for use with the
ODBC API.

5. Click Exit to close the ODBC administrator.

You can add additional SQL Servers data sources for a workstation by
repeating steps 1 through 4 before exiting the ODBC administrator. The
entries you make for each new data source are added to the ODBC.INI
file located in the \WINDOWS directory of the workstation.

Using the Same ODBC Data Sources for All Workstations

If all workstations on the network that use Access will employ the same ODBC data sources, you can install the ODBC Administrator application on the network server instead of installing a copy on each workstation's fixed disk. All workstations then use the same ODBCINST.INI and ODBC.INI files that determine the installed drivers and data sources. Using this process reduces the time required to install ODBC drivers on a large number of workstations.

To set up the ODBC Administrator application on the server, complete the following steps:

1. At one workstation, add all the data sources required by all the workstations by following the procedure described in the preceding section.

2. Create an \ODBC directory on the network server drive.

3. Copy all the files on the ODBC Setup disk to the server's new \ODBC directory.

4. Copy the ODBCINST.INI and ODBC.INI files from the \WINDOWS directory of the workstation to the \ODBC directory of the server.

Now you can run the ODBC Setup application for each workstation from the server instead of the distribution disk. The ODBCINST.INI and ODBC.INI files you created in step 1 will be used by the workstations instead of the default versions supplied on the ODBC Setup disk.

Installing ODBC Drivers on Other Workstations

To install the ODBC drivers from the server on each workstation that will share the common data source(s), complete the following steps:

1. Close all open Windows applications on the workstation.

2. Connect the workstation to the network drive to which you copied the ODBC setup files.

3. Choose **R**un from Program Manager's File menu.

4. Type **n:\odbc\setup /auto** in the Command Line text box, where *n* is the network drive designator. Then press Enter. The /auto command line parameter is required for automatic installation.

5. Proceed with driver installation as described in the preceding section.

To change the data source for one or more of the workstations, you can install a local copy of the ODBC administrator application on the workstation drive to alter the ODBCINST.INI and ODBC.INI files as necessary.

Using Databases Connected by ODBC

After you have added the SQL Server database as a data source, you can attach, import, or export tables in the SQL Server database to your Access database, depending on the permissions granted by SQL Server to each connected workstation. You use tables in the client-server database in the same manner you use dBASE, Paradox, or Btrieve tables. (See Chapter 5, "Attaching, Importing, and Exporting Tables.") You don't specify indexes to be used with client-server tables, because indexes are automatically opened when you open the table for which indexes have been created.

Access

Pubs is a demonstration database, supplied with Microsoft SQL Server, that contains tables for a fictional book distributor. Pubs' tables include information on imaginary book publishers, titles, and authors. To attach the tables in the Pubs SQL Server database to an Access database, NWIND.MDB in this example, follow these steps:

1. Launch Access and open the Northwind Traders database. Choose **A**ttach Table from the **F**ile menu. The Attach dialog box appears, as shown in figure 21.15.

2. Use the vertical scrollbar to expose the <SQL Database> entry in the Data Source list box. Double-click the <SQL Database> entry or select the entry and choose OK. The SQL Data Sources dialog box appears, as shown in figure 21.16.

3. Double-click or select the data source (network host name) in the Select Data Source list box. The SQL Server Login dialog box appears, as shown in figure 21.17.

FIG. 21.16

Choosing a
network host
name as a SQL
data source.

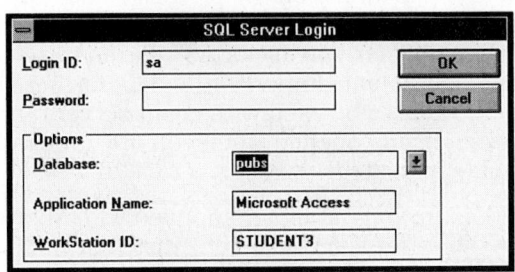

FIG. 21.17

Logging in to the
SQL Server Pubs
database as the
system adminis-
trator.

4. Type your login identification and password in the Login ID and
   Password text boxes. SA (system administrator) is used as the
   Login ID, and no Password is used in this example. Select the Pubs
   database in the Database drop-down list box of the Options section of the SQL Server Login dialog box. The entries in the Application Name and Workstation ID text boxes are added automatically
   for you by Access. Choose OK to log in to SQL Server.

   Once you are connected to the Pubs database with the ODBC API,
   the Attach Tables dialog box appears as shown in figure 21.18.

5. Choose the dbo.authors table (dbo is an abbreviation for data
   base owner), and click the Attach button.

FIG. 21.18

Attaching the
dbo.authors table
from the Pubs
database to the
Northwind
Traders data-
base.

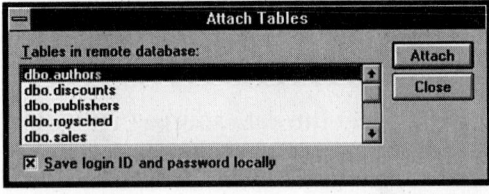

The message box of figure 21.19 indicates that you have successfully attached the table. An underscore substitutes for the period
between dbo and the table name because periods are not allowed
within Access table names. (Periods are separators between table
names and fields in Access.)

FIG. 21.19

The message box
that indicates that
a table has been
attached.

6. Repeat step 5, adding the dbo.titleauthor, dbo.titles, and
   dbo.publishers tables from the Pubs database to the tables attached to NWIND.MDB.

You can view the content of the tables by clicking the Table button in
the Database window then double-clicking the dbo_ table name you
want to examine. To create a query that joins the tables and displays
the author name, book title, and book publisher, follow these steps:

1. Click the Query button in the database window, and then click the
   New button to create a new query that joins the tables you just
   attached. The Add Table dialog box appears.

2. Add the dbo_authors, dbo_titleauthor, dbo_titles, and
   dbo_publishers tables to your query. Then click the Close button.

   Key fields of SQL Server tables are indicated in bold type, the
   same way Access emphasizes key fields in its tables. Access creates joins automatically based on the key fields and identically
   named foreign key fields of the SQL Server tables.

3. Click and drag the au_lname field from the dbo_authors table to
   the field row of the first column of the query.

4. Repeat step 3 for the title field of the dbo_titles table and the
   pub_name field of the dbo_publishers table. Your query design
   window appears as shown in figure 21.20.

5. Click the Run Query button on the toolbar to display your query
   dynaset, as shown in figure 21.21.

FIG. 21.20

The query design
window for the
example based
on tables
attached from the
Pubs database.

FIG. 21.21

The query
dynaset that
results from the
query design of
figure 21.20.

Table

6. To remove the attached tables from the Northwind Traders database, choose Database:NWIND from the Windows menu, click the Tables button, and select the name of the attached table to delete. Press the Delete key. A message box appears that requests you to confirm that you want to delete the table. Choose OK because you do not delete the table; you delete the attachment to the table.

The preceding example, using the Pubs and Northwind Traders databases, is typical of the procedure that you use to attach tables from any client-server database for which an ODBC driver is available.

You can change two entries in the [ODBC] section of your MSACCESS.INI file if you are having difficulty logging on the SQL Server or processing queries based on SQL Server tables. Following are the entries and their default values, in seconds:

```
[ODBC]
QueryTimeout=5
LoginTimeout=20
```

You can change these entries, if necessary, with Windows Notepad to provide additional time to process a query or connect to SQL Server.

Sharing Your Access Database Files with Other Users

While you are learning to use Access and designing your first Access applications, you use Access in single-user mode and maintain exclusive use of the database files you create. If your application is designed for use on a single computer, using files exclusively is satisfactory. If your application is designed for use in a networked environment, you need to set up a workgroup for the users that will share the database that includes the application you created.

Creating Database Applications for File Sharing

Sharing a database application requires that each user of the database share a common system file, SYSTEM.MDA, that contains information on the members of the workgroup and their levels of authority (permissions) to use the objects in the database file. Permissions are discussed in a later section of this chapter, "Maintaining Database Security."

When you develop an application that is intended for shared use, you should create a new SYSTEM.MDA file specifically for the application and develop the application in its own directory. When the application is completed, you can copy the files in this directory to the workgroup directory of the network or peer-to-peer server that is used to share them.

The location of the SYSTEM.MDA file that Access uses when it is launched is specified by the SystemDB= entry of the [Options] section of the MSACCESS.INI file in your \WINDOWS directory. The options section of MSACCESS.INI contains two entries, typically the following:

```
[Options]
UtilityDB=C:\ACCESS\UTILITY.MDA
SystemDB=C:\ACCESS\SYSTEM.MDA
```

You need to change the SystemDB= entry to specify the new SYSTEM.MDA file for the application you develop.

To establish a directory for the development of a shared database application, complete the following steps:

1. Launch File Manager and add a subdirectory, called **\SHARED** in this example, to your \ACCESS directory.

2. Copy SYSTEM.MDA from your \ACCESS directory to the \ACCESS\SHARED subdirectory.

3. If you already have created the database file you intend to share, copy the database file from the \ACCESS directory to \ACCESS\SHARED.

4. Close File Manager, launch Notepad, and open MSACCESS.INI.

5. Locate the [Options] section of MSACCESS.INI and edit the SystemDB= entry to specify the SYSTEM.MDA file in the new subdirectory:

```
SystemDB=C:\ACCESS\SHARED\SYSTEM.MDA
```

Close Notepad, and close Access, if it is running.

Access

6. Launch Access. Access reads the MSACCESS.INI file only during the loading process.

7. If you copied an existing database file from the \ACCESS directory, open the file to verify its operation with the new SYSTEM.MDA file. Otherwise, choose **N**ew Database from Access's **F**ile menu to create the new database file.

The dedicated SYSTEM.MDA file contains information pertaining only to the database application to be shared and the Northwind sample database. You can develop the application using Access's default operating options, and then change the options to provide for file sharing when the application is completed.

You can change the SYSTEM.MDA file that Access uses when launched with the Access Setup application. The procedure is described in the section, "Choosing Workgroups with the Setup Application," later in the chapter.

Minimize the number of database objects you create when you develop applications to be shared. Use SQL statements to replace query objects when possible (see Chapter 20). Combine related Access macros so that you have as few individual macro objects as possible (see Chapter 17). Criteria for combining macros are the subject of a tip in the "Granting and Revoking Permissions" section, later in this chapter. Minimizing the number of objects reduces the number of entries you need to make when you establish database security restrictions (permissions) for your application.

Preparing To Share Your Database Files

Setting up Access to share database files requires several changes to the operating options for Access that are determined by settings in the Multiuser Options dialog box. You open this dialog box by choosing **O**ptions from the **V**iew menu and then choosing Multiuser from the list of options presented. The changes you make to the default multiuser settings, which apply to all databases you open thereafter, follow:

- Access opens database files for exclusive use by a single user in its default operating mode. You need to change the file-opening mode of your workgroup database to Shared mode so that more than one user can open the file.

- You can gain additional area on the display by removing the toolbar from view. Users are unlikely to be allowed to modify your application, so you can remove the toolbar if your applications don't require that users employ any of its actions.

- You can set the locking mode and adjust the refresh interval and the number of update *retries* from their default values, if necessary. *Record locking* prevents more than one user from making simultaneous changes to the same record. *Refresh interval* determines how often the data displayed in a datasheet or form is rewritten automatically to reflect changes made by other members of the workgroup. Access attempts to update a locked record the number of times specified as *retries* before issuing a message box that the record is locked and cannot be updated. Access doesn't lock records in a SQL Server table attached with the ODBC API, but the records in the table you attach can be locked by users of SQL Server.

To set the operating options of the system database you are using (SYSTEM.MDA) for shared use of Access database files, complete the following steps:

1. Choose **O**ptions from the **V**iew menu. The Options dialog box appears, as shown in figure 21.22.

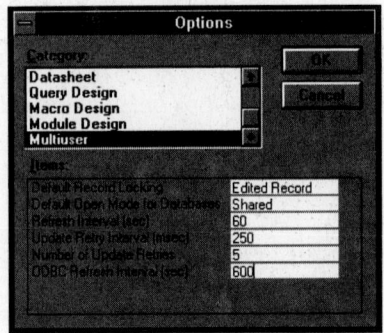

FIG. 21.22

The Options
dialog box for
setting the
multiuser
properties of a
database.

2. Choose Multiuser from the Categories list box.

3. Open the Default Record Locking list box, and choose Edited
   Record. When a user updates a record, no other user can update
   the record simultaneously. If you choose All Records, no other
   user will be able to make changes to a table when another user
   opens the table, and you will not be able to view or query attached SQL Server tables.

4. Open the Default Open Mode for Databases list box, and choose
   Shared to make the databases you open shareable.

5. You edit the values for Refresh Interval, Update Retry Interval,
   Number of Update Retries, and ODBC Refresh Interval in the remaining text boxes. The default values, except for Number of Retries, are adequate for most network installations. You can set the
   Number of Update Retries to a more conservative value of 5; this
   results in a 1.25-second wait before you receive the Can't Update
   message box if your Update Retry Interval is 250 milliseconds.

6. When you have completed your entries as shown in figure 21.22,
   choose OK. The values you have entered are saved in the
   SYSTEM.MDA system database file.

Now that you have set up the database files for shared use, you need to
set up the workstations so that they can join the workgroup for the
application.

Record locking is a misnomer in Access. An Edited Record lock is
applied to a 2K page that may contain many records if the fields of
the records have small Size property values. Use of No Locks, the
default speeds operation of Access in a multiuser environment,
because the time required to lock and unlock table pages is saved.
No Locks is called *optimistic locking*; optimistic locking assumes
that the probability is low that two or more users might attempt

to alter the same record simultaneously. If you attempt to update a record in a table with No Locks that is being updated simultaneously by another user, Access displays a message box that lets you choose to accept or overwrite the other user's changes. The conservative approach is to use Edited Record locking. No Locks should be reserved for users that ordinarily edit but don't append new records; use Edit Record locking for users that add new records to a table when more than one user is authorized to do so.

Creating Workgroup Directories for Database Files

Workgroups are established by creating directories to hold the database file(s) and a copy of the system file, SYSTEM.MDA. Each member of the workgroup shares the copy of the SYSTEM.MDA file in the workgroup directory. Members of the workgroup use the database(s) in the workgroup directory, but they can attach, import, or export tables located in other workgroup directories, depending on their permissions to use the foreign files.

If you create separate Access databases for the Accounting, Sales, and Production departments, for example, you may locate the database and dedicated SYSTEM.MDA files in \ACCESS\ACCOUNT, \ACCESS\SALES, and \ACCESS\PRODUCT directories of the network or peer-to-peer server. These directories appear to workstations as separate drives, perhaps D, E, and F. To use the same drive designator for all databases at the workstation level, you add another layer to the server directory structure, \ACCESS\DATABASE\ACCOUNT, for example. The DATABASE subdirectory is then shared as drive D on the workstations.

To create a workgroup directory on a network or peer-to-peer server, complete the following steps:

1. Create the directory on the server computer that will be shared with the members of the database workgroup.

2. Designate the names of the workstation computers that are authorized for access to the new directory. Make sure you designate read-write access for each workstation, even if the workstation isn't to be allowed to modify data. Any directory that contains a SYSTEM.MDA file must not be made read-only.

3. Copy the files from the directory in which you developed the application to the new server directory. The server directory must contain SYSTEM.MDA and at least one database file.

4. Edit the workstation's MSACCESS.INI file so that the SystemDB=
   entry of the [Options] section designates the path to the
   workgroup directory, as in the following example:

   ```
   SystemDB=d:\account\system.mda
   ```

Access

5. Launch Access from the workstation and open the database file
   on the server.

6. Run your application and make a temporary modification to one
   of the tables to verify that you have read-write authorization in
   the new directory.

7. Make a backup copy of the database and the SYSTEM.MDA file
   from the development directory in which you created it. The purpose of the backup is to maintain a copy of the original application in case you encounter problems when you establish database
   security.

8. You can now safely delete the development copy of the database
   file on your computer. You may, however, want to keep the file
   as a local copy for modification and further development as
   required.

Always make a backup copy of the related SYSTEM.MDA file when
you back up a database file. If your SYSTEM.MDA file or the file for
a workgroup becomes corrupted and cannot be repaired, you may
not be able to open the database, even from a restored backup
copy. Backing up database files is discussed in the section, "Administering Databases and Applications," near the end of this
chapter.

Choosing Workgroups with the Setup Application

You can allow users to choose the workgroup they join by adding the
Access Setup applications icon to Program Manager's Access applications group. To add the Access Setup application on the workstation if
it is not already installed, perform the following steps:

1. Activate the Access applications group in Program Manager.

2. Choose New from Program Manager's File menu, and click the
   Program Item option button, if necessary, in the New Program
   Object dialog box that appears. Then choose OK. The Program
   Item Properties dialog box appears.

3. Type a brief title, such as **Access WG**, in the Description text box.

4. Type **c:\access\stfsetup.exe /w** in the Command Line text box. Alter the drive and path if STFSETUP.EXE is located elsewhere. The /w command line parameter (option) tells the setup application to limit its purpose to choosing a workgroup. Do not make an entry in the Working Directory text box, because Program Manager does this for you.

5. Choose OK. The Access Setup application appears with the Specify Workgroup dialog box shown in figure 21.23.

6. The path to the SYSTEM.MDA file you are currently using appears in the Path text box. Enter the well-formed path (WFP, the drive and path) of the workgroup directory, but not the filename, in the text box. Choose OK. Depending on the network operating system you are using, you may need to type a network share name, such as **\\DATABASE\ACCESS**.

Setup checks to see if a copy of SYSTEM.MDA exists in the specified directory; if not, you receive an error message. If SYSTEM.MDA exists, Setup changes the SystemDB= entry in the [Options] section of MSACCESS.INI to correspond with your entry. You can choose Cancel if you decide not to join a workgroup or the File Open button to open a dialog box that enables you to search for SYSTEM.MDA files in other directories.

Using Command Line Options To Open a Database

Access provides a number of options that you can employ to customize how Access starts for each user. All users in a workgroup share a common database, for example, but you may want individual users to start Access with a different form. If you are using Access in single-user mode with a particular database, opening the database automatically saves a few steps in the process.

You can open a workgroup database automatically, execute a macro, and supply a user name or password when you start Access by entering options on the command line that you use to start Access for each workgroup member, as in the following example:

```
d:\msa_path\msaccess.exe [n:\mdb_path\mdb_name.mdb ]
[/User user_name ][/Pwd pass_word ][/X macro_name ][/Ro ][/
Excl ]
[/Cmd cmd_value]
```

Table 21.2 describes the elements of the Access start-up command line options.

Table 21.2. Command Line Options for Launching Access

Command Line Element	Function
d:\msa_path\msaccess.exe	Command to launch Access
n:\mdb_path\mdb_name.mdb	Path and name of start-up database file
/User user_name	Start with user_name as user name
/Pwd pass_word	Start with pass_word as password
/X macro_name	Run macro_name on start-up
/Ro	Open mdb_name for read-only use
/Excl	Open mdb_name for exclusive use
/Cmd cmd_value	Specify a value to be returned by the Access Basic Command function

Do not use the /Ro option if you want some members of the workgroup to be able to modify the tables of the database. If you specify the /Ro option for one workstation, all workstations in the workgroup are restricted to read-only use of the database. Use the permissions features of Access, described in the "Maintaining Database Security" section of this chapter, to designate those users who may update the data in tables and those who may not.

The sequence in which you enter the command line options doesn't affect the options' operation; however, a convention is that the name of the file to open always immediately follows the command that launches the application. Do not use the /Excl option if you want other users to be able to share the database. When you omit the /Excl option, shared or exclusive use of databases is determined by the Default Open Mode for Databases choice of the Multiuser Options, discussed in a previous section, "Preparing to Share your Database Files."

The following example starts Access, opens the Northwind Traders sample database using *Gabriel* as the user name and *Marquez* as the password, and runs the PA Open Form macro. Access is assumed to be located in network directory E:\ACCESS, and SALES.MDB and SYSTEM.MDB are located in the network directory N:\SALES. The procedure also assigns a special icon for the application. To create an icon that uses these command-line parameters to open Access, follow these steps:

1. Open or select the Windows program group in which you want to install the icon for Access.

2. Choose New from Program Manager's **F**ile menu, and choose Program Item in the New Program Object dialog box. Choose OK; the Program Item Properties dialog box appears.

3. Type a short title of your application, such as **PA Form**, in the Description text box of the Program Item Properties dialog box.

4. Type the following in the Command Line text box; then press Tab:

   ```
   e:\access\msaccess.exe n:\sales\sales.mdb /User
   Gabriel /Pwd Marquez /X PA Open Form
   ```

5. Type **n:\sales** in the Working Directory text box and press Tab. This entry establishes the workgroup directory as the working directory when the user launches Access.

6. Click the Change Icon button. The Change Icon dialog box appears, as shown in figure 21.24.

7. Choose the Form icon from those offered in the Current Icon box, and choose OK to close the dialog box. Icons are provided for forms, tables, reports, queries, macros, and modules. The icons from which you can choose correspond to the icons used by Access when you minimize the window of a database object.

8. Your application now is assigned the new icon in the Program Items Properties dialog box, as shown in figure 21.25.

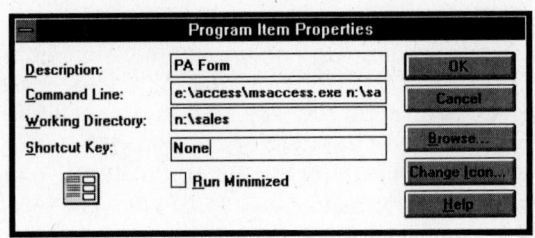

FIG. 21.25

The Program Item Properties dialog box for automatic start-up of Access.

9. Choose OK to accept your entries.

You need to repeat these steps for each workstation in the workgroup, changing the /X macro_name entry as necessary to start each workstation with the appropriate form.

Adding a user's password as an option to the start-up command line violates one of the basic rules of database security: Do not disclose your password to any other person. The preceding example that uses a password as a command line option does so only for the purpose of completely defining the options available. You should not use the /Pwd command line option under any circumstances.

Maintaining Database Security

Database security prevents unauthorized persons from accidentally or intentionally viewing, modifying, deleting, or destroying information contained in a database. Database security is of primary concern in a multiuser environment, although you may want to use Access's security features to prevent others from viewing or modifying databases stored on your single-user computer. This section describes the multi-layered security features of networked Access databases and how you use these features to ensure a secure database system.

Specifying the Principles of Database Security on a LAN

Ten basic principles of database security exist for databases that are installed on a LAN. Five of these principles are associated with the network operating system:

1. Each user of a network must be positively identified before he or she can gain access to the network. Identification requires a unique user name and secret password for each user. Users must not share their passwords with one another, and all passwords used should be changed every 60 to 90 days.

2. Each identified user of the network must be authorized to have access to specific elements of the network, such as server directories, printers, and other shared resources. Each user has a network *account* that incorporates the user's identification data and authorizations. The network file that contains this information is always encrypted and is accessible only by the network administrator(s).

3. Actions of network users should be monitored to determine whether users are attempting to access elements of the network for which they don't have authorization. Users that repeatedly attempt to breach network security should be locked out of the network until appropriate administrative action can be taken.

4. The network should be tamper-proof. Tamper-proofing includes installing security systems that are immune to "hacking" by ingenious programmers, and testing routinely for the presence of viruses.

5. Data stored on network servers must be protected against hardware failure and catastrophic destruction (fires, earthquakes, hurricanes, and so on) by adequate and timely backup. Backup systems enable you to reconstruct the data to its state at the time the last backup occurred.

   The measures required to establish the first five principles are the responsibility of the network administrator for a server-based system. In a peer-to-peer network, network security measures are the responsibility of each person that shares his or her resources with others.

   The remaining five principles of database security are determined by the security capabilities of the database management system and the applications you create with it:

6. The contents of tables in a database should be encrypted to prevent viewing the data with a file-reading or other "snooping" utility.

7. Users must be further identified before they are allowed to open a database file. A secret password, different from the user's network access password, should be used. The database file that contains user identification and password data (database user accounts) must be encrypted. The encryption technique used should be sophisticated enough to prevent hackers from deciphering it. Only the database administrator(s) have access to this file.

8. Users must be assigned specific permission to use the database and the tables it contains. If users are to be restricted from viewing specific columns of a table, access to the table should be in the form of a query that includes only the fields that the user is authorized to view. The database management system must provide for revoking specific permissions as the need arises.

9. The data in tables should be auditable. Lack of auditability is an incentive to computer-based embezzling. Updates made by users to tables that contain financial data should be maintained in a log, preferably in another database, that identifies the user that made the entry and the date and time that the update was made. Logs are useful in reconstructing database entries that occurred between the time the database was last backed up and the time data was restored from the backup copy.

10. Operations that update records in more than one table should be accomplished by transaction techniques that can be reversed (rolled back) if updates to all the tables involved cannot be completed immediately.

Most network operating systems in use on PCs provide for the first five database security principles, but enforcement of password secrecy, monitoring of user transgressions, and virus surveillance often are ignored, especially in peer-to-peer networks. Access provides all five of the database security principles, but you must take specific actions to invoke and maintain these principles.

One of the most frequent breaches of database security occurs when a temporary worker is hired to stand in for a user who is ill or on vacation. Instead of establishing a new network account, including user name and password, and a new user (or guest) account for the database, the employee's user names and passwords are divulged to the temporary worker for the sake of expediency. A temporary worker should be assigned his or her own identification for the network and database; the temporary worker's authorizations should be removed when the regrular employee returns to the job.

Establishing Groups and Users

Access and most client-server databases establish the following three groups of database users:

- *Administrators* (Admins) that have the authority to view and update existing tables, and add or delete tables and other database objects from the database. Members of the Admins group usually have permission to modify the applications contained in databases.

- *Regular members of workgroups* (Users) that are assigned permission to open the database and are granted permissions to view and modify databases on a selective basis. Users ordinarily aren't granted permissions to modify Access applications.

- *Occasional users of databases* (Guests) that are granted limited rights to use a database and the objects it contains but aren't assigned a user account. Guest privileges often are assigned to persons being trained in the use of a database application.

When you install Access, you automatically are made a member of the Admins group with the name Admin and have all permissions granted. You have an empty password and Personal ID Number (PIN); this means that you don't need to enter a password to log on to the database(s) associated with the SYSTEM.MDA installed in the \ACCESS directory. When you are learning Access, you have little reason to establish database security. Once you begin to create a useful database application, you should implement basic security provisions on your own computer.

Establishing Your Own Admins Name, Password, and PIN

Access has two levels of security: *application* level and *file* level. The application-level security system requires that each user of Access enters a user name and a password to start Access. Establishing single-user application-level security and preparing for multiuser security requires that you perform the following tasks:

1. Activate the log-on procedure for Access. This action requires that you add a password for the Admin user. To remain "Admin," you need not complete the remaining steps, but the only security will be your password.

2. Create a new account for yourself as a member of the Admins group.

3. Log on to Access using your new Admin user account.

4. Delete the default Admin user account. The Admins group should include entries for active database administrators only.

Before you begin the following procedure, make a disk backup copy of the SYSTEM.MDA file in use and any database files that you created or modified while using this SYSTEM.MDA file. If you forget the user name or password you assigned to yourself, after deleting the Admin user, you will not be able to log on to Access. In this case, you must restore the original version of the SYSTEM.MDA file. Then you may not be able to open the database files with which the original version of the SYSTEM.MDA file is associated unless you restore the backed-up versions.

To activate the log-on procedure for Access, complete the following steps:

1. A temporary password to the Admin user is necessary to activate Access's log-on procedure. Open a database so that the **S**ecurity menu choice is displayed. Choose **C**hange Password from the **S**ecurity menu to display the Change Password dialog box shown in figure 21.26.

If you don't change the Admin user's password, you are logged on as Admin automatically each time you start Access.

2. Press the Tab key to bypass the Old Password text box (this enters the equivalent of an empty password) and enter a temporary password, such as **Temp**, in the New Password text box. Your entry is shown as a series of asterisks to prevent disclosing your password to others as you enter it. Passwords are case-sensitive, so *Temp* is a different password than *temp*.

3. Type the password in the Verify text box to test your entry. The verification test is *not* case-sensitive.

   Choose OK. If you receive the message, `No permissions for Admin user`, choose OK because you will delete the Admin user in the steps that follow.

4. Exit Access and launch it again from Program Manager. The Logon dialog box shown in figure 21.27 appears.

Access

5. Type **Admin** in the Name text box, press Tab, and enter the password, exactly as you typed it in step 2. Press Enter or choose OK. If you entered the password correctly, Access continues the start-up procedure.

To add your new user account in the Admins group, perform the following steps:

1. Open a database so that the **S**ecurity menu choice appears. Choose **U**sers from the **S**ecurity menu. The Users dialog box shown in figure 21.28 appears. All members of the Admins group automatically are included (and must be included) in the Users group. Both Admins and Users appear in the Member Of list box.

2. Click the New button to add your new account. The New User/ Group dialog box shown in figure 21.29 appears.

3. Type the name you want to use to identify yourself to Access in the Name text box and a four-digit PIN in the Personal ID Number text box. The PIN, with the Name entry, uniquely identifies your account. This precaution is necessary because two people may use the same log-on name; the Name and PIN values are combined to create a no-duplicates index on the Users table in SYSTEM.MDA. Choose OK to close the New User/Group dialog box and return to the Users dialog box.

Access

4. You *don't* enter a password for the new user at this time, because you still are logged on to Access as Admin. Click the Close button to close the Users dialog box, and exit Access.

5. Launch Access, type your new user name in the Logon dialog box, and press Enter or choose OK. Do not enter a password, because you have an empty password at this point. User names aren't case-sensitive; Access considers *NewAdmin* and *newadmin* to be the same user.

6. Open a database and choose **C**hange Password from the **S**ecurity menu. The Password dialog box appears. Press Tab to bypass the Old Password text box and type the password you plan to use until it is time to change your password (to maintain system security). Passwords can be up to 14 characters long and may contain any character, except ASCII character 0, the Null character. Verify your password, and then press Enter or choose OK to close the Password dialog box.

7. Choose **U**sers from the **S**ecurity menu. The Users dialog box appears. Open the Users list box and select your new user name from the list. Verify that you are a member of the Admins and Users group. Open the Users list box again and choose Admin; then click Delete. You are asked to confirm deletion by the message box shown in figure 21.30. Choose OK to confirm deletion.

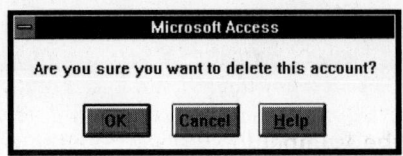

8. Exit Access, and then launch it again from Program Manager. Test your new password during the log-on procedure.

You use the same procedure to add other users as members of the default Admins, Users, or Guests group, or of new workgroups you create.

Be sure to write down and save your own PIN, and the PIN of every user you add to the workgroup, for future reference. User names and PINs aren't secure elements, so you can safely keep a list without compromising system security. This list should be accessible only to database administrators. You need a user's PIN so that the user can be recognized as a member of another workgroup when the need arises. (See the "Granting Permissions for a Database in Another Workgroup" section near the end of this chapter.)

Establishing Members of Access Groups

Groups within Access's security system are not the same as workgroups. As discussed previously, a workgroup shares the same SYSTEM.MDA file that is located in a specific directory. The entries you made in the preceding steps have been saved in the SYSTEM.MDA file that is located in your \ACCESS directory (unless you specified a different directory in a previous section of this chapter). Workgroups will have their own SYSTEM.MDA files in different directories.

To add a new user to a group, you must be logged on to Access as a member of the Admins group and complete the following steps:

1. Choose Users from the Security menu to open the Users dialog box.

2. Click New. The New User/Group dialog box appears. Type the new user's name and PIN. Choose OK to create the account and close the dialog box. The Users dialog box reappears. Make a note of the PIN you used to add the new user. You need to know the user's PIN so that you can duplicate an entry for the new user in other workgroups.

3. The default group for all new users is Users. To add the user to the Admins group, choose Admins in the Available Groups list box and click the Add >> button to add Admins to the Member Of list (see fig. 21.28). All users must be members of the Users group, except for members of the Guests group. To change the group membership of a current user to the Guests group, you need to delete the user's account and then add the user with only Guests appearing in the Member Of list box. Use the << Remove button to delete the User group assignment. Click Close to return to Access's main window when your selections are complete.

4. Request the new user to log on to Access with the user name and change his or her password from the default empty value to a legitimate password.

5. You can improve the level of security by typing the new user's password yourself, so that users cannot bypass the password step by leaving their passwords blank.

   To enter a password for a new user, close Access, log on as the new user, choose Change Password from the Security menu, and enter the user's chosen password.

Before you add a significant number of users, you should decide whether you need additional groups and determine the permissions that should be assigned to each group other than Admins. These aspects of database security are discussed in the sections that follow.

When requesting new users to enter their first password, emphasize the advantage of the use of longer passwords that combine upper- and lowercase characters and numbers because they improve system security. Users should not use their initials, names of spouses or children, birth dates, or nicknames; these are the entries that unauthorized users will try first to gain access to the system.

Adding a New Group

In most cases, Admins, Users, and Guests are the only groups necessary for each workgroup you create. Members of a group usually share the same permissions to use database objects (which is the subject of the next section). Adding a new Access group is not necessary, therefore, unless you have a category of users who are to have a different set of permissions than members of the Users or Guests groups. Such a category may distinguish Users (who may be limited to viewing data) from members of "Data Entry" who have permission to update the data in tables.

To add a new group, perform the following steps:

1. Choose Groups from the Security menu. The Groups dialog box shown in figure 21.31 appears.

FIG. 21.31

Adding a new user group to a database.

2. Click the New button to open the New User/Group dialog box (see fig. 21.29).

3. Type the name of the Group in the Name dialog box and a four-digit Personal ID Number, and then press Enter or choose OK. The Groups dialog box reappears.

Group names may be up to 20 characters long and may contain spaces, but punctuation symbols aren't allowed. You don't need to make a note of the PIN in the case of groups, because the PIN is used only for indexing purposes.

4. Click Close from the Groups dialog box. You can delete the newly added group by clicking the Delete button now.

Once you have added a new group, you need to assign the default permissions that apply to all members of the group by the procedure outlined in the "Granting and Revoking Permissions" section that follows.

Deleting Users and Groups

Members of the Admins group have the authority to delete users from any group and to delete any group except Admins, Users, and Guests. To delete a user or group, choose Users or Groups from the Security menu, choose the user or group to delete from the list box, and click Delete. You are asked to confirm the deletion. Admins, Users, and Guests groups must each contain one user account; you cannot delete all users for any of these groups.

Clearing Forgotten Passwords

If a user forgets his or her password and if you are logged in to Access as a member of the Admins group, you can delete the user's password, so that you or the user can enter a new password.

To clear a user's password, complete the following steps:

1. Choose Users from the Security menu.

2. Open the Name list box and choose the user whose password you want to clear.

3. Click the Clear Password button (see fig. 21.28).

4. Make sure that the user whose password you cleared enters a new password, or log on to Access as the new user and enter a new password for the user.

As mentioned previously, entering the user's password as the database administrator is the only means of ensuring that the database security is enforced.

Granting and Revoking Permissions

The second layer of Access security is at the database level. Access lets the database administrator grant or revoke *permissions* to use specific database objects to all members of a group. Permissions grant authority for users to view or alter specific database objects. The permissions granted to the group are inherited by each member as he or she is added to the group. You can grant additional permissions to individual members of a group, but you cannot revoke permissions that individual members inherit from the group. Permissions are stored in the database file as properties of database objects.

When you modify permissions for a database, you establish accounts for users in the database file. If you have deleted the Admin user and have assigned yourself a new user name and PIN in the Admins group, any changes you make to the permissions by clicking the Assign button in the Permissions dialog box will be made a permanent element of the database. You must log on to Access with your new user name and password. Do not use the Assign button unless you are satisfied with the user name(s) you created in previous sections of this chapter. Choose Cancel after making any changes to permissions you do not want to make permanent.

Table 21.3 lists the permissions offered by Access for database objects, ranked in descending level of authority. Full Permissions allow the user to use all the features of Access, including design functions. The description of the specific action allowed by a permission is listed in the Explicit Permissions column. Permissions at an authority level below Full Permissions require other permissions to operate; these required permissions are called *Implicit* Permissions.

Table 21.3. Permissions To Use Access Database Objects

Permission	Database Objects	Explicit Permissions	Implicit Permissions
Full (Admin)	All database objects	All permissions	Not applicable
Modify Definitions	All	Alter, replace, or delete objects	Modify Data and Execute

Permission	Database Objects	Explicit Permissions	Implicit Permissions
Execute	Forms, reports, macros	Use or run objects	Read Data
Modify Data	Tables, queries, forms	Update data in objects	Read Data
Read Data	Tables, queries, forms	View data in objects	Read Definitions
Read Definitions	All	View objects	Execute for macros only

If, for example, you allow a user to modify definitions, this user also must be able to modify data and execute objects. Therefore, Modify Data and Execute permissions are implied by the Modify Definitions permission. This user, and any other users that are allowed to modify data, must be able to read data. All users having permission to read data must be able to read definitions. When you establish permissions for a database object, Access adds the implicit permissions automatically.

The Admins and Users groups have full permissions, and the Guests group has Read Definitions and Read Data permissions for any new database objects you create. If you intend to share the database with other users, it is not likely that you want all members of the Users group to have permission to update database tables, nor should all Guests be able to view all objects. A more conservative set of permissions for the three groups follows:

■ *Admins:* Full permissions for all objects. Admins privileges should be assigned to as few individuals as possible, consistent with the availability of backup database administrators to cover for the absence of the primary administrator. Members of the Admins group also must be members of the Users group.

■ *Users:* Execute and Read Data permissions. Modify Data permissions are granted for specific forms and reports. Users ordinarily aren't granted Modify Definitions permission in databases.

■ *Guests:* No group permissions. All permissions are granted to each guest on an *ad hoc* basis. Members of the Guests group are deleted when they no longer need access to the database.

You can use the Run with Owner's Permissions check box or the WITH OWNERACCESS OPTION in SQL statements to enable users without the required permissions to execute a query or to prevent them from doing so. *Owner* is a misnomer in Access; unlike SQL Server and other client-server DBMs, no owner is defined for Access database objects. *Owner* in Access implies the permission to modify data but not to modify definitions.

Altering Group Permissions

After you design your hierarchy of permissions and add any new user groups you need, you are ready to assign group permissions for each of the objects in your database. Only members of the Admins group can alter permissions for Groups or Users.

To change the permissions for a group, complete the following steps:

1. Open the database file for which group permissions are to be granted or revoked.

2. Choose **P**ermissions from the **S**ecurity menu. The Permissions dialog box appears, as shown in figure 21.32.

FIG. 21.32

The default permissions for the Users group.

3. Click the Groups option button to display the permissions for groups of users.

4. Open the Type list box and choose the type of database object whose permissions you want to change.

5. Open the Name list box and choose the specific object to which the new permissions will apply.

6. Open the User/Group list box and choose the Group whose permissions you want to revise, Users for this example. Figure 21.32 shows the Full permissions that Access assigns by default to the Users group.

7. Permissions currently granted to the group are shown by an X in the Permissions check boxes. Click the Modify Definitions and Modify Data check boxes to allow the users groups only to read definitions and read data. The X in the Full Permissions check box is removed by Access. Your Permissions dialog box appears as shown in figure 21.33.

FIG. 21.33

Revising permissions for the OLE Objects table for the Users group.

8. Click the Assign button to make the new permissions effective for the selected database object.

9. Repeat steps 4 through 8 for each database object whose user permissions you want to change.

The Permissions check boxes that are enabled depend on the type of object you choose. Execute, for example, is enabled only for form, report, and macro objects.

When you create macro objects that contain several individual named macros (to minimize the number of objects in the database), make sure that each macro object contains named macros that correspond to a specific category of permissions. Named macros, for example, that invoke action queries to modify tables or add new records should be grouped in one macro object, and named macros that only display the contents of database objects should be located in a different macro object. When you assign permissions to execute macro objects, you need to assign Modify Data permission to those users who can execute macro objects that run action queries.

Granting Additional Permissions to Specific Users

The process of granting additional permissions to a specific user is similar to the process used to alter Group permissions. Permissions that are inherited by the user from the group to which the user is assigned are *not shown* in the Permissions dialog box. To grant additional permissions to a specific user, complete the following steps:

1. Choose Permissions from the Security menu. The Permissions dialog box appears.

2. Click the Users option button to display the permissions for a specific user, and then open the User/Group list box and choose the user, as shown in figure 21.34.

FIG. 21.34

The Permissions dialog box for a user that does not display inherited permissions.

NewUser is a member of the Users group. As mentioned in the introduction to this section, the Read Definitions and Read Data permissions that have been inherited by NewUser from the modified permissions of the Users group aren't shown in the Permissions check boxes.

3. To assign Modify Data permission to a specific user so that the user can update an object, choose the object using the Type and Name list boxes, and then click the Modify Data list box. The implicit permissions—Read Definitions and Read Data—associated with the explicit permission, Modify Data, are marked automatically by Access, as shown in figure 21.35. Click the Assign button after selecting each object whose permissions you want to change.

FIG. 21.35

The Permissions dialog box for a new user with the Modify Data permission added.

Implicit permissions for individual users are displayed in the Permissions check boxes, regardless of whether the implicit permissions also were inherited from group membership.

4. Repeat step 3 for each user that requires permissions for an object that aren't inherited from the user's group permissions. Click the Close button when you complete the permission changes for all users who require such changes.

You can use the /Ro command line option, described in the preceding section, "Using Command Line Options to Open a Database," to revoke Modify Data permissions for the database on specific workstations. This isn't a secure method, because the user can edit the command line option, remove the /Ro entry, and log in again with read-write privileges. If you use this method, Access displays a message box indicating that the database is being opened in read-only mode and that the user cannot modify data.

Granting Permissions for a Database in Another Workgroup

If your application requires that you attach a table in a secure database used by a different workgroup, the user needs to be a member of a group in the other workgroup and needs to be assigned appropriate permissions for the attached table. At this point, you need the list of PINs for users, mentioned in the "Establishing Your Own Admins Name, Password, and PIN" section earlier in this chapter.

To grant permission for a user to modify data in a table attached from another workgroup's database, perform the following steps:

1. Close Access; you need to relaunch Access when you choose another workgroup.

2. Launch the Access Setup application and specify the path to the SYSTEM.MDA file of the workgroup that uses the database that contains the table to be attached.

Access

3. Launch Access and open the database that contains the table to be attached.

4. Add an account for the user to the Users group with exactly the same user name and PIN as was used to add the user account to his or her workgroup.

5. If you don't want this user to join the other workgroup, enter a password and don't disclose the password to the user.

6. Open the Permissions dialog box, choose the table object to be attached, and assign the Modify Data permission for the table for the user.

You need to use the same PIN for the user in both workgroups, because the account for the user is created from the user name and PIN, and the accounts must be identical in both databases. You also must use the same PIN number to reinstate the user's account if your SYSTEM.MDA file becomes corrupted, you don't have a current backup, and Access cannot repair it.

Encrypting and Decrypting Database Files

File-level security isn't complete until you have encrypted the database so that others cannot read its contents with a text editing or disk utility application, such as is included with Symantec's Norton Utilities. Encryption of databases causes Access's operations on tables to slow perceptibly because of the time required to decrypt the data. Only members of the Admins group can encrypt or decrypt a database. You can use the procedure that follows to determine whether a file is encrypted.

To encrypt or decrypt an Access database file, complete the following steps:

1. Make sure that the disk drive of the computer on which the database is stored has sufficient free space to create a copy of the database you intend to encrypt or decrypt. Access makes a new copy of the file during the process.

2. All other workstations, including your own, need to close the database file to be encrypted. You cannot encrypt or decrypt a database file that is in use on any workstation.

3. Activate the Database window and choose Encrypt/Decrypt Database from the File menu. The Encrypt/Decrypt dialog box appears.

4. Choose the name of the database file to be encrypted and choose OK.

5. If the file is already encrypted, it will be decrypted, and vice versa. The title bar of the dialog box that opens indicates whether the file will be encrypted or decrypted in this operation. If you are interested only in whether the file has been encrypted, you can choose Cancel now.

6. Type the name of the encrypted or decrypted file to create and choose OK. Normally, you type the same name as the original file; Access will not replace the original copy of the file if the process does not succeed.

Databases are compacted by Access when they are encrypted or decrypted.

You do not need to encrypt files while you're developing applications using files that aren't shared with others unless the files contain sensitive information. Once the files are made shareable, a good security practice is to encrypt them, even if they don't contain confidential data.

For Related Information:

◀◀ "Compacting Databases," p. 117.

◀◀ "Encrypting and Decrypting Databases," p. 119.

FROM HERE...

Administering Databases and Applications

Administering a multiuser database involves a number of duties besides adding and maintaining user accounts. The most important function of the database administrator is to ensure that periodic valid backup copies are made of database and system files. The database administrator's other responsibilities consist of routine database maintenance, periodic compacting of database files, and repairing databases.

Backing Up and Restoring Databases

The following maxims relate to maintaining backup copies of database files:

- The time interval between successive backups of databases is equal to the amount of data you are willing and able to reenter in the event of a fixed disk failure. Except in unusual circumstances, such as little or no update activity, daily backup is the rule.

- Rotate backup copies. Make successive backups on different tapes or disk sets. One of the tapes or disks may have defects that prevent restoring the backup. The backup device, such as a tape drive, can fail without warning you that the recorded data isn't valid.

- Test backup copies of databases periodically. You should test one different copy in the backup rotation sequence for restorability. If you rotate five daily backup tapes, for example, you should randomly choose one of the tapes, restore the database file from the tape, and open it with Access to ensure its validity every fifth day. Access tests each database object for integrity when you open the database file.

- Maintain off-site backups that you can use to restore data in case of a disaster, such as a fire or a flood. The copy of the backup tape or disk that you test for restorability is a good candidate for an off-site backup copy.

You can back up database files on a network server by copying them to a workstation that has a fixed disk, but this technique doesn't provide backup security. The user of the workstation can erase or damage the backup copy if you don't create the off-site copy required for security against disasters.

Backing up data on network and peer-to-peer servers usually is accomplished with a tape drive device. These devices usually include an application that backs up all data on a network server or selected files on peer-to-peer servers at intervals and times you select. The simpler the backup operation, the more likely you are to have current backups. Regardless of how automated the backup procedure, however, you need to manually restore the test copy.

Compacting and Repairing Database Files

Compacting and repairing database files was discussed in Chapter 4, "Working with Access Databases and Tables." You should compact database files in which applications add and delete data to recover the disk space occupied by the deleted data. The procedure for compacting a database is similar to that described for encrypting and decrypting databases, except that you choose Compact Database instead of Encrypt/Decrypt Database from the File menu.

If you have a fixed disk defragmentation utility, such as Norton Utilities' SpeedDisk or Allen Morris' Disk Organizer (DOG), you can improve the operating speed of Access if you periodically defragment database files. Most defragmentation utilities tell you whether a disk drive has sufficient fragmentation to justify running the utility.

If you receive a message that a database is corrupted or if the database behaves in an irregular manner, one or more of the objects it contains may have become corrupt as the result of a hardware error. Databases can become corrupt as the result of a power failure when the computer is writing to the database file. The Repair Database choice of Access's File menu will attempt to repair the damage. If Access cannot repair the corruption, you must restore the latest backup copy. Test the backup copy with the existing SYSTEM.MDA file; in some cases, you may need to restore the prior SYSTEM.MDA file that contains the user account data for the database.

Modifying and Updating Multiuser Applications

The queries, forms, and reports you create when you develop a multiuser application are likely to be altered in response to suggestions from users and the needs of a growing organization. Modifying an existing application requires that you make a temporary unshared copy of the database file, make the modifications to the test file, and then test the modifications or additions you made. Then you need to export the modifications to the multiuser database.

To modify or update the multiuser copy of the database file, perform the following steps:

1. Have all users close the database file that is to be updated or modified.

2. Make a backup copy of the multiuser database file and the related SYSTEM.MDA file.

3. If you have made changes to the structure of any tables, import the corresponding table with a different name to your temporary database, and then append the data from the table to your new table structure (only) with an append query.

4. Export the objects that you have added or altered to the multiuser database.

5. Test the operation of the updated multiuser application.

The procedure for importing and exporting database objects is covered in Chapter 5, "Attaching, Importing, and Exporting Tables."

Chapter Summary

Although this chapter was devoted primarily to using Access in a multiuser environment, many of the elements of database security that were discussed apply to single-user applications. Even if you don't have a network now, if you use Access in an organization of more than 10 employees, multiuser applications likely will be a part of your future. This chapter provided a brief explanation of PC-based networks and the combination of hardware and software required to implement them. This chapter also described using the ODBC Administrator utility to connect to SQL Server databases. The methods you use as Database Administrator to share files and add new users to a network implementation of Access were explained, and establishing and maintaining database security was discussed. The chapter closed with a short description of the additional duties of a database administrator.

Chapter 22, "Writing Access Basic Code," begins Part VI of this book and introduces you to Access Basic, the programming language of Access. The remaining chapters of Part VI deal with programming-related topics, such as dynamic data exchange and creating Help files to assist the users of your applications.

Programming with Access Basic

Writing Access Basic Code

Most Access applications you create do not require you to write a single line of Access Basic code. Many commercial Access applications, such as MTX International's Accounting SDK for Access, use a minimal amount of Access Basic code. Sequences of Access actions, contained in macro objects, are usually sufficient to provide the methods you need to respond to events, such as running queries, displaying forms, and printing reports. The built-in functions of Access enable you to perform complex calculations. You may, however, want or need to use Access Basic code for any of the following reasons:

- ■ To create user-defined functions (UDFs) that substitute for complex expressions you use repeatedly to validate data, compute values for text boxes, and perform other duties. Creating a UDF that you refer to by a short name minimizes potential typing errors and enables you to document the way your expression works.

- ■ To write expressions that include more complex decision structures than allowed by the standard IIf( ) function (in an If...Then...Else...End If structure, for example), or to write expressions that need loops for repetitive operations.

- ■ To perform actions that are not available from standard Access macros, such as transaction processing with the Access Basic equivalents of SQL COMMIT, and ROLLBACK statements.

- To execute DDE operations that you cannot perform with the standard DDE( ) and DDESend( ) functions of Access, or to execute DDE operations over which you need more control than is offered by these functions. Using Access Basic's DDE capabilities is the subject of Chapter 23.

- To open more than one database in an application where attaching a table or using the SQL IN statement is not sufficient for your application.

- To provide hard-copy documentation for your application. If you include actions in Access Basic code instead of macros, you can print the Access Basic code to improve the documentation for your application.

This chapter describes Access Basic, introduces you to Access Basic modules and procedures, shows you how to use the Module window to enter and test Access Basic code, and helps you start writing user-defined functions. The chapter also includes examples of Access Basic programs.

Introducing Access Basic

Several years ago, Bill Gates, the founder and chairman of Microsoft Corporation, stated that all Microsoft applications that used macros would share a common macro language built on BASIC. BASIC is the acronym for Beginners All-Purpose Symbolic Instruction Code. Gates's choice of BASIC is not surprising when you consider that Microsoft was built on the foundation of Gates's BASIC interpreter that ran in 8K on the early predecessors of the PC. He reiterated his desire for a common macro language in an article that appeared in *One-to-One with Microsoft* in late 1991.

Before Access was released, the results of Gates's edict were observed in only one Microsoft product, Word for Windows. If you have created Word for Windows macros, or just made minor changes to macros you recorded, you will find that Access Basic is very similar to WordBasic. Access Basic, however, is a programming language, not a macro language. You create your own macro actions with Access Basic functions and procedures. To execute the Access Basic functions and procedures that you write, you use Access's macro language. You can execute any macro-action keyword from Access Basic by preceding the keyword with a DoCmd and a space. Many macro-action keywords appear to be the same as Access Basic keywords. Except for MsgBox and SendKeys, macro-action and Access Basic keywords that are identical in name, use a different syntax and perform different but usually related functions.

The Object Basic Root Language

Access Basic and Visual Basic are two members of a family of languages collectively called Object Basic, which is becoming the Esperanto for Microsoft Windows application programming. A sea of change may not occur immediately, but the decision has been made: before long you will be able to use Object Basic dialects with Microsoft Excel, FoxBase, and any of Microsoft's other mainstream applications. If you have used Visual Basic, writing Access Basic code will be a snap. Version 2 of Visual Basic, the language on which Access Basic is modeled, includes many of the new keywords added by Access to the Object Basic root language.

Although programmers who use "more sophisticated" languages, such as C++ and Pascal, heaped derision on the original dialects of BASIC, Access Basic is a full-featured language. Like other programming languages, Access Basic offers the same constructs, such as conditional statements and loops.

Access Basic Compared with xBase, PAL, and Visual Basic

Programmers who have experience with dBASE III, dBASE IV, or other xBase dialects, such as Clipper and FoxBase, will find that Access Basic uses many of the same xBase keywords or minor variations of familiar xBase keywords. Borland's PAL is related to xBase, so PAL programmers will also find the translation of PAL to Access Basic keywords straightforward.

User-defined functions are almost identical in structure in Access Basic, xBase, and PAL. This similarity in code structure ends, however, with user-defined functions. Writing code for Windows applications in general, and for Access in particular, requires an entirely different code structure. Applications for DOS DBMs use top-down programming techniques, which means that a main program calls (executes) other subprograms or procedures that perform specific actions. The user of the application makes choices from a menu that determine which subprograms or procedures are invoked. Menus that let the application remain idle are enclosed within DO WHILE...ENDDO loops while the user decides what menu command to choose next. Your code is responsible for all actions that occur while the application is running.

User-defined functions

xBase

PDOX

Program
structure

The situation with Windows and Access differs from that of top-down programming. Access itself is the main program and Windows is responsible for many functions that you must code in DOS DBM languages. This fact is a blessing for new programmers because Windows and Access simplify the development of complex applications. However, Access's and Windows' contributions are a curse for top-down DOS programmers because Access and Windows require an entirely new approach to writing DBM code. The guiding principles for DOS DBM developers writing Access Basic applications are the following:

- Don't even *think* about writing Access Basic code during the development stage of your applications. Most applications do not need any code other than an occasional user-defined function. Those applications that do need code usually do not require very much of it.

- Use command buttons and associated macro actions to substitute for the traditional menu commands of DOS DBMs. In most applications, you should create a menu that gives the user only the **Q**uit command from a **F**ile menu. All other user-initiated choices in the application are handled by control objects on forms.

- Concentrate on using macro actions to respond to application-initiated events, such as opening forms. Study the event-oriented properties of form and control objects and the macro actions available to respond to the event properties. Learn the full capabilities of each macro action native to Access before you write your own actions in Access Basic. Event properties combined with the appropriate macro actions usually can substitute for about 95 percent of the code you write for DOS DBMs.

- After your application is up and running, consider writing Access Basic code to add the nuances that distinguish professionally written database applications. If you are a programmer, you may find that implementing macro actions in code is preferable to using macro objects to contain those actions, because you can print code to document your application.

Visual Basic programmers will find only one major difference in Access Basic code: macros intervene between events and event-handling code. In Access, there is no provision for calling a procedure directly from an event property of a query, form, or report, or from a control object on a form or report. You must specify a named macro, choose the RunCode action, and name the procedure (written in the form of a function) that handles the event. One of the reasons for the intervening macro layer is database security; you can assign permission implicitly or explicitly to execute macros, but the modules that contain Access Basic code do not have permissions.

For Related Information:

◄◄ "Granting and Revoking Permissions," p. 908.

FROM HERE...

Where You Use Access Basic Code

You probably will first use Access Basic to create functions that make complex calculations. Creating an Access Basic function to substitute for calculations with many sets of parentheses is relatively simple and a good introduction to writing Access Basic code. Writing expressions as Access Basic functions enables you to add comments to the code that make the purpose and construction of the code clear to others. Also, comments aid your memory when you decide to revise an application after using it for a few months.

Your next step is to create Access Basic functions that you can call from macros using the RunCode action. You use functions to perform operations that cannot be accomplished by macro actions. The RunCode action executes Access Basic functions, but the RunCode action ignores the function's return value if it has one. Access Basic functions actually are procedures disguised in the form of functions. You write the procedures you need as functions, or you can write a short function that calls one or more procedures.

Typographic Conventions Used for Access Basic

This book uses a special set of typographic conventions for references to Access Basic keywords in Access Basic examples:

- Monospace type is used for all Access Basic code in the examples, as in `dwItemCounter`.

- **Boldface monospace** type is used for all Access Basic keywords and type-declaration symbols, as in **Dim** and **%**. Standard function names in Access Basic, as described in Chapter 7, "Understanding Operators and Expressions In Access," are also set in boldface type so that keywords, standard function names, and reserved symbols stand out from variable and function names and values you assign to variables.

■ *Italic monospace* type indicates a replaceable item, as in **Dim** *DataItem* **As String**.

■ **Bold italic monospace** type indicates a replaceable keyword, such as a data type, as in **Dim** *DataItem* **As** **DataType**; DataType is replaced by a keyword corresponding to the desired Access Basic data type.

■ Conventional, proportionally spaced type is used for properties of Access objects when the value of property is determined by an entry for the object in the Properties dialog box, instead of by Access Basic code.

■ Optional elements are included within square brackets, as in [*OptionItem*]. Square brackets also enclose object names that contain spaces or special punctuation symbols.

■ Ellipsis (...) substitutes for code not shown in syntax and code examples, as in **If...Then...Else If...End If**.

Names of macro actions that serve as arguments of the DoCmd MacroName statement are not set in bold type because macro-action names are not reserved words in Access Basic. When a keyword in Access Basic is used in Access database objects other than modules, the typeface is determined by the context in which the word is presented.

Modules, Functions, and Procedures

A *module* is a container for Access Basic code, just as a form is a container for control objects. You create a module to contain your Access Basic code the same way that you create any other new database object—click the Module button in the Database window, and then click the New button.

A module consists of a *declarations section* and one or more *procedures* or *functions*. As the name suggests, the declarations section of a module is used to declare items (usually variables, the subject of a following section) that are used by the procedures and functions contained in the module.

Procedures are typically defined as subprograms that are referred to by name in another program. Referring to a procedure by name *calls* or *invokes* the procedure; the code in the procedure executes, and then the sequence of execution returns to the program that called the procedure. Another name for a procedure is *subroutine*. Procedures can call other procedures, in which case the called procedures are called *subprocedures*. Procedures are defined by beginning (Sub) and end (End Sub) keywords, as in the following example:

```
Sub ProcName
    [Start of procedure code]
    ...
    [End of procedure code]
End Sub
```

You can refer to the procedure name to invoke the procedure, but Access Basic provides a keyword, Call, that explicitly invokes a procedure. Prefixing the procedure name with Call is a good programming practice because this keyword identifies the name that follows as the name of a procedure instead of a variable.

Functions are a class of procedures that return values to their names, as explained in Chapter 7. C programmers would argue that procedures are a class of functions that do not return values. Regardless of how you view the difference between functions and procedures, keep the following points in mind:

- Access requires that you write Access Basic functions (not procedures) to act as macro actions and user-defined functions. Functions are the entry point to all the Access Basic code you want.

- The only way you can call a procedure is from an Access Basic function or from another procedure. You cannot directly execute a procedure from any Access database object.

- To execute an Access Basic function in Access Basic code, you must use the function in an expression, such as wReturnValue=wFunctionName, even when the function returns no value.

Functions are created within a structure similar to procedures, as in the following example:

```
Function FuncName
    [Start of function code]
    ...
    [End of function code]
End Function
```

You cannot use Call to execute a function; you must refer to the function by name. Function calls are identified by the parentheses that follow the function name, even if the function requires arguments.

You can add to a module as many individual procedures and functions as you want. If you write a substantial amount of Access Basic code, you should create separate modules for code associated with a particular class of object, such as forms. Module objects are assigned names and stored in the open database, like all other Access database objects.

Data Types and Database Objects in Access Basic

When you create Access Basic tables, all data types that you use to assign field data types and sizes (except for OLE and Memo data types) have counterparts in Access Basic. With the exception of the Variant and Currency data types, Access Basic data types are represented in most other dialects of BASIC, such as Microsoft QuickBASIC and the QBasic interpreter supplied with MS-DOS 5+. All these data types, including Variant, are now supported by Visual Basic 2.0.

Traditional BASIC dialects use a punctuation symbol called the type-declaration character, such as $ for the String data type, to designate the data type. The Access Basic data types, the type-declaration characters, the corresponding field data types, and the ranges of values are shown in the AB Type, Symbol, Field Type, Minimum and Maximum Value columns of table 22.1, respectively. The Field Types Byte, Integer, Long Integer, Counter, Single, and Double correspond to the Field size property of the Number data type in tables, queries, forms, and reports.

Table 22.1. Access Basic and Corresponding Field Data Types

AB Type	Symbol	Field Type	Minimum Value	Maximum Value
Integer	%	Byte, Integer, Yes/No	-32,768	32,767
Long	&	Long Integer, Counter	-2,147,483,648	2,147,483,647
Single	!	Single	-3.402823E38 1.401298E-45	-1.401298E-45 3.402823E38
Double	#	Single, Date/Time	-1.79769313486232E308 4.94065645841247E-324	4.9406564841247E-324 1.79769313486232E308
Currency	@	Currency	-922,337,203,685, 477.5808	922,337,203,685, 477.5807
String	$	Text	0 characters	65,500 characters (+/-)
Variant	None	Any	January 1, 0000 (date) Same as Double (numbers) Same as String (text)	December 31, 1999 (date) Same as Double (numbers) Same as String (text)

You can dispense with the type-declaration character if you explicitly declare your variables with the Dim...As DataType statement, discussed later in this section. If you do not explicitly declare the variables' data type or use a symbol to define an implicit data type, Access Basic variables default to the Variant data type.

The # sign is also used to enclose values specified as dates, as in NewYears# = #1/1/94#. In this case, bold type is not used for the enclosing # signs, because these symbols are not intended for the purpose of the # reserved symbol.

Database objects, such as tables, queries, forms, and reports, all of which you used in prior chapters, also have corresponding data types in Access Basic. Here Access Basic departs from other BASIC languages, including Visual Basic. The new database object types of Access Basic are listed in table 22.2.

Table 22.2. Database Object Data Types Supported by Access Basic

Object Data Type	Corresponding Database Object
Database	Access databases
Form	Forms, including subforms
Report	Reports, including subreports
Control	Controls on forms and reports
QueryDef	Query definitions (SQL statement equivalents)
Table	Tables of databases
Dynaset	Results of queries (recordsets) that are updatable
Snapshot	Results of queries (recordsets) that are not updatable

The Dynaset and Snapshot data types are called *recordset objects* because variables of these data types consist of sets of records from queries.

Variables and Naming Conventions

Variables are named placeholders for values of a specified data type that change when your Access Basic code is executed. You give variables names, as you name fields, but the names of variables cannot

include spaces or any other punctuation except the underscore character (_). The other restriction is that a variable cannot use an Access
Basic keyword by itself as a name; keywords are called *reserved words*
for this reason. The same rules apply to giving names to functions and
procedures. Variable names in Access Basic typically employ a combination of upper- and lowercase letters to make them more readable.

Implicit Variables

You can create variables by assigning a value to a variable name, as in
the following example:

```
NewVar = 1234
```

A statement of this type *declares* a variable, which means to create a
new variable with a name you choose. The statement in the example
creates a new implicit variable, NewVar, of the Variant data type with a
value of 1234. When you do not specify a data type for an implicit variable by appending one of the type-declaration characters to the variable name, the Variant data type is assigned by default. The following
statement creates a variable of the Integer data type:

```
NewVar% = 1234
```

Declaring variables of the Integer or Long type when decimal fractions
are not required speeds the operation of your code. Access takes
longer to compute values for Variant, Single, and Double variables.

Explicit Variables

It is better programming practice to declare your variables and assign
those variables a data type before you give variables a value. Programming languages such as C, C++, and Turbo Pascal require you to declare
variables before you use them. The most common method of declaring
variables is by using the Dim...As structure, where As specifies the data
type. This method declares explicit variables. An example follows:

```
Dim NewVar As Integer
```

If you do not add the As Integer keywords, NewVar is assigned the Variant data type by default.

You can require that all variables must be explicitly declared prior to
their use by adding the statement, Option Explicit, in the declarations
section of a module. The advantage of using Option Explicit is that Access will detect misspelled variable names and display an error message when misspellings are encountered. If you do not use Option

Explicit and you misspell a variable name, Access creates a new implicit variable with the misspelled name. Resulting errors in your code's operation can be difficult to diagnose.

Scope and Duration of Variables

Variables have a property called *scope*, which determines when they appear and disappear in your Access Basic code. Variables appear the first time you declare them and then disappear and reappear on the basis of the scope you assign to them. When a variable appears, it is said to be *visible*, meaning that you can assign the variable a value, change its value, and use it in expressions. Otherwise, the variable is *invisible*; if you use a variable's name while it is invisible, you create a new variable with the same name instead.

The following lists the three scope levels in Access Basic:

- *Local (procedure-level) scope:* The variable is visible only during the time when the procedure in which the variable is declared is executed. Variables that you declare, with or without using the Dim...As keywords in a procedure or function, are local in scope.

- *Module-level scope:* The variable is visible to all procedures and functions contained in the module in which the variable was declared. You declare variables with module scope in the declarations section of the module, using the Dim...As keywords.

- *Global scope:* The variable is visible to all procedures and functions within all modules. You declare variables with global scope in the declarations section of the module, using the Global...As keywords.

The scope and visibility of variables declared in two different modules of the same database, both having two procedures, are illustrated by the diagram in figure 22.1. In each procedure, variables declared with different scopes are used to assign values to variables declared within the procedure. Invalid assignment statements are shown crossed out in the figure. These assignment statements are invalid because the variable used to assign the value to the variable declared in the procedure is not visible in the procedure.

Variables also have a property called *duration*, or lifetime. The duration of a variable is your code's execution time between the first appearance of the variable (its declaration) and its disappearance. Each time a procedure or function is called, local variables declared with the Dim...As statement are set to default values, with 0 for numeric data types and the empty string ("") for string variables. These local variables have a duration equal to the lifetime of the function—from the time the function is called until the End Function statement is executed.

FIG. 22.1

Valid and invalid assignment statements for variables of different scopes.

To preserve the values of local variables between occurrences (called *instances*) of a procedure or function, you substitute the keyword Static for Dim. Static variables have a duration of your Access application, but their scope is determined by where you declare them. Static variables are useful when you want to count the number of occurrences of an event. You can make all variables in a function or procedure static variables by preceding Sub or Function with the Static keyword.

 Minimize the number of local variables that you declare Static. Local variables do not consume memory when they are not visible. This characteristic of local variables is especially important in the case of arrays, discussed in the "Access Basic Arrays" section that follows shortly, because arrays are often very large.

User-Defined Data Types

You can create your own data type consisting of one or more Access data types. User-defined data types are discussed in this section pertaining to variables because you need to know what a variable is before you can declare a user-defined data type. You declare a user-defined data type between the Type...End Type keywords, as in the following example:

```
Type DupRec
    Field1 As Long
    Field2 As String * 20
    Field3 As Single
    Field4 As Double
End Type
```

User-defined data types are particularly useful when you create a variable to hold the values of one or more records of a table that uses fields of different data types. The String * 20 statement defines Field2 of the user-defined data type as a *fixed-length* string of 20 characters, usually corresponding to the Size property of the Text field data type. String variables in user-defined data types are always specified with a fixed length. You must declare your user-defined data type (called a *record* or a *structure* in other programming languages) in the Declarations section of a module.

You must explicitly declare variables to be of the user-defined type with the Dim, Global, or Static keywords because there is no reserved symbol to declare a user-defined data type, as in Dim CurrentRec As DupRec. To assign a value to a field of a variable with a user-defined data type, you specify the name of the variable and the field name, separating them with a period, as in CurrentRec.Field1 = 2048.

Access Basic Arrays

Arrays are variables that consist of a collection of values, called elements of the array, of a single data type in a regularly ordered structure. Implicitly declared arrays are not allowed in Access Basic (or in Visual Basic). You declare an array with the Dim statement, adding the number of elements in parentheses to the variable name for the array, as in the following example:

```
Dim NewArray (20) As String
```

This statement creates an array of 21 elements, each of which is a conventional, variable-length string variable. You create 21 elements because the first element of an array is the 0 (zero) element, unless you specify otherwise by adding the To modifier, as in the following example:

```
Dim NewArray (1 To 20) As String
```

The preceding statement creates an array with 20 elements.

You can create multidimensional arrays by adding more values, separated by commas. The statement

```
Dim NewArray (9, 9, 9) As Long
```

creates a three-dimensional array of 10 elements per dimension. This array, when visible, occupies 4,000 bytes of memory (10 * 10 * 10 * 4 bytes/long integer).

You can create a dynamic array by declaring the array using Dim without specifying the number of elements, and then using the ReDim keyword to determine the number of elements the array contains. You can ReDim an array as many times as you want; each time you do so, the values stored in the array are reinitialized to their default values, determined by the data type. The follow sample statements create a dynamic array:

```
Dim NewArray ( ) As Long
ReDim NewArray (9, 9, 9)
```

Dynamic arrays are useful when you don't know how many elements an array requires when you declare it. You can ReDim a dynamic array to 0 elements when you no longer need the values it contains; this enables you to recover the memory that the array consumes while it is visible. Arrays declared with Dim are limited to eight dimensions. You can use the ReDim statement within a procedure without preceding it with the Dim statement to create local-scope arrays with up to 60 dimensions.

Scope, duration rules, and keywords apply to arrays in the same way in which they apply to conventional variables. You can declare dynamic arrays with global and module-level scope by adding the Global or Dim statement to the declaration section of a module, and then use the ReDim statement by itself in a procedure. If you declare an array with Static, instead of Dim, the array retains its values between instances of a procedure.

Do not use the Option Base keyword to change the default initial element of arrays from 0 to 1. Option Base is included in Access Basic for compatibility with Visual Basic. In Visual Basic, Option Base is for compatibility with other BASIC dialects. Many arrays you create from Access Basic objects must begin with element 0. If you are concerned about the memory occupied by an unused zeroth element of an array, use the Dim ArrayName (1 To N) As DataType declaration. In most cases, you can disregard the zeroth element.

Named Database Objects as Variables in Access Basic Code

Properties of database objects you create with Access can be treated as variables and assigned values within Access Basic code. You can assign a new value to the text box that contains the address information for a customer by name, for example. Use the following statement:

```
Forms!Customers!Address = "123 Elm St."
```

The keyword Forms defines the type of object. The exclamation point (called the *bang* symbol by programmers) separates the name of the form and the name of the control object. The ! symbol is analogous to the \ path separator that you use when you are dealing with DOS files. If the name of the form or the control object contains a space or other punctuation, you need to enclose the name within square brackets, as in the following statement:

```
Forms!Customers![Contact Name] = "Joe Hill"
```

Alternatively, you can use the Set keyword to create your own named variable for the control object. This procedure is convenient when you need to refer to the control object several times; it is more convenient to type txtContact than the full "path" to the control object, in this case a text box.

```
Dim txtContact As Control
Set txtContact = Forms!Customers![Contact Name]
txtContact = "Joe Hill"
```

You can assign any database object to a variable name by declaring the variable as the object type and using the Set statement to assign the object to the variable. You do not create a copy of the object in memory when you assign it a variable name; the variable refers to the object in memory. Referring to an object in memory is often called *pointing* to an object; many languages have a pointer data type that holds the value of the location in memory where the variable is stored. Access Basic does not support pointers.

Variable Naming Conventions

In the unlikely event that you need to write large amounts of Access Basic code, you probably will employ a large number of variable names and many different data types. On forms and reports, many different types of named control objects can be used, each of which you can assign to a variable name with the Set keyword in your Access Basic code. As your code grows in size, remembering the data types of all the variables becomes difficult.

Greg Reddick, one of the members of the Access beta-test forum on CompuServe, has proposed a set of variable-naming conventions for Access Basic. His proposed naming conventions are called *Hungarian notation*, which is used primarily in the C and C++ languages. Hungarian refers to the nationality of the method's inventor, who was involved in the development of Access, and the fact that only Hungarians are likely to be able to correctly pronounce some of the abbreviations involved, such as "sz." Reddick adapted Hungarian notation for use in the Access Basic environment.

Hungarian notation uses a set of codes for the data type. You prefix the variable name with the code in lowercase letters. As an example, the prefix code for a text box is txt, so the variable name for the text box in the preceding example is txtContact. Strings in C code are identified by the prefix lpsz, an abbreviation for long pointer to a string, zero-terminated (with Chr$(0) or ASCII Null). Access Basic does not support the pointer data type (but it does use pointers for the location of string variables), and it does not use zero-terminated strings. The sz prefix is used here, because Access Basic strings are passed to Windows functions you declare.

The data type identifier of a user-defined data type is called a *created tag*. In Hungarian notation, created tags are capitalized as in the following:

```
Type REC
    dwField1 As Long
    szField2 As String
    sField3 As Single
    dField4 As Double
End Type
```

A variable of type REC is declared with the rec prefix, such as in the following:

```
Dim recCurRecord As REC
```

Created tags should be short, but should not duplicate one of the standard data type prefix codes.

Using standard data type prefixes makes your code easier to read and understand. Many of the code examples in this book use the new proposed naming conventions. The complete list of Greg Reddick's notation for Access Basic appears in Appendix B.

Symbolic Constants

Symbolic constants are named placeholders for values of a specified data type that do not change when your Access Basic code is executed. You precede the name of a symbolic constant with the keyword, Const, as in Const sPI = 3.1416. You declare symbolic constants in the declarations section of a module. Precede Const with the Global keyword if you want to create a global constant that is visible to all modules, as in Global Const sPI = 3.1416. Constants only have global or module-level scope.

Typically, symbolic constants take names in all capital letters to distinguish them from variables. Often underscores are used to make the names of symbolic constants more readable, as in sVALUE_OF_PI.

You do not need to specify a data type for constants, because Access Basic chooses the data type that stores the data most efficiently. Access Basic can do this, because it knows the value of the data when it compiles your code. Compiling code is discussed in a section that follows, "Compiling Access Basic Code."

Access System-Defined Constants

Access includes seven system-defined constants, True, False, Yes, No, On, Off, and Null that are created by Access when launched. Of these seven, you can use True, False, and Null in Access Basic code. The remaining four are valid for use with all database objects except modules. When the system-defined constants True, False, and Null are used in Access Basic code examples in this book, they are capitalized.

The global constants TRUE and FALSE must be explicitly declared in Visual Basic. You cannot declare these constants in Access Basic. If you attempt to declare TRUE, FALSE, or NULL as constants in Access Basic, you receive the error message, Expected: identifier.

Access Intrinsic Constants

Access Basic provides a number of pre-declared intrinsic symbolic constants for actions (prefixed with A_), databases (prefixed with DB_) and the variant data type (prefixed with V_). The names appear in the Help window for the Constants subject. You may not use any of these intrinsic constants' names as names for constants that you define.

Controlling Program Flow

Useful procedures must be able to make decisions based on the values of variables and then take specified actions based on those decisions. Blocks of code, for example, may need to be repeated until a specified condition occurs. Statements used to make decisions and repeat blocks of code are the fundamental elements that control program flow in Access Basic and all other programming languages.

All programming languages require methods of executing different algorithms based on the results of one or more comparison operations. You can control the flow of any program in any programming language with just three types of statements: conditional execution (If ... Then), repetition (Do While ... Loop and related structures), and termination (End...). The additional flow control statements in Access Basic and other programming languages make writing code more straightforward.

The code examples used in this section do not include Dim statements, so Hungarian notation is not used here, and data type identification symbols are used to indicate the data types of variables.

For Related Information:

◄◄ "Assignment and Comparison Operators," p. 269.

FROM HERE...

Branching and Labels

If you have written DOS batch files or WordPerfect macros, you are probably acquainted with branching and labels. Both the DOS batch language and the WordPerfect macro language include the GoTo *Label* command. DOS defines any word that begins a line with a colon as a label; WordPerfect requires use of the keyword LABEL and then the label name.

When BASIC was first developed, the *only* method of controlling program flow was through its GOTO *LineNumber* and GOSUB *LineNumber* statements. Every line in the program required a number that could be used as a substitute for a label. GOTO *LineNumber* caused the interpreter to skip to the designated line and continue executing the program from that point. GOSUB *LineNumber* caused the program to follow that same branch, but when the BASIC interpreter that executed the code encountered a RETURN statement, program execution jumped back to the line following the GOSUB statement and continued executing at that point.

Skipping Blocks of Code with GoTo

Procedural BASIC introduced named labels that replaced the line numbers for GOTO and GOSUB statements. Access Basic's GoTo Label statement causes your code to branch to the location named Label; and continue from that point. Note the semicolon following Label; it identifies the single word you assigned as a label. However, the semicolon is not required after the label name following the GoTo. In fact, if you add the semicolon, you get a "label not found" error message.

A label name *must* begin in the far left column (1) of your code. This often interferes with orderly indenting of your code, explained in the next section, just one more reason, in addition to those below, for not using GoTo.

Avoiding "Spaghetti Code" by Not Using GoTo

The sequence of statements in code that uses multiple GoTo statements is very difficult to follow. It is almost impossible to understand the flow of a large program written in line-numbered BASIC because of the jumps here and there in the code. Programs with multiple GoTo's are derisively said to contain "spaghetti code."

The GoTo statement is required for only one purpose in Access Basic: handling errors with the On Error GoTo Label statement. Although Access Basic supports BASIC's ON ... GOTO and ON ... GOSUB statements, using those statements is not considered good programming practice.

Conditional Statements

A conditional statement executes the statements between its occurrence and the terminating statement if the result of the relational operator is true. Statements that consist of or require more than one statement for completion are called *structured statements*, *control structures*, or just *structures*.

The If ... Then ... End If Structure

The syntax of the primary conditional statement of procedural BASIC is as follows:

```
If Condition1% = TRUE Then
    Statements to be executed if Expression1 is true
[Else[If Condition2% = TRUE Then]]
    Optional statements to be executed if Condition1%
    is false [and Condition2% is true]
End If
```

The = True elements of the preceding conditional statement are optional and typically not included when you write actual code. If Condition1% Then and If Condition1% = True produce the same result.

You can add a second condition with the ElseIf statement that must be true to control execution of the statements that are executed if Condition1% is false. Note that no space is needed between Else and If. An If ... End If structure that incorporates the ElseIf statement is the simplified equivalent of the following:

```
If Condition1% = TRUE Then
    Statements to be executed if Expression1 is true
Else
    If Condition2% = TRUE Then
        Statements to be executed if Condition1% is
    false and Condition2% is true]
    End If
End If
```

Whether a statement is executed is based on the evaluation of the immediately preceding expression. This expression may include additional If ... End If or other flow control structures. If ... End If structures within other If ... End If structures are said to be *nested*, as in the preceding example. The number, or *depth*, of If ... End Ifs that may be nested within one another is unlimited.

Note that the code between the individual keywords that make up the flow control structure is indented. Indentation makes code within structures easier to read. You usually use the tab key to create indentation.

To evaluate whether a character is a letter and to determine its case, you can use the following code:

```
If Asc(Char$) > 63 And Asc(Char$) < 91 Then
    CharType$ = "Upper Case Letter"
ElseIf Asc(Char$) > 96 And Asc(Char$) < 123 Then
    CharType$ = "Lower Case Letter"
End If
```

You have seen a single-line version of the If ... End If statement, IIf( ), in the "Assignment and Comparison Operators" section of Chapter 7. The single-line version does not require the terminating End If statement. Although acceptable for simple statements, the single-line version's use is questionable (not necessarily poor) programming practice, so this book avoids it.

You use the If ... End If statement more often than any other flow control.

The Select Case ... End Select Structure

When you must choose among many alternatives, If ... End If structures can become very complex and deeply nested. The Select Case ... End Select statement was added to procedural BASIC to overcome this complexity. In addition to testing whether an expression evaluates to true or false, Select Case can evaluate variables to determine whether those variables fall within specified ranges. The generalized syntax is in the following example:

```
Select Case VarName
    Case Expression1[, Expressions, ...]
        (Statements executed if the value of VarName
    = Expression1 or Expressions)
    [Case Expression2 To Expression3
        (Statements executed if the value of VarName
    is in the range of Expression2 to Expression3)]
    [Case Is RelationalExpression
        (Statements executed if the value of
    VarName = Expression1)]
    [Case Else
        (Statements executed if none of the
    above cases is met)]
End Select
```

Select Case evaluates VarName, which can be a string or numeric variable. It then tests each Case expression in sequence. Case expressions can take one of the following four forms:

- A single or list of values to which to compare the value of VarName. Successive members of the list are separated from the predecessor by commas.

- A range of values separated by the keyword To. The value of the first member of the range limits must be less than the value of the second. Strings are compared by the ASCII value of their first character.

■ The keyword Is, followed by relational operator, such as <>, <, <=, =, >=, or >, and a variable or literal value.

■ The keyword Else. Expressions following Case Else are executed if no prior Case condition is satisfied.

The Case statements are tested in sequence, and the code associated with the first matching Case condition is executed. If no match is found and the Case Else statement is present, the code following the statement is executed. Program execution then continues at the line of code following the End Select terminating statement.

If VarName is a numeric type, all expressions with which it is to be compared by Case, are forced to the same data type.

The following example is of Select Case using a numeric variable, Sales#:

```
Select Case Sales#
    Case 10000 To 49999.99
        Class% = 1
    Case 50000 To 100000
        Class% = 2
    Case Is < 10000
        Class% = 0
    Case Else
        Class% = 3
End Select
```

Note that because Sales# is a double-precision real number, all the comparison literals also are treated as double-precision (not the default single-precision) real numbers for the purposes of comparison.

A more complex example that evaluates a single character follows:

```
Select Case Text$
    Case "A" To "Z"
        CharType$ = "Upper Case"
    Case "a" To "z"
        CharType$ = "Lower Case"
    Case "0" To "9"
        CharType$ = "Number"
    Case "!", "?", ".", ",", ";"
        CharType$ = "Punctuation"
    Case ""
        CharType$ = "Null String"
    Case < 32
        CharType$ = "Special Character"
    Case Else
        CharType$ = "Unknown Character"
End Select
```

This example demonstrates that Select Case, when used with strings, evaluates the ASCII value of the first character of the string, either as the variable being tested or the expressions following Case statements. Thus Case < 32 is a valid test, although Text$ is a string variable.

Repetitive Operations—Looping

There are many instances in which you must repeat an operation until a given condition is satisfied, whereupon the repetitions terminate. You may want to examine each character in a word, sentence, or document, or assign values to an array with many elements. Loops are used for these and many other purposes.

Using the For ... Next Statement

Access Basic's For ... Next statement enables you to repeat a block of code a specified number of times, as shown in the following example:

```
For Counter% = StartValue% To EndValue% [Step
Increment%]
      Statements to be executed
      [Conditional statement
            Exit For
      End of conditional statement]
Next [Counter%]
```

The block of statements between the For and Next keywords is executed (EndValue%-StartValue% +1) / Increment% times. As an example, if StartValue% = 5, EndValue% = 10, and Increment% = 1, execution of the statement block is repeated 6 times. You need not add the keyword Step in this case—the default increment is 1. Although integer data types are shown, long integers may be used. The use of real numbers as values for counters and increments is possible, but uncommon.

The dividend of the above expression must always be a positive number if execution of the internal statement block is to occur. If EndValue% is less than StartValue%, Increment% must be negative; otherwise, the For ... Next statement is ignored by Access Basic.

If you use a numeric variable for Increment% in a For ... Next loop and the value of the variable becomes zero, the loop repeats indefinitely and locks up your computer, requiring you to reboot the application or Access Basic. Make sure your code traps any condition that could result in Increment% becoming zero.

The optional Exit For statement is provided so that you can prematurely terminate the loop using a surrounding If ... Then ... End If conditional statement. Changing the value of the counter variable within the loop itself to terminate its operation is discouraged as a dangerous programming practice. You might make a change that would cause an infinite loop.

The repetition of Counter% following the Next statement is optional, but is considered good programming practice, especially if you are using nested For ... Next loops. Adding Counter% keeps you informed of which loop you are counting. If you try to use the same variable name for a counter of a nested For ... Next loop, you receive an error message.

When the value of Counter% exceeds EndValue% or the Exit For statement is executed, execution proceeds to the line of code following Next.

Using For ... Next Loops To Assign Values to Array Elements

One of the most common applications of the For ... Next loop is to assign successive values to the elements of an array. If you have declared a 26-element array named Alphabet$( ), the following example assigns the capital letters A through Z to its elements:

```
For Letter% = 1 To 26
    Alphabet$(Letter%) = Chr$(Letter% + 63)
Next Letter%
```

The preceding example assigns 26 of the array's 27 elements if you used Dim Alphabet$(26) instead of Dim Alphabet$(1 To 26). 63 is added to Letter% because the ASCII value of the letter A is 64 and the initial value of Letter% is 1.

Understanding Do While ... Loop and While ... Wend

A more general form of the loop structure is Do While ... Loop, which uses the following syntax:

```
Do While Condition% = TRUE
    Statements to be executed
    [Conditional statement
        Exit Do
    End of conditional statement]
Loop
```

This loop structure executes the intervening statements only if Condition% equals TRUE (-1), and continues to do so until Condition% no longer equals TRUE or the optional Exit Do statement is executed. Note that Condition% need not equal FALSE (0) for the loop to terminate; the Not TRUE (<> -1) condition is the test for termination.

From the above syntax, the previous For ... Next array assignment example can be duplicated by the following structure:

```
Letter% = 1
Do While Letter% <= 27
    Alphabet(Letter%) = Chr$(Letter% + 63%)
    Letter% = Letter% +1
Loop
```

Another example of a Do loop is the Do Until...Loop structure which loops as long as the condition is not satisfied, as in the following example:

```
Do Until Condition% <> TRUE
    Statements to be executed
    [Conditional statement
        Exit Do
    End of conditional statement]
Loop
```

The While ... Wend loop is identical to the Do While ... Loop structure, but you cannot use the Exit Do statement within it. The While ... Wend structure is provided for compatibility with QBasic and QuickBASIC and should be abandoned in favor of Do While ... Loop in Access Basic.

Making Sure Statements in a Loop Occur at Least Once

You may have observed that the statements within a Do While ... Loop structure are never executed if Condition% is NOT TRUE when the structure is encountered in your application. You also can use a structure in which the conditional statement that causes loop termination is associated with the Loop statement. The syntax of this format is in the following example:

```
Do
    Statements to be executed
    [Conditional statement then
        Exit Do
    End of conditional statement]
Loop While Condition% = TRUE
```

A similar structure is available for Do Until...Loop:

```
Do
     Statements to be executed
     [Conditional statement
          Exit Do
     End of conditional statement]
Loop Until Condition% = TRUE
```

These structures ensure that the loop executes at least once *before* the condition is tested.

Avoiding Infinite Loops

You have already received warnings about infinite loops in the descriptions of each of the loop structures. If you create a "tight" loop, (one with few statements between Do ... and Loop) that never terminates, executing the code causes Access Basic to appear to freeze. You cannot terminate operation, and you must use Ctrl+Alt+Delete to reboot Access Basic and correct the code.

These apparent infinite loops are often created intentionally with code such as the following:

```
Temp% = TRUE
ExitLoop% = FALSE
Do While Temp% = TRUE
     Call TestProc(ExitLoop%)
     If ExitLoop% = TRUE Then
          Exit Do
     End If
Loop
```

The above example repeatedly calls the procedure TestProc, whose statements are executed, until ExitLoop% is set true by code in TestProc. Structures of this type are the equivalent of DO WHILE .T. ... ENDDO structures in dBASE. You must make sure that ExitLoop% eventually becomes TRUE, one way or another, no matter what happens when the code in TestProc is executed.

Typically you can write the Do While line as Do While Temp%, not Do While Temp% = TRUE. Displaying the relational operator, as in Temp% = TRUE, however, makes your code more readable and is used in this chapter's examples for clarity.

To avoid locking up Access Basic with tight infinite loops, include the DoEvents( ) function in loops during the testing stage, as in the following example:

```
Do While Temp% = TRUE
    Call TestProc(ExitLoop%)
    If ExitLoop% = TRUE Then
        Exit Do
    End If
    DoEvents( )
Loop
```

DoEvents( ) tests the Windows environment to determine whether
any other event messages, such as a mouse click, are pending. If
so, DoEvents( ) allows the messages to be processed and then
continues at the next line of code. You can then remove
DoEvents( ) to speed up the loop, after your testing verifies that
infinite looping cannot occur.

Handling Run-Time Errors

No matter how thoroughly you test and debug your code, run-time
errors appear eventually. Run-time errors are errors that occur when
Access executes your code. Use the On Error GoTo instruction to control what happens in your application when a run-time error occurs. On
Error is not a very sophisticated instruction, but it is your only choice
for error processing. You can branch to a label, creating "spaghetti
code," or you can ignore the error. The general syntax of On Error
GoTo follows:

```
On Error GoTo LabelName
On Error Resume Next
On Error GoTo 0
```

On Error GoTo LabelName branches to the portion of your code with
the label LabelName. LabelName must be a label; it cannot be the name
of a procedure. The code following LabelName, however, can (and usually does) include a procedure call to an error handling procedure,
such as ErrorProc:

```
On Error GoTo ErrHandler
...
[RepeatCode:]
(Code using ErrProc to handle errors)
...
GoTo SkipHandler
ErrHandler:
Call ErrorProc
[GoTo Repeat Code}
SkipHandler:
...
(Additional code)
```

In this example, the On Error GoTo instruction causes program flow to branch to the ErrHandler label that executes the error-handling procedure ErrorProc. Ordinarily, the error handler code is located at the end of the procedure. If you have more than one error handler, or if the error handler is in the middle of a group of instructions, you need to bypass it if the preceding code is error-free. Use the GoTo SkipHandler statement that bypasses ErrHandler instructions. To repeat the code that generated the error after ErrorProc has done its job, add a label such as **RepeatCode:** at the beginning of the repeated code, and then branch to the code in the ErrHandler: code.

On Error Resume Next disregards the error and continues processing the succeeding instructions.

After an On Error GoTo statement executes, it remains in effect for all succeeding errors until another On Error GoTo instruction is encountered or until error processing is explicitly turned off with the On Error GoTo 0 form of the statement.

If you do not trap errors with an On Error GoTo statement or if you have turned error trapping off with On Error GoTo 0, a dialog box with the appropriate error message appears when a run-time error is encountered.

The Err function (no arguments) returns an integer representing the code of the last error, or 0 if no error occurs. This function is ordinarily used within a Select Case structure to determine the action to take in the error handler based on the type of error incurred. Use the Error$( ) function to return the text name of the error number specified as its argument, as in the following example:

```
ErrorName$ = Error$(Err)
Select Case Err
    Case 58 To 76
        Call FileError 'procedure for handling file
    errors
    Case 281 To 297
        Call DDEError ' procedure for handling DDE
    errors
    Case 340 To 344
        Call ArrayError 'procedure for control array
    errors
End Select
Err = 0
```

Most of the error codes returned by the Err function are listed in the Error Codes topic of the Access help file. Choose **S**earch from the **H**elp menu to display the Search dialog box. Then type **Error Codes** in the text box and press Enter. The Error Codes Help window displays a list of code numbers and their descriptions. Click the underlined description text to display a window that describes each error code in detail.

You can substitute the actual error processing code for the Call instructions shown in the preceding example, but using individual procedures for error handling is the recommended approach. The Err *statement* is used to set the error code to a specific integer. This statement should be used to reset the error code to 0 after your error handler has completed its operation, as shown in the preceding example.

The Error statement is used to simulate an error so that you can test any error handlers you have written. You can specify any of the valid integer error codes or create a user-defined error code by selecting an integer that is not included in the list. A user-defined error code returns "User-defined error" to Error$( ).

Exploring the Module Window

You write Access Basic functions and procedures in the Module window. To display a module window, click the Module button in the Database window. Then double-click the name of the module you want to display. To start a new Access Basic module, click the New button. A Module window, which demonstrates the use of Access Basic to execute SQL queries, appears as shown in figure 22.2. The Module window incorporates a text editor, similar to Windows Notepad, in which you type your Access Basic code.

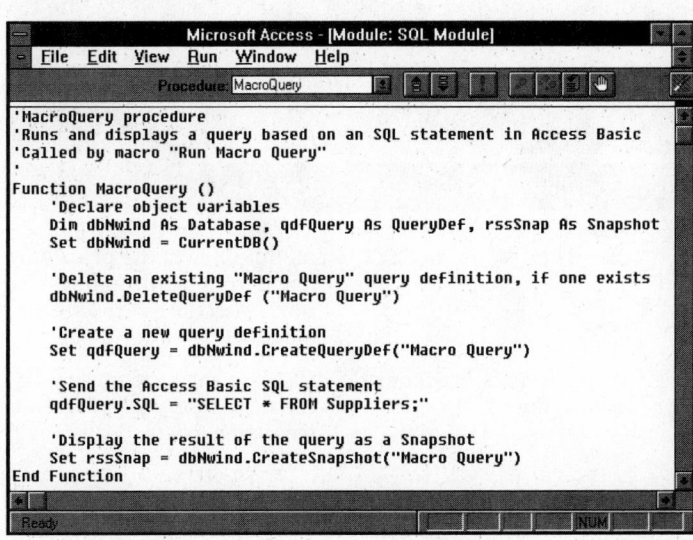

FIG. 22.2

The Access Basic Module window.

The Access Basic code in figure 22.2 demonstrates two principles of writing code in any language: add code comments that explain the purpose of the statements, and use indentation to make your code more readable. Comments in Access Basic are preceded with an apostrophe ('); alternatively, use the prefix Rem (for "remark" in earlier versions of BASIC) to indicate that the text on the line is a comment. Rem must be the first statement on a line (unless preceded by a colon that separates statements), but the apostrophe prefix may be used anywhere in your code. Comments that precede the code identify the procedure, explain its purpose, and indicate the macro or other procedure that calls the code. If the function returns a value, a description of the returned value and its data type is included.

The Toolbar of the Module Window

Figure 22.3 identifies the elements in the toolbar of the Module window. Table 22.3 lists the the purpose of each item in the toolbar, and the menu commands and key combinations that you can substitute for toolbar components.

FIG. 22.3

The toolbar of the Access Basic Module window.

Table 22.3. Elements of the Module Window's Toolbar

Button	Item	Alternate Method	Purpose
N/A	Procedure List Box	View Procedures... or press the F2 key (see figure 22.3)	Displays a procedure in the module. Select the procedure name from the drop-down list box. Procedures are listed in alphabetical order by name.
▲	Previous Procedure	View Previous Procedure or Ctrl+Cursor Up	Displays the procedure with the next name higher in the list, if one exists.

Button	Item	Alternate Method	Purpose
	Next Procedure	**View N**ext Procedure or Ctrl+Cursor Down	Displays the procedure with the next name lower in the list, if one exists.
	Continue	**R**un **C**ontinue or press F5	Continues execution of the procedure after execution of a procedure has been halted by a break condition or after use of the Single Step or Procedure Step button.
	Single Step	**R**un **S**ingle Step or press F8	Moves through an Access Basic procedure one statement (line) at a time.
	Procedure Step	**R**un **P**rocedure Step or press Shift+F8	Moves through an Access Basic procedure one subprocedure at a time.
	Re-initialize	**R**un **R**einitialize	Terminates execution of an Access Basic procedure and reinitializes all variables to their default values.
	Breakpoint	**R**un **T**oggle Breakpoint or press F9	Toggles a breakpoint at the line of the code in which the caret is located. Breakpoints are used to halt execution at a specific line. If a breakpoint is set, the Breakpoint button turns it off.
	Undo	**E**dit **U**ndo	Rescinds the last keyboard or mouse operation performed if possible.
	Help	F1 key	Displays help for Programming Topics (an alphabetical list of Access Basic keywords). If the caret is located on an Access reserved word, help is displayed for that reserved word (see "The Access Basic Help System" that follows).

The View Procedures dialog box, which appears when you press the F2 key (see fig. 22.4), enables you to select any module in the database and then choose to display a function or procedure of the selected module.

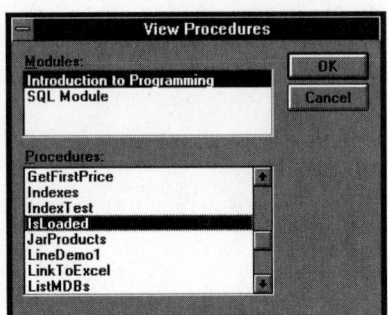

Module Shortcut Keys

Additional shortcut keys and key combinations listed in table 22.4 can help you as you are write and edit Access Basic code. Two key combinations, Ctrl+N and Ctrl+Y, are not commonly used in Windows applications. These two combinations were implemented in the original version of the WordStar application and were later adopted by Borland International for its code-editing applications.

Table 22.4. Key Combinations for Entering and Editing Access Basic Code

Key Combination	Purpose
F3	Finds next occurrence of a search string.
Shift+F3	Finds previous occurrence of a search string.
F9	Clears all breakpoints.
Tab	Indents a single line of code by four (default value) characters.
Tab with selected text	Indents multiple lines of selected code by four (default) characters.
Shift+Tab	Unindents a single line of code by four characters.

Key Combination	Purpose
Shift+Tab with selected text	Unindents multiple lines of selected code by four characters.
Ctrl+N	Inserts a new blank line above the caret.
Ctrl+Y	Deletes the line on which the caret is located.

You can change the default indentation of four characters per tab stop by choosing **O**ptions from the **V**iew menu, choosing Module Design from the Category list box, and entering the desired number of characters in the Tab Stop Width text box.

Menu Commands in the Module Window

Menu commands to perform operations not included in table 22.3 are listed in table 22.5. Menu commands common to other database objects, such as **F**ile **S**ave, are not included in the table.

Table 22.5. Module Window Menu Commands

Menu	Commands	Purpose
File	Load Text	Displays the Load Text dialog box to select a text file (ASCII format) of Access Basic code to replace or merge with the existing module's code.
	Save Text	Displays the Save Text dialog box to save the module's code to a text file in ASCII format.
	Print	Displays the Print dialog box to print all or part of the code contained in the module.
	Run Macro	Displays a dialog box with a list of macro objects so you can run the code from the macro that calls the Access Basic function.
Edit	Find	Displays the Find dialog box to search for specific text strings or regular expressions entered in the Find text box.

continues

Table 22.5. Continued

Menu	Commands	Purpose
	Find Next	Locates and highlights the next occurrence of the search string entered in the Find dialog box.
	Find Previous	Locates and highlights the previous occurrence of the search string entered in the Find dialog box.
	Replace	Replaces all or selected occurrences of the text entered in the Find text box with the text in the Replace text box.
	New Procedure	Displays a dialog box with a text box in which you can enter the name of a new procedure to add to the module.
View	Split Window	Divides the Module window into two windows that can display the code of individual procedures.
	Immediate Window	Displays the Immediate window that you use to determine the value of variables. The Debug.Print object writes the value of a variable argument to the Immediate window.
Run	Compile All	Recompiles all code in the module and reinitializes all procedures (see "Compiling Access Basic Code" in this chapter).
	Clear All Breakpoints	Clears all breakpoints set in the module. (Active only when breakpoint(s) are set. See "Adding a Breakpoint to the IsLoaded( ) Function" in this chapter.)
	Modify Command$	Displays a dialog box with a textbox into which you enter command line parameters to simulate Access Basic parameters added to the startup command line.

The Access Basic Help System

Microsoft provides an extensive, multilevel help system to help you learn and use Access Basic. If you place the caret on a keyword or select a keyword and then press the F1 key, or click the Help button on the toolbar, for example, a help window for the keyword appears. If you click the Example hot spot under the name of the keyword, you see an example of the keyword used in Access Basic (see fig. 22.5).

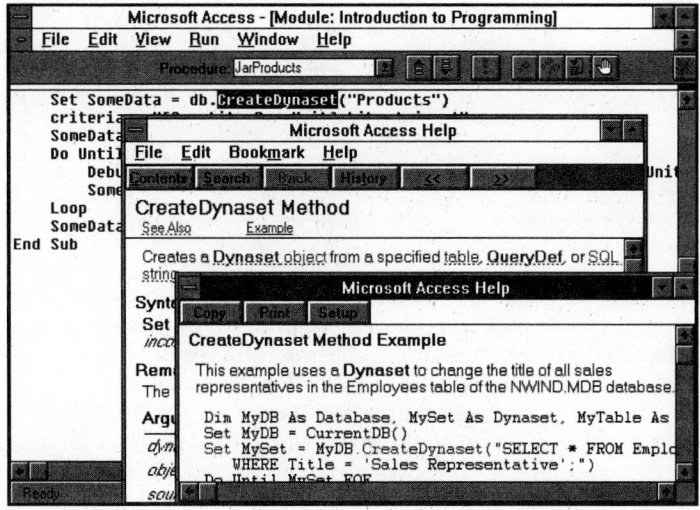

FIG. 22.5

A help window for a method and an example window, showing this window's use.

If you press the F1 key when the caret is not located on a keyword, the help system presents you with an alphabetic list of Access Basic keywords and reserved symbols (see fig. 22.6). You can narrow the list to a particular keyword class by clicking the Actions, Functions, Properties, or Methods Reference hot spots. A list of error messages and the message meanings also is available when you click the Error Messages Reference hot spot.

The Access Basic Compiler

Programming languages, such as Pascal and C, use compilers. *Compilers* are applications that convert the code statements—*source code*—you write into instructions the computer can understand—*object code*. These languages use punctuation symbols to identify where statements begin and end; Pascal, for example, uses a semicolon to tell the compiler that a statement is complete. Separating code into individual statements and determining which words in a statement are keywords is *parsing* the code.

FIG. 22.6

The Programming Topics help window for Access Basic.

After you compile Pascal or C code, you link the code with *libraries* to create an *executable* file. *Libraries* are additional object code that perform standard operations, such as mathematical calculations. Libraries in Access Basic, such as WIZARD.MDA, have a similar purpose. An executable file for a Windows application has the extension .EXE; you run executable files as independent applications. Compiling and linking an application, especially a Windows application, can be a complex process. Borland International's C++ compiler, version 3.1, for example, requires more than 40M of disk space, just to install the compiler.

Traditional BASIC languages, such as QBasic and also the native dBASE and Paradox programming languages, employ interpreters to execute code. An *interpreter* is an application that reads each line of code, translates the code into instructions for your computer, and then tells the computer to execute these instructions. The interpreter parses code line by line, beginning with the first nonblank character on a line and ending with the newline pair, carriage return (CR, Chr$(13)), and line feed (LF, Chr$(10)). A *newline pair* is created by pressing the Enter key. Compilers for the dBASE language, such as Clipper or Arago, also use the newline pair to indicate the end of a statement.

You must execute interpreted code within the application in which the code was created. You run QBasic code, for example, from QBasic, not as a stand-alone application. An interpreter's advantage is that it can test the statements you enter for proper syntax as you write them. Compiled languages issue error messages after you compile the source code to object code. Another advantage of interpreters is that you don't need to go through the process of compiling and linking the source code every time you make a change in the code. Unfortunately, interpreters usually execute code more slowly than the computer executes a compiled (.EXE) application.

Access combines the features of both a compiler and an interpreter. Access interprets the code you write when you terminate a line with the Enter key. If possible, Access corrects your syntax; otherwise you receive a syntax error message, which usually is accompanied by a suggestion for correcting the mistake. Each line of code, therefore, must contain a syntactically correct statement. Some languages, such as xBase and Paradox, enable you to continue a statement; xBase, including Clipper, uses the semicolon for this purpose. There is no statement continuation character in Access Basic. No matter how long your Access Basic statement is, it must be written on a single line.

Multiline statements

After you write the source code, Access compiles this code into a cross between interpreted and object code known as *pseudo-code*, or p-code. Pseudo-code runs faster than conventional interpreted code. Access compiles to p-code the code you write or modify the first time the code is used in an application. Access discovers most errors not caught during entry as the code compiles. You can choose Compile **A**ll from the **R**un menu to force Access to compile all the code into a module. Forcing compilation before running the code—especially if the form or macro that executes the code takes a long time to load—can save substantial time during development.

Examining the Introduction to Programming Module

One recommended way to learn a new programming language is to examine simple examples of code and analyze the statements used in the example. Microsoft includes representative code examples from the Access Basic documentation's *Introduction to Programming* manual in a module of the same name in the Northwind Traders sample database. Some of these examples are called by macros in NWIND.MDB.

This section shows how to open a module, display a function in the Module window, and then relate the function to the macro action that calls the function and the database object with which the macro is associated. Examples of the use of the Immediate window, breakpoints, and the Debug object also are provided.

Viewing the IsLoaded( ) Function and the Country Filter Macro

To view the IsLoaded( ) user-defined function used in the example in the "Synchronizing Forms to the Same Record" section of Chapter 18, follow these steps:

1. Open the Database window and click the Module button.

2. Double-click Introduction to Programming in the Module list box. The declarations section of the module appears (see fig. 22.7). When you open a module, the declarations section appears in the Procedure list box.

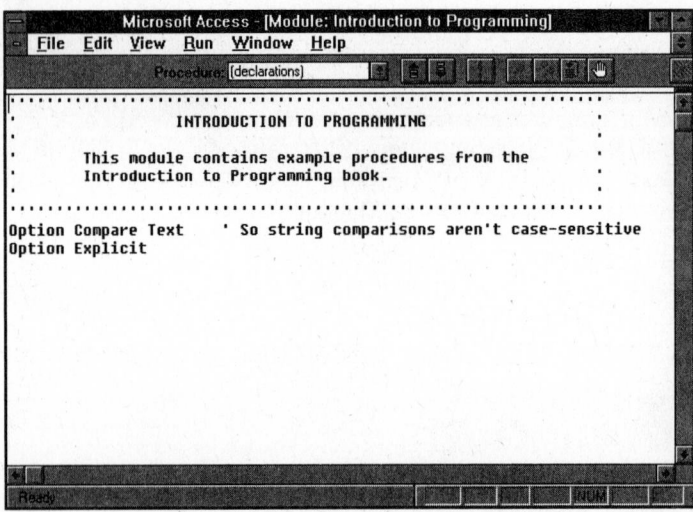

The Option Compare Text keyword is explained in the following section, "Text Comparison Options." Option Explicit establishes the requirement that all variables are declared before the variables are assigned a value. Module-level variables are not declared for use by the Introduction to Programming procedures.

3. Open the Procedures list box and select the IsLoaded function. The Module window for the IsLoaded( ) function appears (see fig. 22.8).

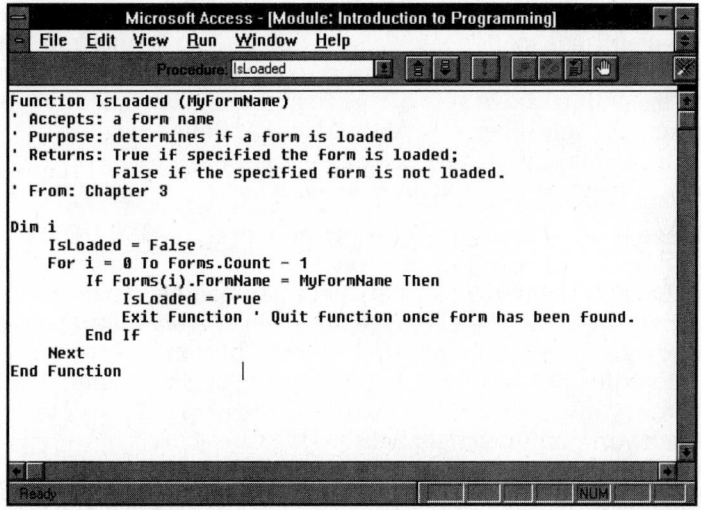

The purpose of the IsLoaded( ) function is to determine whether
an application loaded a form with a name specified by the argument, MyFormName, passed in the expression that calls
IsLoaded( ).

4. IsLoaded( ) is called by the Country Filter macro that responds to
the OnOpen event of the Customer Mailing Labels report. To see
this macro, open the Database window, click the Macro button,
select the Country Filter macro, and click the Design button. The
macro design sheet for the Country Filter macro appears as
shown in figure 22.9.

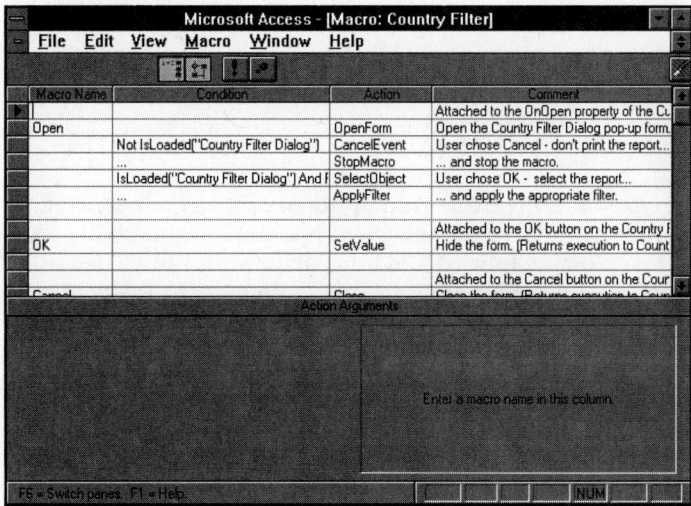

The IsLoaded( ) function returns True if the Country Filter Dialog pop-up form is loaded and False if this pop-up form is not loaded. In this macro, IsLoaded( ) is used to return a condition to control the execution of two sets of macro actions. If IsLoaded( ) returns False, the CancelEvent and StopMacro actions execute. If IsLoaded( ) returns True, execution continues with the SelectObject and ApplyFilter actions.

5. To see how the Country Filter macro works, open the Database window, click the Report button, and double-click Customer Mailing Labels. When you run the Customer Mailing Labels report, a modal dialog box appears (see fig. 22.10). *Modal* dialog boxes are boxes that you must close by clicking a button before you can perform further actions. If you click the Specific Country option button, you can enter in the text box the name of the country for which you want mailing labels.

   If you click Cancel or press Esc, the Country Filter dialog box closes. The Country Filter macro tests the condition Not IsLoaded ("Country Filter dialog box") to determine if the user canceled the request for mailing labels.

FIG. 22.10

The Country Filter dialog box that runs the Country Filter macro.

Adding a Breakpoint to the IsLoaded( ) Function

When you examine the execution of Access Basic code written by others, and when you debug your own application, Breakpoints are useful. This section explains how to add a breakpoint to the IsLoaded( ) function so that the Customer Mailing Labels Report stops executing when the Country Filter macro calls the IsLoaded( ) function and Access displays the code in the Module window.

To add a breakpoint to the IsLoaded( ) function, follow these steps:

1. Choose Module:Introduction to Programming from the **W**indow menu.

2. Place the caret on the line IsLoaded = True.

3. Click the Breakpoint button on the toolbar, choose **T**oggle Breakpoint from the **R**un menu, or press the F9 key. The breakpoint you create is indicated by changing the attribute of the line to bold (see fig. 22.11).

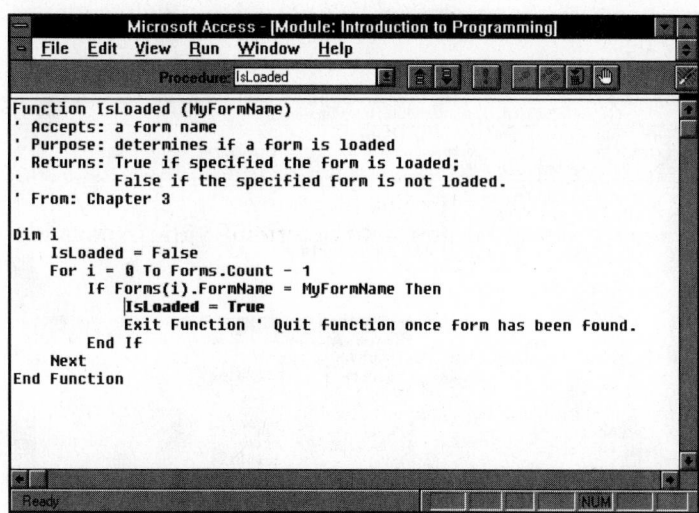

FIG. 22.11

The IsLoaded( ) procedure with a breakpoint set.

4. Choose Report:Customer Mailing Labels from the **W**indow menu, or click the Report button of the Database window. Then double-click Customer Mailing Labels to run the Customer Mailing Labels report.

5. Click the All Countries option button, and then click OK. When execution of the Country Filter macro reaches the IsLoaded( ) function, execution of IsLoaded( ) begins with the Dim i line that assigns variable i the variant data type (the Integer data type is more appropriate for counter variables).

   The value that IsLoaded( ) returns, unless changed later, is specified by the line IsLoaded = False. The function name is used as the variable name so that a return value is assigned to the function name.

The For i = 0 To Forms.Count -1 ... Next loop tests each of the forms loaded to determine if the name of a specific form exists. Forms is a predefined array whose elements consist of all loaded forms, beginning with the zeroth element. The Count property of Forms returns the number of forms currently loaded.

The element of the Forms array tested is specified by Forms(i) and the name of each form, returned by Forms(i).FormName, is compared with the value of MyFormName, Country Filter dialog box in this case. If the result of the comparison is true, the line that contains the breakpoint is reached, execution halts, and the Module window displays the module code. The line with the breakpoint is enclosed in a highlighting rectangle (see fig. 22.12).

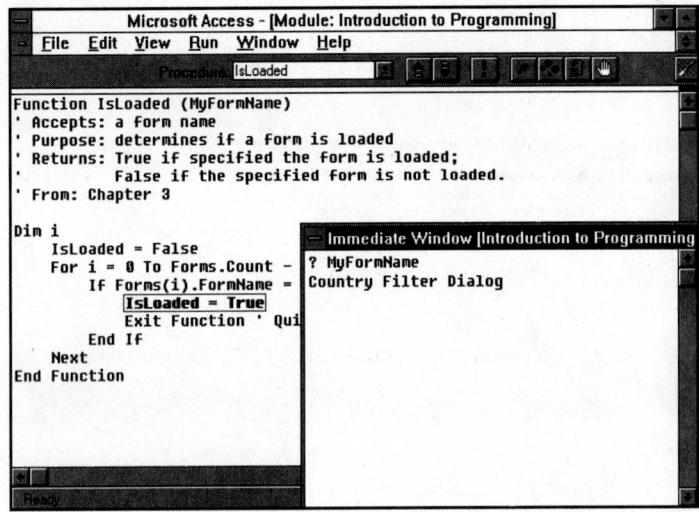

FIG. 22.12

The IsLoaded( ) procedure when the breakpoint is reached and the Immediate window opened.

Using the Immediate Window

In Chapter 7, "Using the Immediate Window to Experiment With Functions" section, you learned to use the Immediate window to display the results of computations and values returned by functions. The Immediate window also is useful when you want to display the value of variables when the breakpoint is encountered.

To open the Immediate window and display the value of a variable, follow these steps:

1. Choose Immediate Window from the View menu.

2. Type **? MyFormName** and press Enter to display the value of this variable (see fig. 22.12). The ? symbol is shorthand for the keyword, Print.

3. You can display the value of the variable, i, by typing **? i** and pressing Enter. You cannot, however, type **? IsLoaded** to determine the value of the function; you receive an error message if you try.

4. Type **? IsLoaded(MyFormName)** and press Enter. The Immediate window executes the function again (a second instance of the function), but execution stops at the breakpoint.

5. Click the Single Step button on the toolbar, choose **S**ingle Step from the **R**un menu, or press the F8 key to continue execution of the function. The Exit Function statement is encountered, and execution jumps to the End Function line. Click the Single Step button, or press F8 again. IsLoaded( ) then returns -1 (TRUE) in the Immediate window.

6. Continue clicking the Single Step button. Execution of the first instance of the function continues until Exit Function is reached; then you see the Customer Mailing List report in Print Preview mode.

7. Choose Clear All Breakpoints from the **R**un menu to toggle the breakpoint off.

When you write your own code, the Immediate window is handy for debugging purposes.

Printing to the Immediate Window with the Debug Object

When you need to view the values of several variables, you can use the Debug object to automate printing to the Immediate window. If you add the Debug object to the IsLoaded( ) function, you can create a list in the Immediate window of all the forms that are open.

To modify the IsLoaded( ) function to list all open forms, follow these steps:

1. Load three or four forms by repeatedly opening the Database window, clicking the Form button, and double-clicking a form name in the list box. The Customers, Categories, Forms Switchboard, and Main Switchboard forms are good choices because these forms do not take a long time to load.

2. Choose Module:Introduction to Programming from the **W**indow menu.

3. Place the caret on the line that contains If Forms(i)... and press Ctrl+N to insert a new line above this line.

4. Type the following text in the new line and press Enter:

   ```
   Debug.Print Forms(i).FormName
   ```

   This statement prints the name of each open form in the Immediate window.

5. Add an apostrophe in front of the line Exit Function to turn the statement into a comment. Without Exit Function, all forms are listed, regardless of when Country Filter dialog box is encountered during execution of the loop.

6. Place the caret on the last line of the function, End Function, and press the F9 key to create a breakpoint. This causes the Module window to appear when the function is run by the macro.

7. Open the Database window, click the Report button, and double-click Customer Mailing Labels. Click OK in the Country Filter dialog box.

8. When you use the Debug.Print statement in a procedure, execution is halted at the first line of the procedure. Click the Single Step button, or press the F8 key repeatedly to step through the function.

   As you single-step through the loop, the name of each form is added to the Immediate window by the Debug.Print statement (see fig. 22.13).

9. Double-click the document control symbol, or choose **C**lose from the **F**ile menu. Do not save changes to the Introduction to Programming module. Then close the other forms that you opened for this example.

The Debug.Print statement is particularly useful in displaying the values of variables that change when you execute a loop. When you have completed testing of your procedure, you delete the Debug statements.

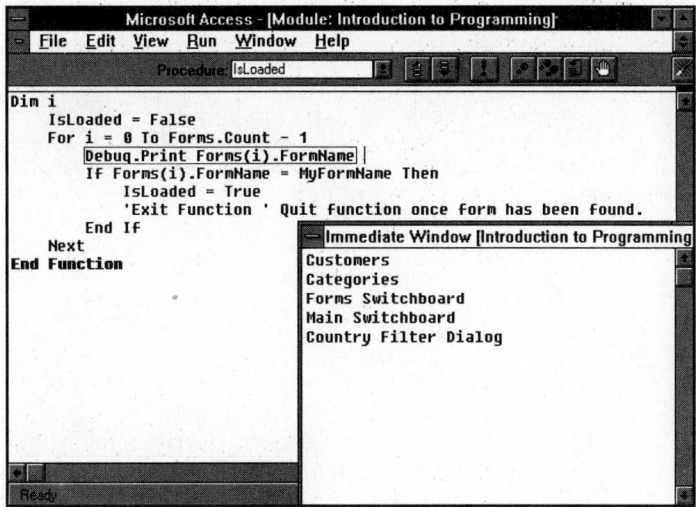

FIG. 22.13

The Debug object used to print values of variables to the Immediate window.

Using Text Comparison Options

The comparisons that the IsLoaded( ) function made between the values of MyFormName and Forms(i).FormName in the preceding examples are based on the value of the Option Compare Text statement, which appears in the declarations section of the Introduction to Programming module. To determine how text comparisons are made in the module, you can use any of the following statements:

■ Option Compare Binary comparisons are case-sensitive. Lowercase letters are not equivalent to uppercase letters. To determine the sort order of characters, Access uses the character value assigned by the ANSI character set of Windows.

■ Option Compare Text comparisons are not case-sensitive. Lowercase letters are treated as the equivalent of uppercase letters. The sort order of characters is determined by the sCountry=.setting in the [intl] section of the WIN.INI file. For most North American users, the sort order is the same as Option Compare Binary, ANSI. Unless you have a reason to specify a different comparison method, use Option Compare Text.

■ Option Compare Database comparisons are case-sensitive and the sort order is that specified for the database.

Option Compare Binary is the default if you do not include an Option Compare statement in the declarations section of the module. However, Access adds Option Compare Database and a comment to the declarations section when you create a new module, overriding the default. Binary and Database are reserved words in Access Basic; for compatibility with changes in possible future releases of Access, you should not use Compare or Text as names of variables.

Writing Your Own Functions and Procedures

You do not need to be an Access Basic expert to write a user-defined function. The information you learned about operators and expressions in Chapter 7, as well as the introduction to Access Basic statements presented in this chapter, enable you to create UDFs that supplement Access Basic's repertoire of standard functions. Once you master user-defined functions, you can try your hand at writing functions—actually, procedures in the form of functions—that are executed by the RunCode action of macro objects. Access Basic procedures offer flexibility in manipulating database and control objects, but require more knowledge of programming techniques than is needed to create UDFs. This section describes how you write a simple user-defined function and how to create a short procedure that employs several database objects.

Writing a User-Defined Function

User-defined functions are required when you need a conditional statement more complex than that accommodated by the IIf( ) function. An example is a fixed set of quantity discounts that apply to all or a group of products. You can create a table of quantity discounts; however, a user-defined function that returns the discount is easier to implement and faster to execute.

For this example, the discounts are 50 percent for 1,000 or more of an item, 40 percent for 501 to 999, 30 percent for 100 to 499, 20 percent for 50 to 99, 10 percent for 10 to 49 and no discount for purchases of fewer than 10 items. Discount structures of this type lend themselves well to Select Case...End Select structures.

To create the user-defined function Discount( ) that returns a fractional percent discount based on the value of the argument, Quantity, follow these steps:

1. Click the Modules button of the Database window and double-click the Introduction to Programming Module.

2. Position the cursor on the line following Option Explicit and type **Function Discount(Quantity)**. After you press Enter, Access opens a new Module window with the function name on the first line and adds the End Function statement. This process is easier than choosing New Procedure from the Edit menu.

3. Position the caret at the beginning of the blank line and press Tab. To establish the discount schedule, enter the following lines of code:

```
Select Case Quantity
    Case Is >= 1000
        Discount = .5
    Case Is >= 500
        Discount = .4
    Case Is >= 100
        Discount = .3
    Case Is >= 50
        Discount = .2
    Case Is >= 10
        Discount = .1
    Case Else
        Discount = 0
End Select
```

You don't need to enter the Is keyword because Access checks the syntax of each statement you write when you press Enter. If you omit the Is keyword, Access adds it for you.

Use the Tab key to duplicate the indentation illustrated in the preceding example. Case statements are executed from the first statement to the last, so quantities are entered in descending sequence. If Quantity = 552, the criterion is not met for Case Is >= 1000, so the next Case statement is tested. Case Is >= 500 is satisfied, so Discount receives the value .4 and execution proceeds directly to the End Select statement.

4. To make sure that the function is acceptable to Access Basic's compiler, choose Compile All from the Run menu. Access converts the entries to a form that it can process. When you compile the code, Access indicates any errors not caught by line-by-line syntax checking.

5. You do not need to create a table or macro to test the function; the Immediate window performs this task adequately for sample code. If the Immediate window is not open, choose **Immediate Window** from the **View** menu.

6. Test the Discount( ) function by entering **? Discount(*Quantity*)** in the Immediate window, and then press Enter. Substitute numeric values for *Quantity*, (see fig. 22.14).

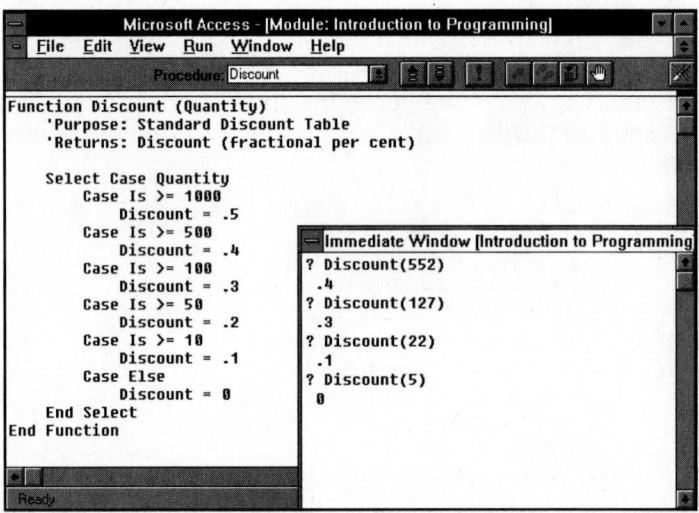

FIG. 22.14

Code for the Discount( ) user-defined function.

7. To save the UDF, add the explanatory comments, preceded by an apostrophe, immediately after the Function Discount(Quantity) line, and then choose **S**ave from the **F**ile menu.

You can employ user-defined functions in expressions to compute values for calculated fields, validate data entry, construct queries, and other purposes where an expression can be used.

Microsoft has provided another example of a user-defined function, DueDate( ), which calculates the first weekday of the month following a date supplied as the argument, AnyDate.

Writing a Procedure that Uses Database Objects

All database objects that you can create and manipulate with Access's graphical development environment also can be created and manipulated with Access Basic code. You could use Access Basic to create a new table, add records to the table, define a query to select records from the table, create a form to display the data, and then print a report. In other words, you can use Access Basic to create an application exactly the same way you use the dBASE language or PAL. The purpose of Access's graphical development environment, however, is to minimize the need for code in applications.

The MacroQuery procedure you write in this example uses the QueryDef database and Snapshot data types to create a query with an SQL statement and then display that query in Datasheet view. To run the procedure, you need a simple macro object Run MacroQuery that contains a RunCode action. This example shows you how to test the procedure by choosing **R**un Macro from the **F**ile menu.

Writing the MacroQuery Procedure

The MacroQuery Procedure contains a number of Access Basic keywords that have not been explained in this chapter. Describing every Access Basic keyword requires a book in itself, as you can see by the length of the Access Basic Language Reference included in the Access documentation. As you enter the keywords in this example, place the caret inside the keyword and press the F1 key to obtain a detailed explanation of the keyword and its use from Access Basic's Help system.

To create the MacroQuery procedure, follow these steps:

1. Open the Database window, click the Module button, and click the New button to create a new module.

2. You can accept the default Option Compare Database statement that Access adds to the declarations section of a new module, or change the compare modifier to Text to make comparisons not case-sensitive.

3. To create the new procedure, enter Function MacroQuery( ) below the Option Compare statement. Access Basic procedures called by macros must be written as functions, although these procedures do not return usable values to the macro action.

4. You need to declare and assign data types to the variables that the procedure uses. Below Function MacroQuery( ), enter the following statements:

```
Dim dbNwind As Database, qdfQuery As QueryDef,
rssSnap As Snapshot
```

You can use a single Dim statement to declare a number of variables by separating the variables with a comma, or you can use individual Dim statements, as in the following:

```
Dim dbNwind  As Database
Dim qdfQuery As QueryDef
Dim rssSnap  As Snapshot
```

The QueryDef data type is a query definition, the object you create when you define a query in Design mode. A variable you declare as of the Snapshot data type holds (points to) a query result table that you cannot modify; Snapshots are instantaneous representations of the result of a query. If you declare a variable as of the type Dynaset, the query data can be updated.

5. You need to specify the database, NWIND.MDB, that contains the tables for the query. Type the following text:

   Set dbNwind = CurrentDB()

   CurrentDB() returns the currently open database object, NWIND.MDB, and Set assigns the database object to dbNwind.

6. You cannot have two QueryDef objects of the same name, so you need to delete the QueryDef created by multiple executions of the procedure with the DeleteQueryDef method. Enter the following text:

   ```
   On Error Resume Next
   dbNwind.DeleteQueryDef ("Macro Query")
   On Error GoTo 0
   ```

   An error is not generated if the QueryDef you attempt to delete doesn't exist. The Macro Query doesn't exist the first time you run the macro, so an error occurs. The On Error Resume Next statement causes Access to disregard errors that occur in code below the statement. On Error GoTo 0 resumes run-time error checking.

7. You need a variable to hold (point to) the definition of the query. Enter the following:

   ```
   Set qdfQuery = dbNwind.CreateQueryDef("Macro
   Query")
   ```

   CreateQueryDef creates the query object Macro Query that appears in the Database window's Query list when you run the MacroQuery procedure. Properties and methods of objects are separated from the object by a period. Notice that you do not enclose object names within square brackets in expressions that require object names only.

8. Now you enter the SQL statement that you use to create and run the query. Enter the following:

   ```
   qdfQuery.SQL = "SELECT * FROM Suppliers WHERE
   [Supplier ID] < 11;"
   ```

In this case, you use the square brackets to enclose Supplier ID because you are not assigning an object name. Database objects with spaces or other punctuation must be enclosed between square brackets in Access Basic SQL statements.

9. Finally, you assign the result of the query to a variable by creating a Snapshot. Enter the following statement:

```
Set rssSnap = dbNwind.CreateSnapshot("Macro
Query")
```

You use methods with the rssSnap variable to extract data from the rows and columns of the query it represents. If you want to be able to update the query records, substitute CreateDynaset() for CreateSnapshot().

10. Your Module window appears (see fig. 22.15), but without the explanatory comments.

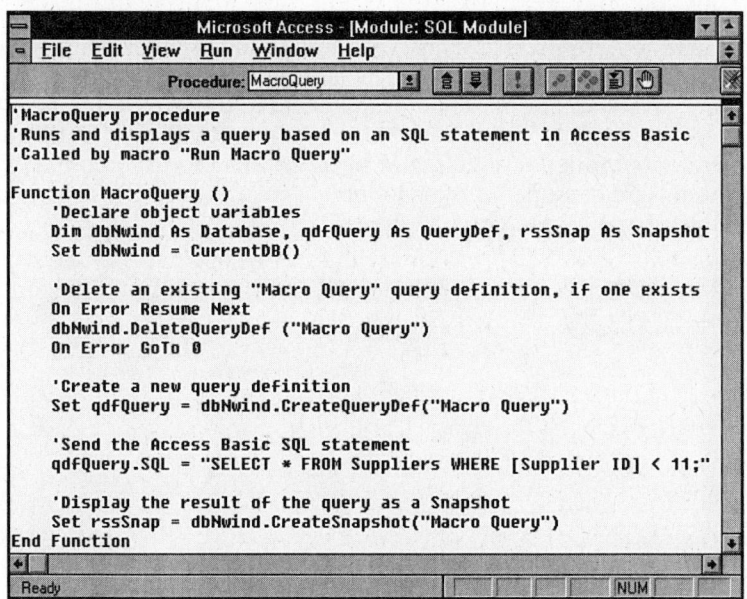

FIG. 22.15

Code for the MacroQuery procedure.

11. Choose Compile **A**ll from the **R**un menu to verify the syntax of the code.

12. Enter the comments as shown in figure 22.15, and then choose **S**ave from the **F**ile menu and give the new module a name, such as **SQL Module**.

Now you need to create a two-line macro object so you can run the procedure and display the Snapshot.

Running the MacroQuery Procedure

Procedures written as functions in Access VBasic require that you write a macro that includes the RunCode( ) macro action to describe the Access Vbasic procedure you want to execute. You then run the macro, which in turn executes the procedure.

To run the MacroQuery Procedure, follow these steps:

1. Open the Database window, click the Macro button, and then click the New button.

2. Open the Actions list for the first line of the macro and select RunCode from the drop-down list. Enter **MacroQuery( )** in the Function Name text box. This action runs the procedure.

3. Open the Actions list for the second line of the macro and select OpenQuery from the drop-down list. Type **Macro Query** in the Query Name text box, select Datasheet from the View list box, and select Read Only in the Data Mode list box. Read-only is the appropriate mode for a Snapshot because this mode cannot be updated. You can open a Dynaset object in Edit mode. The macro design appears as shown in figure 22.16.

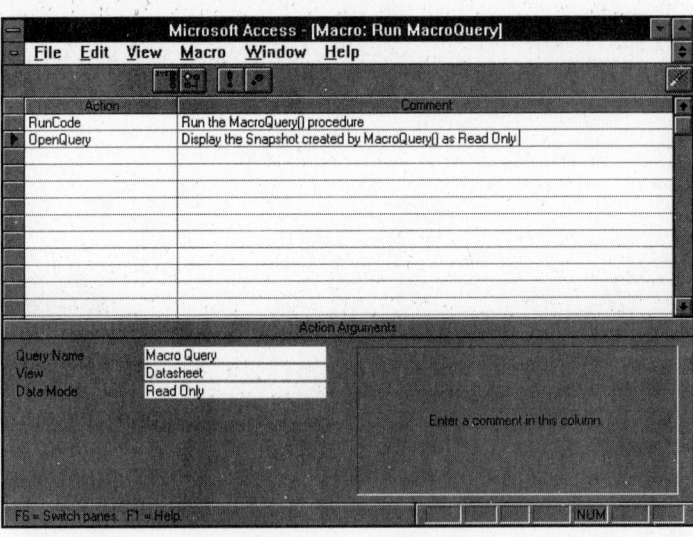

FIG. 22.16

The Run MacroQuery macro in Design mode.

4. Save the macro with an appropriate name, such as **Run MacroQuery**.

5. Click the Run button on the toolbar to run the new macro and execute the MacroQuery( ) procedure. The RunCode action creates the query, and the OpenQuery action displays the resulting query datasheet (see fig. 22.17).

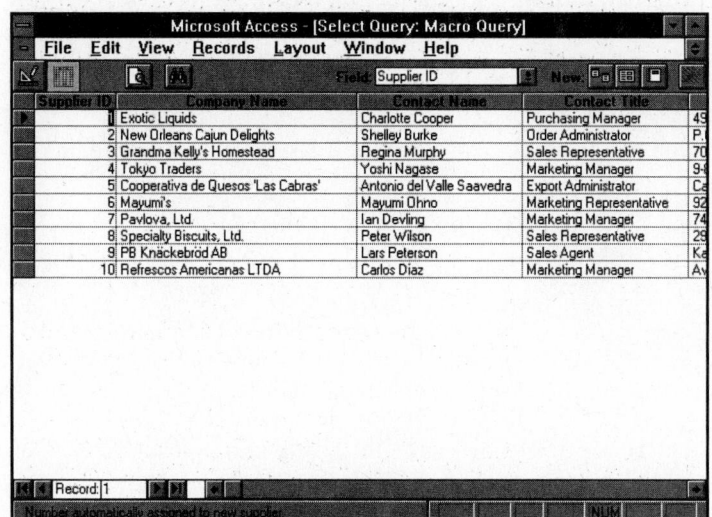

FIG. 22.17

The Datasheet view of the Snapshot query created by the MacroQuery( ) procedure.

Chapter Summary

This chapter introduced you to Access Basic code so you can create user defined functions and simple procedures. This chapter described ways to use the Module window to enter and edit code, and explained the compiling process for Access Basic in the context of compilers and interpreters for other programming languages. The use of conditional statements and different types of loops were covered. You combined the expressions you learned in Chapter 7 with the Access Basic keywords presented here so you could write short examples of Access Basic code. The methods you use to handle run-time errors were explained briefly.

Chapter 23 describes how to use Access Basic to create procedures that interact with other applications via dynamic data exchange (DDE). It is likely that you will want to use DDE in many applications that exchange data, because DDE is a faster and less obtrusive process than OLE in many cases. Many Windows applications do not yet support OLE, but most support DDE; so you need to master DDE techniques to interact with applications that lack OLE capabilities. DDE also enables you to establish multiple simultaneous conversations with other applications.

Exchanging Data with Access Basic DDE

C hapter 15, "Using Access with Microsoft Excel," demonstrated how you can use Windows' dynamic data exchange (DDE) capabilities, the DDE() and DDESend() functions in particular, to transfer data between Excel and Access using the Clipboard as an intermediary. Access Basic has its own set of DDE methods that provide more flexibility than the DDE() and DDESend() functions. Using Access Basic for DDE data transfers is faster than using the DDE() and DDESend() functions because you can make multiple requests for data after you establish a DDE communications channel.

This chapter describes how DDE works and how to use the DDE statements and functions of Access Basic to exchange information with other Windows applications. Most applications' documentation attempts to explain the DDE syntax of an application in isolated code snippets. In contrast, the DDE example presented in this chapter is a complete application, including a test form, Access Basic procedures, and the macros necessary to run the code you write. The purpose and operation of each Access Basic procedure you write is described in detail.

Using Access as a DDE server with other DDE client applications is explained at the end of this chapter. This chapter also covers Access server protocol because the DDE procedures you write in the macro languages of client applications are quite similar to those used with Access Basic DDE. In the case of Word for Windows' WordBasic macro language, the DDE keywords are identical to those of Access Basic.

Exploring Dynamic Data Exchange

DDE is a method of interprocess communication that allows applications to exchange data on a real-time basis. The process of exchanging data is called a DDE *conversation*. The application that initiates the conversation is called the DDE *client*, and the application that provides the data is called the DDE *server*. DDE clients also can supply unsolicited data to DDE servers (called *poking* data) and can send commands for servers to execute. An application can engage in several DDE conversations simultaneously, acting as a server in some and a client in others.

The basic elements of a DDE conversation consist of a request from a client to a server to initiate a conversation, exchange of information between the server and the client, and termination of the conversation. These elements, called DDE *transactions*, comprise the DDE protocol. DDE transactions take place between windows in each of the participating applications that are dedicated to the DDE conversation. These windows are usually invisible. Figure 23.1 is a diagram of a DDE conversation; optional transactions of the conversation are shown in gray type.

 The client usually initiates the Terminate Conversation transaction, but the server also can terminate a transaction.

To execute the DDE protocol, the client and server send a series of Windows messages to the message queue maintained by the Windows operating system. Windows processes the messages and then removes each message from the message queue in first-in, first-out (FIFO) sequence.

The six elements of the conversation shown in figure 23.1 involve many Windows messages. Several messages may be passed between the client and server to implement one element of the conversation. To maintain the proper timing of messages, the client can request that the server acknowledge all request messages. This type of conversation is called an *asynchronous* DDE conversation.

FIG. 23.1

The elements
of a DDE
conversation.

In an asynchronous conversation, the client waits until it receives an acknowledgment from the server, indicating that it has processed a request message, before the client sends the server the next message. Most DDE conversations are asynchronous. *Synchronous* conversations use a time-out method; the client sends a series of messages and then awaits a response. If the expected response isn't received within the time-out period, an error message results.

Understanding Service Names, Topics, and Items

DDE uses a three-level hierarchy to identify the data that the client transmits to the server:

- *Service name:* Identifies the client application. Prior to Windows 3.1, *service name* was called *application name*. The service name is usually the name of the application's executable file, less the .EXE extension, such as EXCEL, WINWORD, or MSACCESS. An application may have more than one service name; the application's documentation usually provides the application's DDE service name(s).

- *Topic:* Identifies the context of the information that is the subject of the conversation. In most cases, the topic is the name of a file, such as an Excel worksheet or a Word for Windows document. If an application doesn't use files, the topic is usually a string that is specific to the application. A third type of topic, the system topic, is described in the following section.

- *Item:* A specific piece of data contained in a topic, such as text specified by a bookmark in a word processing document.

Understanding the System Topic

Most applications that support DDE provide an additional topic called System. If the server application fully supports the System topic, you can use SysItems to obtain information about the server and its status.

SysItems returns a comma-separated list of all valid items that you can use in conjunction with the System topic. In most cases, at least the following two SysItems are supported:

- *Topics:* Provides a list of the files that are open in the application, if the application is file-based. Otherwise, it provides a list of the names of application-specific strings.

- *Formats:* Supplies a list of the Clipboard formats that the server application supports. Excel, for example, supports 11 different Clipboard formats for DDE data. The client application automatically selects the format that suits it best. Access requires that the format be plain text (the Clipboard's CF_TEXT format). Access cannot, for instance, process graphic images (using Clipboard's CF_BITMAP format) with DDE. You cannot alter the DDE Clipboard format in Access Basic.

Many applications don't include the information returned by SysItems in the product documentation. You must write a short DDE application to find out this information. The SysItems supported by Access as a DDE server are listed in the section, "Using the System Topic," near the end of this chapter.

Choosing between DDE and OLE

Access is biased toward the use of OLE for interprocess communication because OLE simplifies the interprocess communication. OLE is the only practical method of transferring large blocks of data, such as graphic images, between Access and other applications. The maximum length of a DDE string in Access is about 32K, and Access, as noted previously, cannot handle graphics formats with DDE.

DDE, however, is the only practical method of transferring individual data items to and from worksheets and word processing documents, as discussed in Chapter 15. In the case of Word for Windows, DDE is the only method of transferring data because Access doesn't support the OLE format used by Word in either bound or unbound object frames. DDE is a much faster method of processing data in many cases because you open the server, if it isn't running, in the minimized (iconic) style. The server doesn't need to open a window to participate in the DDE conversation.

As a rule, you use OLE when you want to view or play (using multimedia terminology) an object. You use DDE when you need to process individual items of data contained in an object. DDE consumes fewer memory resources than the equivalent OLE process, so DDE is the method of choice if you have less than 4M of RAM in the computer using the application.

Choosing between DDE() and DDESend() and Access Basic DDE

When you used the DDE() and DDESend() functions in Chapter 15 to obtain data from or send data to an Excel spreadsheet, you specified the service name, topic, and item for each transaction. When you use these functions, Access does most of the work for you. DDE() initiates a conversation, specifies the topic, requests the particular data item, and then terminates the conversation with a single command. Similarly, DDESend() transfers a data item to a server with a single function.

If you need to transfer substantial numbers of data items between two applications, using DDE() or DDESend becomes quite cumbersome. In the majority of cases, you need a separate control object to hold the value of each data item. The alternative is to use a table with records that contain the values to identify the data item; this technique was used for the Stock Prices example of Chapter 15. Creating a table to specify the addresses of a large number of data items is, at best, a tedious process. If the data items are properly organized, you can write an Access Basic procedure to append the data to a table. An example of an Access Basic procedure that appends records from the STK_21.XLS worksheet to a table is given later in this chapter.

Using Access Basic for DDE

Access Basic includes a set of six keywords that are used to initiate, process, and terminate DDE conversations. The four statements and two functions that comprise the DDE keywords of Access Basic are listed in table 23.1.

If you have written macros using DDE in Word for Windows' WordBasic language, you already know how to use these commands. The one difference is the lack of the string type identification character in the DDERequest() function; DDERequest() in Access Basic returns data of the Variant data type; DDERequest$() in WordBasic always returns a string. Excel DDE macro functions dispense with the DDE prefix, but otherwise use similar commands. Visual Basic substitutes Link for DDE and requires more statements to process a DDE conversation, but the overall approach of Visual Basic to DDE is similar to that of other Microsoft applications.

Table 23.1. DDE Keywords of Access Basic

Keyword	Type	Purpose
DDEExecute	Statement	Sends a command recognized by a DDE server over an open DDE channel.
DDEInitiate()	Function	Initiates a conversation with a DDE server and returns an integer that serves as the DDE channel number.
DDEPoke	Statement	Sends unsolicited data to a DDE server.
DDERequest()	Function	Requests a specific item of information from a DDE server over an open DDE channel.
DDETerminate	Statement	Closes an open DDE channel specified by number.
DDETerminateAll	Statement	Closes all open DDE channels.

Understanding the Structure and Syntax of Access Basic DDE Statements

The structure of a simple Access Basic DDE conversation that requests a data item (*ItemName*) from a topic (*TopicName*) of an application (*ServiceName*) follows:

```
wChannel = DDEInitiate("ServiceName", "TopicName")
DDERequest(wChannel, "ItemName")
DDETerminate wChannel
```

The DDEInitiate() function returns an integer that all succeeding DDE statements use to identify the communication channel for the service name and topic. This set of instructions assumes the application is loaded before the DDEInitiate() function is called. Unlike OLE, if the application isn't loaded, you receive an error message. You then must start the application with Access Basic's Shell function.

Using the Shell Command To Load an Application

The operation of the Shell command is similar to running an application from the **R**un command of Program Manager's **F**ile menu. The syntax of the Shell command is as follows:

```
hTask = Shell("AppFile", wStyle)
```

In this case, AppFile is the full file name, including the .EXE extension, of the application you want to run: EXCEL.EXE, for example. If AppFile isn't on your DOS path, you need to add the well-formed path to the file name.

The wStyle argument specifies the presentation of the application when it is loaded. Assigning a wStyle of 6 is the equivalent of checking the Run Minimized checkbox in the Run dialog box; Windows starts the application in iconic style without the focus. Unless you have a specific reason to display the server in a window, always use the iconic style without the focus when opening a DDE server.

If you call the Shell() function when an application is already running, you launch another instance of the application. This consumes resources that you may need to keep Access operating. To determine whether the application is presently running, you can use the On Error GoTo instruction, but the most straightforward method is to test the error value with the Err function and then use Shell(). If an error occurs because the application isn't running, the value of Err isn't.

You can create a procedure that includes the Shell() function that other procedures and functions can call to open the application, if necessary, and supply the channel number for the ensuing DDE transactions. The advantage of writing a general purpose procedure is that it can be used for any DDE server and topic of your application. A typical procedure for initiating a DDE conversion is OpenDDEChannel, described in the section, "Using the OpenDDEChannel Procedure," in the following example of a DDE application.

Adding Records to a Stock Price Table from a Worksheet

One of the most useful applications for Access Basic DDE procedures is appending data from worksheets to database tables, especially when you are appending a substantial amount of data or appending repetitive data from a worksheet in a standard format. The advantage of using

DDE over simply importing the worksheet to an Access table is that you determine an optimum structure for the table, rather than the design of the worksheet imposing a table structure. The Stock Price application that follows is an example of a moderately complex DDE process.

This example uses Microsoft Excel and the original version of STK_21.WK1 found in the Chapter 15 examples. You can use any Windows spreadsheet application that can act as a DDE server, such as Lotus 1-2-3 for Windows or Borland's Quattro Pro for Windows, by substituting the DDE service name of the application for Excel in this example. STK_21.WK1 has a challenging structure, but you can modify the code examples to employ any worksheet with a similar format. Chapter 15 gives instructions for obtaining STK_21.WK1 from CompuServe. Alternatively, you can enter the data in Appendix D into a smaller sample worksheet.

Designing the Application

The objective of the Stock Prices application is to append the stock price data contained in STK_21.XLS to a table that enables you to use conventional select queries to determine the quotations and trading volume for any stock on any date. A secondary objective is to enable cross-tab queries to determine average values and other statistical summaries to create graphs. These objectives determine the design of the table and your application.

The table must be open-ended so that you can add as many records for different stocks and dates as you want. Using multiple make-table and append queries to create an open-ended table from the closed-ended tables you created in Chapter 15 would be very laborious. Writing your first real Access Basic application is no snap, either, but investing time in creating an application results in time saved when you periodically add new data to the table. You also learn how to write Access Basic code in the process.

In addition to the table to which the worksheet data is appended, you need a form that contains at least a Start button. You also need a Stop button so that you can stop the process to test the result. A DDE status display is desirable because a number of individual steps are necessary to start the DDE conversation. Text boxes on the form provide status data, such as what record you are currently appending and how many records are in the table.

Macros also are necessary to run your Access Basic code. The OnPush actions of the two command buttons initiate the macro actions. Finally, you need to create a new module to contain the Access Basic functions and procedures that are used to achieve the application's objectives. The macros require that your Stock Prices module have at least two functions, one to respond to the Start Append button (GetStockPrices()) and one to respond to the Stop Append button (StopAppend()).

Figure 23.2 shows a diagram of the Stock Prices application.

FIG. 23.2

A diagram of the Stock Prices Access Basic DDE application.

Break your code into functional units so that Access employs separate procedures to initiate the DDE conversation with Excel (OpenDDEChannel) and to obtain and add the data transferred by DDE to the table (AppendDDEData). OpenDDEChannel is designed for general purpose use; by making it a separate procedure, you can copy it into other DDE applications.

Defining the Stock Prices Database Structure

After you have a basic design for your application, the first step is to create the Stock Prices table. An open-ended table requires one record for each stock on each date for which data is available. The original version of STK_21.XLS has 21 days of data for each stock; therefore, 21 records are appended to Stock Prices for each row of the worksheet. If you enter the five-day stock price data from the data supplied in Appendix D, five records are created for each stock. Figure 23.3 shows the appearance of STK_21.XLS, with the required dates in the first row.

FIG. 23.3

Using the
STK_21.XLS
worksheet as the
data source.

High, low, and close quotations and daily trading volume are required
for each record. The close quotation is the data in the row that includes the stock ticker symbol in column A. These requirements define
a table with the structure shown in table 23.2.

Table 23.2. Field Specifications for Stock Prices Table

Field Name	Data Type	Size	Decimals	Description
Symbol	Text	10	N/A	NYSE stock ticker symbol
Date	Date/Time	Short Date	N/A	Trading date
High	Number	Single	3	High quotation on Date
Low	Number	Single	3	Low quotation on Date
Close	Number	Single	3	Closing price on Date
Volume	Number	Single	0	Trading volume on Date

Delete the 0 default value in each of the four fields with the number
data type: High, Low, Close, and Volume. This action causes Null values
to occur in fields of records in which no data exists for the field in the
corresponding column of the worksheet.

The repetition of the stock ticker symbol and trading date in each record causes the database file to be larger than the worksheet file. This result is an unavoidable consequence of using a relational structure for a database. The size penalty is lower in Access than in database management systems, such as xBase and Paradox, that use fixed-width fields. Access's variable-length field for Symbol occupies only the space required to contain the value.

Because only one record should exist for a stock with a particular symbol on a given date, a composite (multiple) primary key field, consisting of Symbol and Date, is appropriate. Access automatically creates a composite index on these two fields.

To create the Stock Prices table, follow these steps:

1. Open the Database window.

2. If you created a new database for the examples of Chapter 15, you can use the database for this example. Otherwise, create a new database called Stock Prices by choosing New Database from the File menu, naming the database STOCKS.MDB.

3. Click the Tables button, and then click the New button of the Database window.

4. Enter the field names, data types, size, decimal, and description properties for the seven fields shown in table 23.2.

5. Hold down the left mouse button and drag the mouse pointer over field selection buttons at the left of the window to select both the Symbol field and the Date field.

6. Click the Key Field button on the toolbar to make a composite primary key from the Symbol and Date fields. Make sure the indexed property of both the Symbol and Date fields has the value No. Access automatically creates an index on the primary key field.

7. Choose the Save **As** command from the **F**ile menu and name your table *Stock Prices*.

A composite primary key is necessary for this table because the index is used to test for duplicate appended data.

Adding Stub Functions and Procedures

Programmers commonly create the basic structure of an application by writing stubs for functions and procedures. A *stub* is simply the beginning and end of a procedure's function, with no arguments, parameters, or intervening code added. Stubs enable you to test the forms and macros you create to run your Access Basic code without actually writing any code.

To create the stubs for the functions and procedures of the Stock Prices application, follow these steps:

1. Open the Database window.

2. Click the Module button, and then click the New button. The declarations section of the new module appears with the Option Compare Database line added.

3. Add the following line after the Option Compare Database line:

   Dim f StopAppend As Integer 'Stop appending flag

   The module-level variable, fStopAppend, is a flag variable that the StopAppend() procedure uses to halt operation of the append process.

4. Then add the following line:

   Function GetStockPrices( )

   Access creates a stub with End Function added.

5. After End Function, add the following line:

   Function StopAppend( )

   Access again completes the stub for you.

6. Add the following line after End Function:

   Sub OpenDDEChannel

   Access adds an End Sub line.

7. Add the line for the last stub after the End Sub line:

   Sub AppendDDEData

8. Open the Procedures list box on the toolbar and verify that each stub appears in the list, as shown in figure 23.4.

9. Choose Save As from the File menu and save your module as **Stock Prices**.

You create stubs for the two Sub procedures, even though there is no code that calls them, because creating all your stubs at one time, or at least those that you know you need before writing any code, is a good practice.

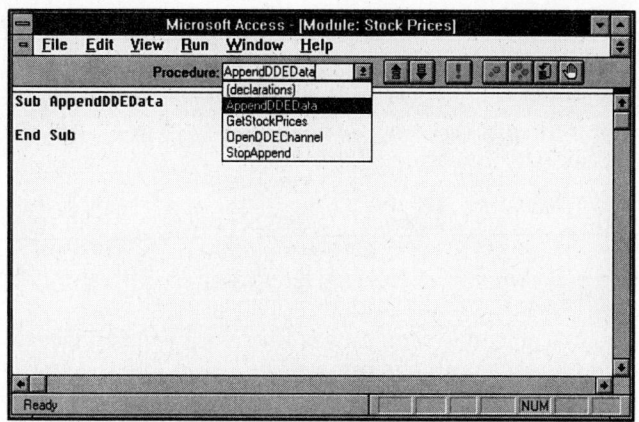

FIG. 23.4

Verifying the function and procedure stub entries for the Stock Prices module.

Adding the Necessary Macros

After you have a table and a set of stubs, you can write the macro that calls the two functions and displays the table when the process is complete. Creating macros is the subject of Chapter 17, "Understanding Access Macros." Table 23.3 lists the macro actions necessary for the StartAppend and StopAppend macros, the parameters for the actions, and the purpose of the actions.

Table 23.3. Actions and Parameters for Stock Prices Macros

Macro Name	Action	Parameter	Value	Purpose
StartAppend	Close	Object Type	Table	Closes table, if open
		Object Name	Stock Prices	
	RunCode	Function Name	GetStockPrices()	Runs Access Basic code
	OpenTable	Table Name	Stock Prices	Displays resulting table
		View	Datasheet	
		Data Mode	Edit	
	GoToRecord	Object Type	Table	Goes to end of table
		Object Name	Stock Prices	

continues

Table 23.3. Continued

Macro Name	Action	Parameter	Value	Purpose
		Record	Last	
		Offset	(leave blank)	
StopAppend	RunCode	Function Name	StopAppend()	Halts appending records

The Close macro action, which closes the Stock Prices table, is important. If the stock prices table is open when you append records with Access Basic, you may not see records appended when the OpenTable action is executed. Access Basic appends records to an invisible copy of the table. You need to open this copy while the AppendDDEData procedure appends records.

To create the Stock Prices macro, follow these steps:

1. Open the Database window, click the Macros button, and then click the New button.

2. Click the Macro Names button on the toolbar so that you can enter multiple macros in a single macro object.

3. Enter the macro name, action, parameter(s), and purpose for each macro action from the list of table 23.3 (see fig. 23.5).

4. Choose the Save **As** command from the **File** menu and save your macro object as Stock Prices.

Creating the Stock Prices Form to Control the Application

The Stock Price form that you use to call the macros and display the status of the append operation requires three text boxes and two command buttons, as shown in figure 23.6. Creating forms is the subject of Chapter 10, "Designing Custom Forms." The label that provides the title is optional. You use the Stock Price form only for testing the application, so don't waste effort on beautifying the form with background colors and embossed frames. The objective is to spend as much time as possible working on your code.

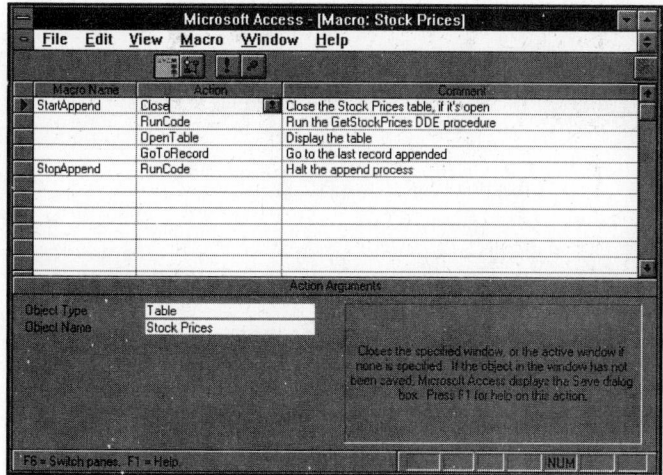

FIG. 23.5

Creating macros for the Stock Prices application.

FIG. 23.6

The design of the Stock Prices test form.

Table 23.4 lists the object type, control name, important property employed, and the value assigned to the property for each of the six control objects in the Stock Prices form. Control names are important when you use Access Basic because you must refer to control objects by name when you want to change their values.

Table 23.4. Test Form Control Object Specifications

Object Type	Control Name	Property	Value of Property or Purpose
Label	lblForm	FontSize	14 point bold
Text Box	txtSymbol	N/A	Displays ticker symbol
Text Box	txtDate	N/A	Displays trading date
Text Box	txtAction	N/A	Displays messages from module
Button	cmdStartAppend	OnPush	[Stock Prices].StartAppend macro
Button	cmdStopAppend	OnPush	[Stock Prices].StopAppend macro
		Enabled	False

To create the new Stock Prices form and add the control objects shown in Figure 23.6, follow these steps:

1. Open the Database window.

2. Click the Form button, and then click the New button.

3. Choose **T**oolbox from the **V**iew menu if the toolbox isn't visible.

4. Drag the right margin to about 4 3/8 inches and the bottom margin to about 2 1/8 inches.

5. Use the toolbox to create the label, the three text boxes, and the two buttons, each approximately the size shown in figure 23.6.

6. Click the command buttons and add the **Start Appending** and **Stop Appending** captions shown in figure 23.6. Add an ampersand (**&**) before the A of Start Appending and before the S of Stop Appending, if you want to use Alt key combinations to activate these buttons. The ampersand assigns the following letter as the Alt-key selection letter and underlines the letter in the caption of the command button.

7. Click the Properties button on the toolbar to display the Properties dialog box.

8. Enter the Control Name properties listed in table 23.4 in the Control Name text box.

9. Click the toolbar's Form Run Mode button to verify the design of your form.

10. Choose Save **As** from the **File** menu and save your form as **Stock Prices**.

When you create your own DDE application, you can copy the controls of the Stock Price form to the Clipboard and then paste them into your new application.

Testing Your Form and Macros with the Function Stubs

Before you write any code, test the form and macros to make sure they are error-free. Testing ensures that you entered the macro names correctly and that the parameters of the two RunCode actions of your macro are correct.

To test your form and macros, follow these steps:

1. Choose Form:Stock Prices from the **Window** menu.

2. Click the Start Appending button. The StartAppend macro displays the Stock Prices table in Datasheet view.

3. Click the Stop Appending button. Nothing happens because the StopAppending button is disabled.

4. If you added shortcut key ampersands to the command button captions, try Alt+A to test the Start Appending shortcut. You cannot test the Stop Appending button, because it is disabled.

If you receive an error message, correct the problem and repeat the test until you don't receive any error messages.

Understanding the GetStockPrices() Function

The GetStockPrices() function is the equivalent of a main procedure in conventional programming languages. GetStockPrices() has four basic elements:

■ Declaring the variables you need to establish the DDE conversation

■ Calling OpenDDEChannel to establish the conversation with Excel, if possible

■ Calling AppendDDEData to append the records to the table if a valid DDE channel is open

■ Closing any open DDE channels when the append operation is complete or terminated by the StopAppend() function

The balance of the code of GetStockPrices() is devoted to the administrative duties required to clear prior entries from text boxes, set the mouse pointer to the hourglass while the application runs, and return the mouse pointer to its default shape when the application's execution completes or is terminated.

Open the Modules window, select the GetStockPrices function in the Procedures list box of the Modules window, and enter the following Access Basic code in the GetStockPrices() function stub:

```
'FUNCTION: GetStockPrices( ) called by Stock Prices macro
'Uses:     OpenDDEChannel procedure for stock prices
'Returns:  Nil
Function GetStockPrices ( )
    'Declare DDE variables
    Dim wChannel   As Integer 'Channel number
    Dim szName     As String  'Service Name
    Dim szTopic    As String  'Topic
    Dim szCommand As String   'Command string to open topic
    Dim hTask As Integer      'Windows task handle
    'Disable the StopAppend button
    Forms![Stock Prices]![cmdStopAppend].Enabled = False
    'Clear prior entries from text boxes
    Forms![Stock Prices]![txtSymbol] = ""
    Forms![Stock Prices]![txtDate] = ""
    'Make the mouse pointer an hourglass
    DoCmd Hourglass Yes

    'Assign values to variables
    szName = "Excel"
    szTopic = "c:\excel\stk_21.xls"    'a well-formed path
to your topic
    'The command structure is application-specific
    szCommand = "[OPEN(" & Chr$(34) & szTopic &
Chr$(34) & ")]"

    'Use OpenDDEChannel to open the channel
    Call OpenDDEChannel(wChannel, szName, szTopic,
szCommand, hTask)
    If wChannel <> 0 Then
        'If the channel number is valid, append the
worksheet data
        Call AppendDDEData(wChannel)
    End If
```

```
      'Terminate all open DDE conversations
      DDETerminateAll
      'Change the mouse pointer back to the default type
      DoCmd Hourglass No
End Function
```

After you have entered the code and corrected any typographic errors reported by message boxes, choose Compile **A**ll from the **R**un menu to make a final test of your code. Occasionally, line-by-line syntax checking misses a coding error. You also receive error messages indicating an Argument count mismatch when your procedure attempts to execute a subprocedure in the form of a stub. You can add the arguments to the stubs you created earlier in the chapter to avoid this type of error; just duplicate the arguments within the parentheses of the calling statement. If you want an explanation of the syntax or another example of a keyword's use, place the caret on the keyword and press the F1 key.

> All lines that precede the Function keyword must be comments, prefixed with an apostrophe.

The bang symbol (ObjectType!ObjectName!ControlName) is used as a path separator when you specify a control object on a form or report, as in the following:

```
Forms![Stock Prices]![cmdStopAppend].Enabled = False
```

A period separates properties, in this case the Enabled property, from the control object name.

If your copy of STK_21.XLS isn't in C:\EXCEL, revise the code for the line that contains c:\excel\stk_21.xls accordingly. Make sure that your worksheet has the dates, beginning with 10-Apr-92 in column B, not the numbers that you substituted for dates when you modified the worksheet for the examples in Chapter 15. Also, delete the dashes in row 2 of the worksheet, if they appear. If you didn't convert STK_21.WK1 to Excel format, substitute the .WK1 extension for .XLS. If you aren't using Excel, enter the DDE service name of your Windows spreadsheet application in the line szName = "Excel".

The line

```
szCommand = "[OPEN(" & Chr$(34) & szTopic & Chr$(34) & ")]"
```

is the syntax that Excel expects when you send commands with the DDEExecute statement to open a worksheet file. The two Chr$(34) entries are the embedded quotation marks that Excel requires to surround a filename. Using double quotation marks to create quotation marks embedded in strings isn't a recommended practice, because it makes your code hard to read. Refer to the application's documentation for the syntax of DDEExecute commands if you aren't using Excel.

Understanding the StopAppend() Function

The StopAppend() function sets the value of the module-level flag (integer) variable, fStopAppend, to True. The code in the AppendDDEData procedure tests the value of this flag before it adds a new record. If fStopAppend is true, execution of AppendDDEData halts. AppendDDEData needs to have module-level scope so that it is visible both to StopAppend() and AppendDDEData.

Choose StopAppend from the Procedures list box and type the following code in the StopAppend() stub:

```
'FUNCTION:     StopAppend
'Purpose:      Sets macro-level variable to halt the append
   process
'Called by:    StopAppend sub-macro of Stock Prices macro
'Returns:      Nil
Function StopAppend ()
     fStopAppend = True
End Function
```

Notice that there is more explanatory material than code for this function. Regardless of how simple the procedure or function, a description of its purpose is very useful when you return to the application six months after you wrote it and try to remember what each component does (or is supposed to do).

Using the OpenDDEChannel Procedure

OpenDDEChannel is a general purpose procedure that you can use in any application to initiate communication with a DDE server. The device-specific values assigned to szName and the application-specific values assigned to szTopic and szCommand are passed as parameters by the calling procedure or function. You can replace the path for the messages directed to the [txtAction] control object on the [Stock Prices] form in this procedure with names suited to the other application. You can make OpenDDEChannel more universal by passing the form name and the text box name to the procedure as parameters.

To complete the OpenDDEChannel procedure stub, select OpenDDEChannel from the Procedures list box on the toolbar, and then type the code that follows:

```
'PROCEDURE:   OpenDDEChannel, opens a DDE channel, server
   if necessary
'Parameters:  wChannel, DDE channel number
'             szName, Service Name
'             szTopic, Topic name
'             szCommand, command string for DDEExecute
'             hTask, Windows handle to task from Shell
'Called by:   Standard procedure
Sub OpenDDEChannel (wChannel, szName, szTopic, szCommand,
   hTask)
    Dim szMsgTitle As String
    Dim szDDEMsg   As String
    Dim szOpenTopics   As String
    szMsgTitle = szAppName & " DDE Error"
    szDDEMsg = szName & " with topic " & szTopic & "."
    On Error Resume Next 'Do not display error messages
    Forms![Stock Prices]![txtAction] = "Opening DDE channel
to " & szName & "."
    wChannel = DDEInitiate(szName, "System")

    If Err Then
        Forms![Stock Prices]![txtAction] = "Launching
server " & szName & "."
        Err = 0  'Reset error code
        hTask = Shell(szName, 6)
        If Err Then    'Could not launch application
            'Display a message box describing error
            MsgBox "Unable to start application " &
szName & ".", 48, szMsgTitle
            Exit Sub 'Abandon hope
        Else
            'Open the System Topic
            wChannel = DDEInitiate(szName, "System")
        End If
    End If
    szOpenTopics = DDERequest(wChannel, "Topics")
    Forms![Stock Prices]![txtAction] = "Topics for " &
szName & ": " & szOpenTopics

    If InStr(UCase$(szOpenTopics), UCase$(szTopic)) = 0
Then
        Forms![Stock Prices]![txtAction] = "Opening file "
& UCase(szTopic) & " with command " & szCommand & "."
        Err = 0  'Reset error code
        DDEExecute wChannel, szCommand
        If Err Then     'Could not find the topic
            'Display a message box describing error
            MsgBox "Unable to open " & szDDEMsg, 48,
szMsgTitle
                DDETerminate wChannel     'Close the system
channel
            Exit Sub 'Abandon attempt
        End If
    End If
```

```
        DDETerminate wChannel 'Close the system channel
        Forms![Stock Prices]![txtAction] = "Opening DDE
    channel to topic " & szTopic & "."
        wChannel = DDEInitiate(szName, szTopic)
        If Err Then   'Could not find the topic
            'Display a message box describing error
            MsgBox "Unable to open channel to " & szDDEMsg,
    48, szMsgTitle
            wChannel = 0
        End If
        On Error GoTo 0 'Resume error messages
    End Sub
```

Channel numbers returned by the DDEInitiate() function can be positive or negative values; a return value of 0 indicates that DDEInitiate() failed to establish a connection. Notice that when you use the Call keyword, parameters that you pass to procedures are enclosed in parentheses. You use the value of the Windows task handle, hTask, to determine whether Excel was already opened (hTask = 0) or whether your application used the Shell command to open Excel (hTask > 0).

Now choose Compile **A**ll from the **R**un menu to make a final test of this block of your code.

The OpenDDEChannel procedure takes several steps to initiate the DDE conversation with the server:

1. wChannel = **DDEInitiate**(szName, "System") tests to see whether the application is running. Virtually all Windows DDE server applications now support the System topic.

2. If an error occurs in step 1, the application is assumed not to be running. The line hTask = **Shell**(szName, 6) uses the Shell command to start the server application. The parameter, 6, tells the application to open minimized to an icon and without the focus.

3. **Err** = 0 resets the error code so that it can be used in successive tests. You need to reset the error code each time it is used to determine the outcome of execution of a DDE statement. Message boxes created with the **MsgBox** statement advise you about the source of the problem.

4. An error that occurs in step 2 can result from insufficient resources (memory or disk space for the swap file, for instance) or an error in specifying the service name of the server. If the server cannot be opened, continuing on is pointless, so **Exit Sub** causes execution to resume at the **End Sub** statement.

5. If the application is loaded, the following statement returns a list of the server's currently valid topics:

   szOpenTopics = **DDERequest**(wChannel, "Topics")

This list is used to determine whether the topic is presently open in the server application. One of the reasons for this test is to accommodate servers that don't use file-based topics but return the names of strings that include data items.

6. **If InStr(UCase$**(szOpenTopics), **UCase$**(szTopic)) = 0 **Then** makes a case-insensitive test to see whether szOpenTopics includes szTopic.

7. If the desired topic isn't open, **DDEExecute** wChannel, szCommand sends the required command to the server to open the file. If the server cannot open the file corresponding to **szTopic**, perhaps because the wrong path or filename was specified, an error message is displayed and **Exit Sub** is invoked to terminate further activity.

8. After the topic is open, wChannel = **DDEInitiate**(szName, szTopic) initiates the conversation with the topic, returning the DDE channel number, wChannel, that is used to continue the conversation. There is little likelihood that execution would fail at this point, but an error trap is provided in case it does.

9. **On Error GoTo 0** returns **On Error Resume Next** to its default state.

Examples of Basic code often use the **On Error GoTo** statement rather than testing errors in line by evaluating the **Err** value after execution of a specific command. If you can avoid the use of GoTo statements in your code, do so. GoTo statements and labels create spaghetti code that is hard to decipher.

Using the AppendDDEData Procedure

AppendDDEData is the procedure that does the real work of the application. All of the code you type to create AppendDDEData is shown in a single block to make it easier to enter. Each code block (a group of lines of code that, in combination, perform a single function) contained in AppendDDEData is described in a section that follows the example code.

You need two loops, one nested within the other, to extract the data from the STK_21.XLS worksheet and add the data items in proper form and sequence to the table. Nested loop structures of this type are quite common in processing worksheet data; the outer loop processes rows, and the inner loop processes columns.

The *outer loop* begins with Do While Not fStopAppend and ends with Loop. The outer loop processes four rows of data, representing the close, high, and low prices and trading volume for a single stock, in row sequence. You aren't sure how many rows the worksheet contains, so the condition to exit the loop is either a blank cell that contains the Symbol data (executes Exit Do) or the fStopAppend flag set by clicking the Stop Appending button (the Do While criterion).

The *inner loop* processes data for a single date. The STK_21.XLS worksheet has 21 days of data. The inner loop begins with For irgwCol = 2 To 22 (substitute 6 for 22 if you are using the five-day version created from the data in Appendix D) and ends with Next irgwCol. The irgwCol identifier Next is optional, but it is a good programming practice to identify the end of your loops. If worksheets have a variable number of columns, you can determine the number of columns to process by detecting a blank cell where a date should be found. Records are appended to the table within this loop.

Select AppendDDEData from the Procedures list box and type the following code in the stub:

```
'PROCEDURE:    AppendDDEData, appends data to the table from
    the worksheet
'Parameters:   wChannel, valid DDE channel number
'Called by:    Standard procedure
Sub AppendDDEData (wChannel)
    'Create an array of date values from columns 2 through
    22
    Static rgdDate(23) As Double

    'Declare other variables
    Dim szDate   As String    'Date from worksheet
    Dim wRow     As Integer   'Worksheet row
    Dim wCol     As Integer   'Worksheet column
    Dim vClose, vHigh, vLow, vVolume 'variant data type
    'Stock prices from DDERequest( )
    Dim dwCount     As Long      'Total appended records
    Dim fTestDups   As Integer   'Duplicate test flag for
    partial append
    Dim fDupData    As Integer   'Duplicate data, skip 4 rows

    'Declare database object variables
    Dim dbStocks   As Database
    Dim tblStocks  As Table
    Set dbStocks = CurrentDB( )
    Set tblStocks = dbStocks.OpenTable("Stock Prices")
    'Set index to primary key index
    tblStocks.Index = "PrimaryKey"
```

```
'Reset module-level variable to zero
fStopAppend = 0
'Get the beginning record count
dwCount = DCount("[Symbol]", "Stock Prices")

'Create an array of dates for all entries
'Substitute 6 for 22 if you are using the 5-day version
For irgwCol = 2 To 22
     szDate = DDERequest(wChannel, "R1C" & irgwCol)
     If irgwCol = 2 Then
          Forms![Stock Prices]![txtAction] = "Creating
data array starting with " & szDate & "."
     End If
     rgdDate(irgwCol) = DateValue(szDate)
Next irgwCol
'Enable the StopAppend button
Forms![Stock Prices]![cmdStopAppend].Enabled =
True

'Start process at row 2
wRow = 2
Do While Not fStopAppend
     'Get stock ticker symbol
     szSymbol = DDERequest(wChannel, "R" & wRow & "C1")
     If Len(RTrim(szSymbol)) < 2 Then
          'Mark the worksheet as having been appended
          DDEPoke wChannel, "R1C1", "Done"
          'Exit the loop when a blank row (no symbol)
is reached
          Exit Do
     End If
     'Substitute 6 for 22 if you are using the 5-day
version
     For wCol = 2 To 22
          'Test for duplicate entry to avoid key
violation errors
          tblStocks.Seek "=", szSymbol, rgdDate(wCol)
          If tblStocks.NoMatch Then
               fDupData = False
          Else
               'Duplicate entry, exit the loop
               If Not fTestDups Then
                    fTestDups = MsgBox("Duplicate entry
for " & szSymbol & " on " & Format(rgdDate(wCol),
"mm/dd/yy") & ". Test for unappended records?", 20,
"Primary Key Violation")
                    If fTestDups = 6 Then
                         '6 is value for the "Yes"
choice
                         fTestDups = True
                    End If
               End If
```

```
            If Not fTestDups Then
                    'Exit If duplicate occurred and no
test desired
                    Exit Do
            End If
            fDupData = True
        End If
        If fDupData Then
            Forms![Stock Prices]![txtAction] =
"Skipping duplicate entry for " & szSymbol & " on " &
Format(rgdDate(wCol), "mm/dd/yy") & "."
        Else
            'Get the closing, high, low and volume
data for each date
            vClose = DDERequest(wChannel, "R" & wRow
& "C" & wCol)
            vHigh = DDERequest(wChannel, "R" & (wRow
+ 1) & "C" & wCol)
            vLow = DDERequest(wChannel, "R" & (wRow
+ 2) & "C" & wCol)
            vVolume = DDERequest(wChannel, "R" &
(wRow + 3) & "C" & wCol)
            'Append a new record
            tblStocks.AddNew
            'Assign values to fields
            tblStocks("Symbol") = szSymbol
            tblStocks("Date") = rgdDate(wCol)
            'Test for blank cells, leave null field
values
            If Val(vHigh) > 0 Then
                tblStocks("High") = vHigh
            End If
            If Val(vLow) > 0 Then
                tblStocks("Low") = vLow
            End If
            If Val(vClose) > 0 Then
                tblStocks("Close") = vClose
            End If
            If Val(vVolume) > 0 Then
                tblStocks("Volume") = vVolume
            End If
            'Commit append edit
            tblStocks.Update
            'Update text boxes
            Forms![Stock Prices]![txtSymbol] =
szSymbol
            Forms![Stock Prices]![txtDate] =
Format(rgdDate(wCol), "mm/dd/yy")
            Forms![Stock Prices]![txtAction] =
"Appending record " & dwCount
        End If
```

```
                    'Update the record count
                    dwCount = dwCount + 1
                    'Test for other messages (e.g., Stop
      Appending)
                         DoEvents
                Next wCol
                'Advance to next set of data
                wRow = wRow + 4
           Loop

           Forms![Stock Prices]![txtAction] = "Closing Table and
      Database Object."
            'Close the table
            tblStocks.Close
            'Close the database object (not the database)
            dbStocks.Close
      End Sub
```

Choose Compile **A**ll from the **R**un menu to test your code.

The sections that follow describe code blocks that perform functions that haven't already been discussed.

Working with Database and Table Objects in AppendDDEData

The Stock Prices application requires that you declare variables that point to a hierarchy of database objects: the database itself, the table to which records are to be appended, and the index of the table. Chapter 22, "Writing Access Basic Code," discusses how to use the Set statement. Database object variable declaration occurs in the following code block:

```
      'Declare database object variables
      Dim dbStocks    As Database
      Dim tblStocks   As Table
      Set dbStocks = CurrentDB()
      Set tblStocks = dbStocks.OpenTable("Stock Prices")
      'Set index to primary key index
      tblStocks.Index = "PrimaryKey"
```

The database is open, so you use the CurrentDB() function to assign dbStocks as a pointer to the database itself. You use the OpenTable() method to assign the Stock Prices table to tblStocks. You use the Index property of a table to determine the index in use. The value assigned to the Index property, enclosed in quotation marks, can be PrimaryKey, if you add a primary key to the table. The value can also be Index1 through Index5 for supplemental indexes.

When you use a composite index, you can substitute the name of the first field in the index if you want to find records based on a partial index value. For example, you can use the expression tblStocks.Index = "Symbol" to find all stocks with a given symbol, using the Seek method that is described shortly.

Closing the database objects you create when a procedure no longer needs to use them is a good programming practice; it conserves memory resources. The statements at the end of the following procedure close the table and close the database object:

```
'Close the table
tblStocks.Close
'Close the database object (not the database)
dbStocks.Close
```

If the database object is the current database, the database itself doesn't close; only the database object variable that represents the database object, dbStocks, closes.

Creating the Date Array with the DDERequest( ) Function

The array, rgdDate, that is declared in the line

```
Static rgdDate(23) As Double
```

holds the 21 date values found in columns 2 though 22 of the first row of the worksheet. Creating an array to hold the date values, rather than using DDERequest( ) to obtain the value for each entry, speeds operation of your code. Arrays declared within procedures must be declared with the Static keyword, rather than the Dim keyword. The array needs 23 elements because the first element is element 0; making the index correspond to the column number simplifies your code. This is accomplished with the following block of code:

```
'Create an array of dates for all entries
For irgwCol = 2 To 22
    szDate = DDERequest(wChannel, "R1C" & irgwCol)
    If irgwCol = 2 Then
        Forms![Stock Prices]![txtAction] = "Creating data
array starting with " & szDate & "."
    End If
    rgdDate(irgwCol) = DateValue(szDate)
Next irgwCol
```

The For...Next loop assigns the 21 values of the dates in worksheet cells R1C2 through R1C22 to szDate with the DDERequest( ) function. The string value is in one of the standard formats, mm-dd-yy, recognized by Access as a date, so you can use the DateValue( ) function to convert the string to the required Date/Time field data type that corresponds to the Double data type in Access Basic.

Testing the Symbol Value and Poking the Worksheet

The value of the stock ticker symbol in the Symbol field is the primary identifying value for each record in the database. The same value is used for 21 consecutive appended records, so DDERequest() is used to assign its value to a variable, szSymbol, as follows:

```
'Get stock ticker symbol
szSymbol = DDERequest(wChannel, "R" & wRow & "C1")
If Len(RTrim(szSymbol)) < 3 Then
    'Mark the worksheet as having been appended
    DDEPoke wChannel, "R1C1", "Done"
    'Exit the loop when a blank row (no symbol) is
reached
    Exit Do
End If
```

The minimum valid length of a stock ticker symbol in the worksheet is three characters. These characters correspond to a stock identified by a single letter, followed by a hyphen and a letter that identifies the type of the security, such as S for stock. All valid stock data in the worksheet must have a symbol, so you use the length of the symbol string to test for the end of the worksheet. Using RTrim() ensures that trailing spaces aren't counted in the test.

When a blank symbol cell is detected, you can use the DDEPoke statement to mark the worksheet as having been appended in its entirety to the Stock Prices table. DDEPoke sends unsolicited data to the specified item of the current topic. DDEPoke in Access Basic is the equivalent of the DDESend() function that you can use with other database objects; you cannot use DDE() or DDESend() in Access Basic statements. In this case, cell R1C1 of the worksheet is normally empty, so item R1C1 is poked with the value Done. Exit Do then causes execution of the code to jump to the statement following the Loop statement, terminating the procedure.

Using the Seek Method To Test for Duplicate Records

The composite primary key, consisting of Symbol and Date, doesn't permit duplicate data for a particular stock on a given date to be added to the table. If you stop appending records before all the data in the worksheet has been added to the table and then attempt to begin the process again, key violations result. A partial set of records can result from this premature use of the StopAppend() function or can be caused by a full disk drive, a hardware problem, or a power failure. You need a code that detects key violations before you try to add a duplicate record.

The following code block uses the Seek method to determine whether a record with the same stock ticker symbol and trading date exists in the table. The Access Basic Seek method is similar to that of xBase, but the Access method is more flexible. You have previously specified the active index with the tblStocks Index property.

To use the Seek method, you specify the comparison operator, "=" in this case, and the value(s) for find as parameters of Seek. The following code block is located within the inner loop of the procedure. This code block demonstrates the use of the Seek method to trap duplicate records and to offer the user of the application the choice of abandoning the append or bypassing duplicate records and appending only records that create unique primary key values:

```
'Test for duplicate entry to avoid key violation errors
tblStocks.Seek "=", szSymbol, rgdDate(wCol)
If tblStocks.NoMatch Then
    fDupData = False
Else
    'Duplicate entry, exit the loop
    If Not fTestDups Then
        fTestDups = MsgBox("Duplicate entry for " &
szSymbol & " on " & Format(rgdDate(2), "mm/dd/yy") & ".
Test for unappended records?", 20, "Primary Key
Violation")
        If fTestDups = 6 Then
            '6 is value for the "Yes" choice
            fTestDups = True
        End If
    End If
    If Not fTestDups Then
        'Exit If duplicate occurred and no test desired
        Exit Do
    End If
    fDupData = True
End If
```

Executing the Seek method assigns a value to the NoMatch property of the table. The NoMatch property is the equivalent of xBase's EOF() function after an xBase SEEK operation and the opposite of the FOUND() function. If a match is found, NoMatch is False; otherwise, it is True.

In addition to the conventional "=" operator used to find a matching value, you can use <, <=, >= and > comparison operations with the Seek method. The comparison operator is enclosed in quotation marks. The

=, >= and > operators begin the search at the top of the index, while <= and < begin the search at the end of the index. Seek finds the first record that satisfies the criteria established by the operator and value(s) parameters you supply.

The duplicate test code block also demonstrates the use of flags to control execution within a procedure. A *flag* is a logical (Boolean) variable that has either the value True (–1) or False (0). You *set* flags to the True value and *reset* them to the False value. The AppendDDEData procedure uses the fTestDups flag to determine whether the user sees a message box when a value that duplicates an existing record is encountered in the worksheet. The fTestDups flag is reset to 0 when you declare it as a variable. When a duplicate value is encountered, the user is presented with a message box that provides a Yes/No choice between testing for duplicate values and appending only nonduplicate records or exiting the procedure with the Exit Do statement.

The MsgBox() function with a type value of 20 designates a message box with a critical stop (red stop sign) icon and Yes and No buttons. Clicking the No button returns 0. Clicking the Yes button returns 6. Place the caret on MsgBox() and press the F1 key for additional information about this function.

If the user elects to test for duplicate data, the fDupData flag is used in the If fDupData Then...Else...End If structure to determine whether a record is appended to the table. A message in the txtAction text box informs the user that duplicate records are being skipped.

Obtaining the Balance of the Data

The high, low, and close quotations and the trading volume for each stock are obtained for each date if the data isn't duplicative. This information is contained in successive rows of a single date column; executing the DDERequest() function obtains the four values. The current row value, corresponding to the row in which the stock ticker symbol appears, is incremented by 1 to specify the cell of each row in sequence, as shown in the following code block:

```
'Get the closing, high, low and volume data for each date
vClose = DDERequest(wChannel, "R" & wRow & "C" & wCol)
vHigh = DDERequest(wChannel, "R" & (wRow + 1) & "C" &
wCol)
vLow = DDERequest(wChannel, "R" & (wRow + 2) & "C" &
wCol)
vVolume = DDERequest(wChannel, "R" & (wRow + 3) & "C" & wCol)
```

```
'Append a new record
tblStocks.AddNew
'Assign values to fields
tblStocks("Symbol") = szSymbol
tblStocks("Date") = rgdDate(wCol)

'Test for blank cells, leave null field values
If Val(vHigh) > 0 Then
    tblStocks("High") = vHigh
End If
If Val(vLow) > 0 Then
tblStocks("Low") = vLow
End If
If Val(vClose) > 0 Then
    tblStocks("Close") = vClose
End If
If Val(vVolume) > 0 Then
    tblStocks("Volume") = vVolume
End If

'Commit append edit
tblStocks.Update
```

You append a new current record to a table with the AddNew method. If you want to change the value of an existing record, you use the Edit method instead of the AddNew method.

Specifying the table object variable and adding the field name enclosed within parentheses and quotation marks assigns values to individual fields of the currently selected record. Although the structure of this expression looks like a conventional function, the statement tblStocks("High") = vHigh technically isn't a function. This statement assigns a value to the High field of the table; functions return values to their names. When you reverse the expression, such as vHigh = tblStocks("High"), the expression becomes a function, because the expression returns the value of the field High to vHigh.

You must test the numeric value of each variable with the Val() function; otherwise, a wrong field data type error occurs when you encounter blank cells. You want blank cells in the worksheet to create null values in the corresponding fields of the appended record, because a blank cell indicates no data available, not a 0 value. If you don't assign a data value to a field, the default null value, established when the record is appended, remains.

After you have assigned values to the fields of the appended record, you need to save the record with the Update method. Executing the Update method in Access Basic has the same effect as changing the record selection in the datasheet view of a table.

The DoEvents statement at the end of the inner loop tests the Windows message queue to determine whether any messages, such as a message indicating that you clicked the Stop Appending button, have been sent while the application is running. If you don't include a DoEvents statement in loops that take a long time to complete, you may not be able to halt them with a macro action such as StopAppend().

You can speed the process of acquiring DDE data from worksheets by specifying a range of cells in a single DDERequest() statement, using the form R#C#:R#C# for the data item, where # symbolizes the numbers that specify a rectangular block of cells. If you use this approach, you must write code that uses a nested loop to parse the data. Rows are separated by newline pairs so that the outer loop detects Chr$(10) as the end of a row. Columns are separated by tab characters, so the inner loop tests for Chr$(6). This example uses individual DDE transactions for the sake of simplicity in presentation; an application designed for maximum speed would parse a 4-row by 21-column matrix of cells with Access Basic code.

Running the Stock Prices Code

The acid test of your typing skills occurs when you run the code you entered from the examples presented in the prior sections. If you are using the complete STK_21.WK1 worksheet you downloaded from CompuServe or the STK_21.XLS worksheet you created from it, appending Stock Price records for all 305 stocks (a total of 21 * 305 or 6,405 records) can be a time-consuming process. The amount of time required depends on the processor and the amount of RAM available in your computer, as well as the average access time of your disk drive. Use of a permanent rather than a temporary Windows swap file often makes a significant improvement in the performance of Access applications. Refer to the *Windows User's Guide* for additional information on swap files.

Running Stock Prices for the First Time

To run the Stock Prices application, follow these steps:

1. Use Windows' Task Manager to close any applications other than Access before you run the Stock Prices application. This step frees memory resources that Access needs to run the application efficiently, minimizing the use of your temporary or permanent swap file.

2. Choose Form:Stock Prices from the **Window** menu. The Stock Prices test form appears.

3. Click the Start Appending button of the Stock Prices test form. Depending on the amount of RAM in your computer, there may be a delay while resources in RAM are transferred to the swap file.

   Messages appear in the Action text box describing the steps taken to initiate the DDE conversation with Excel. Your code launches Excel; then the command string opens the STK_21 worksheet, and finally the DDE communications channel is established.

   As records are appended to the Stock Prices table, the Stock Prices test form appears, as shown in figure 23.7.

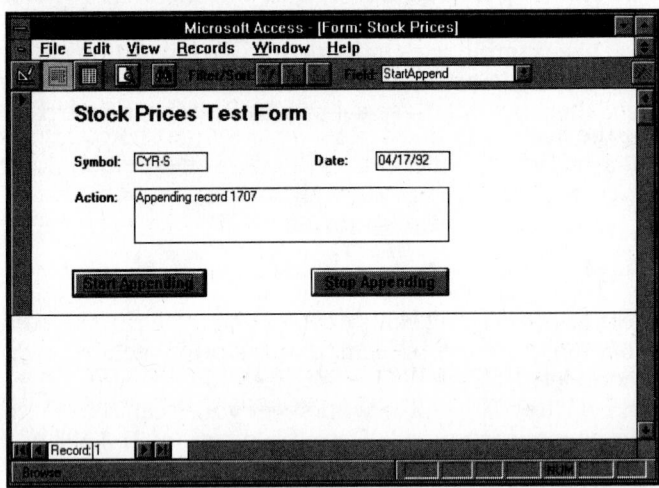

FIG. 23.7

Appending
records with the
Stock Prices
application.

4. After appending a few records, click the Stop Appending button. You may need to click the button more than once to stop the process.

You can use several DoEvents statements at the end of the inner loop to make clicking the Stop Appending button more decisive, but each DoEvents statement you add slows operation of the procedure as a whole.

The Open macro action causes the table created by the Stock Prices application to appear (see fig. 23.8).

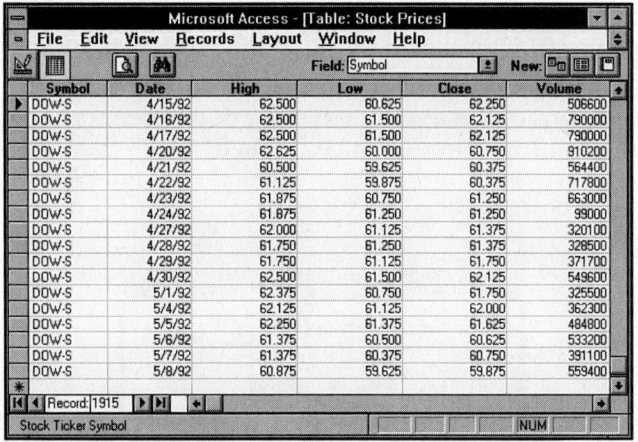

FIG. 23.8

Viewing the records appended to the Stock Prices table.

If you encounter run-time errors during execution of your Access Basic code, make the necessary corrections to the code and then choose Compile **A**ll from the **R**un menu. Compiling your code also reinitializes your module, resetting the values of all variables to the defaults. This procedure is the equivalent of choosing **R**einitialize from the **R**un menu.

If DDE Timeout messages appear, choose the **O**ptions command from the **V**iew menu and click General from the Categories list box. The default value in the OLE/DDE Timeout text box is 30 seconds. Increase this value until you no longer receive DDE Timeout messages.

Running Stock Prices after Appending Some Records

To verify proper operation of the duplicate records test included in the AppendDDEData procedure, follow these steps:

1. Choose Form:Stock Prices from the **W**indow menu. The Stock Prices test form appears.

2. Click the Start Appending button. Excel is presently open with STK_21.XLS as a valid topic, so the DDE initiation process is faster.

3. When the DDERequest() function returns the first symbol, the message box shown in figure 23.9 appears. Click the Yes button to continue with duplicate record testing.

As the Stock Prices application skips duplicate records, the Stock Prices test form appears, as shown in figure 23.10. After all the duplicate records have been skipped, the AppendDDEData procedure starts appending new records.

FIG. 23.9

The custom message box indicating a pending key violation.

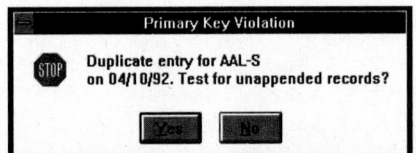

FIG. 23.10

Skipping duplicated records.

You can adapt the code in the Stock Prices application to almost any worksheet that displays repetitive groups of data values in repeating blocks of cells.

Using Access as a DDE Server

Access can act as a DDE server to other DDE client applications. Access recognizes a set of DDE instructions issued by the client applications that is more versatile than the set offered by most DDE server applications. The flexibility of Access's DDE server instruction set compensates for the application's inability to act as an OLE server. In the majority of cases, DDE is a better choice than OLE for transferring columnar data to a client spreadsheet application.

Using the System Topic

When a client application initiates a DDE channel on the System topic and specifies Topics as the data item in a DDERequest() statement, Access returns a list of the topics it currently supports. For example, type and then execute the following Word for Windows macro:

```
Sub MAIN
    Channel = DDEInitiate("MSAccess", "System")
    Topics$ = DDERequest$(Channel, "Topics")
    DDETerminate(Channel)
    Insert Topics$
End Sub
```

Access returns a tab-separated string and Word for Windows inserts this string, similar to that in the following example, at Word's current insertion point:

```
System[ma]UTILITY[ma]WIZARD[ma]EXCEL
```

The System topic is supported by all Windows DDE servers. UTILITY, WIZARD, and EXCEL are the names of open databases; UTILITY and WIZARD are libraries, but the System topic treats them as if they were databases. If you have opened database objects, such as a table or query, Access appends multiple copies of the database name to the string. In this case, you receive a string such as the following:

```
System[ma]UTILITY[ma]WIZARD[ma]EXCEL[ma]EXCEL[ma]EXCEL
```

The System supports the SysItems data item that returns a list of valid data items that you can use to determine additional information about Access's capabilities as a server. Run the following Word for Windows macro:

```
Sub MAIN
    Channel = DDEInitiate("MSAccess", "System")
    SysItems$ = DDERequest$(Channel, "SysItems")
    DDETerminate(Channel)
    Insert SysItems$
End Sub
```

The macro inserts the following comma-separated list of valid data items for the System topic:

```
Status,Formats,SysItems,Topics
```

If you substitute Formats for SysItems in the preceding macro, Access returns the two types of Clipboard formats it supports:

```
Text  CSV
```

CSV is an abbreviation for comma-separated values, the format in which Access returns the examples shown previously.

The data items supported by the System topic are summarized in table 23.5.

Table 23.5. Data Items Supported by Access's System Topic

Data Item	Purpose
Status	Returns Ready or Busy
Formats	Returns a list of the formats Access can copy onto the Clipboard, presently CSV and Text
SysItems	Returns a list of the data items, except *MacroName*, supported by the System topic
Topics	Returns a list of all open databases, including libraries
MacroName	Enables a macro in the current database to be executed with the DDEExecute statement using the System topic

As an example of the MacroName System topic, the following Word macro executes the StopAppend macro in the Stock Prices macro object if the database that contains the macro object is open:

```
Sub MAIN
    Channel = DDEInitiate("MSAccess", "System")
    DDEExecute Channel, "[Stock Prices].StopAppend"
    DDETerminate(Channel)
End Sub
```

Don't attempt to execute the StartAppend macro with a DDEExecute statement because the StartAppend macro doesn't load the Stock Prices form that is required to display the messages sent to the form's text boxes. Word presents a time-out message because the GetStockPrices() function generates an error.

Returning Information about Other Topics

You can obtain four different sets of data by specifying the name of the open database:

- *Database object lists:* To obtain these lists, use the name of the database as the topic in the DDEInitiate() statement and use one of the following keywords as the data item in a DDERequest() statement: TableList, QueryList, FormList, ReportList, MacroList, and ModuleList.

- *Data from tables:* To obtain this data, specify the database (followed by a semicolon), the keyword TABLE, and the name of the table as the topic in the DDEInitiate() statement. Then use one of the following keywords as the data item in a DDERequest() statement: All, Data, FieldNames, FirstRow, NextRow, PrevRow, LastRow, and FieldCount.

- *Data from a query:* To obtain this data, specify the database (followed by a semicolon), the keyword QUERY, and the name of the query as the topic in the DDEInitiate() statement. Then use one of the same keywords for the TABLE topic as the data item in a DDERequest() statement.

- *Data from an SQL statement:* To obtain this data, specify the database (followed by a semicolon), the keyword SQL, and a valid SQL statement in the DDEInitiate() statement. Then use one of the same keywords for the TABLE topic as the data item in a DDERequest() statement.

The sections that follow give the syntax and an example of an Excel macro that executes each of these DDE client processes. The information in these sections assumes some familiarity with the command macros features of Microsoft Excel.

You can execute macros over DDE channels initiated with the *DatabaseName* topic in the same manner as those initiated with the System topic. You specify the *MacroName* of a macro contained in the open database as the data item in a DDERequest() statement.

Listing Database Object Names with the DatabaseName Topic

You can obtain lists of all database objects in an Access database you specify with the *DatabaseName* topic. *DatabaseName* can be NWIND or NWIND.MDB, for example, if NWIND.MDB is open. Otherwise, you need to include the Shell command in your macro.

After initiating the DDE conversation with the *DatabaseName* topic, you can use the data items listed in table 23.6 with the DDERequest() request function to return a CSV string listing the names of database objects in the database.

Table 23.6. Data Items Recognized with the DatabaseName Topic

Data Item	Purpose
TableList	A list of tables in *DatabaseName*
QueryList	A list of queries in *DatabaseName*
MacroList	A list of macros in *DatabaseName*
ReportList	A list of reports in *DatabaseName*
FormList	A list of forms in *DatabaseName*
ModuleList	A list of modules in *DatabaseName*

For example, the following Excel macro returns the first three entries in a list of the tables in the Northwind Traders sample database, assuming NWIND.MDB is open:

```
=INITIATE("MSAccess","NWIND")
=INDEX(REQUEST(A2,"TableList"),1)    Categories
=FORMULA(A3,B3)
=INDEX(REQUEST(A2,"TableList"),2)    Customers
=FORMULA(A5,B5)
=INDEX(REQUEST(A2,"TableList"),3)    Employees
=FORMULA(A7,B7)
=TERMINATE(A2)
=RETURN()
```

Enter the macro statements of the example in a macrosheet in rows 1 through 9 of column A. Select cell A1, and then choose **R**un from Excel's **M**acros menu. Choose OK or press Enter when the Run Macro dialog box appears. The values appear in cells B3, B5, and B7.

Using the TableName and QueryName Topics To Obtain Data

You can add a qualifier to *DatabaseName* to specify a table or query object contained in *DatabaseName* as the topic. The syntax is as follows:

```
DatabaseName;TABLE TableName
DatabaseName;QUERY QueryName
```

Table 23.7 lists the data items that are valid for use with both the *TableName* and *QueryName* topics, plus the *SQLStatement* topic discussed in the next section.

Table 23.7. Data Items Recognized by the TableName, QueryName, and SQLStatement Topics	
Data Item	**Purpose**
All	Returns all data in the table, preceded by a row of field names
Data	Returns all rows of data without a row of field names
FieldNames	Returns a list consisting of all field names
FirstRow	Returns the data in the first row of the table or query
NextRow	Returns the data in the next row in the table or query. If Next Row is the first request, the data in the first row is returned. NextRow fails if the current row is the last record.
PrevRow	Returns the previous row in the table or query. If PrevRow is the first request, the data in the last row of the table or query is returned. PrevRow fails if the current row is the first record.
LastRow	Returns the data in the last row of the table or query
FieldCount	Returns the number of fields in the table or query
MacroName	Enables a macro in the current database to be executed with the DDEExecute statement using the System topic

The following Excel macro returns the first three fields of the first row of the Categories table:

```
=INITIATE("MSAccess","NWIND;TABLE Categories")
=INDEX(REQUEST(A2,"FirstRow"),1)          BEVR
=FORMULA(A3,B3)
=INDEX(REQUEST(A2,"FirstRow"),2)          Beverages
=FORMULA(A5,B5)
=INDEX(REQUEST(A2,"FirstRow"),3)          Soft drinks, ...
=FORMULA(A7,B7)
=TERMINATE(A2)
=RETURN()
```

Enter and run the macro using the procedure described previously in the *DatabaseName* section.

Running a Query with the SQLStatement Topic

The *SQLStatement* topic returns a valid SQL statement following the SQL keyword. The syntax for the *SQLStatement* topic is as follows:

DatabaseName;SQL *SQLStatement*;

The SQL statement must end with a semicolon.

An Excel macro that executes the SQL statement, SELECT * FROM Customers and lists the names of the first three customers in the resulting dynaset is as follows:

```
=INITIATE("MSAccess","NWIND;SQL SELECT * FROM Customers;")
=INDEX(REQUEST(A2,"FirstRow"),2)     Always Open Quick...
=FORMULA(A3,B3)
=INDEX(REQUEST(A2,"NextRow"),2)      Andre's Continental...
=FORMULA(A5,B5)
=INDEX(REQUEST(A2,"NextRow"),2)      Anthony's Beer and Ale
=FORMULA(A7,B7)
=TERMINATE(A2)
=RETURN()
```

In the majority of cases, you write macros in the client application's macro language that contain loops to process multiple rows of data, similar to the Stock Prices' loop structure, which was described earlier in the chapter. The design of macros in the languages of other applications is beyond the scope of this book. Ron Person's *Using Excel 4 for Windows,* Special Edition, also published by Que Corporation, is an excellent resource for learning more about the command macro syntax of Excel.

Chapter Summary

This chapter demonstrates that DDE is an effective method for appending records from spreadsheets and other documents that contain ordered sets of data. When you are faced with repetitive updating of data in Access tables based on information generated by other applications, DDE is usually the most efficient approach. The sample application presented in this chapter is typical of the Access Basic code you need to write to use Access as a DDE client.

Using Access as a DDE server to other DDE client applications is relatively simple, especially when compared with alternative choices of DDE servers designed for use with database tables. The flexibility of the extended DDE topics offered by Access and the data item keywords make writing client DDE macros a pleasure, rather than a chore.

Chapter 24 explains how to complete an Access application for transaction processing or decision support so that users are presented only with the menu choices they need to run the application. Creating help files for users of Access applications also is described in detail.

Adding On-Line Help for Users

O n-line Help is an indispensable element of the Access applications you create for others to use, especially if the applications are complex. Users of Windows applications are reported to take advantage of on-line Help more frequently than those using the same applications under DOS. The reason is undoubtedly the easy-to-use WinHelp engine, as well as its navigation and search features.

This chapter explains how to create Windows Help files to provide context-sensitive Help for your applications. To create Help files, you need a word processing application that creates Rich Text Format (.RTF) files, such as Word for Windows 1.1a or 2.0+. (.RTF is a method of including formatting data with text in a readable ASCII file; .RTF is described in, "Taking a Brief Look at the Rich Text Format," later in this chapter.) You also need HC31.EXE, the Microsoft Help compiler that converts the .RTF files to a form readable by the Windows 3.1 Help engine, WinHelp. HC31.EXE is not included with Access but is included with the Microsoft Software Development Kit (SDK) for Windows 3.1 and the Professional Edition of Visual Basic 2.0. Recent versions of most language compilers that are designed for creating Windows applications, such as Borland C++ Version 3.1, also include HC31.EXE. Or you can purchase HC31.EXE as a stand-alone product directly from Microsoft Corporation.

The information in this chapter is intended to be a supplement to, not substitute for, the *Help Author's Guide* or other documentation accompanying HC31.EXE, the Microsoft Help compiler application. That documentation also deals with advanced topics such as Help macros, which are not covered in this chapter.

Understanding How the WinHelp Engine Works

The WinHelp engine, WINHELP.EXE, is used by all applications to display the contents of Help files. WINHELP.EXE contains a single function, WinHelp(), whose arguments determine the name of the Help file to use and the topic to display. WinHelp files are a special type of file, with the extension .HLP, designed for use with the WinHelp engine. WinHelp files are created from .RTF files that use special codes, embedded as footnote markers, to create indexes to topics. These indexes then are used by WinHelp() to locate the topics in the file, find keyword search entries, enable the user to browse topics in sequence, and create a history of the Help screens viewed by the user.

Creating Help files for Windows applications is a more complex process than writing Help text files for DOS applications. You need to create an .RTF file with special topic, browsing, and keyword entries; create a *project file* (also called a *make file*); and then compile your .RTF files to WinHelp.HLP with the Help compiler.

With the WinHelp engine, you have much more flexibility than you have with the simple text files that you use for Help for DOS-based database management applications. WinHelp enables you to illustrate your Help files with bit maps and meta files, add music or sound to the Help windows, and format your text in any typeface and font available on the user's computer. This chapter shows you how to create WinHelp files that use the following methods to display Help windows explaining specific topics:

■ *Context strings* enable you to use hot spots to display a window identified by the context string. *Hot spots* add hypertext-like capabilities to your application's Help system. (Hypertext is explained in the next section, "Understanding Hypertext Links in Help Files.") Context strings are names that identify a particular Help window. When the user clicks a green hot spot with which a context string is associated, a new Help window identified by the context string appears. You can choose between conventional nonmodal windows for Help text and graphics and modal pop-up windows that usually provide definitions of terms.

- *Keywords* assigned to a topic enable the user to search the WinHelp file for other topics that include the same word in a keyword list. A list box of all topics identified with the chosen keyword enables the user, rather than the WinHelp file, to make the navigation decisions.

- *Browse-sequence numbers* establish the sequence in which windows for topics appear when the user clicks the << and >> buttons of the Help window.

- *Context-sensitive Help* uses context ID numbers coupled to the context strings associated with individual topics. You can specify the WinHelp file to be used for a form or report by assigning the file name to the Help File property of a form or report, or a control object on a form or report. Then you assign the context ID value to the Help Context ID property of a control object. You select the control to give it the focus, press the F1 key, and the Help window with the designated topic appears.

Context strings, keywords, browse-sequence numbers, and context ID numbers are placed in footnotes in the Help text files. The Help compiler uses the footnote text to create the indexes needed to make the WinHelp file operable.

The techniques for creating Help files that use each of these WinHelp features are explained in the balance of this chapter. But first you need to understand the structure of WinHelp files, the difference between Help compiler versions, and how to plan and design your Help files. These subjects are included in the sections that follow.

Understanding Hypertext Links in Help Files

Hypertext was invented to make related items in complex documents easily accessible. A table of contents presents the topics of a book in an orderly, linear form, telling you where to find topics from the front to the back of the book. Hypertext works differently. Hypertext links are nonlinear and are similar to the nonclustered indexes for database tables described in Chapter 19. Hypertext links, also called *jumps*, save you the trouble of looking up the topic in the index and turning to the appropriate pages. The green hot spots of the Access Help windows are hypertext links to other related topics. These related topics have hot spots that link to even more related topics. Glossary-type hot spots provide jumps to definitions of unfamiliar terms in a pop-up window.

Comparing the Windows 3.1 and 3.0 Help Engines

If you have written Help files for applications with the Windows 3.0 Help compiler, HC.EXE, you need to be aware of changes made to the new version, HC31.EXE, used with Windows 3.1+. If you install Access under Windows 3.0, Access copies the Windows 3.1 version of WINHELP.EXE over the 3.0 version so that Access can use the new features of the Windows 3.1 Help engine. Many other recent Windows applications do the same. Existing Windows 3.0 Help files are backward-compatible with the Help files of Windows 3.1 applications.

These two major changes have been made to HC.EXE 3.0+ versions:

- Browse buttons no longer appear automatically when browse-sequence numbers are incorporated in your Help file. You must add the BrowseButtons() Help macro to the [CONFIG] section of your Help project file.

- You must change the INDEX= option entry to CONTENTS= in the [OPTIONS] section of your HC.EXE Version 3.0+ project files.

In addition, the WinHelp engine supplied with Windows 3.1 and the Windows 3.1 version of the Help compiler, HC31.EXE, add the following seven new features:

- Multicolumn tables. With HC.EXE, displaying tabular information required side-by-side columns. Those of you who have attempted to deal with several side-by-side columns can especially appreciate this addition.

- The capability to embed objects such as charts and diagrams directly in text. An OLE object, such as a diagram created by MS Draw or a chart from MS Graph, displays exactly as it appears in your Word for Windows 2.0 (Version 2+ is required) document. Packaged embedded objects, such as Media Player and an MIDI file, however, are inoperable; the icon appears in the Help display, but double-clicking it does nothing.

- Compression of Help files at differing levels.

- Definition of Help window placement and colors.

- Creation of nonscrolling regions.

- Incorporation of secondary windows.

- The capability to establish jumps between different Help files.

The two most important of these new features are the multiple-column tables and the capability to embed objects, which alone justify the cost of acquiring HC31.EXE. Tables enable you to format text and even small graphic images in aligned columns, with or without borders around the cells. Embedding with OLE enables you to add sound, animation, and digital video to WinHelp files. Acquiring HC31.EXE, instead of attempting to "get by" with Windows 3.0's HC.EXE in a Windows 3.1 world, is strongly recommended.

Word for Windows 2.0 is known to have incompatibilities with HC.EXE. These problems do not arise with HC31.EXE. If you plan to use Word for Windows 2+ to create Help files, you need to acquire HC31.EXE.

You can implement multimedia elements for Help files, such as sound effects and music, only if you and your users have installed Windows 3.1 or the Multimedia Extensions 1.0 for Windows 3.0. Users of Help files that incorporate sound must, of course, have an MPC-compatible audio card. Windows 3.1, by itself, supports only the basic audio multimedia functions. If you plan to use other multimedia features in your Help files, acquiring the current version of Microsoft's Multimedia Development Kit (MDK) is recommended.

At the time this book was written, an extended version of the Windows 3.1 Help compiler, called HCP.EXE (Version 3.10.504 (extended)), was available for downloading as HCP.ZIP from Library 16 of the Windows SDK forum (GO WINSDK) on CompuServe. A simple Word for Windows Help file template, similar to VBHELP.DOT, can be downloaded from Library 3 of the same forum as HELP.DOT.

Planning Help Files for Your Applications

Creating a Help file is much like writing a book. You determine your intended audience, develop a master outline of the parts of the Help system, and then fill in the lower outline levels of each part with the topic titles covering each aspect of your application. This process creates the hierarchy of your Help file. Finally, you add the text for each topic, written to accommodate the user's level of familiarity with computers in general, the operating system in use, and similar applications. With the advent of the CD-ROM, you can expect Help files to grow to encyclopedic length. Microsoft's Multimedia Works and Lotus's SmartHelp for Lotus 1-2-3 for Windows are early examples of this trend—the Help files are contained in CD-ROM tracks and consist of 500M to 600M of text and images.

The Help file and your application's operating manual usually cover much of the same material. A good Help file can reduce by more than half the time needed to prepare printed documentation. You can use standardized Help files for various, related applications because WinHelp can find topics in any file that you include in your final Help file list.

Build your Help file as you develop the Access application. One of the advantages of this approach is that you can evaluate the application's ease of use. If you can explain a step clearly in a paragraph or two of a Help file, the user probably will understand what you intend; otherwise, consider altering the application to clarify the actions required of the user. Simultaneous creation of Help files also aids in eliminating the omission of important topics. The topic you forget to include in your WinHelp file is always the one that users don't understand. Another benefit is the Help file's capability to document your application as you proceed with its development. When you return to writing code after your vacation, use the Help file to refresh your recollection of what the application was intended to accomplish and to remind you of where you were when you left. Creating a Help file-tracking database also assists in preventing critical omissions. (For more information, see the "Creating a Help File-Tracking Database" section in this chapter.)

Aiming at the User's Level of Expertise

You should direct the structure and contents of your Help file to the experience level of your audience, not only with computers in general and Windows in particular, but also with applications that are similar to the one you are creating. If you are developing a database front end for your firm, for example, your users may be experienced data entry persons or management colleagues who are familiar with the terminology of your industry and the content of your databases. But what happens when a "temp" replaces your vacationing data-entry person, and you are in Teaneck training sales representatives?

Users can be classified within five basic groups with increasing levels of competence:

1. *Computing novice:* A person who has never used a personal computer or who is making the transition from use of a mainframe terminal to a self-contained or networked PC. Special applications often are written for trainees or employees in transition from one job classification to another.

2. *Windows novice:* An individual who is familiar with DOS or uses an Apple Macintosh, but is new to the Windows GUI. Your Help file should include details on effective use of the mouse and keyboard

shortcuts. A glossary of Windows terminology is a definite requirement, and diagrams for menu choices are Helpful. Simple diagrams created with the Microsoft Draw applet usually suffice.

3. *Application novice:* One who is experienced with Windows but not with the type of application you are creating. An example is a word processing operator assigned to use your database front end. You may not need to include information on how to use the keyboard and mouse for these users.

4. *Application-familiar user:* A person who is familiar with Windows and the type of application you are developing. Such a person may be a data entry operator who regularly uses the database features of a Windows spreadsheet application, or an executive who has used applications developed with a client-server front end for Windows. The Help file need only explain those elements of the application that are not intuitive or that differ from commercial implementations of similar applications. You may be able to dispense with printed documentation for application-familiar users.

5. *Power user:* A person who does not read the documentation or use your Help file. Power users believe no application has ever left the beta stage. They find warts (anomalies) and bugs in Version 7.6 of your application.

The first four classifications require distinctly different contents in their Help files. One way of accomplishing this differentiation is to create a different Help file for each user level and supply the appropriate file or include a dialog box to select the appropriate Help file at startup. An alternative is to create a single Help file and change the topic name of the entry point in the file for each subject at different skill levels. You can create a browse sequence to enable the user to obtain information about the subject at a higher or lower level of detail.

Examining the Standard Structure of Help Topics

Most Help files are arranged in a structure corresponding to the basic subject matter covered by the application and include assistance to users in the translation of menu commands. The structure of a typical Help file for a full-scale Access application appears in figure 24.1. Solid lines show the topic selection paths in a linear, hierarchical structure. Topic windows comprise the lowest level of the hierarchy. Dashed lines show nonlinear, hypertext links.

FIG. 24.1

A sample Help
file structure for
an order entry
and billing
application.

In this example, the Commands Menu Index and Procedures Index are
secondary indexes that list the topics within each category and provide
quick access to a specific topic. Individual topics in different categories, however, may be related, so they are joined by dashed lines in
figure 24.1. The dashed lines do not follow the usual top-to-bottom sequence in a category of related topics. You can provide hot spots to
create cross-category jumps, or use common keywords that give the
user quick access to a related topic in another category.

All Help files have an entry point, usually called a *Help Index*, from
which you select the Help category you want. In some cases, selecting a
category, such as Commands, leads to another Help window that enables you to access commands through the main menu. You choose the
command for which you need Help, and a window appears explaining
the command. You make choices in Index windows and receive Help,
textual or graphic, in topic windows.

If you plan to create a number of related applications, you may want to
create individual Help files for each category or for a particular category that is the same for all the applications. As an example, if you are
writing a number of database front ends for your firm, the glossary
portion of the Help file may be the same for all applications. You therefore can create the glossary as a separate .RTF file and then compile it
with other .RTF files written specifically for the particular applications.
The project file for the Help compiler, described in this chapter's section "Creating the Project File," can include as many .RTF Help files as
you want to include in the compiled WinHelp .HLP file.

Creating the Text for Help Files

As mentioned at the beginning of this chapter, you must create Windows Help files in a word processing application that exports files in Rich Text Format (.RTF) and is capable of creating hidden text. Alternatively, you can manually add the required .RTF control words and symbols to unformatted text with a conventional text editor such as Windows Notepad, but this process is extremely laborious. Word for Windows, Ami Pro, and WordPerfect for Windows provide .RTF export capability. If you have the Professional Toolkit for Visual Basic 1.0, using Word for Windows is especially recommended because the Toolkit includes the VBHELP.DOT template that can assist you with Help file generation (see "Using the Visual Basic VBHELP.DOT Template," later in this chapter). Note that the Professional Toolkit for Visual Basic 1.0 has HC.EXE, not HC31.EXE; you need to upgrade to the Professional Edition of Version 2.0 to obtain HC31.EXE.

In the following paragraphs, you take a look at the Rich Text Format needed for Help files and familiarizing yourself with many of the common codes used in a Help file. Then you learn how to create Help files by using a commercial Help authoring system and by building the Help file manually.

Taking a Brief Look at the Rich Text Format

.RTF (Rich Text Format) is a Microsoft Corporation standard for Interprocess Communication (IPC) transfer of formatted text and graphics. .RTF is a valid Windows Clipboard format for many applications. You can use .RTF files for IPC transfers between Windows applications and DOS, OS/2, or Apple Macintosh applications created by Microsoft and many other software publishers.

An .RTF file consists of control words, symbols, and groups combined with unformatted text in ANSI (Windows), PC-8 (used by Hewlett-Packard laser printers), Macintosh, or IBM PC character sets. An .RTF file of the first two sentences of the preceding paragraph (less most of the header section added by Word for Windows) appears as

```
\paperw12240\paperh31680\margl1800\margr1800\margt1440
\margb1440\gutter0\deftab360\widowctrl\ftnbj{\*\templa
te F:\\WINWORD2\\QUE_BOOK.DOT}\sectd \linex0\endnhere
\pard\plain \qj\fi504\sa120\keep \f4\fs21\lang1033
```

```
.RTF (Rich Text Format) is a Microsoft Corporation standard
for Interprocess Communication (IPC) transfer of for matted
text and graphics. .RTF is a valid Windows Clipboard format
for many applications.\par
```

A backslash character precedes .RTF control words and symbols, which are used to indicate text formatting. Double backslashes are used to include a backslash in the text. The original version of *Microsoft Word for Windows Technical Reference*, published by Microsoft Press to accompany Word for Windows 1+ versions, includes a complete description of the format of .RTF files. .RTF is not discussed in *Using WordBasic*, a manual offered by Microsoft with the purchase of Word for Windows 2+. Fortunately, you do not need a full understanding of .RTF syntax to write Windows Help files.

Examining the Basic Elements of Help Files

Windows Help files consist of a combination of formatted text, double-underlined hot spots that specify hypertext jumps, single-underlined hot spots for pop-up windows, footnote symbols and text, and hidden text. Footnote symbols serve as codes to tell HC31.EXE how to use the information included in the footnotes and hidden text. Context strings (hidden text used to identify hot spots), footnote symbols, and footnote text do not appear in the Help window viewed by the user. Table 24.1 lists common footnote codes.

Table 24.1. Common Footnote Codes Used in .RTF Help Documents		
Help Element	**Footnote Code**	**Description**
Context string	#	Identifies each topic in a Help file. Context strings are optional and are used by WinHelp to find a specific topic when the user initiates a jump to it.
Topic title	$	Displays topics in the dialog boxes for the Search and History buttons, as well as those topics marked by using the Bookmark menu.
Keyword	K	Provides entries for lists that appear in the Search dialog box, enabling the user to jump to any topic that contains the keyword.

Help Element	Footnote Code	Description
Browse sequence	+	Displays groups of topics in a predetermined sequence. These topics are accessed in sequence by the << and >> buttons of the Help menu.

Each of the commonly used .RTF codes for WinHelp files is described in table 24.2. Lowercase codes shown in bold type are .RTF formatting instructions (\v stands for hidden text, for example).

Table 24.2. Common .RTF Codes Used in .RTF Help Documents

Help Element	.RTF Code	Description
Jump	**uldb** *JumpText* **v** *TopicName*	Links related topics in a manner similar to hypertext. When the user clicks a coded word or bit map, *JumpText*, WinHelp moves to *TopicName*. You identify a jump by double-under-lining the text. With HC31.EXE, users can jump to topics in different files.
Pop-up window topic	**ul** *JumpText* **v** *TopicName*	Displays the text identified by *TopicName* in a modal dialog box when the user clicks a single-underlined hot spot, *JumpText,* in the Help file.
16-color bit-map reference	bmc *picture.ext*	Inserts a 16-color bit map (BMP or DIB) or meta-file (WMF) image, *picture.ext*, into a Help file. Images are positioned as if they were characters or may be formatted with optional parameters. You also may copy a bit map to the Clipboard with CopyBmp if the bit map is identified as a hot spot. (If you are using Word for Windows,

continues

Table 24.2. Continued

Help Element	.RTF Code	Description
		you can simply use **Insert Picture** to insert the bit map in the text.)
Nonscrolling region	**\keepn**	Keeps a region containing text immediately below the menu bar from scrolling with the balance of the text when the scroll bar is used.
Nonwrapping text	**\keep**	(Keep with next formatting.) Prevents an area of the screen from wrapping if the user reduces the width of the Help window. This option is frequently used with tabular information.
Embedded window	ew ...	Enables the display of 256-color bit maps or animation sequences and can play sound files.

Depending on the Windows word processing program (and its version) that you use, the program usually inserts most or all of the preceding codes when you save a file as an .RTF file. You can use many other codes in addition to those shown in tables 24.1 and 24.2 when authoring WinHelp files, but the use of special-purpose codes is beyond the scope of this book. The documentation accompanying the Help compiler explains the use of special-purpose codes not listed here.

Using Commercial Help Authoring Systems To Create Help Files

You can speed up the process of creating Help files by using a commercial Help authoring system. One example is RoboHelp, which is offered by Blue Sky Software Corp. of La Jolla, California. Specifically designed for use with Word for Windows 2+, RoboHelp uses a sophisticated template, ROBOHELP.DOT, and includes the additional files required to automate the Help file-creation process. The Professional Toolkit for Visual Basic 1.0 contains another Word for Windows template, VBHELP.DOT. In the following sections, you learn how to use these templates to Help you create your Help files.

Using the RoboHelp Template

The main advantage of using a commercial Help authoring system is that you can create WinHelp files quickly. RoboHelp also does most of the housekeeping for you, such as adding footnotes and assigning Help context strings, which can save up to 50 percent of the time needed to create a Help file.

To create a Help file with RoboHelp, follow these steps:

1. Launch Word for Windows, open the File menu, and choose New. The Use Template dialog box appears.

2. Choose the ROBOHELP template from the Word 5 Use Template list box; then choose OK or press Enter. The Save File As dialog box appears.

3. Save the file with the name that you want to give your Help file— **NWIND**, for example. This step establishes the name of your Help file as a variable in the RoboHelp macro.

   RoboHelp automatically inserts the Help Index topic for you when you start a new Help file and opens its Help Index window.

4. Click RoboHelp's Topic button to add a topic to the Help Index window. RoboHelp displays an Insert New Help Topic dialog box.

5. Click the Advanced >> button to display additional data about the topic in the New Help Topic dialog box.

6. Enter the topic title, such as **Commands**, in the Topic Title text box. RoboHelp automatically adds the same title to the Search Word(s) text box, as shown in figure 24.2. You can add more search words if you prefer; separate each word from the preceding word with a semicolon. Search words appear in the list box in the Search dialog box that appears when you choose Search from the Help menu.

   RoboHelp creates entries in the Context String, Browse Sequence, and Build Tag text boxes. The browse-sequence numbers are incremented by 5 each time you add a topic. Choose OK, and RoboHelp adds a hard page break and the new topic title, Commands, to a new page.

FIG. 24.2

RoboHelp's dialog box for adding a new Help topic.

7. Position the caret on the line in the Help Index page where you want to create the hot spot for the new topic (Commands, in this example). Click the Jump button to create a hypertext link between the hot spot and the topic. The Create New Hypertext Jump to Help Topic dialog box appears.

8. In the Click Text text box, enter the text that you want the user to click (or select with the Tab key) to display the Help window for the Help topic; **Commands** is a good choice for this example. Choose the context string (IDH_Commands, in this example) from the Jump To list box. (The IDH_ prefix is an abbreviation for Index Help.) Your completed Create New Hypertext Jump to Help Topic dialog box appears as shown in figure 24.3.

You can create as many levels in your Help file structure as you want by repeating this step to add new subtopics to the main topic (Commands, in this example). Figure 24.4, for example, shows the beginning of a Help file with a three-level hierarchy—index, category, and topic—based on the structure of figure 24.1 at the beginning of this chapter. The footnotes that RoboHelp creates for you are shown in the Footnotes pane of figure 24.4. The footnote that uses the asterisk (*) symbol is called the *build tag*, which enables you to compile the Help file with or without topics identified by the build tag. The use of build tags is optional.

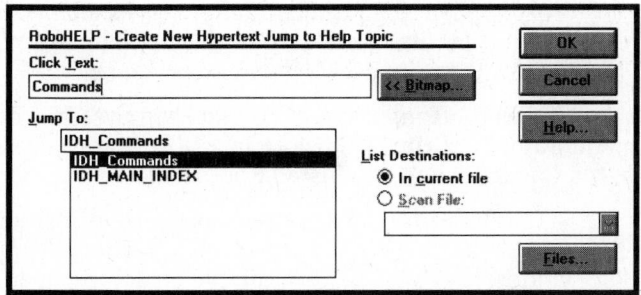

FIG. 24.3

The Create New
Hypertext Jump
to Help Topic
dialog box.

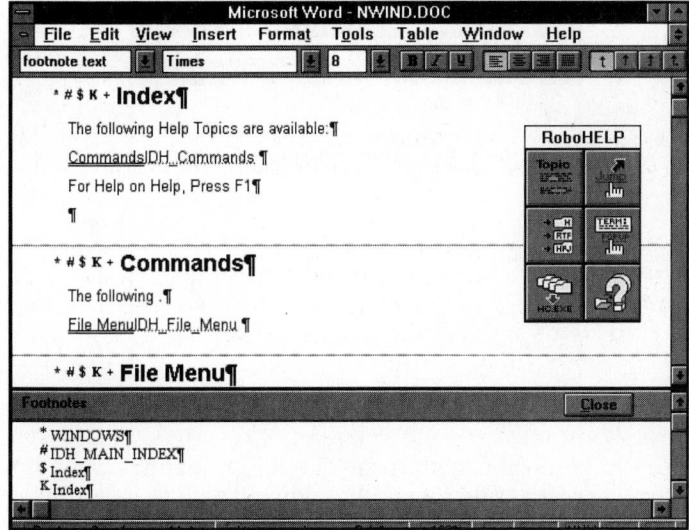

FIG. 24.4

The beginning
of a Help file
in Word for
Windows 2+.

9. Add the Help text to your topic. You can add bit-map graphics
   files, drawings created in Microsoft Draw, or other objects created
   by OLE servers by choosing **P**icture or **O**bject from Word's **I**nsert
   menu and then selecting the appropriate graphics file or object.

10. When you have created the basic structure of your Help system,
    choose Save and **G**enerate Code from Word's **F**ile menu. RoboHelp
    adds several of its own menu items to Word's **F**ile, **E**dit, **V**iew,
    Insert, and **T**ools menus.

11. Enter a descriptive title, such as **Northwind Traders Help System**,
    when RoboHelp requests a title for the title bar of your Help
    windows.

RoboHelp has created NWIND.RTF, the file that serves as the source code for your NWIND.HLP file. To use HC31.EXE to compile NWIND.RTF to NWIND.HLP, follow these steps:

1. Click the HC.EXE button, or choose **M**ake Help System from the **F**ile menu. RoboHelp runs HC31.EXE in a DOS window from a PIF file that is created when you install RoboHelp.

2. Click the Run Help button, or choose **R**un the Help System from the **F**ile menu. Your new WinHelp file appears. Figure 24.5 shows the Help window created from the sample structure given in figure 24.1.

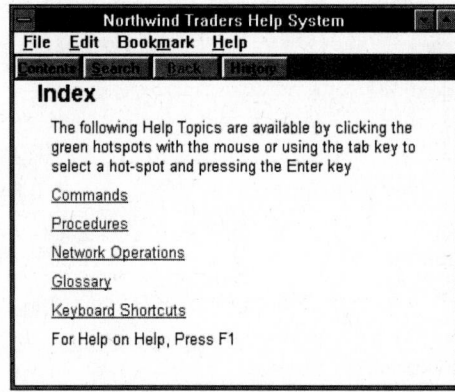

FIG. 24.5

A Help window created with the aid of RoboHelp.

From this Help file, you can click the green Commands hot spot to display the topic, such as File Menu, that you entered at lower levels in the hierarchy.

RoboHelp takes most of the drudgery out of creating a WinHelp file, but the organization and contents of the file are up to you. RoboHelp does not include HC31.EXE, so you need to purchase it or a compiler that includes it, such as Visual Basic 2.0.

Using the Visual Basic VBHELP.DOT Template

The Professional Toolkit for Visual Basic 1.0 includes HC.EXE for Windows 3.0 and a Word for Windows template called VBHELP.DOT that supplies styles and macros to aid in creating WinHelp files. VBHELP.DOT adds menu commands for creating new topics but is not as fully automated as RoboHelp. You need to enter your own topic hot spots and context ID strings when you use VBHELP.DOT.

To use VBHELP.DOT, first copy it to the directory in which WINWORD.EXE is located. Then, as in step 2 of the preceding series of steps, assign VBHELP.DOT as the template when you open a new Help file. You add topics to the document by choosing **T**opic from the **I**nsert menu and then entering data in the Title, ContextID, and Browse text boxes of the Insert Topic dialog box shown in figure 24.6. In the Place New Topic box in the lower-left corner, you can choose to add new topics at the location of the insertion point (caret) or at the end of the file.

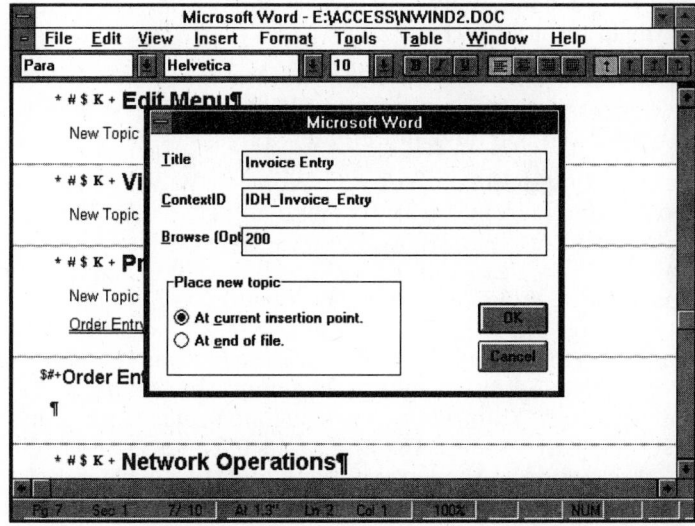

FIG. 24.6

VBHELP.DOT's dialog box for adding a new topic.

You can see the other macro functions that VBHELP.DOT provides by choosing **M**acro from Word's **T**ools menu, choosing **E**dit, and choosing a macro name to edit. Word for Windows' WordBasic macro-editing window appears. The comments at the beginning of the file include a description of the function of the macro.

Two of the VBHELP.DOT menu macros perform utility functions. **Call Help** runs the CallHelp Visual Basic application from Word for Windows when CALLHELP.EXE is in the current directory or on your path. Call Help is a Visual Basic application that you can use to test your Help file after you compile it. **HC Test** brings up a dialog box that enables you to choose to create a test WinHelp file, automatically named TEST.HLP, from a single topic or the entire Help file that you are creating. The HC macro runs HC.EXE to compile TEST.HLP and then runs the WinHelp engine to display it. TEST.HPJ must be in the current directory or on your path in order for the HC Test macro to operate properly. If you are familiar with WordBasic macro programming, you can edit the macro code to add more appropriate paths for the files.

Creating Help Text Files Manually

Using RoboHelp or the VBHELP.DOT template to write WinHelp files is convenient but not necessary. You can create your text file with any Windows word processor that creates .RTF files, with any template, and in any format you want. The rules for inserting footnotes and codes, designating hot spots, and separating individual topics with page breaks are described in the steps that follow.

To create a Help file manually, using Word for Windows 2.0 and beginning with the index, follow these steps:

1. Choose New from Word for Windows' File menu and choose the template you want to use for your Help file text. Choose the Normal template if you have not created a template for Help files.

   When creating Help text files with Word for Windows 2.0, choose Options from the Tools menu and click the View button. Choose the Hidden Text, Paragraph Marks, Tabs, Line Breaks and Fonts as Printed, and Table Grid lines check boxes to mark them. You need to view hidden text entries, and the other settings aid you in formatting the text. Choose Page Setup from the Format menu and then click the Size and Orientation option button. Set the height to 22 inches, the maximum allowed by Word. You then can create long topics without inserting soft page breaks. Space paragraphs 0.5 lines apart by choosing Paragraph from the Format menu and then clicking Before or After so that .5 appears in the text box. Using half a line instead of inserting a full line between paragraphs not only saves space in the screen, but also improves readability.

2. Choose Footnote from the Insert menu. The Footnote dialog box appears.

3. In the Custom Footnote Mark text box, type $, the symbol used to identify the title of the topic (see fig. 24.7). The purpose of the footnote symbols is described in table 24.1, in the earlier section, "Examining the Basic Elements of Help Files."

FIG. 24.7

The Word for Windows Footnote dialog box.

Footnote	
○ Auto-Numbered Footnote	OK
◉ Custom Footnote Mark: $	Cancel
	Options...

4. The footnote pane opens with the caret positioned after the $ footnote symbol. Enter the title of the topic, **Index**.

5. Repeat steps 2 through 4, substituting the # footnote symbol in the Custom Footnote Mark text box to indicate a context string and then entering the context string **IDH_MAIN_INDEX**. (The context strings used in this example follow RoboHelp conventions; IDH is an abbreviation for Index Help.)

6. Repeat steps 2 through 4, substituting the **K** footnote symbol that denotes members of the keywords list. Then enter **Index;Help;** as the footnote text.

7. Repeat steps 2 through 4 again, entering the + footnote symbol and then a browse-sequence number in the footnote pane. Enter a number with a low value for the index, such as **000005**. The leading zeroes, used by RoboHelp, are optional. You can precede the browse-sequence number with a Help file name and a colon, as in NWIND:000005, to identify the .RTF file if you are using more than one file.

8. Enter the text for your Help window. Begin with the title, **Index**, and then enter the text that explains how to use the Help index. Enter the names of each topic to which you want to create hot-spot jumps, each on a separate line, but do not apply special formatting to these names yet.

9. Each topic that comprises an individual window in a Help text file needs to be separated from the next topic by a hard page break. When you have completed the text portion of your Help Index window, press Ctrl+Enter (or choose **B**reak from the **I**nsert menu, and then choose **P**age Break). The hard page break causes the footnote markers in the text ($, #, K, and +) to be associated only with this, the index topic. Soft page breaks do not divide topics. Figure 24.8 shows an example of how your Help window might look.

10. Create the additional category index and topic Help windows that you need by repeating steps 2 through 9, substituting body and footnote text appropriate to the topic. When you are writing Help files manually, you first create the topic text and then add the formatting and context ID strings to create the hypertext links between the topics.

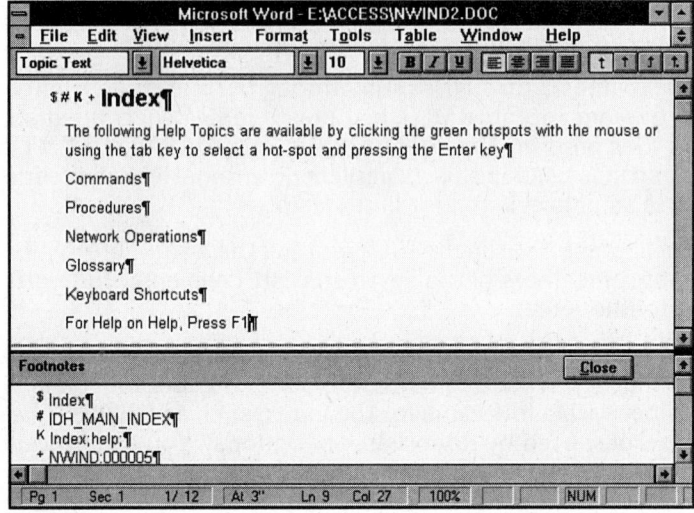

FIG. 24.8

A Help topic page prior to applying formatting.

Now you need to create the hypertext links to the topic names that you added for each category in step 8 of the preceding example. To create hot spots and the links, follow these steps:

1. Add the context ID string of the topic to which you want to link immediately after the name of the topic in the text of the index page. As an example, type **CommandsIDH_Commands**, as your first entry in which Commands is the hot spot and IDH_Commands is the context string.

2. Select (highlight) the name of the topic—Commands, for example—and press Ctrl+D to add the double-underline attribute.

3. Select the context ID string and press Ctrl+H to make the context ID string hidden text.

4. Repeat steps 1 through 3 for each of the names of the topics for which you want jumps. When you complete your entries for the Index topic, the index page appears as shown in figure 24.9.

The double-underlined text shown in figure 24.9 indicates a hot-spot jump to the topic identified by the context ID that follows, formatted as hidden text. The hot spot appears in green underlined type when you execute the Help file. Hidden text does not display. The footnote text contains the indexing information that HC31.EXE uses to create the required hypertext links, browse sequences, and keyword lists that the user can search.

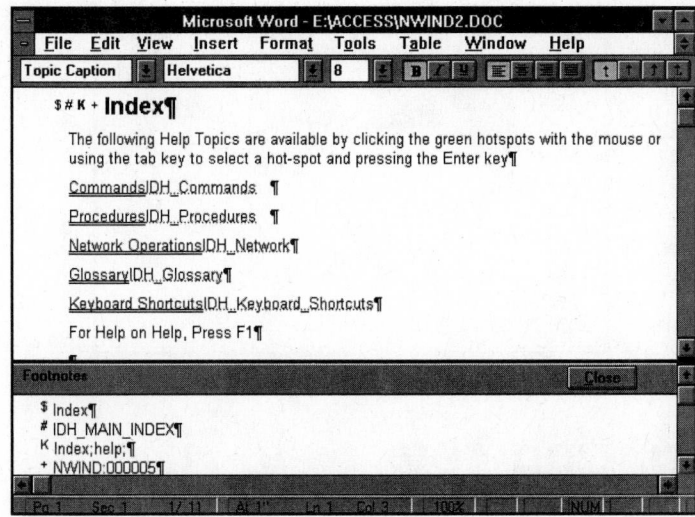

FIG. 24.9

The Help index
page after hot
spots have been
formatted.

You can substitute a pop-up window for a hypertext jump by formatting
a word with the single-underline attribute and then adding a hidden-
text context string immediately after the word. Single-underlined text
appears in the Help window, green and without the underline. After you
(or the users for whom you have created the Help file) click this type of
hot spot, the topic appears in a modal window. Clicking the pop-up
window makes it disappear.

When you have completed your entries to the point where you want to
test the Help file with your application, follow these steps:

1. Choose **S**ave from Word for Windows' **F**ile menu to save your Help
   file in Word format.

2. Choose Save File **As** from the **F**ile menu.

3. Choose Rich Text Format from the Save File as Type drop-down
   list box.

4. Give your file the same name as the database file with which it is
   to be used, **NWIND** for example, and add the .RTF extension.

   The Save As dialog box appears, as shown in figure 24.10.

5. Choose OK to save your file.

Creating the Help project file and running HC31.EXE to compile your
WinHelp file, the next two tasks needed to complete the Help file-
creation process, are covered in "Compiling Your Help Files," later in
this chapter.

FIG. 24.10

The Save As dialog box for a Rich Text Format text file.

Enhancing Your Help Files

You can add bit-map images, vector-based drawings, sound, and even video clips to your .RTF Help files. Such embellishments can make your WinHelp windows more attractive and interesting for users. WinHelp macros enable you to extend the capabilities of your WinHelp files with external programs stored in Windows dynamic link libraries (DLLs). The following sections show you how to use Word for Windows 2.0 and other Windows applications to enhance your WinHelp system.

Adding Illustrations to Your Help Files

You can use the (**bmc** *BitmapName*) tab, formatted as hidden text, to incorporate a bit map into your Help file by reference. Inserting a bit map directly into your Word for Windows Help document, however, is a much simpler process. If you have a commercial screen capture application, such as Inner Media's Collage Plus or Horizon Technologies' SnagIt, you can use it to create .BMP files of your application's windows that you then can insert into Help topic windows. Otherwise, you can use Windows Paintbrush to create the .BMP illustrations. First you need to retrieve the image you want to use. Follow these steps:

1. Set up the application that includes the image you want and display the image. If the window is less than one full screen, minimize any windows that appear underneath it to provide a neutral gray background, and position the window you want to copy at the upper left corner of the display.

2. Press the PrtSc key to copy the entire display to the Clipboard.

With the image in your Clipboard, you're ready to use Paintbrush to edit the image and add it to your Help file. Follow these steps:

1. Launch Windows Paintbrush, and choose **P**aste from the **E**dit menu to copy the Clipboard image to Paintbrush's editing window. A dashed line surrounds the image, indicating that the entire image is selected.

2. Click anywhere within the screen image, and while holding down the left mouse button, drag the image diagonally downward about one-fourth inch to expose a blank margin at the top and left edges of the image.

3. Click the blank margin to deselect the image. The dashed selection lines disappear.

4. Using the Scissors tool with the rectangular box, drag a selection box around the area you want to incorporate in the illustration, as shown in figure 24.11. Because enclosing precisely the area you want to save is difficult, add a margin to be edited (cropped) later.

5. Choose C**o**py To from the **E**dit menu to save your bit map in a file. The Copy To dialog box appears.

6. In the File Name text box, enter the path to your Help file and the file name for the bit map (with the extension .BMP), as shown in figure 24.12. Do not use the **S**ave or Save **A**s commands of the **F**ile menu; these commands save the entire image.

7. Choose **N**ew from the **F**ile menu and do not save the existing image.

FIG. 24.11

Selecting the bit-map image to copy to a file.

8. Choose Paste From from the Edit menu and enter the path and file name you used in step 6. You paste the image, rather than open the file, so that you can position the image where you want it in Paintbrush's editing window.

9. Edit the image as required. You can use Paintbrush's line and text tools to add callouts or to modify the image.

10. When you are satisfied with the illustration, use the Scissors tool to enclose the area you want to save. Choose Copy To from the Edit menu. In the Copy To dialog box, enter the path to your Help file and the file name for the bit map (with the extension .BMP).

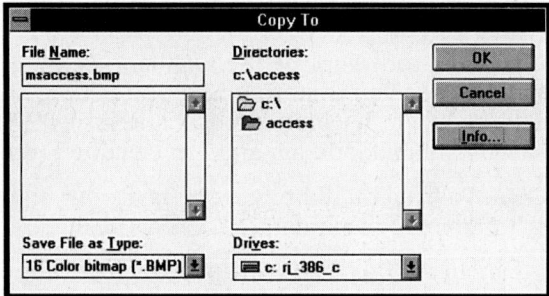

FIG. 24.12

Copying the selected bit-map image to a 16-color .BMP file.

To add the bit-map image to your Help file, open the Help file in Word for Windows and position the caret where you want to place the bit map. Choose Picture from the Insert menu and double-click the name of your bit-map file. Figure 24.13 shows an example of a Help Page file with a bit-map icon for Access added at the top of the window.

When you compile your WinHelp file with HC31.EXE (see "Using the Help Compiler," later in this chapter), the image you inserted appears as shown in figure 24.14.

You also can insert drawings in the form of Windows meta files. If you have Microsoft Draw and HC31.EXE, you can import the bit-map file, add callouts or other graphic elements to it, and embed the resulting .WMF file in your text or add a {**bmp** ... } reference to it.

For Related Information:

◄◄ "Using Microsoft Draw To Embed Vector Images," p. 567.

◄◄ "Editing the Logo with Windows Paintbrush," p. 595.

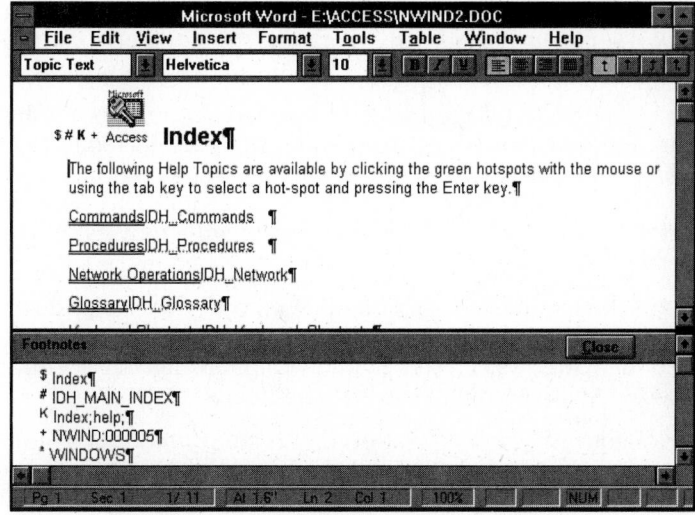

FIG. 24.13

The Help topic page with a bit-map icon added.

FIG. 24.14

The WinHelp window displaying the Access icon.

Incorporating Multimedia Objects in Help Files

Using Word for Windows 2+ as an OLE client makes adding multimedia objects to your Help file a simple process. A few of the objects you can embed in your Word for Windows file to enhance your WinHelp file follow:

■ Waveform audio narration in .WAV files using Sound Recorder as the OLE server.

- MIDI music and sound effects in .MID files with the Media Player 2.0 OLE server included with Microsoft's new Video for Windows application.

- Animated images created with Macromedia's Director application on an Apple Macintosh computer and then converted to DOS-format .MMM files with the CONVERT.EXE application supplied with Microsoft's Multimedia Development Kit (MDK). You use Media Player 2.0 to embed .MMM (multimedia movies) in your Word for Windows file.

- Video clips created with Video for Windows' VidCap (video capture) and VidEdit (video editing) applications (components of Video for Windows) in .AVI (audio-video interleaved) format and embedded with Media Player 2.0.

Each user of your Access application that includes multimedia objects needs a copy of the OLE server used to embed the object in the Help file and a Windows-compatible audio adapter card (except for multimedia movie files). Users with Windows 3.1 and an audio adapter card can play audio narration embedded with Sound Recorder because Sound Recorder is included with Windows 3.1. To play other types of multimedia objects, users need to substitute Media Player 2.0 for the original version of Media Player supplied with Windows 3.1. A Word for Windows file with three embedded multimedia objects is shown in figure 24.15.

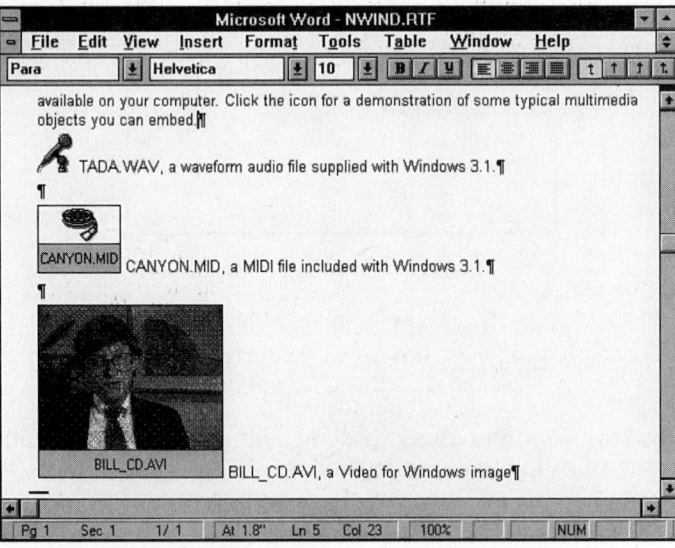

A WinHelp .RTF file with embedded waveform audio, MIDI music, and Video for Windows multimedia objects.

Word for Windows supplies all of the required .RTF codes necessary to play the multimedia objects in the compiled .HLP file. Embedding long .WAV files and even short .AVI files significantly increases the size of your WinHelp .HLP file. Embedding 10 seconds of 8-bit mono .WAV audio narration recorded at 11.025 kHz, as an example, adds about 110K to the file. A 10-second video clip in .AVI format may cause the file to grow by as much as 1.5M. Multimedia movie and MIDI files are much smaller in size (about 30K and 2K for 10 seconds of playing time, respectively), so these types of files are more practical for WinHelp files that are stored on fixed disks, rather than CD-ROMs.

Using WinHelp Macros

Another way to enhance your Help files involves using macros. The WinHelp engine includes its own macro language. You can use WinHelp macros to add or remove buttons and menu items, change the functions of buttons and menu items, and execute functions contained within external *dynamic link libraries* (DLLs). You can execute a WinHelp macro when a Help file is first opened; when the user displays a particular topic in the Help file; or when the user clicks a button, menu item, or hot spot containing a macro. The general .RTF syntax for executing a WinHelp macro follows:

```
{\uldb \{hot-spot text\}}{\v !macroname}
```

In Word for Windows, you double-underline the text constituting the hot spot and then follow it with a hidden-text exclamation point (bang) and the macro name, also in hidden text. When you save the file in .RTF format, Word creates the .RTF syntax shown in the example preceding this paragraph. Space limitations preclude listing the WinHelp macros and their syntax here. Full descriptions are provided in the WinHelp documentation supplied with HC31.EXE.

Creating a Help File-Tracking Database

When you create a Help file having any degree of complexity, you need to keep track of the files and topics that comprise the Help file, as well as the last edit date, who wrote the text, and the text's status. You can do so with a Help file-tracking database, which you can create with Access. If you are an expert WordBasic programmer, you can write a Word for Windows macro that updates the Access database using DDE when you create or edit WinHelp files.

You can create a relational structure for the Help tracking database that includes separate tables for Help files, categories of Help topics, and the Help topics themselves. Relations are established between the file names and context ID values, as shown in the query of figure 24.16.

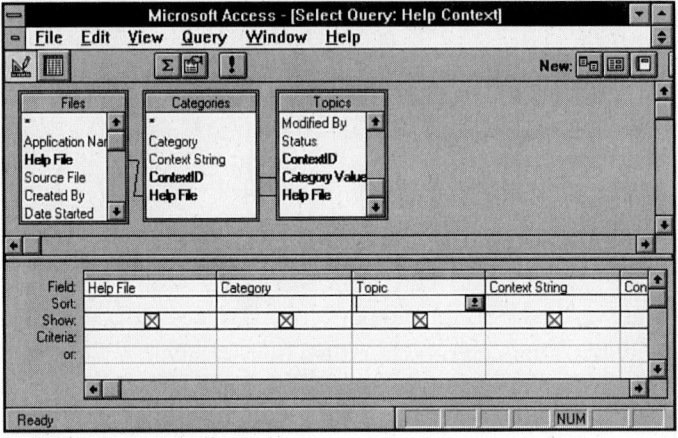

FIG. 24.16

An Access query for displaying data in a relational Help tracking database.

When you run the query of figure 24.16, the Help file name, topic category, topic title, context string, and context ID number for each Help topic appear as shown in figure 24.17.

Help File	Category	Topic	Context String	ContextID
NWIND.HLP	Commands	New	IDHfile_new	110
NWIND.HLP	Commands	Open	IDHfile_open	120
NWIND.HLP	Commands	Close	IDHfile_close	130
NWIND.HLP	Commands	Exit	IDHfile_exit	140
NWIND.HLP	Procedures	Orders	IDHproc_orders	210
NWIND.HLP	Procedures	Invoices	IDHproc_invs	220
NWIND.HLP	Procedures	Customers	IDHproc_custs	230
NWIND.HLP	Network Operation	Logon	IDHnet_logon	310
NWIND.HLP	Network Operation	Logoff	IDHnet_logoff	320

FIG. 24.17

The result table of the query of figure 24.16.

If you plan to update the table automatically, using a Word for Windows macro to send data by DDE to Access, you may choose a simple flat file structure to make the data-transfer process simpler to code. The table should include, at the minimum, Category, Topic, Context String, and Context ID fields. You can choose the Context String or Context ID field as the Primary Key field. Add a No Duplicates index to whichever of these two fields is not the primary key so that you do not duplicate values in the Context String or Context ID fields. You can choose to use a separate table for each Help file or to combine all of your Help files in a single table. If you choose the single-table approach, you need to add a File Name field and make File Name the first field of the primary key.

Making use of the browse buttons requires adding a Browse field to contain browse-sequence numbers. Browse-sequence numbers determine the sequence in which windows are displayed when you click the Browse Forward or Browse Backward buttons in the Help menu. Browse buttons are a standard feature of Windows 3.0 Help windows, but are optional in Version 3.1. Browse buttons seldom are used in Windows 3.1 applications because the Back, History, and Search menu choices serve a similar purpose. If you add the Browse field, use the Integer data type and format the field with leading zeros (use 000# or the like for the Format property) because browse-sequence numbers are sorted by the Help compiler by their ASCII character, not numeric, value.

You can add other optional fields to the table, such as an OLE field that contains a link to the page in your Word for Windows document for the record's topic. Creating an OLE link to the Help text file enables you to view and edit your Help topic content from within Access. To create an OLE link to the originating WinHelp document, follow these steps:

1. Add a field of the OLE Object data type to your Help table and give the field an appropriate name, such as **Content**.

2. Open Word for Windows, and select the contents of the page that comprise the topic by using the mouse or the Shift+Arrow keys.

3. Choose **C**opy from Word's **E**dit menu to copy the selected text and any graphics that are included in the selection to the Clipboard.

4. Activate Access and choose Paste **L**ink from Access's **E**dit Menu. The Paste Link dialog box appears.

5. Choose OK to create the link. Access enters `Word Document` in the OLE Object field of the selected record.

6. Repeat steps 2 through 5 for each topic record in your table.

When you double-click a data cell in your Content field that contains a Word Document link, Word for Windows appears with the designated page of your Help file in its window. If you use a form to enter or edit Help tracking records, add a bound object frame for the Content OLE field. The presentation of a Word for Windows Document is a large (64×64 pixel) icon. Double-clicking the Word icon displays the Word for Windows document. You do not need to manually update the linked data (with the **U**pdate Now command of the Word Document **O**bject choice of Access's **E**dit menu) because linked OLE objects that use icons as their presentation automatically display the latest version of the linked object.

Compiling Your Help Files

As you have learned in this chapter, Windows requires that you compile .RTF files to a specific format with the Microsoft Help compiler. If you want to use Word for Windows 2.0, incorporate tables in your Help files, or use the other new WinHelp 3.1 features described in the preceding sections, you must use a Help compiler that has a version number of 3.10 or higher. You can determine the version number by running the compiler without command-line parameters.

In the sections that follow, you learn how to create a Help project file, use the Help project file with the Help compiler, and understand error messages you may receive from the Help compiler.

Creating the Project File

Before you can create, using the Help compiler, a WinHelp.HLP file from your .RTF file, you need to create a project file. This file provides instructions that tell HC.EXE or HC31.EXE which files to compile and which indexes you want the Help compiler to create. Project files are similar in concept to the .MAK files of Visual Basic and C compilers.

The Help compiler uses a project file with the extension .HPJ, such as HELPFILE.HPJ. The compiled Help file has the same name as the project file, but with the extension HLP, as in HELPFILE.HLP. You create Help project files with a standard text editor such as Windows Notepad. The only entry *required* in the project file for a simple WinHelp file is the FILES section header, enclosed in square brackets and followed by the names of your .RTF files on separate lines, as in this example:

```
[FILES]
hlpfile1.rtf
hlpfile2.rtf
hlpfile3.rtf
```

You need to enter the full path to the files if you do not set the path with the ROOT= line in the [OPTIONS] section of your Help project file. The sections that you may include in your Help project file, and some of the common [OPTIONS] keywords used, are listed in table 24.3. Values shown for [OPTIONS] keywords in the table are those most commonly used in creating conventional WinHelp files. (You also can include comments in the Help project file by preceding each comment line with a semicolon.)

Table 24.3. Required and Optional Sections of a Help Project File

Section of File	Required?	Description
[OPTIONS]	No	Defines any options required to control the Help compilation process. Some of the more common options include the following:
OPTIONS Keywords		
ROOT=*d:\path*		Defines the path to your Help files.
INDEX=*ContextString*		Sets the context string for the index topic. Valid only when you're using HC.EXE (Windows 3.0).
CONTENTS=*ContextString*		Sets the context string for the index topic with the Windows 3.1 Help compiler, HC31.EXE.
TITLE=*AppName Help*		Sets the title for the Help file, which appears in the Help title bar.
ICON=*IconFile.ICO*		Sets the icon that is displayed when the Help window is minimized.
COMPRESS=0 I FALSE		Controls file compression. 0, or False, means do not compress files. 1, or True, compresses the file. Compressing .HLP files saves disk space at the expense of speed in displaying Help windows (due to the time required to decompress the file). HC31.EXE supports varying degrees of compression.

continues

Table 24.3. Continued		
Section of File	**Required?**	**Description**
	WARNING=3	Determines what errors are reported. 0 through 3 control the level of error reporting: 0 = no error reports; 1 = most severe warnings; 2 = intermediate warning level; and 3 = report all warnings.
	REPORT=1|ON	Determines whether progress reports of the compilation are provided. 1, or On, = Report progress of compile; 0, or Off, = no report.
[FILES]	Yes	Specifies the Help files included in the compilation.
[BUILD]	No	Specifies topics to include in or exclude from the compiled file.
[BUILDTAGS]	No	Names valid build tags, enabling the selection of topics to be compiled within a file.
[CONFIG]	No (HC.EXE) Yes (HC31.EXE, if DLLs are used)	Registers DLLs used with WinHelp macros in the Help file. Must include the BrowseButtons macro if they are to appear in the Help menu bar when you're using HC31.EXE. Browse buttons are added automatically by HC.EXE Version 3.0 if browse sequence numbers are detected in the Help file.
[BITMAPS]	No	Specifies bit-map files used in the compilation and not inserted into the text of your Help document. This element is

Section of File	Required?	Description
		required if you used the ROOT option to specify the path to the files.
[MAP]	No	Associates context strings with context ID numbers. You need a map section to use the Context ID property of Access forms, reports, and control objects.
[ALIAS]	No	Assigns more than one context string to a subject.
[WINDOWS]	No	Describes the main Help window and any secondary window types in the Help file. HC31.EXE enables you to define the size, placement, and color of Help windows.
[BAGGAGE]	No	Names any additional data files that are to be incorporated within the WinHelp file.

Although only the [FILES] section is needed for simple WinHelp files created with Word for Windows or another Windows words processor, adding the [OPTIONS] section and the following keyword entries to all .HPJ files is common practice:

```
[OPTIONS]
ROOT=c:\access
BUILD=WINDOWS
CONTENTS=IDH_Main_Index (substitute INDEX= for HC.EXE)
TITLE=Northwind Traders Help
WARNING=3
REPORT=1
```

The BUILD=WINDOWS line suppresses a noncritical error message that appears if you do not specify a BUILD name. (You can substitute any name you want for WINDOWS.) If you add BUILD=WINDOWS to the [OPTIONS] section to suppress the error message, you need to add another section with the following entries:

```
[BUILDTAGS]
WINDOWS
```

The COMPRESS keyword is optional because COMPRESS=0 is the default value. You change the ROOT, INDEX, and TITLE entries to values that are appropriate to the WinHelp file you are creating.

You need a [MAP] section in your .HPJ file to assign context ID numbers to context strings. The value you assign to Help category and topic windows is discussed in the section that follows. The other sections listed in table 24.3 seldom are required in WinHelp files created with Windows word processing applications.

Adding a [MAP] Section for Context ID Numbers

Applications, such as Access and Visual Basic 2.0, that enable you to add context-sensitive Help with Help File and Context ID properties require that you add a [MAP] section to your project file. This procedure will enable you to assign a context ID number to each of the Help windows that you want to associate with an object in the application you create. Using the Help File and Context ID properties of Access forms, reports, and control objects is the subject of a following section, "Linking Help Topics to Your Access Application."

The numbers that correspond to context strings can be arbitrary, but following a regular pattern is a good practice. As an example, the .RTF file used as a demonstration in the preceding sections has a Help Index window and four categories of Help windows, as shown in table 24.4. You assign the Index window a low value, such as 1 or 10. You give Help categories numbers such as 100 or 1000 so that you can assign numbers such as 110 to topics belonging to the 100 category. Using even hundreds to identify categories enables you to establish a four-level hierarchy: index, category, subcategory, and topic. Four levels is usually sufficient for even the most complex application. Adding a Help context ID number to the Help Index window lets you set the Help Index window as the context when there is no Help window applicable to the object you select in Access.

Using a Help file-tracking database, such as that shown in figure 24.17, can assist in preventing duplication of context ID numbers if you assign the Context ID field as the primary key or create a No Duplicates index on the Context ID field.

Table 24.4. Sample Context ID Numbers Assigned to Context Strings

Category Context String	Context ID	Topic Context String	Context ID
IDH_Main_Index	10		
IDH_Commands	100		
IDH_File	110	IDHfile_new	111
		IDHfile_open	113
		IDHfile_close	115
		IDHfile_exit	119
IDH_Edit	120	IDHedit_undo	121
IDH_Procedures	200	IDHproc_orders	211...219
		IDHproc_invs	221...229
		IDHproc_custs	231...239
IDH_Network	300	IDHnet_logon	311
		IDHnet_logoff	321
IDH_Keyboard_Shortcuts	400		

After you determine the context ID values for each of your Help windows, you add the [MAP] section to your Help project file and then add the context ID strings, a space (you also can use a Tab as a separator), and the corresponding context ID value, as in the following example:

```
[MAP]
IDH_Main_Index 10
IDH_Commands 100
IDH_Procedures 200
IDH_Network 300
IDH_Keyboard_Shortcuts     400
```

You can add the lines to complete the context ID assignment for Help topic windows under the category entries or in groups that follow the category assignments; the entries do not need to be in numerical sequence.

Figure 24.18 shows TEST.HPJ, the Help project file used to compile the test version of this chapter's examples, as the file appears in Windows Notepad.

Using the Help Compiler

You execute HC.EXE or HC31.EXE, a DOS application, from the DOS command line. The following lines show the two appropriate syntaxes:

```
HC HELPFILE[.HPJ]
```

```
HC31 HELPFILE[.HPJ]
```

The file name of the Help project file is a required parameter, but the .HPJ extension is optional and thus enclosed in brackets in the preceding examples.

The messages displayed by HC31.EXE when you compile the test WinHelp file with TEST.HPJ are shown in figure 24.19. The message lines describe each phase of the compilation process as it occurs. If you set Report = 0 or Report = Off, only the name of the project file appears when you run the Help compiler.

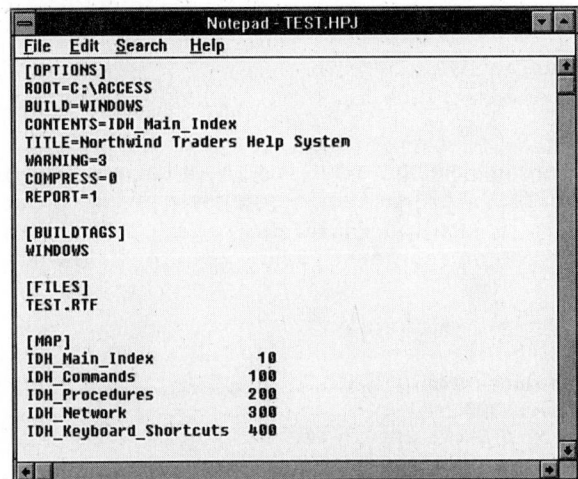

FIG. 24.18

The project file used to create the TEST.HLP file.

FIG. 24.19

Compiling TEST.HPJ, with HC31.EXE and the REPORT keyword set to 1.

```
Microsoft (R) Help Compiler Version 3.10.358
Copyright (c) Microsoft Corp 1990 - 1991. All rights reserved.
e:\access\test.HPJ

Compiling file E:\ACCESS\TEST.DOC...
Resolving browse sequences.
Resolving context strings.
Resolving keywords.
```

Creating a Program Information File (PIF) for the Help Compiler

When you are developing a Help file, create an HC.PIF program information file so that you can run the Help compiler in a DOS window.

Using a .PIF file and running the Help compiler in a window accelerates the inevitable edit-compile-test sequence when you are creating a new WinHelp file.

To create HC.PIF for HC.EXE or HC31.EXE, follow these steps:

1. Launch the PIF Editor from Program Manager's Accessories group. PIF Editor's dialog box appears.

2. Type **hc.exe** or **hc31.exe** in PIF Editor's Program Filename text box. Add the path to the directory in which the Help compiler is located if the directory is not on your path.

3. Type **HC3.0** or **HC3.1** in the Window Title text box, depending on the version of the Help compiler you are using.

4. Type the name of your project file, for example **test.hpj**, in the Optional Parameters text box.

5. Type the name of the directory where your Help project file is located, such as **c:\access**, in the Start-up Directory text box, if you are not using RoboHelp, VBHELP.DOT, or another Help file authoring application that supplies the name of the current Help project file as a DOS command line parameter.

6. Type **256** in the KB Required and **384** in the KB Desired text boxes of the Memory Requirements section. HC.EXE and HC31.EXE will run in 256K of DOS memory.

7. Click the Windowed option button in the Display Usage section and the Background check box of the Execution section. This second selection allows HC.EXE or HC31.EXE to run while you are using other Windows applications.

8. Click the Close Window on Exit check box if it is not marked. (If you want the DOS window to remain open to display error messages, do not mark the Close Window on Exit check box.) Your PIF Editor window (for HC31.EXE, not used with a Help file authoring application in this example) appears as shown in figure 24.20.

9. Choose Save **As** from the **File** menu. The Save As dialog box appears.

10. Type **hc.pif** in the File Name text box (regardless of the version of the Help compiler you are using); then choose OK. PIF Editor saves your file, and the dialog box closes.

PIF Editor - [Untitled]

File   Mode   Help

Program Filename:	hc31.exe
Window **T**itle:	HC3.1
Optional Parameters:	test.hpj
Start-up Directory:	c:\access

Video Memory: ● Text   ○ Low Graphics   ○ High Graphics

Memory Requirements: KB **R**equired `256`   KB **D**esired `384`

EMS Memory: KB R**e**quired `0`   KB L**i**mit `1024`

XMS Memory: KB Re**q**uired `0`   KB L**i**mit `1024`

Display Usage: ○ F**u**ll Screen   Execution: ☒ **B**ackground
　　　　　　　　　● **W**indowed   ☐ **E**xclusive

☒ **C**lose Window on Exit   [Advanced...]

Press F1 for Help on Close Window on Exit.

FIG. 24.20

The HC.PIF file
used to run
HC31.EXE in a
DOS window.

Now you need to add an icon to run HC.PIF in one of Program Manager's groups. If you have an Access program group, this is a logical place to add the icon for HC.PIF.

To add HC.PIF to your Access program group, follow these steps:

Access

1. Open the Access program group; or if the Access program group is open, click its window to activate it.

2. Choose **New** from Program Manager's **File** menu. The New Program Object dialog box appears.

3. Click the Program Item option button, if it is not selected, and then choose OK. The Program Item Properties dialog box appears.

4. Type **Help Compiler 3.1** (or **3.0** if you are using HC.EXE) in the Description text box, and type **hc.pif** in the Command Line text box.

5. Click the Change Icon button. A message box appears advising you that HC.PIF does not have an icon and that you can select one from those supplied with Program Manager.

6. Choose OK, and the Change Icon dialog box appears.

7. Use the horizontal scroll bar to expose the icon for the Swiss Army knife, or choose another likely candidate from the selection of icons. Click the icon to select it, and then choose OK. The Program Item Properties dialog box appears with the icon you selected.

8. Choose OK to add the icon for HC.PIF to your Access program group and close the Program Item Properties dialog box. Your Access program group appears as shown in figure 24.21.

9. Double-click the Help Compiler icon to test your HC.PIF file. If you added the BUILD= option and the [BUILDTAGS] section, your HC31.EXE DOS window appears as shown in figure 24.22.

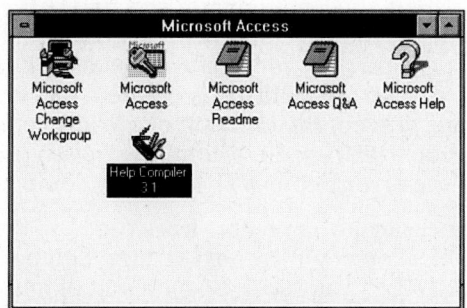

FIG. 24.21

The Microsoft Access program group with the Help compiler icon added.

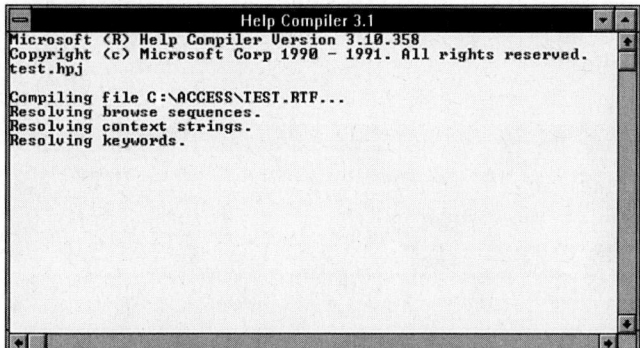

FIG. 24.22

HC31.EXE compiling TEST..RTF in a DOS window.

If you did not mark the Close Window on Exit check box when you created HC.PIF, remember to use Task Manager (press Ctrl+Esc) and close the inactive windows created by successive compilations of your Help file. In this case, Windows adds a new Help Compiler window each time you compile your Help file.

Examining Help Compiler Error Messages

HC.EXE and HC31.EXE display messages if errors are encountered in creating the WinHelp file. The sequence number of the topic in the file or the file name that contains the error is included in the error message. If your text file does not contain soft page breaks, the error number corresponds to the page number. Messages that begin with Error are fatal. Fatal errors are reported regardless of the value of the REPORT keyword, and no WinHelp file is created. Messages beginning with Warning do not prevent the creation of a WinHelp file, but the file may not operate properly. Most Help compiler messages are quite specific in identifying the error in the .RTF file being compiled.

The most typical messages you receive from the Help compiler are the result of typographical errors in context strings. Some of the warning messages (4098 and 4056) you receive as a result of misspelling context strings in the TEST.HPJ file are shown in figure 24.23. If you don't include the BUILD= assignment and the [BUILDTAGS] section, you receive a warning message (3178) that you can safely ignore. Messages prefaced with Warning do not prevent the Help compiler from creating a new .HLP file.

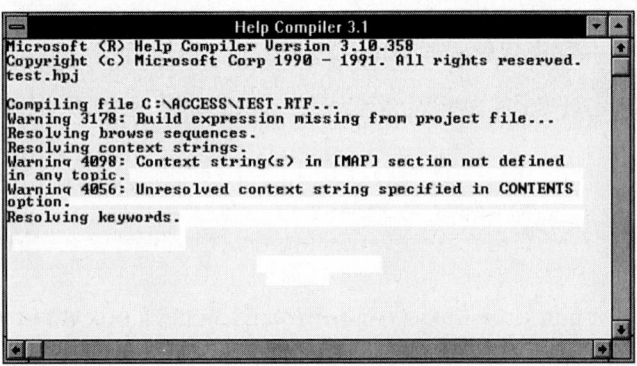

FIG. 24.23

Warning messages resulting from missing build information and errors in context string designation.

Errors result from the inability of the Help compiler to locate an .RTF file, omitting the [FILES] section, or errors of similar magnitude. Figure 24.24 shows the error messages resulting from typing the wrong file name in the [FILES] section of the .HPJ file. Messages prefaced with Error are fatal, and a new .HLP file is not created.

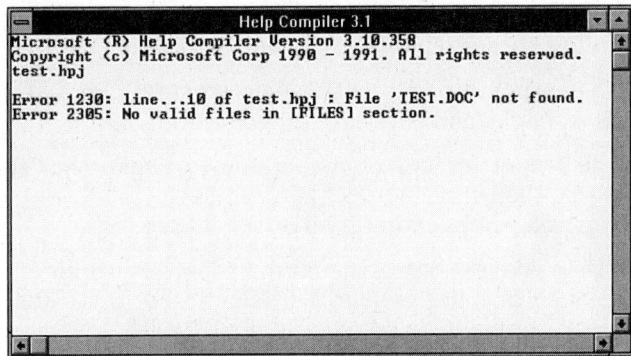

FIG. 24.24

Fatal errors that result from the inability of the Help compiler to find a required file.

Linking Help Topics to Your Access Application

You can create context-sensitive Help for your Access applications, similar to that used by Access's own Help system, by using one of two methods:

- You can use the Help File property of a form or report to designate the WinHelp file that is to be used. You then assign the context ID number as the value of the Context ID property of a control to display a specific Help window when the user selects the control and presses F1 for Help.

- You can use the WinHelp() function of the WinHelp engine in Access Basic procedures and functions. The Access Basic code you use to declare and then use WinHelp() in Access Basic is typical of the method for using any of the functions of Windows and third-party dynamic link libraries (DLLs).

The following sections give you more details about these two procedures.

Assigning Help Files and Context IDs to Access Objects

You can specify a Help file and a Help Context ID value to be used for a form or report, plus each control object on the form or report. The capability to assign a specific Help file to a form or report enables you to write smaller Help files that load faster.

To assign a Help file and a context ID number to a form and a control on a form, follow these steps:

1. Click the Form button of the Database window, choose Customers for this example, and click the Design button.

2. Click the Properties icon on the toolbar to display the Properties dialog box; then choose Select Form from the Edit menu to select the form as a whole, rather than one of its sections.

3. In the Help File text box of the Form Properties window that appears, enter the name of your WinHelp file. For this example, enter **TEST.HLP**, the Help file created by TEST.HPJ.

4. In the Help Context ID text box, enter the value of the Help Context ID of the Help topic that applies to the form as a whole. In this example, the value 200 is used for the Procedures category, so enter **200** in the Help Context ID text box. Your Form dialog box appears as shown in figure 24.25.

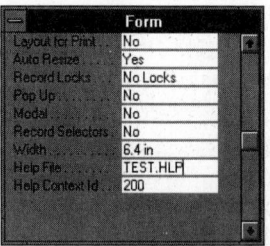

FIG. 24.25

The Form Properties window when assigning a Help file and context ID value.

5. Select the Customer ID bound text box and enter the context ID value for the Help topic that applies to the control object in the Help Context ID text box, as shown in figure 24.26. The value assigned to the Customer Data Entry topic is 255 in this example, so enter **255** in the Help Context ID text box. Properties dialog boxes for control objects do not have a Help File text box because the Help file applies to the form and all the control objects it contains.

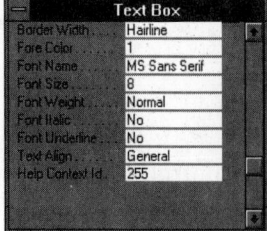

FIG. 24.26

The Text Box properties dialog box when you're assigning context ID value to a control object.

6. Click the Run Mode icon on the toolbar. The Customer ID field is selected when the Customers form loads. Press the F1 key, and the Customer Data Entry Help topic is displayed in the Northwind Traders Help System window. The Customer Data Entry topic has a single-underlined Customer ID topic that displays a pop-up window describing the Customer ID field, as shown in figure 24.27.

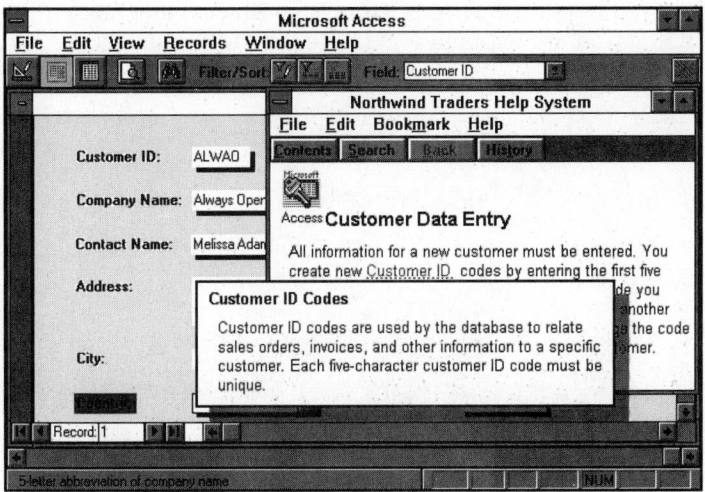

The Customer Data Entry topic of the TEST.HLP file.

You can create Help topics for each of the form's fields by assigning different Help Context ID values to each text box or other control object on the form. Alternatively, you can assign to control objects a Help Context ID value of 0 so that all control objects on the form display the Help topic with the Help Context ID value assigned to the form. If you set the Help Context ID value of the form to 0, Access displays its own Help window when you press the F1 key. The procedure described in the preceding steps also applies to reports.

Adding Calls to WinHelp in Access Basic Code

Assigning Help files to forms and reports and Help Context ID values to forms, reports, and control objects provides all the WinHelp capabilities you need for most applications. If you use Access Basic procedures that change how control objects behave, however, you may need to set the Help Context values in your Access Basic procedures.

To control the action of the WinHelp engine with Access Basic code, you call the WinHelp function when you need to change a Help file name or context ID value. The syntax of the WinHelp() function is as follows:

```
wHelpOK = WinHelp(hWnd, szHelpFile, wCommand, dwData)
```

In the preceding syntax, wHelpOK is an integer variable used to receive the return value of the WinHelp() function. The arguments of the WinHelp function are explained in the following sections.

FROM HERE...

For Related Information:

◄◄ "Data Types and Database Objects in Access Basic," p. 928.

►► "Naming Conventions for Access Objects," p. 1117.

Declaring Windows Functions in Access Basic

You call Windows functions in the same manner that you call Access Basic functions within Access Basic procedures. You need to inform Access Basic of your intention to use an external function, however, before using that function in your code. For this task, which is called *declaring a function prototype*, you use the Declare keyword. The syntax of the declaration statement follows:

```
Declare Function WinHelp Lib "User" (ByVal hWnd As
Integer, ByVal szHelpFile As String, ByVal wCommand
As Integer, dwData As Any) As Integer
```

The following list explains the statement's components:

- *ByVal:* A keyword that tells Access to transfer the data in the argument to the Windows function with a data type that is compatible with the C language in which Windows is written.

- *hWnd:* A Windows handle (code number or integer) to the window that is active when the Help function is called with the F1 key.

- *szHelpFile:* The name of the Help file, including the .HLP extension.

- *wCommand:* Table 24.5 lists and describes the wCommand constant values for you.

■ *dwData:* An argument whose data type depends on the value of the wCommand argument you choose; so the dwData argument is declared an As Any data type and is not prefixed with the ByVal keyword.

Table 24.5. WinHelp wCommand Constant Values and Their Actions

wCommand Constant	Value	Description
HELP_CONTEXT	1	Causes a specific Help topic, identified by a Long integer specified as the dwData argument, to be displayed.
HELP_QUIT	2	Notifies WinHelp that the specified Help file is no longer in use and can be closed. The dwData argument is ignored.
HELP_INDEX	3	Displays the index of the specified Help file, as designated by the author. The dwData argument is ignored.
HELP_HELPONHELP	4	Displays Help for using the WinHelp application itself. The dwData argument is ignored.
HELP_SETINDEX	5	Sets the context number specified by the dwData argument, a long integer, as the current index for the specified Help file.
HELP_KEY	257	Displays the first corresponding topic found in a search for the keyword specified by the dwData argument, in this case, As String (as a string variable).
HELP_MULTIKEY	513	Displays Help for a keyword found in an alternate keyword table. The dwData argument is a data structure containing the size of the string, the letter of the alternate table, and the keyword string.

Table 24.5 describes how the data type of the dwData argument changes with the value of wCommand. The dwData argument may be a long integer, a string, or a user-defined data type. Therefore, dwData is declared As Any and is passed by reference, not by value. When you want dwData to be ignored by WinHelp( ), you should set dwData to &H0 (null, rather than decimal 0) in your application.

The additions to the declarations section of your module to take advantage of all the features WinHelp( ) offers follow:

```
'Declare WinHelp function prototype
Declare Function WinHelp Lib "User" (ByVal hWnd As Integer,
ByVal szHelpFile As String, ByVal wCommand As Integer,
dwData As Any) As Integer

'Declare global constants for wCommand
Global Const HELP_CONTEXT = &H1            'Display a specified
topic
Global Const HELP_QUIT = &H2                       'Terminate WinHelp
for application
Global Const HELP_INDEX = &H3              'Display the Help
index
Global Const HELP_HELPONHELP = &H4                 'Display Help on
using Help
Global Const HELP_SETINDEX = &H5           'Set the current
Help index
Global Const HELP_KEY = &H101              'Display a topic for
keyword
Global Const HELP_MULTIKEY = &H201                 'Use the alternate
keyword table
Global Const KEY_F1 = &H70                         'Key code for Help
key

'Declare the multikey Help user-defined variable type
(structure)
Type MKH 'Multikey Help
  wSize            As Integer                 'Size of record
  sfKeylist        As String * 1              'Code letter for keylist
  sfKeyphrase      As String * 100            'String length is arbitrary
End Type

'Declare global Help variables
Global szHelpFile As String                   'Name of Help file
Global wCommand   As Integer                  'Help command
constant
Global dwHelpCtx As Long                      'Help context value when
numeric
Global szHelpKey As String                    'Help keyword for search
when string
Global wHelpOK    As Integer                  'Return value from WinHelp()
```

You do not need to add the constants to the declarations section of your module if you want to substitute the integer values shown in table 24.5 as the wCommand argument when you use the WinHelp( ) function. You must, however, declare the MKH (multikey Help) structure in your global module, declare a record variable, and assign values to its fields in your code if you plan to use more than one Help key in your application. A good practice is to make the name of your Help file a global variable.

Using the WinHelp API Function in Your Access Basic Code

Assign the name of your Help file to szHelpFile and default values to wCommand and dwHelpCtx in the declarations section of the module. These variables are made global so that they retain the last value set to all modules contained in your Access database. You set dwHelpCtx to the value of the context ID of the topic you want to display when the user requests Help at a particular point in your code. For example,

```
'Assign initial values to Help variables
szHelpFile = "TEST.HLP"
wCommand = HELP_CONTEXT
dwHelpCtx = 255
```

To display Help, create the function AppHelp( ) as shown in this example:

```
Function AppHelp()
   HelpOK = WinHelp(hWnd, szHelpFile, wCommand, ByVal
dwHelpCtx)
End Function
```

Add a Help button to your form or report and assign AppHelp( ) as the function to an AppHelp macro's Run Code action. When you click the Help button, WinHelp( ) displays the appropriate topic.

dwHelpCtx must be passed by value to dwData, but the prototype did not include ByVal, so you must include ByVal with the argument when you call the function. dwHelpCtx is set to &H0 when dwData is ignored.

If wCommand is set to the value of HELP_KEY for a keyword search, the syntax of the call to WinHelp( ) is as follows:

```
wCommand = HELP_KEY
dwHelpKey = "Invoice"
HelpOK = WinHelp(hWnd, szHelpFile, wCommand, ByVal szHelpKey)
```

If you want to use the Multikey command to select an entry in a multikey table, you need to create a variable of the MKH data type, *mkhMultiKey*, and assign values to each of its fields as shown in the following example:

```
Dim mkhMultiKey As MKH
mkhMultiKey.mkSize = Len(mkhMultiKey)
mkhMultiKey.mkKeyList = "A"
mkhMultiKey.szKeyphrase = "A Keyphrase in Keylist A"
```

Then call WinHelp( ) with the following code in your multikey Help function:

```
HelpOK = WinHelp(hWnd, szHelpFile, wCommand, mkhMultiKey)
```

You need an individual macro for each type of Help function you want to use.

Chapter Summary

This chapter showed you the basic steps for creating custom Heip files for your Access applications. You learned how to create the Help file document with a commercial Help file authoring application, and you saw an example of a simple Word for Windows 2+ template that streamlines housekeeping for Help files. The chapter explained how to create Help project files and use them with HC31.EXE, the Microsoft Help compiler, to compile documents in rich text format to WinHelp files. You also learned the methods for assigning custom Help files to forms and reports and setting the Help Context ID values for control objects to display specific topics. A description of how you use the WinHelp( ) function of Windows with your Access Basic code concluded the chapter.

The next and final chapter of this book is a look into the future of Microsoft Access and its present operating environment, Windows 3.1. The success of Windows 3+ has enabled Microsoft Corporation and other suppliers of mainstream Windows applications to devote an increasing amount of resources to the development of new and improved products for the Windows graphical user environment. Chapter 25 gives you a bit of insight as to how these future products will enhance your use of Microsoft Access.

Looking at Future Versions of Access and Windows

Access had a long period of development that began with the development of the ill-fated Omega database application in the late 1980s. One major cause of the repeated delays in bringing Access to the market was that Microsoft wanted to incorporate features to make Access easy to transport to future operating systems and to comply with new standards that were being finalized during the latter stages of Access's development cycle.

This book, which was written in late 1992, is based on several beta versions of Access. Windows 3.1 received excellent reviews in almost all computer-related periodicals, making a substantial contribution to Microsoft's profits. As this book entered the final phases of publication, Windows for Workgroups was being prepared for retail release. Because Windows NT was in the early beta-test stage and wasn't completely implemented, Microsoft said the company would not meet the original late 1992 retail release date. Meanwhile, several microcomputer industry leaders, anxious to blunt the impact of Windows NT, concluded a series of joint-venture and cooperative agreements that related to network operating systems. All these events are certain to alter the future direction of desktop computing.

This last chapter attempts to predict how more immediate changes in the desktop computing industry might affect Access and your use of Access on PCs and other platforms. The predictions in this chapter are drawn from a wide range of sources, including Microsoft press releases and background white papers, industry periodicals, newsletters, and just plain guesses. Only time will authenticate or debunk the predictions.

Size of the Windows Market

A view of the current and prospective size of the Windows market is useful when formulating opinions about future developments. Table 25.1 lists the estimated installed base for Windows as of the end of 1991 and forecasts 1992 sales for PC operating systems. This data was obtained from *The Win32 Application Programming Interface: An Overview*, published by Microsoft in January 1992. This report relies on several industry sources for its sales and market projections.

Table 25.1. Market Perspective for Windows (Microsoft Corp., January 1992)			
PC Operating System	**Installed Base as of 12/31/91, MM Units**	**Forecast Sales, 1992, MM Units**	**Percent of Market, 1/1/93**
Windows 3+	7.90	9.20	26.59%
DOS*	96.00	24.30	70.23%
UNIX	1.00	0.40	1.16%
OS/2	1.20	0.70	2.02%
Total PCs	106.10	34.60	

Does not include Windows 3+ operating under DOS

In this same publication, Microsoft stated, "Between May 1990 and October 1991, more than 7 million personal computer users worldwide licensed Windows Version 3.0." Remember that these are figures for purchases, not users. Estimating the number of unlicensed copies of Windows in use is difficult, if not impossible. Figure 25.1 displays the data of table 25.1 for Windows 3+ (including Windows NT and Windows for Workgroups) and OS/2 in graphic form and then projects sales of both products for four months.

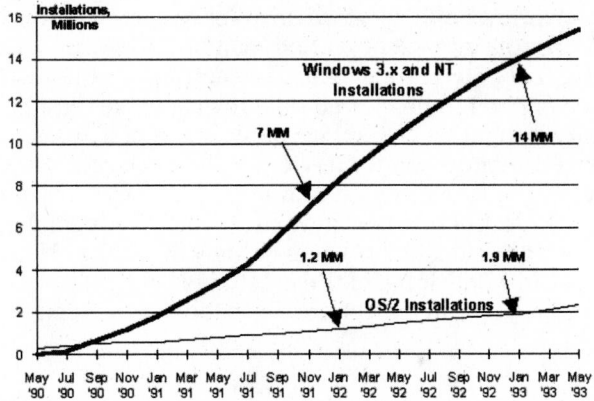

FIG. 25.1

Current and projected sales of Windows 3+ and OS/2, May 1990 to May 1993.

Sales volumes of operating systems are as important to users and developers of applications as those sales are to the marketing departments of software publishers. Successful operating systems breed successful applications, such as Microsoft Excel, Word for Windows, and Project, Aldus PageMaker, CorelDRAW!, and Micrografx Picture Publisher. Successful applications generate a variety of additional third-party products that enhance the applications. Windows 3+, for example, influenced the market significantly. Beginning about January 1992, the only significant new application releases by mainstream software publishers were for Windows.

PC Week reported that the 1992 Software Industry Business Practices Survey, published by Price Waterhouse, demonstrates the effects of marketplace momentum. According to the report, of the companies surveyed, 40 percent with 100 or more employees were developing Windows applications in 1992. Another 37 percent planned to develop Windows applications in 1993, representing a total of 77 percent of these firms. Slightly more than 27 percent of the firms with 100+ employees surveyed plan to start developing Windows NT applications in 1993.

Future Versions of Access and Windows

Microsoft Windows is a moving target; new variations on the Windows 3.1 theme now appear every few months. In late 1992, Microsoft released Windows for Workgroups and Modular Windows and distributed tens of thousands of copies of the preliminary software development kit for Windows NT. Windows for Workgroups and Windows NT may have a pronounced effect on how you use Access in a network environment, and both are discussed in sections that follow. Modular Windows is designed to be viewed on a television set equipped with a special Tandy-designed CD-ROM player. Instead of a mouse, you use a special infrared remote control device to click enlarged buttons to navigate through consumer-oriented multimedia applications. You can rest assured that there will be other new and improved special-purpose versions of Windows 3.1 in 1993. It is equally likely that Microsoft will update Access in 1993. Some of the most likely short-term enhancements to Access you can expect are described in the next section.

Updates and Upgrades to Access Version 1.0

Access is a product with remarkable capabilities, especially when you consider these two factors: database managers are the most complex of mainstream Windows applications, and you are using Version 1.0 of Access. One of the adages of writers for PC-oriented periodicals is, "Never use Version 1.0 of any software product," but this statement does not apply to Access. The extended development cycle of Access and the efforts of those who evaluated Access during its one-year alpha- and beta-testing period ensure that Access is close to a bulletproof product. Here is what you can expect in the first few months after the release of Access:

■ One or more maintenance releases to correct minor deficiencies, some of which were known but not corrected due to the pressure to meet a release deadline of mid-November 1992, corresponding to the date of the Fall COMDEX exposition held in Las Vegas. Maintenance releases are common even for mature Windows applications (Microsoft Word for Windows 2.0b is the second and Excel 4.0a is the first maintenance release for these "old-timers").

■ Additional, certified drivers to add the capability to attach tables of Digital Equipment Corp.'s Rdb, Oracle Corp.'s Oracle, IBM DB2 and other databases to Access (discussed in the section of this chapter "Extension of the ODBC API").

■ The run-time version of Access that you can use to create standalone Access applications that do not require each user to have a copy of Access. The run-time version of Access is likely to be supplied in the form of a Windows dynamic link library (DLL), similar to VBRUN200.DLL provided for Visual Basic 2.0, together with an accompanying (.EXE) file or an application to create the .EXE file required for all Windows applications. Run-time Access is slated for release in early 1993.

■ A developer's toolkit for Access, similar in scope and purpose to the Microsoft Professional Toolkit for Visual Basic. According to Microsoft, the Access developer's tool kit will contain "new documentation, tools, and sample code." Look for this toolkit in mid- to late-1993.

You can keep up-to-date on new Access developments through the Microsoft Access Forum on CompuServe (GO MSACCESS). Updated versions of components of the files in the retail release of products are often available in the libraries of CompuServe forums before they are sent to registered users by the software publisher. Procedures to circumvent problems you encounter with Access, called *work-arounds,* will appear in the Access forum and in the Microsoft Knowledge Base, a product support database that Microsoft maintains on CompuServe (GO MSKB). Search on the product name, Access, to find applicable technical tips.

Look for Version 2.0 of Access in the Spring of 1994. Microsoft typically issues major upgrades to its Windows applications at 15- to 18-month intervals. Some of the changes you may expect in Access 2.0, based on the comments of Access beta testers, follow:

■ Closer resemblance to other mainstream Microsoft applications. Enhancements are likely to include expanded use of drag-and-drop techniques, capability to select individual fields or groups of fields for copy-and-paste operations (instead of having to select entire records), and perhaps even the equivalent of Excel's formula bar to replace Access's Shift+F2 Zoom dialog box.

■ Features provided by OLE 2.0, including the capability to edit linked or embedded objects in Access windows, rather than the window of the OLE server. You'll also be able to make extensive use of drag-and-drop techniques with OLE 2.0.

■ Full implementation of Access as a 32-bit Windows application designed for use under the Windows NT operating system. Windows NT and 32-bit implementation will increase the operating speed of Access and other 32-bit applications you use with Access, especially 32-bit OLE servers. You will be able to run the 32-bit applications under Windows 3.1 by employing the Win32s extensions that were in the beta-testing stage when this book was written.

Windows NT

Network operating systems will change in future versions of Windows. As Access faces a DBM market with 70 percent of the user base held by Borland, Microsoft LAN Manager competes with the Novell NetWare Goliath, which reportedly commands a similar percentage of all network operating system installations. Although LAN Manager generally is said to provide better performance than NetWare with client-server databases, multiple database servers, and Windows applications, its future has been clouded in the minds of many current and prospective users because LAN Manager's latest Version, 2.1, still must be run under the Microsoft or IBM version of OS/2.

The rift between Microsoft and IBM filled many thousands of column-inches in computer-related periodicals. The rift was created when Microsoft abandoned the jointly developed OS/2 in favor of a new 32-bit operating system built on the Windows model. Microsoft announced its intent to develop OS/2 3.0 with built-in networking capabilities in January 1991, and renamed the product Windows NT in July 1991. Windows NT and OS/2 2.0 are designed to take full advantage of the 32-bit protected mode of Intel 80386, 80486, and future 08x86 microprocessors. Both programs promise to reduce or eliminate performance differences between DOS and applications that use a graphical user interface.

Some of the more interesting features reported to be included in Windows NT appear in the following list:

■ *Cross-platform compatibility:* Windows NT will operate on PCs using Intel 80386 and higher microprocessors and will operate on RISC (Reduced-Instruction Set Computing) workstations built around the MIPS Computer Systems, Inc., R3000/R4000-series and Digital Equipment Corporation Alpha chip sets.

■ *Support for network clients and servers:* Functions to accommodate Microsoft LAN Manager will be built into Windows NT. Microsoft announced that two versions will be produced: one version optimized for network server applications, and the other as a client. Preemptive multitasking will allow Windows applications to run as lower-priority processes, so dedicated file servers will not be required. High-performance multiserver systems, therefore, will become more common.

■ *Capability to run multiple types of applications efficiently:* Windows NT will run DOS, Windows 3+ (16-bit), Windows NT (32-bit), 16-bit (and possibly 32-bit) OS/2 client applications, and UNIX applications written to the Portable Operating System Interface for UNIX

(POSIX) standard. The initial version of Windows NT will be limited to running existing 16-bit OS/2 database server applications, such as Microsoft SQL Server. Although Microsoft has announced that a future version of NT will support 32-bit OS/2 servers, few users will be willing to bet the farm on this commitment.

- *Improved network security:* Initial versions of Windows NT will be submitted for certification at the federal C2 security level, but future versions are expected to gain the much more secure B1 classification. Security systems are designed to prevent unauthorized access to the network, especially through "back doors" created to serve remote clients via Wide-Area Networks (WANs), which hackers might tap. Windows NT will use a "client impersonation" system to maintain all security checks at a single point, the server.

Like OS/2, Windows NT will be compatible with both conventional DOS file systems that use the familiar File Allocation Table scheme and high-performance file system (HPFS) designed for use with client-server databases. In addition, Microsoft will add a CD-ROM file format and its NTFS (New Technology File System), a "recoverable" file format riding on HPFS. NTFS will provide a transaction log that aids in data recovery in the event of a disk crash. NTFS will include incentives for future enhancements, such as On-Line Transaction Processing capabilities for such applications as airline and hotel reservation systems.

The minimum hardware configuration for a PC running Windows NT is expected to be an 80386 CPU with 8M of RAM; however, an 80486-based system with 12M to 16M of RAM will undoubtedly be the practical lower limit for Windows NT when it is used as a file server. The cost of upgrading from the common 4M used to run Windows 3.1 to 8M for a Windows NT client is less than $200, based on a mid-1992 street memory price of $45/M. The price difference between 80386DX- and 80486DX-based computers continues to decline. The $129 upgrades to your present suite of 16-bit Windows applications probably will be the major expense involved in converting to Windows NT.

Windows NT's promise of increased speed and cross-platform compatibility are the two most important characteristics for current and potential Access users. Under Windows 3.1, Access 1.0 will not win any awards for fastest PC database.

Multiple users share database information much more extensively than spreadsheet or word processing document files. In the future, therefore, the capability to run Access on a variety of computer architectures will warrant and receive a topic of its own. For users of Access, the significance of many of the other features, as well as other Windows applications, will not be realized until the 32-bit Windows NT versions are released. The code used to create Access was written with Windows NT in mind, and an NT-compatible version will be announced with or shortly after the official release of the 32-bit operating system, now reportedly scheduled for the first half of 1993.

Windows for Workgroups

Windows for Workgroups, originally referred to as Windows 3.1+ or by the code name Sparta, allows users of DOS and Windows to share files and peripherals, such as modems and printers, without installing a separate network operating system or a dedicated server computer. Because peer-to-peer networking capability is incorporated within Windows itself, the relatively large DOS terminate-and-stay-resident (TSR) applications and network device drivers required for a conventional network of this type, such as Novell's NetWare Lite and Artisoft's LANtastic, are not necessary. (You do, however, need a DOS device driver for Windows for Workgroups' network adapter card.) This frees the resources otherwise required for use by Windows.

Peer-to-peer networks are an economical way for smaller organizations to establish a LAN and, when necessary, change to a server-based system to accommodate larger numbers of users or expanding data files. Memory requirements are smaller than those requirements for Windows NT, perhaps 4M for a client and 8M for a client-server combination. The cost of the 16-bit EtherNet adapter cards, suitable for most clients, dropped dramatically in mid-1992. Low-cost 10-BASE-T cards allow high-speed communication over standard, twisted-pair telephone wires. EtherNet adapter cards are available at street prices of less than $100. Small peer-to-peer LANs require a minimum of network administration; therefore, implementation and maintenance costs are low enough to meet the budget constraints of even the smallest business.

You can reasonably expect that the built-in network operating system of Windows for Workgroups will provide access to future Windows NT servers. When the need arises, therefore, users of Access running under Windows for Workgroups have an upgrade path to more powerful network systems. When Windows NT and the 32-bit version of Access are released, workstation power users will gain substantial performance benefits.

Network Wars

The battle between Windows NT and OS/2 2.0 is a minor skirmish compared to Microsoft and Novell's looming contest for dominance in the network operating systems market. OS/2 never was able to capture a significant portion of stand-alone PC installations or the client side of networks. If the projections shown in figure 25.1 are believable, OS/2 Version 2.0 ultimately will not fare much better than its predecessors.

If you are already using Access on a network, chances are about 7 in 10 that you will be using Novell NetWare; the probability is even higher that you will continue to use it. In the client-server network operating system market, brand loyalty is very strong because of the cost and inconvenience of changing network horses in midstream. If your organization has more than a few PCs and does not presently use a LAN, the organization very likely will install a network by 1994. Trade publications estimate that more than 90 percent of all sites with five or more PCs in use will connect those PCs with a LAN by 1995. The only question is which LAN they will choose.

To ward off the network attack from archrival Microsoft, Novell has signed mutual defense treaties with IBM, Digital, Hewlett-Packard, and Sun Microsystems. IBM will resell red NetWare, a direct competitor for its true-blue OS/2 LAN Server. Both Digital and Hewlett-Packard are now major users of Microsoft LAN Manager, but will include NetWare in their product lines, too. In the network operating system market table, relations are clearly many-to-many.

Novell is planning a major thrust through its Univel joint venture with UNIX System Laboratories into systems based on UNIX servers. Univel plans a 32-bit UNIX clone that will run both DOS and UNIX applications and incorporate NetWare client functions. To run these applications efficiently under UNIX, Novell acquired the necessary DOS expertise through the acquisition of Digital Research, Inc., and its DR DOS products. The Univel product will make NetWare more accessible to third-party developers because writing UNIX applications is far simpler than creating the arcane NetWare Loadable Modules required to run applications, such as database servers, directly under NetWare 3+'s operating system.

Sites that have standardized on Windows applications with stand-alone PCs undoubtedly will be better served by a Windows-based LAN, either client-server or peer-to-peer. A network operating system for Windows applications built into Windows itself is much easier to install, use, and maintain than an application specifically oriented for running DOS and/or UNIX applications. Consequently, the success of Windows for Workgroups and Windows NT as network operating systems relies on a continued increase in the market share of Windows 3+ applications.

If you plan to share your Access data with more than five users, first consider a client-server network operating system. Microsoft SQL Server is the logical choice, because Access's database file structure is built on the SQL Server model. With the ODBC Administrator, attaching SQL Server table to an Access database is an easy process. To speed the operation of applications, many routine operations that require Access Basic code can be converted to SQL Server's stored procedures. The change from Access to SQL Server database files is surprisingly painless.

Workgroup Applications and E-Mail

No discussion of networks and workgroups is complete without a few comments on workgroup applications, such as E-mail and joint appointment schedulers. Microsoft Mail and a simple scheduling application are built into Windows for Workgroups. In its annual strategy briefing in the fall of 1992, Microsoft introduced a suite of 19 additional applications designed to join the activities of workgroups. Several of these applications were developed by Microsoft using Access. All the new Microsoft applications are low-cost products designed to compete with existing integrated workgroup solutions, such as Lotus Development's Notes. Again, only time will determine whether Microsoft's piecemeal approach will undermine the market penetration of integrated workgroup applications. Microsoft's use of Access for commercial applications is an encouraging seal of approval for Access.

Access on Other Platforms

Another feature of Windows NT significant to Access users is the assurance of multiple upgrade paths for the Access applications you create. You make a major investment in the time required to write and test applications and to train users in the application's operations. Ultimately, you will be able to operate all Access applications under Windows NT and, consequently, run these applications on Intel and RISC microprocessor systems based on the MIPS chip set or those supplied by Digital using the Alpha CPU. Obviously, you cannot discount the importance of Apple's Macintosh product line, especially with the price reductions that took place in 1991. Macs are here today and Windows NT is not, so Macs get first priority in this chapter.

Apple Macintosh

The two mainstream Microsoft applications for Windows, Excel and Word, have equivalents designed for Apple's Macintosh product line. Both Mac Word and Excel for the Mac have a larger share (of a smaller market) than their Windows counterparts. System 7 enables you to use OLE for inter-application communication.

Microsoft announced that the WordBasic macro languages will be added to a future version of Mac Word. In all probability, this iteration of Word's macro language will more closely resemble Access Basic than the macro language incorporated in Word for Windows 2.0. The use of the same source code to create applications for PCs and Macintoshes was one reason the FoxBase DBM succeeded. You can be certain that Microsoft will complete its triad for Apple computers with Access for the Mac, making Object Basic the standard macro language for all Microsoft applications running on Macs, too—it's just a matter of time.

Access for the Mac is expected to allow transparent access to Access and other common database files on PC networks, whether those are of the NetWare, LAN Manager, or Windows NT variety. NetWare 3.11 and LAN Manager 2.1 presently provide Macintosh connectivity. Because Windows NT incorporates LAN Manager technology, a compatible version of Microsoft LAN Manager Services for the Macintosh should accompany or shortly follow Windows NT's release. Whether you will be able to use Workgroups for Windows on your Mac to participate in peer-to-peer relationships with PCs remains speculative.

RISC Workstations

The late 1991 agreement between Microsoft Corp. and Digital marked another alliance between giants. This alliance followed the creation of the Apple-IBM Taligent venture and the round of agreements relating to network operating systems between Novell Inc., and major players in the industry. Prior to its new agreement with Microsoft, Digital had used portions of LAN Manager in its Pathworks network operating system. Now it has officially joined Microsoft's Strategic Integrator Program to resell LAN Manager in enterprise-wide systems.

The most important element of the announcement, however, is Digital's decision to run Windows NT on its new workstations and other products that use the Alpha RISC (Reduced-Instruction Set Computing) microprocessor. Digital developed the RISC to compete with an advanced version of IBM's RS/6000 RISC chip. IBM's upgraded RS/6000 is the heart of "Pink," the new object-oriented operating system that will be developed by the Taligent (*Tal*ent + intelli*gent*) combination of IBM and Apple. OS/2's future is doubly in doubt because, if successful, Pink will replace OS/2 on IBM and advanced Apple desktop computers. The second joint venture between Apple and IBM, called Kaleida (from kaleidoscope), concentrates on multimedia applications.

Microsoft and Digital are members of the Advanced Computing Environment (ACE) consortium, along with MIPS, the Santa Cruz Operation (SCO), and about 200 other firms with a stake in RISC technology. ACE's charter states a goal of developing open standards for both MIPS Rx000 RISC and Intel 80x86 microprocessor-based systems to accommodate future advances in chip technology.

Unwritten objectives are to prevent IBM from creating a *de facto* industry standard, either single-handedly or in conjunction with Apple, and to prevent Sun Microsystems, Inc., from doing the same with its SPARC-based RISC workstations. A similar group created Extended Industry Standard Architecture (EISA) specification, which successfully blocked IBM's attempt to make its patented Multi-Channel Architecture a new PC standard. SCO's Open Desktop and Windows NT are the two operating systems presently sanctioned by ACE.

Whether RISC technology will ever gain presence in the mass market afforded conventional Industry Standard Architecture (ISA) PCs is questionable. When applications can be run interchangeably on either, the point becomes moot. Microsoft demonstrated the capability to rewrite a portion of the "Executive" or kernel of Windows NT to accommodate different RISC chips in its adaptation of Windows NT to the Digital Alpha microprocessor.

Writing a modified "microkernel," about 50K of compiled code for use with IBM or Hewlett-Packard RISC workstations, would not necessarily be a major hurdle for Microsoft's programming staff. Your Access applications, therefore, will not depend solely on Intel's capability to create increasingly powerful 80x86 chips. If RISC-based servers offer price-performance advantages over PC architecture, your Access clients running under Windows NT will access them without any modification.

The cross-platform compatibility offered by Windows NT will have two beneficial effects: more applications will become available, because a larger market will exist, and the larger potential volume ultimately will reduce the cost of applications to the end-user. The present pricing differentials between costly POSIX-compliant applications designed for UNIX-based servers and workstations and their moderately priced counterparts for Windows are likely to be reduced or eliminated as Windows NT gains market share in 1993 and beyond.

Windows 3.2 and Macro Manager

Bill Gates stated that all Microsoft applications with macros would share a common macro language built on BASIC. Now Mr. Gates' edict has been extended to two mainstream applications, Access and Word for Windows. Only Microsoft Excel remains as a member of the triad without its own "Excel Basic" dialect. OLE 2.0, which was in the development stage at Microsoft when this book was written, and a future application called Microsoft Macro Manager will be the likely combination to realize Mr. Gates' objective to create a common macro language for all Windows applications. Both OLE 2.0 and Macro Manager are expected to be incorporated in a future version of Windows—possibly Windows 3.2 or 4.0.

OLE 2.0 will add *Command Architecture* to its current capabilities and will use a database to store the macro commands of other OLE-compliant applications. These applications then will add their vocabulary of macro instructions or keywords into the database. Macro Manager will employ the database to allow macros written in one application to be used in another that can communicate via OLE 2. In essence, the combination would be an OLE counterpart of Access Basic's DDEExecute method, with Macro Manager creating the command strings for you. In addition, you will not have to go through the exercise of parsing SysItems strings; their equivalents will be in the registration database of Windows 3.1, REG.DAT. Microsoft also plans a future version of Visual Basic that will allow you to read, edit, and compile the inter-application macros you create with Macro Manager.

Macro Manager will allow you to orchestrate the use of multiple Windows applications. You could, for example, write a macro to create a monthly report on the fifth day of each month. The macro would call Access to query the appropriate database, insert the updated information into an Excel spreadsheet, create a graph of the results, and then incorporate a portion of the spreadsheet and the graph into a Word for Windows document. You could do all this with your mouse—without writing a single line of programming code.

Macro Manager will not be limited to use with only Microsoft's Windows applications. Aldus, Borland, Lotus, Micrografx, and WordPerfect, which collaborated in the design and development of OLE 1.0, are participants in the OLE 2.0 definition process. As OLE is enhanced in new versions, less need will exist to write complex DDE code for Windows interprocess communication.

Access Programming Languages

One of the principal factors you should consider, especially if you are choosing a PC-based DBM to use in your organization as a whole, is language standardization. Training employees to use new macro and programming languages can exceed the purchase cost of the application by factors of 10 to 100. Standardized macro action keywords and similar macro syntax across all your most-used applications will reduce the cost of training users to reach the intermediate and advanced skill levels.

Without question, dBASE (which was derived from BASIC), is presently the root PC database system language. All xBase languages are derived from it, and each xBase dialect adds its own particular set of keywords to enhance the root language's usefulness. A standardized dialect of Visual Basic, Object Basic, Microsoft's root language for creating your own macro actions in Windows, will be used with Microsoft's word processing, spreadsheet, database, project management, and even multimedia authoring applications of the future. If you presently use or plan to convert to other Microsoft applications, Access is a wise choice for a company-wide DBM. The time you spend learning Access Basic will pay when you or your firm's staff turn to programming macros in other Microsoft applications.

When Microsoft designed Access, it made the Access Basic language a module of Access. In a 1992 interview in *DBMS* magazine, executives in charge of Microsoft's database development program stated that Access was designed for "language independence." Language independence means the capability to create Access applications if you replace or supplement the use of Access Basic with other programming languages, such as xBase dialects or ANSI C++. According to Microsoft's Tod Nielsen, group manager for the Fox product line, the capability to use the FoxBase dialect of xBase within Access may occur in 1994 or 1995.

SQL is, and will continue to be, the preeminent data handling language for client-server DBMS. Most PC-based DBMS now support SQL, either as a primary language or as an alternative to the DBM's native language. You can absorb most of SQL by studying the SQL syntax of the QBE queries you create in Access's SQL window.

Extensions to Access

A wide range of third-party add-in applications, supplied as object code libraries, are available for xBase DBMS, such as Clipper and FoxPro. Visual Basic, which uses the same techniques as Access to increase its repertoire of control objects and add new programming functions, had more than 200 commercial supplements when this book was written. The catalog of third-party enhancements for Access included in the retail version of the product is only a small proportion of the add-ons that ultimately will become available once Access establishes its foothold in the Windows application marketplace.

Third-Party Toolkits for Access

Many standardized applications, which you can modify to meet your own specific requirements, are available for xBase and PAL programmers using the DOS versions of these DBMS. You can choose from a variety of accounting packages that you can customize for xBase, such as the AccountMate and SBT offerings, and modify those packages to create financial packages tailored for your specific industry or profession.

Several firms that produce accounting packages that run under DOS-based DBMS are adapting their products as Access toolkits. An example of such a product is the software development kit for Access produced by MTX International, Inc., of Englewood, Colorado. The initial MTX accounting development kit consists of accounts receivable, accounts payable, and general ledger modules. Payroll and construction job-costing modules are available as add-on products. A typical data entry form of the MTX SDK is illustrated in figure 25.2.

FIG. 25.2

One of the data entry forms from MTX International's Access software development kit.

You can expect third-party developers to develop Access toolkits for the most popular applications of DBMS, such as personal information managers, large-scale mailing list maintenance, bar-code reading and printing, point-of-sale applications for such retailers as videotape rental firms, and so on. The advantage of Access SDKs over those for PAL and xBase is that most Access toolkits are designed with a minimum amount of Access Basic code. Modifications are made primarily to forms, reports, and macros. This approach avoids the tedium of deciphering other programmers' code writing styles (or lack of styles).

Access Libraries and DLLs

Version 1.0 of Access does not provide Visual Basic's capability to add third-party control objects by means of custom controls. You can, however, use libraries created by third-party developers to add functionality to your Access applications. The Wizards and Analyzer libraries supplied with Access demonstrate the power of add-in libraries. Libraries are Access Basic databases with the .MDA instead of the .MDB file extension. Most third-party products not supplied in the form of toolkits are expected to be distributed as Access libraries.

WordBasic and VisualBasic, for example, give you the capability to use functions in the dynamic link libraries of Windows itself, as well as in third-party DLLs. You use the same Declare keyword and syntax in Access Basic to register a function in any DLL written for Windows. Once registered, you can use any of the Access-compatible functions the DLL contains as an adjunct to your Access Basic code. Many DLLs developed for Visual Basic, such as those that include transcendental and statistical functions not provided in Access, can be called by Access Basic functions.

Extension of the ODBC APIs

Only two ODBC drivers for use with client-server database managers were supplied with the initial retail version of Access 2.0. Both drivers were written for Microsoft Corp. and are designed for SQL Server: one for Microsoft SQL Server, designed to run on PCs, and the other for Sybase SQL Server, which runs under OS/2 and on other computer platforms. Microsoft SQL Server is based on the Sybase product, but distinct differences exist between the Microsoft and Sybase implementations.

Microsoft has committed to supply ODBC drivers for Oracle, Digital Rdb, and IBM DB2 database systems but has not announced when these additional drivers will be certified and released. Other suppliers of client-server database systems, such as Gupta, have announced that they will support the ODBCs by writing and certifying drivers for their products.

Chapter Summary

You are on your own with Access. This chapter has given you some insight into what's in store for Access in the future. Unfortunately, much of what is known about the future of Windows and its applications is shrouded in secrecy imposed by the confidentiality requirements of the non-disclosure agreements that authors must execute to obtain access to unreleased products. The information in this chapter has been gleaned from computer-based periodicals, newsletters, and other reliable sources.

This book's objective has been to provide you the information you need to master the development of Access applications at the beginning and intermediate levels. Access is a very sophisticated application, and publishing limitations preclude complete descriptions of its every function and keyword. Such a book might exceed 2,000 pages in length! Appendix A provides a glossary of terms that may be unfamiliar to many readers. Other reference material pertinent to Access also is appended.

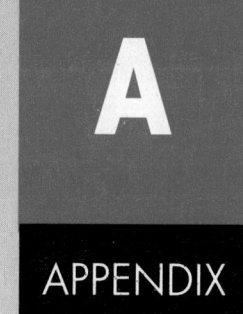

Glossary

Accelerator key A key combination that provides a way to select a menu choice, macro, or other function of the application in lieu of selecting with the mouse. Also called a *shortcut key.*

Active In Windows, the currently running application or the window to which user input is directed (the window with the focus).

Address The numerical value, usually in hexadecimal format, of a particular location in your computer's random-access memory (RAM).

Aggregate functions AVG, SUM, MIN, MAX, ANY, and COUNT. Aggregate functions calculate summary values (average, total, minimum, maximum, and number of records) from a group of values in a specified column and usually are associated with GROUP BY and HAVING clauses.

Alias A temporary name assigned to a table in a self join. Alias is also an embedded keyword option for the Access Basic Declare statement used to register prototypes of functions in DLLs. Access then may use the other name (alias) to call the functions from the programs.

ANSI An acronym for the American National Standards Institute. In Windows, ANSI refers to the ANSI character set that Microsoft decided to use for Windows rather than the IBM PC character set, the OEM. The OEM includes special characters, such as characters used for line drawing. The most common character set is ASCII (the American Standard Code for Information Interchange) which, for English alphabetical and numeric characters, is the same as ANSI.

API An abbreviation for Application Programming Interface. Generically, a method by which a program can obtain access to or modify the operating system. API, for example, can refer to the 550 or so Windows 3 functions that enable applications to open and close windows, read the keyboard, interpret mouse movements, and perform other operations. Programmers call the functions *hooks*. Access Basic provides access to these functions with the Declare statement.

Applet A Windows application designed to accomplish a single, often simple task and usually included with a commercial product, but not sold as a product by itself. The Packager and Character Map applications sold with Windows 3.1 are applets.

Application The software product that results from creation of a program. The application often is used as a synonym for the program code that creates it. Microsoft Word for Windows, Microsoft Excel, Adobe Type Manager, and 1-2-3 are Windows applications. Applications are distinguished by their purpose and the operating system for which they are designed (Windows, DOS, Macintosh, and UNIX, for example). Windows applications carry the DOS executable file extension, *.EXE.

Argument Data supplied to a function that the function acts on or uses to perform its task. Arguments are enclosed in parentheses. Additional arguments, if any, are separated by commas. Arguments of functions are equivalent to parameters of procedures.

Array An ordered sequence of values (elements) stored within a single variable and accessed by referring to the variable name with the number of the element (index or subscript) in parentheses: Value$ = Array$(3), for example. Arrays in Access Basic that have more than one dimension include indexes for each dimension: Value$ = Array$(3,3).

ASCII An acronym for the American Standard Code for Information Interchange. A set of standard numerical values for printable (text), control (such as Tab), and special characters (including letters in languages other than English) used by PCs and most other computers. Other commonly used codes for character sets are ANSI (used by Windows) and EBCDIC (Extended Binary Coded Decimal Interchange Code used by IBM for mainframe computers).

Assembler An application that uses a source code written in an assembly language to create a code (called the *object code*) that a computer can use to perform a program. MASM (the Microsoft Assembler) is the most commonly used application with PCs.

Assembly language A low-level language that provides for direct operation of the hardware of a PC. An application written in assembly language is compiled into Object code, the native language of most computers.

Assign To give a value to a variable.

Background In multitasking operations, the application or procedure that is not visible on-screen and that will not receive user-generated input. In Windows, an application that is minimized and does not have the focus is operating in the background.

Back up To create a file (a back up file) that duplicates data stored on a fixed disk.

Base date A date used as a reference from which other date values are calculated. In the case of Access and SQL Server, the base date is January 1, 1900.

Base tables The permanent tables from which a view is created. Base tables is a synonym for underlying tables. Each base table in a database is identified by a name unique to the database.

Batch A group of statements processed as an entity: DOS batch files and SQL batch statements, for example.

Binary file A file whose contents do not consist of lines of text. Executable (*.EXE), dynamic link library (*.DLL), and most database files are stored in binary format.

Binary string A string consisting of binary, not text, data that contains bytes outside the range of ANSI or ASCII values for printable characters.

Bit The smallest piece of information processed by a computer. A bit, derived from the contraction of *binary digit*, has two states: On (1) or Off (0). Eight bits make up a *byte*, and 16 combined bits are called a *word*.

BitBlt An assembly-level function used for manipulating graphic images in Windows applications written in the C programming language.

Bit map The representation of a printed or screen image, usually graphic, as a series of bytes.

Bitwise A process that evaluates each bit of a collection of bits, such as a byte or word, rather than process the entire combination as a single element. Logical operations and masks use bitwise procedures.

Blitting The process of using BitBlt functions to modify a bit map.

Boolean A type of arithmetic in which all digits are bits; the numbers may have only two states: On (True or 1) or Off (False or 0). Boolean arithmetic is used widely in set theory and computer programming. Boolean, named after the mathematician George Boole, also describes a data type that may only have two states: True or False. In Access Basic, True is represented by &HFF (all bits of an 8-bit byte set to 1) and False, by &H0 (all bits set to 0). Access Basic does not have a native Boolean or BOOL type; you use Yes/No fields to simulate the Boolean data type.

Break To cause an interruption in program operation. Ctrl+C is the standard DOS break key combination, but it seldom halts the operation of a Windows application. Windows often enables you to use Esc to terminate an operation prior to completion.

Breakpoint A designated statement that causes program execution to halt after executing the statement preceding the breakpoint. Breakpoints may be toggled on or off by an Access Basic menu selection, **R**un/Toggle **B**reakpoint, or by pressing F9.

Bridge An electronic device or software used to connect one type of network or communications protocol (methodology) with another.

Buffer An area in memory of a designated size (number of bytes) reserved to hold a portion of a file or the value of a variable. When string variables are passed as arguments of DLL functions, you must create a buffer of sufficient size to hold the returned string. Before you call the DLL function, use the String$( ) function to create a fixed-length string variable of the necessary size.

Built-in functions Functions included in a computer language. Unlike user-defined functions, the programmer does not create these functions.

Caption The title that appears in the title bar of a window. Access Basic calls the text of a label, check box, frame, command, or option button the Caption property.

Caret The Windows term for the mouse cursor in a text field, usually in the shape of an I-beam. Also called the *insertion point*.

Cartesian product Named for René Descartes, a French mathematician. Access uses Cartesian products in JOIN operations to describe all possible combinations of rows and columns from each table in a database. The number of rows in a Cartesian product is equal to the number of rows in table 1 times the number of rows in table 2 times the number of rows in table 3, and so on. Access disregards the Cartesian rows that do not satisfy the JOIN condition.

Cascading delete A trigger that deletes data from one table based on a deletion from another table. Access usually uses a cascading delete to delete detail data (invoice items, for example) when the master record (the invoice) is deleted.

Case sensitivity A term used to define whether the interpreter or compiler responds to lowercase and uppercase letters as if they are the same character. Most interpreters are case-insensitive. The C programming language is an exception; it is case-sensitive, and all C keywords are in lowercase. Many interpreters, Access Basic included, reformat keywords to their standard: all upper-case for Basic and a combination of uppercase and lowercase letters for Access Basic. Access Basic, however, does not distinguish between uppercase and lowercase letters used as names for variables.

CD-ROM An abbreviation for Compact Disk Read-Only Memory, a photo-optic read-only medium that is similar to an audio compact disc (CD) but contains files that can be read by a computer.

Channel In Windows, channel ordinarily refers to a unique task ID assigned to a dynamic data exchange (DDE) conversation. Some applications, such as Word for Windows and Excel, assign integer channel number aliases, starting with 1 for the first DDE channel opened and numbering sequentially thereafter. Access Basic associates the channel number with the object that acts as the client or server in a DDE conversation. Access Basic also uses channel to identify an I/O port in minicomputers and mainframe computers.

Check box A Windows dialog box and Access Basic object that consists of a square box and an associated caption. The user creates or erases (toggles) a diagonal cross in the box by clicking the box with the mouse or pressing an assigned hot key.

Child (1) In Windows, usually an abbreviation for an MDI child window. *MDI Child windows* are additional windows that are displayed within the confines of a parent window. All user input (keyboard and mouse) and data display in Access is within MDI Child windows. (2) Used in computer programming in general to describe an object that is related to, but lower in the hierarchical level of, a parent object.

Chunk A part of a RIFF or a standard MIDI (Musical Instrument Digital Interface) file that is assigned to a particular function and may be treated as a single element by an application.

Clause The portion of an SQL statement that begins with a nonverb keyword (such as WHERE or GROUP BY) that names a basic operation to be performed.

Client The device or application receiving data from a server device or application. The data may be in the form of a file received from a network file server, an object from an OLE server, or values from a DDE server assigned to client variables.

Clipboard The Windows temporary storage location for text and graphic objects. The Clipboard is the intermediary in all Copy, Cut, and Paste operations. You may use the Program Manager Clipboard applet to view and save the contents of the Clipboard.

Clustered index An index in which the physical and index order is the same. Equivalent to INDEX ON RECNO( ) TO in xBase.

Code Short for *source code*. The readable text you enter in your program to create an application. Code consists of instructions and their parameters, functions and their arguments, objects and their events, properties and methods, constants, variable declarations and assignments, and expressions and comments.

Code template Self-contained groups of modules and resources that perform a group of standard functions. Code templates are implemented as attachable libraries in Access. See also *Library*.

Code window In Access Basic, the window that appears when you select View Code from the Project window or double-click an object. Also called the Code Editing window.

Color palette A means of establishing a foreground or background color in Windows by selecting a color with the mouse from those displayed. The Color Palette then converts the selection to the standard windows RGB (red/green/blue) color format.

Combo box A Windows object that combines a text box and list box into a single element. In Access Basic, combo boxes are drop-down by default. The list portion of a drop-down combo box appears after you click the down arrow to the right of the text box.

Command A synonym for *instruction*. Command specifies an action to be taken by the computer.

Command button A Windows object that, when clicked, causes a command to be executed. In Access, command buttons run an associated macro. A command button is ordinarily a gray rectangle surrounded by a border with rounded corners. See also *Macro*.

Comment Explanatory material within source code that is not designed to be interpreted or compiled into the final application. In Access Basic, comments usually are preceded by an apostrophe (') but also can be preceded by the Rem keyword.

Common dialog box A standardized Windows 3.1 dialog box that is created by a Windows API function call. Common dialog boxes include FileOpen, FileSave, Print and Printer Setup, Color Palette, Font, and Search and Replace.

Common User Access See *CUA*.

Comparison operators See *Operator*.

Compile To create an executable or object (machine language) file from source (readable) code.

Composite key or index A key or index based on the values in two or more columns of a table. Equivalent to an INDEX ON *field1* + *field2* + O *index_filename* statement in xBase.

Compound In computer programming, a set of instructions or a statement that requires more than one keyword or group of related keywords to complete. An example of a compound statement in Access Basic follows:

```
Select Case...
Case...
Case...
End Select
```

Concatenation Combining two expressions, usually strings, to form a longer expression. The concatenation operation is & or + in Access Basic and only & in SQL.

Concurrency When more than one user has access to a specific set of records or files at the same time.

Constant A variable name to which your source code assigns a permanent value. Once you declare it, you do not change the value of a constant while your application is running.

Control A synonym for a dialog object in Access Basic. Controls include labels, text boxes, bound objects, unbound objects, list boxes, combo boxes, option buttons, command buttons, and option frames.

Conversation In DDE operations, the collection of Windows messages passed between two different applications, the client and the server, during an interprocess communication.

Correlated subquery A subquery that cannot be evaluated independently. Subqueries depend on an outer query for their results. See also *Outer query*, *Subquery*, and *Nested query*.

CUA An abbreviation for Common User Access, an element of the IBM SAA (Systems Application Architecture) specification. CUA establishes a set of standards for user interaction with menus, dialog boxes, and other user-interactive elements of an application. The CUA was first implemented in Windows and OS/2 and has been an integral part of these graphic user interfaces (GUIs) since their inception.

Current statement The statement or instruction being executed at a particular time. In debugging or stepwise operation of interpreted applications, such as Access Basic, the current statement is the next statement that will be executed by the interpreter when Access resumes the program operation.

Data definition The process of describing databases and database objects, such as tables, indexes, views, procedures, rules, default values, and triggers.

Data dictionary A set of system tables that contain the data definitions of database objects.

Data element The value contained in a data cell, also called a data item, or simply an element. A data element is a piece of data that describes a single property of a data entity, such as a person's first name, last name, Social Security number, age, sex, or hair color.

Data entity A distinguishable object that is the subject of a data table and usually has at least one unique data element. A data entity can be a person (unique Social Security number), an invoice (unique invoice number), or a vehicle (unique vehicle ID number; license plate numbers are not necessarily unique across state lines).

Data integrity Maintaining rules to prevent inadvertently or intentionally modifying the contents of a database and thereby affecting its accuracy or reliability.

Data modification Changing the content of one or more tables in a database. Data modification includes adding, deleting, or changing information with the INSERT, DELETE, and UPDATE SQL statements.

Data sharing The capability to enable more than one user or application to access information stored in a database.

Data type The description of how the computer is to interpret a particular item of data. Data types generally are divided into two families: strings that usually have text or readable content and numeric data. The types of numeric data supported vary with the compiler or interpreter used. Most programming languages support a user-defined, record, or structure data type that can contain multiple data types.

Database Related data tables and other database objects, such as a data dictionary, which are organized as a group and accessed with the SQL FROM statement.

Database administrator The individual responsible for the administrative functions of databases. The database administrator has PRIVILEGES (permissions) for all commands that the DBM may execute. The administrator ordinarily is responsible for maintaining system security, including user access to the DBM, and for performing backup and restoration functions.

Database device A file in which databases and related information, such as transaction logs, are stored. Database devices usually have physical names (a DOS or OS/2 file name) and a logical name.

Database manager See *DBM*.

Database object In client/server terminology, a component of a database. Client/server database objects include tables, views, indexes, procedures, columns, rules, triggers, and defaults. The Database object in Access Basic is the topmost member of the class of objects that relate to the presently open database. All objects within a database are subclasses of the Database object.

Database owner The user who originally created a database. The database owner has control over all objects in the database but may delegate control to other users.

Date function A function that provides date and time information or manipulates these values.

DBM An abbreviation for DataBase Manager, an application that is capable of creating, organizing, and editing databases; displaying data through user-selected views; and printing formatted reports. Most DBMs include at least a macro or macro language, and most provide a system programming language. dBASE III and IV, Paradox, FoxBase, and FoxPro are DBMs. Because it does not incorporate a user interface, Nantucket Clipper is a database program compiler, not a DBM. DBMS (database management system) is commonly used as a synonym for DBM, but DBMS encompasses database files, special operating systems required (such as OS/2 for Microsoft SQL servers), and sometimes the network operating system under which the database operates.

DDE An abbreviation for dynamic data exchange, an Interprocess Communication (IPC) used by Windows and OS/2 to transfer data between different applications.

Deadlock A condition that occurs when two users with a lock on one data item attempt to lock the other's data item in order to edit it. Most DBMs can detect this condition, prevent its occurrence, and advise both users of the situation.

Debug The act of finding and removing errors in the source code for an application.

Declaration A statement that creates a user-defined data type, names a variable, creates a constant, or registers the prototypes of functions incorporated within dynamic link libraries.

Declaration section A section of an Access Basic module reserved for statements containing declarations.

Declare (1) In text and not as a keyword, to create a user-defined data type, data holder for a variable, or constant. (2) As an Access Basic keyword, to register a function contained in a dynamic link library in the global module.

Default A value assigned or option supplied when no value is specified by the user or assigned by a program statement.

Default database The logical name of the database assigned to a user when he or she logs in on the database application.

Demand lock Precludes more shared locks from being set on a data resource. Successive requests for shared locks must wait for the demand lock to be cleared.

Dependent A condition in which detail data in a subsidiary table, such as invoice items, is associated with data in a master table, such as invoice items. In this case, invoice items are dependent on invoices.

Design mode One of two modes of operation of Access Basic, also known as design time. The Design mode enables you to create and modify forms and control objects, enter code, and execute the application. *Run* is the mode in which the application executes.

Detail data Data in a subsidiary table that derives its meaning from data in a master table. If you delete the master invoice records, the subsidiary table's detail data for items included in the invoice lose their reference in the database; they become orphan data.

Detail table A table that depends on a master table. Detail tables usually have a many-to-one relationship with the master table. See also *Detail data*.

Device A computer system component, such as a keyboard, display, printer, disk drive, or modem, capable of sending or receiving data.

Device context A Windows term describing a record containing a complete definition of all variables required to fully describe a window containing a graphic object. Some variables include the dimensions of the graphic area (viewport), drawing tools (pen, brush), fonts, colors, and drawing mode. Windows provides a handle (hDC) for each device context.

Dialog box A pop-up modal window that requests information from the user. Dialog boxes include message boxes, input boxes, and user-defined dialog boxes for applications such as choosing files to open.

DIB An acronym for Device Independent Bit map, a Windows-specific bit map format designed to display graphic information. DIB files use the extension *.DIB and are similar to the *.BMP format.

Difference In data tables, data elements that are contained in one table but not in another.

Directory list box An element of a file selection dialog box that selectively lists the subdirectories of the designated directory of a specified logical drive.

DLL An abbreviation for Dynamic Link Library, a file containing a collection of Windows functions designed to perform a specific class of operations. Applications call or invoke functions within DLLs to perform a desired operation.

Drag and drop A Windows process in which you use a mouse to move (drag) and place (drop) an icon representing an object, such as a file, into another location, such as a different directory. Access Basic provides drag-and-drop capabilities for control objects.

Drive The logical identifier of a disk drive, usually specified as a letter. When the drive is part of a path, the drive letter must be followed by a colon and backslash, as in C:\.

Drive list box An element of a file selection dialog box (usually a drop-down list box) that selects the logical drive for subsequent display of directory and file lists.

Dynamic Data Exchange See *DDE*.

Dynamic Link Library See *DLL*.

Enabled In Access Basic, the capability of a control object to respond to user actions such as a mouse click.

Environment A combination of the computer hardware, operating system, and user interface. A complete statement of an environment follows: a 386DX computer with a VGA display and two-button mouse, using the DOS 5.0 operating system, and running the Windows 3.1 Graphical User Interface in its Enhanced mode with Multimedia Extensions 1.0.

Environmental variable A DOS term for variables declared by PATH and SET statements, usually made in an AUTOEXEC.BAT file, and stored in a reserved memory location by DOS. Variables may be used by applications to adjust their operation for compatibility with user-specific hardware elements or directory structures.

Equi-join A join in which the values in the columns being joined are compared for equality. Equi-joins are called INNER JOINS in Access SQL.

Error trapping A procedure by which errors generated during the execution of an application are rerouted to a designated group of lines of code, called an *error handler*, that performs a predefined operation, such as ignoring the error. If Access Basic does not trap an error, the standard message box appears showing the text message for the error that occurred.

Event An action initiated by the user of an application that causes the application or its operating system to respond with an action. Events usually are related to mouse movements and keyboard action; however, events also can be generated by Access Basic code or another application (through a DDE link, for example).

Event-driven The property of an operating system or environment that implies the existence of an idle loop. When an event occurs, the idle loop is exited, and event-handler code specific to the event is executed. After the event handler has completed its operation, execution returns to the idle loop, awaiting the next event.

Exclusive lock A lock that prevents others from locking data items until the exclusive lock is cleared. The update operations INSERT, UPDATE, and DELETE can place exclusive locks on data items.

Executable Code, usually in the form of a disk file, that the operating system in use can run to perform a particular set of functions. Executable files in Windows carry the extension *.EXE and may obtain assistance from dynamic link libraries (DLLs) in performing their tasks.

Exponent The second element of a number expressed in scientific notation, the power of 10 by which the first element, the mantissa, is multiplied to obtain the actual number. For +1.23E3, the exponent is 3, so you multiply 1.23 by 1,000 (10 to the third power) to obtain the result, 1,230.

Expression A combination of variable names, values, functions, and/or operators that will return a result, usually assigned to a variable name. Result = 1 + 1 is an expression that returns 2 to the variable named Result. DiffVar = LargeVar – SmallVar returns the difference between the two variables to DiffVar. Functions may be used in expressions; the Mid$( ) function in the example, and StringVar$ = Mid$(StringVar$, 2, 3), will replace the value of StringVar$ with three of its characters, starting at the second character.

Family One or more typefaces having a related appearance. Courier Roman (standard), bold, italic, and bold italic constitute the Courier family of faces.

Field Synonym for a column of data contained in a table.

Fifth normal form The relational database rule requiring that a table that has been divided into multiple tables must be capable of being reconstructed to its exact original structure by one or more JOIN statements.

File A collection of related information. In dBASE, for example, each table is a single *.DBF file. Access and most client-server databases store an entire database in a single file.

File handle A number assigned, usually by DOS, to a disk file when it is opened. The application then may refer to the integer file handle, instead of the name of the file, in subsequent file operations.

File list box A special type of Windows list box that displays the file names, usually having predetermined file extensions, of the files in a selected directory of a specified file.

First normal form The relational database rule for dictating that tables be flat. Flat tables can contain only one data value set per row. Members of the data value set, called *data cells*, are contained in one column of the row and must have only one value.

Flag A variable, usually Boolean (True/False), used to determine the status of a particular condition within an application. The term *set* often is used to indicate turning a flag from False to True, and the term *reset* is used for the reverse.

Flow control In general usage, conditional expressions controlling the sequence in which instructions or statements are processed in the source code of an application. If...Then...End If is a flow control statement, for example. Flow control also is used for diagrams that describe the mode of operation of an application.

Focus A Windows term indicating the currently selected application, or one of its windows, to which all user-generated input (keyboard and mouse operations) is directed. The title bar of a window with the focus usually is blue.

Font A typeface in a single size, usually expressed in points, of a single style or having a common set of attributes.

Foreground In multitasking operations, the application or procedure that is visible on-screen and to which user-generated input is directed. In Windows, the application that has the focus is in the foreground.

Foreign key A column or combination of columns whose values match a primary key in another table. Foreign keys need not be unique for each record or row.

Form In Access, a window that displays and enables you to update data, usually from one or more tables and/or queries. Forms contain control objects for displaying and updating data in fields of tables or columns of queries. Access provides the capability to print forms.

Fourth normal form The relational database rules requiring that only related data entities be included in a single table and that tables not contain data related to more than one data entity when many-to-one relationships exist among the entities.

Frame In Windows, an enclosure, usually with a border of a single pixel, that encloses a group of objects, usually dialog boxes.

Front end When used with database management systems, a window or set of windows by which the user may access, view, add to, or edit database records. Front end also describes application launchers that function similarly to the Windows Program Manager.

FTP An abbreviation for File Transfer Protocol, an Internet communication protocol for performing file transfer operations on a UNIX host.

Function Functions are classified as internal to the application language when their names are keywords. You may create your own, user-defined functions in Access Basic by adding code between Function FunctionName...End Function statements.

Global Pertaining to the program as a whole. Global variable and constants are accessible to and may be modified by code at the module and procedure level. See also *Module* and *Procedure*.

Grid A preset group of imaginary vertical and horizontal lines used in aligning the position of graphic objects. In Design mode, Access Basic shows the intersection of the imaginary lines as dots. Control objects automatically align their outlines to these dots if the snap-to-grid option is enabled.

Hierarchical menu A menu with multiple levels, consisting of a main menu that leads to one or more levels of submenus from which choices of actions are made. Almost all Windows applications use hierarchical menu structures.

Icon A 32-by-32-pixel graphic image used to identify the application.

Identifiers A synonym for *name*, usually applied to objects (such as databases, tables, and forms) and Access Basic variables.

Idle In Windows, the condition or state in which Windows and the application have processed all pending messages in the queue from user- or hardware-initiated events and are waiting for the next event to occur. The idle state is entered in Access Basic when the interpreter reaches the End Sub statement of the outermost nesting level of procedures for a form or control object.

Immediate window In Access Basic, a nonmodal dialog box in which you may enter expressions and view results without writing code in a code editing window. You also may direct information to be displayed in the Immediate window by using the Debug object.

Index With arrays, the position of the particular element with respect to others, usually beginning with 0 as the first element. When used with database files or tables, index refers to a lookup table, usually in the form of a file, that relates the value of a field in the indexed file to its record number. The record number, similar to the index of an array, indicates the position of the record within a database file, usually the sequence in which the records were created originally and most often starting with 1.

Infinite loop A Do While...Loop, For...Next, or similar program flow control structure, in which the condition to exit the loop and continue with succeeding statements is never fulfilled. In For...Next loops, an infinite loop occurs by resetting the loop counter to a value less than the value assigned to the To embedded keyword within the structure.

Initialize In programming, setting all variables to their default values and resetting the point of execution to the first executable line of code. Access Basic initializes automatically when you start an application.

Inner query Synonym for *subquery*.

Insertion point The position of the cursor within a block of text. The cursor in a Windows text box is called the *caret*.

Instance A term used by Windows to describe the temporary existence of a loaded application or one or more of its windows.

Integer A whole number. In most programming languages, an integer is a data type that occupies two bytes (16 bits). Integers may have signs (as in Access Basic), taking on values from –32,768 to +32,767, or may be unsigned. In the latter case, integers can represent numbers up to 65,535.

Interface A noun describing a connection between two dissimilar devices. A common phrase is *user interface*, meaning the connection between the display-keyboard combination and the user. Adapter cards constitute the interface between the PC data bus and peripheral devices such as displays, modems, and CD-ROMs. Drivers act as a software interface between Windows and the adapter cards. A bridge is an interface between two dissimilar networks. Using *interface* as a verb is jargon.

Intersection The group of data elements that is included in both tables in a join.

Invocation path The route through which an object or routine is invoked. If the routine is deeply nested, the path may be quite circuitous.

Invoke To cause execution of a block of code, particularly a procedure or subprocedure.

Items The elements of a list box.

Join A basic operation, initiated by the JOIN statement, that links the rows or records of two or more tables by one or more columns in each table. Equivalent to the dBASE SET RELATION TO command.

Jump In programming, execution of code in a sequence that is not the same as the sequence in which the code appears in the source code. In most cases, a jump skips over a number of lines of code, the result of an evaluation of a conditional expression. In some cases, a jump causes another subroutine to be executed.

Key or **Key field** A field that identifies a record by its value. Tables usually are indexed on key fields. See also *Primary key* and *Foreign key*.

Key value A value of a key field included in an index.

Keyword A word that has specific meaning to the interpreter or compiler in use and causes predefined events to occur when encountered in source code. You cannot use keywords as variable, procedure, or function names.

Label In Access Basic programming, a target line in the source code to which execution is directed when a **GoTo** *LableName* instruction is encountered. A label is also an Access Basic control object that displays only text.

LAN An acronym for Local Area Network, a system with multiple computers physically interconnected through adapter cards and cabling. LANs enable one computer to share the specified devices, such as disk drives, printers, and modems, of another computer on the LAN.

Launch To start a Windows application. The Windows Program Manager is an application launcher.

Leaf level The lowest level of an index. Indexes derive the names of their elements from the objects found on trees, such as trunks, limbs, and leaves.

Library (1) In Access, a database that is attached to Access by an instruction in the MSACCESS.INI file. You may use any object within the Access library in your application. WIZARD.MDA and ANALYZER.MDA are libraries supplied with Access. (2) In computer programming, a collection of functions, compiled as a group and accessible to applications by calling the function name and any required arguments. DLLs are one type of library; libraries used by compilers to provide built-in functions are another.

Link To combine one or more object files into a single executable file structure. This process is called *static linking* because the object files are made a permanent part of the executable file structure which, at least in DOS, may consist of an executable element and one or more overlay files. Dynamic link libraries, on the other hand, are linked to executable files loaded in memory, not files created by linking one or more object files.

List box A dialog box that provides a list of items from which the user may choose by using the mouse or the cursor keys.

Live lock A request for an exclusive lock on a data item that is repeatedly denied because of shared locks imposed by other users.

Local The scope of a variable declared within a procedure rather than at the module level. Local variables are visible (defined) only within the procedure in which they were declared.

Local area network See *LAN*.

Lock Restricting access to a table, portion of a table, or data item to maintain the data integrity of a database. Locks may be exclusive or shared (more than one user can access the locked elements). The user with the exclusive lock prevents other users from creating simultaneous shared or exclusive locks on the elements.

Logical A synonym for *Boolean*. Logical is a data type that may have True or False values only. Logical also is used to define a class of operators that can result only in True or False.

Loop A compound program flow control structure that is executed repeatedly until a given condition is satisfied.

Machine language Program code in the form of instructions that can be acted on by the computer hardware and operating system used. Object files compiled from source code are in machine language, as are executable files that consist of object files linked with library files.

Macro In Access, the means by which you choose how Access responds to events (such as clicking a command button or opening a form). Macros consist of one or more macro actions. Macros automate the operation of Access database applications. See also *Macro action*.

Macro action One of a collection of 42 predefined Access instructions, such as Beep (which sounds the Windows message beep) that may be incorporated into a macro.

Mantissa The first element of a number expressed in scientific notation that is multiplied by the power of 10 given in the exponent to obtain the actual number. For +1.23E3, the exponent is 3, so you multiply the mantissa, 1.23, by 1,000 (10 to the third power) to obtain the result, 1,230.

Master database A database that controls user access to other databases, usually in a client/server system. SYSTEM.MDA is the master database of Access.

Master table A table containing data on which detail data in another table is dependent. Master tables have a primary key that is matched to a foreign key in a detail table. Master tables often have a one-to-many relationship with detail tables.

MDI Child window See *Child*.

Menu A set of choices from which the user determines the next set of actions to take. The design of menus in Windows is governed by the CUA or Common User Access specification developed by IBM.

Meta file A type of graphics file that stores the objects displayed in the form of mathematical descriptions of lines and surfaces. Windows meta files that use the extension *.WMF are a special form of meta files.

Method One of the characteristics of an object and a classification of keywords in Access Basic. Methods determine the behavior of Access Basic objects.

Mission-critical A cliché used in software and hardware advertising to describe the necessity of using the promoted product if users want to create a reliable database system.

Modal A dialog box that must be closed before further action can be taken by the user.

Modeless A window or dialog box that may be closed or minimized by the user without taking any other action; the opposite of modal.

Module A block of code consisting of one or more functions or procedures for which the source code is stored in a single database object. In compiled language, a code module would be compiled to a single object file.

Module-level Variables and constants that are declared in the declarations section of a module. These have module-level scope and are visible (defined) to all procedures that are contained within the module.

Monitor A name often used in place of the more proper terms, *display* or *graphic display.*

Multimedia The technology that enables combining sound and graphic images within a single application for the purpose of selling new computer hardware and software.

Multitasking The capability of a computer with a single CPU to simulate the processing of more than one task at a time. Multitasking is effective when one or more of the applications spends most of its time in an idle state waiting for a user-initiated event, such as a keystroke or mouse click.

Multiuser Concurrent use of a single computer by more than one user, usually through the use of remote terminals.

Natural join A join in which the values of the columns involved in the join are compared. All columns of each table in the join that do not duplicate other columns are compared. A natural join is like an equi-join except that the joined columns are not duplicated in the result.

Nested An expression applied to procedures that call other procedures within an application. The called procedures are said to be nested within the calling procedure. When many calls to subprocedures and sub-subprocedures are made, the last one in the sequence is said to be deeply nested.

Nested query A SELECT statement that contains subqueries. See also *Subquery.*

NewLine A combination of a carriage return, the Enter key CR or Chr$(13) and line feed LF or Chr$(10), used to terminate a line of text on-screen or within a text file. Other characters or combinations may be substituted for the CR/LF pair to indicate the type of newline character (such as soft, hard, or delete), usually in word processing applications.

Nonclustered index An index that stores key values and pointers to data based on the values. In a nonclustered index, the leaf level points to data pages rather than to the data itself, as would be the case for a clustered index. Equivalent to SET INDEX TO *field_name* in xBase.

Normal forms A set of rules, the first three originally defined by Dr. E. F. Cobb, used to design relational databases. Five normal forms generally are accepted in the creation of relational databases. See also *First*, *Second*, *Third*, *Fourth*, and *Fifth normal form*.

Normalization Creating a database according to the five generally accepted rules of normal forms. See also *Normal forms*.

Not-equal join A JOIN statement that specifies that the columns engaged in the join do not equal one another. Access uses the WHERE clause with the <> (not equal) operator to create not-equal joins.

Null Having no value assigned. The NULL value is explicit in Access, and does not correspond to a zero numeric value, a blank (""), or null string value.

Object In programming, elements that combine data (properties) and behavior (methods) in a single container of code called an object. An Access Basic form or control object is a member of the class of Access Basic objects, of which a particular control object is a subclass member. Objects inherit their properties and methods from the classes above them in the hierarchy. Objects can modify the inherited properties and methods to suit their own purposes. The code container may be part of the language itself, or you may define your own objects in source code. An example of user-defined objects is the Access Basic custom control DLL in which you may create user-defined objects of the Access Basic class in the C language.

Object code Code in machine-readable form that can be executed by your computer's CPU and operating system.

Object permission Permission granted by the database owner for others to modify the values of database objects. See also *Statement permission*.

Offset The number of bytes from a reference point, usually the beginning of a file, to the byte of particular interest. When offset is used for location, the first byte in a file is always 0.

Operand One of the variables or constants on which an operator acts. In 1 + 2 = 3, 1 is an operand, as is 2; + and = are the operators.

Operating system Applications that translate basic instructions, such as keyboard input, to language understood by the computer. The most common operating systems used with personal computers are DOS (Disk Operating System), UNIX, and OS/2.

Operator A keyword or reserved symbol that acts on a single variable (in its unary form) or on two variables to give a result. Operators may be of the conventional mathematical type such as +, – (subtraction), /, and * (multiplication), as well as logical, such as And or Not. The unary minus (–), when applied to a single variable in a statement such as NumVar% = –NumVar%, inverts the sign of NumVar% from – to + or + to –.

Option button A synonym for *radio button*, the original terminology in the CUA specification. Option buttons are circular control objects with centers that fill when they are selected. If the option has a group of buttons, only one radio button of a group may be selected.

OS/2 An operating system developed jointly by Microsoft and IBM as a substitute for DOS. OS/2 Presentation Manager provides a CUA-compliant GUI similar to Microsoft Windows. Microsoft LAN Manager, the local area network under which the Microsoft SQL server commonly is run, operates under OS/2. Version 2 of OS/2 was released by IBM for distribution in 1992.

Outer join A join in which all rows of the joined tables are returned, whether or not a match is made between columns. The *= operator in a join returns all rows in the preceding table (a LEFT JOIN in Access), and =* returns all rows in the succeeding table (a RIGHT JOIN in Access).

Outer query A synonym for the primary query in a statement that includes a subquery.

Parameter The equivalent of an argument of a function but associated with a procedure. The terms *parameter* and *argument* often are used interchangeably. A parameter is a variable required by a procedure to perform its function, which is passed to the procedure by the calling statement. A parameter may be passed by reference; in this case, the procedure using it may change its value. If the parameter is passed by value, the value of the parameter as seen in the calling program is unchanged by any action on it by the procedure. The distinction is made between arguments of functions and parameters of procedures in this book, because Windows API functions often change the value of arguments passed to them, despite the precedence of the ByVal keyword in their prototype declarations.

Parse The process of determining whether a particular expression is contained within another expression. Parsing breaks program statements into keywords, operators, operands, arguments, and parameters for subsequent processing of each by the computer. Parsing string variables involves searching for the occurrence of a particular character or set of characters in the string and then taking a specified set of actions when the character or set is found or not found.

Permission Authority given by the system administrator or database owner to perform operations on a network or on data objects in a database.

Persistent (graphics) A Windows graphic image that survives the movement, resizing, or overwriting of the window in which it appears. Persistent images are stored in global memory blocks and are not released until the window containing them is destroyed.

Picture box An Access Basic object that can display graphics in the form of *.BMP and *.WMF files or code.

Pixel The smallest unit of measurement for video displays, representing the grain of the screen. Standard VGA color displays measure 640 by 480 pixels. Advanced (super) VGA displays are capable of displaying 800 by 600 pixels and, often, $1,024 \times 768$ pixels.

Point (1) In typography, the unit of measurement of the vertical dimension of a font, about 1/72 of an inch. (2) In Windows, a unit of measurement representing exactly 1/72 of a logical inch or 20 *twips*.

Poke In DDE terminology, the transmission of a data item that has not been requested to a DDE server by the DDE client. In Basic terminology, POKE is placing a byte of data in a specific memory location. Access Basic does not support the Basic POKE keyword and uses the DDEPoke method for DDE operations.

Precedence The order in which the operators in a statement are executed.

Primary key The column or columns with individual or combined values that uniquely identify a row in a table.

Print zone The area of a sheet of paper on which a printer can create an image. For most laser printers and standard dot-matrix printers, this area is 8 inches wide. The vertical dimension is unlimited for dot-matrix printers and usually 13.5 inches for a laser printer with legal-size paper capabilities.

Printer object An Access Basic object representing the printer chosen as the default by the Control Panel Printers Set Default option.

Procedure A self-contained collection of source code statements, executable as an entity. All Access Basic procedures begin with the reserved words Sub or Function and terminate with End Sub or End Function.

Program All the code required to create an application, consisting basically of declarations, statements, and, in Windows, resource definitions and Help files.

Project In Access Basic, a name for an application and its project file. The project file contains the names of the forms and modules that make up the program for the application and is similar to the MAKE files used with compilers and linkers.

Project Window The Access Basic window listing the names of the files making up the application. You can use the Project window to replace the default names of forms and modules with other names more representative of their use within the application.

Projection A projection identifies the desired subset of the columns contained in a table.

Property A principal characteristic of objects (the first is methods). Properties may be defined for an object or for the class of objects to which the particular object belongs, (called an *inherited* property).

Qualification A search condition that data values must meet to be included in the search.

Qualified To have the name of the database and the object's owner precede the name of a database object, or to have the drive designator and path precede the name of a file.

Query A request to retrieve data from a database with the SELECT command.

Random access files A category of files, defined by Access Basic (and other Basic dialects), consisting solely of the user-defined (or record) data type.

Record The logical equivalent of the row of a table. A set of related fields or columns of information that are treated as a unit by a DBM application.

Recursion A condition in which a procedure or function calls itself. As a general rule, you should avoid recursive procedures and functions in Access Basic unless you are an experienced programmer.

Referential integrity Rules that govern the relationships between primary keys and foreign keys of tables within a relational database and determine data consistency. Referential integrity requires that the values of every foreign key in every table be matched by the value of a primary key in another table.

Relation Synonym for *table* or *data table*.

Relational database management system or **RDBM** A database management system (DBM) that conforms to the rules for relational databases originally established by Dr. E. F. Codd. Unless otherwise specified, DBMs for personal computers are relational DBMs. DBMs that do not have relational capabilities are called *flat-file managers* or *file managers*. The Windows Cardfile applet is an example of a simple flat-file manager.

Relational operators Relational operators consist of operators such as >, <, <>, and = that compare the value of one operand with another and return True or False. The relational operators are sometimes called *comparative operators*.

Reserved word A synonym for *keyword*, sometimes used to indicate a subset of keywords that do not include embedded keywords.

Restriction A query statement that defines a subset of the rows of a table based on the value of one or more of its columns.

RGB A method of defining colors by using numbers to specify the individual intensities of red, green, and blue components—the colors created by the three guns of the color display CRT.

Rollback Canceling a proposed transaction that will modify one or more tables and undo changes, if any, made by the transaction before a COMMIT or COMMIT TRANSACTION statement.

Routine A synonym for *procedure*.

Row A set of related columns that describes a specific data entity. Row is a synonym for *record*.

Row aggregation functions Functions such as SUM, AVG, MIN, MAX, and COUNT. When the functions are located in a SELECT statement that includes a COMPUTE instruction, they generate a new row that contains their value.

Rule A specification that determines the type of data and value of data that may be entered in a column of a table.

Run mode The mode of Access Basic operation during which the interpreter is executing your source code. Microsoft calls Run mode *run-time*. The term run-time, however, normally refers to errors that occur while running the executable version of an application.

Sample In audio terminology, a digital representation of a sound created by a combination of microphone, amplifier, and analog-to-digital converter. Samples usually begin as relatively short and then are digitally processed by looping or other forms of repetition to create sounds of longer duration. Digital signal processing is used to change the pitch and other characteristics of samples so that a single sample may be used to create a range of notes.

Sampling rate The speed with which successive digital samples of a sound are recorded. Standard sample rates are 11.025, 22.05, and 44.l KHz. The fidelity of the sample improves with increasing sampling rate or frequency, but storage requirements also increase.

Scope In programming, the extent of visibility (definition) of a variable. Access Basic has this scope: global (visible to all procedures in the application), form (visible to all objects and procedures within a single form), module (visible to all procedures in a single module file), and local (visible only within the procedure in which declared). The scope of a variable depends on where it is declared. See also *Global*, *Local*, and *Module-level*.

Screen object An Access Basic object and object class defined as the entire usable area of the video display unit. All visible form and control objects are members of subclasses of the screen object.

Scroll bar In Access Basic, vertical and/or horizontal bars at the right side and bottom, respectively, of a multiline text box that enable the user to scroll the window to expose otherwise hidden text. Other Windows applications enable you to scroll windows containing graphic objects; Access Basic does not.

Second normal form The relational database rule that requires columns which are not key fields to each be related to the key field. A row may not contain values in data cells that do not pertain to the value of the key field. In an invoice item table, for example, the columns of each row must pertain solely to the value of the invoice number key field.

Seek To locate a specific byte, record, or chunk within a disk file.

Select list The list of column names, separated by commas, that specify the columns to be included in the result of a SELECT instruction.

Selection See *Restriction*.

Self-join A join used to compare values within a single column of a table. Self-joins join a table with itself, requiring that the table have two different names, one of which must be an alias.

Separator A reserved symbol used to distinguish one item from another. An example is the use of the exclamation point (bang character) in Access Basic to separate the name of an object class from a specific object of the class, and an object contained in specified object: Forms![Personnel Actions]![txtID], for example.

Sequencer A device or application that records and plays back musical compositions in MIDI message format. Computer sequencers enable you to compose and edit MIDI scores. High-end keyboard synthesizers often incorporate sequencers.

Sequential access file A file in which one record follows another in the sequence applicable to the application. Text files usually are sequential.

Server (computer network) A computer on a LAN that provides services or resources to client computers by sharing its devices. Servers may be dedicated, sharing their resources but not using the resources themselves except in performing administrative tasks. Servers in client/server databases usually are dedicated. Servers also may be used to run applications for users. In the latter case, such servers often are called *peer-to-peer* servers, because any client on the LAN that supports peer-to-peer servers may share its resources with any other client.

Server (DDE and OLE) The device or application that provides data to a client device or application that may use, modify, and return the data to the server. The data may be in the form of a file on a network file server, an object in an OLE server, or the topic of a DDE server (usually a file).

Shared lock A lock, created by read-only operations, that does not enable its creator to modify the data. Other users can place shared locks on data so that they can read it, but no user may apply an exclusive lock on the data while any shared locks are in effect.

Shortcut key A key combination that provides quick access to a menu choice, macro, or other function of the application in lieu of selection with the mouse. Also called an *accelerator key*.

Single-stepping A debugging process by which the source code is executed one line at a time to enable you to inspect the value of variables, find infinite loops, or remove other types of bugs.

Sizing handles The small black rectangles on the perimeter of Access Basic control objects in Design mode. You drag the rectangles to shrink or enlarge sizeable control objects.

Source code The readable form of code that you create in a high-level language. Source code is converted to machine language object code by a compiler or interpreter.

SQL An acronym, pronounced "sequel" or "seekel," for Structured Query Language, a language developed by IBM for processing data contained in mainframe computer databases. SQL now has been institutionalized by the creation of an ANSI standard for the language.

Statement An instruction to the computer that contains at least one keyword or operator valid in the language. Statement often is used as a synonym for *command*. In SQL, statements must begin with an SQL keyword.

Statement permission Permission granted by the owner of a database for other users to execute specified SQL statements that act on the database's objects.

Static (1) A variable that will retain its last value until another is assigned, although the procedure in which it is defined has completed execution. All global variables are static. Variables declared static are similar to global variables; however, their visibility is limited to their declared scope. (2) Distinguishes between statically linked (conventional) executable files and those that use DLLs.

Stored procedure A set of SQL statements and, with some DBMs, flow-control statements that are stored under a procedure name that can be executed as a group. Some DBMs, such as Microsoft SQL Server, compile stored procedures in advance so that they execute more rapidly.

String A data type used to contain textual material, such as alphabetical characters and punctuation symbols. Numbers may be included in or may constitute the value of string variables but cannot be manipulated by mathematical operators.

Structure Two or more keywords used together to create an instruction that usually is conditional. See also *Compound*.

Structured Query Language See *SQL*.

Stub A procedure or user-defined function that, in Access Basic, consists only of Sub SubName...End Sub or Function FnName...End Function lines with no intervening code. Stubs are created by Access Basic for events. Stubs are used to block out the procedures required by the application that can be called by the main program. The intervening code statements are filled in during the programming process.

Style In typography, a characteristic or set of attributes of a member of a family of typefaces created by an outline or bit map, designed specifically to implement the style. Styles include bold, italic, bold italic, bold italic condensed, and others. Styles may contain attributes for weight (bold, demi-bold, black), form (italic, Roman), and spacing (compressed, extended) in various combinations.

Submenu A set of choices presented when a main menu choice is made. In Windows, the first level submenu is similar to a drop-down dialog box. The second level submenu is usually a fly-out menu that appears horizontally at the point of the first submenu choice.

Subquery A SELECT statement that is included (nested) within another SELECT, INSERT, UPDATE, or DELETE statement or within another subquery.

Syntax The rules governing the expression of a language. Like English, Spanish, Esperanto, or Swahili, each programming languages has its own syntax. Some programming languages allow much more latitude (irregular forms) in their syntax. Access Basic has a relatively rigid syntax; the C programming language provides more flexibility but is more complex.

System administrator The individual responsible for the administrative functions for all applications on a LAN or users of a UNIX cluster or network, usually including supervising all databases on servers attached to the LAN. If the administrator's responsibility is limited to databases, the term *database administrator* ordinarily is assigned.

System colors The 16 standard colors used by Windows for elements such as backgrounds, scroll bars, borders, and title bars. You may use Control Panel Color and Desktop functions to change the system colors.

System databases Databases that control access to databases on a server or across a LAN. Microsoft SQL Server has three system databases: the master database, which controls user databases; tempdb, which holds temporary tables; and model, which is used as the skeleton to create new user databases. Any database that is not a user database is a system database.

System function Functions that return data about the database rather than about the content of the database.

System tables A data dictionary table that maintains information on DBM users and each database under the control of the system.

Tab order The order in which the focus is assigned to multiple control objects within a form or dialog box with successive presses of the Tab key.

Table A database object consisting of a group of rows (records) divided into columns (fields) that contain data or NULL values. Access treats a table as a database device.

TCP/IP A network protocol originally developed by the U.S. military to create a secure network in case of atomic attack. TCP/IP is now one of the most common protocols used by UNIX networks.

Text box A Windows object designed to receive printable characters typed from the keyboard. Access Basic provides two basic types of objects: single- and multiline. Entries in single-line text boxes are terminated by pressing Enter. Multiline text boxes accept more than one line of text, either by a self-contained word-wrap feature (if a horizontal scroll bar is not present) or by a Ctrl+Enter key combination.

Text file A disk file containing characters with values ordinarily ranging from Chr$(1) through Chr$(127) in which lines of text are separated from one another with newline pairs of Chr$(13) + Chr$(10).

TFTP An abbreviation for Trivial File Transfer Protocol, an Internet communication protocol for transferring files to and from a UNIX host.

Theta join A join operation that uses comparison or relational operators in the JOIN statement. See also *Operator*.

Third normal form The relational database rule requiring that one column may not be dependent on another column when the columns are not key columns. The third normal form generally is considered the most important, because it is the first in the series that is not intuitive.

Time stamp The date and time data attributes applied to a disk file when the user creates or edits the file.

Title bar The heading area, usually blue, of a window in which the title of the window appears, usually in white.

Toggle A property of an object, such as a checkbox, that alternates its state when repeatedly clicked with the mouse or activated by a shortcut key combination.

Toolbar A group of command buttons, arranged horizontally across the top of a window, which perform functions ordinarily requiring one or more menu choices.

Toolbox A collection of command buttons designated as tools, usually with icons substituted for the default appearance of a command button. Toolbox buttons enable you to choose a method applicable to an object (usually graphic) until you select another tool. An example is the Access Basic toolbox.

Topic In DDE conversations, the name of the file or other identifying title of a collection of data. When used with Help files, topic is the name of the subject matter of a single Help screen display.

TRANSACT-SQL ANSI SQL plus additional SQL keywords used by Microsoft SQL Server. TRANSACT-SQL includes flow control instructions and the capability to use stored procedures.

Transaction A group of processing steps that is treated as a single activity to perform a desired result. A transaction can entail all the steps necessary to modify the values in or add records to each table involved when a new invoice is created. DBMs capable of transaction processing usually include the capability to cancel the transaction by a rollback instruction or to cause the transaction to become a permanent part of the tables with the COMMIT or COMMIT TRANSACTION statement.

Trigger A stored procedure that occurs when a user executes an instruction which may affect the referential integrity of a database. Triggers usually occur prior to the execution of INSERT, DELETE, or UPDATE statements so that the effect of the statement on referential integrity can be examined by a stored procedure prior to execution. See also *Stored procedure*.

Twip The smallest unit of measurement in Windows and the default unit of measurement of Access Basic.

Type See *Data type*.

Typeface A set of fonts of a single family in any available size. The set of fonts must have an identical style or set of attributes.

Unary See *Operator*.

Unique index An index in which no two records may have field values or combinations of field values that are equal in the field(s) used to create the index.

UNIX The AT&T registered trademark for a multiuser operating system. Extensions and modifications of UNIX include DEC Ultrix, SCO UNIX, IBM AIX, and similar products.

Update A permanent change to data values in one or more data tables. An update occurs when Access executes the INSERT, DELETE, UPDATE, or TRUNCATE TABLE command.

User-defined A data type, also called a *record*, that may be defined in your Access Basic source code by a Type...End Type declaration statement in the global module.

User-defined transaction A group of instructions combined under a single name and processed as a block when the name is invoked in a statement executed by the user.

Variable The name representing or substituting for a number (numeric), letter, or combination of letters (string).

WAN An acronym for *Wide Area Network*. A system of multiple computers in different geographical locations that are interconnected through the switched telephone network or leased data lines, by optical or other long-distance cabling, or by infrared or radio links.

WAVE file A file containing waveform audio data, usually with a *.WAV extension.

Waveform audio A data type standard of the Windows Multimedia Extensions that defines how digitally sampled sounds are stored in files and processed by Windows API functions calls.

Wild card A character that substitutes for and allows a match by any character or set of characters in its place. Windows applications use the DOS ? and * wild cards similarly.

Workstation A client computer on a LAN or WAN used to run applications and connected to a server from which it obtains data shared with other computers. Some network servers, although not many, can be used as both a server and a workstation: Microsoft LAN Manager and Windows NT, for example.

xBase Any language or database manager built on the dBASE III+ model and incorporating all dBASE III+ commands and functions. Microsoft FoxPro and Computer Associates Clipper are xBase dialects. Most xBase database managers add a substantial number of commands and functions to the dBASE III+ vocabulary. While xBase DBMs often do not use the same index file structure as dBASE III+, they all use the same database file (*.DBF) structure.

Naming Conventions for Access Objects

This appendix describes a set of Access naming conventions compiled by Greg Reddick. The author has made minor additions, a few changes, and some edits to Reddick's text. The conventions listed in this appendix use a method of naming called *Hungarian*, referring to the nationality of the naming conventions inventor, Charles Simonyi (who, incidentally, worked on Access for a period). The naming conventions have been adapted to correspond to the Access development environment.

Using these naming conventions may seem a little strange at first (like reading Hungarian), but soon you find that using them becomes second nature. Eventually, you find reading code that doesn't use these conventions to be tedious.

Access object names consist of three parts: a prefix, a tag, and a qualifier. The prefix and qualifier, however, aren't always present.

Using Tags

Tags generally are short (typically one to four letters) and mnemonic. Some of the tag names in this document derive from the C programming language, so the mnemonic connection is somewhat stretched in Access Basic. For example, *w* is used for integer because integers are stored internally as a word (16 bits, 2 bytes). You cannot use *i* to indicate integer because *i* is used as a data type prefix for indexes.

The following list includes tags for objects used by Access or Visual Basic. Not all of these objects occur in both Access and Visual Basic. *Picture box*, for example, is a Visual Basic object and has no direct counterpart in Access. On the other hand, Access bound object frame objects have no corresponding object type in Visual Basic. Table B.1 lists the proposed naming conventions and provides examples of their uses.

Table B.1. Objects and Their Corresponding Tags

Object	Tag	Example with Qualifier
Bound object frame	bof	bofAudioFile
Chart	cht	chtSales
Check box	chk	chkReadOnly
Combo box	cbo	cboEnglish
Command button	cmd	cmdCancel
Database	db	dbAchievers
Directory list box	dir	dirSource
Drive list box	drv	drvTarget
Dynaset	rsd	rsdOverAchiever
File List box	fil	filSource
Form	frm	frmFileOpen
Frame	fra	fraLanguage
Grid	grd	grdPrices
Horizontal scroll bar	hsb	hsbVolume
Image	img	imgIcon
Label	lbl	lblHelpMessage

Object	Tag	Example with Qualifier
Line	lin	linVertical
List box	lst	lstPolicyCodes
Macro	mcr	mcrMain
Menu	mnu	mnuFileOpen
Module	mod	modLibrary
OLE object	ole	oleObject1
Option button	opt	optFrench
Option group	grp	grpChoices
Page break	brk	brk
Picture box	pic	picDiskSpace
Query object	qry	qryOverAchiever
QueryDef	qdf	qdfOverAchiever
Report	rpt	rptFireList
Shape (for example, rectangle)	shp	shpCircle
Snapshot	rss	rssThisQuery
Subform	sbf	sbfMany
Subreport	sbr	sbrNewReport
Table	tbl	tblCustomer
Text box	txt	txtGetText
Timer	tmr	tmrAlarm
Unbound object frame	uof	uofLogo
Vertical scroll bar	vsb	vsbRate

Note that the *rsd* and *rss* tags for Dynaset and Snapshot, respectively, include *rs* because both are types of record sets.

When you declare a variable with one of the object data types listed in table B.1, the tag defines the variable's data type, and the qualifier is the name of the object (without spaces or punctuation).

Tags for Access Basic Variables

Tags commonly are used to identify the data type and size property of Access Basic variables that have corresponding data types in other languages. In the majority of cases, C or Windows programming conventions are used for these tags. C, of course, doesn't support the Currency and Variant data types of Access Basic and Visual Basic 2.0 and treats fixed-length strings as an array of the char type. C and Windows use *lp* to indicate a pointer of the long type, but neither Access Basic nor Visual Basic supports pointer variables. Therefore, the *dw* tag, an abbreviation for *double-word*, is used to indicate a long integer, as is common in specifying the data type of arguments passed to Windows functions. Table B.2 lists the tags that specify data types not listed in table B.1.

Table B.2. Proposed Tags Based on Data Type

Data Type	Tag	Example with Qualifier
Integer	w	wRetValue
Long	dw	dwParam
Single	s	sLoadFactor
Double	d	dPi
Currency	mny	mnySalary
String, fixed-length	sf	sfContact
String, variable-length	sz	szName
Variant	v	vInput

Tip for C programmers: *sz* usually means *zero terminated string*, which, strictly speaking, isn't how Access Basic stores strings. Access Basic strings can be passed as though they are zero-terminated strings, however, so the same tag is used. The As String keywords are used to declare variables as strings when adding arguments to Windows functions identified by the Declare keyword. Access Basic and Visual Basic pass the argument to the function as a C *lpsz*, a long pointer to a zero-terminated string.

Tags for User-Defined Data Types

When creating a user-defined data type (also called a *record type*), you always use a created tag. By convention, the created tag is capitalized. When you create a user-defined data type with a declarative such as the following:

```
Type NAM
    sfFirst  As String * 15
    sfMiddle As String * 15
    sfLast   As String * 20
End Type
```

you declare variables of type NAM with the created tag in lowercase, as in the following:

```
Dim namAdd As NAM
```

This convention removes any ambiguity about the data type of namAdd, as long as you use one of the standard object tags. When you refer to a field of the record, as in the following:

```
szLastName = RTrim$(namAdd.sfLast)
```

the data types of the record and the field are identified properly.

Context Tags

When you use a value in a context other than a simple variable, you should use a different tag, even if the data type is one listed in table B.2. Table B.3 provides examples of context-based prefixes that you substitute for the data type tags of table B.2. The tag *f*, for *flag*, is used to identify the Boolean or logical variable, typed as an integer in Access Basic and Visual Basic.

Table B.3. Tags Based on Use or Context of a Variable

Use of Variable	Prefix	Example with Qualifier
Boolean (Yes/No)	f	fReturnValue
Character	ch	chLetterLastPressed
Handle	h	hCursor
Handle to a window	hwnd	hwndForm
Handle to a device	hdc	hdcPrinter
Bit	b	bMin

To expand further on context tags, assume that you have written Access Basic code that determines the validity of an address. 1 is a valid address, 2 is the last known address, 3 is no address, and so on. If this code is used frequently, then you invent a new tag, rather than use *w*. For example, *vad* may indicate a valid address; therefore, *vadShipTo* would contain the validity code for the ship to address.

Using Prefixes

Prefixes modify data type tags to provide additional information about the variable. Tags and prefixes are concatenated to create the variable name, as shown in the examples of common prefixes in table B.4.

Table B.4. Common Prefixes for Types of Variables

Type of Data	Prefix	Example with Qualifier	Description
Array	rg	rgwStock	Array of integers
Index into array	i	irgwStock	Index into rgwStock
	i	ilstPickList	Index into a list box
Count	c	cchSzName	Count of chars in szName
	c	clstPickList	Count of items in a list box
Group	gr	grbClass	Group of Class bits
Unused	zz	zzfrmNames	An unused form

The difference between a group and an array is that you can use an index into an array but you must use code to specify a particular member of a group. Indexes are integers unless specified otherwise.

Using Common Variable Qualifiers

Although the prefix and tag are sufficient to fully specify a variable's type, they may not be sufficient to distinguish one variable from another. When two variables of the same type are within the same scope, further specification is required to remove ambiguities. This specification is achieved with qualifiers. A *qualifier* is a short descriptive word that indicates the variable's use. You can use multiple words. The first letter of the qualifier is capitalized, as is the first letter of each additional word. You concatenate the qualifier without using intervening spaces.

The data type prefix *rgw* is a perfectly valid and complete variable name for an array, as are *frm* for a form and *sz* for a string; however, you can have only one distinct variable of each type in a procedure. Table B.5 lists some common qualifiers.

Table B.5. Common Qualifiers for Variable Names

Purpose	Qualifier	Example
First element of set	First	irgwFirst
Last element of set	Last	irgwLast
Lower limit of set	Min	irgszNamesMin
Upper limit of set	Max	irgszNamesMax
Invalid value	Nil	hwndNil
Temporary variable	T	wT
Source	Src	dwBufferSrc
Destination	Dest	dwBufferDest

The common qualifiers usually are appended to the rest of the qualifier name.

When you are constructing a database, you may use the same qualifier name for the following elements: the table, the main form and subform for accessing the table, the main macro sheet for the form, the main report and subreport for the table, the main query for the table. A database has a table called tblCustomerName, for example. The form for entering the customers is called frmCustomerName, for example. The macro for the form is mcrCustomerName. The report that lists all customer names is rptCustomerName.

Using Function Names

You construct function names just as you construct variable names, with the exception that the first letters are the tag of the return type of the function. Always capitalize the first letter of a function. SzGetFormName, for example, returns a variable-length string. A function name without a tag indicates that the function doesn't return a value.

Getting Updates of Proposed Conventions

The name of the file on CompuServe that contained Greg Reddick's (CompuServe ID 71501,2564) compilation was NAMING.ZIP. NAMING.ZIP contains the Word for Windows 2 document file, NAMING.DOC. Reddick dedicated the contents of this document to the public domain. As amendments to the naming conventions are made, the file name probably will change. To find the latest version of the Access Basic naming conventions, use the IBM File Finder (GO IBMFF) and search for files uploaded with the user ID 71501,2564.

Binary and Hexadecimal Arithmetic

A knowledge of binary and hexadecimal arithmetic is useful when you write Access Basic code. In some cases, you cannot avoid dealing with hexadecimal arithmetic. To understand hexadecimal arithmetic, you need to have a grasp of binary notation. This appendix provides the background you need to handle hexadecimal values in Access Basic.

The Windows Calculator has the capability of performing both decimal and hexadecimal arithmetic. Launch the Calculator, choose View, and select Scientific mode. You see the Hex(adecimal), Dec(imal), Oct(al), and Bin(ary) option buttons, with Dec set as the default. You can enter a decimal number and then click the Hex button to see its hexadecimal representation. You also can enter hexadecimal numbers, with the Hex button selected, and convert the numbers to their decimal equivalents by clicking Dec. Octal arithmetic uses 8 digits, instead of 10 (decimal) or 16 (hexadecimal), and Bin expresses numbers as a series of 1s and 0s that represent powers of 2, starting with 0 in the far right position. The logic of this representation is explained in sections of this appendix.

The Basics of Binary Arithmetic

In decimal arithmetic, the position of each digit of a number represents a power of 10, starting at the right. *Powers*, if you don't remember them from school, mean the number of times the number is multiplied by itself. 10 is 10 to the first power (multiplied by 1), 100 is 10 to the second power (multiplied by itself once), 10,000 is 10 to the fourth power, and so on. The number that you multiply is called the *radix* of the number system. By convention, the 0 power of any number is defined as 1. The power of a number also is called its *exponent*.

Binary notation simply substitutes 2 for 10 used by the decimal system. In binary arithmetic, the radix is 2—that is, the position of each digit represents a power of two. Therefore, 4 is 2 to the second power, 16 is 2 to the fourth power, and so on. Table C.1 shows the similarity between decimal and binary notation.

Table C.1. Powers or Exponents in Decimal and Binary Notation

Power or Exponent	Decimal Notation	Binary Notation
0	1	1
1	10	2
2	10 * 10 = 100	2 * 2 = 4
3	10 * 10 * 10 = 1,000	2 * 2 * 2 = 8
4	10 * 10 * 10 * 10 = 10,000	2 * 2 * 2 * 2 = 16
5	10 * 10 * 10 * 10 * 10 = 100,000	2 * 2 * 2 * 2 * 2 = 32

When a number is expressed in binary notation, the far right bit (called the *least-significant*, or *LSB*) represents the decimal number 1, which is equal to 2^0 (2 to the 0 power). Binary notation reads from right to left. Each additional bit to the left of the LSB represents an increasing power of 2, as table C.2 shows.

Table C.2. Decimal Values of the First 8 Powers of 2

Power of 2 (Bit)	7	6	5	4	3	2	1	0
Decimal Value	128	64	32	16	8	4	2	1

The decimal value of a binary number is determined by adding the value of each bit set to 1, as shown in table C.3, which contains a collection of 8 binary bits that represent the binary number 0101 0101.

Table C.3. Adding Decimal Values of Bits to Arrive at the Decimal Value of an 8-Bit Byte									
Bit Pattern	0	1	0	1	0	1	0	1	= 1 byte (8 bits)
Decimal Value		64	+	16	+	4	+	1	= 85 (letter U)

If all 8 bits are set (have the value 1), the decimal value of the resulting binary number, 1111 1111, is 255. Using spaces to set off groups of 4 bits is common when expressing values in binary form.

Bytes, Words, and Hexadecimal Notation

Information used by your computer is classified as instructions or data. Both classes of information are stored in random-access memory (RAM) integrated circuits, called *chips*, and usually are referred to simply as *memory*. PCs store data in 8-bit groups called *bytes*, which are the basic units of measure of your computer's RAM. The 0101 0101 pattern for U, for example, is 1 byte.

Each byte of memory has an assigned location called an *address*. Instructions tell the central processing unit (CPU), the heart of your PC, the addresses of the data they need and what action to perform on the data—such as adding or subtracting numbers or simply moving the data to a new location. Data and instructions are stored in separate areas in memory.

If you tried the Windows Calculator tip, you saw the three option buttons: Word, DWord, and Byte. When 2 bytes are required for data or instructions, they are called *words* and are 16 bits long. Integers are stored in words. Sometimes 4 bytes must be processed together; these 32-bit groups are called *double words* or DWords. DWords are used to store long integers, the Access Basic Long data type. In Appendix B, double words are given the data type tag *dw*.

Hexadecimal notation is the equivalent of representing the value of 4-bit groups within a byte, word, or double word that is represented by the 16 characters 0 through F. This notation is much more convenient than writing four 1s or 0s. Because the 4-bit pattern 1111 represents 15 (1 + 2 + 4 + 8), you need 6 single-character substitutes to represent the numbers 10 through 15. The letters A through F are added for this purpose. Therefore, FF in hexadecimal notation equals decimal 255. Half a byte (4 bits) is called a *nibble*.

When hexadecimal notation is used in texts, you see various types of symbols which identify it as hex, such as %h, %H, &H, 0x, H, h, and so on. Access Basic, QuickBASIC, QBasic, and Visual Basic use the &H prefix, whereas the C programming language identifies hexadecimal numbers with the 0x prefix. Another similar type of notation is called *octal*. This notation uses 8 as its base (or radix) rather than 16. Octal notation seldom is used in today's computers.

As the value of the number increases, it takes more hexadecimal digits to represent it. Therefore, if you enter **123456789** in the Windows Calculator's Decimal mode, changing to Hexadecimal displays 75BCD15, but only if the DWord option button is selected. A double word is necessary to represent 9-digit decimal numbers. The hexadecimal result is truncated from the left if you choose Word or Byte for large values.

Values for the STK_21.XLS Worksheet

This appendix contains data for 50 of the 305 stocks, 7 indexes, and 2 futures whose high, low, and close quotations and trading volume (where applicable) have been compiled by Ideas Unlimited of Bellerose, New York, 11426 (CompuServe ID 76064,3727). Ideas Unlimited has daily data available for the 305 stocks starting from December 1988. Five days of stock prices for the 50 stocks, starting from April 10, 1992, are included here so that you can enter them into an Excel or 1-2-3 for Windows worksheet. You can use this data for the sample applications of Chapter 15, "Using Access with Microsoft Excel," and Chapter 23, "Exchanging Data with Access Basic DDE."

Details for downloading the complete sample worksheet, STK_21.WK1, from CompuServe are provided in Chapter 15. The sample worksheet contains 21 days of data for the 305 stocks and includes a text file and order form. You also can order stock data for specific dates by sending an E-mail message to Ideas Unlimited on CompuServe.

	A	B	C	D	E	F
1		10-Apr-92	13-Apr-92	14-Apr-92	15-Apr-92	16-Apr-92
2	AAL-S	18.500	18.250	18.750	19.125	19.000
3	High	19.250	18.500	18.875	19.250	19.125
4	Low	18.500	18.125	18.500	18.875	18.875
5	Volume	59200.000	52800.000	84000.000	63400.000	16700.000
6	AAQ-S	55.500	56.500	58.750	60.500	59.000
7	High	57.500	56.750	59.250	60.875	60.750
8	Low	55.000	55.250	57.250	57.500	58.500
9	Volume	2447000.000	1078200.000	1289300.000	1940700.000	2309700.000
10	AA-S	68.000	73.750	71.750	74.500	76.625
11	High	68.750	73.875	73.750	74.875	76.750
12	Low	68.000	67.000	71.250	72.000	74.375
13	Volume	381900.000	270800.000	1162900.000	723900.000	1079600.000
14	ABT-S	65.250	65.625	67.250	66.375	64.875
15	High	66.125	65.750	67.875	67.750	66.000
16	Low	64.625	64.875	65.625	65.625	64.375
17	Volume	1328400.000	561800.000	739900.000	898900.000	894700.000
18	ABY-S	12.375	12.375	12.500	12.125	12.250
19	High	12.500	12.375	12.500	12.375	12.250
20	Low	12.375	12.375	12.375	12.125	12.125
21	Volume	2900.000	200.000	1500.000	3700.000	2400.000
22	ACY-S	61.875	62.375	64.375	64.500	62.625
23	High	62.625	62.750	64.375	64.750	64.750
24	Low	61.500	61.750	62.625	63.750	62.500
25	Volume	199400.000	168600.000	340400.000	129100.000	295100.000
26	ADM-S	25.000	25.375	25.625	24.375	23.875
27	High	25.125	25.500	26.000	25.875	24.500
28	Low	24.500	24.875	25.500	24.000	23.625
29	Volume	1819500.000	646900.000	679200.000	2912100.000	3101600.000
30	AEP-S	31.250	31.125	31.625	32.000	32.250
31	High	31.375	31.250	31.875	32.000	32.250
32	Low	31.000	31.000	31.375	31.500	32.000
33	Volume	214300.000	123600.000	296900.000	219600.000	279300.000
34	AET-S	43.500	44.000	43.625	43.125	43.250
35	High	43.750	44.500	44.250	43.750	43.250
36	Low	42.500	43.750	43.625	43.000	42.500
37	Volume	160700.000	294000.000	197200.000	269300.000	186200.000
38	AGC-S	41.875	41.375	42.125	42.375	42.625
39	High	42.000	42.000	42.250	42.375	42.625
40	Low	41.750	41.250	41.250	42.000	42.125
41	Volume	66400.000	107100.000	164000.000	110200.000	217900.000
42	AHC-S	39.375	40.000	41.375	42.375	42.375
43	High	40.500	40.125	41.500	42.375	42.625
44	Low	39.250	39.250	40.000	41.500	42.250
45	Volume	213300.000	133300.000	337100.000	400100.000	244100.000
46	AHM-S	16.375	16.625	16.625	16.625	16.750
47	High	16.625	16.625	16.750	16.875	17.000

	A	B	C	D	E	F
48	Low	16.125	16.250	16.000	16.500	16.500
49	Volume	266000.000	178900.000	321200.000	192800.000	242800.000
50	AHP-S	76.875	77.750	81.625	80.000	78.250
51	High	77.750	77.750	82.000	81.875	80.000
52	Low	76.750	77.000	78.000	79.750	77.750
53	Volume	561800.000	227100.000	1056400.000	443900.000	697500.000
54	AIG-S	85.375	85.500	86.750	87.250	86.750
55	High	86.000	85.625	87.750	87.500	87.500
56	Low	84.750	84.875	86.000	86.375	86.500
57	Volume	226200.000	231000.000	370000.000	335100.000	337700.000
58	AIT-S	58.750	58.875	59.375	59.625	60.750
59	High	58.875	59.375	59.500	59.625	60.750
60	Low	58.625	58.500	58.875	59.250	59.750
61	Volume	336700.000	191200.000	169800.000	250600.000	433400.000
62	ALD-S	53.750	53.750	54.625	55.500	57.000
63	High	54.125	54.375	55.750	55.500	57.125
64	Low	53.000	53.000	53.875	54.500	55.250
65	Volume	368100.000	316600.000	422600.000	415300.000	697500.000
66	ALK-S	18.125	17.750	17.500	17.875	18.125
67	High	18.125	18.000	17.750	17.875	18.250
68	Low	17.500	17.625	17.375	17.375	17.750
69	Volume	37400.000	55200.000	89100.000	64800.000	63800.000
70	AL-S	19.625	20.625	20.125	20.250	20.875
71	High	19.625	20.625	20.375	20.250	21.125
72	Low	19.500	19.500	19.875	20.125	20.375
73	Volume	184200.000	605900.000	599000.000	260800.000	785600.000
74	ALS-S	32.000	32.250	32.125	31.875	32.250
75	High	32.000	32.500	32.500	32.250	32.375
76	Low	31.250	32.000	32.125	31.875	31.750
77	Volume	43000.000	25100.000	50800.000	35300.000	11900.000
78	AMB-S	46.250	46.375	47.750	46.750	46.750
79	High	46.375	46.875	47.750	47.750	47.000
80	Low	45.500	46.375	46.500	46.625	46.375
81	Volume	267600.000	297000.000	239100.000	307900.000	278100.000
82	AMD-S	16.625	16.625	17.375	17.500	16.875
83	High	17.250	16.750	17.750	17.750	17.500
84	Low	16.375	16.375	16.750	17.250	16.625
85	Volume	1669600.000	473900.000	1700100.000	943400.000	824800.000
86	AMH-S	14.375	14.750	15.000	15.125	15.125
87	High	15.000	14.750	15.250	15.250	15.125
88	Low	14.000	14.500	14.875	14.875	14.875
89	Volume	503200.000	262600.000	451100.000	198900.000	163800.000
90	AMI-S	8.875	8.875	9.250	9.000	9.125
91	High	9.000	8.875	9.250	9.250	9.125
92	Low	8.750	8.750	9.000	9.000	8.875
93	Volume	29400.000	15900.000	77300.000	64200.000	57000.000
94	AMP-S	58.000	58.375	59.750	60.625	61.625

	A	B	C	D	E	F
95	High	58.625	58.375	60.000	60.750	61.625
96	Low	58.000	58.000	59.125	59.875	60.500
97	Volume	245400.000	58800.000	280900.000	185800.000	261000.000
98	AMR-S	69.875	67.500	69.875	71.000	70.625
99	High	72.500	69.750	70.375	71.875	71.500
100	Low	69.875	67.250	67.750	69.375	69.875
101	Volume	668200.000	1000900.000	1160200.000	961500.000	400900.000
102	AMX-S	17.750	18.875	19.625	20.125	20.500
103	High	17.750	18.875	20.125	20.125	20.625
104	Low	17.250	17.625	19.125	19.750	20.000
105	Volume	273300.000	354200.000	903200.000	356100.000	525300.000
106	AN-S	43.250	43.250	44.500	45.250	45.500
107	High	44.000	43.375	45.000	45.250	45.750
108	Low	43.125	42.875	42.750	44.250	45.125
109	Volume	466000.000	301400.000	674400.000	561600.000	895500.000
110	ARC-S	106.000	106.750	107.000	103.375	105.250
111	High	106.625	106.750	107.250	105.875	105.250
112	Low	105.125	105.500	106.250	103.250	103.500
113	Volume	171000.000	187300.000	241000.000	473900.000	316500.000
114	ASA-S	44.375	43.875	43.625	41.375	41.375
115	High	45.000	44.500	44.000	43.625	41.500
116	Low	44.250	43.875	43.500	41.250	41.125
117	Volume	51900.000	46800.000	35900.000	111400.000	107900.000
118	ASH-S	32.375	32.375	32.250	32.625	32.500
119	High	32.875	32.625	32.500	32.750	32.750
120	Low	32.375	32.125	32.000	32.250	32.125
121	Volume	21200.000	103500.000	60200.000	182900.000	70400.000
122	AS-S	5.625	5.625	5.625	5.875	5.875
123	High	5.625	5.625	5.750	5.875	5.875
124	Low	5.375	5.500	5.500	5.750	5.625
125	Volume	156600.000	110700.000	143600.000	209200.000	165200.000
126	AUD-S	43.875	43.500	45.125	46.375	46.500
127	High	44.000	43.875	45.125	47.000	46.500
128	Low	43.625	43.500	43.625	45.625	45.375
129	Volume	318200.000	166800.000	386900.000	409100.000	259500.000
130	AVP-S	48.875	48.750	49.875	49.875	49.375
131	High	49.000	49.125	49.875	50.125	50.000
132	Low	47.375	48.625	48.875	49.500	48.000
133	Volume	264700.000	208800.000	219700.000	270800.000	550200.000
134	AVT-S	24.750	25.375	26.000	25.875	25.750
135	High	25.000	25.375	26.000	26.000	25.875
136	Low	24.750	24.750	25.250	25.875	25.375
137	Volume	147900.000	188300.000	263700.000	193400.000	148600.000
138	AXP-S	22.375	22.500	22.625	22.875	23.000
139	High	22.875	22.625	23.125	22.875	23.125
140	Low	22.125	22.125	22.500	22.500	22.750
141	Volume	967400.000	508100.000	1840200.000	1300700.000	1887100.000

	A	B	C	D	E	F
142	BAC-S	41.125	41.250	43.000	42.625	43.500
143	High	41.375	41.250	43.625	43.625	43.875
144	Low	40.625	40.875	41.625	42.625	43.250
145	Volume	796200.000	466600.000	1464000.000	919600.000	1182600.000
146	BA-S	44.750	45.750	46.375	47.125	47.250
147	High	45.000	45.875	46.625	47.125	47.500
148	Low	43.625	45.000	46.125	46.375	46.875
149	Volume	1019000.000	730700.000	1099000.000	1032700.000	1463300.000
150	BAX-S	36.750	37.375	38.625	39.250	37.875
151	High	37.125	37.500	39.000	39.500	39.250
152	Low	36.500	36.875	37.500	38.875	37.500
153	Volume	596700.000	594400.000	1009100.000	851900.000	902200.000
154	BCC-S	21.125	21.000	20.875	21.500	22.500
155	High	21.250	21.125	21.125	21.625	22.750
156	Low	20.750	21.000	20.375	20.875	21.750
157	Volume	97100.000	37200.000	150000.000	161500.000	212100.000
158	BC-S	15.000	14.875	15.250	15.625	16.375
159	High	15.125	15.000	15.500	15.625	16.375
160	Low	14.750	14.750	14.875	15.250	15.625
161	Volume	161600.000	249900.000	343300.000	351900.000	621900.000
162	BDK-S	23.500	24.250	24.750	24.625	23.750
163	High	23.750	24.375	24.875	25.125	24.750
164	Low	23.000	23.375	24.000	24.500	23.750
165	Volume	330500.000	260000.000	308900.000	171100.000	343900.000
166	BDX-S	70.375	70.375	70.625	70.250	70.375
167	High	70.375	70.375	70.875	71.250	70.875
168	Low	69.500	70.000	70.125	70.250	69.875
169	Volume	243800.000	76800.000	100400.000	158900.000	84700.000
170	BEL-S	41.250	41.500	41.875	42.375	42.750
171	High	41.375	41.750	41.875	42.375	43.000
172	Low	40.875	41.000	41.625	41.875	42.500
173	Volume	1078700.000	421400.000	612500.000	655600.000	1042000.000
174	BFI-S	21.125	21.125	21.500	22.125	22.125
175	High	21.500	21.375	21.750	22.125	22.125
176	Low	20.750	21.125	20.875	21.625	21.875
177	Volume	189000.000	185900.000	814400.000	463800.000	232700.000
178	BLS-S	44.375	44.250	44.250	45.500	45.625
179	High	44.875	44.500	44.750	45.500	46.000
180	Low	44.250	44.000	43.875	44.250	45.000
181	Volume	529700.000	509500.000	818300.000	748400.000	843800.000
182	BLY-S	6.125	6.250	6.250	6.000	6.000
183	High	6.500	6.250	6.375	6.250	6.125
184	Low	6.125	6.000	6.125	6.000	5.750
185	Volume	143400.000	122100.000	145000.000	76700.000	156200.000
186	BMY-S	76.375	77.625	78.125	77.500	75.500
187	High	76.375	77.875	78.500	79.250	75.875
188	Low	75.625	76.125	77.250	77.375	74.000

	A	B	C	D	E	F
189	Volume	991500.000	753200.000	1216700.000	974700.000	3300000.000
190	BNI-S	41.000	41.375	43.000	43.875	44.500
191	High	41.750	41.500	43.375	43.875	45.000
192	Low	40.750	41.125	41.500	43.000	43.375
193	Volume	560600.000	119300.000	197600.000	247700.000	420900.000
194	BN-S	33.375	34.125	34.500	34.375	34.125
195	High	33.375	34.250	34.500	34.750	34.500
196	Low	32.625	33.125	33.750	34.125	33.625
197	Volume	440300.000	570100.000	499200.000	431900.000	501100.000
198	BOL-S	48.750	48.500	49.750	49.250	48.625
199	High	49.250	48.625	50.000	50.375	49.500
200	Low	47.750	47.875	48.500	48.750	48.250
201	Volume	270400.000	69000.000	235800.000	214100.000	119000.000

Data Dictionary for the Personnel Actions Table

You use the Personnel Actions table in examples in the following chapters:

 9 "Creating and Using Forms"
10 "Creating Custom Forms"
14 "Using Graphics and Color with Forms and Reports"
18 "Creating Macros for Forms, Reports, and Custom Menus"

The step-by-step procedures for creating the Personnel Actions table and adding the first nine records to the table are included in Chapter 4, "Working with Access Databases and Tables."

Tables E.1 through E.5 provide a tabular data dictionary for the Personnel Actions table.

Table E.1 lists the values of the Field Name, Caption, Data Type, Field Size, and Format properties of the Personnel Actions table. These values are entered in the Properties text boxes for each field.

Table E.1. Field Properties for the Personnel Actions Table

Field Name	Caption	Data Type	Field Size	Format
PA ID Number	ID	Number	Long Integer	General
PA Type	Type	Text	1	@> (all caps)
PA Initiated By Number	Initiated By	Number	Integer	General
PA Scheduled Date	Scheduled	Date/Time	N/A	Short Date
PA Approved By Number	Approved By	Number	Integer	General
PA Effective Date	Effective	Date/Time	N/A	Short Date
PA Rating Number	Rating	Number	Integer	General
PA Amount	Amount	Currency	N/A	##,##0.00#
PA Comments	Comments	Memo	N/A	None

Table E.2 lists the entries you make to assign default values to each field for which default values are required. You enter these values in the Default Values text box of the indicated field.

Table E.2. Default Field Values for the Personnel Actions Table

Field Name	Default Value	Comments
PA Type	Q	Quarterly performance reviews are the most common personnel action
PA Scheduled Date	=Date( )	The expression to enter today's (DOS) date
PA Effective Date	=Date( )	Today's date

Table E.3 lists the values you enter as Validation Rules and the accompanying Validation text that is displayed in the status bar if an entry violates one of the rules. Only those fields with validation rules are shown in table E.3.

Table E.4 lists the key fields, indexes, and relationships for the Personnel Actions table. A composite key field is used so that duplication of an entry of a record for an employee is precluded. The default index that Access creates on the primary key field is shown for completeness; you do not add this index because Access creates indexes on key fields automatically. Index1 is for demonstration purposes only and is not used in the examples. You establish the relationship with the Employees table by opening the Database window, choosing **R**elationships from the **E**dit menu, and making the selections that are listed for the Relationship property in table E.4 in the Relationships dialog box.

Table E.3. Validation Criteria for Fields of the Personnel Actions Table

Field Name	Validation Rule	Validation Text
PA ID	>0	Please enter a valid employee ID number.
PA Type	"H" Or "S" Or "Q" Or "Y" Or "B" Or "C"	Only H, S, Q, Y, B, and C codes may be entered.
PA Initiated By	>0	Please enter a valid supervisor ID number.
PA Scheduled Date	Between Date() –3650 And Date () +365	Scheduled dates cannot be more than 10 years ago nor more than 1 year from now.
PA Approved By	>0 Or Null (see below)	Please enter a valid manager ID number or leave blank if not approved.
PA Effective Date	>=[PA Scheduled Date] Or Is Null	Effective date must be on or after scheduled date or left blank.
PA Rating	Between 0 And 9 Or Is Null	Rating range is 0 for terminated employees, 1 to 9, or blank.

Table E.4. Key Fields, Indexes, and Relationships for the Personnel Actions Table

Property	Value
Key Fields	PA ID;PA Type;PA Scheduled Date
Index0 (default)	PA ID;PA Type;PA Scheduled Date
Index1	PA Type;PA Scheduled Date
Relationships	Primary table: Employees Related table: Personnel Actions Enforce Referential Integrity: True (checked)

Table E.5 lists the first nine entries in the Personnel Actions table that are used to demonstrate use of the table. The (PA) Scheduled (Date) and (PA) Effective (Date) entries are based on the Hired Date information in the Employees table. Enter these values after you have created the composite primary key for the table. Assigning performance ratings (except 0, terminated) to the records is optional.

Table E.5. First Nine Entries for the Personnel Actions Table

ID	Type	Init. By	Scheduled	Appr. By	Effective	Rating	Amount	Comments
1	H		01-Apr-87		01-Apr-87		2,000	Hired
2	H		15-Jul-87		15-Jul-87		3,500	Hired
3	H	2	01-Mar-88	2	01-Mar-88		2,250	Hired
4	H	2	01-Apr-88	2	01-Apr-88		2,250	Hired
5	H	2	15-Sep-89	2	15-Sep-89		2,500	Hired
6	H	5	15-Sep-89	2	15-Sep-89		4,000	Hired
7	H	5	01-Dec-89	2	01-Dec-89		3,000	Hired
8	H	2	01-Feb-90	2	01-Feb-90		2,500	Hired
9	H	5	15-Oct-91	2	15-Oct-91		3,000	Hired

Installing Access

The procedure described in this appendix is for a conventional, single-user installation on the fixed disk drive of your computer. To learn how to install Access on a network server or on a peer-to-peer server running under Windows for Workgroups, refer to Chapter 21, "Using Access in a Network Environment." To install Access on your computer, you need the following available disk space:

■ You need about 11.5M of free disk space for the files that are contained in the \ACCESS subdirectory.

■ If you are running Windows 3.0, you need an additional 1.5M of free disk space in your \WINDOWS directory in order to install the upgrade files and Microsoft Graph. *Upgrade files* are components of Windows 3.1 that are necessary to run Access under Windows 3.0 and are installed in your \WINDOWS\SYSTEM directory. Upgrade files commonly are known as *shared files* or *distributables* and are listed in table F.1. In this case, the total disk space requirement in the two directories is approximately 13M.

■ If you are running Windows 3.1 and haven't previously installed Microsoft Graph (supplied with other Microsoft applications such as Word for Windows 2 and PowerPoint 3), you need an additional 1M (approximately) in your \WINDOWS directory. Microsoft Graph is installed in the \WINDOWS\MSAPPS\MSGRAPH and \WINDOWS\MSAPPS\GRPHFLT directories. In this case, the total disk space requirement in the two directories is about 12.5M.

■ Installing the Open Database Connectivity Administrator and its associated files requires an additional 14K in the \ODBC directory and about 200K in the \WINDOWS\SYSTEM directory.

Table F.1. Windows 3.1 Upgrade Files Installed in \WINDOWS\SYSTEM

File Name	Size, in Bytes	Purpose
COMMDLG.DLL	97,808	Creates the common dialog boxes used by Windows 3.1 applications for opening and saving files, printer operations, font selection, and color choices
DDEML.DLL	38,400	The Dynamic Data Exchange Management Library that streamlines use of DDE operations
OLECLI.DLL	83,456	Provides OLE client services to applications
OLESVR.DLL	24,064	Provides OLE server functions to applications
SHELL.DLL	41,600	Adds OLE and other services to File Manager
VER.DLL	9,008	Tests to make sure that any shared files being installed are newer than existing versions

The disk space requirements for the upgrade files may vary a bit from those shown, depending on the version supplied by Microsoft. If you don't have sufficient free disk space for a complete installation of Access, the following section shows you how to choose a minimum installation that requires about 3.6M of disk space in your \ACCESS directory and, if you are presently running Windows 3.0, about 300K in your \WINDOWS\SYSTEM directory.

Starting the Installation Process

You install Access from within Windows, as you do most other Windows applications. The files included on the distribution disks are compressed, so you cannot just copy the files to your fixed disk and then run Access. The Setup application enables you to choose the type of installation you want, and then selects the files to be installed. Setup uses the Microsoft EXPAND.EXE application to decompress the files on the disk and install the expanded versions in the proper directories.

To start installing Access, follow these steps:

1. Launch Windows, if it isn't already running.

2. Choose **R**un from Program Manager's **F**ile menu. Program
Manager's Run dialog box appears.

3. Type the drive designator (**a:** or **b:**) for the Access distribution
disks, followed by **\setup** in the command line text box, as shown
in figure F.1. Choose OK. The User Information dialog box appears.

FIG. F.1

Program
Manager's Run
dialog box.

4. Type your name and the name of your organization, if applicable,
in the text boxes. Choose OK. Access asks you to confirm your
entry in another dialog box. Choose OK. Access then displays the
Specify Directory dialog box as shown in figure F.2.

FIG. F.2

The Specify
Directory dialog
box.

5. The default directory for Access is C:\ACCESS. Type a different
drive or directory, if you want, and then click the Continue button.
Access displays the Installation Options dialog box, as shown in
figure F.3.

1142

The Installation
Options dialog
box of the
Access Setup
application.

6. If your fixed disk has adequate free space, click the Complete Installation button and skip to the section, "Completing the Installation Process." Otherwise, click the Custom Installation button and proceed with the following section for further instruction.

The Minimum installation option saves a substantial amount of disk space, but doesn't install the Help file. The Help file is indispensable when you are learning to use Access. A better choice than Minimum installation is to use the Custom installation option, selecting only those elements of the application you need.

Choosing Custom Installation Options

When you choose the Custom Installation option, the Microsoft Access Setup Options dialog box shown in figure F.4 appears.

To complete the custom installation, follow these steps:

1. The default check box choices install all the Access files, the equivalent of the Complete Installation option. Click the check boxes to unmark any options you do not want to install. The Space Required entries change, depending on the options you select.

2. If you don't anticipate importing, exporting, or attaching a particular type of foreign database file structure, click the Select button to display the ISAM Options dialog box shown in figure F.5. ISAM is an acronym for *Indexed Sequential Access Method*, a description of the relational database family to which dBASE, FoxPro, Paradox, Btrieve, and Access belong.

   See the last section of this appendix, "Installing the Open Database Connectivity Administrator," to learn how to install Access for use with Microsoft and Sybase SQL Server databases.

3. All compatible file types are selected by default. Click the check box to unmark those file types you don't need, and then choose OK. You can install drivers for any supported file type later by running the Setup program again.

4. Only the files associated with check boxes containing an X in the Microsoft Access Setup Options dialog box will be installed. For any of the ISAM drivers to be installed, for example, the dBASE, Paradox, and/or Btrieve Drivers check box must be marked.

5. Choose OK when you have completed your selections.

Three sample database files are installed when you mark the
Sample Files check box. You can use File Manager to delete
PIM.MDB and ORDENTRY.MDB files to save about 1M of disk
space after completing the installation process. The Northwind
Traders sample database, NWIND.MDB, is essential for learning to
use Access.

Completing the Installation Process

The remainder of the installation process is completed automatically
by the Setup application, except for insertion of the appropriate distribution disk. The installation proceeds with the following steps:

1. The Setup application expands each source file, if necessary, and
   copies the expanded version to the directory and file shown in the
   Destination File line of the Progress Indication dialog box shown
   in figure F.6.

   The blue bar indicates the percentage of the distribution disk that
   has been processed, not the percentage of completion of the
   entire installation.

   Messages appear in dialog boxes on your display as the application progresses. A typical dialog box is shown in figure F.7.

FIG. F.6

The Setup
applications
dialog box.

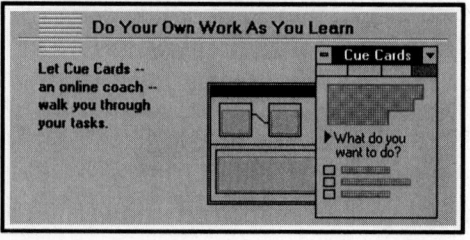

FIG. F.7

One of the sales-
pitch messages
for Access that
appears during
installation.

2. After the required files contained on the distribution disk have been copied to your fixed disk, the Microsoft Access Setup Message dialog box shown in figure F.8 indicates the next disk to insert. Insert the requested disk and choose OK. Disks are skipped if you choose the Minimum Installation option.

   If you insert a disk other than the one requested, Windows beeps and the Microsoft Access Setup Message dialog box reappears.

3. Access requires that DOS' SHARE.EXE application be installed prior to running Windows. If you haven't installed SHARE.EXE, Access will do so for you, proposing to add the line SHARE /L:200 to your AUTOEXEC.BAT file. If you have installed SHARE.EXE by an entry in your AUTOEXEC.BAT file and haven't specified the \L: (Locks) option with 200 or more available locks, you receive the message shown in figure F.9.

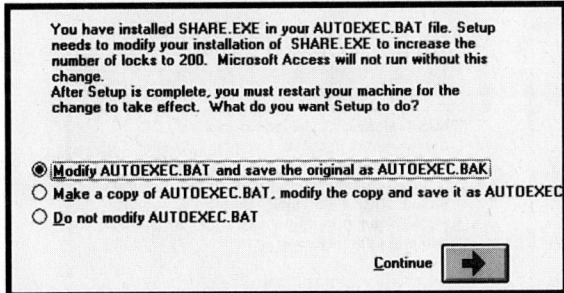

4. Unless you have a specific reason *not* to modify your AUTOEXEC.BAT file, choose the Modify AUTOEXEC.BAT and Save the Original as AUTOEXEC.BAK option. If you choose the Make a Copy... option, an AUTOEXEC.ACC file is created that you may examine. Copy as AUTOEXEC.BAT if it is satisfactory. Click the Continue button after you make your choice.

5. Access often requires more DOS file handles than most other Windows applications. If you have specified fewer than 50 files in the FILES= line of your CONFIG.SYS file, you receive the message shown in figure F.10.

In this case, Access doesn't make the change for you. Use Windows' SysEdit or Notepad applets to edit the FILES= line of your CONFIG.SYS file to read FILES=50 after the installation is completed. Then choose OK.

6. The Open Database Connectivity Administrator application and its required files aren't installed automatically by the Setup application. When the basic installation of Access is complete, you receive the message shown in figure F.11. Installation of the ODBC Administrator is covered in the following section. Contrary to the instructions in the message box, knowing the name of your database server isn't necessary now.

FIG. F.10

The message box requesting that you increase the number of file handles available to DOS.

FIG. F.11

The message box signaling completion of the basic Access installation.

7. Choose OK. Access creates its own Windows application group with icons for the Change Workgroup setup function, Access itself, two text files, and the Access Help system, as shown in figure F.12.

8. Double-click the Access Readme button to display the README.TXT file, as shown in figure F.13. README.TXT provides updated information that didn't make it into the Access documentation. You can print the README.TXT file from Notepad.

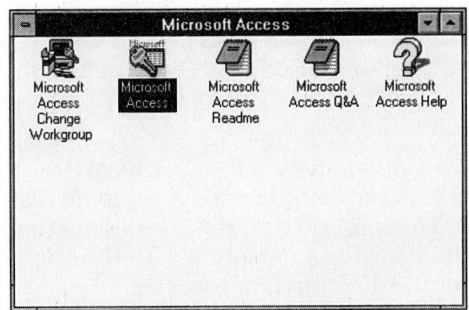

The Access Application Group window created by the Setup application.

```
━━━━━━━━━━━━━━━━━━━━━━━━━━━━━━━━━━━━━━━━━━
            Notepad - README.TXT
 File  Edit  Search  Help
━━━━━━━━━━━━━━━━━━━━━━━━━━━━━━━━━━━━━━━━━━
│
        Microsoft Access Version 1.0 README File
                 September 21, 1992
        ━━━━━━━━━━━━━━━━━━━━━━━━━━━━━━━━━━


           (C) Copyright Microsoft Corporation, 1992


 This document provides complementary or late-breaking
 information as a supplement to the standard Microsoft
 Access documentation.


 ━━━━━━━━━━━━━━━━━━━━━━━━━
 How to Use This Document
 ━━━━━━━━━━━━━━━━━━━━━━━━━

 To view README on screen in Windows Notepad, maximize
 the Notepad window.

 To print README, open it in Windows Write, Microsoft
 Word, or another word processor.  Then select the entire
 document and format the text in 10-point Courier before
```

The README.TXT file as it appears in Windows' Notepad applet.

9. If you want additional information about the use of Access, click the Microsoft Access Q&A icon. The Access Q&A text file consists of the most frequently asked questions by Access beta testers and answers from Microsoft. As with README.TXT, you can print this file from Windows' Notepad.

10. If Access modified your AUTOEXEC.BAT file (step 3) or you changed your CONFIG.SYS file (step 5), exit Windows and reboot your computer so that the changes to AUTOEXEC.BAT and/or CONFIG.SYS take effect.

If you plan to use Access with Microsoft or Sybase SQL Server, you need to install the Open Database Connectivity files as described in the following section.

Installing the Open Database Connectivity Administrator

The Open Database Connectivity (ODBC) Administrator application and ODBC-related files are contained on a separate distribution disk designated ODBC. This section describes installing the files required to use the ODBC Administrator application with the Microsoft SQL Server ODBC driver but not setting up data sources. To establish an ODBC database as a data source, refer to Chapter 21, "Using Access in a Network Environment."

To install the ODBC Administrator application, complete the following steps:

1. Insert the ODBC distribution disk into the appropriate drive.

2. Choose **R**un from Program Manager's **F**ile menu and type **d:\setup**, where *d*: is the drive designator (a: or b:) of the disk drive.

3. When the first Microsoft ODBC 1.0 Setup dialog box appears, click the Continue button. The second Microsoft ODBC 1.0 Setup dialog box appears, as shown in figure F.14. This dialog box installs the ODBC drivers and the ODBC Administrator application by default.

4. Click the Continue button. The default directory appears, as shown in figure F.15.

5. Accept the default directory, C:\ODBC, or choose another directory for the two small files (about 50K) that comprise the ODBC Administrator utility. Click the Continue button. A confirmation dialog box appears, as shown in figure F.16.

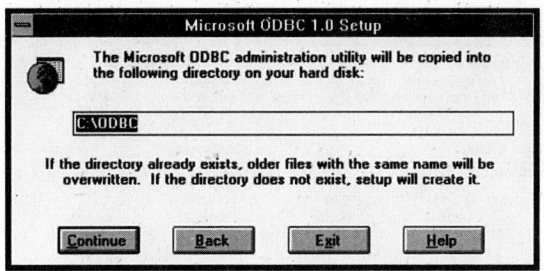

FIG. F.15

Selecting a
directory in
which to install
the ODBC
Administrator.

FIG. F.16

The ODBC
Administrator
directory
confirmation
dialog box.

6. Confirm creation of the new directory by clicking the Create Directory button. The driver installation dialog box shown in figure F.17 appears.

   Only the driver for Microsoft SQL Server is supplied with the version of the ODBC Application Programming Interface (API) supplied with Access.

7. Click the SQL Server entry in the Available Drivers list box to highlight it, and then click the Install –> button. The selected entry is copied to the Installed Drivers list box, as shown in figure F.18.

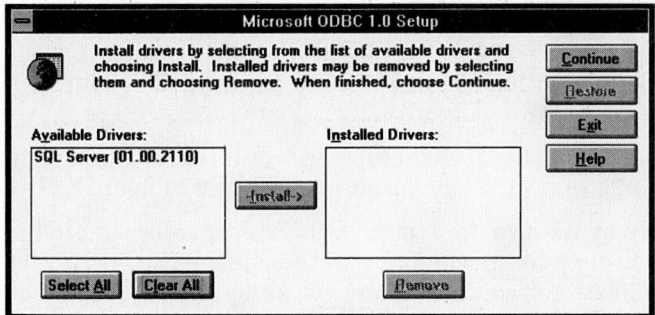

FIG. F.17

The ODBC Driver
installation
dialog box prior
to adding the
Microsoft SQL
Server driver.

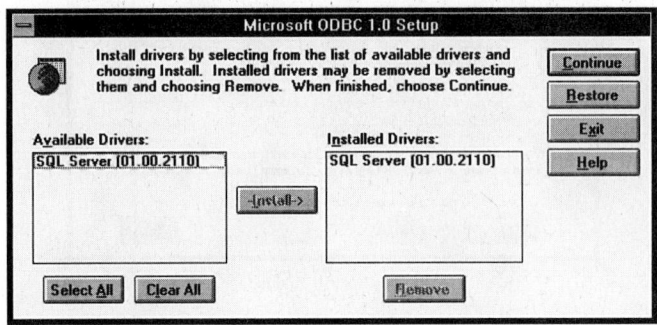

FIG. F.18

The ODBC Driver
installation
dialog box after
adding the
Microsoft SQL
Server driver.

8. Click the Continue button. The data source installation dialog box appears, as shown in figure F.19. You don't need to install a data source for the ODBC driver at this time. Chapter 21, "Using Access in a Network Environment," discusses ODBC data sources and how you install them.

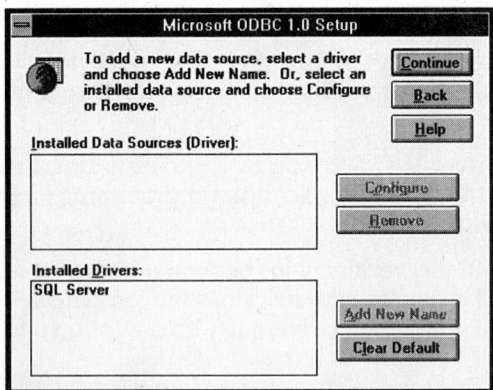

FIG. F.19

The dialog box
used by the
ODBC Setup
application to
install an SQL
Server data
source.

9. Click the Continue button without adding a data source. The message box shown in figure F.20 appears.

10. Choose OK. The ODBC Setup application creates a separate application group with a single entry, as shown in figure F.21.

11. You may want to drag the ODBC Administrator icon to the Access application group window, and then delete the Microsoft ODBC Administrator application group window by selecting it and pressing the Delete key.

12. Exit and restart Windows to make the ODBC driver you installed available to Access.

The message box that confirms completion of the ODBC Setup application.

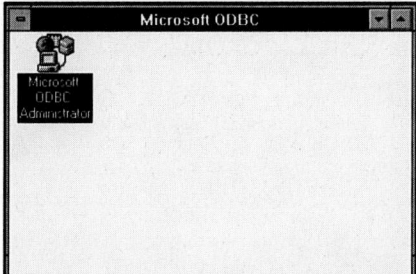

The ODBC Application Group created by the ODBC Setup application.

The installation of the files required to use the ODBC Application Programming interface now is complete. Refer to Chapter 21, "Using Access in a Network Environment," for instructions on how to install and use Microsoft SQL Server data sources.

Symbols

A

D

I